RICHARD S. CESARO

$48

D0578245

HAVE 1, 6, 7, 8,
9, 10, 12

THERMODYNAMICS AND
PHYSICS OF MATTER

BOARD OF EDITORS

THEODORE VON KÁRMÁN, *Chairman*
HUGH L. DRYDEN
HUGH S. TAYLOR
JOSEPH V. CHARYK, General Editor, 1952–
Associate Editor, 1949–1952
MARTIN SUMMERFIELD, General Editor, 1949–1952

I. Thermodynamics and Physics of Matter. Editor: F. D. Rossini
II. Combustion Processes. Editors: B. Lewis, R. N. Pease, H. S. Taylor
III. Fundamentals of Gas Dynamics. Editor: H. W. Emmons
IV. Laminar Flows and Transition to Turbulence. Editor: C. C. Lin
V. Turbulent Flows and Heat Transfer. Editor: C. C. Lin
VI. General Theory of High Speed Aerodynamics. Editor: W. R. Sears
VII. Aerodynamic Components of Aircraft at High Speeds. Editors: A. F. Donovan, H. R. Lawrence
VIII. High Speed Problems of Aircraft and Experimental Methods. Editors: A. F. Donovan, H. R. Lawrence, F. Goddard, R. R. Gilruth
IX. Physical Measurements in Gas Dynamics and Combustion. Editors: R. W. Ladenburg, B. Lewis, R. N. Pease, H. S. Taylor
X. Aerodynamics of Turbines and Compressors. Editor: W. R. Hawthorne
XI. Design and Performance of Gas Turbine Power Plants. Editors: W. R. Hawthorne, W. T. Olson
XII. Jet Propulsion Engines. Editor: O. E. Lancaster

VOLUME I

HIGH SPEED AERODYNAMICS

AND JET PROPULSION

THERMODYNAMICS

AND

PHYSICS OF

MATTER

EDITOR: FREDERICK D. ROSSINI

PRINCETON, NEW JERSEY

PRINCETON UNIVERSITY PRESS

1955

Copyright, 1955, by Princeton University Press

London: Geoffrey Cumberlege, Oxford University Press

L. C. card 55-8069

Reproduction, translation, publication, use, and disposal by and for the United States Government and its officers, agents, and employees acting within the scope of their official duties, for Government use only, is permitted excepting: Fig. B,12; Fig. B,15; Table B,19a; and Table B,19b. At the expiration of ten years from the date of publication, all rights in material contained herein first produced under contract Nonr-03201 shall be in the public domain.

Printed in the United States of America by
The Maple Press Inc., York, Pennsylvania

FOREWORD

On behalf of the Editorial Board, I would like to make an acknowledgement to those branches of our military establishment whose interest and whose financial support were instrumental in the initiation of this publication program. It is noteworthy that this assistance has included all three branches of our Services. The Department of the Air Force through the Air Research and Development Command, the Department of the Army through the Office of the Chief of Ordnance, and the Department of the Navy through the Bureau of Aeronautics, Bureau of Ships, Bureau of Ordnance, and the Office of Naval Research made significant contributions. In particular, the Power Branch of the Office of Naval Research has carried the burden of responsibilities of the contractual administration and processing of all manuscripts from a security standpoint. The administration, operation, and editorial functions of the program have been centered at Princeton University. In addition, the University has contributed financially to the support of the undertaking. It is appropriate that special appreciation be expressed to Princeton University for its important over-all role in this effort.

The Editorial Board is confident that the present series which this support has made possible will have far-reaching beneficial effects on the further development of the aeronautical sciences.

Theodore von Kármán

PREFACE

Rapid advances made during the past decade on problems associated with high speed flight have brought into ever sharper focus the need for a comprehensive and competent treatment of the fundamental aspects of the aerodynamic and propulsion problems of high speed flight, together with a survey of those aspects of the underlying basic sciences cognate to such problems. The need for a treatment of this type has been long felt in research institutions, universities, and private industry and its potential reflected importance in the advanced training of nascent aeronautical scientists has also been an important motivation in this undertaking.

The entire program is the cumulative work of over one hundred scientists and engineers, representing many different branches of engineering and fields of science both in this country and abroad.

The work consists of twelve volumes treating in sequence elements of the properties of gases, liquids, and solids; combustion processes and chemical kinetics; fundamentals of gas dynamics; viscous phenomena; turbulence; heat transfer; theoretical methods in high speed aerodynamics; applications to wings, bodies and complete aircraft; nonsteady aerodynamics; principles of physical measurements; experimental methods in high speed aerodynamics and combustion; aerodynamic problems of turbo machines; the combination of aerodynamic and combustion principles in combustor design; and finally, problems of complete power plants. The intent has been to emphasize the fundamental aspects of jet propulsion and high speed aerodynamics, to develop the theoretical tools for attack on these problems, and to seek to highlight the directions in which research may be potentially most fruitful.

Preliminary discussions, which ultimately led to the foundation of the present program, were held in 1947 and 1948 and, in large measure, by virtue of the enthusiasm, inspiration, and encouragement of Dr. Theodore von Kármán and later the invaluable assistance of Dr. Hugh L. Dryden and Dean Hugh Taylor as members of the Editorial Board, these discussions ultimately saw their fruition in the formal establishment of the Aeronautics Publication Program at Princeton University in the fall of 1949.

The contributing authors and, in particular, the volume editors, have sacrificed generously of their spare time under present-day emergency conditions where continuing demands on their energies have been great. The program is also indebted to the work of Dr. Martin Summerfield who guided the planning work as General Editor from 1949–1952. The cooperation and assistance of the personnel of the Princeton University Press and of the staff of this office has been noteworthy. In particular, Mr. H. S. Bailey, Jr., the Director of the Press, and Mr. R. S. Snedeker, who has supervised the project at the Press and drawn all the figures, have been of great help. Special mention is also due Mrs. H. E. H. Lewis of this office who has handled the bulk of the detailed editorial work for the program from its inception.

Joseph V. Charyk
General Editor

PREFACE TO VOLUME I

This volume brings together the basic principles of the thermodynamics and physics of matter, presented from the standpoint of their applicability to a better understanding of high speed aerodynamics and jet propulsion.

Section A by Rossini covers the fundamentals of thermodynamics. In Section B, Herzfeld and Griffing discuss quantum mechanics, molecular structure, bond energies, and activation energies, and Hirschfelder, Curtiss, Bird, and Spotz present statistical mechanics and the kinetic theory of gases. Section C, by Beattie, gives a complete treatment of the thermodynamic properties of real gases and their mixtures. In Section D, Hirschfelder, Curtiss, Bird, and Spotz discuss the transport properties of gases and gaseous mixtures. In Section E, Rice covers critical phenomena, including association and condensation. Section F, by Richardson and Brinkley, presents the theories of liquids and liquid solutions. In Section G, Ewald discusses solids and solid solutions, covering crystals, conductors, insulators, energy bands, and cooperative phenomena. Section H, by Herzfeld, covers relaxation phenomena in gases, including theory and experiment. In Section I, Estermann presents a discussion of gases at low densities, including molecular beams. In Section J, Curtiss discusses the thermodynamics of irreversible processes, including flow processes, viscosity, thermal conductivity, and diffusion.

Because of the nature of such a cooperative enterprise, most of the sections were completed in 1951 and 1952. The references in each section will indicate to what date the review of the literature for that section has covered. In particular, Section G by Ewald, Section H by Herzfeld, Section I by Estermann, and Section J by Curtiss were all completed in 1951. The reader should take these dates into account to bring himself up to date.

The volume editor is grateful for the excellent cooperation extended by the authors of the several sections, by the General Editor and his staff, and by the Princeton University Press.

Frederick D. Rossini
Volume Editor

CONTENTS

CONTENTS

L. Spotz, Department of Chemistry, University of Wisconsin, Madison, Wisconsin

CONTENTS

CONTENTS

CONTENTS

Chapter 4. The Lewis and Randall Rule

Chapter 5. The Gibbs-Dalton Law

Joseph O. Hirschfelder, C. F. Curtiss, R. B. Bird, and Ellen L. Spotz, Department of Chemistry, University of Wisconsin, Madison, Wisconsin

CONTENTS

⟨ xiv ⟩

CONTENTS

CONTENTS

Immanuel Estermann, Department of Physics, Carnegie Institute of Technology, Pittsburgh, Pennsylvania (now with the U.S. Office of Naval Research, Washington, D.C.)

CONTENTS

THERMODYNAMICS AND
PHYSICS OF MATTER

SECTION A

FUNDAMENTALS OF THERMODYNAMICS

FREDERICK D. ROSSINI

A,1. Introduction and Definition of Terms. Thermodynamics[1] provides laws that govern the transfer of energy from one system to another, the transformation of energy from one form to another, the utilization of energy for useful work, and the transformation of matter from one molecular, atomic, or nuclear species to another. In fixed electric, magnetic, and gravitational fields, all matter of specified composition may be considered to have five fundamental thermodynamic properties. Knowledge of the proper manner of applying the first and second laws of thermodynamics to a system and its fundamental properties permits one to subject all changes of energy and matter to the powerful scrutiny of thermodynamics.

It is important to note that thermodynamics does not evaluate the rate at which a given reaction proceeds or chemical equilibrium is attained, and does not specify the mechanism by which the molecules are transformed from the initial to the final state, and vice versa.

The terms frequently encountered in thermodynamics include the following: A *thermodynamic system* is that part of the universe which is being subjected to thermodynamic scrutiny. A *homogeneous system* is one whose properties are uniform throughout, or, if not uniform, vary in a continuous manner. A *heterogeneous system* is one which consists of two or more regions of homogeneity. The *state* of a system is specified when its properties and composition are adequately known. A *thermodynamic process* constitutes the changes which take place in the system or systems being subjected to thermodynamic examination. The *properties* of a system are classed as intensive or extensive, according to whether the given property is independent of or dependent on the mass of the substance. *Equilibrium* may be said to exist in a system when its composition and properties undergo no observable change. *Molal properties* are those for which values are expressed per mole or gram-formula-weight of the compound whose chemical formula is written.

---

[1] The material of this section is based largely on the book by the writer entitled "Chemical Thermodynamics" [1], with permission of the publishers, John Wiley & Sons, Inc.

In expressing the composition of a solution, the mole fraction X_i, of a given component is the ratio of the number of moles of the given component to the total number of moles in the solution. In the case of aqueous solutions, the composition is usually expressed in terms of the molality m, defined as the number of moles of solute per 1,000 grams (or 55.506 moles) of water.

Appropriate superscripts are used to denote thermodynamic standard state, pure state of a given substance, infinite dilution, etc. The subscripts used include the simple integral numbers $_1$, $_2$, $_3$, etc., which refer to the components of the solution, taken with the solvent first, etc., and other numerical subscripts representing the absolute temperature, e.g. $_0$, $_{298.16}$, or $_{1,000}$. The context always makes clear the meaning of such superscripts and subscripts.

A,2. Scale of Temperature. The "zero-pressure" gas scale of temperature, which is identical with the thermodynamic scale of temperature, is established essentially from measurements of the pressure-volume product of a fixed mass of gas at successively lower and lower pressures at suitable reference temperatures.

Using a fixed, but not necessarily measured, quantity of any real gas at a given temperature T, measurements of the pressure and volume are made at several finite low pressures. These values, in the form of the pressure-volume product, are extrapolated to zero pressure to obtain the value of the pressure-volume product at zero pressure at the given temperature for the quantity of gas involved. If these measurements are repeated at another temperature on the same quantity of the same gas, there is obtained a value of the pressure-volume product at zero pressure for the second temperature. A satisfactory and fundamental scale of temperature is established by letting these values of the pressure-volume product at zero pressure be proportional to the temperature on this zero-pressure gas scale, as

$$(pV)_T^{p=0} = AT \qquad (2\text{-}1)$$

In Eq. 2-1, A is the constant of proportionality for the quantity of gas involved and T is the temperature on this zero-pressure gas scale.

The constant of proportionality may be evaluated in either of two ways: (1) by defining the number of degrees between two selected fixed points which are realizable in the laboratory; or (2) by defining the absolute value of temperature to be assigned to one fixed point realizable in the laboratory with reference to the origin or zero on the zero-pressure gas scale of temperature. In the former method, which is the one currently in use, the difference in the values of temperature between the two selected fixed points is defined and never changed, but the absolute values of the temperature of the two selected fixed points may change as the result of improvements in experimentation with the zero-pressure gas thermometer. In the second method, the absolute value of the temperature of one fixed point with reference to the origin or absolute zero is defined and never changed, but the absolute value of the temperature of any other point may change as the result of improvements in experimentation.'

Basic, reproducible, fixed points on any scale of temperature are most easily realized by using the temperature of the thermodynamic equilibrium between two or more phases of a given pure substance. In general, the equilibrium between a solid and a liquid is easier to reproduce than one between a liquid and a gas because the temperature of the latter is very much more sensitive to changes in pressure.

In the method currently in use for defining the zero-pressure gas scale of temperature, the two realizable fixed points which are used to define the scale are (1) the temperature at which solid water is in thermodynamic equilibrium with liquid water in air at a pressure of 1 atmosphere and (2) the temperature at which liquid water is in thermodynamic equilibrium with gaseous water at a pressure of 1 atmosphere. The difference in the temperature of these two fixed points, which are commonly called the "ice" and "steam" points, respectively, is defined as exactly 100 units or degrees. The temperature at which solid water is in thermodynamic equilibrium with liquid water at saturation pressure, in the absence of air, which is the triple point, is 0.0100°C higher than the ice point involving water saturated with air at 1 atmosphere. On the foregoing scale of temperature, the interval between the triple point and the steam point of water is 99.9900°C.

If values of the pressure-volume product at zero pressure have been determined for the quantity of the given gas, at the ice and steam points, respectively, then for the first method of defining the zero-pressure gas scale of temperature, the following relations hold:

$$T_{steam} - T_{ice} = 100 \quad \text{defined constant} \tag{2-2}$$

$$T_{ice} = 100 \, \frac{(pV)^{p=0}_{T_{ice}}}{(pV)^{p=0}_{T_{steam}} - (pV)^{p=0}_{T_{ice}}} \tag{2-3}$$

Eq. 2-3 serves to evaluate the absolute temperature of the ice point on the zero-pressure gas scale of temperature, according to the current method of defining this scale of temperature by using two realizable fixed points.

Any other unknown temperature, including any additional fixed (but not defining) points, may be evaluated fundamentally from measurements on a given, but not necessarily measured, quantity of a suitable gas. Such measurements would determine the pressure-volume product at zero pressure at the given unknown temperature and at the two defining fixed points, the ice and steam points. The value of the unknown temperature T_x on this scale would be given by the following relation:

$$T_x = \frac{(pV)_{T_x}^{p=0}}{100\ (pV)_{T_{\text{steam}}}^{p=0} - (pV)_{T_{\text{ice}}}^{p=0}} \qquad (2\text{-}4)$$

In such determinations, maximum precision and accuracy in the evaluation of the unknown temperature T_x are obtained by having the pressure-volume measurements at all three temperatures made with the same apparatus and procedure and by having the extrapolation of the experimental data to zero pressure made uniformly in the same way.

In the second method of defining the zero-pressure gas scale of temperature, using only one realizable fixed point and the origin or absolute zero, the absolute temperature of the ice point is defined; any other unknown temperature T_x would be evaluated fundamentally from this defined value of the ice point and the ratio of the pressure-volume product of a suitable gas at zero pressure at the unknown temperature and at the ice point. In this case, arbitrarily defining the absolute value of the ice point according to its present best value on the scale of temperature defined by two realizable fixed points, the relations involved are the following:

$$T_{\text{ice}} = 273.16 \quad \text{defined constant} \qquad (2\text{-}5)$$

$$T_x = 273.16 \frac{(pV)_{T_x}^{p=0}}{(pV)_{T_{\text{ice}}}^{p=0}} \qquad (2\text{-}6)$$

If, instead of the ice point fixed by the thermodynamic equilibrium between water, ice, and liquid water saturated with air at 1 atmosphere, one used the triple point of water fixed by the same equilibrium in the absence of air, the same equations would be used with the pressure-volume product at zero pressure at the triple point in place of the pressure-volume product at the ice point, and with 99.9900 in place of 100.0000 and 273.17 in place of 273.16.

The evaluation of temperatures by the use of a zero-pressure gas thermometer is essentially limited to the national standardizing laboratories and to certain other laboratories possessing the necessary apparatus and experience. This is because the use of a zero-pressure gas thermometric system with high precision and accuracy is laborious, difficult, and costly. For general use in science and technology, it has become necessary to establish a practical or working scale of temperature. To do this, one goes back to the selection of a specified thermometric substance, a specified property of that substance, and a specified mathematical function relating values of the given property of the given substance to values of the temperature. Before making any measurements on the selected thermometric substance and property, it is necessary to determine experimentally the values of the temperature of a necessary number

⟨ 6 ⟩

of fixed points which are to be used in connection with the practical or working scale of temperature. The number of such fixed points will depend upon the number of constants to be evaluated in the selected mathematical function relating, with the necessary precision and accuracy, the values of the selected thermometric property of the selected thermometric substance to the values of the temperature of the selected fixed points.

The absolute value of the temperature of the ice point on the zero-pressure gas scale is currently selected to be 273.160 ± 0.010°. Therefore, the absolute values of the temperature of the water-ice triple point and of the steam point are higher by 0.0100° and 100.0000°, respectively. Additional fixed points necessary to establish a practical or working scale of temperature are selected on the basis of their reproducibility and the range of temperature to be covered. Such basic fixed points, together with the values of temperature which have been assigned to them on the above zero-pressure gas scale of temperature, as a result of measurements with a gas thermometer system, are as follows, with the two defining points, ice and steam, included for completeness:

Substance	Equilibrium	Assigned temperature (degrees absolute)
Oxygen	liquid-gas, at 1 atm	90.19
Water	solid-liquid, in air at 1 atm	273.16
Water	solid-liquid, saturation pressure	273.17
Water	liquid-gas, at 1 atm	373.16
Sulfur	liquid-gas, at 1 atm	717.76
Silver	solid-liquid, at 1 atm	1233.96
Gold	solid-liquid, at 1 atm	1336.16

The uncertainties in the absolute values of temperature on the zero-pressure gas scale of temperature assigned to the above fixed points are about 0.01° for the oxygen, ice, and steam points, near 0.1° for the sulfur point, and near 0.5° for the silver and gold points.

For convenience in the use of a practical or working scale of temperature in ordinary scientific and technological work, as well as for historical reasons, the defining ice and steam points are assigned values of 0 and 100 degrees, respectively. The values on this practical scale are called degrees Centigrade (Celsius), or °C. The above fixed points have the following values on the Centigrade (Celsius) scale, obtained by subtracting 273.16° from the values: oxygen, −182.970°C; ice, 0°C (exactly); ice, triple point, 0.0100°C; steam, 100°C (exactly); sulfur, 444.60°C; silver, 960.80°C; gold, 1063.00°C.

The next step is to select suitable thermometric substances, properties, and mathematical functions. It has been found that the electrical resistance of pure platinum wire increases in a roughly linear manner with temperature. With three or four constants in a second or third degree polynomial, it is possible to relate the electrical resistance of platinum to temperature on the above scale with considerable precision and accuracy, from $-183°$ to $630°C$, as follows:

For the range $-183°C$ to $0°C$, the relation of resistance to temperature is

$$r_t = r_0(1 + at + bt^2 + ct^3) \tag{2-7}$$

where r_t and r_0 are the electrical resistances of the platinum resistance thermometer at the temperature t and at $0°C$, respectively, and a, b, and c are constants evaluated from measurement of the resistance of the thermometer at the oxygen, steam, and sulfur points.

For the range $0°C$ to $630°C$, the relation of resistance to temperature is

$$r_t = r_0(1 + at + bt^2) \tag{2-8}$$

where the three constants are evaluated from measurement of the resistance of the thermometer at the ice, steam, and sulfur points.

For temperatures from $630°C$ to $1063°C$, the electromotive force of a standard platinum vs. platinum-rhodium thermocouple is used for the working scale of temperature, with the following relation:

$$e = a + bt + ct^2 \tag{2-9}$$

Here e is the electromotive force of the standard thermocouple, one junction of which is kept at $0°C$ and the other at the given temperature t, and the three constants a, b, and c are evaluated from measurements of the electromotive force of the thermocouple at the antimony, silver, and gold points. The value of the temperature to be assigned to the antimony point in this calibration is evaluated with the platinum resistance thermometer for the given sample of antimony. (Pure antimony has a freezing point of $630.5°C$.)

Measurements of temperature below $-183°C$ are made with gas thermometers, or with resistance thermometers or thermocouples that have been calibrated against a gas thermometric system, or with resistance thermometers or thermocouples that have been calibrated against other resistance thermometers or thermocouples that have been calibrated against a gas thermometric system.

Measurements of temperature above the gold point are made with optical pyrometers. The measurements involve determination of the ratio of the intensity of monochromatic visible radiation of a given wavelength emitted by a black body at the unknown temperature to the intensity of the same radiation of the same wavelength emitted by a black body at the gold point. The unknown temperature T_x is evaluated from the radiation formula:

$$\frac{J_{T_z}}{J_{T_{Au}}} = \frac{e^{c_2/\lambda T_{Au}} - 1}{e^{c_2/\lambda T_z} - 1} \tag{2-10}$$

In this equation, J_{T_z} and $J_{T_{Au}}$ are the radiant energies per unit wavelength interval at the given wavelength λ (cm), emitted per unit time by unit area of a black body at the temperatures T_z and T_{Au}, respectively; T_z and T_{Au} are the absolute values of the unknown temperature and the temperature of the gold point, respectively; c_2 is the second radiation constant and is equal to hc/k or 1.438 cm degrees.

The International Temperature Scale, which is essentially the practical or working scale described above, was first adopted in 1927 by the Seventh General Conference of Weights and Measures, and was revised in 1948 at the Ninth General Conference of Weights and Measures.

A,3. Fundamental Constants and Conversion Factors. The fundamental constants required in thermodynamics may for simplicity be divided into three categories: basic, derived, and defined.

The basic constants are those for which the values are determined by experimental measurements and include the following: the velocity of light c, the Avogadro constant N; the Faraday constant $\mathfrak{F}$; the Planck constant h; the absolute temperature of the ice point, $T_{0°C}$; the pressure-volume product for one mole of a gas at 0°C and zero pressure, $(pV)_{T_{0°C}}^{p=0}$.

The derived constants are those for which the values are determined from appropriate physical relations involving one or more of the basic constants and the given derived constant, and include the following:

the gas constant per mole, R, obtained from the relation

$$R = \frac{(pV)_{T_{0°C}}^{p=0}}{T_{0°C}} \tag{3-1}$$

the charge on the electron e, obtained from

$$e = \frac{\mathfrak{F}}{N} \tag{3-2}$$

the Boltzmann constant k, obtained from

$$k = \frac{R}{N} \tag{3-3}$$

the second radiation constant c_2, obtained from

$$c_2 = \frac{hc}{k} \tag{3-4}$$

the Einstein constant Y, relating mass and energy, from

$$Y = c^2 \tag{3-5}$$

and the constant Z, relating spectroscopic wave number and energy, from

$$Z = Nhc \qquad (3\text{-}6)$$

The defined constants are those for which the values are fixed entirely by definition, and include the following: the standard value of the acceleration of gravity, g_0; the standard atmosphere, atm; the inch; the pound; the gallon; the thermochemical calorie, cal; the I.T. steam calorie, I.T. cal; and the British thermal unit, BTU.

From the time of the early work of Count Rumford near 1800 to the early part of the present century, the most convenient and readily applicable method of measuring quantities of heat arising from processes occurring at or near room temperature was to observe the rise of temperature produced in a known mass of water contained in a suitable vessel or calorimeter. In this way, it was possible to measure with considerable precision a quantity of energy in terms of a given mass of water and its rise of temperature. With the calorie defined as the quantity of heat required to raise the temperature of 1 gram of water through one Centigrade degree, the experimenter was thus able to express the result in calories, obtained as the product of the mass of water in grams and the rise of temperature in Centigrade degrees. As the measurements increased in precision, it became necessary to take proper cognizance of the heat capacity of the container, thermometer, stirrer, etc.; to define the scale of temperature; and to specify accurately the various conditions attending the absorption of the heat by the water, such as the mean temperature or the interval of temperature, the pressure, etc. The specification of the mean temperature gave rise in itself to various calories, such as the 0° calorie, the 4° calorie, the 15° calorie, the 18° calorie, the 20° calorie, and the mean (0 to 100°C) calorie. By about 1905, experimental calorimetry had advanced to a stage where measurements of heat in terms of the heat capacity of water could be made with a precision of about 1 part in 1,000. It was early recognized, however, that, notwithstanding the relative ease with which measurements of heat could be made in terms of the heat capacity of water, it was necessary to ascertain to what quantity of energy in absolute units (ergs or joules) a given calorie was equivalent. This gave rise to the long series of different investigations on the mechanical equivalent of heat. Throughout all of this work, it was apparent that the uncertainty of the value giving the number of joules equivalent to a given calorie was always comparable with the uncertainty with which a given quantity of heat could be measured in terms of the heat capacity of water. As long as this situation existed, it was desirable, for purposes of high precision, to continue to use as the unit of heat energy the heat capacity of water under specified conditions.

However, with the development of accurate electric standards near the beginning of the present century, it became possible to measure electric energy with high precision. As soon as this precision in the measurement of the electric energy introduced into a calorimeter became equal to or exceeded that of measuring heat in terms of the heat capacity of water, the real need for retaining the latter as a unit of heat energy was removed. It was not until about 1930, however, that definite steps were taken to separate the calorimetric unit of energy from any connection with the actual heat capacity of water under specified conditions.

Electric measurements of energy are based upon the mean solar second as the unit of time and upon working standards of electromotive force and resistance maintained at the various national standardizing laboratories. These working standards are saturated cadmium (Weston) cells and wire (usually manganin) resistance coils. When redefined in 1908, the units internationally agreed upon, and specified in terms of the mercury ohm and the silver voltameter, were identical with the absolute units within the limits of which the latter could then be determined. Since that time, however, the accuracy of the absolute measurements has increased and more accurate determinations of the relation between the international units and the absolute units (ohm and ampere) have been made. In 1930, the relation between the international and absolute electric units was such that

$$1 \text{ international joule} = 1.0004 \text{ absolute joules} \qquad (3\text{-}7)$$

Later and more accurate evaluations yielded values more nearly approaching unity. In 1939, the relation was

$$1 \text{ international joule} = 1.00020 \pm 0.00005 \text{ absolute joules} \qquad (3\text{-}8)$$

In 1947, the relations selected as best by the National Bureau of Standards for purposes of certification of standard cells and resistances was such that

$$1 \text{ international joule} = 1.000165 \pm 0.000025 \text{ absolute joules} \qquad (3\text{-}9)$$

All measurements of electric energy made from about 1910 to 1948 by means of standard cells and resistances are actually in terms of international joules. Since January 1, 1948, the National Bureau of Standards, along with the national standardizing laboratories of other countries, has certified standard cells and resistances in absolute volts and ohms, so that the resulting energy is measured in absolute joules.

Notwithstanding the fact that practically all accurate calorimetric measurements made after about 1910 were actually based on electric energy, most investigators continued until about 1930 to express their final results in such a way as to make it appear that the unit of energy was in some way still connected with the heat capacity of water. Actually, what they did was to convert their values, determined in international joules, into one or more of the several calories based on the heat capacity of water, usually for comparison with older values in the literature reported in calories. This procedure should have been reversed: that is, the older data should have been converted to the modern unit of energy. But the conversion to the older unit, the calorie, was favored because most chemists and physicists were reluctant to change from their habits of thinking of energy in terms of a unit the size of a calorie.

An important effort to accustom chemists and physicists to the use of the joule as the unit of energy was made in connection with many of the tabulations of chemical thermodynamic data in the International Critical Tables. This attempt to change over to the joule was not popular. It appeared then that the calorie would at least have to be retained as the name of the unit of heat energy. It was also realized that every association with the heat capacity of water would have to be separated from the new calorie, or else all the thermodynamic values would have to be changed every time someone determined the heat capacity of water with an accuracy greater than that already existing. It would also be necessary for the new calorie to have a size approximately equal to that of the traditional calorie. The obvious solution was to have an artificial, conventional calorie, defined as equal to a given number of electric joules, the unit in which the calorimetric measurements were actually made. The investigators would then report their results in terms of the unit in which the measurements were actually made, and, for the benefit of those who preferred to continue thinking of energy in terms of a unit having the name and size of the calorie, would also give the values in terms of the artificial calorie by using the conventional factor for the conversion. In line with the foregoing development, there came into use independently about 1930 two different, artificial, conventional, defined calories, one in the engineering steam tables and the other in thermochemistry and chemical thermodynamics.

The artificial conventional calorie used in the engineering steam tables is designated as the I.T. calorie (International Table calorie), which was first defined in 1929 by the International Steam Table Conference by the relation

$$1 \text{ I.T. calorie} = \tfrac{1}{860} \text{ international watt-hour} \qquad (3\text{-}10)$$

By common consent, the British thermal unit (BTU) used in the engineering steam tables is defined in terms of the steam calorie so as to retain the convenient relation

$$1 \text{ I.T. calorie/gram} = 1.8 \text{ BTU/lb} \qquad (3\text{-}11)$$

The artificial, conventional thermochemical calorie that was used after about 1930 in all the research laboratories in the United States dealing with thermochemistry and chemical thermodynamics was defined completely by the relation

$$1 \text{ calorie} = 4.1833 \text{ international joules} \qquad (3\text{-}12)$$

Beginning January 1, 1948, this calorie was redefined in terms of absolute joules, using the 1947 National Bureau of Standards relation between the international and absolute electric units, so that

$$1 \text{ calorie} = 4.1840 \text{ absolute joules} \qquad (3\text{-}13)$$

With this new definition, the thermochemical calorie represents exactly the same quantity of energy as before, and all the values previously reported in terms of the thermochemical calorie remain unchanged. As is obvious from the definition, the thermochemical calorie is independent of the heat capacity of water.

Table A,26 gives the values of the fundamental constants recommended as of July 1, 1951 by the Committee on Physical Chemistry of the Division of Chemistry and Chemical Technology of the National Research Council.

A,4. Energy and the First Law of Thermodynamics. The property of every thermodynamic system called its energy, E, is characterized by the fact that it is fully conserved over all systems in every process. Energy can enter or leave a system only through its surroundings. The existence of energy is manifested to us through observations of the changes which it produces in material things. It is important to note that distinction between various kinds of energy is made only as regards energy being transferred from one system to another. Once a given quantity of energy of a given kind has been taken up by a system, it is merged into the energy of the given system as a whole.

Different processes may have associated with them quite appreciably different amounts of energy. The following examples illustrate the tremendous variation in the magnitude of the changes in energy which accompany different processes: (1) processes involving changes in the nuclei of atoms, as in the nuclear fission of uranium 235 with one neutron to form one atom of barium, one atom of krypton, and an assumed number of three neutrons, in which process the energy given up by the system to the surroundings is approximately 4×10^{12} cal/mole; (2) processes involving changes in the valence electrons of atoms or molecules, as in the recombination of an electron with a proton to form a neutral hydrogen atom, in which process the energy given up by the system to the surroundings is about 3×10^5 cal/mole; (3) processes involving changes in molecular structure, as in the reaction of hydrogen with oxygen to form water, in which process the energy given up by the system to the surroundings is about 6×10^4 cal/mole; (4) processes involving changes of state, from solid to liquid or liquid to gas, as in the condensation of water vapor to liquid water, in which process the energy given up by the system to the surroundings is about 10^4 cal/mole; (5) processes involving changes in translational, rotational, and vibrational energy in a molecule, as in the process of cooling gaseous water from $1,000°K$ to $300°K$, where the energy given up by the system is about 5×10^3 cal/mole; (6) processes involving changes in mechanical potential energy, as when a mass of water is dropped from a height of 555 ft, where the energy given up by the system to its surroundings is about 7 cal/mole; (7) processes involving changes in mechanical kinetic energy, as in the stopping of a mass of water traveling with a speed of 50 miles per hour, where the energy given up by the system to its surroundings is about 1 cal/mole.

In every process that occurs, every change in energy must be in accord with the first law of thermodynamics. This law governs not only the transfer of energy from one place to another, but also all the transformations of energy in any of its many forms.

The first law of thermodynamics may be summed up in the statement that whenever any process occurs the sum of all the changes in energy of all the systems involved is zero:

$$\sum dE = 0 \qquad (4\text{-}1)$$

In subjecting a given process to the scrutiny of the first law, it is usually convenient to specify or define a particular system which is inclosed by a surface through which passes, in or out, energy in its various forms, and to let all the other possible systems constitute one large surrounding system. Whenever any process occurs, the net energy taken up by the given system will be exactly equal to the energy lost by the surroundings, and vice versa. The increase in the energy of a given system participating in a process will be equal to the sum of all the different kinds of energy taken up by the system from the surroundings less the sum of all the different kinds of energy given up by the system to the surroundings. For convenience in later derivations and calculations, it is desirable to distinguish three kinds of energy transferred between the system and its surroundings and to take the algebraic sign of each as positive when the given energy is taken up or absorbed by the system. This may be expressed by the relation[2]

$$dE = \delta q + \delta w + \delta u \qquad (4\text{-}2)$$

[2] The differential symbol d is used to mean the infinitesimal increment or differential increase of a given property, as dE, the increment or differential increase in the energy of the system. The symbol δ is used to represent an infinitesimal value of something, as of one of the kinds of energy transferred in the process, as δq, an infinitesimal quantity of heat energy absorbed by the system.

In Eq. 4-2, dE is the differential increase in the energy of the system and δq, δw, and δu are infinitesimal quantities of the different kinds of energy taken up by the system, with q representing heat energy, w representing "pV" work energy, and u representing all other forms of energy. In order to be added properly, the energies q, w, and u must be expressed in the same unit of energy, and must be labeled properly with respect to sign. Positive values of q, w, or u indicate that the given energy has been taken up by the system from the surroundings. Correspondingly, negative values of q, w, or u indicate that the given energy has been lost by the system to the surroundings.

Since the energy of the system in the state A is fixed completely by the properties of state A, and similarly for state B, the increase in energy, $E_B - E_A$, or ΔE, as the system passes from state A to state B, is independent of the path followed in going from A to B. That is to say, for given states A and B, the value of ΔE is invariant. But q, w, and u may have any values whatsoever so long as their algebraic sum is equal to ΔE.

It is important to note that the first law of thermodynamics is concerned only with changes in the energy of material systems and not with the absolute value of the energy of any system. However, in making thermodynamic calculations of energy, particularly of the energy of chemical reactions, it is convenient to select certain reference states of the substances to which are assigned values of zero energy. Such reference states may be, for example, the chemical elements in the physical state in which they occur naturally at 25°C, the chemical atoms in the gaseous monatomic state at the absolute zero of temperature, or, also at the absolute zero of temperature, the neutrons, protons, and electrons from which atoms may be formed. The selection of any such set of reference states, including the last named, is essentially arbitrary, since it is conceivable that even more fundamental units of matter may be discovered. The use of any given set of arbitrary reference states for assigning values of energy is desirable insofar as their use facilitates the making of thermodynamic calculations.

A,5. Equivalence of Mass and Energy. Embodied in the principle of relativity announced by Einstein in 1905 is the following important relation:

$$E = \frac{m_0 c^2}{\left(1 - \dfrac{v^2}{c^2}\right)^{\frac{1}{2}}} \tag{5-1}$$

In this equation, E is the energy of the body, m_0 is the mass of the body at rest, v is the velocity of the body, and c is a constant whose value is the velocity of light. The expression on the right side of the equation may be expanded into a series for which, at ordinary velocities, the terms beyond the second are negligible, so that, for velocities which are small compared to the velocity of light, the relation reduces to

$$E = m_0c^2 + \tfrac{1}{2}m_0v^2 \tag{5-2}$$

In this equation, the term $\tfrac{1}{2}m_0v^2$ is the ordinary mechanical kinetic energy of a moving body and the term m_0c^2 is the energy of the body at rest.

Considering systems at rest, the foregoing equation reduces to

$$E = m_0c^2 \tag{5-3}$$

indicating that the energy of a system at rest is equal to the square of the velocity of light times the mass of the system. The great practical usefulness of Einstein's theory, as expressed in Eq. 5-3, lies in the fact that it relates changes of mass with changes of energy. If the equation is applied to a given system that has gone from an initial state A to a final state B, then

$$E_B - E_A = (m_{0_B} - m_{0_A})c^2 \tag{5-4}$$

or

$$\Delta E = c^2 \Delta m_0 \tag{5-5}$$

According to this equation, any gain or loss in energy by a given system is accompanied by a corresponding and proportional gain or loss in the mass of the given system. Letting the Einstein constant of proportionality be represented by the symbol Y, one may write

$$\Delta E = Y \Delta m_0 \tag{5-6}$$

The value of the Einstein constant Y is (approximately) 2.15×10^{13} cal/g. That is to say, a gain in mass of 1 g corresponds to a gain in energy of more than 2.1×10^{13} cal or 2.5×10^7 kw-hr.

It is instructive to calculate the changes in mass accompanying the several representative types of thermodynamic processes listed in the preceding article. Taking the processes in the order given, we find the changes in mass, Δm_0, to be, in g/mole, -0.2, -1.4×10^{-8}, -3×10^{-9}, -5×10^{-10}, and -2×10^{-10}, for the first five processes. In each of the foregoing processes involving a decrease in energy, there is a corresponding decrease in mass. But, except for the reaction involving nuclear fission, the changes in mass are too small to be detected on the most sensitive balance available. Every system that has a change in energy has at the same time a corresponding and proportional change in mass, although for all ordinary chemical reactions and processes the change in mass is far too small to be detected, let alone measured. If it were possible to have a balance of unlimited sensitivity, measurements of energy could be made entirely by means of such a balance and calorimetric measurements would no longer need to be made.

Since nuclear reactions usually involve extremely large changes in energy, it became possible with them for the first time to subject the Einstein relation between mass and energy to experimental test. It was found that the changes in mass and energy were in accord with the Einstein relation within the accuracy and precision of the experimental observations.

The nuclear reaction of protons with lithium to form helium is one in which the system undergoes a decrease in mass and a decrease in energy. The energy lost by the reacting system is given up to the surroundings. However, this is not a reaction which may be used as a source of energy because many of the high speed protons do not react and the kinetic energy that was given to them is wasted. The energy which is supplied to the many nonreacting protons is far greater than the energy released by the few reacting atoms. That is to say, a far greater quantity of energy is required to maintain the reaction than is liberated by it.

In 1939, the discovery of the fission of uranium was reported. As was made evident by the truly tremendous amount of work done on this nuclear reaction during the recent war period, the fission of uranium can be made a self-sustaining chain reaction. In the case of such reactions, one or more of the products of the reaction are particles which are reactants necessary to maintain the reaction. In the fission of uranium 235, the decrease in mass is about 0.001 g per g. Therefore, the fission of 1 gram of uranium 235 would result in the transfer to the surroundings of an energy equal to 2.1×10^{10} cal, or about 2.5×10^4 kw-hr. These figures mean that the energy released in the fission of 1 mass unit of uranium 235 is about the same as that released in the combustion of 3,000,000 mass units of coal.

A,6. Energy, Heat Content (Enthalpy), and Heat Capacity. When a system participates in any process,

$$dE = \delta q + \delta w + \delta u \qquad (6\text{-}1)$$

In this equation q, w, and u represent heat energy, pV work energy, and all other kinds of energy, respectively. When a given process involves only heat energy and pV work energy, then this equation reduces to

$$dE = \delta q + \delta w \qquad (6\text{-}2)$$

Suppose that the system is in pressure equilibrium with the surroundings in the sense that, if the pressure exerted by the system on the surroundings is p, then the pressure exerted by the surroundings on the system is either $p + dp$ or $p - dp$. Under these circumstances, the pV work energy is

$$\delta w = -pdV \qquad (6\text{-}3)$$

where dV is the differential increase in the volume of the system. If the volume of the system increases, then the value of dV is positive and the value of δw is negative, indicating that the system gives up a positive amount of pV work energy to the surroundings. If the volume of the system decreases, then the value of dV is negative and the value of δw is positive, indicating that in such case the system takes up a positive amount of pV work energy from the surroundings. When the pressure exerted by the surroundings on the system is constant, then Eq. 6-3 becomes

$$\delta w = -d(pV) \tag{6-4}$$

For such a process at constant pressure, with only heat energy and pV work energy involved, we have

$$dE = \delta q - d(pV) \tag{6-5}$$

or

$$d(E + pV) = \delta q \tag{6-6}$$

This equation shows that, for any process occurring at constant pressure, with only heat energy and pV work energy involved, the heat absorbed from the surroundings is equal to the increment in the function $E + pV$.

Because many processes actually occur at constant pressure (often that of the atmosphere) with only heat energy and pV work energy involved, and because under these circumstances the heat energy absorbed by the system from the surroundings is equal to the increment in the value of the function $E + pV$ for the system, it has been found convenient to define

$$H = E + pV \tag{6-7}$$

The function H is called the **heat content** or **enthalpy**. With this nomenclature, Eq. 6-6 becomes

$$dH = \delta q \tag{6-8}$$

If the given process of this kind takes place between an initial state A and a final state B, then, on integration,

$$\int_A^B dH = H_B - H_A = \Delta H = q \tag{6-9}$$

Calorimetric measurements of the heat energy associated with a process occurring in a calorimetric reaction vessel at constant pressure, with no other energy than heat energy and work energy of the "pV" kind involved, yield a value for the increment in heat content (or enthalpy) of the given process, in accordance with the foregoing equation.

Just as was the value of ΔE, the value of ΔH is uniquely determined for a given system by the initial and final states, A and B, respectively, and is independent of the path followed in going from state A to state B. While the thermodynamic function, $H = E + pV$, was defined initially because of its utility in connection with processes occurring at constant pressure, the fact that it is a thermodynamic property of a system makes its use possible under any conditions of temperature, pressure, etc. In aerodynamics problems, enthalpy is frequently considered in processes involving changes of pressure.

The heat capacity C of a system is defined as the ratio of the heat energy absorbed by the system from the surroundings to the increase in temperature of the system, as

$$C = \frac{\delta q}{dT} \tag{6-10}$$

In general, the heat capacity of a system is determined by adding a measured quantity of heat energy to the system and measuring the resulting change in temperature, with the quantity of heat energy added being such as to produce not too large a change in temperature. The heat capacity so defined is perfectly general and may be applied to any system of one or more components and of one or more phases.

The heat capacity at constant volume, C_V, of a system is defined as the ratio of the heat energy absorbed by the system from the surroundings to the increase in temperature of the system, while the system remains at constant volume,

$$C_V = \left(\frac{\delta q}{dT}\right)_V \tag{6-11}$$

In this process, there is no work energy of the pV kind because the volume is constant, and the only energy involved is heat energy. Application of the first law to this process yields $dE = \delta q$, whence

$$C_V = \left(\frac{\partial E}{\partial T}\right)_V \tag{6-12}$$

The heat capacity at constant pressure, C_p, of a system is defined as the ratio of the heat energy absorbed by the system from the surroundings to the increase in temperature of the system, all at constant pressure,

$$C_p = \left(\frac{\delta q}{dT}\right)_p \tag{6-13}$$

In this process, the work energy is of the pV kind, and, since the pressure is constant, is equal to the pressure times the change in volume. Application of the first law yields

$$dE = \delta q + \delta w = \delta q - pdV \tag{6-14}$$

Since the pressure is constant, $pdV = d(pV)$ and

$$d(E + pV) = dH = \delta q \tag{6-15}$$

Then

$$C_p = \left(\frac{\partial H}{\partial T}\right)_p \tag{6-16}$$

The relation between the heat capacity at constant volume and the heat capacity at constant pressure may be derived from the definition of the heat content, letting the energy E be a function of V and T. The relation between C_p and C_V is

$$C_p - C_V = \left(\frac{\partial V}{\partial T}\right)_p \left[p + \left(\frac{\partial E}{\partial V}\right)_T\right] \tag{6-17}$$

An equation similar to this but containing the pressure as a variable instead of the volume may be derived by letting the energy be expressed as a function of pressure and temperature and proceeding as before.

A,7. Application of the First Law to Gases. One of the important applications of the first law of thermodynamics is in connection with processes involving the compression and expansion of gases. Such processes may be isothermal or adiabatic and reversible or irreversible. Any process that takes place at a constant temperature, or any process that is fully specified by the initial and final states when these are at the same temperature, is an isothermal process. Any process occurring in such a way that no heat energy is absorbed or lost by the given system through the boundary which separates the system from the surroundings is an adiabatic process. A simple reversible process is one occurring in such a manner that the restoring force differs from the deforming force only by a differential amount. In the simple reversible expansion of a gas, the deforming force is the pressure p of the gas itself, and the restoring force is represented by an opposing pressure, $p - dp$. Similarly, in the simple reversible compression of a gas, the deforming force is an external pressure, $p + dp$, operating against a restoring force represented by the pressure p of the gas. A process involving fluid dynamics may be a rapid one and still remain reversible. In such cases, reversibility is maintained if the state of the system or element of mass is definable in a thermodynamic sense at each stage of the process. In general, an irreversible process is one which is not reversible.

In any discussion concerning the thermodynamic properties of a gaseous substance, it is convenient to define what has come to be known as the ideal gas. In the words of Lewis and Randall [2], the ideal gas is an invented substance, defined by certain properties which are not possessed by any actual substance, but which are supposed to be approached by every actual gas as its pressure is indefinitely diminished. The ideal gas is defined by the following relations:

$$pV = RT \tag{7-1}$$

$$\left(\frac{\partial E}{\partial V}\right)_T = 0 \tag{7-2}$$

The work performed in the expansion or compression of a gas is evaluated from the physical relation that the amount of work is equal to the pressure multiplied by the change in volume. If w is the pV work energy absorbed by the gas during a given process, then, during either expansion or compression,

$$\delta w = -p\,dV \quad \text{and} \quad w = -\int p\,dV \tag{7-3}$$

On the expansion of a gas from a volume V_A to a volume V_B, different amounts of work may be performed by the gas on the surroundings, depending upon the resisting pressure. If the expansion is performed reversibly, with the resisting pressure differing from the pressure of the gas itself only by a differential amount, then the work done by the gas on the surroundings is a maximum. If during the expansion the resisting pressure is a constant and equal to the final pressure p_B, then the work done by the gas is evaluated as $p_B(V_B - V_A)$. If the resisting pressure during the expansion is zero, as by expansion of the gas into an evacuated space, then the work performed by the gas is zero.

If the relation between the pressure and volume of the gas undergoing reversible expansion or compression is known and expressible by means of an equation explicit in terms of either the pressure or the volume, then the pV work energy may be calculated analytically. For example, in the case of an ideal gas at constant temperature,

$$\delta w = -p\,dV = -(RT/V)dV = -RT\,d \ln V \tag{7-4}$$

or, for the finite change from an initial volume V_A to a final volume V_B,

$$w = -RT \ln (V_B/V_A) \tag{7-5}$$

When an ideal gas is expanded or compressed, with only heat energy and pV work energy involved, the process conforms to the first law, $\Delta E = q + w$. Since the energy of an ideal gas at constant temperature is constant and independent of the volume, then in the isothermal expansion or compression of an ideal gas, $\Delta E = 0$, and $q + w = 0$, or $q = -w$. This tells us that in the isothermal expansion of an ideal gas, the heat energy taken up by the gas from the surroundings is equal to the pV work energy performed by the gas on the surroundings (which is the negative of the pV work energy absorbed by the gas from the surroundings). Similarly, in the isothermal compression of an ideal gas, the pV work energy absorbed by the gas from the surroundings is equal to the heat energy given up by the gas to the surroundings (which is the negative of the heat energy absorbed by the gas from the surroundings).

In the reversible expansion or compression of an ideal gas in an isothermal process,

$$w = -RT \ln (V_B/V_A) \tag{7-6}$$

This equation gives the value of the pV work energy in the isothermal expansion or compression of an ideal gas. Since, for such a process, the heat energy absorbed is equal to the negative of the pV work energy absorbed, we can also write the heat energy absorbed in such a process as

$$q = RT \ln (V_B/V_A) \tag{7-7}$$

Because for an ideal gas

$$V_B/V_A = p_A/p_B \tag{7-8}$$

these equations may also be expressed in terms of the initial and final pressures.

In the adiabatic expansion or compression of a gas, with only pV work energy involved, the first law reduces to $dE = \delta w$. For the ideal gas, the energy is independent of the volume, and at constant volume,

$$dE = C_V dT \tag{7-9}$$

Then

$$C_V dT = -p dV \tag{7-10}$$

Substituting RT/V for p and integrating, assuming C_V constant, one obtains

$$T V^{\frac{R}{C_V}} = c \tag{7-11}$$

The isothermal expansion or compression of a real gas, with only heat energy and pV work energy involved in the process, is governed by the relation

$$\Delta E = q + w \tag{7-12}$$

In the case of the ideal gas, this equation is simplified because at constant temperature the change in energy is zero. Further, with the ideal gas in an isothermal reversible process, the pV work energy is readily evaluated from the initial and final volumes and hence the heat energy becomes known. However, with a real gas in an isothermal reversible expansion or compression a knowledge is required of how the energy of the gas changes with pressure or volume, in order to evaluate ΔE, and of how the pressure is related to the volume, in order to evaluate the pV work energy.

In the adiabatic expansion or compression of a gas, with only pV work energy involved, the first law relates the change in energy to the pV work. If the expansion or compression is reversible, then $dE = -p dV$. In order to apply this equation to the adiabatic expansion or compression of a real gas, data must be available on the p, V, T relations of the gas or on the energy as a function of the volume and temperature.

A,8. Entropy and the Second Law of Thermodynamics. Every system, if left to itself, changes spontaneously at a slow or rapid rate in such a way as to approach a definite final state of rest or equilibrium. Some simple examples of such spontaneous change are the following: (1) the free expansion of a gas from a region of high pressure to one of low pressure; (2) the diffusion of a solute from a region of high concentration to one of low concentration; (3) the passage of heat from a region of high temperature to one of low temperature; and (4) the occurrence of a chemical reaction, as the combustion of carbon in oxygen to produce carbon dioxide. In each of these cases, the spontaneous change continues until equilibrium is attained, that is until (1) the pressure becomes uniform, (2) the concentration becomes uniform, (3) the temperature becomes uniform, and (4) what we may at this point call the thermodynamic stability becomes uniform. As these systems move toward equilibrium, they lose some measure of their capacity for spontaneous change.

In each of the above examples, it follows that the reverse change of moving away from equilibrium will not occur spontaneously, and, further, that some external energy or force is necessary to move the given system in a direction away from the state of equilibrium, that is, to increase the capacity for spontaneous change in the given system. It is obvious, also, that in each of the above cases the capacity of the given system for spontaneous change is greater (1) the greater the difference in pressure, (2) the greater the difference in concentration, (3) the greater the difference in temperature, and (4) the greater the difference in the thermodynamic stability between the initial state and the equilibrium state. It is important to note that in many such spontaneous changes there may be no change whatever in the energy of the given system. A simple example of such a case is the isothermal expansion of an ideal gas, in which expansion the gas loses some measure of its capacity for spontaneous change, but undergoes no change in energy.

This brings us to the idea that there exists a property of every thermodynamic system called its entropy, S, which is associated with its capacity for spontaneous change. Qualitatively, we can arrange that this property of entropy of a system shall increase in value as the system undergoes some spontaneous change and hence loses some of its capacity for spontaneous change. That is, in the case of the isothermal expansion of an ideal gas, the entropy of the gas would increase with increase in its volume and decrease with decrease in its volume.

Given a system capable of spontaneous change from state A to state B, it would be possible theoretically to include in the process a mechanism whereby, as the spontaneous change occurred and the capacity for spontaneous change of the given system decreased, an increase in capacity for spontaneous change would be built up in the surroundings in an amount equal in magnitude to the decrease in capacity for spontaneous change occurring in the given system. Such a process would be what we have already called a reversible process, wherein there exist no forces (or pressures) differing by more than a differential amount, and wherein no heat energy is produced from other kinds of energy by friction, electrical resistance, etc. It is important to note that a reversible process is one from which have been eliminated all friction, electrical resistance, and other causes of the dissipation of energy. The reversible process is therefore not an actual process but an ideal process which is approached in the limit by an actual process as the dissipation of energy is reduced further and further through friction, etc. Every actual process that occurs, therefore, is accompanied by a decrease in capacity for spontaneous change, or an increase in entropy, the decrease in capacity for spontaneous change, or the increase in entropy, being greater the greater the departure from reversibility of the given process. In the study of gas dynamics, the local stagnation pressure is a measure of the capacity of the gas to flow at high velocity, and this capacity is diminished as the stagnation pressure diminishes. The meaning of entropy in this sense is discussed by Ferri [7].

According to the second law, entropy is fully conserved over all systems in every reversible process. That is, for a reversible process, the sum of all the changes in entropy, taken over all the systems participating in the process, is zero. If the process is not a reversible one, then for all systems participating, the sum of all the changes in entropy is greater than zero. We can then say that for any process that may occur, for all systems participating, the sum of all the changes in entropy will be equal to or greater than zero.

In subjecting a given process to the scrutiny of the second law, it is usually convenient to specify or define a particular system which is inclosed by a surface and to let all the other possible systems constitute one large surrounding system. Whenever any reversible process occurs, the entropy gained by the system will be exactly equal to the entropy lost by the surroundings, and vice versa. Quantitatively, the increase in entropy of a given system participating in a reversible process is defined as

$$dS = \frac{\delta q}{T} \tag{8-1}$$

At the same time, the surroundings will undergo a decrease in entropy of exactly the same amount.

We have seen how the property of entropy of a system is associated with its capacity for spontaneous change, with the value of entropy reaching a maximum as the capacity for spontaneous change reaches a minimum. To appreciate better the significance of the property of entropy, it is helpful to associate entropy with probability. Here we are concerned with the relation between the entropy of a system in a particular state as related to the probability of its existence in that particular one of its (usually many) allowable states of existence. Consider a system, at a given temperature T, consisting of a rectangular box having a volume V_B and containing one single molecule of an ideal gas. Suppose the box is arranged in such a way that, without involving any energy, a partition can be passed through the walls to separate instantaneously a volume V_A of the total volume V_B. The probability that the molecule of gas will at a given instant be found in the volume V_A is equal to the ratio of the volume V_A to the total volume V_B. If the box contained two molecules of the ideal gas instead of one, the probability that both molecules would at any instant be found in the volume V_A would be $(V_A/V_B)^2$. If the box contained x molecules of the ideal gas, the probability that all the molecules would at any instant be found in the volume V_A would be $(V_A/V_B)^x$, and if the box contained one mole N of molecules of the ideal gas, then the probability that all the molecules would at any instant be found in the volume V_A would be $(V_A/V_B)^N$. Since the probability for the existence of the molecules in the total volume V_B is unity, the relation also gives the ratio of the probability of the existence of the molecules in the volume V_A to the probability for their existence in the total volume V_B, as

$$W_A/W_B = (V_A/V_B)^N, \quad \text{or} \quad W_B/W_A = (V_B/V_A)^N \qquad (8\text{-}2)$$

Let us now arbitrarily define the following relation between entropy, per mole of molecules in the ideal gaseous state, and the probability of existence, corresponding to the number of states of existence available to the system:

$$S = k \ln W \qquad (8\text{-}3)$$

In this equation, the constant of proportionality is the Boltzmann gas constant. According to this relation, for the one mole of molecules in the ideal gas state, the increase in entropy from state A to state B is

$$S_B - S_A = k \ln (W_B/W_A) \qquad (8\text{-}4)$$

Substituting, one obtains

$$S_B - S_A = k \ln (V_B/V_A)^N = Nk \ln (V_B/V_A) = R \ln (V_B/V_A) \qquad (8\text{-}5)$$

A,9. Entropy of Substances in Relation to Temperature, Volume, Pressure, and Physical State. If any substance is subjected to a reversible process in which only heat energy and pV work energy are involved, then by combining the first and second laws, we obtain

$$dE = TdS - pdV \qquad (9\text{-}1)$$

This equation is an important relation describing how the five fundamental thermodynamic properties of a given substance are related as that substance is subjected to reversible changes in which are involved only heat energy and the pV work energy arising from the reversible changes in pressure and volume.

If a given substance absorbs a small amount of heat energy, δq, in a reversible process with no other energy involved except pV work energy, there will occur, in general, corresponding changes in the five fundamental thermodynamic properties, dp, dV, dT, dE, and dS. But we have defined the increase in entropy to be $\delta q/T$ and the heat capacity to be $\delta q/dT$. Hence

$$TdS = CdT \tag{9-2}$$

or

$$dS = (C/T)dT = Cd \ln T \tag{9-3}$$

If the pressure is constant, the heat capacity is that at constant pressure, C_p, and we can write,

$$\left(\frac{\partial S}{\partial T}\right)_p = \frac{C_p}{T} \tag{9-4}$$

Similarly, if the process occurs at constant volume, we can write

$$\left(\frac{\partial S}{\partial T}\right)_v = \frac{C_V}{T} \tag{9-5}$$

Since

$$C_p = \left(\frac{\partial H}{\partial T}\right)_p \tag{9-6}$$

we have

$$\left(\frac{\partial S}{\partial T}\right)_p = \frac{1}{T}\left(\frac{\partial H}{\partial T}\right)_p \tag{9-7}$$

Differentiating both sides with pressure at constant temperature, we have

$$\frac{\partial^2 S}{\partial T \partial p} = \frac{1}{T}\frac{\partial^2 H}{\partial T \partial p} = \frac{1}{T}\left(\frac{\partial C_p}{\partial p}\right)_T \tag{9-8}$$

or

$$\frac{\partial^2 H}{\partial T \partial p} = T\frac{\partial^2 S}{\partial T \partial p} \tag{9-9}$$

Similarly, we can derive the relation

$$\frac{\partial^2 S}{\partial T \partial p} = \frac{1}{T}\frac{\partial^2 E}{\partial T \partial p} = \frac{1}{T}\left(\frac{\partial C_V}{\partial V}\right)_T \tag{9-10}$$

or

$$\frac{\partial^2 E}{\partial T \partial p} = T\frac{\partial^2 S}{\partial T \partial V} \tag{9-11}$$

For a substance subjected to a reversible process at constant temperature, with only heat energy and pV work energy involved, Eq. 9-1 may be divided by dV at constant T, whence

$$\left(\frac{\partial E}{\partial V}\right)_T = T\left(\frac{\partial S}{\partial V}\right)_T - p \tag{9-12}$$

Differentiating with temperature at constant volume, we obtain

$$\frac{\partial^2 E}{\partial V \partial T} = T\frac{\partial^2 S}{\partial V \partial T} + \left(\frac{\partial S}{\partial V}\right)_T - \left(\frac{\partial p}{\partial T}\right)_V \tag{9-13}$$

Combining with Eq. 9-11, we have

$$\left(\frac{\partial S}{\partial V}\right)_T = \left(\frac{\partial p}{\partial T}\right)_V \tag{9-14}$$

From the definition

$$H = E + pV \tag{9-15}$$

we can write

$$dH = dE + pdV + Vdp \tag{9-16}$$

Combination of Eq. 9-1 and 0 16 gives

$$dH = TdS + Vdp \tag{9-17}$$

Dividing Eq. 9-17 by dp at constant T, we obtain the relation

$$\left(\frac{\partial H}{\partial p}\right)_T = T\left(\frac{\partial S}{\partial p}\right)_T + V \tag{9-18}$$

Differentiating with temperature at constant pressure, we obtain

$$\frac{\partial^2 H}{\partial p \partial T} = T\frac{\partial^2 S}{\partial p \partial T} + \left(\frac{\partial S}{\partial p}\right)_T + \left(\frac{\partial V}{\partial T}\right)_p \tag{9-19}$$

Combining with Eq. 9-9, we obtain

$$\left(\frac{\partial S}{\partial p}\right)_T = -\left(\frac{\partial V}{\partial T}\right)_p \tag{9-20}$$

At some given temperature and pressure, a substance can change from one phase to another with the absorption or liberation of heat energy. Examples of such changes in phase that involve absorption of heat energy, with a corresponding increase in the energy content of the phase that is formed, are the transition from one crystalline form to another, melting of a crystal to liquid, vaporization of liquid to gas, and sublimation of a solid to gas. In each case, at the given temperature and pressure, the reverse process occurs with liberation of energy by the substance. At the given equilibrium temperature and pressure, we can write for the change in phase, in general terms,

$$MX \text{ (phase } a) = MX \text{ (phase } b) \tag{9-21}$$

Since this is a reversible process, with the change from one phase to another taking place on the absorption or liberation of heat energy, we may write from the second law,

$$dS = \delta q/T' \tag{9-22}$$

But we have found that for a process taking place at constant pressure

$$\delta q = dH \tag{9-23}$$

Therefore,

$$dS = dH/T \tag{9-24}$$

and, since the temperature is constant,

$$S_B - S_A = (H_B - H_A)/T \tag{9-25}$$

or

$$\Delta S = \Delta H/T \tag{9-26}$$

For the several kinds of changes in phase, this equation would be written as follows:

$$\Delta S \text{ (transition)} = \Delta H \text{ (transition)}/T \tag{9-27}$$

$$\Delta S \text{ (melting)} = \Delta H \text{ (melting)}/T \tag{9-28}$$

$$\Delta S \text{ (vaporization)} = \Delta H \text{ (vaporization)}/T \tag{9-29}$$

$$\Delta S \text{ (sublimation)} = \Delta H \text{ (sublimation)}/T \tag{9-30}$$

It should be noted that the foregoing equations are applicable only for the temperature and pressure at which the two given phases are in equilibrium.

Given $n_1, n_2, n_3, \ldots, n_i$ moles of different ideal gases, each at the same pressure p and temperature T, and having volumes $V_1, V_2, V_3, \ldots, V_i$, respectively. Suppose these gases are in adjoining compartments in a large box, with the partitions between the compartments occupying an insignificant volume. It is desired to evaluate the change in entropy occurring when the partitions are removed and the several gases are permitted to mix, all at constant temperature, and with the pressure remaining unchanged. After mixing, the total volume is the sum of the volumes of the separate gases before mixing, and the mole fraction X_i of each gas in the mixture is equal to its original volume divided by the total volume. On mixing, each gas passes from its original volume V_i to the common final volume $\sum V_i$. The increase in entropy for this change in volume for each gas is independent of the presence of the other ideal gases, and the total change in entropy is obtained by adding together the increases in entropy for each of the gases. If the total amount of all the gases is taken as one mole, then the number of moles of each gas is equal to its mole fraction. The increase in entropy, ΔS_i, for each gas on passing from its original volume to the final volume is given by

$$\Delta S_i = X_i R \ln \frac{\sum V_i}{V_i} \tag{9-31}$$

Substituting, the mole fraction of the given component for the ratio of its initial volume to the final volume, this equation becomes

$$\Delta S_i = X_i R \ln (1/X_i) = -R X_i \ln X_i \tag{9-32}$$

The sum of the increases in entropy for all the gases involved is

$$\Delta S \text{ (mixing)} = \sum \Delta S_i = -R \sum X_i \ln X_i \tag{9-33}$$

This equation gives the entropy of mixing ideal gases when the pressures of the different gases before mixing are identical and the same as the final pressure after mixing. In such a case, it follows that the final volume of the mixture is the sum of the original volumes of the separate cases. This equation also shows that for ideal gases the entropy of a given kind of gas occupying a given volume is independent of what other gases occupy the identical space. To calculate the entropy of mixing ideal gases which are originally at different pressures to form a mixture in which the final pressure is also different, a simple procedure is to evaluate the change in entropy for bringing each of the different gases to a common pressure, to evaluate the entropy of mixing the gases at this common pressure, and to evaluate the change in entropy on bringing the final mixture from this common pressure to the specified final pressure. The sum of all these changes in entropy will give the total entropy of mixing for the specified case.

A,10. Energy in Relation to Pressure and Volume. From the equations of the preceding article, we obtain

$$\left(\frac{\partial E}{\partial V} \right)_T = T \left(\frac{\partial p}{\partial T} \right)_V - p \tag{10-1}$$

This equation permits us to calculate for any substance its change of energy with volume at constant temperature from a knowledge of the temperature, pressure, and the change of pressure with temperature at constant volume. In other words, if the p, V, T relations for any substance (solid, liquid, or gas) are known, the change of energy with volume at constant temperature may be calculated.

From the equations of the preceding article, we obtain

$$\left(\frac{\partial H}{\partial p} \right)_T = -T \left(\frac{\partial V}{\partial T} \right)_p + V \tag{10-2}$$

This equation makes it possible to calculate the change of heat content (enthalpy) with pressure at constant temperature of any given substance from a knowledge of the temperature, volume, and the change of volume with temperature at constant pressure. The change of heat content with pressure at constant temperature may be calculated for any substance (solid, liquid, or gas) for which the p, V, T relations are known.

From the definition of the heat content, we may write

$$E = H - pV \qquad (10\text{-}3)$$

Differentiating with pressure at constant temperature, we obtain

$$\left(\frac{\partial E}{\partial p}\right)_T = \left(\frac{\partial H}{\partial p}\right)_T - p\left(\frac{\partial V}{\partial p}\right)_T - V \qquad (10\text{-}4)$$

whence

$$\left(\frac{\partial E}{\partial p}\right)_T = -T\left(\frac{\partial V}{\partial T}\right)_p - p\left(\frac{\partial V}{\partial p}\right)_T \qquad (10\text{-}5)$$

This equation permits the calculation of the change of energy with pressure at constant temperature for any substance for which the p, V, T relations are known or for which, specifically, the values of the expansion with temperature and the compression with pressure are known.

The foregoing equations on the change of energy and heat content with volume or pressure are applicable to any substance in any physical state. In general, however, the change in energy with pressure for a condensed substance, liquid or solid, is not large because the values of expansion with temperature and compression with pressure are not large and, further, are of opposite sign and largely tend to cancel. With regard to gases, we have seen that for the ideal gas, by definition, the energy is independent of the volume or pressure at constant temperature. For real gases, however, there is a measurable change of energy with pressure or volume, and several methods of measurement have been developed and used to obtain data on the change of energy or heat content with volume or pressure.

In 1845, Joule described the following experiment: Two large spheres, connected by a valve, were placed in a water bath the temperature of which was measured with a thermometer. One sphere was filled with a gas at a given pressure, and the other sphere was evacuated. When equilibrium with temperature was established, the thermometer was read. Then the valve was opened and the gas permitted to flow into the second sphere until the pressure was equalized. The thermometer was again read. Joule found that there was no observable change in temperature. He concluded, therefore, that within the limits of precision of his measurements, the value of $(\Delta E/\Delta V)_T$ was zero. We know now, however, that

Joule's experiment was not sensitive enough to measure the small change in energy involved in such an experiment.

In 1853, Joule and Thomson reported the results of a different and much more sensitive kind of measurement designed to disclose the change of energy or heat content of a gas with change in pressure. In this experiment, which is shown schematically in Fig. A,10a, a gas is made to flow continuously through a tube containing a porous plug. At state A, in this figure, one mole of the continuously flowing gas is outlined momentarily on the inlet side of the porous plug, and at state B the same mole of gas is outlined at an appropriate later time on the exit side of the porous plug. The drop in pressure due to the flow of gas in the open tube is negligible,

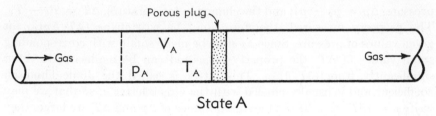

State A

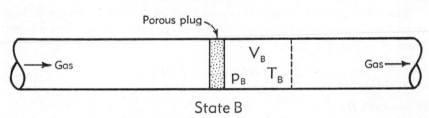

State B

Fig. A,10a. Schematic diagram of the adiabatic Joule-Thomson experiment. After [1] by permission.

for the given rate of flow, compared to the drop in pressure caused by the flow of the gas through the porous plug. The entire tube is completely isolated thermally from the surroundings, so that no heat enters or leaves the gas through the walls of the tube. The process is, therefore, an adiabatic one. In state A, one mole of gas has a pressure p_A, volume V_A, and temperature T_A, and in state B, the corresponding values p_B, V_B, and T_B. The process may be looked upon as transferring one mole of gas from state A to state B. As the gas enters the porous plug from the inlet side, it is being acted upon by the gas behind it at a pressure p_A through the volume V_A. As the gas leaves the porous plug on the exit side, it is acting upon the gas ahead of it at a pressure p_B through the volume V_B. The system is taken as the one mole of the gas. Then according to the first law

$$E_B - E_A = \Delta E = q + w + u \qquad (10\text{-}6)$$

Since the process is adiabatic, and no work other than pV work is involved, $q = 0$, and $u = 0$. The net pV work energy absorbed by the system is equal to

$$w = p_A V_A - p_B V_B \tag{10-7}$$

Hence

$$E_B - E_A = p_A V_A - p_B V_B = -(p_B V_B - p_A V_A) \tag{10-8}$$

or

$$(E_B + p_B V_B) - (E_A + p_A V_A) = H_B - H_A = \Delta H = 0 \tag{10-9}$$

The given process is therefore one that occurs with no change in heat content or that occurs at constant H. In the experiment, the quantities that are measured are the initial or the final pressure; the change in pressure, $\Delta p = p_B - p_A$; and the change in temperature, $\Delta T = T_B - T_A$. The property measured, therefore, may be written as $(\Delta T/\Delta p)_H$, for given values of pressure. Since Δp may be made small, with corresponding small values of ΔT, the property measured can be made not to differ significantly from $(\partial T/\partial p)_H$. This latter is called the Joule-Thomson coefficient and is usually labeled with the Greek letter μ, so that we may write $\mu = (\partial T/\partial p)_H$. If the measured values of Δp and ΔT are large, they may be treated analytically or graphically to obtain the values of the differential coefficient $(\partial T/\partial p)_H$, for given values of pressure.

The relation of the Joule-Thomson coefficient to the change in heat content with pressure at constant temperature can be derived as follows: Given $H = f(p, T)$. Therefore,

$$dH = \left(\frac{\partial H}{\partial T}\right)_p dT + \left(\frac{\partial H}{\partial p}\right)_T dp \tag{10-10}$$

At constant H,

$$0 = \left(\frac{\partial H}{\partial T}\right)_p dT + \left(\frac{\partial H}{\partial p}\right)_T dp \tag{10-11}$$

or

$$0 = \left(\frac{\partial H}{\partial T}\right)_p \left(\frac{\partial T}{\partial p}\right)_H + \left(\frac{\partial H}{\partial p}\right)_T \tag{10-12}$$

or

$$\left(\frac{\partial H}{\partial p}\right)_T = -\left(\frac{\partial T}{\partial p}\right)_H \left(\frac{\partial H}{\partial T}\right)_p \tag{10-13}$$

Therefore

$$\left(\frac{\partial H}{\partial p}\right)_T = -\mu C_p \tag{10-14}$$

This equation permits the calculation of the change of heat content with pressure at constant temperature from values of the heat capacity C_p and the Joule-Thomson coefficient.

The Joule-Thomson experiment is one in which the heat content is constant and changes occur in the pressure and temperature. In 1903 Buckingham suggested, and later Keyes and Collins and Eucken, Clausius, and Berger independently carried out, the porous plug experiment in a new way, by adding heat energy to the gas on the exit side of the porous plug to keep the temperature of the gas the same before and after the change in pressure. Fig. A,10b gives a schematic diagram of the experiment, which involves a gas flowing continuously through the porous plug. At state A, in this figure, one mole of the continuously flowing gas is outlined momentarily on the inlet side of the porous plug, and at state B the same mole of gas is outlined at an appropriate later time on the exit side of the porous plug. As in the Joule-Thomson experiment, the drop in pressure due to the flow of gas in the tube is negligible,

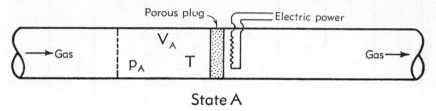

State A

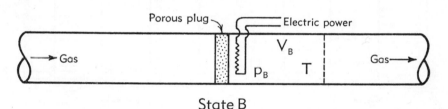

State B

Fig. A,10b.   Schematic diagram of the isothermal Joule-Thomson experiment. After [1] by permission.

for the given rate of flow, compared to the drop in pressure caused by the flow of gas through the porous plug. The quantities measured in this experiment are the following: the pressure on one side of the porous plug; the drop in pressure through the porous plug or the difference in pressure between the two sides of the porous plug; the amount of gas flowing in unit time; and the electric power input. Applying the first law to the process occurring between the states A and B, we can write

$$\Delta E = E_B - E_A = q + w + u \qquad (10\text{-}15)$$

But $u = 0$,

$$w = -(p_B V_B - p_A V_A) \qquad (10\text{-}16)$$

and q is measured electrically. Hence

$$q = E_B - E_A + p_B V_B - p_A V_A = H_B - H_A = \Delta H \qquad (10\text{-}17)$$

⟨ 33 ⟩

The property measured in this experiment may therefore be written as $(\Delta H/\Delta p)_T$ or, if the change in pressure is sufficiently small compared with the variation of heat content with pressure, as $(\partial H/\partial p)_T$. If the measured differences in pressure, Δp, are large, the experimental values of ΔH and Δp may be related analytically, or plotted graphically, in such a way as to permit evaluation of the values of $(\partial H/\partial p)_T$ by appropriate differentiation.

In the Washburn experiment, a known quantity of gas is contained at a known pressure in a suitable vessel in a calorimeter and permitted to expand against the pressure of the atmosphere, at constant temperature. Fig. A,10c gives a schematic diagram of the experiment, showing at

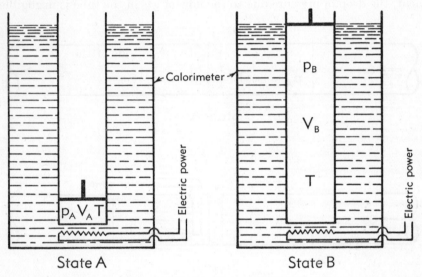

Fig. A,10c.   Schematic diagram of the Washburn experiment. After [1] by permission.

state A the gas before expansion and at state B the gas after expansion to the pressure of the atmosphere. In this experiment, the quantities measured are the following: the mass m, the pressure p_A, and the volume V_A, of the gas in the vessel at the beginning of the experiment; the quantity of electric energy, required to be added to the system to maintain the constant temperature; and the pressure of the atmosphere, p_B. In the expansion of the gas from the initial pressure p_A to the final pressure p_B, work is performed by the gas on the surroundings in an amount equal to the constant pressure of the atmosphere p_B, multiplied by the change in volume $V_B - V_A$. In the actual experiment, it is not practical to contain all of the gas in the calorimeter at its final volume, but the same result is obtained by letting the gas escape from the calorimeter at the constant temperature. This may be accomplished by letting the gas issue from the vessel through a long length of coiled tubing immersed in the water of the calorimeter. It is also necessary to see that the gas issuing from the calorimeter possesses no significant amount of directed kinetic energy or to take account of it if it is significant. The opening at the exit end of the tubing may be made large so that the issuing gas has a small velocity. In the Washburn experiment, the temperature is constant, the electric energy is absorbed by the system as heat energy, and the system performs some pV work on the surroundings. According to the first law, the change in energy of the gas from the initial pressure p_A, to the final pressure p_B, is equal to

$$E_B - E_A = \Delta E = q - w \tag{10-18}$$

where q is the heat produced by the measured electric energy, and w is the work done by the gas in "pushing back" the atmosphere, or $p_B(V_B - V_A)$. Hence

$$E_B - E_A = q - p_B(V_B - V_A) \tag{10-19}$$

or

$$E_B - E_A = q + p_B V_A - p_B V_B \tag{10-20}$$

In this equation, the first and second terms on the right are evaluated from the directly measured quantities. Since the final volume V_B is not measured, the last term on the right side is evaluated from the value of the pV product for the given gas at the given temperature and the atmospheric pressure. For the gases which are likely to be subjected to measurements in the Washburn experiment, there will be known the value of the compressibility factor, $z = pV/RT$, at the given temperature and atmospheric pressure. At this pressure, the compressibility factor will be nearly unity, so that the value of $p_B V_B$ will be nearly equal to RT. In any case,

$$p_B V_B = z_B RT \tag{10-21}$$

so that Eq. 10-20 may be written as

$$E_B - E_A = q + p_B V_A - z_B RT \tag{10-22}$$

and the value of each of the terms on the right side is known. Measurements are made for different values of the initial pressure p_A, and there results a series of values of $E_B - E_A$ for different values of $p_A - p_B$, where p_B is near 1 atmosphere and p_A covers the range of values of the initial pressure. Suitable analytic or graphical treatment of the data will yield values of the coefficient $(\Delta E/\Delta p)_T$, or, in the limit, $(\partial E/\partial p)_T$. The Washburn experiment, therefore, evaluates the change of energy of the gas with pressure at constant temperature.

A,11. Heat Capacity of Substances. It has been largely a matter of experimental convenience that data on the change of energy or heat content with temperature have been obtained mostly in the form of heat capacity at various temperatures rather than as energy or heat content at various temperatures. The values of heat capacity are then expressed analytically or graphically as a function of the temperature, and the values of the energy or heat content as a function of the temperature are obtained from the equations by analytic integration or from the plots by graphical integration. The heat capacity of a substance in a given physical state may be expressed analytically as a function of temperature over a specified range of temperature,

$$C_p = a + bT + cT^2 + \cdots \tag{11-1}$$

or in the form

$$C_p = a' + b'T + \frac{c'}{T^2} \tag{11-2}$$

It is important to note that all such equations must be labeled as to the physical state and the range of temperature for which they are applicable. In order to obtain the heat content explicitly as a function of temperature, the foregoing equations may be integrated. The heat capacity at constant pressure is related as follows to the heat content:

$$dH = C_p dT \tag{11-3}$$

Then, if the range of applicability is from T_A to T_B, one obtains, for any temperature T in the range T_A to T_B,

$$H - H_A = \int_{T_A}^{T} C_p dT \tag{11-4}$$

With the heat capacity given in the form of Eq. 11-1, we have

$$H - H_A = \left(aT + \frac{b}{2} T^2 + \frac{c}{3} T^3 + \cdots \right)$$
$$- \left(aT_A + \frac{b}{2} T_A^2 + \frac{c}{3} T_A^3 + \cdots \right) \tag{11-5}$$

With the heat capacity given in the form of Eq. 11-2, the corresponding equation is

$$H - H_A = \left(a'T + \frac{b'}{2} T^2 - \frac{c'}{T} \right) - \left(a'T_A + \frac{b'}{2} T_A^2 - \frac{c'}{T_A} \right) \tag{11-6}$$

It should be noted again that equations such as the above giving the heat content as a function of temperature for a given physical state of the substance should be used only in the range of temperature for which the corresponding equations for heat capacity are valid. In the case where the heat content itself is measured as a function of the temperature, then equations for heat content may be obtained directly from the experimental data, and the corresponding equations for heat capacity are obtained by differentiation. In such case, the equations for heat capacity will be valid only in the range of temperature for which the corresponding equations for heat content hold. Combination of Eq. 6-21 and Eq. 10-1 yields

$$C_p - C_V = T \left(\frac{\partial V}{\partial T}\right)_p \left(\frac{\partial p}{\partial T}\right)_V \tag{11-7}$$

But for a given substance, the pressure can be expressed as a function of volume and temperature, and

$$\left(\frac{\partial p}{\partial T}\right)_V = - \left(\frac{\partial V}{\partial T}\right)_p \left(\frac{\partial p}{\partial V}\right)_T \tag{11-8}$$

Substituting, we obtain

$$C_p - C_V = -T \left(\frac{\partial V}{\partial T}\right)_p^2 \left(\frac{\partial p}{\partial V}\right)_T \tag{11-9}$$

Letting the coefficient of expansion be

$$\alpha = \frac{1}{V} \left(\frac{\partial V}{\partial T}\right)_p \tag{11-10}$$

and the coefficient of compressibility be

$$\beta = - \frac{1}{V} \left(\frac{\partial V}{\partial p}\right)_T \tag{11-11}$$

we may write Eq. 11-9 as

$$C_p - C_V = \frac{\alpha^2 V T}{\beta} \tag{11-12}$$

For most solid substances, the value of $C_p - C_V$ is small, though it becomes appreciable for substances having large values of the coefficient of expansion. The following values illustrate the magnitude of $C_p - C_V$ for a number of elements in the solid state at room temperature, in cal/deg mole: Li, 0.3; C, 0.0; Na, 0.5; Al, 0.2; Si, 0.1; S, 0.4; K, 0.6; Cr, 0.1; Mn, 0.1; Fe, 0.1; Co, 0.1; Ni, 0.2; Cu, 0.2; Zn, 0.3; As, 0.0; Ag, 0.3; Cd, 0.3; I, 0.9; W, 0.1; Pt, 0.2; Au, 0.3; Pb, 0.4; Th, 0.1. These values range up to 10 per cent of the value of C_V. For a substance in the liquid state, the value of $C_p - C_V$ will usually be larger than for the same substance in the solid state, since the value of the coefficient of expansion is usually greater for the liquid state. For the ideal gas, the value of $C_p - C_V$ can be derived easily, using the two conditions that define the ideal gas, and

$$C_p - C_V = R \tag{11-13}$$

For real gases at low pressure, the value of $C_p - C_V$ will not be greatly different from R.

From Eq. 9-20, we obtain

$$\left(\frac{\partial^2 S}{\partial T \partial p}\right) = -\left(\frac{\partial^2 V}{\partial T^2}\right)_p \tag{11-14}$$

Combination of this with Eq. 9-9 yields

$$\left(\frac{\partial C_p}{\partial p}\right)_T = -T\left(\frac{\partial^2 V}{\partial T^2}\right)_p \tag{11-15}$$

Similarly, utilizing the corresponding equations involving C_V, we can derive the relation

$$\left(\frac{\partial C_V}{\partial V}\right)_T = T\left(\frac{\partial^2 p}{\partial T^2}\right)_V \tag{11-16}$$

For the energy and heat capacity of crystalline solid, per gram atom, Debye's equations are

$$E - E_0 = 3RT\left[3\left(\frac{T}{\theta}\right)^3 \int_0^{\frac{\theta}{T}} \left(\frac{x^3}{e^x - 1}\right) dx\right] \tag{11-17}$$

and

$$C_V = 3R\left[3\left(\frac{T}{\theta}\right)^3 \int_0^{\frac{\theta}{T}} \left(\frac{x^4 e^x}{(e^x - 1)^2}\right) dx\right] \tag{11-18}$$

In these equations, the following abbreviations are used:

$$x = \frac{h}{kT}\nu \tag{11-19}$$

$$\theta = \frac{h}{k}\nu_{\text{max}} \tag{11-20}$$

$$\frac{\theta}{T} = \frac{h}{kT}\nu_{\text{max}} = x_{\text{max}} \tag{11-21}$$

The Debye equations lead to the limiting values of energy and heat capacity, as follows: as $T \rightarrow$ large value, $E \rightarrow 3RT$, $C_V \rightarrow 3R$; and as $T \rightarrow 0$, $E \rightarrow 0$, $C_V \rightarrow 0$. For sufficiently small values of temperature, the Debye equations for energy and heat capacity reduce to the following values, per gram atom:

$$E - E_0 = 3R\frac{\pi^4}{5\theta^3}T^4 \tag{11-22}$$

$$C_V = 3R\frac{4\pi^4}{5\theta^3}T^3 \tag{11-23}$$

The heat capacities of practically all elements in the solid crystalline state, and of most compounds in the isotropic crystalline state, are fairly well represented as a function of the temperature by the Debye relation.

Fig. A,11a gives a plot of C_V against T/θ, as given by Eq. 11-18. The values of C_V for most isotropic crystalline solids will fall on or near this curve. If the value of θ is known for a given isotropic crystalline solid, the value of its heat capacity C_V at any given temperature can be estimated. Similarly, if the temperature is known at which the heat capacity C_V for a given solid has a known value between about $\frac{1}{2}R$ and $\frac{5}{2}R$, per gram atom, the value of θ can be deduced and values of the heat capacity C_V for other temperatures can be estimated. Values of the Debye θ, evaluated from the values of the heat capacity C_V as a function of temperature, for a number of elements and compounds in the crystalline state, are approximately as follows: Cs, 68; Rb, 85; Pb, 88; Tl, 96; Hg, 97;

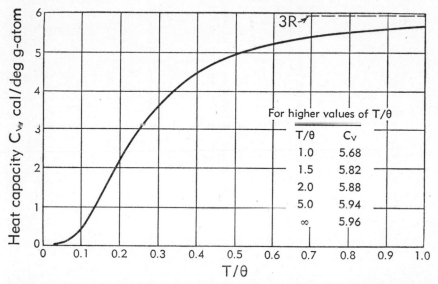

For higher values of T/θ

T/θ	C_V
1.0	5.68
1.5	5.82
2.0	5.88
5.0	5.94
∞	5.96

Fig. A,11a. The heat capacity, C_V, calculated from the Debye equation for the heat capacity of solids, plotted as a function of T/θ. The scale of ordinates gives the value of the heat capacity at constant volume, C_V, per gram atom, as given by the Debye equation, and the scale of abscissas gives the value of the absolute temperature divided by the Debye constant, T/θ. After [1] by permission.

I_2, 106; Bi, 111; Sn, 119; K, 115; Cd, 165; Au, 175; Na, 180; Ag, 215; Pt, 225; Ca, 226; Zn, 235; Ge, 290; Mg, 290; W, 310; Cu, 315; Fe, 370; Ni, 375; Al, 396; Fe, 420; Li, 510; Be, 900; C (diamond), 1850; KBr, 177; KCl, 220; NaCl, 287; CaF_2, 474; FeS_2, 630.

A gas at low pressure may be looked upon as an ensemble of molecules each of which is so far removed from the others that the intermolecular forces are negligible. In such case, the value of a given thermodynamic property for one mole of the gas is Avogadro's number N times the value for each molecule. For the property of heat capacity, the picture may be developed in a simple way in terms of the several classical degrees of freedom of the gaseous molecule. For any gaseous molecule, the total

Table A,11. Classical degrees of freedom and their contributions to the heat capacity of gaseous molecules.

Gaseous molecule	Classical degrees of freedom (total $= 3n$)†			Contributions to the heat capacity C_v, when the given degrees of freedom are fully excited			
	Translation	Rotation	Vibration	Translation	Rotation	Vibration	Total
Monatomic	3	0	0	$\frac{3}{2}R$	0	0	$\frac{3}{2}R$
Polyatomic, linear	3	2	$3n - 5$	$\frac{3}{2}R$	R	$(3n - 5)R$	$(3n - \frac{5}{2})R$
Polyatomic, nonlinear	3	3	$3n - 6$	$\frac{3}{2}R$	$\frac{3}{2}R$	$(3n - 6)R$	$(3n - 3)R$

† n is the number of atoms in the molecule.

number of degrees of freedom allocated to translation, rotation, and vibration is $3n$, where n is the number of atoms in the molecule. Each molecule has 3 degrees of translational freedom, each of which, when fully excited, carries a contribution of $\frac{1}{2}R$ to the heat capacity. The sum of the degrees of freedom for rotation and vibration is therefore $3n - 3$. If the molecule is monatomic, with $n = 1$, there are no degrees of freedom for rotation or vibration. If the molecule is polyatomic $(n > 1)$, there are 2 degrees of freedom for rotation if the molecule is linear or 3 degrees of freedom if the molecule is nonlinear, with each degree of rotational freedom contributing, when fully excited, $\frac{1}{2}R$ to the heat capacity. For polyatomic molecules $(n > 1)$, the number of degrees of freedom for vibration is therefore $3n - 5$ for linear molecules and $3n - 6$ for non-linear molecules, with each degree of freedom for vibration contributing,

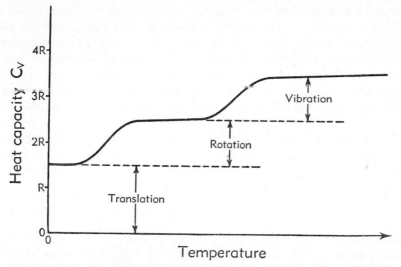

Fig. A,11b. Schematic diagram of the heat capacity, C_v, for an ideal diatomic gas as a function of the temperature. After [1] by permission.

when fully excited, R to the heat capacity (the energy of the fully excited vibrator being $\frac{1}{2}RT$ for the mean kinetic energy and $\frac{1}{2}RT$ for the mean potential energy, or a total energy of RT). Table A,11 summarizes the foregoing discussion regarding classical degrees of freedom and their contributions to the heat capacity of gaseous molecules.

Fig. A,11b shows schematically how the heat capacity C_v for an ideal diatomic gas varies with the temperature. This plot indicates how the degrees of freedom for translation are fully excited even near the absolute zero of temperature; how, as the temperature is increased, the degrees of freedom for rotation become fully excited; and how, following that, the degrees of freedom for vibration become fully excited. This curve also illustrates the difficulty of expressing the heat capacity of a gas over the entire range of temperature by means of one simple mathematical function.

For the ideal gas, we have seen that the difference between C_p and C_V is the gas constant R. For the ideal gas, or for real gases near zero pressure, therefore, the value of the ratio of the heat capacity at constant pressure to that at constant volume has certain simple values, from the relation

$$\frac{C_p}{C_V} = 1 + \frac{R}{C_V} \qquad (11\text{-}24)$$

For the ideal gas, composed of monatomic molecules, the ratio C_p/C_V is $1\frac{2}{3}$. For the ideal gas composed of polyatomic linear molecules with the degrees of freedom for translation and rotation being fully excited but with the degrees of freedom for vibration being not excited at all, the ratio is $1\frac{2}{5}$. For the ideal gas composed of polyatomic nonlinear molecules with the degrees of freedom for translation and rotation being fully excited but with the degrees of freedom for vibration being not excited at all, the ratio is $1\frac{1}{2}$. For the ideal gas composed of diatomic molecules with all the degrees of freedom for translation, rotation, and vibration being fully excited, the ratio is $1\frac{2}{7}$. For real gases, the value of the ratio C_p/C_V may change markedly with pressure, especially at low temperatures.

A,12. Useful Energy, Free Energy, and Criteria of Equilibrium.
For a reversible process which involves the transfer, between the system and its surroundings, of energy in addition to heat energy and pV work energy, we can write from the first law

$$dE = \delta q + \delta w + \delta u \qquad (12\text{-}1)$$

where, as before, dE is the increase in energy of the system, δq is the heat energy, δw is the pV work energy, and δu is all other energy absorbed by the system from the surroundings. Substituting in the usual way TdS for δq and $-pdV$ for δw, we obtain

$$dE = TdS - pdV + \delta u \qquad (12\text{-}2)$$

where δu represents all energy other than heat energy and pV work energy absorbed by the system from the surroundings. The term δu, therefore, is identified as useful energy absorbed by the system from the surroundings. Conversely, the useful energy made available by the system to the surroundings is $-\delta u$. From this equation, we can write the useful energy made available by the system to the surroundings as

$$-\delta u = -(dE + pdV - TdS) \qquad (12\text{-}3)$$

This equation is a most important relation, because it tells us that for any process performed reversibly, the useful energy obtainable from the system is completely expressible in terms of the five fundamental thermodynamic properties, p, V, T, E, and S.

It is important to note the simplification occurring in the value of the useful energy in terms of the fundamental thermodynamic properties for various special cases, as follows: At constant volume, $dV = 0$ and

$$-\delta u = -(dE - TdS) \tag{12-4}$$

At constant pressure, $pdV = d(pV)$ and

$$-\delta u = -[dE + d(pV) - TdS] = -(dH - TdS) \tag{12-5}$$

At constant temperature, $TdS = d(TS)$ and

$$-\delta u = -[d(E - TS) + pdV] \tag{12-6}$$

At constant entropy, $dS = 0$ and

$$-\delta u = -(dE + pdV) \tag{12-7}$$

At constant volume and constant entropy,

$$-\delta u = -dE \tag{12-8}$$

At constant pressure and constant entropy,

$$-\delta u = -d(E + pV) = -dH \tag{12-9}$$

At constant volume and constant temperature,

$$-\delta u = -d(E - TS) \tag{12-10}$$

At constant pressure and constant temperature,

$$-\delta u = -d(E + pV - TS) = -d(H - TS) \tag{12-11}$$

Because many processes occur at constant pressure and constant temperature, the particular combination of the five fundamental thermodynamic properties occurring in Eq. 12-11, namely, $E + pV - TS$ or $H - TS$, recurs with great frequency in thermodynamic calculations. It has accordingly been found desirable to use an abbreviation F for this particular combination of properties and to call this function the free energy. Thus, by definition,

$$F = E + pV - TS = H - TS \tag{12-12}$$

This function is frequently called the Gibbs' or Lewis free energy. From Eq. 12-11, it is seen that, for a reversible process occurring at constant pressure and temperature, the useful energy, $-\delta u$, is equal to $-d(E + pV - TS)$ or $-d(H - TS)$, or, by our new definition,

$$-\delta u = -dF \tag{12-13}$$

That is to say, for a reversible process at constant pressure and temperature, the decrease in the free energy for the process is the energy which is free to be put to some useful purpose.

Abbreviations similar to that above may be used for other combinations of the fundamental properties, as for example, the combination $E - TS$, for which the symbol A is frequently used, so that, by definition, one may write

$$A = E - TS \qquad (12\text{-}14)$$

This function is frequently called the Helmholtz free energy.

Every system if left to itself tends to change toward its final state of rest or equilibrium. If a given system has some capacity for spontaneous change, an appropriate mechanism can, in principle, always be introduced to harness the system to obtain some amount of useful energy as the system passes reversibly from its initial state toward the state of equilibrium. For every process that occurs spontaneously, therefore, some amount of useful energy may be obtained from the system. To make the given system move away from the state of equilibrium, that is, in a nonspontaneous or unnatural direction, it is necessary to supply some useful energy to the system. The algebraic sign of the useful energy obtainable from the system, therefore, serves to tell us whether the given process is one in which the system is moving toward or away from equilibrium. If the value of δu is negative, useful energy is obtainable from the system and we know that the change is a naturally occurring one in the direction toward the state of equilibrium. If the value of δu is positive, useful energy is required to be supplied to the given system to bring about the desired change and we know that the change is an unnatural one in the direction away from equilibrium. It follows that if the value of δu is zero, the system is already at the state of equilibrium with respect to the prescribed change.

The value of δu for any given system in any reversible process is given by Eq. 12-3 in terms of the five fundamental thermodynamic properties of the system. We have just seen that when the value of δu is zero for any given change in a reversible process, the system is at the state of equilibrium. This condition may therefore be used as the general criterion of equilibrium. That is, equilibrium exists in a system with respect to any prescribed change occurring reversibly whenever δu is zero, or

$$dE + p\,dV - T\,dS = 0 \qquad (12\text{-}15)$$

This equation is the general criterion of equilibrium for any prescribed change in a reversible process.

Just as it was desirable to evaluate the useful energy for special cases, it is important to ascertain the simplification occurring in the general criterion of equilibrium for various special cases. The criterion of equilibrium reduces to the following for the indicated special cases:

Conditions	Criterion of Equilibrium	
Constant volume	$dE - TdS = 0$	(12-16)
Constant pressure	$dH - TdS = 0$	(12-17)
Constant temperature	$d(E - TS) + pdV = 0$	(12-18)
Constant entropy	$dE + pdV = 0$	(12-19)
Constant volume and entropy	$dE = 0$	(12-20)
Constant volume and energy	$dS = 0$	(12-21)
Constant pressure and entropy	$dH = 0$	(12-22)
Constant volume and temperature	$d(E - TS) = 0$	(12-23)

Constant pressure and temperature

$$d(E + pV - TS) = d(H - TS) = dF = 0 \quad (12\text{-}24)$$

A,13. Relations among the Thermodynamic Properties and Functions. When a substance is subjected to a reversible process involving only heat energy and pV work energy, application of the first and second laws yields

$$dE = TdS - pdV \quad (13\text{-}1)$$

For the same process for which Eq. 13-1 is valid, namely, a reversible process involving only heat energy and pV work energy, similar equations may be derived to give the corresponding relations for the defined thermodynamic functions H, A, F, as follows:

By definition,

$$H = E + pV \quad (13\text{-}2)$$

On differentiation,

$$dH = dE + pdV + Vdp \quad (13\text{-}3)$$

whence

$$dH = TdS + Vdp \quad (13\text{-}4)$$

Similarly, from the definition of A (Eq. 12-14),

$$dA = dE - TdS - SdT \quad (13\text{-}5)$$

and

$$dA = -SdT - pdV \quad (13\text{-}6)$$

Similarly from the definition of F (Eq. 12-12),

$$dF = dE + pdV + Vdp - TdS - SdT \quad (13\text{-}7)$$

and

$$dF = -SdT + Vdp \quad (13\text{-}8)$$

Interesting and important thermodynamic relations may be obtained from these equations, for various special cases, as follows:

From Eq. 13-1, we have at constant volume,

$$dE = TdS \tag{13-9}$$

or

$$(\partial E/\partial S)_V = T \tag{13-10}$$

and at constant entropy,

$$dE = -pdV \tag{13-11}$$

or

$$(\partial E/\partial V)_S = -p \tag{13-12}$$

Similarly,

$$(\partial H/\partial S)_p = T \tag{13-13}$$

$$(\partial H/\partial p)_S = V \tag{13-14}$$

$$(\partial A/\partial T)_V = -S \tag{13-15}$$

$$(\partial A/\partial V)_T = -p \tag{13-16}$$

$$(\partial F/\partial T)_p = -S \tag{13-17}$$

$$(\partial F/\partial p)_T = V \tag{13-18}$$

The general exact differential equation may be written in the form

$$dG = Mdx + Ndy \tag{13-19}$$

But

$$dG = \left(\frac{\partial G}{\partial x}\right)_y dx + \left(\frac{\partial G}{\partial y}\right)_x dy \tag{13-20}$$

Hence

$$M = \left(\frac{\partial G}{\partial x}\right)_y \quad \text{and} \quad N = \left(\frac{\partial G}{\partial y}\right)_x \tag{13-21}$$

But

$$\frac{\partial^2 G}{\partial x \partial y} = \frac{\partial^2 G}{\partial y \partial x} \tag{13-22}$$

so that

$$\left(\frac{\partial M}{\partial y}\right)_x = \left(\frac{\partial N}{\partial x}\right)_y \tag{13-23}$$

Eq. 13-1, 13-4, 13-6, and 13-8, which are exact differential equations, may be utilized in this way to obtain many useful thermodynamic relations, such as

$$\left(\frac{\partial T}{\partial p}\right)_s = \left(\frac{\partial V}{\partial S}\right)_p \tag{13-24}$$

and

$$\left(\frac{\partial V}{\partial T}\right)_p = -\left(\frac{\partial S}{\partial p}\right)_T \tag{13-25}$$

A,14. Heats and Energies of Reactions and Processes. One of the important thermodynamic facts to be known about a given chemical reaction or process is the change, or increment, in energy ΔE, or heat content ΔH, associated with the reaction or process at some specified reference temperature, as at 25°C, with each of the reactants and products in an appropriate reference state. As will be seen later, such reference states, formally called standard states and denoted by a superscript on the thermodynamic symbol, e.g. H^0, may be ones realizable only in theory but are such that a given substance can be readily converted from the actual state to the appropriate standard state with the necessary few data. Unless otherwise specified, it is usually assumed that a given reaction or process involves each of the reactants and products in their standard states. Unless the context provides a complete description of the reaction or process, as to temperature, pressure, concentrations, etc., such information should be given explicitly in the writing of the chemical equation describing the process.

In addition to specifying the actual state of each of the reactants and products participating in the given reaction or process, it is important to specify the thermodynamic property which is measured, such as the increment in energy ΔE, or the increment in heat content ΔH, or the heat capacity $(\partial E/\partial T)_V$ or $(\partial H/\partial T)_p$.

In the case of chemical reactions, the thermodynamic property measured may usually be labeled as ΔE or ΔH depending upon whether the substances participating in the reaction are confined at constant volume or at constant pressure. Consider, for example, the reaction of a stoichiometric mixture of two diatomic ideal gases MX and X_2 to form the triatomic ideal gas MX_2:

$$MX \text{ (g)} + \tfrac{1}{2}X_2 \text{ (g)} = MX_2 \text{ (g)} \qquad (14\text{-}1)$$

If the reaction takes place in a calorimeter in a closed bomb at constant volume, and if the total pressure of the reactant gases is p_A, then the reaction may be specified as follows, at the given temperature:

$$MX \text{ (g, } p = \tfrac{2}{3}p_A) + \tfrac{1}{2}X_2 \text{ (g, } p = \tfrac{1}{3}p_A) = MX_2 \text{ (g, } p = \tfrac{2}{3}p_A) \quad (14\text{-}2)$$

According to the first law, for any process,

$$\Delta E = q + w + u \qquad (14\text{-}3)$$

where q is the heat energy, w is the pV work energy, and u is any other energy, each absorbed by the system during the process. But in this calorimetric experiment, u is zero, and, since the volume is constant, w is also zero. Hence, the calorimetrically measured heat energy absorbed, q, is equal to ΔE, and for this reaction we may write,

$$\Delta E = q \qquad (14\text{-}4)$$

Since the gases are ideal and the energy of ideal gases is independent of the pressure and of the presence of other gases, the designation of pressure is unnecessary. For real gases, however, the specification of the pressure must be made insofar as it is significant.

If the reaction takes place in a calorimeter at constant pressure, with each reactant gas disappearing at the pressure p_A and the product gas appearing at the pressure p_A, then the reaction may be specified as follows at the given temperature:

$$MX\ (g,\ p_A) + \tfrac{1}{2}X_2\ (g,\ p_A) = MX_2\ (g,\ p_A) \qquad (14\text{-}5)$$

According to the first law, Eq. 14-3 holds for any process. But in this calorimetric experiment, u is zero. Since the system undergoes a change in volume and is subjected to a constant confining pressure, the pV work energy is $-p\Delta V$. Substitution gives

$$\Delta E = q - p\Delta V \qquad (14\text{-}6)$$

Hence

$$\Delta E + p\Delta V = \Delta(E + pV) = \Delta H = q \qquad (14\text{-}7)$$

That is, the calorimetrically measured heat energy absorbed, q, is equal to ΔH, the increment in heat content for the given reaction.

For any specified reaction or process, the difference between the value of ΔE and ΔH may be evaluated from the relation

$$\Delta H = \Delta E + \Delta(pV) \qquad (14\text{-}8)$$

In this equation, $\Delta(pV)$ is simply the sum of the product of pressure and volume for each of the products less the sum of the product of pressure and volume for each of the reactants, for the specified reaction or process. The value of pV for liquid and solid substances will be small compared to the value of pV for gaseous substances. For reactions in which all the reactants and products are liquids or solids, therefore, the difference between ΔE and ΔH will be relatively small. For reactions in which the number of moles of gaseous reactants is the same as the number of moles of gaseous products, the difference between ΔE and ΔH will also be relatively small. For other reactions, the difference between ΔE and ΔH will depend on the difference in the number of moles Δn of gaseous reactants and gaseous products. In the case of a reaction wherein each of the substances involved is an ideal gas, the difference between ΔE and ΔH may be readily evaluated from Eq. 14-8 because

$$\Delta(pV) = (\Delta n)RT \qquad (14\text{-}9)$$

Hence

$$\Delta H = \Delta E + (\Delta n)RT \qquad (14\text{-}10)$$

In the case of processes such as those of transition, fusion, and vaporization, occurring in a calorimeter, the calorimetrically measured value of the heat energy is equivalent to ΔH if the process occurs at constant pressure and ΔE if the process occurs at constant volume. Similarly, if the process is one of simply taking a given substance from one temperature to a slightly higher temperature, in order to determine the heat capacity of the given substance, as the ratio of the heat absorbed to the rise in temperature, the measured property will be the heat capacity at constant volume C_V if the process occurs at constant volume, and the heat capacity at constant pressure C_p if the process occurs at constant pressure. In any case, the property will be that of the substance in the physical state or states in which it actually exists in the calorimetric vessel in which it is contained.

When the value of the change in heat content ΔH is known for a specified reaction or process at some temperature, the value at any other temperature may be readily calculated if there are known, for each of the individual reactants and products, the values of heat capacity C_p or of the heat content H (referred to some selected temperature), over the range of temperature for which the calculation is to be made.

Given the simple reaction

$$M = N \tag{14-11}$$

with the state of each substance being adequately specified. The change in heat content for this reaction at the given temperature T is equal to

$$\Delta H = H_N - H_M \tag{14-12}$$

At constant pressure,

$$\frac{d(\Delta H)}{dT} = \frac{dH_N}{dT} - \frac{dH_M}{dT} = C_{p_N} - C_{p_M} = \Delta C_p \tag{14-13}$$

Suppose that over a given range of temperature T_1 to T_2,

$$C_{p_N} = a_N + b_N T + c_N T^2 \tag{14-14}$$

and

$$C_{p_M} = a_M + b_M T + c_M T^2 \tag{14-15}$$

Subtraction of these equations gives

$$\Delta C_p = (\Delta a) + (\Delta b)T + (\Delta c)T^2 \tag{14-16}$$

where $\Delta a = a_N - a_M$, $\Delta b = b_N - b_M$, and $\Delta c = c_N - c_M$. Combination of Eq. 14-13 and Eq. 14-16 gives

$$\frac{d(\Delta H)}{dT} = (\Delta a) + (\Delta b)T + (\Delta c)T^2 \tag{14-17}$$

This equation may be readily integrated over the given range of temperature to give the value of ΔH at some temperature T within the given range with reference to the value of ΔH at T_1:

$$\Delta H - \Delta H_{T_1} = (\Delta a)(T - T_1) + \frac{(\Delta b)}{2}(T^2 - T_1^2)$$
$$+ \frac{(\Delta c)}{3}(T^3 - T_1^3) \quad (14\text{-}18)$$

Eq. 14-17 may be integrated without specific limits of temperature to give the relation

$$\Delta H = \Delta H_* + (\Delta a)T + \frac{(\Delta b)}{2}T^2 + \frac{(\Delta c)}{3}T^3 \quad (14\text{-}19)$$

where ΔH_* is the constant of integration required to make the equation valid over the range of applicability. In this equation, the values of the constants Δa, Δb, and Δc are obtained from the equations for the heat capacity of each of the reactants and products, and ΔH_* is evaluated from the foregoing constants and the value of ΔH at a known temperature in the range T_1 to T_2. Although the substitution of $T = 0$ in this equation makes ΔH_* appear formally to be the value for $0°K$, it must be remembered that this equation is valid only over the range of temperature for which heat capacities are known, and within which range of temperature the actual value of ΔH is known at some one temperature.

The heat capacity of each of the products and reactants in the given reaction may frequently be expressed as a function of temperature over the range T_1 to T_2 by means of an equation of the form

$$C_p = a' + b'T + \frac{c'}{T^2} \quad (14\text{-}20)$$

In such case, the corresponding equations are, respectively, as follows:

$$\frac{d(\Delta H)}{dT} = (\Delta a') + (\Delta b')T + \frac{(\Delta c')}{T^2} \quad (14\text{-}21)$$

$$\Delta H - \Delta H_{T_1} = (\Delta a')(T - T_1)$$
$$+ \frac{(\Delta b')}{2}(T^2 - T_1^2) - (\Delta c')\left(\frac{1}{T} - \frac{1}{T_1}\right) \quad (14\text{-}22)$$

$$\Delta H = \Delta H_* + (\Delta a')T + \frac{(\Delta b')}{2}T^2 - \frac{(\Delta c')}{T} \quad (14\text{-}23)$$

Frequently, there are known, for each of the reactants and products of a given reaction, values at various temperatures of the heat content $H - H_0$, which is the heat content at a given temperature referred to the heat content at $0°K$. In such cases, the value of ΔH for other temperatures may be readily calculated from the value of ΔH at one temperature. Suppose that the value of ΔH at $25°C$ is known. Then the actual value of ΔH at $0°K$ is equal to

$$\Delta H_0 = \Delta H_{298.16} - \Delta(H_{298.16} - H_0) \quad (14\text{-}24)$$

where

$$\Delta(H_{298.16} - H_0) = \sum (H_{298.16} - H_0) \text{ (products)}$$
$$- \sum (H_{298.16} - H_0) \text{ (reactants)} \quad (14\text{-}25)$$

The value of ΔH at any other temperature may be obtained from the relation

$$\Delta H = \Delta H_0 + \Delta(H - H_0) \quad (14\text{-}26)$$

where

$$\Delta(H - H_0) = \sum (H - H_0) \text{ (products)}$$
$$- \sum (H - H_0) \text{ (reactants)} \quad (14\text{-}27)$$

These equations may be readily proved by considering the symbol Δ as an operator and multiplying it into each term inside the parentheses.

The modern thermochemical method aims to determine as directly as possible the quantity of energy associated with a unit amount of given

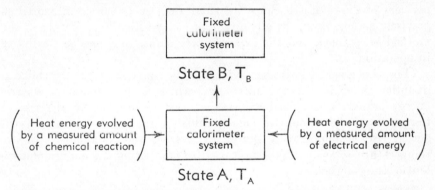

Fig. A,14a.   Schematic diagram of the thermochemical method of determining the heats of exothermal reactions. After [1] by permission.

reaction or process. The thermochemical investigation consists of a calorimetric part, involving the measurement of energy, and a chemical part, involving the measurement of the amount of the given reaction or process. The desired result is the ratio, in appropriate units, of the quantity of energy to the amount of the reaction or process.

For a chemical reaction or process that is exothermal, that is, evolves heat energy as it takes place, the method is schematically illustrated in Fig. A,14a. Here, A represents a fixed calorimeter system at the "standard" initial temperature T_A and B represents the same fixed calorimeter system at the "standard" final higher temperature T_B. In one kind of experiment, the heat evolved by a measured amount of the given chemical reaction or process is used to take the calorimeter system from its initial state A and temperature T_A, to its final state B and temperature T_B. In another kind of experiment, with the same calorimeter system at the same initial state, the heat evolved by a measured amount of electric energy is used to take the calorimeter system from the same initial state A and temperature T_A, to the same final state B and temperature T_B. In this manner, there is obtained a direct equivalence between the measured amount of chemical reaction and the measured amount of electric energy, using the fixed calorimeter system as the absorber and comparator of the two kinds of energy.

In actual practice it is easy to use a fixed calorimeter system but impracticable to try to obtain exactly the same rise of temperature in all experiments. Instead, with the fixed calorimeter system, the rise of temperature is made substantially the same in all experiments, and the small differences from one experiment to another are measured in order to effect the correction to the common or standard value of the rise of temperature. In most cases, the amount of electric or chemical energy added to the calorimeter can be so regulated that the differences in the rise of temperature in the various experiments will be less than several per cent of the total rise. Since the small differences can be measured as precisely as necessary, the advantage of the substitutional nature of the method is retained, and the experimenter gains some needed flexibility in operation.

For the given calorimeter system it is convenient to determine a quantity called its energy equivalent,[3] which is the amount of electric energy added to the fixed calorimeter system divided by the rise of temperature, the amount of energy added being regulated so that the actual rise of temperature differs little from the "standard" rise of temperature. The simple relation used in computing the energy equivalent of the calorimeter is

$$\text{(energy equivalent)} = \text{(electrical energy)}/\Delta t_e \qquad (14\text{-}28)$$

where Δt_e is the rise of temperature in the experiment with electric energy. From a series of such experiments, an average value of the energy equivalent is determined.

In a series of calorimetric reaction experiments, there is measured the amount of chemical reaction that produces, in the calorimeter, a rise of temperature substantially equal to the selected "standard" rise of temperature. The relation used to evaluate the "reaction equivalent" is

$$\text{(reaction equivalent)} = \Delta t_r/n \qquad (14\text{-}29)$$

[3] The energy equivalent is substantially the same as that which in the early days was called the heat capacity of the calorimeter, but the latter designation is not recommended because it implies that the investigator has a knowledge of the actual physical boundaries of the material system to which the heat capacity is ascribed, and that the heat capacity of the calorimeter may be evaluated by a summation of the heat capacities of its component parts.

where Δt_r is the rise of temperature in the experiment with chemical energy (measured with the same thermometer over substantially the same range), and n is the number of moles of reaction measured by the mass and molecular weights of the substance that is used to determine the amount of reaction. From a series of such experiments, an average value of the reaction equivalent is determined.

The experimental value of the change in energy or heat content for the given reaction, per mole, is then evaluated by the relation

$$-q = [(\text{electric energy})/n][(\Delta t_r)/(\Delta t_e)] \qquad (14\text{-}30)$$

It will be noted from this equation that the rises of temperature in the two kinds of experiments substantially cancel. It follows that the temperature need be known in an accurate sense, as distinguished from precision of differences, only to the extent required to specify the temperature to which the measured thermodynamic property is to be assigned.

Examples of exothermal reactions for which the decrease in energy or heat content may be measured in the above way are those of the following kinds: combustion of gaseous, liquid, or solid substance in oxygen, such as the combustion of gaseous methane, or liquid normal octane, or solid normal octadecane, in oxygen to form gaseous carbon dioxide and liquid water; solution of a gaseous, liquid, or solid substance in a liquid solvent, such as the solution of hydrogen chloride in water to form aqueous hydrochloric acid, or the solution of liquid sulfuric acid in water to form aqueous sulfuric acid, or the solution of solid potassium hydroxide in water to form aqueous potassium hydroxide; neutralization, in the liquid phase, of an acid with a base, such as the neutralization of aqueous nitric acid with aqueous sodium hydroxide to form aqueous sodium nitrate; reaction of a gaseous, liquid, or solid substance with a liquid to form an aqueous solution, with or without a gaseous product or solid product, such as the reaction of solid sodium with liquid water to form aqueous sodium hydroxide and gaseous hydrogen; reaction of two gaseous substances to form a gaseous product, as in the hydrogenation or chlorination of ethylene; and formation of a gaseous, liquid, or solid product from its elements, gaseous, liquid, or solid, as in the formation of liquid water from gaseous hydrogen and oxygen, or the formation of gaseous sulfur dioxide from solid sulfur and gaseous oxygen, or the formation of solid sodium chloride from solid sodium and gaseous chlorine, or the formation of gaseous hydrogen chloride from gaseous hydrogen and gaseous chlorine.

If the reaction or process is an endothermal one, that is, absorbs heat energy as it takes place, then, in principle, the method is simplified. In this case, a measured quantity of electric energy is added to the calorimeter system in an amount that is just sufficient to maintain the temperature constant, balancing the energy absorbed by the reaction or process as it proceeds. This is illustrated schematically in Fig. A,14b. For this experiment, the initial and final states of the calorimeter system are the same and the calorimeter neither absorbs nor gives up energy. In this way, a direct equivalence (except for sign) is obtained between the measured amount of electric energy and the measured amount of the given reaction or process.

Examples of endothermal reactions or processes for which the increase in energy or heat content may be measured isothermally in the above way include any reactions of the kinds mentioned earlier which may be endothermal, together with endothermal reactions of the following types: decomposition of a gaseous substance into gaseous, liquid, or solid products, such as the decomposition of gaseous lead tetramethyl into solid lead and gaseous ethane; vaporization of a liquid substance to the gaseous state, such as the vaporization of liquid water to gaseous water; sublimation of a solid substance to the gaseous state, such as the sublimation of the solid octane, 2,2,3,3-tetramethylbutane; melting or fusion of a solid substance to the liquid state, such as the melting or fusion of water ice

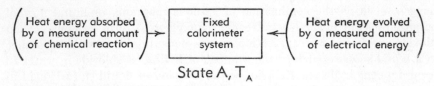

$$\text{State A, } T_A$$

Fig. A,14b. Schematic diagram of the thermochemical method of determining the heats of endothermal reactions. After [1] by permission.

to liquid water; and transition of a solid substance from one stable crystalline form to another, such as the transition of carbon tetrachloride from crystalline form II to crystalline form I.

In cases when exothermal reactions are to be measured, and the investigator does not have available apparatus for measuring the electric energy with adequate accuracy, there may be substituted for the experiments with electric energy calibrating experiments with a similar chemical reaction the decrease in energy or heat content of which has previously been determined accurately in another laboratory. It is preferable that such calibrating reactions be ones which have been agreed upon by the leading investigators in the field. Examples of the use of such calibrating reactions are the following: evaluation of the "energy equivalent" of a calorimeter system in which the reaction vessel is a closed bomb, using the combustion of standard benzoic acid under certain standardized conditions; evaluation of the "energy equivalent" of a calorimeter system in which the reaction vessel is one designed to burn gases in a flame at constant pressure, using the combustion of hydrogen in oxygen to form water; and evaluation of the "energy equivalent" of a calorimeter system for measuring heats of solution of solids in water to form aqueous solutions, using the solution of a solid the heat of solution of which has previously been accurately determined.

Similarly, for endothermic reactions, if the investigator does not have available apparatus for measuring electric energy with adequate accuracy, it is possible to determine the ratio of the amount of the given reaction or process to the amount of a calibrating reaction or process associated with the same quantity of energy. This may be done either by ascertaining what amount of the calibrating reaction is needed to produce the same change (decrease) in the temperature of the calorimeter system as is produced by a known amount of the given reaction, or by ascertaining what amount of the given reaction is brought about by the same, but not accurately measured, amount of electric energy as is needed to bring about a known amount of the calibrating reaction.

In processes involving no chemical reaction as such, and where the substance under investigation does not change its state, as in the determination of the heat capacity of a liquid or a solid substance, the experiment involves measurement of the energy required to produce a measured change of temperature for the substance and the container. In such cases, the "energy equivalent" or heat capacity of the containing vessel must be accounted for. The most reliable way of doing this is to perform two sets of experiments, in one of which the calorimetric container is full of the substance under investigation and in the other of which the container holds only a small amount of the given substance. The difference in the two sets of experiments serves, in effect, to determine the heat capacity of that amount of the given substance corresponding to the difference in mass of the two charges. With such a procedure, the container is under more nearly identical conditions than would be the case if the container were measured actually empty in the second set of experiments.

For any of the cases where a calibrating reaction or process is used, for energy either evolved or absorbed, it is possible, in principle, to devise a twin calorimeter arrangement, wherein the values of the "energy equivalent" of the two calorimeters are the same or have a known ratio one to the other. With such an apparatus, the given reaction and the calibrating reaction are run simultaneously, and the experiment serves, in effect, to determine the ratio of the amounts of the two reactions with which equal amounts of energy or heat content are associated.

In the chemical part of the thermochemical investigation, it is necessary, first, to establish that the actual reaction or process that occurs is the specified one, and, second, to measure with the necessary accuracy the amount of the given reaction or process that occurs in each experiment for which the heat energy has been evaluated.

In the examination of the purity of the chemical reaction being studied, the investigator should demonstrate with reasonable certainty, by means of appropriate chemical or physical tests, that the reaction which actually occurs in the calorimetric reaction vessel is one that does not differ significantly from the theoretically pure reaction. Or, if there is a side reaction, its amount and effect must be evaluated with the necessary accuracy. Having first decided that the reaction being studied is reasonably complete and clear-cut, one can investigate the purity of the reaction as it actually occurs in the reaction vessel in the calorimeter, first, by establishing the purity of the reacting substances, and, second, by examining the products of the reaction for the presence of possible foreign substances. The permissible amounts of impurities in the reacting substances, and the permissible amounts of side reactions, depend to a large extent upon the method by which the amount of the reaction is determined and upon the amount of heat energy contributed by the side reactions involved. One of the vital points in any thermochemical investigation is the method of determining the amount of chemical reaction that occurs in any given experiment. The method selected should be precise and accurate with respect to true mass and the amount should be accurately expressible in terms of moles. This latter requirement involves an accurate knowledge of the molecular weight of the substance whose mass determines the amount of reaction.

For purposes of intercomparison and tabulation of data on the energies or heats of reactions and processes, it is desirable that each substance participating in the given reaction or process be corrected to an appropriate reference or standard state. For example, with regard to energy or heat content, it is convenient and desirable to select for the reference state at the given temperature, say 25°C, the pure liquid or solid substance at an actual pressure of 1 atmosphere and the gas in the ideal state at 1 atmosphere. Other appropriate reference states are required for aqueous and other solutions. For every reaction or process that takes place in a calorimeter, it is imperative that significant data be recorded as to the phase, pressure, temperature, and concentration of each of the substances at the beginning and at the end of the reaction. A study of each reaction will indicate with what significance the various properties must be known and recorded.

For every reaction or process which is carried out in a calorimeter and for which a value of the change in energy or heat content is determined, it is important to assign with adequate accuracy the value of temperature to which the given thermodynamic property is to be ascribed. In the case of those experiments where each reactant enters the calorimeter, and each product leaves the calorimeter, on the average, at the mean temperature of the experiment, the value of the given thermodynamic property may usually be assigned to the mean of the initial and final temperatures of the calorimeter in the given experiment. On the other hand, if the reaction takes place in a system such that all of the reactant material is in the calorimeter at the beginning of the experiment at the initial temperature T_A, and all of the product material is in the calorimeter at the end of the experiment at the final temperature T_B, one has a choice of using as the assigned temperature of the given property the initial temperature T_A, the final temperature T_B, or the mean temperature $(T_A + T_B)/2$. If the energy equivalent of the calorimeter is taken as that of the final system, then the assigned temperature is the initial temperature. If the energy equivalent of the calorimeter is taken as that of the initial system, then the assigned temperature is the final temperature. If the energy equivalent of the calorimeter is taken as the mean of the initial and final systems, then the assigned temperature is the mean of the initial and final temperatures. Actually, also, the assigned temperature may be any intermediate temperature provided the appropriate fractions of the initial and final systems are used to evaluate the energy equivalent of the calorimeter.

The ideal table of heats of reaction is one which will permit calculation of the heat of every possible chemical reaction. Obviously it would be impractical to list in a table every chemical reaction and its corresponding change in heat content, but the same end is accomplished by listing for each chemical substance its heat of formation from its elements in selected reference states. It is evident that, by proper selection, the number of chemical reactions whose heats must be measured will be about the same as the number of substances listed in the table. Some saving in the number of reactions to be measured will occur because of the correlations of energy with molecular structure which are possible among certain organic compounds, particularly hydrocarbons. The value of the heat of formation of a given substance from its elements may be the result of the determination of the heat of one reaction, as for the heat of formation of liquid water:

$$H_2 \ (g) + \tfrac{1}{2}O_2 \ (g) = H_2O \ (liq) \tag{14-31}$$

For many other substances, however, the value will result from the measurement of the heats of a number of reactions, as for the heat of formation of crystalline sodium hydroxide:

$$Na \ (c) + H_2O \ (liq) = NaOH \ (aq) + \tfrac{1}{2}H_2 \ (g) \tag{14-32}$$

$$H_2 \ (g) + \tfrac{1}{2}O_2 \ (g) = H_2O \ (liq) \tag{14-33}$$

$$NaOH \ (c) = NaOH \ (aq) \tag{14-34}$$

Combination of these equations gives the desired result:

$$Na \ (c) + \tfrac{1}{2}O_2 \ (g) + \tfrac{1}{2}H_2 \ (g) = NaOH \ (c) \tag{14-35}$$

Similarly the heat of formation of carbon monoxide is evaluated from data on the following reactions:

$$CO \text{ (g)} + \tfrac{1}{2}O_2 \text{ (g)} = CO_2 \text{ (g)} \qquad (14\text{-}36)$$

$$C \text{ (c, graphite)} + O_2 \text{ (g)} = CO_2 \text{ (g)} \qquad (14\text{-}37)$$

Subtraction of Eq. 14-37 from 14-36 gives

$$C \text{ (c, graphite)} + \tfrac{1}{2}O_2 \text{ (g)} = CO \text{ (g)} \qquad (14\text{-}38)$$

which is the desired result. In every case the reactions selected for measurement must be ones that can be made to proceed adequately and be handled quantitatively in a calorimeter.

There are certain basic values in the table of heats of formation which will be used very frequently in the derivation of other values. These basic values, which should preferably be known with the highest accuracy, include the heats of formation of water, carbon dioxide, nitric acid, sulfuric acid, hydrogen chloride, hydrogen sulfide, etc. Because of this interdependence of many of the values of heats of formation, it is desirable that the basic values be carefully selected, and, when any change is made in any one of the basic values, corresponding changes should be made in all the values which depend upon it. It is for this same reason that the addition or subtraction of values of heats of formation from different tables is a procedure fraught with uncertainty.

For the primary table of heats of formation of the chemical compounds, it is necessary to have a reference temperature and a reference state for each substance. For each element, the heat of formation is given as zero for that phase in which it naturally exists at the reference temperature, when it is in the reference state. As previously mentioned, for liquid and solid substances, the reference state is taken as the real state at a pressure of 1 atmosphere, while for gases the reference state is taken as the ideal gaseous state at 1 atmosphere.

A,15. Thermodynamic Functions from Statistical Calculations.
In the simple picture, we may consider that there is a complete set of discrete quantum levels of energy associated with each degree of freedom of a gaseous molecule. Each set of levels of energy may be represented schematically by the diagram in Fig. A,15. The levels of energy are numbered as indicated, beginning with zero at the bottom, lowest, or ground level. The energy of each level is represented by ϵ_0, ϵ_1, ϵ_2, ϵ_3, . . . , ϵ_i. The multiplicity, or number of individual states of virtually the same energy existing at each level of energy, is given by g_0, g_1, g_2, g_3, . . . , g_i. While the individual states labeled for the same level actually have extremely small differences in energy, these differences become important only at extremely low temperatures, near $0°K$. At any given temperature, the distribution of molecules among the possible states of

energy is given by the Boltzmann distribution law:

$$n_i = n_0 e^{-\frac{\epsilon_i - \epsilon_0}{kT}} = n_0 e^{-x} \tag{15-1}$$

where

$$x = \frac{\epsilon_i - \epsilon_0}{kT}$$

In this equation, n_i is the statistical average number of molecules in each quantum state of energy ϵ_i, n_0 is the statistical average number of molecules in each state at the ground level of energy ϵ_0, e is the base of the natural logarithms, k is the Boltzmann constant, and T is the absolute temperature.

Eq. 15-1 gives the statistical average of the population of each state of energy ϵ_i in terms of the population of a state at the ground level having an energy ϵ_0. The calculation requires only the specification of

Levels of energy	Number of the given level	Energy of the given level	Number of states at the given level
———	i	ϵ_i	g_i
•	•	•	•
•	•	•	•
•	•	•	•
———	3	ϵ_3	g_3
———	2	ϵ_2	g_2
———	1	ϵ_1	g_1
———	0	ϵ_0	g_0

Fig. A,15. Schematic diagram of energy levels. After [1] by permission.

the temperature T, and a knowledge of the difference in energy between the given level and the ground level, $\epsilon_i - \epsilon_0$. Simple application of this equation indicates that as the temperature approaches the absolute zero the population tends to converge at the ground level, and that as the temperature becomes very large, in comparison with the value of $(\epsilon_i - \epsilon_0)/k$, the population tends to become equally distributed over all the possible states of energy. When the value of T is very large in comparison to $(\epsilon_i - \epsilon_0)/k$, the degree of freedom giving rise to the particular set of energy levels is said to be fully "excited" to its classical value.

The order of magnitude of the spacing of the levels of energy near the ground level for the sets of levels of energy arising from the ordinary degrees of freedom is approximately as follows, in cal/mole: translational, 10^{-21}; rotational, 10 to 100; and vibrational, 1,000 to 10,000. From the foregoing, it may readily be seen that the translational degrees of freedom will be fully excited to their classical values even at extremely low temperatures, the rotational degrees of freedom will tend to be fully excited near room temperature, while the bulk of the molecules will be in the ground state of vibrational energy.

At sufficiently high temperatures, we need to consider, in addition to translation, rotation, and vibration, the degrees of freedom arising from the excitation of the valence electrons in the molecule, which gives rise to a set of levels of electronic energy. It may readily be calculated that the population of molecules in an electronic state having an energy of 10 kcal/mole, referred to the ground level, will usually be entirely negligible at ordinary temperatures.

The entire method of calculating the thermodynamic properties of a given molecule statistically is based on the fact that it is possible to calculate the energy of one mole of molecules at any given temperature in the ideal gaseous state. This calculation may be repeated for all temperatures of interest. Once the energy is known as a function of the temperature, the other basic thermodynamic properties may be evaluated through the regular thermodynamic relations:

$$C_V = \left(\frac{\partial E}{\partial T} \right)_V \tag{15-2}$$

$$S = \int C_V \, d \ln T \tag{15-3}$$

The evaluation requires first the calculation, for each temperature, of the fractional population at each level, covering as many vibrational levels, beginning with the ground level, as have any significant population. Then there is summed the product of the population times the energy at each level, referred to the ground level, counted for each state at each level. For our calculation, we take the total number of molecules as one mole, N. Then at a given temperature

$$N = \sum n_i g_i \tag{15-4}$$

Substituting the value of n_i from Eq. 15-1 gives

$$N = \sum n_0 g_i e^{-x} \tag{15-5}$$

or, since at the given temperature n_0 is constant, this equation may be solved for n_0 to give

$$n_0 = \frac{N}{\sum g_i e^{-x}} \tag{15-6}$$

The population of each state of the ground level at any temperature is thus given in terms of known factors, namely, N, g_i, $\epsilon_i - \epsilon_0$, k, and T.

Combination of Eq. 15-1 and 15-6 permits calculation of the population of each state at the level i, in terms of known factors:

$$n_i = N \frac{e^{-x}}{\sum g_i e^{-x}} \tag{15-7}$$

The total energy of one mole of molecules, referred to the ground level, is then at the given temperature:

$$E - E_0 = \sum n_i g_i (\epsilon_i - \epsilon_0) \tag{15-8}$$

Substituting the value for n_i given by Eq. 15-7 yields for the energy at the given temperature

$$E - E_0 = N \frac{\sum g_i (\epsilon_i - \epsilon_0) e^{-x}}{\sum g_i e^{-x}} \tag{15-9}$$

In order to simplify the writing of Eq. 15-9 and the other equations that may be derived from it, we may use the following abbreviations:

$$A_i = g_i e^{-x} \tag{15-10}$$

$$B_i = (\epsilon_i - \epsilon_0) A_i \tag{15-11}$$

$$D_i = (\epsilon_i - \epsilon_0) B_i = (\epsilon_i - \epsilon_0)^2 A_i \tag{15-12}$$

It may be noted that

$$\frac{dA_i}{dT} = \frac{B_i}{kT^2} \tag{15-13}$$

and

$$\frac{dB_i}{dT} = \frac{D_i}{kT^2} \tag{15-14}$$

The sum of the A_i terms over all levels is called the partition function, and, for any temperature, is equal to the series

$$A_i = A_0 + A_1 + A_2 + A_3 + \cdots \tag{15-15}$$

or

$$\sum A_i = g_0 + g_1 e^{\frac{-(\epsilon_1 - \epsilon_0)}{kT}} + g_2 e^{\frac{-(\epsilon_2 - \epsilon_0)}{kT}} + \cdots \tag{15-16}$$

With these abbreviations, the energy of one mole of molecules, in the given set of levels of energy, at the temperature T, is

$$E - E_0 = N \frac{\sum B_i}{\sum A_i} \tag{15-17}$$

Since the calculation is being made for the molecules in the ideal gaseous reference state, of unit pressure, we can indicate this by the appropriate superscript on the symbol for the energy, so that Eq. 15-17 may be written as

$$E^0 - E_0^0 = N \frac{\sum B_i}{\sum A_i} \tag{15-18}$$

Once the energy of one mole of molecules is known as a function of the temperature, then the other thermodynamic functions may be evaluated from the regular thermodynamic relations. As will become evident later, it is convenient to evaluate the following five thermodynamic properties or functions of the given substance in the ideal gaseous reference state of unit pressure:

$(H^0 - H_0^0)/T$, the heat content (or enthalpy) function;

$(F^0 - H_0^0)/T$, the free energy function;

S^0, the entropy;

$H^0 - H_0^0$, the heat content (or enthalpy);

C_p^0, the heat capacity at constant pressure.

In the foregoing symbols, the superscript ^{0} denotes the ideal gaseous reference state and the subscript $_0$ denotes the absolute zero of temperature. For one mole of molecules in the ideal gaseous standard state, the following relations hold:

$$pV = RT \tag{15-19}$$

$$H^0 = E^0 + (pV)^0 = E^0 + RT \tag{15-20}$$

$$F^0 = E^0 + (pV)^0 - TS^0 = E^0 + RT - TS^0 \tag{15-21}$$

$$C_p^0 = C_V^0 + R = (\partial E^0/\partial T)_V + R \tag{15-22}$$

At 0°K,

$$H_0^0 = E_0^0 \tag{15-23}$$

Subtracting Eq. 15-23 from Eq. 15-20 and dividing by T, we obtain

$$(H^0 - H_0^0)/T = (E^0 - E_0^0)/T + R \tag{15-24}$$

which, in terms of the statistically evaluated quantities, is, for each set of levels of energy or each degree of freedom,

$$\frac{H^0 - H_0^0}{T} = R + \frac{N}{T} \frac{\sum B_i}{\sum A_i} \tag{15-25}$$

The heat content is obtained by multiplying the heat content function by the temperature:

$$H^0 - H_0^0 = RT + N \frac{\sum B_i}{\sum A_i} \tag{15-26}$$

The heat capacity C_V^0 is obtained by differentiating Eq. 15-18 with temperature,

$$C_V^0 = \left[\frac{\partial(E^0 - E_0^0)}{\partial T} \right]_V \tag{15-27}$$

or

$$C_V^0 = \frac{N}{kT^2} \left[\frac{\sum D_i}{\sum A_i} - \left(\frac{\sum B_i}{\sum A_i} \right)^2 \right] \qquad (15\text{-}28)$$

The heat capacity C_p^0 is then

$$C_p^0 = C_V^0 + R \qquad (15\text{-}29)$$

From the definition of the free energy, we can write for one mole of our molecules in the ideal gaseous standard state

$$F^0 = E^0 + (pV)^0 - TS^0 = H^0 - TS^0 \qquad (15\text{-}30)$$

Subtracting H_0^0 from both sides and dividing by T gives the free energy function as

$$(F^0 - H_0^0)/T = (H^0 - H_0^0)/T - S^0 \qquad (15\text{-}31)$$

Substituting for the terms on the right side their equivalents from previous equations, we obtain

$$\frac{F^0 - H_0^0}{T} = R + \frac{E^0 - E_0^0}{T} - \int_0^T \left(\frac{\partial (E^0 - E_0^0)}{\partial T} \right)_V d \ln T \qquad (15\text{-}32)$$

But the last term on the right side may, for an ideal gas, be simplified to

$$\int_0^T \frac{1}{T} d(E^0 - E_0^0) \qquad (15\text{-}33)$$

and

$$\frac{F^0 - H_0^0}{T} = R + \left(\frac{1}{T} \right) (E^0 - E_0^0) - \int_0^T \left(\frac{1}{T} \right) d(E^0 - E_0^0) \qquad (15\text{-}34)$$

But the last two terms on the right side may be combined in accordance with the mathematical relation

$$xy - \int y\,dx = \int x\,dy \qquad (15\text{-}35)$$

Then

$$\frac{F^0 - H_0^0}{T} = R + \int_0^T (E^0 - E_0^0) d \left(\frac{1}{T} \right) \qquad (15\text{-}36)$$

But

$$E^0 - E_0^0 = N \frac{\sum B_i}{\sum A_i} \qquad (15\text{-}37)$$

and

$$\sum B_i = kT^2 \frac{d(\sum A_i)}{dT} \qquad (15\text{-}38)$$

so that

$$E^0 - E_0^0 = NkT^2 \frac{1}{\sum A_i} \frac{d(\sum A_i)}{dT} \qquad (15\text{-}39)$$

or

$$E^0 - E_0^0 = +RT^2 \frac{d \ln (\sum A_i)}{dT} \tag{15-40}$$

Hence

$$(E^0 - E_0^0)d\left(\frac{1}{T}\right) = -Rd \ln (\sum A_i) \tag{15-41}$$

and

$$\int_0^T (E^0 - E_0^0)d\left(\frac{1}{T}\right) = -R \int_0^T d \ln (\sum A_i) \tag{15-42}$$

But

$$\int_0^T d \ln (\sum A_i) = \ln (\sum A_i)_T - \ln (\sum A_i)_0 \tag{15-43}$$

From Eq. 15-15 and 15-16, the value of $\sum A_i$ for $T = 0$ would appear to be equal to the multiplicity of the ground level, g_0. But at a temperature sufficiently near the absolute zero, when g_0 is greater than unity, cognizance must be taken of the fact that the several states at the ground level actually have small differences in energy, which become significant in comparison with kT as T approaches zero. Therefore, as T approaches zero, the ground level may be treated as a series of levels of energy, g_0 in number, with one of them being lowest in energy. Giving this latter one the number 00 and the others the numbers 01, 02, etc., up to $0g_0$, the value of the partition function at the absolute zero reduces to $A_i = A_{00} = g_{00} = 1$. Therefore

$$\ln (\sum A_i)_0 = 0 \tag{15-44}$$

and

$$\int_0^T (E^0 - E_0^0)d\left(\frac{1}{T}\right) = -R \ln (\sum A_i) \tag{15-45}$$

Then

$$\frac{F^0 - H_0^0}{T} = R - R \ln (\sum A_i) \tag{15-46}$$

The entropy may be written as the heat content function less the free energy function,

$$S^0 = (H^0 - H_0^0)/T - (F^0 - H_0^0)/T \tag{15-47}$$

and may be evaluated from these latter functions if their values have already been calculated. In terms of the components of the statistical calculations,

$$S^0 = \frac{N}{T}\frac{\sum B_i}{\sum A_i} + R \ln (\sum A_i) \tag{15-48}$$

From the foregoing equations, it may be seen that the free energy function is the thermodynamic property most easily calculated statistically because it involves only the simple summation of the series of terms of A_i.

From the foregoing, it is seen that when the complete diagram of levels of energy is known for each degree of freedom for a given molecule in the ideal gaseous state, the value of each thermodynamic function may be calculated in a straightforward manner for each set of levels of energy and summed for all the different sets of levels of energy, one for each degree of freedom in the molecule. That is, the over-all value of a given thermodynamic property G is, for example,

$$G = G \text{ (translation)} + G \text{ (rotation)} + G \text{ (vibration)}$$
$$+ G \text{ (electronic)} \quad (15\text{-}49)$$

In summing the several contributions to obtain the over-all value of the given thermodynamic property, it is important to note that, in the case of the heat content function $(H^0 - H_0^0)/T$ and the free energy function $(F^0 - H_0^0)/T$, the value of the gas constant R, which arises from the substitution of RT for pV and subsequent division by T, is counted for the entire molecule in the contribution from the translational degrees of freedom and is not to be included again with any of the other contributions. That is to say, for the contributions following translation, the heat content function would be given by the term $(N/T)(\sum B_i/\sum A_i)$, and the free energy function would be given by the term $-R \ln (\sum A_i)$.

It is important to note that the thermodynamic properties evaluated statistically are values of the several given thermodynamic properties for a given substance in the ideal gaseous state with reference to the value of that given property at the absolute zero of temperature, except for the property of the heat capacity. In the case of the properties of the entropy and the free energy function, the reference values at the absolute zero of temperature are zero. In the case of the heat capacity, which is the temperature coefficient of the energy, the differentiation eliminates the constant of reference. In the case of the energy, $E^0 - E_0^0$, or the heat content, $H^0 - H_0^0$, the reference value is of course the absolute energy content, $E_0^0 = H_0^0$, of the given substance in the ideal gaseous state at the absolute zero of temperature. Statistical calculations do not evaluate the difference in energy content of different molecules, which difference, if known, would permit the calculation of the heat of any reaction involving the given molecules.

From Eq. 15-48, we have the entropy given as

$$S^0 = \frac{N}{T} \frac{\sum B_i}{\sum A_i} + R \ln (\sum A_i) \quad (15\text{-}50)$$

As the temperature approaches the absolute zero of temperature, both of the terms on the right side of Eq. 15-50 approach zero, and, in the limit, we may write, $S_0^0 = 0$. In the simple picture presented above, the given pure substance is in the ideal gaseous state and the molecules are distributed among the various states of the given set of levels of energy at the given temperature according to the Boltzmann distribution law. By this simple picture, we would have, at the absolute zero of temperature, all the molecules in the lowest state at the ground level. From an earlier article (Art. 8), we have seen that the entropy may also be defined as $S = k \ln W$, where W is the probability of existence and corresponds to the number of states of existence available to the system. If there is only one state available, as at the absolute zero of temperature according to the simple picture presented above, then W is unity, its logarithm is zero, and, as before, $S_0^0 = 0$. Each of the possible sets of levels of energy or degrees of freedom would be treated in the same way, and the entropy at the absolute zero of temperature would be the sum of the several contributions, each of which, according to the simple picture, would have the value zero. At this point, it is necessary to point out that actually at very low temperatures the Boltzmann distribution law must be replaced by that of the Einstein-Bose statistics or the Fermi-Dirac statistics, in accordance with the requirements of the given system. However, the net result is the same as far as the entropy at the absolute zero is concerned, in that, in each case, the ideal gaseous molecules at the absolute zero of temperature have only one state of existence available to them and the entropy has the value zero.

The levels of energy associated with the three translational degrees of freedom, for a particle of mass m in the ideal gaseous state in a cubic space of volume V are given by the expression

$$(\epsilon_i - \epsilon_0) \text{ (translation)} = (n_x^2 + n_y^2 + n_z^2) \frac{h^2}{8mV^{\frac{2}{3}}} \qquad (15\text{-}51)$$

where h is the Planck constant, and n_x, n_y, and n_z are integral positive quantum numbers associated with the three coordinates of the system, x, y, and z, and have values running from zero to infinity. This leads [2] to the following partition function for the three degrees of translational freedom:

$$\sum A_i \text{ (translation)} = \left(\frac{2\pi mkT}{h^2}\right)^{\frac{3}{2}} \frac{Ve}{N} \qquad (15\text{-}52)$$

Substituting this value of $\sum A_i$ (translation) into the appropriate preceding equations, one obtains for the three degrees of translational freedom:

$$(E_0 - E_0^0) \text{ (translation)} = \tfrac{3}{2}RT \qquad (15\text{-}53)$$

$$C_V^0 \text{ (translation)} = \tfrac{3}{2}R \qquad (15\text{-}54)$$

$$\frac{F^0 - H_0^0}{T} \text{ (translation)} = -R \ln\left[\left(\frac{2\pi mkT}{h^2}\right)^{\frac{3}{2}} \frac{N}{V}\right] \qquad (15\text{-}55)$$

$$\frac{H^0 - H_0^0}{T} \text{ (translation)} = \frac{5}{2} R \qquad (15\text{-}56)$$

$$S^0 \text{ (translation)} = \frac{5}{2} R + R \ln\left[\left(\frac{2\pi mkT}{h^2}\right)^{\frac{3}{2}} \frac{V}{N}\right] \qquad (15\text{-}57)$$

In the case of the contributions to the thermodynamic functions arising from the rotational degrees of freedom, the most accurate procedure is to use the actual levels of rotational energy as determined from appropriate spectral data. The value of the partition function $\sum A_i$ may be obtained by summation over the actual levels of rotational energy, term by term. Or the energy of the various levels may be expressed in terms of an appropriate series and the value of $\sum A_i$ obtained by analytic summation.

Whenever the actual diagram of the levels of rotational energy is not known for a given molecule, a very good approximation for ordinary temperatures may be obtained by using the levels of rotational energy deduced theoretically for an ideal rigid rotator. The calculation requires that there be known the value of the moment of inertia for each degree of rotational freedom.

For a diatomic molecule, which has effectively only two degrees of rotational freedom, the levels of rotational energy for a rigid rotator are given by the following relation [3]:

$$(\epsilon_i - \epsilon_0) \text{ (rotation)} = j(j+1)\frac{h^2}{8\pi^2 I} \qquad (15\text{-}58)$$

In this equation, I is the moment of inertia about the axis of rotation and j is the rotational quantum number. The partition function for the diatomic molecule becomes

$$\left(\sum A_i\right) \text{ (rotation)} = \frac{8\pi^2 IkT}{h^2} \qquad (15\text{-}59)$$

For any polyatomic nonlinear molecule, which will have three degrees of rotational freedom, similar equations may be derived. For small values of the quantity $h^2/8\pi^2 IkT$, the partition function for rotation for a polyatomic nonlinear molecule, taken as a rigid rotator, reduces to [3]

$$\left(\sum A_i\right) \text{ (rotation)} = \left(\frac{8\pi^2 kT}{h^2}\right)^{\frac{3}{2}} (\pi I_x I_y I_z)^{\frac{1}{2}} \qquad (15\text{-}60)$$

Here I_x, I_y, and I_z are the moments of inertia about the three axes of the polyatomic nonlinear molecule. It is shown theoretically that whenever the diatomic molecule is composed of identical atoms, the number of states of rotational energy is only half that given for the diatomic molecule composed of dissimilar atoms. The effect of this is to introduce the factor $\frac{1}{2}$ into the value of the partition function for rotation. Similarly, it is shown that for any polyatomic molecule having two or more identical atoms, the allowable number of states of rotational energy is only $1/\sigma$ times the number for polyatomic molecules composed of dissimilar atoms, where σ is the symmetry number, a small integer, evaluated as the number of ways the molecule may be superimposed upon itself by rotation of the entire molecule. The effect of this is to introduce the factor $1/\sigma$ into the value of the partition function for rotation for the polyatomic molecule. Examples of the value of the symmetry number for several polyatomic molecules are: OCO, carbon dioxide, 2; CH_4, methane, 12; NH_3, ammonia, 3; NNO, nitrous oxide, 1; HCCH, acetylene, 2; H_2CCH_2, ethylene, 4. Taking cognizance of the symmetry number σ, the partition function for rotation for any molecule taken as a rigid rotator has the following values:

$$(\textstyle\sum A_i) \text{ (rotation, linear molecule)} = \frac{8\pi^2 IkT}{h^2\sigma} \tag{15-61}$$

$$(\textstyle\sum A_i) \text{ (rotation, nonlinear molecule)} = \left(\frac{8\pi^2 kT}{h^2}\right)^{\frac{3}{2}} \frac{(\pi I_x I_y I_z)^{\frac{1}{2}}}{\sigma} \tag{15-62}$$

Substituting the value of the partition function into the appropriate preceding equations, we obtain the following rotational contributions to the thermodynamic properties for molecules taken as rigid rotators:

For any linear molecule:

$$(E^0 - E_0^0) \text{ (rotation)} = RT \tag{15-63}$$

$$C_V^0 \text{ (rotation)} = R \tag{15-64}$$

$$(F^0 - H_0^0)/T \text{ (rotation)} = -R \ln [8\pi^2 IkT/h^2\sigma] \tag{15-65}$$

$$\left(\frac{H^0 - H_0^0}{T}\right) \text{ (rotation)} = R \tag{15-66}$$

$$S^0 \text{ (rotation)} = R + R \ln \left(\frac{8\pi^2 IkT}{h^2\sigma}\right) \tag{15-67}$$

For any nonlinear molecule:

$$(E^0 - E_0^0) \text{ (rotation)} = \tfrac{3}{2}RT \tag{15-68}$$

$$C_V \text{ (rotation)} = \tfrac{3}{2}R \tag{15-69}$$

$$\left(\frac{F^0 - H_0^0}{T}\right) \text{ (rotation)} = -R \ln \left[\left(\frac{8\pi^2 kT}{h^2}\right)^{\frac{3}{2}} \frac{(\pi I_x I_y I_z)^{\frac{1}{2}}}{\sigma}\right] \tag{15-70}$$

$$\left(\frac{H^0 - H_0^0}{T}\right) \text{ (rotation)} = \frac{3}{2} R \tag{15-71}$$

$$S^0 \text{ (rotation)} = \frac{3}{2} R + R \ln \left[\left(\frac{8\pi^2 kT}{h^2}\right)^{\frac{3}{2}} \frac{(\pi I_x I_y I_z)^{\frac{1}{2}}}{\sigma}\right] \tag{15-72}$$

As previously indicated, the foregoing equations for the rigid rotator give a good approximation for the rotational contributions to the thermodynamic properties at ordinary temperatures. Corrections to the equations for the rigid rotator to account for the "stretching" of the molecule in the states of higher rotational energy have been derived and may be applied whenever the population of molecules in such states is large enough.

In the case of the contributions to the thermodynamic functions arising from the vibrational degrees of freedom, the most accurate procedure is to use the actual levels of vibrational energy as determined from appropriate spectral data. As in the case of the rotational contributions, the value of the partition function $\sum A_i$ for vibration may be obtained by summation over the actual levels of vibrational energy, term by term. Or the energy of the various levels may be expressed in terms of an appropriate series and the value of $\sum A_i$ obtained by analytic summation.

Whenever the actual diagram of the levels of vibrational energy is not known for a given molecule, a very good approximation for ordinary temperatures may be obtained by using the levels of vibrational energy deduced theoretically for a harmonic oscillator. The calculation requires that there be known the value of the fundamental frequency of vibration for each of the degrees of vibrational freedom in the molecule, which, for a molecule of n atoms, are $3n - 5$ in number for a linear molecule and $3n - 6$ in number for a nonlinear molecule. For a diatomic molecule, which has only one degree of vibrational freedom, the levels of vibrational energy for the harmonic oscillator are given by the following expression [3]:

$$(\epsilon_i - \epsilon_0) \text{ (vibration)} = v_i h \nu \tag{15-73}$$

In this equation, ν is the fundamental frequency of vibration and v_i is the vibrational quantum number, having values from zero to infinity. For the vibrational levels, the multiplicity is unity, and the partition function for vibration for a diatomic molecule taken as a harmonic oscillator becomes, with $x = h\nu/kT$,

$$(\sum A_i) \text{ (vibration)} = \frac{1}{1 - e^{-x}} \tag{15-74}$$

Substituting the value of the partition function into the appropriate preceding equations, we obtain the following vibrational contributions to the thermodynamic properties for molecules taken as harmonic oscillators, for each degree of vibrational freedom:

$$(E^0 - E_0^0) \text{ (vibration)} = RT \frac{x}{e^x - 1} \tag{15-75}$$

$$C_V^0 \text{ (vibration)} = R \frac{x^2 e^x}{(e^x - 1)^2} \tag{15-76}$$

$$\left(\frac{F^0 - H_0^0}{T}\right) \text{(vibration)} = R \ln (1 - e^{-x}) \tag{15-77}$$

$$\left(\frac{H^0 - H_0^0}{T}\right) \text{(vibration)} = R \frac{x}{e^x - 1} \tag{15-78}$$

$$S^0 \text{(vibration)} = R \left[\frac{x}{e^x - 1} - \ln (1 - e^{-x})\right] \tag{15-79}$$

No significant error occurs in the use of the foregoing equations to calculate the vibrational contributions to the thermodynamic properties for low temperatures, and very little uncertainty occurs in the calculations for ordinary temperatures. For extremely high temperatures, however, the population of the higher levels of vibrational energy becomes large and the approximation of a uniform spacing of the levels of vibrational energy brings significant errors into the calculations. Corrections to the simple equations for the harmonic oscillator may be made to take cognizance of the fact that the spacing of the vibrational levels of energy actually decreases slowly with increase in the vibrational quantum number. The total vibrational contribution is obtained by adding the contribution from each degree of vibrational freedom. The labor of such calculation is greatly lessened by making use of published tables which give values of the functions.

The contributions to the thermodynamic functions arising from electronic states of energy must be calculated using values of the energies of the electronic states of the molecule as determined from appropriate spectral data.

The contributions to the thermodynamic properties arising from the electronic states of energy are given by the following equations:

$$(E^0 - E_0^0) \text{(electronic)} = N \frac{\sum B_i}{\sum A_i} \tag{15-80}$$

$$C_V^0 \text{(electronic)} = \frac{N}{kT^2} \left[\frac{\sum D_i}{\sum A_i} - \left(\frac{\sum B_i}{\sum A_i}\right)^2\right] \tag{15-81}$$

$$\left(\frac{H^0 - H_0^0}{T}\right) \text{(electronic)} = \frac{N}{T} \frac{\sum B_i}{\sum A_i} \tag{15-82}$$

$$\left(\frac{F^0 - H_0^0}{T}\right) \text{(electronic)} = -R \ln (\sum A_i) \tag{15-83}$$

$$S^0 \text{(electronic)} = \frac{N}{T} \frac{\sum B_i}{\sum A_i} + R \ln (\sum A_i) \tag{15-84}$$

In the case of polyatomic molecules having a group of atoms bonded to another group of atoms, one of the vibrational degrees of freedom of the molecule will be associated with the oscillation, about the bond joining the two groups, of one of the groups with respect to the other. Such oscillation may be highly restricted and of small amplitude, nearly corresponding to pure vibrational motion, or it may be little restricted and of large amplitude, approaching nearly free rotation about the given bond. Ascertaining the proper set of levels of energy to be associated with such a degree of freedom is considerably more complicated than in the case of essentially pure rotation or pure vibration. When the restriction to rotation is extremely large, the levels of energy approach those of a simple harmonic oscillator, while, when the restriction to rotation is very small, the levels of energy approach those of a simple rotator. In the case of a degree of freedom involving such restricted internal rotation, it is assumed that the potential energy of the rotating group may be expressed as a function involving the cosine of the angle of rotation. Specifically, for the molecule ethane, in which one methyl group may oscillate, with respect to the second methyl group, about the carbon—carbon bond joining the two groups, the potential energy for the restricted internal rotational degree of freedom is taken as follows:

$$U = U_{max}(1 - \cos 3\alpha)(\tfrac{1}{2}) \qquad (15\text{-}85)$$

Here U_{max} is the maximum value of the potential energy, α is the angle of rotation, and 3 is the number of maxima in the potential energy occurring in a complete rotation of the methyl group. Pitzer and Gwinn [4] have calculated the levels of energy associated with a restricted internal rotational degree of freedom and have prepared extensive tables giving the contribution to the thermodynamic properties of energy, free energy function, entropy, and heat capacity arising from such a degree of freedom. The tabulated values cover, in suitable combination, an appropriate range of values of the maximum of the potential energy, the temperature, and the reduced moment of inertia for the given rotation.

A,16. Entropy and the Third Law of Thermodynamics. We have seen that when a system participates in a reversible process, its increase in entropy is equal to the heat energy absorbed divided by the absolute temperature:

$$dS = \frac{\delta q}{T} \qquad (16\text{-}1)$$

If the temperature is known as a function of the quantity of heat absorbed, beginning at the absolute zero of temperature, this equation can be integrated to give the entropy at the temperature T:

$$S = S_0 + \int_0^T \frac{\delta q}{T} \qquad (16\text{-}2)$$

⟨ 71 ⟩

In this equation, S_0 is the entropy of the given system at the absolute zero of temperature. From the discussion in the preceding article, it is clear that when the given substance is taken down to the absolute zero of temperature, the ensemble of molecules constituting the given substance will end up in a single permitted state of energy, provided opportunity is given for the free passage of each of the molecules among all the permitted states of energy in accordance with the appropriate distribution law. If the given ensemble of molecules is in a single quantum state at the absolute zero of temperature, the entropy of the ensemble is zero. This constitutes the third law of thermodynamics, which may be formally stated as follows: The entropy of any substance of which all component parts are in complete internal equilibrium becomes zero at the absolute zero of temperature.

The investigator begins his observations at T_*, the lowest temperature of measurement, and the value of the integral below T_* is obtained by extrapolation, from T_* to 0°K, of the measurements made above T_*. Indicating this fact, we may write

$$S = S_0 + \left(\int_0^{T_*} \frac{\delta q}{T} \right)_{\text{extrap}} + \int_{T_*}^{T} \frac{\delta q}{T} \tag{16-3}$$

In this equation, the last term is derived completely from the experimental measurements (of heat capacity, heat of transition, heat of fusion, and heat of vaporization, as appropriate), and the second term on the right side is evaluated by extrapolating from T_* to 0°K the measurements of heat capacity made above T_*, in conjunction with an appropriate theoretical equation, usually the Debye equation for the heat capacity of solids. The extrapolation from T_* to 0°K in this way accounts for the ordinary thermal entropy resident in the substance at T_*, the lowest temperature of measurement. Therefore, the term S_0 represents the entropy of the substance at 0°K as determined essentially by its quantum condition at T_*.

A simple statement of the requirements for the application of the third law is the following: "If at the lowest temperature of measurement T_*, a substance is in a single pure quantum state of energy, except for the ordinary thermal energy characteristic of T_* which is accounted for by the extrapolation from T_* to 0°K, then S_0, its entropy at 0°K, may be placed equal to zero." When this condition holds, Eq. 16-3 reduces to

$$S = \left(\int_0^{T_*} \frac{\delta q}{T} \right)_{\text{extrap}} + \int_{T_*}^{T} \frac{\delta q}{T} \tag{16-4}$$

and the entropy of the given substance is determined with substantial completeness from the experimental observations. It is clear that, for such experiments, T_* should be made as low as practicable so that the extrapolation introduces as little error as possible. It is important to note that the above statement of the requirements for the application of the third law places no limitation on the physical state of the substance, solid, liquid, or gas, although practically all substances investigated down to near 10°K will be in the solid state. The only requirement that needs to be fulfilled is that at the lowest temperature of measurement T_*, the given substance, solid, liquid, or gas, shall be in a substantially single quantum state of energy except for that energy which will be accounted for by the extrapolation, from T_* to 0°K, of the measurements made above T_*. That is to say, the situation is such that the extrapolation, from T_* to 0°K, of the observations above T_*, has the effect of reducing all the molecules of the given substance to a single quantum state of energy (usually but not necessarily the ground level) at 0°K in the same physical state, solid, liquid, or gas, in which it existed at T_*. However, if the given substance is in the liquid or gaseous state at T_*, and a change of state occurs below T_*, as from liquid to solid or gas to liquid, accompanied by a finite change in energy, it is obvious that the extrapolation, from T_* to 0°K, of the observations above T_* will not properly account for the term

$$\int_0^{T_*} \frac{\delta q}{T}$$

and the system will not conform to the requirements of the third law. In general, we may say that the requirements for the application of the third law are that, for some range of temperature above the lowest temperature of measurement T_*, the molecules of the given substance are distributed among the available quantum states in accordance with the normal distribution law, and that as the temperature is lowered, the distribution of the molecules among the available levels of energy changes progressively in such a way that in the limit, at 0°K, the molecules will have available only one state of existence.

We have already seen that the entropy of a mole of molecules in the ideal gaseous state at the absolute zero of temperature becomes zero when the mole of molecules has available only one state of existence. The third law is essentially, then, a statement of this fact applied to the evaluation of entropy from experimental measurements of energy as a function of temperature. It is important to note also, in this connection, that the third law does not limit the given substance to existence in only one of two or more possible crystalline forms. The given substance may at the lowest temperature of measurement be in any one of several possible crystalline forms and each of the different crystalline forms, pure in itself, may conform to the requirements of the third law.

For a substance that conforms to the requirements of the third law, and has two stable crystalline forms, the entropy of the gas at the given pressure at the temperature T is given by the following relation:

$$S \text{ (gas)} = \left(\int_0^{T_*} \frac{\delta q}{T} \right)_{\text{extrap}} + \int_{T_*}^{T_{\text{tr}}} C_p \text{ (c, II)} d \ln T + \frac{\Delta H_{\text{tr}}}{T_{\text{tr}}}$$

$$+ \int_{T_{\text{tr}}}^{T_{\text{m}}} C_p \text{ (c, I)} d \ln T + \frac{\Delta H_{\text{m}}}{T_{\text{m}}} + \int_{T_{\text{m}}}^{T_{\text{v}}} C_p \text{ (liq)} d \ln T$$

$$+ \frac{\Delta H_{\text{v}}}{T_{\text{v}}} + \int_{T_{\text{v}}}^{T} C_p \text{ (gas)} d \ln T \quad (16\text{-}5)$$

In the practical application of the third law, it is necessary to consider the problem of what substances are likely to conform, and what substances are likely not to conform, to the requirements for the application of the third law. By comparison of the values of entropy calculated for the ideal gaseous state in an accurate way statistically with the values of entropy evaluated from experimental measurements of energy as a function of temperature, appropriately corrected by a small amount to the ideal gaseous state, it has been found that the following substances, among many others, conform to the requirements for the application of the third law: O_2, N_2, Cl_2, HCl, HBr, HI, H_2S, SCO, CO_2, NH_3, CS_2, CH_4, C_2H_2, C_2H_4, C_2H_6, C_3H_6 (propylene), C_6H_6 (benzene), plus a large number of other hydrocarbons. The following values indicate the degree of accord between values of the entropy at 25°C for the given substance in the ideal gaseous state at 1 atmosphere obtained (1) by application of the third law, from Giauque and collaborators, and (2) by the method of statistical calculations, the values being given in that order (in cal/deg mole) and having respective uncertainties as indicated below: O_2, 49.1, 49.003; N_2, 45.9, 45.767; HCl, 44.5, 44.617; HBr, 47.6, 47.437; HI, 49.5, 49.314; H_2S, 49.1, 49.15; SCO, 55.3, 55.34; CO_2, 51.1, 51.061; NH_3, 45.9, 46.01. Actually, it appears that, except for certain small molecules of the types discussed below, any substance obtainable in a pure crystalline form is likely to conform to the requirements of the third law. The uncertainties are, in cal/deg mole, approximately ± 0.1 to ± 0.2 for the "third law" values and ± 0.005 to ± 0.05 for the statistically calculated values.

Possible causes of nonconformity with the requirements for the application of the third law, that is, causes which would result in the given substance not being in a single pure quantum state at T_* (except for those states which will become normally depopulated as the observations above T_* are extrapolated from T_* to 0°K), are the following: existence of nuclear spin; existence of isotopes; existence of randomness in the structure of the crystal; existence of a nonequilibrium distribution of molecules among the quantum states of energy; existence of a solution or mixture of different molecules; existence of the substance in a glassy instead of a crystalline form. Examples of these cases are discussed in [1].

A,17. Equilibrium Constant and Change in Free Energy for Reactions of Ideal Gases. When a given system participates in a reversible process in which only heat energy and pV work energy occur, we have seen that, at constant temperature,

$$dF = Vdp \tag{17-1}$$

For an ideal gas, this becomes

$$dF = \frac{RT}{p} dp = RTd \ln p \tag{17-2}$$

On integrating for a given gas between states of different pressure, A and B, at constant temperature, we obtain the relation

$$F_B - F_A = RT \ln \frac{p_B}{p_A} \tag{17-3}$$

In an earlier article, we derived the relation giving the change in entropy on mixing different ideal gases. For the case of bringing together gases initially at identical pressures to form a mixture at the same pressure, the change in entropy, calculated per mole of the mixture, was found to be, per mole of the mixture,

$$\Delta S \text{ (mixing)} = -R \sum X_i \ln X_i \tag{17-4}$$

where X_i is the mole fraction of component i in the mixture and the summation is carried over all the components.

From the definition of the ideal gas we can write, for constant temperature,

$$\Delta E \text{ (mixing)} = \Delta H \text{ (mixing)} = 0 \tag{17-5}$$

But by definition of the free energy for a given substance we can write, for a process or reaction at constant temperature,

$$(F_B - F_A) = (H_B - H_A) - T(S_B - S_A) \tag{17-6}$$

or

$$\Delta F = \Delta H - T\Delta S \tag{17-7}$$

Applying this equation to the above process of mixing ideal gases, and substituting from the preceding equations, we obtain, at constant temperature, per mole of mixture,

$$\Delta F \text{ (mixing)} = RT \sum X_i \ln X_i \tag{17-8}$$

This equation gives the change in free energy, per mole of mixture, on mixing different ideal gases brought together in different amounts from initially identical pressures to form a mixture at the same pressure.

It is convenient to define what we may term the "proper quotient of pressures," as well as the equilibrium constant, for reactions of ideal gases. Given the following reaction in which each reactant and product is an ideal gas:

$$bB \text{ (g)} + cC \text{ (g)} = mM \text{ (g)} + nN \text{ (g)} \tag{17-9}$$

This equation states that b moles of the gas B react with c moles of the gas C to form m moles of the gas M and n moles of the gas N. For any such reaction, the "proper quotient of pressures" is here defined as

$$Q_p = \frac{(p_M)^m (p_N)^n}{(p_B)^b (p_C)^c} \tag{17-10}$$

That is to say, the numerator is the product of the pressure of each of the product gases with each pressure raised to a power equal to the stoichiometrical number of moles of the given gas, and the denominator is the product of the pressure of each of the reactant gases, with each pressure raised to a power equal to the stoichiometrical number of moles of the given gas. The proper quotient of pressures, Q_p, may be written for any reaction of ideal gases in any states. When, however, the pressure of each reactant and each product gas is that which it has at thermodynamic equilibrium for the given reaction, the proper quotient of pressures is then specified for the equilibrium states Q_p (equilibrium), or Q_p^e, and it is convenient to write this as the equilibrium constant K. For the reaction of ideal gases given by Eq. 17-9, the equilibrium constant is

$$K = Q_p^e = \frac{(p_M^e)^m (p_N^e)^n}{(p_B^e)^b (p_C^e)^c} \tag{17-11}$$

Consider the reaction given by Eq. 17-9 as occurring at some constant temperature T. We may write for the change in free energy for the given reaction, for any specified set of conditions,

$$\Delta F = mF_M + nF_N - bF_B - cF_C \tag{17-12}$$

In this equation, F_M, F_N, F_B, and F_C are the free energies per mole for the gases M, N, B, and C, respectively, and m, n, b, and c are, respectively, the number of moles of the given gases participating in the reaction. Suppose we consider this reaction as taking place under two different sets of conditions, one in which the participating gases are in certain states s, and the other in which the participating gases are in certain states e, and let us be concerned with the difference in the change in free energy for the given reaction under the two sets of conditions. For the states s, we write

$$\Delta F^s = m(F_M^s) + n(F_N^s) - b(F_B^s) - c(F_C^s) \tag{17-13}$$

And for the states e, we write

$$\Delta F^e = m(F_M^e) + n(F_N^e) - b(F_B^e) - c(F_C^e) \tag{17-14}$$

Subtraction gives

$$\Delta F^s - \Delta F^e = m(F_M^s - F_M^e) + n(F_N^s - F_N^e)$$
$$- b(F_B^s - F_B^e) - c(F_C^s - F_C^e) \quad (17\text{-}15)$$

But from Eq. 17-3, for the gas M,

$$F_M^s - F_M^e = RT \ln \frac{p_M^s}{p_M^e} \quad (17\text{-}16)$$

and

$$m(F_M^s - F_M^e) = RT \ln \left(\frac{p_M^s}{p_M^e}\right)^m \quad (17\text{-}17)$$

Similar relations hold for the other gases, and substitution gives

$$\Delta F^s - \Delta F^e = RT \left[\ln \left(\frac{p_M^s}{p_M^e}\right)^m + \ln \left(\frac{p_N^s}{p_N^e}\right)^n - \ln \left(\frac{p_B^s}{p_B^e}\right)^b - \ln \left(\frac{p_C^s}{p_C^e}\right)^c \right] \quad (17\text{-}18)$$

The terms on the right side may be rearranged to bring together the factors involving the same states rather than the same molecules, as follows:

$$\Delta F^s - \Delta F^e = RT \ln \frac{(p_M^s)^m (p_N^s)^n}{(p_B^s)^b (p_C^s)^c} - RT \ln \frac{(p_M^e)^m (p_N^e)^n}{(p_B^e)^b (p_C^e)^c} \quad (17\text{-}19)$$

or

$$\Delta F^s - \Delta F^e = RT \ln Q_p^s - RT \ln Q_p^e \quad (17\text{-}20)$$

Now we may for convenience identify the states s as the reference or standard states in which each of the ideal gases has a pressure of unity, so that

$$p_M^s = p_N^s = p_B^s = p_C^s = 1 \quad (17\text{-}21)$$

Then

$$Q_p = 1 \quad \text{and} \quad \ln Q_p^s = 0 \quad (17\text{-}22)$$

Following the usual nomenclature, the reference or standard state may be indicated by the superscript ^{0}, so that the change in free energy for the s states becomes the standard change in free energy: $\Delta F^s = \Delta F^0$. Since we are interested in the states of the participating gases at thermodynamic equilibrium, we identify the e states as those of thermodynamic equilibrium for the given reaction at the given temperature. In such case, the proper quotient of pressures is the equilibrium constant $Q_p^e = K$. But we have seen that at constant temperature and constant pressure, the change in free energy at thermodynamic equilibrium is equal to zero, so that $\Delta F^e = 0$. On appropriate substitution of the foregoing, we have

$$\Delta F^0 = -RT \ln K \quad (17\text{-}23)$$

It should be noted that, of the two pairs of corresponding terms in Eq. 17-19, one term applying to the standard states and one term applying to the equilibrium states have been eliminated, so that in Eq. 17-23 there remain two noncorresponding terms, one relating to the standard states, ΔF^0, and one to the equilibrium states, $RT \ln K$. This equation (Eq. 17-23), which has been derived for any reaction of ideal gases at a given temperature, is one of the most powerful relations in the practical application of chemical thermodynamics. With this relation, the equilibrium constant may be evaluated from a knowledge of the standard change in free energy, and vice versa. Later on, it will be seen how the powerful simplicity of this equation can be retained for use in reactions of any substances in any states, solid, liquid, or gas.

If each of the reactants and products of the given reaction are in their respective standard reference states, then

$$\Delta F^0 = \Delta H^0 - T\Delta S^0 \tag{17-24}$$

where each of the thermodynamic properties applies to each reactant and product in its standard reference state.

But since

$$\Delta F^0 = -RT \ln K$$

combination of these equations gives

$$\Delta H^0 - T\Delta S^0 = -RT \ln K \tag{17-25}$$

or

$$\ln K = \frac{\Delta S^0}{R} - \frac{\Delta H^0}{RT} \tag{17-26}$$

From this equation, it is seen how one may calculate the equilibrium constant for a given reaction at a given temperature, if there is known the value of the heat of the reaction, ΔH^0, and the value of the standard change in entropy for the reaction, ΔS^0. We have seen how the value of the heat of the given reaction, ΔH^0, may be determined calorimetrically. The value of ΔS^0 for the given reaction is obtained simply as the sum of the entropies of the products less the sum of the entropies of the reactants, each in its standard reference state.

A,18. Equilibrium Between Different Phases of One Pure Substance. We have seen that thermodynamic equilibrium exists in any process at constant temperature and pressure when $dF = 0$, or, for a finite change, $\Delta F = 0$. If a given assembly of atoms or molecular species has an open path leading to a state in which the value of the free energy, $F = E + pV - TS$, per mole, is lower (algebraically), it will pass to the state of lower free energy. If the second state has a value of the free energy, per mole, equal to that of the first state, the two states will be in thermodynamic equilibrium. In general, we may say that, if the molal free energy of any substance is greater in one state than it is in another state, with the path between the states being open, the given substance will pass from the former state to the latter state. Or, in other words, any given substance has, thermodynamically, a tendency to pass from a state of higher free energy, per mole, to one of lower free energy, per mole, and will do so whenever the path between the two states is open.

A system is said to possess f degrees of freedom when at least f data are required to fix the system completely. A system composed of one component in one phase, solid, liquid, or gaseous, can be completely fixed by specifying the temperature and the pressure, if all other conditions, such as the gravitational field and magnetic field, are constant. That is, under these conditions, a system of one component in one phase has two degrees of freedom, while, if two phases of the one component exist together at equilibrium, the system has only one degree of freedom. In the latter case, the specification of either the temperature or the pressure fixes the system completely. If the given component exists in three phases together at equilibrium, then, under these conditions, the system has no degrees of freedom and is invariant, meaning that the three phases of the one component can exist together only at one temperature and pressure. The foregoing statements are summarized in the phase rule of Gibbs, that, whatever the number of variables, the number of degrees of freedom of the complete system is equal to the number of variables needed to fix the state of the individual phases less the number of phases beyond the first. That is, for a system of one component in one or more phases,

$$f = r - (P - 1) = r + 1 - P \tag{18-1}$$

where f is the number of degrees of freedom, P is the number of phases, and r is the number of all the variables needed to fix the state of the individual phases. If, as is usually the case, the variables of temperature and pressure are adequate to fix the state of the individual phases, then

$$f = 3 - P \tag{18-2}$$

Consider the thermodynamic equilibrium between two different phases, a and b, of the same pure substance, MX:

$$MX(a) = MX(b) \tag{18-3}$$

At equilibrium at constant temperature and pressure,

$$F_a = F_b \tag{18-4}$$

and if equilibrium is maintained as a result of any change in the variables,

$$dF_a = dF_b \tag{18-5}$$

The free energy may be expressed as a function of pressure and temperature, so that

$$dF_a = \left(\frac{\partial F_a}{\partial p}\right)_T dp + \left(\frac{\partial F_a}{\partial T}\right)_p dT \tag{18-6}$$

and

$$dF_b = \left(\frac{\partial F_b}{\partial p}\right)_T dp + \left(\frac{\partial F_b}{\partial T}\right)_p dT \qquad (18\text{-}7)$$

But

$$\left(\frac{\partial F}{\partial p}\right)_T = V \qquad (18\text{-}8)$$

and

$$\left(\frac{\partial F}{\partial T}\right)_p = -S \qquad (18\text{-}9)$$

Therefore,

$$dF_a = V_a dp - S_a dT \qquad (18\text{-}10)$$

and

$$dF_b = V_b dp - S_b dT \qquad (18\text{-}11)$$

Combination of these equations gives

$$(V_b - V_a)dp = (S_b - S_a)dT \qquad (18\text{-}12)$$

or

$$\frac{dp}{dT} = \frac{S_b - S_a}{V_b - V_a} \qquad (18\text{-}13)$$

For the process represented by Eq. 18-3, Eq. 18-13 may be written as

$$\frac{dp}{dT} = \frac{\Delta S}{\Delta V} \qquad (18\text{-}14)$$

But at thermodynamic equilibrium,

$$\Delta S = \frac{\Delta H}{T} \qquad (18\text{-}15)$$

so that we may write

$$\frac{dp}{dT} = \frac{\Delta H}{T \Delta V} \qquad (18\text{-}16)$$

This equation, commonly called the Clapeyron equation, gives, for the equilibrium between two different phases of the same pure substance, the ratio of the change in the equilibrium pressure to the change in temperature in terms of the absolute temperature and the difference in heat content, and the difference in volume of the substance in the two phases. This equation can be recast to give either the value of the increment in heat content or the increment in volume explicitly:

$$\Delta H = T(\Delta V)\frac{dp}{dT} \qquad (18\text{-}17)$$

and

$$\Delta V = \frac{\Delta H}{T}\frac{dT}{dp} \qquad (18\text{-}18)$$

That is, for the given process involving the equilibrium between phase a and phase b, the increment in heat content can be evaluated if the increment in volume and the change of pressure with temperature are known. Similarly, the increment in volume can be calculated if the increment in heat content and the change of pressure with temperature are known.

If the equilibrium under consideration is that between the liquid and gaseous phases of the same pure substance, i.e.

$$MX \text{ (liq)} = MX \text{ (g)} \tag{18-19}$$

then

$$\frac{dp}{dT} = \frac{H \text{ (g)} - H \text{ (liq)}}{T[V \text{ (g)} - V \text{ (liq)}]} = \frac{\Delta H_v}{T\Delta V_v} \tag{18-20}$$

where ΔH_v and ΔV_v represent, respectively, the increment in heat content and the increment in volume for the process of vaporization, and ΔH_v is the heat of vaporization. It is important to note that the increments in heat content and in volume apply to the given phases at the equilibrium pressure and temperature. If, for the given substance MX in the gaseous state, the value of the compressibility factor pV/RT is known for the given temperature and pressure, we may write the following:

$$z = \frac{pV}{RT} \tag{18-21}$$

and

$$V \text{ (g)} = \frac{zRT}{p} \tag{18-22}$$

Substitution yields

$$\frac{dp}{dT} = \frac{\Delta H_v}{T\left[\dfrac{zRT}{p} - V \text{ (liq)}\right]} \tag{18-23}$$

At sufficiently low pressures the value of the compressibility factor approaches unity and the volume of the liquid, per mole, is small in comparison with the value (in the same units) of RT/p. Under these conditions of sufficiently low pressures, then, this equation becomes the following approximation:

$$\frac{dp}{dT} = (\Delta H) \frac{p}{RT^2} \tag{18-24}$$

or

$$\frac{d \ln p}{dT} = \frac{\Delta H_v}{RT^2} \tag{18-25}$$

or

$$\frac{d \ln p}{d(1/T)} = - \frac{\Delta H_v}{R} \tag{18-26}$$

This equation, commonly called the Clausius-Clapeyron equation, is an approximation good only at sufficiently low pressures.

If the equilibrium is that between the solid and liquid phases of the same pure substance, i.e.

$$MX \text{ (c)} = MX \text{ (liq)} \qquad (18\text{-}27)$$

then

$$\frac{dp}{dT} = \frac{\Delta H_m}{T[V \text{ (liq)} - V \text{ (c)}]} = \frac{\Delta H_m}{T(\Delta V_m)} \qquad (18\text{-}28)$$

where ΔH_m and ΔV_m represent, respectively, the increment in heat content and the increment in volume for the process of melting or fusion, and ΔH_m is the heat of fusion. As before, it is to be noted that the increments in heat content and volume apply to the given phases at the equilibrium temperature and pressure. If the equilibrium is that between the solid and gaseous phases of the same pure substances, i.e.

$$MX \text{ (c)} = MX \text{ (g)} \qquad (18\text{-}29)$$

then

$$\frac{dp}{dT} = \frac{H \text{ (g)} - H \text{ (c)}}{T[V \text{ (g)} - V \text{ (c)}]} = \frac{\Delta H_s}{T(\Delta V_s)} \qquad (18\text{-}30)$$

where ΔH_s and ΔV_s represent, respectively, the increment in heat content and the increment in volume for the process of sublimation, and ΔH_s is the heat of sublimation. As previously noted, the increments in heat content and volume apply to the given phases at the equilibrium temperature and pressure.

If the equilibrium is that between two different solid phases of the same pure substance, i.e.

$$MX \text{ (c, II)} = MX \text{ (c, I)} \qquad (18\text{-}31)$$

then

$$\frac{dp}{dT} = \frac{\Delta H_{tr}}{T(\Delta V_{tr})} \qquad (18\text{-}32)$$

where ΔH_{tr} and ΔV_{tr} represent, respectively, the increment in heat content and the increment in volume for the process of transition. Since the value of ΔH_{tr} (c, II → c, I) is always positive, the value of dp/dT will be positive or negative according to the value of ΔV_{tr}, the change in volume for the transition.

A,19. Fugacity. Standard States. In the equilibrium involving one pure substance in several different phases, the given substance has a tendency to leave each phase in which it exists and to pass into every other phase which is open to it. At equilibrium, the escaping tendency has a constant value throughout every phase of the system, as does the molal free energy. When the phases under consideration are condensed ones, liquid or solid, the molal free energy serves as a satisfactory quantitative measure of the escaping tendency. However, when the gaseous phase is involved, the molal free energy becomes a rather inconvenient measure of the escaping tendency because the value of the free energy of an ideal gas approaches minus infinity as the pressure approaches zero. Since any real gas approaches the ideal gas as the pressure is indefinitely reduced, it follows that the free energy of any real gas approaches minus infinity as the pressure approaches zero. It is obvious, then, that a more convenient measure of the escaping tendency than the free energy is needed in the case of gases, particularly for ordinary and low pressures.

For the ideal gas the pressure itself is a satisfactory measure of the escaping tendency, because, for the ideal gas at constant temperature, the pressure is related to the molal free energy by a simple mathematical relation involving no unknown constants:

$$F_p - F_{p=1} = RT \ln p \tag{19-1}$$

However, real gases depart significantly from the relations for an ideal gas, and the simple form of this equation does not hold. Nevertheless, it is possible to retain the simplicity of this equation in the case of real gases by inventing a new thermodynamic function, called the fugacity [1] and labeled f, which will be evaluated in such a way that the substitution of values of the fugacity for pressure will make Eq. 19-1 valid for real gases as well as for the ideal gas.

The form in which the fugacity must be defined to achieve the foregoing end is the following:

$$RT \ln f = RT \ln p - \int_0^p \alpha dp \tag{19-2}$$

or

$$\ln \frac{f}{p} = - \frac{1}{RT} \int_0^p \alpha dp \tag{19-3}$$

or

$$\frac{f}{p} = e^{-\frac{1}{RT} \int_0^p \alpha dp} \tag{19-4}$$

or

$$f = pe^{-\frac{1}{RT} \int_0^p \alpha dp} \tag{19-5}$$

where

$$\alpha = V_{\text{ideal}} - V_{\text{real}} = \frac{RT}{p} - V_{\text{real}} \tag{19-6}$$

From the foregoing definition of fugacity, it is seen that for any gas at constant temperature the fugacity may be evaluated as a function of pressure from values of the molal volume of the actual gas at various pressures. If $\alpha = (RT/p - V)$ is plotted on the scale of ordinates for various pressures, the area under the curve from zero pressure to the pressure p, multiplied by the negative reciprocal of RT, is the value of the natural logarithm of the ratio of the fugacity to the pressure, at the given pressure.

If the p, V, T data for a given temperature are expressible by an equation of state that gives the volume explicitly in terms of the pressure, the foregoing operation may be performed analytically in a very simple way. If the p, V, T data for a given temperature are expressible by an equation of state that gives the pressure explicitly in terms of the volume, fugacity may still be calculated analytically, although the procedure is more complicated. For the ideal gas, it is easily seen that $f = p$. The fugacity may be looked upon as a sort of corrected pressure such that it permits the retention of the simplicity of the relation with free energy given by Eq. 19-1. It will be seen that this is important in the relations between the equilibrium constant and the free energy for reactions involving real gases.

In the preceding equations, it was convenient to use a reference state of unit pressure from which to measure changes in free energy. In the practical application of chemical thermodynamics, such reference states will be used quite frequently and it is desirable to define formally the thermodynamic standard reference state that is to be used for gases. For gases, the thermodynamic standard reference state is taken to be the ideal gaseous state of unit pressure (in atmospheres, unless otherwise specified) at each temperature. This standard state is designated by the usual superscript on the appropriate thermodynamic symbols, i.e. F^0 or f^0. Any real gas may be taken from its real state at the pressure p to the ideal state of unit pressure by proceeding along the path of the real gas from the pressure p to zero pressure and then passing from zero pressure to the pressure p along the path of the ideal gas.

It is important to note that, at constant temperature, the energy and heat content of a gas in the hypothetical ideal condition are constant. At constant temperature, the energy and heat content of a gas in its real condition vary with the pressure.

With reference to the thermodynamic standard state, we can write for any real gas, at a given pressure at constant temperature,

$$F - F^0 = RT \ln \frac{f}{f^0} \tag{19-7}$$

or, since for the standard state, $f^0 = 1$,

$$F - F^0 = RT \ln f \tag{19-8}$$

We have already derived the relation giving the difference in the free energy of a gas between the real and the ideal conditions at the same temperature at a given pressure, in terms of α:

$$(F_{real} - F_{ideal})^p = - \int_0^p \alpha dp \qquad (19\text{-}9)$$

Similarly, we have [1]

$$(S_{real} - S_{ideal})^p = \int_0^p \left(\frac{\partial \alpha}{\partial T}\right)_p dp \qquad (19\text{-}10)$$

and

$$(H_{real} - H_{ideal})^p = - \int_0^p \alpha dp + T \int_0^p \left(\frac{\partial \alpha}{\partial T}\right)_p dp \qquad (19\text{-}11)$$

If the volume of a gas can be expressed explicitly as a function of the pressure and temperature, it becomes a relatively simple matter to evaluate the difference in the properties of a gas between the real and the ideal states.

Although, as we have already indicated, the fugacity is more useful in connection with substances in the gaseous state than with substances in the liquid and solid states, it is sometimes desirable to evaluate the fugacity of a substance in a condensed phase. This may be done simply by evaluating the fugacity of the given substance in the gaseous phase when it is in equilibrium with the substance in the liquid or solid phase. It is to be noted that the vapor pressure of liquids and solids under ordinary conditions is usually low, under which circumstances the fugacity of the gaseous phase will not differ greatly from its pressure, so that the fugacity of ordinary pure liquid and solid substances may be taken as approximately equal to the vapor pressure. Further discussion of the thermodynamic properties of gases may be found in Sec. C of this volume.

In connection with pure liquids and solids, it is convenient to select a standard state to use for reference, just as in the case of gaseous substances. However, because the fugacity of a substance in the liquid and solid phase is usually very low, it is desirable to use a different reference state than that of the gaseous phase. A satisfactory thermodynamic standard reference state for pure liquids and solids at a given temperature is the real state of the liquid or solid substance at a pressure of 1 atmosphere. Just as in the case of gases, we can write for any solid or liquid substance at a given pressure and temperature, with reference to the selected thermodynamic standard state,

$$F - F^0 = RT \ln \frac{f}{f^0} \qquad (19\text{-}12)$$

It is to be noted that, whereas, for the gaseous phase, the fugacity of the standard state, f^0, is unity, for the liquid and solid phases the fugacity of the standard state will be different from unity, except by coincidence, and will usually be less than unity.

The variation of fugacity with temperature at constant pressure, and with pressure at constant temperature, is given by the following relations:

$$\left(\frac{\partial \ln f}{\partial T}\right)_p = -\frac{H - H^0}{RT^2} \tag{19-13}$$

$$\left(\frac{\partial \ln f}{\partial p}\right)_T = \frac{V}{RT} \tag{19-14}$$

A,20. Solutions. Partial and Apparent Molal Properties. It is usually best to specify the composition of a solution of two or more components by giving the mole fraction for the components, the mole fraction X being defined as the number of moles of the given component divided by the total number of moles in the solution. The specification of the composition of a solution by means of the mole fractions of the components is simple and exact. However, in the case of aqueous solutions, there has grown up a system of expressing the composition in terms of the molarity, which is defined as the number of moles of solute per liter of the solution, or the molality, which is defined as the number of moles of solute per 1,000 grams of the solvent, water. The expression of composition in terms of the number of moles per liter of solution is disadvantageous because, for a given solution, the volume changes with temperature, and, as the temperature changes, the concentration changes, without addition or removal of any components.

In scrutinizing a system of two or more components thermodynamically, it is important to decide what part of the total value of a given thermodynamic property of the solution is due to each component. For this purpose, it is convenient to define what is called by Lewis the partial molal quantity, for a component i:

$$G_i = \left(\frac{\partial G}{\partial n_i}\right)_{p,T,n_1,n_2,\ldots,n_j} \tag{20-1}$$

That is, for any property G of the solution, the partial molal quantity for component i is denoted[4] by G_i and is defined as the rate of change of the property G of the solution with change in the number of moles of component i, with the number of moles of all other components being held constant, all at constant pressure and temperature. For example, if the property involved is the volume, then the partial molal volume of component i is the change in the volume of the solution, ΔV, which takes place on the addition of n_i moles of component i, divided by n_i, the number of moles of component i added, the ratio being taken in the limit as n_i approaches zero, all at constant pressure and temperature.

[4] A small capital letter—for example, G—is used to denote a partial molal quantity.

Similarly, the partial molal volume of component i would be the change in the volume occurring on the addition of one mole of component i to an exceedingly large quantity of solution, the quantity of solution being taken so large that the addition of one mole of component i does not significantly change the composition, all at constant pressure and temperature.

It is clear that the partial molal property is one which may not always be conveniently measurable experimentally with the required precision. For the purpose of providing a simpler means of evaluating the partial molal quantity, it is convenient to define what Lewis and Randall [2] term the apparent molal property of a solute. The apparent molal property of a given solute component j in a solution of two components is defined as the value of the property G of the given solution less the value of the property G for the same solution with all of the given solute component j removed, divided by the number of moles of solute component j in the original solution. Usually, the apparent molal property is most used in connection with binary solutions in which water is the main component and the apparent molal property is applied to the solute. That is, the apparent molal property of the solute is

$$\phi G_2 = \frac{G_{(n_1+n_2)} - G_{(n_1)}}{n_2} = \frac{\Delta G}{n_2} \tag{20-2}$$

It is to be noted that at infinite dilution,

$$G_2^0 = \phi G_2^0 \tag{20-3}$$

Two important basic partial molal equations are the following [1,2]:

$$G = G_1 n_1 + G_2 n_2 + G_3 n_3 + \cdots = \sum G_i n_i \tag{20-4}$$

$$n_1 dG_1 + n_2 dG_2 + n_3 dG_3 + \cdots = \sum n_i dG_i \tag{20-5}$$

In these equations n_1, n_2, n_3, and n_i represent the number of moles of components 1, 2, 3, and i, respectively. The corresponding equations in terms of mole fractions are [1,2]

$$G = G_1 X_1 + G_2 X_2 + G_3 X_3 + \cdots = \sum G_i X_i \tag{20-6}$$

$$X_1 dG_1 + X_2 dG_2 + X_3 dG_3 + \cdots = \sum X_i dG_i \tag{20-7}$$

The importance of the foregoing basic partial molal equations becomes more obvious in the case of a binary solution, whence

$$G = G_1 X_1 + G_2 X_2 \tag{20-8}$$

$$X_1 dG_1 + X_2 dG_2 = 0 \tag{20-9}$$

On division by dX_2, the last equation yields

$$\frac{\dfrac{d\text{G}_1}{dX_2}}{\dfrac{d\text{G}_2}{dX_2}} = -\frac{X_2}{X_1} \tag{20-10}$$

The foregoing equation relates the slopes of the curves of G_1 and G_2 plotted as a function of mole fraction.

All of the thermodynamic relations given previously involving properties such as heat capacity, heat content, free energy, entropy, and volume, for one mole of substance, may be shown to hold for the corresponding partial molal properties. Examples of such relations are the following:

$$\text{F}_1 = \text{H}_1 - T\text{s}_1 \tag{20-11}$$

$$\left(\frac{\partial \text{F}_1}{\partial T}\right)_p = -\text{s}_1 \tag{20-12}$$

$$\left(\frac{\partial \text{F}_1}{\partial p}\right)_T = \text{v}_1 \tag{20-13}$$

$$\text{c}_{p_1} = \left(\frac{\partial \text{H}_1}{\partial T}\right)_p \tag{20-14}$$

and

$$\left[\frac{\partial \left(\dfrac{\text{F}_1}{T}\right)}{\partial T}\right]_p = -\frac{\text{H}_1}{T^2} \tag{20-15}$$

In each of the above relations, the partial molal property has been labeled for component 1 in the solution. The same relations hold for each of the other components of the solution.

Methods of evaluating partial molal properties, utilizing values of apparent molal properties where known, are described in [1].

A,21. The Ideal Solution. The ideal solution, which may be gaseous, liquid, or solid, is defined as one in which the fugacity of each component is proportional to its mole fraction, over the entire range of composition. and at all temperatures and all pressures:

$$f_i = k_i X_i \tag{21-1}$$

The proportionality constant k_i is a constant for a given temperature and pressure, and holds for all concentrations at that temperature and pressure. When the mole fraction of the given component becomes unity, then $X_i = 1$, $f_i = k_i$, $f_i = f_i^*$, and k_i, the constant of proportionality, becomes identified as f_i^*, the fugacity of pure component i in the same state as the solution, gas, liquid, or solid, at the given temperature and pressure. Therefore, we may write

$$f_i = X_i f_i^* \tag{21-2}$$

Consider component i in a pure gas phase in equilibrium with component i in an ideal solution, gas, liquid, or solid. From the definition of fugacity, we may write for component i in the pure gas phase,

$$F_i\,(g) = F_i^0\,(g) + RT \ln f_i\,(g) \tag{21-3}$$

But if component i in the pure gas phase is in equilibrium with component i in the solution, we have

$$F_i\,(g) = \mathrm{F}_i(\text{soln}) \quad \text{and} \quad f_i\,(g) = f_i(\text{soln})$$

Therefore,

$$\mathrm{F}_i = F_i^0\,(g) + RT \ln f_i\,(\text{soln}) \tag{21-4}$$

This equation applies to any mole fraction in the solution, so that for $X_i = 1$, we may write

$$\mathrm{F}_i^* = F_i^0\,(g) + RT \ln f_i^* \tag{21-5}$$

Subtraction of these equations gives

$$\mathrm{F}_i - \mathrm{F}_i^* = RT \ln \left(\frac{f_i}{f_i^*}\right)(\text{soln}) \tag{21-6}$$

Since $f_i/f_i^* = X_i$, we may write

$$\mathrm{F}_i - \mathrm{F}_i^* = RT \ln X_i \tag{21-7}$$

Since Eq. 21-7 applies to constant temperature and pressure, we may write

$$\left(\frac{\partial \mathrm{F}_i}{\partial X_i}\right)_{p,T} = \frac{RT}{X_i} \tag{21-8}$$

If Eq. 21-7 is differentiated with pressure at constant temperature, we have

$$\left(\frac{\partial \mathrm{F}_i}{\partial p}\right)_T - \left(\frac{\partial \mathrm{F}_i^*}{\partial p}\right)_T = v_i - v_i^* = 0 \tag{21-9}$$

That is to say, for the ideal solution at a given temperature and pressure, the partial molal volume of each component at every mole fraction is equal to its volume in the pure state (gas, liquid, or solid, as in the solution) at the same temperature and pressure. Or in other words, there is zero change in volume on mixing components to form an ideal solution.

Eq. 21-7 may be written as

$$\frac{\mathrm{F}_i}{T} - \frac{\mathrm{F}_i^*}{T} = R \ln X_i \tag{21-10}$$

Differentiating with temperature at constant pressure, we have

$$- \frac{H_i}{T^2} + \frac{H_i^*}{T^2} = -H_i + H_i^* = 0 \tag{21-11}$$

That is, for the ideal solution at a given temperature and pressure, the partial molal heat content of each component at every mole fraction is equal to its molal heat content in the pure state (gas, liquid, or solid, as in the solution) at the same temperature and pressure. In other words, the heat of mixing components to form an ideal solution is zero.

Since

$$H_i = H_i^* \tag{21-12}$$

and

$$c_{p_i} = \left(\frac{\partial H_i}{\partial T}\right)_p, \qquad c_{p_i}^* = \left(\frac{\partial H_i^*}{\partial T}\right)_p \tag{21-13}$$

it follows that

$$c_{p_2} = c_{p_i}^* \tag{21-14}$$

That is, for the ideal solution at a given temperature and pressure, the partial molal heat capacity of each component at every mole fraction is equal to its partial molal heat capacity in the pure state (gas, liquid, or solid, as in the solution) at the same temperature and pressure.

From the definition of the free energy, we may write

$$(F_i - F_i^*) = (H_i - H_i^*) - T(s_i - s_i^*) \tag{21-15}$$

Since $H_i - H_i^* = 0$, we have

$$s_i - s_i^* = - \frac{F_i - F_i^*}{T} = -R \ln X_i \tag{21-16}$$

That is, for component i in an ideal solution, gas, liquid, or solid, the partial molal entropy, referred to its molal entropy in the pure state, gas, liquid, or solid, at the given temperature and pressure, is equal to the negative of the gas constant R multiplied by the natural logarithm of the mole fraction.

Eq. 21-16 may be used to calculate the entropy of mixing n_i moles of pure component 1, n_2 moles of pure component 2, n_3 moles of pure component 3, . . . , and n_i moles of pure component i, to form one mole of an ideal solution. The change in entropy for introducing each component into the solution is

$$n_1(s_1 - s_1^*) = -n_1 R \ln X_1 \tag{21-17}$$

$$n_2(s_2 - s_2^*) = -n_2 R \ln X_2 \tag{21-18}$$

$$n_3(s_3 - s_3^*) = -n_3 R \ln X_3 \tag{21-19}$$

$$n_i(s_i - s_i^*) = -n_i R \ln X_i \tag{21-20}$$

The sum for all the components, which is the entropy of mixing all the components to form the ideal solution, is

$$\Delta S \text{ (mixing)} = -R \sum X_i \ln X_i \qquad (21\text{-}21)$$

This equation gives the entropy of mixing components to form any solution, whether gaseous, liquid, or solid, which conforms to the definition of the ideal solution.

Consider the thermodynamic equilibrium between a pure substance MX in the solid state and an ideal liquid solution in which the other component is NY:

$$MX \text{ (c)} = MX \text{ (in ideal liq soln with NY)} \qquad (21\text{-}22)$$

It may be shown [1] for such a system that, using 1 to denote the component MX,

$$RT d \ln X_1 = -[v_1 - V_1 \text{ (c)}]dp + [s_1 - S_1 \text{ (c)}]dT \qquad (21\text{-}23)$$

Hence, at constant temperature,

$$\frac{d \ln X_1}{dp} = -\frac{v_1^* - V_1 \text{ (c)}}{RT} \qquad (21\text{-}24)$$

and at constant pressure,

$$\frac{d \ln X_1}{dT} = \frac{H_1^* - H_1 \text{ (c)}}{RT^2} \qquad (21\text{-}25)$$

Eq. 21-25 may be integrated [1], assuming the heat of fusion to change linearly with temperature, to give the following relation, which is valid over the entire range of composition:

$$\ln X_1 = -A(\Delta T) \frac{1}{\left(1 - \frac{\Delta T}{T_1^*}\right)} + J\left[\ln\left(1 - \frac{\Delta T}{T_1^*}\right) + \frac{\Delta T}{T_1^* - \Delta T}\right] \qquad (21\text{-}26)$$

In this equation,

$$A = \frac{\Delta H_{m1}^*}{R(T_1^*)^2}, \qquad \Delta T = T_1^* - T, \qquad J = \frac{\Delta C_p}{R} \qquad (21\text{-}27)$$

For values of mole fraction of MX near unity, the following relation may be derived [1]:

$$\ln X_1 = -A(\Delta T)[1 + B(\Delta T) + C(\Delta T)^2 + \cdots] \qquad (21\text{-}28)$$

Here

$$B = \left(1 - \frac{\Delta C_{p1}^* T_1^*}{2\Delta H_{m1}^*}\right)\left(\frac{1}{T_1^*}\right), \qquad C = \left(1 - \frac{2\Delta C_{p1}^* T_1^*}{3\Delta H_{m1}^*}\right)\left(\frac{1}{T_1^*}\right) \qquad (21\text{-}29)$$

For small values of ΔT, the constants B and C become increasingly negligible in that order.

In the limit as X_1 approaches 1, the foregoing relation becomes

$$\ln X_1 = 1 - X_1 = X_2 = A(\Delta T) \tag{21-30}$$

Systems involving equilibrium between an ideal liquid solution and an ideal solid solution of the same components and equilibrium between an ideal liquid solution and a gaseous solution of the same components may be similarly studied [1].

A,22. The Dilute Real Solution. In the preceding article, we discussed the relations holding for the ideal solution, which relations serve as a limiting description of the behavior of the components of many real solutions. There is another class of solutions the properties of which may be similarly described by a set of general thermodynamic relations, which, however, hold only over a limited range of composition. This additional class of solutions is covered by the general name of the dilute real solution. Consider a dilute solution of two components, X_1 being the mole fraction of the solvent and having a value near unity and X_2 being the mole fraction of the solute and having a value near zero. The dilute real solution is defined as one for which, from $X_2 = 0$ to some small value of X_2, the fugacity of the solute is proportional to its mole fraction, i.e.

$$f_2 = k_2 X_2 \tag{22-1}$$

It is important to note that the range of composition covered by different real solutions satisfying the foregoing definition may be quite different. For some solutions, the range of applicability may be large and for others it may be exceedingly small. It is also to be noted that the value of the constant of proportionality is different for each solute and must be determined experimentally for each case. The experimental determination of k will also usually determine the range of composition over which the ratio of f_2/X_2 is constant.

In the very dilute range, the molality is proportional to the mole fraction, so that, in this range, the relation may be written as

$$f_2 = \frac{k_2' m}{55.506} \tag{22-2}$$

A similar linear relation holds in the dilute range between the fugacity of the solute and the concentration expressed in moles per liter of solution. If the gaseous phase of component 2 in equilibrium with the solution may be taken as ideal, then the partial pressure of component 2 may be substituted for the fugacity, so that, as an approximation,

$$p_2 = k_2' X_2 \tag{22-3}$$

and

$$p_2 = \frac{k_2' m}{55.506} \tag{22-4}$$

These equations are expressions of Henry's law for the vapor pressure of the solute in a dilute solution.

From the definition of the dilute real solution as given by Eq. 22-1, we can derive [1] the following important relation between the mole fraction of the solvent and its fugacity, over the same range of composition for which Eq. 22-1 is valid:

$$f_1 = X_1 f_1^* \qquad (22\text{-}5)$$

From the definition of the dilute real solution given by Eq. 22-1 and the laws of thermodynamics, we have derived the important relation given by Eq. 22-5, which states that in a dilute real solution the fugacity of the solvent is proportional to its mole fraction. It may be noted that, over the range of composition for which they are applicable, these equations for the dilute real solution are identical with the corresponding equations for the ideal solution. In fact, over the range of concentration for which the fugacity of the solute is proportional to its mole fraction, the dilute real solution has all the properties of an ideal solution in which the solute is a hypothetical one whose fugacity up to $X_2 = 1$ is a continuation of the linear relationship between f_2 and X_2 in the dilute range. It follows that, within the foregoing limitations, in the dilute real solution, the partial molal volumes, heat contents, and heat capacities of the components are, as in the ideal solution, independent of the composition over the given range of composition near $X_1 = 1$, and the same laws applying to the ideal solution apply also to the dilute real solution over the given range of composition. In this manner may be derived [1] the laws governing the lowering of the freezing point, elevation of the boiling point, distribution of a solute between two solvents, osmotic pressure, etc.

A,23. Real Solutions. Activity and Activity Coefficient. For any component i of any solution, the partial molal properties are related by the usual equations:

$$F_i = H_i - T S_i \qquad (23\text{-}1)$$

$$\left(\frac{\partial F_i}{\partial p}\right)_T = V_i \qquad (23\text{-}2)$$

$$\left(\frac{\partial F_i}{\partial T}\right)_p = -S_i \qquad (23\text{-}3)$$

$$\left(\frac{\partial H_i}{\partial T}\right)_p = c_{p_i} \qquad (23\text{-}4)$$

and so forth.

In considering the fugacity of gases, we found it convenient to use a standard reference state, for which the fugacity is unity and is denoted by f^0. In this case, we write for the difference in free energy of the gas in a given state and in the standard state, at constant temperature,

$$F - F^0 = RT \ln \frac{f}{f^0} \tag{23-5}$$

In the case of the ideal solution, we may write, at constant temperature and pressure, the partial molal free energy as

$$F_i - F_i^* = RT \ln \frac{f}{f^*} \tag{23-6}$$

If the pure state of component i in the ideal solution is taken as its standard reference state at unit pressure, then this equation may also be written as

$$F_i - F_i^0 = RT \ln \frac{f}{f^0} \tag{23-7}$$

In the case of the ideal gas, $f = p$ and, since $f^0 = 1$, this equation becomes

$$F_i - F_i^0 = RT \ln p \tag{23-8}$$

In the case of the ideal solution at unit pressure, we have for each component

$$X_i = \frac{f_i}{f_i^*} = \frac{f_i}{f_i^0} \tag{23-9}$$

so that, for each component in the ideal solution at unit pressure

$$F_i - F_i^0 = RT \ln X_i \tag{23-10}$$

We thus see that in the case of the ideal gas the molal free energy, referred to the standard state, is expressed simply in terms of the pressure. Similarly, in the case of the ideal solution, the partial molal free energy, referred to the standard state, is expressed simply in terms of the mole fraction. For most real solutions, the simple relation given by Eq. 23-10 does not hold over the entire range of composition for any of the components. In order to retain the simplicity of the form of this equation, it becomes convenient to define a new thermodynamic function, called the activity. From Eq. 23-7, we can see that it is necessary to define the activity of any given component in any state as equal to the ratio of its fugacity in the given state to its fugacity in the standard state:

$$a_i = \frac{f_i}{f_i^0} \tag{23-11}$$

It follows that, for any component i in a solution,

$$F_i - F_i^0 = RT \ln a_i \tag{23-12}$$

In the systematic study and correlation of the thermodynamic properties of pure substances and solutions, it is convenient to agree formally upon a choice of standard states. We have already selected suitable thermodynamic standard reference states for pure substances in the gaseous, liquid, and solid states.

For a gas, the standard state, at each temperature, is taken as the hypothetical ideal state of unit fugacity. It should be noted again that, except for those properties which are primarily a function of the concentration of molecules, such as entropy and free energy, the properties, such as heat content and heat capacity, of a gas in the hypothetical thermodynamic standard reference state of unit fugacity are the same as those of the real gas at zero pressure. The foregoing standard state may be used not only for pure gases but also for the components of any gaseous solution.

Since $a = f/f^0$ and, for a gas, $f^0 = 1$, it follows that for gases the activity is equal to the fugacity, i.e. $a = f$. Since the fugacity approaches the pressure in value as the pressure approaches zero, that is, f/p approaches 1, then, also, a/p approaches 1.

For pure liquids and solids, we have already selected the thermodynamic standard reference state, at each temperature, as the pure liquid or solid at unit pressure. The activity of the pure liquid or solid at some other given pressure at the given temperature is then given by the ratio of the fugacity at the given pressure to the fugacity in the standard state, in accordance with the definition of activity.

For a liquid or solid that may serve as a solvent, the standard state may be taken as the same as that for the pure liquid or solid, namely, the pure liquid or solid at unit pressure. As a solute is added to such a substance to form a liquid solution or a solid solution, the activity of the solvent for a given concentration is $a_1 = f_1/f_1^0$. It is to be noted here that, at unit pressure, $f_1^0 = f_i^*$.

For a solute in any liquid or solid solution, the standard state is most conveniently selected as that hypothetical state in which the solute would exist if its fugacity, given in the dilute region by the relation $f_2 = k_2 X_2$, continued along the same relation to a value of X_2 equal to unity, all at unit pressure. This hypothetical standard state is evaluated from measurements at unit pressure of the ratio of fugacity to mole fraction in the dilute range, where $f_2 = k_2 X_2$ or $X_2 = f_2/k_2$. It is seen that at unit pressure $f_2^0 = k_2$. Over the range of composition for which the fugacity of the solute is proportional to its mole fraction, at unit pressure, $a_2 = f_2/f_2^0 = f_2/k_2 = X_2$, i.e. the activity is equal to the mole fraction. It is to be noted that, also at unit pressure, the fugacity of the pure solute, f_2^*, may differ appreciably from the fugacity in the hypothetical standard state, f_2^0. It is also to be emphasized that if component 2 is considered as the solvent, a different standard state should be selected, namely, that of the pure substance, in which case f_2^0 and f_2^* will be identical, at unit pressure.

For a solute in aqueous solution when the composition is expressed in terms of molality, it is convenient to select a different hypothetical standard than that where X_2 is unity, namely, one in which the molality is unity.

It is important to note that where the standard state of a given component i of a solution has been selected to be the given component in a real or hypothetical system with $X_i = 1$, that is, the given component in a real or hypothetical pure condition, the standard state at a given temperature is taken as that of the given state at unit pressure (1 atmosphere, unless otherwise stated) in order to conform to the standard state that we have already agreed to use for pure liquids and pure solids. In the case where the standard state is not the given component i, in a real or hypothetical pure condition with $X_i = 1$, but at unit molality as in aqueous solutions, we likewise restrict the hypothetical standard state to the state at 1 atmosphere, in order to conform to the selection made for the standard states of the components of solutions having their composition measured in mole fraction. With this convention, we find that at a given temperature the thermodynamic properties of the standard state are independent of the pressure. For that component of any solution for which the standard state is taken as the real pure system of the given component $X_1 = 1$, it follows that at a given temperature f_i^* at 1 atmosphere is equal to f_i^0 but f_i^* at any other pressure is not equal to f_i^0. Similarly, by this convention, for the solute in any aqueous solution at a given temperature the standard state is the solute in the hypothetical one-molal solution at a pressure of one atmosphere, and the hypothetical one-molal solution at any significantly different pressure does not give the properties of the solute in the standard state. We have seen that in an ideal solution f_i is equal to $X_i f_i^*$ at every temperature and every pressure. By reason of the particular standard state that has been selected, namely, that at unit pressure, it follows that f_i^* is equal to f_i^0 only at 1 atmosphere at the given temperature. From the foregoing we see that the activity a_i of a component of an ideal solution, which is defined as f_i/f_i^0, is equal to f_i/f_i^* only at 1 atmosphere, and, hence, while X_i is always equal to f_i/f_i^*, X_i is equal to f_i/f_i^0 or a_i only at 1 atmosphere.

It is important to note that for a given component that is in thermodynamic equilibrium in two or more phases the fugacity of that component is identical in each of the phases, but its activity will not be identical unless f_i^0 is identical in the different phases.

The following equations may be derived [1] to show how the activity varies with pressure and temperature:

$$\left(\frac{\partial \ln a_i}{\partial T}\right)_p = -\frac{H_i - H_i^0}{RT^2} \tag{23-13}$$

$$\left(\frac{\partial \ln a_i}{\partial p}\right)_T = \frac{V_i}{RT} \tag{23-14}$$

If values of a partial molal property are known for one component of a binary solution over the range of composition, corresponding values for the other component may be obtained from a relation [1,2] of the following kind:

$$G_1 - G_1^* = -\int_{X_2=0}^{X_2} \left(\frac{X_2}{X_1}\right) dX_2 \qquad (23\text{-}15)$$

Values of activity for the components of a solution may be determined, as appropriate, from vapor pressures, from the distribution of a solute between two solvents, from the lowering of the freezing point, from the elevation of the boiling point, etc. [1,2].

For the study of solutes in dilute solution, it has been found convenient to define the ratio of activity to the composition function, X_i or m_i, as the activity coefficient, γ_i. For aqueous solutions,

$$\gamma_i = \frac{a_i}{m_i} \qquad (23\text{-}16)$$

For solutions in which the composition is given in mole fraction,

$$\gamma_i = \frac{a_i}{X_i} \qquad (23\text{-}17)$$

For gases,

$$\gamma_i = \frac{f_i}{p_i} \qquad (23\text{-}18)$$

For details regarding the activity and activity coefficient of strong electrolytes in aqueous solution, the reader is referred to [1,2].

A,24. Equilibrium Constant and the Standard Change in Free Energy. For any reaction at any given temperature and pressure,

$$bB + cC = mM + nN \qquad (24\text{-}1)$$

the change in free energy for any given set of states of the reactants and products is

$$\Delta F = mF_M + nF_N - bF_B - cF_C \qquad (24\text{-}2)$$

and the standard change in free energy, with each reactant and product in its thermodynamic standard reference state, is

$$\Delta F^0 = mF_M^0 + nF_N^0 - bF_B^0 - cF_C^0 \qquad (24\text{-}3)$$

The difference in the change in free energy for the given set of states and for the standard states is

$$\Delta F - \Delta F^0 = m(F - F^0)_M + n(F - F^0)_N$$
$$- b(F - F^0)_B - c(F - F^0)_C \quad (24\text{-}4)$$

But, for any substance in any state,

$$F_i - F_i^0 = RT \ln a_i \qquad (24\text{-}5)$$

where F_i and a_i refer to the same given state for substance i and F_i^0 refers to the standard state. Eq. 24-4 then becomes

$$\Delta F - \Delta F^0 = RT \ln \frac{(a_M)^m (a_N)^n}{(a_B)^b (a_C)^c} \tag{24-6}$$

The proper quotient of activities for any reaction such as that given by Eq. 24-1 is defined as

$$Q_a = \frac{(a_M)^m (a_N)^n}{(a_B)^b (a_C)^c} \tag{24-7}$$

That is, in the proper quotient of activities, the numerator is the product of the activity of each of the products of the reaction, each raised to a power equal to the number of moles of the given product, and the denominator is the corresponding product for the reactants of the reaction. The proper quotient of activities is thus identical with the terms in parentheses on the right side of Eq. 24-6.

The equilibrium constant is defined as the proper quotient of activities when each reactant and product is in its equilibrium state for the given reaction, i.e.

$$K = Q_a^e = \frac{(a_M^e)^m (a_N^e)^n}{(a_B^e)^b (a_C^e)^c} \tag{24-8}$$

When the given reaction takes place with each reactant and product in its standard state, the change in free energy is the standard change in free energy, ΔF^0, and is equal to the value given by Eq. 24-3. When the given reaction takes place with each reactant and product in its equilibrium concentration or pressure for the given conditions, then

$$\Delta F \text{ (equil)} = \Delta F^e = mF_M^e + nF_N^e - bF_B^e - cF_C^e \tag{24-9}$$

The difference in the change in free energy for the two sets of conditions, standard states and equilibrium states, is

$$\Delta F^e - \Delta F^0 = m(F^e - F^0)_M + n(F^e - F^0)_N$$
$$- b(F^e - F^0)_B - c(F^e - F^0)_C \tag{24-10}$$

Since, for any substance in its equilibrium state,

$$F_i^e - F_i^0 = RT \ln a_i^e \tag{24-11}$$

we have

$$\Delta F^e - \Delta F^0 = RT \ln \frac{(a_M^e)^m (a_N^e)^n}{(a_B^e)^b (a_C^e)^c} \tag{24-12}$$

But at constant temperature and pressure, the change in free energy at equilibrium is zero, so that ΔF^e is zero. Substituting K for the terms in parentheses, we have

$$\Delta F^0 = -RT \ln K \tag{24-13}$$

This equation is an important equation relating the standard change in free energy and the equilibrium constant.

Differentiation of $\Delta F/T$ at constant pressure for the components of a reaction gives, for standard states,

$$\frac{d\left(\dfrac{\Delta F^0}{T}\right)}{dT} = -\frac{\Delta H^0}{T^2}\, dT \tag{24-14}$$

In an earlier article, we derived an expression for the change in heat content, ΔH, for a reaction, as a function of temperature. Indicating by means of the appropriate superscripts that this expression is to be applied to the reaction with each substance in its standard state, we have

$$\Delta H^0 = \Delta H^0_* + (\Delta a)T + \frac{(\Delta b)}{2}\, T^2 + \frac{(\Delta c)}{3}\, T^3 \tag{24-15}$$

It is to be recalled that this equation is valid only over the range of temperature for which the original expressions for heat capacity as a function of temperature were valid and that ΔH^0_* is not the value of ΔH^0 at $0°K$. When this equation is substituted into the preceding equation and the latter is integrated, we obtain

$$\frac{\Delta F^0}{T} = \frac{\Delta H^0_*}{T} - (\Delta a)\ln T - \frac{(\Delta b)}{2}\, T - \frac{(\Delta c)}{6}\, T^2 + I \tag{24-16}$$

In this equation, I is the constant of integration. This equation may also be written as

$$\Delta F^0 = \Delta H^0_* - (\Delta a)T \ln T - \frac{(\Delta b)}{2}\, T^2 - \frac{(\Delta c)}{6}\, T^3 + IT \tag{24-17}$$

It is to be emphasized that these equations are valid only over the range of temperature for which the original expressions for the heat capacities of the reactants and products are valid. Furthermore, the constant of integration I must be evaluated from one value of ΔF^0 within the given range of temperature. If the change in heat content were by chance constant with temperature, the factors (Δa), (Δb), and (Δc) would be zero, and these equations would reduce to

$$\Delta F^0 = \Delta H^0 + IT \tag{24-18}$$

By comparison with the relation

$$\Delta F^0 = \Delta H^0 - T\Delta S^0 \tag{24-19}$$

it is seen that the constant of integration I has the nature of the negative of the standard change in entropy for the reaction. The evaluation of the standard change in free energy by Eq. 24-16 and 24-17 is subject to the disadvantage that for a given set of constants the range is limited, and, further, the form of the equations may not be such as to reproduce the experimental observations at different temperatures within their limits of uncertainty.

A much more direct and more accurate way of evaluating ΔF^0 at different temperatures is to use the values of the free energy function of the reactants and products which may be available tabulated at different temperatures. Values of $\Delta F^0/T$ for a series of temperatures in the range of interest are calculated and the value for any particular temperature may be obtained by suitable interpolation. The procedure is as follows: For the given reaction, the value of ΔH_0^0 is obtained from the reference value of $\Delta H_{298.16}^0$ and the values of the heat content at 298.16°K, relative to 0°K, of each of the reactants and products:

$$\Delta H_0^0 = \Delta H_{298.16}^0 - \Delta(H_{298.16}^0 - H_0^0) \tag{24-20}$$

But

$$\Delta\left(\frac{F^0 - H_0^0}{T}\right) = \frac{\Delta F^0}{T} - \frac{\Delta H_0^0}{T} \tag{24-21}$$

or

$$\frac{\Delta F^0}{T} = \frac{\Delta H_0^0}{T} + \Delta\left(\frac{F^0 - H_0^0}{T}\right) \tag{24-22}$$

where

$$\Delta\left(\frac{F^0 - H_0^0}{T}\right) = \sum\left(\frac{F^0 - H_0^0}{T}\right)(\text{products}) - \sum\left(\frac{F^0 - H_0^0}{T}\right)(\text{reactants}) \tag{24-23}$$

Since

$$\frac{\Delta F^0}{T} = -R \ln K \tag{24-24}$$

it follows that

$$\ln K = -\frac{\Delta H_0^0}{RT} - \frac{1}{R}\Delta\left(\frac{F^0 - H_0^0}{T}\right) \tag{24-25}$$

It is important to note that for any given temperature the equilibrium constant is directly related to the standard change in free energy. Since, at any given temperature, the free energy in the standard state for each reactant and product, F_i^0, is independent of the pressure, it follows that the standard change in free energy for the reaction, ΔF^0, is independent of the pressure. Therefore, at constant temperature, the equilibrium constant K, as defined by Eq. 24-8 and related to ΔF^0 by Eq. 24-24, is also independent of the pressure.

The fact that, as shown above, the equilibrium constant does not change in value with pressure does not necessarily mean that the concentrations of the components of a chemical reaction at equilibrium remain constant as the pressure is increased. Consider the following reaction at equilibrium at some temperature T, with each component being in the gaseous phase:

$$bB\ (g) + cC\ (g) = mM\ (g) + nN\ (g) \tag{24-26}$$

For this reaction,

$$K = \frac{(a_M^e)^m (a_N^e)^n}{(a_B^e)^b (a_C^e)^c} \tag{24-27}$$

For gases, the activity is equal to the fugacity, so that the equilibrium constant is

$$K = \frac{(f_M^e)^m (f_N^e)^n}{(f_B^e)^b (f_C^e)^c} \tag{24-28}$$

The activity coefficient of each gas is defined as

$$\gamma_i = \frac{f_i}{p_i} \tag{24-29}$$

and the partial pressure is

$$p_i = X_i p \tag{24-30}$$

where X_i is the mole fraction of the given component and p is the total pressure.

Then

$$f_i = X_i \gamma_i p \tag{24-31}$$

Substituting this equation into Eq. 24-28 for each of the components, we obtain

$$K = \left[\frac{(\gamma_M^e)^m (\gamma_N^e)^n}{(\gamma_B^e)^b (\gamma_C^e)^c} \right] \left[\frac{(X_M^e)^m (X_N^e)^n}{(X_B^e)^b (X_C^e)^c} \right] p^{(m+n-b-c)} \tag{24-32}$$

Letting Q_γ^e and Q_X^e denote the proper quotient of activity coefficients (the first bracketed term) and the proper quotient of mole fractions (the second bracketed term), respectively, this equation may be shortened to

$$K = Q_\gamma^e Q_X^e p^{(m+n-b-c)} \tag{24-33}$$

Written explicitly in terms of the proper quotient of mole fractions, this equation becomes

$$Q_X^e = K \left(\frac{1}{Q_\gamma^e} \right) p^{-(m+n-b-c)} \tag{24-34}$$

When the gases involved in the reaction are ideal, the activity coefficient is unity for each gas, so that

$$Q_\gamma^e = 1 \tag{24-35}$$

$$K = Q_X^e p^{(m+n-b-c)} \tag{24-36}$$

and

$$Q_X^e = K p^{-(m+n-b-c)} \tag{24-37}$$

This equation shows that for the reaction of ideal gases the proper quotient of mole fractions at equilibrium is independent of the pressure only when $m + n = b + c$. When the quantity $-(m + n - b - c)$ differs from zero, the proper quotient of mole fractions at equilibrium will vary with the total pressure raised to the power $-(m + n - b - c)$. It is to be noted that the introduction of an inert gas into the system will have no effect on the foregoing relations, except to change the activity coefficients a little in the case of nonideal gases, provided the partial pressure of the inert gas is not included in the value of the total pressure p. That is, the total pressure p given above must be counted as the sum of the partial pressures of the gaseous components participating in the given reaction. If the number of moles of gaseous products is less than the number of moles of gaseous reactants, then $-(m + n - b - c)$ is positive, the proper quotient of mole fractions will increase with the pressure, and the mole fractions of the products will increase at the expense of the mole fractions of the reactants. That is, with increase in pressure, the equilibrium is shifted in favor of the products. Conversely, if the number of moles of gaseous products is greater than the number of moles of gaseous reactants, the equilibrium is shifted in favor of the reactants with increase in pressure. For real gases, the effect of pressure on the concentrations of the components of a chemical reaction at equilibrium will also include the change of the activity coefficient with pressure. This effect may be very large.

It is occasionally necessary to make calculations of the equilibrium concentrations of the components of a chemical reaction at equilibrium in a vessel at constant volume. In lieu of the pressures, there will be known the volume of the space available to the gaseous components and the number of moles of the substances at the beginning. Suppose the temperature is high enough and the volume is large enough, in relation to the number of moles of gaseous reacting substances, for the gases to be assumed ideal. Usually, in such problems, the concentration is given in moles per liter as c_i. Consider the reaction given by Eq. 24-26. Since the gases are assumed ideal, the equilibrium constant is the proper quotient of pressures at equilibrium,

$$K = \frac{(p_M^e)^m (p_N^e)^n}{(p_B^e)^b (p_C^e)^c} = Q_p^e \tag{24-38}$$

But for ideal gases the concentration in moles per liter is related to the pressure by the following relations, where n_i is the number of moles of component i and V is the volume of the space available to the gaseous components:

$$c_i = \frac{n_i}{V} \tag{24-39}$$

$$p_i = \frac{n_i RT}{V} = c_i RT \tag{24-40}$$

Substituting, we have[5]

$$K = \frac{(c_M^e)^m (c_N^e)^n}{(c_B^e)^b (c_C^e)^c} (RT)^{(m+n-b-c)} \qquad (24\text{-}41)$$

Defining the proper quotient of concentrations in the usual manner, this equation becomes

$$K = Q_c^e (RT)^{(m+n-b-c)} \qquad (24\text{-}42)$$

or

$$Q_c^e = K(RT)^{-(m+n-b-c)} \qquad (24\text{-}43)$$

This equation permits the evaluation, for a reaction involving gases assumed ideal, of the proper quotient of concentrations at equilibrium from the value of the equilibrium constant and the stoichiometrical change in the number of moles of gaseous components between reactants and products. If the stoichiometrical number of moles of gaseous products is the same as the number of moles of gaseous reactants, then $Q_c^e = K$. It is important to note that with the concentration in liters, and the equilibrium pressures given in terms of atmospheres, the value of R in these equations must be given in liter atmospheres/mole degree.

A,25. Thermodynamic Calculations. In the modern compilations of selected values of thermodynamic properties, as in [5], there may be found values of the following thermodynamic properties given for the thermodynamic standard state from the absolute zero to high temperatures, for a large number of hydrocarbons and related compounds:

$(F^0 - H_0^0)/T$ free energy function
$(H^0 - H_0^0)/T$ heat content function
S^0 entropy
$H^0 - H_0^0$ heat content (referred to $0°K$)
C_p^0 heat capacity .
ΔH_f^0 heat of formation (from the elements)
ΔF_f^0 free energy of formation (from the elements)
$\log_{10} K_f$ logarithm of the equilibrium constant of formation (from the elements)

In making up such a compilation, the basic values used are the following:

$\Delta H_{f(298.16)}^0$ the standard heat of formation (from the elements) at $25°C$
$(H^0 - H_0^0)/T$ for each temperature for which the thermodynamic values are to be tabulated

---

[5] This equation has c representing two different quantities, namely concentration and the stoichiometrical number of moles of component C. Since this duplication is transient and not ambiguous, it is preferred to the introduction of a new symbol.

$(F^0 - H_0^0)/T$ for each temperature for which the thermodynamic values are to be tabulated

C_p^0 for each temperature for which the thermodynamic values are to be tabulated

From the foregoing basic values, the entire table is made up as follows:

From the heat content function, values of $H^0 - H_0^0$, the heat content at the given temperature referred to the absolute zero, are obtained by simple multiplication of the heat content function by the temperature:

$$H^0 - H_0^0 = T\left(\frac{H^0 - H_0^0}{T}\right) \tag{25-1}$$

Values of the standard entropy S^0 are obtained as the value of the heat content function less the value of the free energy function:

$$S^0 = \frac{H^0 - H_0^0}{T} - \frac{F^0 - H_0^0}{T} \tag{25-2}$$

The value of $\Delta H_{f(0)}^0$ is obtained from the relation

$$\Delta H_{f(0)}^0 = \Delta H_{f(298.16)}^0 - \Delta(H_{298.16}^0 - H_0^0) \tag{25-3}$$

where

$$\Delta(H_{298.16}^0 - H_0^0) = (H_{298.16}^0 - H_0^0) \text{ (compound)}$$

$$- \sum (H_{298.16}^0 - H_0^0) \text{ (elements)} \tag{25-4}$$

When the value of $\Delta H_{f(0)}^0$ is obtained, the values of ΔH_f^0 at all other temperatures are obtained from the relation

$$\Delta H_f^0 = \Delta H_{f(0)}^0 + \Delta(H^0 - H_0^0) \tag{25-5}$$

where

$$\Delta(H^0 - H_0^0) = (H^0 - H_0^0) \text{ (compound)}$$

$$- \sum (H^0 - H_0^0) \text{ (elements)} \tag{25-6}$$

Values of ΔF_f^0 at each temperature are obtained from the relation

$$\Delta F_f^0 = \Delta H_{f(0)}^0 + T\Delta\left(\frac{F^0 - H_0^0}{T}\right) \tag{25-7}$$

where

$$\Delta\left(\frac{F^0 - H_0^0}{T}\right) = \left(\frac{F^0 - H_0^0}{T}\right) \text{ (compound)}$$

$$- \sum \left(\frac{F^0 - H_0^0}{T}\right) \text{ (elements)} \tag{25-8}$$

Values of $\log_{10} K_f$ are obtained at each temperature from the values of ΔF_f^0 from the relation

$$\Delta F_f^0 = -RT \ln K_f \qquad (25\text{-}9)$$

or

$$\log_{10} K_f = -\frac{\Delta F_f^0}{2.30259RT} \qquad (25\text{-}10)$$

The same tables [5] also give values for the following properties:

Heat of formation, free energy of formation, and entropy, for the liquid state, at 25°C
Heat and entropy of fusion
Heat and entropy of vaporization
Standard heat, entropy, and free energy of vaporization, at 25°C
Heat of combustion, for the gaseous and liquid states, at 25°C
Vapor pressures, from 10 to 1500 mm Hg

The tables of [6] list the following thermodynamic properties for all substances for which thermodynamic data are available, except carbon compounds containing more than two carbon atoms per molecule:

Series I: Heat of formation, free energy of formation, logarithm of the equilibrium constant of formation, entropy, and heat capacity, each at 25°C, for solid, liquid, and gaseous states, as appropriate and known; also, where calculable, the heat of formation at 0°K.

Series II: Heat, temperature, and entropy of transition, fusion, and vaporization, including values of pressure as appropriate and known.

Whenever values of $\log_{10} K_f$ are available for the temperature or temperatures of interest for each of the reactants and products in a given chemical reaction, the calculation of $\log_{10} K$ or the equilibrium constant for the given reaction may be made very simply. Consider the reaction

$$bB + cC = mM + nN \qquad (25\text{-}11)$$

Then, for this reaction,

$$\begin{aligned}
\log_{10} K &= \log_{10} K_f \text{ (products)} - \log_{10} K_f \text{ (reactants)} \\
&= m \log_{10} K_{f(M)} + n \log_{10} K_{f(N)} \\
&\quad - b \log_{10} K_{f(B)} - c \log_{10} K_{f(C)} \quad (25\text{-}12)
\end{aligned}$$

For each reactant or product that is an element in the standard state, the value of $\log_{10} K_f$ is of course given in the table as zero since ΔF_f^0 is zero.

In most of the foregoing calculations, the various properties dealt with have usually applied to the thermodynamic reference state, which for gases is the ideal condition of unity fugacity (1 atmosphere, unless otherwise specified) and for pure liquids and solids is the real condition at actual unit pressure (1 atmosphere, unless otherwise specified). We have seen that a simple framework can be assembled to give values for all the important thermodynamic properties as a function of temperature for the thermodynamic standard state. In the solution of a given problem involving real states at some high pressure p, at some elevated temperature T, the procedure is to calculate the results for the standard states at the given temperature, and then to compute, at that constant temperature, the change in the values of the given properties in going from the standard states to the given real states at the pressure p_i^0.

This means that, for example, a complete description and evaluation of the thermodynamic properties of a substance can be provided by means of (1) a tabulation giving values of the several thermodynamic properties for the standard state at each temperature of interest and (2) a tabulation giving, for the same temperatures, values of the difference in the given thermodynamic property between various pressures and the standard state, covering each pressure of interest. In preceding articles, we have seen how values of the several thermodynamic properties may be assembled for the standard state at various temperatures. The next step is to evaluate, as mentioned above, the change of the given thermodynamic property with pressure at the given temperature.

If, at the given temperature, we know how the energy, entropy, and volume change with the pressure, the picture is complete. That is to say, if we know $(\partial E/\partial p)_T$, $(\partial S/\partial p)_T$, and $(\partial(pV)/\partial p)_T$ as functions of pressure, all the other defined thermodynamic properties become known as functions of pressure at the given temperature. Equations are available also for the calculation of $(\partial H/\partial p)_T$ and $(\partial F/\partial p)_T$.

Changes of the defined functions of fugacity and activity with pressure are evaluated by the appropriate equations. It is to be noted from the various relations involved that a knowledge of the p, V, T relations for the given substance, over the range of temperature and pressure to be covered, would serve to give a complete evaluation of the difference in the given thermodynamic property between the standard state and the real state at each pressure of interest, at each temperature. Similarly, it would suffice to have, at each temperature, values of $pV = f(p)$ together with values, at the given temperature, of $(\partial(pV)/\partial T)_p$ at the various pressures involved.

A,26. Data of Thermodynamics.

Original thermodynamic data may be found in the following journals:

The Journal of the American Chemical Society	J. Am. Chem. Soc.
Industrial and Engineering Chemistry	Ind. Eng. Chem.
The Journal of Chemical Physics	J. Chem. Phys.
The Physical Review	Phys. Rev.
The Journal of Physical Chemistry	J. Phys. Chem.
Chemical Engineering Progress	Chem. Eng. Progr.
Journal of the Aeronautical Sciences	J. Aeronaut. Sci.

Proceedings of the American Academy of Arts and Sciences	Proc. Am. Acad. Arts Sci.
Canadian Journal of Research	Can. J. Research
Journal of the Chemical Society (London)	J. Chem. Soc.
The Philosophical Magazine	Phil. Mag.
Proceedings of the Royal Society (London)	Proc. Roy. Soc. London
Nature (London)	Nature
Annales de chimie (Paris)	Ann. chim. Paris
Annales de physique	Ann. physique
Bulletin de la société chimique de France	Bull. soc. chim. France
Comptes rendus hebdomadaires des séances de l'Académie des Sciences	Compt. rend.
Journal de chimie physique et de physicochimie biologique	J. chim. phys.
Proceedings Koninklijke Nederlandsche Akademie van Wetenschappen	Proc. Koninkl. Ned. Akad. Wetenschap.
Recueil des travaux chimiques des Pays-Bas	Rec. trav. chim.
Bulletin des sociétés chimiques belges	Bull. soc. chim. belges
Helvetica Chimica Acta	Helv. Chim. Acta
Helvetica Physica Acta	Helv. Phys. Acta
Gazzetta chimica italiana	Gazz. chim. ital.
Nuovo cimento; Supplements	Nuovo cimento; Suppl.
Atti della Accademia nazionale dei Lincei, Rendiconti, Classe di scienze fisiche, mathematiche e naturali	Atti Accad. nazl. Lincei Rend. Classe sci. fis. mat. e nat.
Annalen der Physik	Ann. Physik
Chemische Berichte	Chem. Ber.
Monatshefte für Chemie und verwandte Teile anderer Wissenschaften	Monatsh. Chem.
Physikalische Zeitschrift	Physik. Z.
Journal für praktische Chemie	J. prakt. Chem.
Angewandte Chemie	Angew. Chem.
Zeitschrift für anorganische Chemie	Z. anorg. Chem.
Zeitschrift für Elektrochemie und angewandte physikalische Chemie	Z. Elektrochem.
Zeitschrift für Naturforschung	Z. Naturforsch.
Zeitschrift für Physik	Z. Physik
Zeitschrift für physikalische Chemie	Z. physik. Chem.
The Science Reports of the Tôhoku Imperial University	Science Repts. Tôhoku Imp. Univ.
Scientific Papers of the Institute of Physical and Chemical Research (Tokyo)	Sci. Papers Inst. Phys. Chem. Research Tokyo
Journal of the Chemical Society of Japan	J. Chem. Soc. Japan
Acta Physicochimica U.R.S.S.	Acta Physicochim. U.R.S.S.
Journal of General Chemistry (U.S.S.R.)	J. Gen. Chem. U.S.S.R.
Journal of Physical Chemistry (U.S.S.R.)	J. Phys. Chem. U.S.S.R.

Reviews, correlations, and summaries of existing data in special areas of thermodynamics as well as occasionally some original data, frequently may be found in the following journals:

Chemical Reviews	Chem. Revs.
Transactions of the American Society of Mechanical Engineers	Trans. Am. Soc. Mech. Engrs.
Transactions of the Electrochemical Society	Trans. Electrochem. Soc.
Chemical Engineering Progress with Transactions of American Institute of Chemical Engineers	Chem. Eng. Progr. (with Trans. Am. Inst. Chem. Engrs.)
Aeronautical Engineering Review	Aeronaut. Eng. Rev.

Engineering	Engineering
The Engineering Journal (Canada)	Eng. J. Can.
Transactions of the Faraday Society	Trans. Faraday Soc.
Science Progress	Science Progr.
Annual Reports on the Progress of Chemistry	Ann. Repts. on Progr. Chem.
(Chemical Society of London)	(Chem. Soc. London)
Bulletin of the International Institute of	
Refrigeration	Bull. Intern. Inst. Refrig.
Chemiker-Zeitung	Chem.-Ztg.

Compilations of thermodynamic data may be found in the following:

Herzberg, G. *Molecular Spectra and Molecular Structure. II. Infrared and Raman Spectra of Polyatomic Molecules.* Van Nostrand, 1945.

Sponer, H. *Molecular Spectra and its Application to Chemical Problems.* Springer, Berlin, 1936.

Harned, H. S., and Owen, B. B. *The Physical Chemistry of Electrolytic Solutions.* Reinhold, 1943.

Gaydon, A. G. *Dissociation Energies and Spectra of Diatomic Molecules.* Wiley, 1947.

Glasstone, S. *Electrochemistry of Solutions.* Methuen, London, 1930.

Rossini, F. D., Pitzer, K. S., Arnett, R. L., Braun, R. M., and Pimentol, G. C. *Selected Values of Physical and Thermodynamic Properties of Hydrocarbons and Related Compounds.* Carnegie Inst. Technol. Press, Pittsburgh, 1953.

Rossini, F. D., Pitzer, K. S., and associates. *Selected Values of Properties of Hydrocarbons (and Related Compounds).* American Petroleum Institute Research Project 44, Carnegie Inst. Technol. (Available in loose-leaf form.)

Rossini, F. D., Wagman, D. D., Evans, W. H., Levine, S., and Jaffe, I. *Selected Values of Chemical Thermodynamic Properties.* Natl. Bur. Standards Circ. 500, U.S. Government Printing Office, 1952.

International Critical Tables. McGraw-Hill, 1926–1933.

Bichowsky, F. R., and Rossini, F. D. *Thermochemistry of the Chemical Substances.* Reinhold, 1936.

Latimer, W. M. *The Oxidation States of the Elements and their Potentials in Aqueous Solutions.* Prentice-Hall, 1938.

Parks, G. S., and Huffman, H. M. *Free Energies of Some Organic Compounds.* Reinhold, 1932.

Kelley, K. K. Contributions to the data on theoretical metallurgy. I–IX. *Bur. Mines Bull. 350, 371, 383, 384, 393, 394, 406, 407, 434* (1932–1941).

Chemical Engineers Handbook. McGraw-Hill, 1950.

Seidell, A. *Solubilities of Inorganic and Metal Organic Compounds,* 3rd ed. Van Nostrand, 1940.

Seidell, A. *Solubilities of Organic Compounds,* 3rd ed. Van Nostrand, 1941.

Annual Tables of Constants and Numerical Data. Hermann, Paris, 1910–1948.

Landolt-Börnstein Physikalisch-Chemische Tabellen, 5th ed. Springer, Berlin, 1923–1936.

Justi, E. *Spezifische Wärme, Enthalpie, Entropie, und Dissoziation technischer Gase.* Springer, Berlin, 1938.

Weibke, F., and Kubaschewski, O. *Thermochemie der Legierungen.* Springer, Berlin, 1943.

van Arkel, A. E. *Reine Metalle.* Springer, Berlin, 1939.

Abhandlungen der Deutschen Bunsen-Gesellschaft, Verlag Chemie, Berlin, 1911–1929.

Methods of estimating values of particular thermodynamic properties for substances for which no data of the given kind are available are discussed in the following:

Hougen, O. A., and Watson, K. M. *Chemical Process Principles.* Wiley, 1943–1947.

Wenner, R. R. *Thermochemical Calculations.* McGraw-Hill, 1941.

Table A,26. Values of the fundamental constants.* Recommended by the National Research Council Committee on Physical Chemistry, as of July 1, 1951.

Name of constant	Symbol or abbreviation	Value and units
Basic constants		
Absolute temperature of the ice point, 0°C	$T_{0°C}$	$273.160 \pm 0.010°K$
Avogadro constant	N	$(6.02380 \pm 0.00011) \times 10^{23}$ number/mole
Velocity of light	c	$(2.997902 \pm 0.000009) \times 10^{10}$ cm/sec
Planck constant	h	$(6.62377 \pm 0.00018) \times 10^{-27}$ erg sec/molecule
Faraday constant	$\mathfrak{F}$	$96,493.1 \pm 0.7$ coulombs/equivalent
Pressure-volume product for one mole of a gas at 0°C and zero pressure	$(pV)_{T_{0°C}}^{p=0}$	2271.16 ± 0.04 joules/mole
Derived constants		
Electronic charge	e	$(1.601864 \pm 0.000031) \times 10^{-19}$ coulomb
Gas constant	R	8.31439 ± 0.00034 joules/deg mole
Boltzmann constant	k	$(1.380257 \pm 0.000062) \times 10^{-16}$ erg/deg molecule
Constant relating wave number and energy	Z	11.96171 ± 0.00039 joule cm/deg mole
Second radiation constant	c_2	1.438675 ± 0.000052 cm deg
Einstein constant relating mass and energy	Y	$(8.987416 \pm 0.000088) \times 10^{13}$ joules/g
Defined constants		
Standard gravity	g_0	980.665 cm/sec²
Standard atmosphere	atm	$1,013,250$ dynes/cm²
Standard millimeter of mercury pressure	mm	$\frac{1}{760}$ atm
Calorie (thermochemical)	cal	4.1840 joules

Auxiliary relations

1 second (mean solar) = 1.00273791 sidereal second
1 joule = 0.999835 ± 0.000052 international joule (NBS)
1 ohm = 0.999505 ± 0.000015 international ohm (NBS)
1 ampere = 1.000165 ± 0.000025 international ampere (NBS)
1 coulomb = 1.000165 ± 0.000025 international coulomb (NBS)
1 watt = 0.999835 ± 0.000052 international watt (NBS)
1 liter = 1000.028 ± 0.004 cm³

Various constants expressed in different units†

$(pV)_{T_{0°C}}^{p=0}$ 2271.16 joule/mole
22,414.6 cm³ atm/mole
22.4140 liter atm/mole

$\mathfrak{F}$ 96,493.1 coulombs/g-equivalent
23,062.4 cal/volt g-equivalent

* All electrical units are absolute unless otherwise indicated.
† See the above regarding the uncertainties.

Table A,26 (continued)

Name of constant	Symbol or abbreviation	Value and units
	e	1.601864×10^{-19} coulombs 1.601864×10^{-20} emu 4.80223×10^{-10} esu
	R	8.31439 joule/deg mole 1.98719 cal/deg mole 82.0567 cm^3 atm/deg mole 0.0820544 liter atm/deg mole
	Z	11.96171 joule cm/mole 2.858917 cal cm/mole
	Y	8.987416×10^{13} joules/g 2.148044×10^{13} cal/g
	cal	4.1840 (exact) joules 4.18331 int. joules 41.2929 cm^3 atm 0.0412917 liter atm

A,27. Cited References and Bibliography.

Cited References

1. Rossini, F. D. *Chemical Thermodynamics.* Wiley, 1950.
2. Lewis, G. N., and Randall, M. *Thermodynamics and the Free Energy of Chemical Substances.* McGraw-Hill, 1923.
3. Mayer, J. E., and Mayer, M. G. *Statistical Mechanics.* Wiley, 1940.
4. Pitzer, K. S., and Gwinn, W. D. *J. Chem. Phys. 10*, 428 (1942).
5. Rossini, F. D., Pitzer, K. S., Arnett, R. L., Braun, R. M., and Pimentel, G. C. *Selected Values of Physical and Thermodynamic Properties of Hydrocarbons and Related Compounds.* Carnegie Inst. Technol. Press, Pittsburgh, 1953.
6. Rossini, F. D., Wagman, D. D., Evans, W. H., Levine, S., and Jaffe, I. *Selected Values of Chemical Thermodynamic Properties.* Natl. Bur. Standards Circ. 500, U.S. Government Printing Office, 1952.
7. Ferri, A. *Elements of Aerodynamics of Supersonic Flows.* Macmillan, 1949.

Bibliography

Dodge, B. F. *Chemical Engineering Thermodynamics.* McGraw-Hill, 1944.
Epstein, P. S. *Textbook of Thermodynamics.* Wiley, 1937.
Fowler, R. H., and Guggenheim, E. A. *Statistical Mechanics.* Macmillan, 1939.
Gibbs, J. W. *Collected Works.* Yale Univ. Press, 1948.
Hawkins, G. A. *Thermodynamics.* Wiley, 1946.
Tolman, R. C. *The Principles of Statistical Mechanics.* Clarendon Press, 1938.
Wenner, R. R. *Thermochemical Calculations.* McGraw-Hill, 1941.
Zemansky, M. W. *Heat and Thermodynamics.* McGraw-Hill, 1948.

SECTION B

FUNDAMENTAL PHYSICS OF GASES

CHAPTER 1. QUANTUM MECHANICS AND APPLICATIONS TO MOLECULAR STRUCTURE

KARL F. HERZFELD

VIRGINIA GRIFFING

B,1. Historical Introduction. From the time of Newton, the three general laws of nature which bear his name were successful in describing and predicting the mechanical behavior of a wide class of phenomena ranging from the motion of the celestial bodies to that of a projectile on the surface of the earth. However, with the discovery of electrons and the study of the behavior of atoms and molecules these laws were found to be inadequate, and, in fact, sometimes gave results that were in direct contradiction to experimental facts. It was necessary to develop a new system of general principles which would describe the motions of small particles. The new system consists of a set of equations called quantum mechanics which are based on concepts which are profoundly different from those of classical mechanics; however, for the heavier bodies of everyday life the quantum mechanics gives the same results as Newtonian mechanics.

The first step in the development of the new system was due to the German physicist Max Planck [1] who proposed that energy of light emitted from a black body was emitted discontinuously as quanta. The magnitude of the quantum he proposed was equal to the frequency of the emitted light multiplied by a new constant of nature now called Planck's constant h. Einstein later extended Planck's assumption to a successful explanation of the photoelectric effect. In 1913, Niels Bohr used the idea of quantization and the value of Planck's constant to deduce quantitatively the spectrum of the hydrogen atom. Bohr's theory as extended by Sommerfeld gave a qualitative understanding of emission and absorption spectra of atoms and molecules and reconciled the Rutherford planetary atom with the stable existence of atoms in certain stationary states.[1] This new theory, called quantum theory of atoms, assumed that Newtonian mechanics gave the correct equations for the motion of electrons in stable circular or elliptical paths about a heavy positively charged nucleus. Only those orbits were stable for which the angular momentum was an integral multiple of $h/2\pi$. Qualitatively these ideas could be carried over to molecules, but the electrons in molecules no longer move in a field of spherical symmetry; furthermore the spectra of more complicated atoms and those involving more than one electron were only qualitatively explained. From the aesthetic point of view the quantum conditions were arbitrarily superposed on classical mechanics without any basis in fundamental principles. Finally, the Bohr theory assumed that an atom can absorb only a full quantum and absorb it instantaneously; however, according to the electromagnetic wave theory of light, the energy would have been spread evenly over a sphere in such a way that the intensity would be so small that it would take an atom a very long time to absorb a quantum. This difficulty disappears if one assumes that light travels in little packets, i.e. quanta, but then one must explain the observed diffraction and interference of light waves. Thus by 1923–24 an impasse had been reached.

The first break in these difficulties came in the dissertation of de Broglie in 1924. De Broglie associated a wavelength λ with every particle of mass m moving with a velocity v where $\lambda = h/mv$. This was verified experimentally by Davisson and Germer and G. P. Thomson who showed that beams of electrons could be diffracted, and later by Stern who showed that particles of atomic mass also exhibited wave properties [2].

When two sets of independent but reliable experiments give an apparent contradiction and there is no error in the logic, then the only solution to the problem is to reexamine the fundamental postulates of the theory upon which the contradictory evidence depends. Thus the fundamental postulates of Newtonian mechanics must be reexamined in the light of these new experiments.

Now, the fundamental postulate of classical mechanics which must be considered can be stated in terms of Eq. 2-4 or Eq. 2-7 given below which say: Given an isolated system of n particles having coordinates $q_1, q_2, \ldots, q_{3n}$ and conjugate momenta $p_1, p_2, \ldots, p_{3n}$, the integration of these equations and the experimental evaluation of the $6n$ constants of integration enable one to describe completely the system at any future time. The $6n$ constants of integration may be the values of the $3n$ coordinates q_i^0 and $3n$ momenta p_i^0 at some given time $t = t_0$.

Heisenberg was the first to point out that mechanical description of

[1] The knowledge of the Bohr theory is invaluable in associating intuitive ideas with the more abstract quantum mechanics. An excellent account of these developments from this point of view are given in [1].

the motion of the electron about the nucleus of an atom required the simultaneous knowledge of the position and momentum of the electron. However, any process that would enable one to determine exactly the position of the electron would cause the electron to separate from the atom, thus changing its momentum. For example, one might be able to observe the electron with a γ-ray microscope but the energy absorbed by the electron in the process ionizes the atom. Thus Heisenberg postulated that classical mechanics is not adequate for the description of atoms and electrons because it is impossible to determine precisely for a given particle both p_i and q_i simultaneously and that the best one can do is given by the following relation $\Delta p_i \Delta q_i \geqq h/2\pi$.

There are other pairs of conjugate variables, related by a similar indeterminacy equation: e.g. energy and time form such a pair. The uncertainty principle proposed by Heisenberg says that for absorption of strictly monochromatic light by an atom, which requires a determined energy $E = h\nu$, the moment of absorption completely eludes observation or more precisely

$$\Delta E \Delta t \geqq \frac{h}{2\pi}.$$

This uncertainty for particles of the ordinary world is so small that it is less than the random disturbances and thus is important only for particles of small mass. Physically, the uncertainty principle says that one can determine the position of a particle precisely but then any previous knowledge of its corresponding momentum has been destroyed by the measurement of position; or, it is possible to determine the momentum precisely but any knowledge of the corresponding position has been destroyed in the process. If the determination of the position, for example, is made only between limits Δq, the measurement of q produces an unknown change of about Δp in the momentum.

The uncertainty relation explains the particle-wave duality by saying that it is impossible to follow a system and to describe it in sufficient detail to distinguish between the wave picture and the particle picture.

Thus the requirements of the new theory are that one must use the wave and particle pictures to describe the same system, while limiting the applicability of these pictures by the uncertainty principle. This leads to the natural introduction of statistical notions into the description of matter and it remains only to formulate a mathematical theory, the results of which can be correlated with experimental results by probability statements. The required mathematical theory was formulated almost simultaneously by Schrödinger and Heisenberg, using different mathematical tools.

Heisenberg believed that the Bohr theory failed because its fundamental quantities (orbits) cannot be measured. So he attempted to set up a system of atomic mechanics which introduced only observable quantities. That is, he assumed that the fundamental entities in the mechanics of atoms are the observable frequencies and their intensities. Using these quantities, Heisenberg, Born, and Jordan developed an entire science called matrix mechanics which has been a highly successful theory; however, it is complicated in mathematical formulation and is not here considered in any detail.

Schrödinger derived a "wave equation" by analogy between mechanics and physical optics which forms the basis of the new theory called wave mechanics. He showed shortly after the development of matrix mechanics and wave mechanics that the two were mathematically equivalent. Thus both are now called quantum mechanics. Because of its more familiar mathematical tools the Schrödinger method is used in this account.

B,2. Classical Mechanics. Newtonian mechanics can best be formulated in terms of Lagrange's equations which are convenient ways of writing Newton's second law and have the advantage that they hold in any sort of coordinate system, and not just in the Cartesian coordinate system. For simplicity consider a particle of mass m and Cartesian coordinates x, y, z, with the components of the velocity u, v, and w, respectively. Then consider that the potential energy is given by a function of the coordinates only, $V(x, y, z)$. Since

$$F_x = - \frac{\partial V}{\partial x}$$

the equations of motion, written in terms of the momenta, are given by

$$\frac{d}{dt}(mu) = - \frac{\partial V}{\partial x} \quad \text{where } u = \frac{dx}{dt} \tag{2-1}$$

as are similar equations for y and z. But the kinetic energy of the particle is given by T where

$$T = \frac{m}{2}(u^2 + v^2 + w^2)$$

thus

$$\frac{\partial T}{\partial u} = mu = p_x \tag{2-2}$$

where p_x is the linear momentum in the x direction and the equations of motion (2-1) can now be written

$$\frac{d}{dt}\left(\frac{\partial T}{\partial u}\right) + \frac{\partial V}{\partial x} = 0, \quad \frac{d}{dt}\left(\frac{\partial T}{\partial v}\right) + \frac{\partial V}{\partial y} = 0 \tag{2-3}$$

or defining the Lagrangian function $L = T - V$, Eq. 2-3 can be written as

$$\frac{d}{dt}\left(\frac{\partial L}{\partial u}\right) - \frac{\partial L}{\partial x} = 0$$

Now to generalize if a system is described by coordinates q_i and their time derivatives are given by $\dot{q}_i$ then the classical equations of motion become

$$\frac{d}{dt}\left(\frac{\partial L}{\partial \dot{q}_i}\right) - \frac{\partial L}{\partial q_i} = 0 \tag{2-4a}$$

where $L = T - V$, and T may now be a function of both q and $\dot{q}$ as occurs, for example, in the rotation of a particle. One may define a generalized momentum, belonging to q_i, by

$$\frac{\partial L}{\partial \dot{q}_i} = p_i \tag{2-4b}$$

Eq. 2-2 is a special case of Eq. 2-4b. Eq. 2-4a can be rewritten

$$\frac{d}{dt}\left(\frac{\partial L}{\partial \dot{q}_i}\right) = -\frac{\partial V}{\partial q_i} + \frac{\partial T}{\partial q_i} \tag{2-5}$$

or

$$\frac{dp_i}{dt} = -\frac{\partial V}{\partial q_i} + \frac{\partial T}{\partial q_i}$$

Since $\partial L/\partial \dot{q}_i$ defines a generalized momentum p_i, the right-hand side of Eq. 2-5 gives the sum of the component of the force derivable from a potential and the last term $\partial T/\partial q_i$ is a fictitious force which arises when Cartesian coordinates are not used and the kinetic energy is no longer a function of $\dot{q}_i$ only.

It is useful to extend this formulation of classical mechanics to an even more symmetric form. Assuming a conservative system then Eq. 2-5 can be replaced by the two relations

$$\frac{dp_i}{dt} = \frac{\partial L}{\partial q_i}, \qquad p_i = \frac{\partial L}{\partial \dot{q}_i} \tag{2-6}$$

and thus the n second order differential equations (2-5) are replaced by $2n$ first order differential equations in (2-6). But now instead of using the Lagrangian function L consider a function H, which in a conservative system is simply the total energy $T + V$ expressed as a function of the generalized coordinates q_i and momenta p_i; then it can be shown that Eq. 2-6 becomes

$$\frac{dq_i}{dt} = \frac{\partial H(p_i, q_i)}{\partial p_i}, \qquad \frac{dp_i}{dt} = -\frac{\partial H(p_i, q_i)}{\partial q_i} \tag{2-7}$$

These are called Hamilton's[2] canonical equations of motion; p_i and q_i are said to be canonically conjugate variables. The Hamiltonian function for a mass m and Cartesian coordinates x, y, z is

$$H = \frac{1}{2m}(p_x^2 + p_y^2 + p_z^2) + V(x, y, z)$$

The law of conservation of energy in this notation is written

$$\frac{dH}{dt} = \sum \left[\frac{\partial H}{\partial q_i} \dot{q}_i + \frac{\partial H}{\partial p_i} \dot{p}_i \right] = 0 \tag{2-8}$$

The equations of motion (2-7) can be rewritten in terms of a convenient function, Poisson's bracket, which is defined as follows: Given two functions of the variables $F_1(p_i, q_i)$ and $F_2(p_i, q_i)$, Poisson's bracket of F_1 and F_2 is written

$$[F_1, F_2] = \sum_{i=1}^n \left[\frac{\partial F_1}{\partial q_i} \frac{\partial F_2}{\partial p_i} - \frac{\partial F_1}{\partial p_i} \frac{\partial F_2}{\partial q_i} \right] \tag{2-9}$$

In this form the equations of motion become

$$\frac{dq_i}{dt} = [q_i, H], \qquad \frac{dp_i}{dt} = [p_i, H] \tag{2-10}$$

and one finds in classical mechanics the following important relations:

$$[q_i, q_j] = 0$$
$$[p_i, p_j] = 0$$
$$[q_i, p_j] = \delta_{ij}$$

B,3. Mathematical Concepts. The mathematical formalism which one uses in quantum mechanics is operator algebra. Since this is an unfamiliar branch of mathematics, a brief discussion of the fundamental rules and definitions are given here before giving the mathematical formulation of quantum mechanics. The proofs are not given but may be found in any standard book on quantum mechanics.

Operators. An operator is defined as a symbol for a rule which tells one how to make one function from another function, that is

$$\alpha\psi(q_1, q_2, \cdots, q_n) = \Phi(q_1, q_2, \cdots, q_n) \tag{3-1}$$

[2] The equivalence of Newton's laws, Lagrange's equations, and Hamilton's equations is proved in [3]. For Cartesian coordinates the equivalence is obvious. The Hamilton equations are not restricted to conservative systems and the definition of the Hamiltonian is more generally

$$H = \sum_i p_i q_i - L_i$$

Here, one says the operator α when applied to the function $\psi(q_1, q_2, \cdots, q_n)$ gives the function Φ. These operators may be of all types, simple multiplication operators, differential operators, etc. For example, if α_1 is the operator representing multiplication by q_2 from the left on $\psi = q_1^2 q_2^2$ then $\Phi = q_2\psi$ or if α_1 is the differential operator $\partial/\partial q_i$ then

$$\frac{\partial}{\partial q_i}\,\psi(q_1, q_2) = 2q_1 q_2^2$$

The sum of two operators α and β is defined by

$$(\alpha + \beta)\psi(q_1, q_2 \cdots q_n) = \alpha\psi + \beta\psi \tag{3-2}$$

The product of two operators α and β is defined by

$$\alpha\beta\psi \equiv \alpha[\beta\psi] \tag{3-3}$$

That is, the function ψ is first operated on by β and the resulting function is then operated on by α. The reverse of this process will in general give a different result. That is

$$\alpha\beta \neq \beta\alpha$$

e.g. if α is the multiplication operator q and $\beta = \partial/\partial q$, then

$$q\,\frac{\partial}{\partial q}\,\psi \neq \frac{\partial}{\partial q}\,(q\psi)$$

Thus one would say that, in general, operators do not commute and one calls the difference $[\alpha\beta - \beta\alpha]$ the commutator of the operators α and β. $\alpha^n\psi$, means α successively operates n times on the function ψ.

The operators used in quantum mechanics are linear operators. A linear operator is defined by the following rule

$$\alpha[\psi_1(q) + \psi_2(q)] = \alpha\psi_1(q) + \alpha\psi_2(q) \tag{3-4}$$

Only certain types of function $\psi(q)$ are of physical interest. These functions may be real or complex but they must be single-valued, finite, and continuous over the complete range of the variables, or at least quadratically integrable, that is

$$\int \psi^*(q)\psi(q)d\tau < \infty \quad \text{where } d\tau = dq_1, dq_2, \cdots, dq_n \tag{3-5}$$

where $\psi^*(q)$ is the complex conjugate of $\psi(q)$.

The only operators of interest in quantum mechanics have the property

$$\alpha\psi = \alpha^*\psi^* \tag{3-6}$$

the α being called a Hermitian operator. Linear combinations of Hermitian operators are also Hermitian; however, the products of two Hermitian operators are Hermitian only if the two operators commute.

Assume that $\psi(q)$ belongs to a class of well-behaved functions and that α is a linear Hermitian operator. If the result of the operation is the function back again multiplied by a constant, that is

$$\alpha\psi(q) = a\psi(q) \quad \text{where } a = \text{real constant} \tag{3-7}$$

then $\psi(q)$ is called an eigenfunction of the operator α and a is called an eigenvalue. In general there will be a set of eigenfunctions $\psi_i(q)$ which when operated on by the operator α will yield a set of eigenvalues a_i. Then the eigenfunctions associated with different eigenvalues are orthogonal. That is

$$\int \psi_i(q)\psi_j(q)dq = \delta_{ij}, \qquad \delta_{ij} \begin{cases} = 1, & i = j \\ = 0, & i \neq j \end{cases} \tag{3-8}$$

When two or more eigenfunctions yield the same eigenvalue, this is a degenerate function. However, it is always possible to choose linear combinations of degenerate eigenfunctions which are orthogonal, and the linear combination will also be an eigenfunction of the operator. Furthermore, if a complete set of orthogonal functions are eigenfunctions of two different operators, α and β, then α and β commute. Conversely, if α and β commute, there exists a set of orthogonal functions which are simultaneously eigenfunctions of both operators.

When the operator is a differential one with several variables, Eq. 3-7 gives a homogeneous linear partial differential equation which can often be split into total homogeneous differential equations with the proper choice of coordinate system for the particular boundary conditions. There the problem often becomes identical with the Sturm-Liouville boundary-value problem discussed below.

Development into orthogonal functions. For simplicity, consider a variable x which is defined for the interval a to b. Consider a function $\psi(x)$ of the type defined in Eq. 3-5 which is continuous, finite, and single-valued in the interval a to b. There is a theorem in analysis which says that it is always possible to find a series made up of given orthogonal functions which will approximate $\psi(x)$ as closely as one likes in the interval from $x = a$ to $x = b$. That is

$$\psi(x) = \sum_{i=1}^{n} C_i\phi_i(x) \tag{3-9}$$

where

$$\int_a^b \phi_j^*\phi_i dx = 0, \quad \text{i.e. orthogonal} \tag{3-10}$$

and

$$\int_a^b \phi_i^*\phi_i dx = 1, \quad \text{i.e. normalized} \tag{3-11}$$

It is necessary that the orthogonal functions ϕ_i satisfy the same boundary conditions as the function $\psi(x)$. The expansion is possible if the set is complete and the series converges. If the expansion is possible

$$C_n = \int_a^b \phi_n f(x)dx \qquad (3\text{-}12)$$

and all values of C_n can be determined by successive integrations according to Eq. 3-12. The condition for normalization of the general function $\psi(x)$ then becomes

$$\sum_{i=1}^n C_i^* C_i = 1 \qquad (3\text{-}13)$$

Examples of orthogonal functions ϕ_n are well known in classical physics where they are solutions of certain well-known linear homogeneous second order total differential equations of the form

$$\frac{d^2y}{dx^2} + [\lambda^2 - f(x)]y = 0 \qquad (3\text{-}14)$$

where $f(x)$ is a known function continuous over the range $x = a$ to $x = b$, with boundary conditions of the form

$$\frac{dy}{dx}(a) - gy(a) = 0, \qquad \frac{dy}{dx}(b) - Gy(b) = 0 \qquad (3\text{-}15)$$

where g and G are constants. Eq. 3-14 and Eq. 3 15 define a Sturm-Liouville boundary-value problem and well-behaved solutions to Eq. 3-14 called eigenfunctions exist for only certain values of the parameter λ called eigenvalues. One is usually able to find these solutions in terms of such well-known functions as Fourier series, Legendre polynomials, Laguerre polynomials, Hermite polynomials, etc.

Eq. 3-14 also has the property that if $F_1(x)$ and $F_2(x)$ are solutions of Eq. 3-14 for the same λ then any arbitrary linear combination

$$y = a_1 F_1(x) + a_2 F_2(x) \qquad (3\text{-}16)$$

is also a solution.

B,4. Introductory Quantum Mechanics. The consequences of the uncertainty principle which must be reflected in the new formulation of mechanics can be stated briefly in terms of two principles.

1. Indeterminacy: Since an exact knowledge of initial conditions of a system is impossible, exact prediction of future behavior is no longer possible but must be replaced by methods of predicting the average behavior of a system or the probability of finding a system in a given state from the knowledge of the initial state allowed within the limits of the indeterminacy principle.

2. Complementariness: According to the indeterminacy principle, increased accuracy in the knowledge of one variable can be obtained only at the expense of knowledge of the conjugated variable, for example, the more accurately one determines q_j the more undetermined p_j becomes; therefore, the description of light from the wave point of view excludes the possibility of determining anything about its particle nature and vice versa.

Furthermore, the formulation of quantum mechanics is carried out according to the Bohr correspondence principle, which states that in the limiting conditions between microscopic and macroscopic systems the results of quantum mechanics and classical mechanics must converge to the same result.

The wave character of light, as shown by interference, is expressed mathematically in such a way that the quantity to which the usual wave equation is applied is the amplitude, which may be positive or negative. Since it is this amplitude which appears in the linear wave equation and to which the principle of superposition applies, the amplitude of light from two slits, for example, is added and because the amplitude may be positive or negative there may be destructive interference. Only after the sum of amplitudes is formed is it squared to give the observable quantity (light intensity) which can never be negative. If, as in the case of noncoherent sources, the intensities are added, there is no interference and the wave character of light does not come into evidence.

Accordingly, a mathematical apparatus which is to express the wave-like properties of particles must apply its linear operators not directly to the density, which can never be negative, but to a quantity which behaves like an amplitude and may be positive or negative or even complex. From this quantity, the density must be formed by getting the square of the absolute magnitude; then the density, like the light intensity, will never be negative, and wavelike properties, like destructive interference, may still be exhibited.

Consider a system of n degrees of freedom which would be described classically by specifying the value of n coordinates $q_1, q_2, \ldots, q_n$ and their conjugate momenta $p_1, p_2, \ldots, p_n$. Now the state of the system is described by a well-behaved function $U(q_1, q_2, \ldots, q_n, t)$ which is called the wave function of the system and has the following properties: $U(q_1, \ldots, q_n, t)$ may be real or complex, may have positive, zero, or negative values, and is interpreted so that $U^*U d\tau$ is the probability of finding the system in a volume element of configuration space $d\tau$. That is for a single particle described in Cartesian coordinates $U^*(x, y, z, t)U(x, y, z, t)dxdydz$ would be the probability of finding the particle in the volume element $dxdydz$. If one assumes the particle is limited to a finite space, then in order to get numerical results the wave functions must be normalized, i.e.

$$\int_\tau U^*U d\tau = 1 \tag{4-1}$$

This says with certainty only that the particle is some place in space. Thus the normalization of orthogonal functions which was done in classical physics for mathematical simplification takes on physical meaning in quantum mechanics.

In quantum mechanics physical quantity is no longer represented by an ordinary variable but to every observable quantity there is assigned a linear Hermitian operator.

A rule for determining the quantum mechanical operator is to write the corresponding classical function, $F(p_j, q_j)$, replace q_j by the multiplication operator q_j, and p_j by the differential operator

$$\frac{h}{2\pi i}\frac{\partial}{\partial q_j}$$

in such a way as to secure a linear Hermitian operator. When defined in this way q_j, p_j and any polynomial constructed from these operators will be linear Hermitian operators. However, products of p_j, q_j do not commute, that is,

$$p_k q_j - q_j p_k = \frac{h}{2\pi i}\delta_{kj}, \qquad \begin{array}{l}\delta_{kj} = 1, \quad \text{for } k = j \\ \delta_{kj} = 0, \quad \text{for } k \neq j\end{array}$$

This follows from the definition of the operator p

$$\left[\frac{h}{2\pi i}\frac{\partial(q_j)}{\partial q_j} - q_j \frac{h}{2\pi i}\frac{\partial}{\partial q_j}\right] U = \frac{h}{2\pi i} U$$

This is the quantum analogue of the classical statement about Poisson brackets (see end of B,2). Functions which contain products of p_j and q_j must be symmetrized, e.g. into $\frac{1}{2}(pq + qp)$. In classical mechanics, p_j and q_j are ordinary numbers and consequently do commute. The uncertainty principle is included in the mathematical description by thus choosing pairs of operators corresponding to a coordinate and its conjugated momentum that do not commute.

Table $B,4$ gives the operators which are used in this discussion.

Table B,4. Some common operators of quantum mechanics.

Observable quantity	Classical operator	Quantum mechanics operators
generalized space coordinate	q_i	q_i
generalized momentum coordinate	p_i	$\dfrac{h}{2\pi i}\dfrac{\partial}{\partial q_i}$
angular momentum in Cartesian coordinates	$M_z = m(x\dot{y} - y\dot{x})$	$\dfrac{h}{2\pi i}\left(x\dfrac{\partial}{\partial y} - y\dfrac{\partial}{\partial x}\right)$
Hamiltonian in Cartesian coordinates	$\dfrac{1}{2m}[p_x^2 + p_y^2 + p_z^2] + V(x, y, z)$	$-\dfrac{h}{8\pi^2 m}\nabla^2 + V(x, y, z)$
some arbitrary function F	$F(p^n, q^m, pq)$	$F\left[\left(\dfrac{h}{2\pi i}\dfrac{\partial}{\partial q}\right)^n, q^m, \dfrac{1}{2}(pq + qp)\right]$

Consider a system, the state of which is described by a wave function ψ_i. If this wave function ψ_i is an eigenfunction of the operator β, this means mathematically that the operation β applied to ψ_i makes out of ψ_i the expression $b_i\psi_i$, b_i being the eigenvalue.

One now makes the physical assumption that a measurement of the observable quantity to which the operator β belongs, will with certainty give the value b_i, the eigenvalue, if the system is described by the eigenfunction ψ_i (this is called a pure state). If the operators α and β commute, the simultaneous determination of the quantities corresponding to α and β will lead to exactly predictable values for both, namely the eigenvalues a_i and b_i.

Assume now that the wave function is not an eigenfunction of α; one can repeat the macroscopic arrangement of a given system and make repeatedly a certain measurement of an observable quantity represented by the operator α. Then the average value of the quantity should be calculated according to the following rule:

$$\bar{\alpha} = \int_\tau U^*\alpha U d\tau \tag{4-2}$$

where U is the wave function that describes the macroscopic state of the system at any given time. Note that Eq. 4-2 tells nothing about the result of a single measurement but represents an expected mean in the usual sense, i.e. if a_1, a_2, a_3, . . . , a_n are, respectively, the results of n measurements of the quantity α then

$$\bar{\alpha} = \frac{1}{n}\sum_{i=1}^{n} a_i$$

The order of writing the operator between U^* and U must be observed as the position matters for differential operators. If $U(q)$ is expanded into a complete set of orthogonal functions

$$U = \sum b_i\psi_i$$

Eq. 4-2 becomes

$$\bar{\alpha} = \int_\tau \sum b_i^*\psi_i^*\alpha\sum b_i\psi_i d\tau = \sum\sum b_i^*b_j \int \psi_i^*\alpha\psi_j d\tau \tag{4-3}$$

Now if ψ_i is an eigenfunction of the operator α, then

$$\alpha\psi_i = a_i\psi_i$$

and Eq. 4-3 becomes

$$\bar{\alpha} = \sum b_i^*b_i a_i$$

where one can interpret $b_i^*b_i$ in the following way: If a system is in a state described by the function U, which can be expanded as above into a series of eigenfunctions of α, and a single measurement of the quantity α is made, then $b_i^* b_i$ is the probability that the measurement will yield the value a_i. Thus if the function U is one of the eigenfunctions ψ_i then all the coefficients are identically zero except b_i and $b_i^* b_i = 1$. Then every measurement will give precisely the value a_i just as in Eq. 4-1. Thus the formulation of quantum mechanics is based on three fundamental postulates:

1. To every observable quantity there is assigned an operator.
2. If ψ_i is an eigenfunction of the operator α, i.e.

$$\alpha \psi_i = a_i \psi_i$$

   a single measurement will yield an exactly predictable value of $\alpha = a_i$.
3. If a system is described by a well-behaved function U, then the expected mean of a large number of measurements is given by $\bar{a} = \int U^* \alpha U d\tau$.

These postulates will now be further elucidated by application to some simple systems.

B,5. The Schrödinger Equation. Assume a system with n degrees of freedom, then $U(q_1, q_2, \ldots, q_n, t)$ describes the system at any time t, and $H(p, q, t)$[3] is the Hamiltonian operator associated with the system according to the above rules. Then $U(q, t)$ is a solution of the following differential equation

$$HU(q, t) = -\frac{h}{2\pi i} \frac{\partial}{\partial t} U(q, t) \tag{5-1}$$

where

$$\int_\tau U^* U d\tau = 1$$

This is the time dependent Schrödinger equation and is exact[4] as long as one excludes velocities which approach the velocity of light. This equation can be written in general[5] as

$$\sum_{j=1}^{n} \nabla_j^2 U - \frac{8\pi^2 M}{h^2} V(q, t) U = \frac{4\pi M}{ih} \frac{\partial}{\partial t} U(q, t) \tag{5-2}$$

where all masses M are assumed equal.

---

[3] $H(p, q, t)$ is a short way of writing $H(p_1, p_2, \ldots, p_n; q_1, q_2, \ldots, q_n, t)$.
[4] One must also exclude certain problems in electrodynamics.
[5] There exists a second equation for the conjugate complex function U^* with $-i$ instead of $+i$, i.e.

$$\sum \nabla^2 U^* - \frac{8\pi^2 M}{h^2} V(q, t) U^* = -\frac{4\pi M}{ih} \frac{\partial}{\partial t} U^*$$

This is a second order linear partial differential equation and can be treated by the ordinary methods of solving boundary-value problems. This is sometimes called the wave equation, because it has the same form[6] as a wave equation in a medium in which the refractive index varies from place to place.

If one assumes that V, the potential energy, is a function of the coordinates only, then an elementary solution of Eq. 5-2 can be written:

$$U(q, t) = \psi(q)f(t) \tag{5-3}$$

Substituting Eq. 5-3 in Eq. 5-2 and separating variables in the usual way one obtains two total differential equations

$$\frac{1}{f}\frac{df}{dt} = -\frac{Lih}{4\pi M} \tag{5-4}$$

$$\sum \nabla_j^2 \psi - \frac{8\pi^2 M}{h^2} V\psi = -L\psi \tag{5-5}$$

$$f(t) = e^{-\frac{ihL}{4\pi M}t}$$

Now calculating the average value of the energy, $\bar{E}$, according to the rule of Eq. 4-2

$$\bar{E} = \int_\tau U^* H U d\tau$$

$$\bar{E} = \int_\tau U^* \left(-\frac{h}{2\pi i}\frac{\partial}{\partial t} U\right) d\tau = -\frac{h}{2\pi i}\int f^* \frac{df}{dt} \psi^*\psi d\tau$$

But

$$f = e^{-\frac{ihL}{4\pi M}t}$$

$$\bar{E} = -\frac{h}{2\pi i}\left(-\frac{ihL}{4\pi M}\right) = \frac{h^2}{8\pi^2 M} L \tag{5-6}$$

Therefore the total energy is a constant, the time dependent Schrödinger equation, Eq. 5-2, has an oscillatory solution, and the frequency is E/h. The equation resulting from Eq. 5-5 by the elimination of L through Eq. 5-6 is called the time independent Schrödinger equation. If this is applied to the special case of a particle of mass m, then Eq. 5-5 becomes

$$\nabla^2 \psi + \frac{8\pi^2 m}{h^2}(E - V)\psi = 0 \tag{5-7}$$

---

[6] Those familiar with the wave equations of classical physics will notice that this has the parabolic form in the place of the usual hyperbolic form, i.e. $\partial u/\partial t$ instead of $\partial^2 u/\partial t^2$. However, i is already included as an explicit factor in front of the time derivative so this is really a wave equation and not a diffusion equation.

The form of ψ is determined by the boundary conditions of the problem and it must be well behaved throughout configuration space. This will be true for only certain values of the energy E; these values may form a discrete set, a continuous set, or both. If the values of E form a discrete set of n values, one says there are n stationary states of the particle and the general wave function ψ can be written as a linear combination of elementary solutions

$$U = \sum_{i=1}^{n} a_i \phi_i e^{-\frac{2\pi i E_i}{h}t} \tag{5-8}$$

where ϕ_i is the eigenfunction associated with the eigenvalue E_i. This means that the system consists of a mixture of states; $a_i^* a_i$ tells how often the particle is in the state i with energy E_i. Usually E_i can be conveniently associated with a series of numbers n called total quantum numbers. Thus the quantum conditions that were arbitrarily imposed on classical mechanics in the old quantum theory arise logically as restrictions that are necessary to obtain well-behaved solutions of the Schrödinger equation in quantum mechanics.

B,6. Perturbation Theory. Assume a system in a stationary state, described by a time independent Schrödinger equation

$$(H - E)\Psi = 0 \tag{6-1}$$

The wave function ψ is determined if, besides the differential equation, the boundary conditions are given, e.g. for an atom, $\psi = 0$ at infinity; or for a stream of electrons, a plane wave at infinity.

Assume then that $\psi_1, \psi_2, \ldots, \psi_n$ form a complete (possibly continuous) set of orthogonal functions, determined by an arbitrary differential or linear operator equation, but restricted by the fact that each ψ satisfies the same boundary conditions as Ψ. One can then always write, as a generalization of a Fourier development, the jth solution of Eq. 6-1 (see Eq. 3-9)

$$\Psi_j = \sum_n b_{jn} \psi_n \tag{6-2}$$

To find the coefficients, one introduces Eq. 6-2 in Eq. 6-1, multiplies the result with a ψ_s^* (s arbitrary), and integrates. One has then, as a result of the orthogonality of the ψ,

$$\sum_n b_n (H_{sn} - \delta_{sn} E) = 0 \tag{6-3}$$

with the definition

$$H_{sn} = \int \psi_s^* H \psi_n d\tau \tag{6-4}$$

In Eq. 6-3, the index j, the first index of the b's, has been left out, since the set of Eq. 6-3 (one for every s) has not one, but an infinite set of solutions, and each set corresponds to a different j (i.e. Ψ_j, E_j).

The set of infinite linear equations for the unknowns b_n is solvable only if the following (infinite) determinant disappears:

$$|H_{sn} - \delta_{sn}E| = 0 \tag{6-5}$$

(secular equation). Each of the roots E of this equation is a possible eigenvalue E_j of Eq. 6-1, and the corresponding b_n's are the coefficients b_{jn} for Eq. 6-2.

To make the series (6-2) well convergent, and the approximate solution of Eq. 6-5 possible, one chooses as development functions ψ solutions of a "neighboring" problem

$$(H_0 - E_n^0)\psi_n = 0 \tag{6-6}$$

The difference,

$$H' = H - H_0 \tag{6-7}$$

is called the perturbation function; it is assumed that all the matrix elements H'_{sn} are small compared with the corresponding H_{sn}. One finds under these conditions, if one develops according to powers of H'_{sn}

$$b_{jn} = \frac{H'_{nj}}{E_j^0 - E_n^0} + \frac{1}{E_j^0 - E_n^0}\left[\sum_s \frac{H'_{ns}H'_{sj}}{E_j^0 - E_s^0} - \frac{(H'_{jj} - H'_{nn})H'_{nj}}{E_j^0 - E_n^0}\right],$$
$$j \neq n \neq s \tag{6-8}$$

$$b_{jj} = 1 - \frac{1}{2}\sum \frac{H'_{js}H'_{sj}}{(E_j^0 - E_s^0)^2} \tag{6-9}$$

$$E_j = E_j^0 + H_{jj} + \sum \frac{H'_{js}H'_{sj}}{E_j^0 - E_s^0} \tag{6-10}$$

Formulas (6-8) to (6-10) may also be found by writing

$$E = \int \Psi^* H \Psi d\tau = \sum_s \sum_n b_s^* H_{sn} b_s \tag{6-11}$$

and minimizing this expression under the condition that Ψ be normalized, i.e.

$$\sum b_n^* b_n = 1$$

These procedures are valid only in nondegenerate cases (the details for degenerate cases are not given here). The closer the ψ' are to the Ψ (i.e. the smaller H'_{sn}) the better the convergence.

B,7. Transitions. There are, in principle, two methods of treating transitions between quantum states; one considers a stationary system, the other considers a time-dependent system.

The former may be used in the investigation of transitions in a molecule induced by collisions with a stream of atoms. Since a transition in the molecule produces a change in the velocity of the atom, an investigation of how many scattered atoms have had their velocity decreased reveals how many collisions have resulted in an internal transition of the molecule to a higher quantum state, while the number of scattered atoms with higher velocity reveals the number of transitions to lower states. The details of such a calculation are given in H,28 and H,29. For transitions induced by light this method would not work, since in the stationary state there are as many excitations as deexcitations and therefore the number of scattered light quanta—the only quantity to be measured, since their frequency is not changed—is not directly affected by these processes. One has therefore to use the method of time dependent perturbation, which is more complicated than that of stationary perturbation. (It could also be used in atomic collisions.)

In the method now considered, one uses the time dependent Schrödinger equation and permits H' (but not H_0) to depend explicitly on time.

One now makes the development not with the time independent but with the time dependent solutions U of Eq. 5-1 and assumes that the coefficients a vary slowly with time (i.e. slow compared to $e^{(2\pi i/h)Et}$).

One therefore writes

$$U_j = e^{-\frac{2\pi i}{h}E_jt}\Psi_j$$

$$= a_{jj}(t)e^{-\frac{2\pi i}{h}E_j{}^0t}\psi_j + \sum_{n\neq j} a_{jn}(t)e^{-\frac{2\pi i}{h}E_n{}^0t}\psi_n \tag{7-1}$$

as generalization of Eq. 5-8. This is inserted into Eq. 5-1

$$(H_0 + H')U = -\frac{h}{2\pi i}\frac{\partial U}{\partial t} \tag{7-2}$$

and leads to

$$\sum_n a_{jn}(t)e^{-\frac{2\pi i}{h}E_n{}^0t}H'\psi_n = -\frac{h}{2\pi i}\sum e^{-\frac{2\pi i}{h}E_n{}^0t}\psi_n\frac{\partial}{\partial t}a_{jn}(t) \tag{7-3}$$

Again multiplying with ψ_s^*, integrating, and omitting the first index j as before, one has,

$$\sum e^{-\frac{2\pi i}{h}(E_n{}^0-E_s{}^0)t}H'_{sn}a_n(t) = -\frac{h}{2\pi i}\frac{\partial}{\partial t}a_s(t) \tag{7-4}$$

This is a set of linear differential equations for a_s. One can integrate them approximately by assuming that at $t = 0$ all the systems were in the state

$$\Psi_j = \psi_j$$

i.e.

$$a_j(0) = 1 \qquad a_n(0) = 0$$

and by using, for a short time interval, these initial values of the a's in the left side of Eq. 7-4. Then

$$-\frac{h}{2\pi i}\frac{\partial a_j}{\partial t} = H'_{jj}$$

This gives only a change of the exponent from

$$-\frac{2\pi i}{h}E^0_j t \quad \text{to} \quad -\frac{2\pi i}{h}(E^0_j + H'_{jj})t$$

in accordance with Eq. 6-10.

For $s \neq j$

$$-\frac{h}{2\pi i}\frac{\partial a_s}{\partial t} = e^{-\frac{2\pi i}{h}(E_j{}^0 - E_s{}^0)t}H'_{sn} \tag{7-5}$$

The next step may be made on different levels of rigor. In the more rigorous case, one considers the system as made up of molecules and photons, and the transition as consisting in the excitation of the molecule and the simultaneous disappearance of a photon. On a less rigorous level, one introduces a potential energy of interaction between the electrical field, $\Xi_0 e^{2\pi i \nu t}$, and the charge displacement er (this would not be legitimate for hard X rays), and writes

$$H' = e(r\Xi_0)e^{-2\pi i \nu t} \tag{7-6}$$

It turns out that, to get reasonable results, one has to assume that the incoming radiation has $\nu \sim (W^0_j - W^0_s)/h$, but is not quite monochromatic. (If it were monochromatic, one would have to wait, according to Heisenberg's uncertainty principle, an infinitely long time, and the question as to what is the transition probability would lose any meaning.)

If one then performs the calculation, one finds

$$|a_s^2| = \frac{8\pi^3}{3hc}|M_{\bar{z}}^2|I_\nu t \tag{7-7}$$

where I_ν is the amount of energy flowing per second through unit area within unit frequency "band width" and M is the component of the electrical moment in the direction of the field

$$M_{js} = e \int \psi_j^* r_{\bar{z}} \psi_s d\tau \tag{7-8}$$

$|a|_s^2$ is the number of particles found in states s at time t, when at zero time all were in state j. This quantity is seen to be proportional to t (this is only valid for times so short that only a small fraction has made the transition; otherwise the approximation made following Eq. 7-4 is not permissible). Therefore

$$\frac{|a_s|^2}{t} = \frac{8\pi^3}{3hc} |M_{\mathsf{z}}^2| I_{\nu} \qquad (7\text{-}9)$$

is the transition probability, i.e. the fraction of particles making the transition in unit time.

A consideration of temperature equilibrium in the field of black body radiation (there must be an equal number of particles per second excited by light absorption as are returning to the lower state through spontaneous emission of a quantum) shows that the probability of spontaneous emission is given by

$$\frac{64\pi^4 \nu^3}{3hc^3} |M^2| \qquad (7\text{-}10)$$

The value of M is determined by the initial wave function ψ_j and the final wave function ψ_s. In order that M be different from zero (the transition be allowed or be a dipole transition), the angular momenta of states j and s may differ by only 1 or 0 (this is a necessary, not a sufficient, condition). But even if M is zero, other transitions may be possible, although with much lower probability. In Eq. 7-6, the system (atom or molecule) was considered negligibly small compared to the wavelength of the light λ, i.e. phase differences between different parts of the atom or molecule were neglected. If the light is propagated in the z direction, Eq. 7-6 must be multiplied by a factor

$$e^{2\pi i \frac{z}{\lambda}} = 1 + 2\pi i \frac{z}{\lambda} - \frac{1}{2}\left(2\pi \frac{z}{\lambda}\right)^2 \cdots$$

In the previous calculation, only the first term was considered. The second gives a contribution

$$\frac{2\pi i}{\lambda} M'$$

where M' is called a quadripole moment and is given by

$$M' = \int \psi_s^* z r_{\mathsf{z}} \psi_j d\tau$$

The resultant quadripole transition probability is found from Eq. 7-10 by replacing $|M^2|$ by $(4\pi^2/\lambda^2) |(M')^2|$ and stands to that for a dipole transition roughly in the ratio

$$\left(2\pi \frac{\text{dimension of atom}}{\lambda}\right)^2 : 1$$

B,8. Application of Quantum Mechanics to Simple Systems. The time independent Schrödinger equation will now be solved for a few simple systems. Since the Hamiltonian operator is invariant under transformation of coordinates, the coordinate system that is most convenient for the problem will be chosen. Consider a particle of mass m, moving along the x axis under the influence of no forces, that is, $V = 0$, then the wave equation $H\psi = E\psi$ becomes

$$\frac{-h^2}{8\pi^2 m}\frac{d^2\psi}{dx^2} = E_x\psi \tag{8-1}$$

$$\psi = Ae^{\frac{2\pi i}{h}\sqrt{2mE_x}\,x} + Be^{-\frac{2\pi i}{h}\sqrt{2mE_x}\,x} \tag{8-2}$$

In order for ψ to be finite for all values of x, $\sqrt{2mE_x}$ must be real, therefore the only restriction is that E_x must be positive. Thus translational motion is not quantized and E_x may vary continuously from 0 to $+\infty$. A and B are arbitrary constants. Since $Ae^{(2\pi i/h)\sqrt{2mE_x}\,x}$ and $Be^{-(2\pi i/h)\sqrt{2mE_x}\,x}$ are linearly independent when $E \neq 0$, the energy spectrum for a free particle is degenerate. These eigenfunctions are not quadratically integrable and thus the problem of normalization presents greater difficulties than in other problems and is not discussed here, but can be found in any one of the texts on quantum mechanics listed in the bibliography. If one uses the wave functions from Eq. 8-2 to calculate the linear momentum according to Eq. 4-2

$$p = \int U^* \frac{h}{2\pi i}\frac{\partial}{\partial x} U d\tau$$

and uses the expression with positive component only or that with negative component only, one finds, in agreement with classical theory,

$$p = \pm\sqrt{2mE_x} \tag{8-3}$$

The wave functions represent plane waves, going to the left or right, with wavelength

$$\frac{h}{\sqrt{2mE}} = \frac{h}{p} \tag{8-4}$$

in agreement with de Broglie's assumption.

The simple harmonic oscillator in one dimension.   A simple harmonic oscillator consists of a particle of mass m held to an equilibrium position Q by a restoring force $F = -k^2 x$ where x is the displacement of the particle from Q. Newtonian mechanics says this particle will oscillate about Q with an arbitrary amplitude and energy with a frequency of

$$\nu = \frac{1}{2\pi}\sqrt{\frac{k^2}{m}}$$

If

$$V = \tfrac{1}{2}k^2 x^2$$

and the origin of the coordinate system is placed at the point Q then $H\psi = E\psi$ becomes

$$\frac{d^2\psi}{dx^2} + \frac{8\pi^2 m}{h^2}\left(E - \frac{1}{2}k^2x^2\right)\psi = 0 \tag{8-5}$$

Changing variables, let

$$y = \left(\frac{4\pi mk^2}{h^2}\right)^{-\frac{1}{4}} x$$

then if $\lambda = \dfrac{2E}{h\nu}$

$$\frac{d^2\psi}{dy^2} + (\lambda - y^2)\psi = 0 \tag{8-6}$$

The problem is now one of finding the values of λ for which Eq. 8-6 has well-behaved solutions, i.e. ψ must decay exponentially as $y \to \infty$. Try a solution of the form

$$\psi = e^{-\frac{1}{2}y^2}f_n(y) \tag{8-7}$$

Differentiating and substituting in Eq. 8-6 one obtains

$$\frac{d^2f}{dy^2} - 2y\frac{df}{dy} + (\lambda - 1)f = 0 \tag{8-8}$$

This differential equation has a solution in terms of a power series

$$f_n(y) = \sum_n a_n y^n \tag{8-9}$$

This solution will cause the wave function (Eq. 8-7) to become infinite as y grows very large, consequently Eq. 8-6 will have well-behaved solutions (Eq. 8-7) only if the series breaks off after a finite number of terms which, it can be shown, requires

$$\lambda = 2n + 1 \quad \text{where } n = 0, 1, 2, \cdots, n$$

Therefore

$$2n + 1 = \frac{2E_n}{h\nu}$$

or

$$E_n = (n + \tfrac{1}{2})h\nu \tag{8-10}$$

The functions $f_n(y)$ are called Hermite polynomials defined by

$$f_n(y) = (-1)^n e^{y^2}\frac{d^n}{dy^n}e^{-y^2} \tag{8-11}$$

Thus quantum mechanically the linear oscillator can no longer have an arbitrary energy but has instead a set of discrete values separated by

$h\nu$ where ν is the classical frequency and furthermore the zero-point energy is $\frac{1}{2}h\nu$. This is necessary to satisfy the minimum condition $\Delta p \Delta q = h$. Thus even in the lowest energy state a simple harmonic oscillator still has an energy $\frac{1}{2}h\nu$. If one extends this to the n-dimensional oscillator as must be done in the case of polyatomic molecules then

$$\frac{E}{h} = \nu_1\left(n_1 + \frac{1}{2}\right) + \nu_2\left(n_2 + \frac{1}{2}\right) + \cdots + \nu_n\left(n_N + \frac{1}{2}\right) \quad (8\text{-}12)$$

where ν_n are the frequencies of the characteristic modes of vibration of the molecule.

The rigid rotator in space. Assume a particle of mass m which rotates about a point O so that the particle is always a distance r from the point. Then choose a spherical polar coordinate system (r, θ, ω) with origin at O. The Laplace operator in spherical coordinates is

$$\nabla^2 = \frac{1}{r^2}\frac{\partial}{\partial r}\left(r^2\frac{\partial}{\partial r}\right) + \frac{1}{r^2}\frac{\partial}{\partial \mu}\left[(1 - \mu^2)\frac{\partial}{\partial \mu}\right] + \frac{1}{r^2(1 - \mu^2)}\frac{\partial^2}{\partial \omega^2} \quad (8\text{-}13)$$

where $\mu = \cos\theta$. If

$$U = e^{-2\pi i \frac{E}{h} t}\psi$$

and only the stationary states are of interest at this time, the Schrödinger equation for the rigid rotator $(r = \text{const})$ can be written

$$\frac{1}{r^2}\frac{\partial}{\partial \mu}\left[(1 - \mu^2)\frac{\partial \psi}{\partial \mu}\right] + \frac{1}{r^2}\frac{1}{1 - \mu^2}\frac{\partial^2\psi}{\partial \omega^2} + \frac{8\pi^2 m}{h^2}E\psi = 0 \quad (8\text{-}14)$$

Making the substitution

$$\sigma^2 = \frac{8\pi^2 m r^2}{h^2}E$$

the equation becomes

$$\frac{\partial}{\partial \mu}\left[(1 - \mu^2)\frac{\partial \psi}{\partial \mu}\right] + \frac{1}{1 - \mu^2}\frac{\partial^2\psi}{\partial \omega^2} + \sigma^2\psi = 0 \quad (8\text{-}15)$$

Eq. 8-15 can be solved in the usual way by separating variables and finding total differential equations which have well-behaved solutions in analogy to the procedure used for the simple harmonic oscillator. Thus one obtains for the orthogonal normalized solutions of Eq. 8-15

$$\psi_{l,m}(\mu, \omega) = \frac{(-1)^l}{2^l l!}\sqrt{\frac{2l + 1}{2}\frac{(l - |m|)!}{(l + |m|)!}}\sin^{|m|}\theta\frac{d^{l+|m|}\sin^{2l}\theta}{d\mu^{l+|m|}}\frac{1}{\sqrt{2m}}e^{im\omega}$$

$$(8\text{-}16)$$

where $l = 0, 1, 2, \cdots$ and $m = 0, \pm 1, \pm 2, \cdots, \pm l$.

The energy values of the rigid rotator are given by

$$\sigma^2 = \frac{8\pi^2 mr^2 E}{h^2} = l(l+1) \tag{8-17}$$

therefore

$$E_l = l(l+1)\frac{h^2}{8\pi^2 mr^2} \tag{8-18}$$

Similarly, it can be shown that the total angular momentum given by

$$M^2 = M_x^2 + M_y^2 + M_z^2$$

can be calculated using the wave functions from Eq. 8-16. One obtains

$$M^2 = \int \psi_{l,m}^* M^2 \psi_{l,m} d\tau = l(l+1)\left(\frac{h}{2\pi}\right)^2 \tag{8-19}$$

Thus the square of the total angular momentum is also quantized and has predictable values given in Eq. 8-19 and can be determined simultaneously with the total energy. The physical meanings of the two quantum numbers l and m then are: l is the total angular momentum quantum number and m is the quantum number associated with different permitted orientations in space, i.e. values of the angle θ. If one writes the operator for the z component of the angular momentum in spherical polar coordinates it becomes $(h/2\pi i)(\partial/\partial\omega)$ and the eigenvalues of this operator can be shown to be $mh/2\pi$; the eigenfunctions are the same as the eigenfunctions for M^2 or H. Therefore not only is the square of the total angular momentum and consequently of the angular velocity of the rigid rotator allowed certain discrete values but also only certain orientations in space are possible.

The next system to be considered is the hydrogen atom. Assume a nucleus of mass m_1, a positive Ze charge,[7] and an electron $(-e$, mass $m_2)$ a distance r from the nucleus under the influence of a Coulomb attraction $V = -Ze^2/r$. The most convenient coordinate system for a discussion of this problem is chosen as follows: Let x, y, z be the coordinates of the center of mass of the system and place a spherical coordinate system (r, θ, ω) at the center of mass. Then the coordinates of the nucleus will be

$$\left(\frac{m_2}{m_1 + m_2} r, \theta, \omega\right)$$

and the coordinates of the electron will be

$$\left(\frac{m_1}{m_1 + m_2} r, \theta, \omega\right)$$

[7] $Z = 1$ for hydrogen but to simplify later discussions it will be kept in the equation as Z.

In this coordinate system the classical Hamiltonian operator H can be written

$$H = \frac{m_1 + m_2}{2}\left[\left(\frac{dx}{dt}\right)^2 + \left(\frac{dy}{dt}\right)^2 + \left(\frac{dz}{dt}\right)^2\right] + \frac{m_1 m_2}{m_1 + m_2}$$
$$\left[\left(\frac{dr}{dt}\right)^2 + r^2\left(\frac{d\theta}{dt}\right)^2 + r^2\sin^2\theta\left(\frac{d\omega}{dt}\right)^2\right] - \frac{Ze^2}{r} \quad (8\text{-}20)$$

and the quantum mechanic operator becomes

$$H = \frac{-h^2}{8\pi^2(m_1+m_2)}\nabla^2(x,\,y,\,z) - \frac{h^2}{8\pi^2}\frac{(m_1+m_2)}{m_1 m_2}\nabla^2(r,\,\theta,\,\omega) - \frac{Ze^2}{r} \quad (8\text{-}21)$$

So that Schrödinger's equation $H\psi = E\psi$ becomes

$$-\frac{h^2}{8\pi^2(m_1+m_2)}\nabla^2(x,\,y,\,z)\psi - \frac{h^2}{8\pi^2\mu}\nabla^2(r,\,\theta,\,\omega)\psi - \frac{Ze^2}{r}\psi = E\psi \quad (8\text{-}22)$$

Let[8] $\psi = F(x,\,y,\,z)\psi(r,\,\theta,\,\omega)$ then in the same way as before, one obtains two equations, one of which is

$$\frac{h^2}{8\pi^2(m_1+m_2)}\nabla^2(x,\,y,\,z)F(x,\,y,\,z) + (E - E^0)F = 0 \quad (8\text{-}23)$$

where E = total energy, E^0 = internal energy, and $E - E^0$ = translational energy of the center of mass. The other equation from Eq. 8-20 becomes

$$\frac{h^2}{8\pi^2\mu}\nabla^2(r,\,\theta,\,\omega)\psi + \left(E^0 + \frac{Ze^2}{r}\right)\psi = 0 \quad (8\text{-}24)$$

Eq. 8-23 is the Schrödinger equation of the three-dimensional translational motion of a mass equal to the total mass of the system located at the center of mass of the system. This equation is like Eq. 8-5 but it is now in three dimensions. The variables can be separated in the usual way and the wave functions determined. The results would be analogous to Eq. 8-7 and one would find that the translational energy of the system calculated in this way is exactly equal to the classical kinetic energy of translation of such a system, and is not quantized but may have all positive energies from zero to high values, as long as one does not approach the velocity of light. It is usually possible to separate out the translational degrees of freedom of any system in this way regardless of the complexity of the system.

Eq. 8-24 is the Schrödinger equation for the internal energy of the hydrogen atom. The internal energy of the hydrogen atom, E^0, must be negative if the electron is bound. This energy is quantized as is shown below; however, if E^0 is positive the energy is no longer quantized but takes on continuous values. This is experimentally observed in the

---

[8] The time factor has already been eliminated by separation of variables.

hydrogen spectrum where the spectrum consists of discrete lines and a continuum.

Eq. 8-24 can be solved in the usual way by separating variables and one will obtain an r-dependent equation and an equation exactly like Eq. 8-14 for the rigid rotator; then the solutions of Eq. 8-24 can be shown to be Eq. 8-16 multiplied by an r-dependent solution. One defines the following quantities

$$\rho = \frac{2Z}{na_0} r \quad \text{and} \quad a_0 = \frac{h^2}{4\pi^2 \mu e^2}$$

a_0 is the radius of the first Bohr orbit as calculated by quantum theory using classical mechanics as a basis.

One obtains for the orthogonal normalized wave functions of the hydrogen atom

$$\psi_{n,l,m} = \frac{1}{\sqrt{2\pi}} e^{im\omega} \left[\frac{(2l+1)(l-|m|)!}{2(l+|m|)!} \right]^{\frac{1}{2}} P_l^{|m|}(\mu)$$

$$\left\{ \left(\frac{2Z}{na_0} \right)^3 \frac{(n-l-1)!}{2n[(n+l)!]^3} \right\}^{\frac{1}{2}} e^{-\rho/2} \rho^l L_{n+l}^{2l+1}(\rho) \quad (8\text{-}25)$$

where $P_l^{|m|}(\mu)$ are the associated Legendre functions and $L_{n+l}^{2l+1}(\rho)$ are the associated Laguerre polynomials.

Just as in the case of the rigid rotator, l is the total angular momentum quantum number usually called the orbital angular momentum as $l(l+1)$ gives the possible values of the square of the momentum of the electron moving about the nucleus in stable orbits measured in units $(h/2\pi)^2$; m gives the allowed orientations of these orbits.

In order to obtain well-behaved solutions for the r-dependent equations it is necessary to select another hitherto undetermined constant, as an integer. This defines another quantum number, n', called the radial quantum number which can have values 0, 1, 2, . . . ; or the total quantum number is defined as $n = n' + l + 1$ where n appears explicitly in the wave function given in Eq. 8-25. Its physical significance becomes apparent if one uses the eigenfunctions $\psi_{n,l,m}$ to calculate the allowed energy values E_n^0, in the usual manner.

Thus having obtained the eigenfunctions of the Schrödinger equation of the hydrogen atom, one can calculate the allowed energies (eigenvalues) according to the equation

$$H\psi_{n,l,m} = E_n \psi_{n,l,m} \qquad (8\text{-}26)$$

and one obtains

$$-E_n = \frac{4\pi^2 Z^2 e^4}{n^2 h^2} \left(\frac{m_1 m_2}{m_1 + m_2} \right) \qquad (8\text{-}27)$$

Therefore the energy values are dependent only on the total quantum number n. The electronic energies given in Eq. 8-27 are the same energies as those calculated by the old Bohr theory and the energy differences for different values of n correspond exactly to the observed spectra of the hydrogen atom $(Z = 1)$, that is,

$$E_n - E_m = \frac{-2\pi^2e^2m_1m_2}{h^2(m_1 + m_2)}\left(\frac{1}{n^2} - \frac{1}{m^2}\right)$$

$$= Rhe\left(\frac{1}{n^2} - \frac{1}{m^2}\right) \tag{8-28}$$

This is the Balmer formula for observed spectral series; since the energy depends only upon n, these energy values are degenerate because one can obtain the same values of n for different values of l and m. Since $n = n' + l + 1$ and $m = \pm l, \pm(l-1), \pm(l-2), \cdots, 0$ for every value of l there are $2l + 1$ values of m that give the same value of n and $l = n - 1$, $n - 2, \cdots, 0$ so the degeneracy of the eigenvalues given in Eq. 8-27 is

$$\sum_{l=0}^{n-1} 2l + 1 = 1 + 3 + \cdots 2n - 1 = n(n - 1) + n = n^2$$

This says that for a given value of n there are n^2 different states in which the electron can move with the same energy E_n. These states are characterized by different angular momenta (l) and different orientations in space (m). Usually m is called the magnetic quantum number because, if the atom is placed in a magnetic field, the energies of the electron in the different states characterized by m are no longer equal but depend on the orientation of the state with reference to the applied magnetic field; one says the energy of the magnetic field has split the degeneracy. If the Schrödinger equation is solved, including the term due to the applied magnetic field, the solutions of Eq. 8-24 contain m explicitly for different energy eigenvalues. This effect is observed experimentally and is called the Zeeman effect.

Thus the stable states of the electron in the hydrogen atom are completely described by the three quantum numbers n, l, and m and the following notation taken from spectroscopy is used. Electronic states for which $l = 0, 1, 2, 3$ are described by the letters s, p, d, and f, respectively, and the value of n is written in front of the letter to designate the state. Thus the electronic structure of the ground state of the hydrogen atom is given by $1s^1$ which is a shorthand way of saying one electron (superscript) is in the $n = 1$, $l = 0$ orbit. The notation is further illustrated below.

$n = 1$	2	2	3	3	3 $\cdots$ 4
$l = 0$	0	1	0	1	2 $\cdots$ 3
state = $1s$	$2s$	$2p$	$3s$	$3p$	$3d \cdots 4f$

B,9. Qualitative Discussion of Extension of Quantum Mechanics to Atoms Containing More Than One Electron. Although the hydrogen atom represents the limit of the problems for which the Schrödinger equation can be solved exactly, considerable qualitative understanding of more complicated systems can be obtained by analogy with the hydrogen atom.

For example, assume that a more complex atom consists of a nucleus with charge $+Ze$ surrounded by Z electrons moving in the field of the nucleus and attracted to the nucleus by a Coulomb potential. Then one treats the problem as if each electron moved independently of the other electrons in the atom and were influenced only by the average field due to the other electrons and the field due to the nucleus. With these simplifying assumptions, it is now possible to consider the motion of each electron moving in an average central field that can be characterized by an effective nuclear charge Z' and each electron will be in its own state characterized by a hydrogenlike wave function. The electronic eigenfunctions in more complicated systems can still be given in terms of the three quantum numbers n, l, and m, but two electrons with the same n value but different l values will now have different energies. This is because the electron with smaller angular momentum goes closer to the nucleus and the attractive potential is stronger there because the nucleus is less completely screened at this point by the other electrons. Thus for a given n, the states of lowest l have the lowest energy. The m degeneracy still exists in the absence of an external magnetic field.

Many of the properties of atoms can be qualitatively understood from a consideration of the form of the one-electron wave functions given in Eq. 8-25. $\psi^*\psi d\tau$ is the probability of finding the electron in a volume element $d\tau$. This can be interpreted either as the fraction of a chosen time interval that a point electron spends in $d\tau$ or considered as if the electron were smeared out into a diffuse cloud so that the charge density at any point is given by $e\psi^*\psi$ where e is the charge on the electron.

The r-dependent factor of the square of the wave function multiplied by $4\pi r^2$ gives the relative probability of finding the electron at a distance r from the nucleus. The angular distribution of the electrons in a given orbit must also be considered. The angular distribution function varies with the quantum numbers l and m and is independent of the value of n. When $l = 0$, $m = 0$ the electron is said to be in an ns state and will always have spherical symmetry as can be seen from Eq. 8-25. (See Fig. B,9(a).) A $2p$ electron belongs to an orbit designated by the following quantum numbers, $n = 2$, $l = 1$, and $m = -1$, 0, or $+1$. The three values of m represent three independent wave functions. One can represent these three $2p$ wave functions in three mutually perpendicular planes of a Cartesian coordinate system with the nucleus at the origin. The charge distribution of an electron in the p orbitals is best represented by the drawings in Fig. B,9(b). When all three $2p$ orbits are occupied they give a combined electron cloud of spherical symmetry. The charge distributions for other combinations of quantum numbers are given in Fig. B,9(c, d).

Each curve is plotted symmetrically on each side of the vertical axis and the three-dimensional picture of the angular distribution of charge

(a) $l = 0$, s orbital

(b) $l = 1$, p orbitals

(c) $l = 2$, d orbitals

(d) $l = 3$, f orbitals

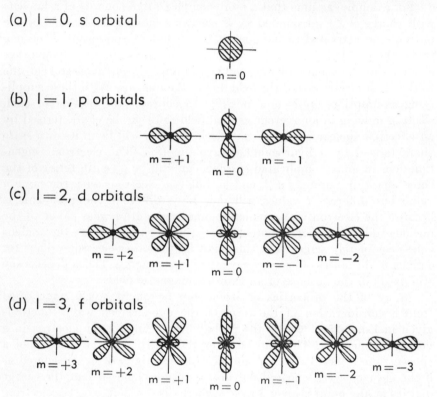

Fig. B,9.   Angular distribution functions for different electronic states of hydrogenlike atoms. After [*24*] by permission.

can be represented by the solid of revolution formed by rotating each figure about its vertical axis. It should be emphasized that the electron is not confined to the shaded area in each figure but the length of the straight line joining the origin and any point on a given curve is a measure of the probability of finding the electron in the direction of that line. The importance of these wave functions becomes apparent in the discussion of molecules in Art. 12.

B,10.   The Pauli Exclusion Principle and the Periodic Table.   In the extension of quantum mechanics to describe atoms containing more than one electron, the mathematical problem becomes too complicated to obtain an exact solution of the Schrödinger equation. However, it is possible to obtain satisfactory quantitative laws for the motion of more than one electron in an atom by introducing an assumption about the distribution of electrons in the allowed orbits about the nucleus which will give agreement with the known experimental evidence. This principle is called the Pauli exclusion principle.

In its simplest form, this principle states that no two electrons can occupy orbits characterized by the same quantum numbers. This means that the necessary and sufficient difference between wave functions which must be fulfilled for the two wave functions to accommodate two electrons is that the two wave functions must be orthogonal. Consider an atom with atomic number Z. This atom consists of a nucleus with charge $+Z$ with the Z electrons moving in hydrogenlike orbits about the nucleus. The z electrons in the atom would thus be expected to fill successively the $1s$, $2s$, $2p_x$, $2p_y$, etc., states where the number of electrons that can simultaneously occupy a single state is restricted by the Pauli exclusion principle. Thus the state characterized by $n = 1$ would accommodate 1 electron and the state $n = 2$ would accommodate 4 electrons, i.e. $2s$, $2p(m = 1)$, $2p(m = -1)$, $2p(m = 0)$, etc. According to this scheme a periodic system of the elements could be built up in which hydrogen formed the first group, helium, lithium, beryllium, and boron would give a second group; but this differs from the well-known periodic classification of the elements developed by the chemists, if one expects that the chemical properties of atoms are due to the configuration of the electrons in the atoms. However, if one assumes that two electrons can occupy each hydrogenlike orbit, then one obtains the chemical periodic table. All electrons having the same value of the total quantum number n are said to belong to the same shell. Electrons with the same n and same l belong to the same subgroup. The periodicity of the chemical properties of elements is due to the fact that the chemical properties of an element are largely determined by the number of electrons in the outermost shell.

As the atoms get more complex, interactions between electrons become important, and some deviations in order from the simple picture occur; however, the correct periodic table can be constructed from spectroscopic data of neutral atoms and their ions (i.e. atoms from which electrons have been removed) along with the changes of electronic configuration in a strong magnetic field as determined by the Zeeman effect. Interpretation of spectroscopic data also requires that at most two electrons occupy the same orbit (and many orbits are actually occupied by two) if the orbits are defined by the three quantum numbers n, l, and m. However, if we define a fourth quantum number s, which can have only two values for electrons, then the Pauli principle is valid and states that no two electrons can have all four quantum numbers n, l, m, and s in common.

B,11. The Electron Spin. It remains to explain the reason for the additional quantum number s. The electron has an internal degree of freedom which must be quantized even after the position (n, l) and momentum (l, m) of the electron have been determined. This internal degree of freedom[9] is due to the angular momentum of the spin of the electron about its own axis. There are only two independent possibilities for s, namely, $\pm\frac{1}{2}$; thus the magnitude of the electronic spin angular momentum of an electron along an arbitrary axis is $\frac{1}{2}(h/2\pi)$. The spin does not greatly influence directly the energy of an electron moving in a given orbit. However, it is of great importance in determining the chemical properties of atoms and their combination with one another to form molecules.

B,12. Formation of Molecules. In principle, quantum mechanics enables one to write down the Schrödinger equation for any system of nuclei and electrons. The exact solution of this equation would then provide a complete description of the equilibrium configuration of the nuclei, the orbits and energies of the electrons, and in general the chemical and physical properties of the system. However, in practice, it is impossible to solve the Schrödinger equation except for a few simple idealized systems. Nevertheless a great deal of qualitative understanding of the combination of atoms to form stable molecules can be achieved by relatively simple considerations of the motion of electrons in the individual atoms as the atoms are moved close enough for the atomic wave functions to overlap. Since the empirical rules of valency, which had been introduced into chemistry to explain the combination of atoms to form molecules, had made possible the formulation of a periodic table almost exactly like the periodic table discussed in the last article on the basis of the electronic structure of the atoms, it was concluded that the electrons in the molecules can be divided into two separate sets, first those which continue to move in the field of the atomic nuclei as if each atom were isolated, and second, the outer shell (valence) electrons which are responsible for the formation of chemical bonds between two or more atoms. When two atoms A and B are brought sufficiently close to each other, the valence electrons from A and the valence electrons from B may interact in such a way as to counteract the Coulomb repulsive forces between the positively charged nuclei and form a stable molecule at some equilibrium position. The way in which electrons can interact to form stable molecules can be made plausible by a consideration of the form of the one-electron wave functions shown in Fig. B,9(a, b, c, and d).

---

[9] Uhlenbeck and Goudsmit [4] had introduced the idea of an intrinsic angular momentum of the electron into classical quantum theory and Stern and Gerlach [2, pp. 159–166] measured the magnitude of the magnetic moment due to spin.

A new assumption is introduced, known as the principle of maximum overlap[10], which can best be illustrated by considering its application to the water molecule [5, pp. 192–194]. Each hydrogen atom is in a $1s$ state; thus the distribution of the electron is spherically symmetric about each hydrogen nucleus. The oxygen atom has an electronic structure $1s^2$, $2s^2$, $2p^4$. The two $1s$ electrons form a closed shell and the two $2s$ electrons form a closed subgroup about the oxygen nucleus but the four $2p$ electrons are distributed as follows: two fill the $2p_z$ orbit, perpendicular to the plane of the paper and do not take part in the binding; one of the remaining electrons moves in the $2p_x$ and one in the $2p_y$ orbit shown in

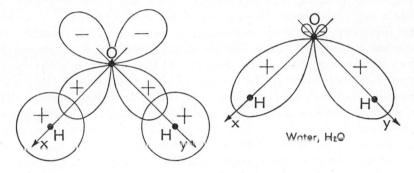

Observed bond angle, 105°

Fig. B,12.   The water molecule. After [5] by permission.

Fig. B,12 and these alone take part in the binding of the water molecule. Now the principle of maximum overlap says the greatest binding energy and thus the most stable configuration is obtained by those electron arrangements which provide the largest negative charge between adjacent nuclei and thereby give the largest attraction. In the water molecule, this is obtained by placing one hydrogen atom along the x axis, and the other along the y axis so that there is maximum overlap of "electron clouds" as shown in Fig. B,12. Thus, the HOH angle in water should be about 90°. Experiment shows this angle to be 105° but here the mixing between the $2s$ and $2p$ orbits and the repulsion between hydrogen atoms has been neglected. Thus the directional properties of the wave functions shown in Fig. B,9(a, b, c, and d) are important and much qualitative information can be obtained about the size and shape of molecules by this type of consideration. Furthermore, the Pauli principle is still valid in molecular orbits formed by the interaction of two atomic orbits, so one can also predict in a qualitative way which combinations of atoms are allowed. For example, one can say two hydrogen atoms combine to form

[10] It is assumed that this is a qualitative description of the results of exact calculations which are too difficult to make.

a stable molecule because the two 1s wave functions in the two independent atoms combine to form a single wave function usually called a σ function which will accommodate two electrons, one with a spin $+\frac{1}{2}$ and one with a spin $-\frac{1}{2}$. On the other hand, two helium atoms do not combine because a single helium atom has two electrons in its 1s shell and so because of the Pauli principle, when two helium atoms are brought near to each other, neither can allow another electron in its orbit $n = 1$. Thus helium exists as a very stable monatomic substance.[11]

B,13. Structure of Molecules. Because of the complexity of the many-body problem, approximation methods had to be developed. To obtain any quantitative description of the energy states of molecules one important assumption is nearly always made which simplifies the problem considerably. Since the nuclei are relatively so much heavier than the electrons, the nuclear masses and the electron motions can be treated independently; so the motions of all the electrons are calculated assuming that the nuclei remain fixed in their equilibrium positions. The equilibrium positions and nuclear configuration can often be determined experimentally from spectra or by electron diffraction experiments. Then the motion of the nuclei is calculated assuming that they move in the field of an average steady state motion of the electrons. In this way one can write two independent Schrödinger equations, one for the electronic motions and one for the nuclear motions.

Two main approximation methods for the solution of the electronic motions of molecules have been developed. They are the Heitler-London-Slater-Pauling (HLSP)[12] method developed by the men for whom it is named and the molecular orbital (M.O.)[13] method of Lennard-Jones, Hund, Herzberg, and Mulliken.

It is beyond the scope of this book to give more than a qualitative idea of the quantum mechanics description of the structure of molecules.

The HLSP method starts with each electron moving in the spherically symmetric field of its own nucleus and then attempts to calculate the

[11] However, it is possible to form the He_2 molecule by exciting one electron into a 2s state; but this requires much energy.

[12] The HLSP approach has been widely used by chemists in formulating a theoretical basis for the chemical properties of compounds; [6] makes extensive use of this method. Craig [7] and Coulson [8] have used this method extensively in recent years but it is rapidly being replaced by the M.O. (molecular orbital) method.

[13] This method has been more successful in explaining the spectra of molecules but due to the greater mathematical complexity has been slow in developing. However, in the last five years due to the work of Mulliken and his coworkers [9] and independently of Lennard-Jones [10] and Coulson and his coworkers, extensive progress has been made in the development of the molecular orbital method. It appears that this method will be superior to the HLSP in calculating the properties of molecules making use of a minimum number of approximations and empirical facts. An excellent comparison of the M.O. and HLSP methods in their primitive form is given in [11].

interaction between the electrons as the nuclei are brought near to each other. Two definite electrons are assigned to each single bond, four to each double bond, etc. The M.O. method assumes that the nuclei are rigidly held in some equilibrium position and then feeds the electrons into the field of the entire molecule one by one. Every electron is considered as belonging, in principle, to the molecule as a whole. Up until the present time such drastic simplifications were necessary before the mathematical problem could be solved that only a few very simple molecules have been treated. However, present developments in the field give some promise that more theoretical calculations may be feasible in the near future (see [7,8,9,10,12,13]).

At present one must depend upon the spectra of polyatomic molecules and chemical properties to get even a roughly quantitative picture of their electronic structure. The electrons in molecules can be roughly ascribed to three classes. The most tightly bound electrons which form the inner shells in the free atoms are still essentially bound to a particular atomic nucleus and will take little or no part in binding the atoms in the molecule. If such an electron is excited, the resulting spectra will be like atomic spectra and will often be in the high energy (far ultraviolet) range of the spectrum. The next less energetic electrons are the so-called localized electrons which are shared between two nuclei but seldom move out of the range of these two nuclei. These electrons, if in pairs with opposite spin, are responsible for the single bonds between two atoms; but if these electron pairs have parallel spins, they may be antibonding in which case they will weaken bonds formed by other electrons between the same atoms. Finally, molecules contain weakly bound electrons which are sometimes called mobile electrons because they do not belong to any atom or isolated group of atoms but move through the entire molecule. These are analogous to the valence electrons in atoms and are responsible for some of the characteristic chemical properties of the molecule as well as the characteristic electronic spectra of many molecules.

The nuclear motions of molecules can be described in terms of the following Schrödinger equation

$$\sum_{i=1}^{N} \frac{1}{m_i} (\nabla_i^2 \psi) + \frac{8\pi^2}{h^2} [E - V]\psi = 0 \qquad (13\text{-}1)$$

where ψ is the wave function, E = the total energy, V = potential energy function averaged over the electron wave functions, m_i = mass of the nucleus, N = total number of atoms in the molecules, ∇_i^2 = Laplacian in Cartesian coordinates. The evaluation of $V(x_1, y_1, z_1, \ldots, x_N, y_N, z_N)$ by theoretical means requires a knowledge of the average field between adjacent nuclei due to the motions of the electrons. Thus far very little completely theoretical work has been done but the following treatment in combination with experiment has been one of the most reliable sources of information concerning the structure of polyatomic molecules. One assumes that the potential energy of the nuclei in the molecule is equal to zero for some equilibrium position for each atom. Then if one allows only small displacements of each nucleus from its equilibrium position one can treat the molecule as if it consisted of N oscillators tied to their equilibrium positions by springs with force constant k_{ii} and coupled to each other by springs with force constants k_{ij}. If one makes this assumption the mathematics is identical with the mathematics of coupled oscillators and it is usually possible to introduce $3N$ normal coordinates ξ_i in the place of the $3N$ Cartesian coordinates in Eq. 13-1. Furthermore, the wave function $\psi(x_1, y_1, z_1, \ldots)$ can be replaced by $\psi_1(\xi_1)\psi_2(\xi_2) \ldots \psi_i(\xi_i) \ldots \psi_{3N}(\xi_{3N})$. With these substitutions Eq. 13-1 can be resolved into a sum of $3N$ equations

$$\frac{1}{\psi_i}\frac{\partial^2 \psi_i}{\partial \xi_i^2} + \frac{8\pi^2}{h^2}\left[E_i - \frac{1}{2}\lambda_i\xi_i^2\right] = 0 \qquad (13\text{-}2)$$

with $E = E_1 + E_2 \cdots E_i + \cdots E_{3N}$. But Eq. 13-2 is exactly like Eq. 8-5 of the simple harmonic oscillator. Thus the vibrational motion of the molecule may be considered to a good approximation as a superposition of simple harmonic motions in the $3N$ normal coordinates. The only difference between this and the classical oscillator problem is that the allowed energy values E_i are quantized and have a zero-point energy as was shown in the case of the oscillator. Thus

$$E = h\nu_1(n_1 + \tfrac{1}{2}) + h\nu_2(n_2 + \tfrac{1}{2}) \cdots h\nu_{3N}(n_{3N} + \tfrac{1}{2}) \qquad (13\text{-}3)$$

where ν_i's are the classical vibration frequencies and are the roots of the $3N$ equations of Eq. 13-2 solved simultaneously. For a nonlinear molecule six of these vibrations (for a linear molecule, five) are "nongenuine vibrations" (i.e. translations and rotations) and thus have a zero frequency and do not contribute to the vibrational energy. Thus there are $3N - 6$ genuine normal vibrations to be determined for each molecule ($3N - 5$ for linear molecules). These six (or five for linear molecules) coordinates can be separated out and one determines then another independent Schrödinger equation for the three translational degrees of freedom of the center of mass of the molecule; this will give an equation like Eq. 8-1 with continuous eigenvalues, i.e. continuous range of values of the translational energy of the molecules. These are of no interest in the structure of the molecule but are important in the treatment of the macroscopic properties of an aggregate of molecules such as discussed in statistical mechanics. Another equation can be written for the rotational motion of a polyatomic molecule. If the coordinates are properly chosen, the rotational motion can be represented by three equations (two, for linear molecules) like Eq. 8-14 where the three mutually perpendicular axes are chosen so that the moment of inertia (I_A) about one is a maximum, the moment of inertia about another (I_C) is a minimum and the moment of inertia about a third (I_B) is intermediate between I_A and I_C. (These are the principal axes of a rigid body.) For a linear molecule the rotational energy is given by Eq. 8-18

$$E_r = \frac{h^2}{8\pi^2 I}[j(j+1)] \tag{13-4}$$

where I is the moment of inertia about a point through the center of mass of the molecule and perpendicular to the molecule. The energy terms are a little more complicated for other more complicated molecules but have been solved and can be found in [14].

This is only a first approximation and in practice there is often interaction between rotation and vibration, but a large number of molecules have been studied and even these interactions and anharmonicities can be taken into account for a particular molecule. The rotational frequencies can be measured in the rotational infrared spectrum for non-symmetric molecules. These experimental values combined with the calculation of the principal axes usually enable one to get a pretty good idea of the interatomic distances. Recent measurements in microwave spectroscopy [15] have given a very accurate means of determining interatomic distances in many molecules.

The vibrational frequencies are more complicated. One is entirely dependent on experiment to determine the frequencies or the potential function. All of the fundamental frequencies do not always occur in the Raman and infrared spectra; there are more force constants in the potential energy equation than there are frequencies, so it is impossible to determine the potential energy function even when all the frequencies are known. However, there are often only a few possible structures consistent with the known chemical composition of a given molecule. Molecules with the same symmetry have similar Raman and infrared spectra. If the geometric configuration of a molecule is known it is possible to calculate the forms of the normal vibrations, and predict which one will occur in the Raman and which ones will occur in the infrared. For example, if the same frequency occurs in both the Raman and infrared spectra, the molecule can have no center of symmetry. Thus by a combination of calculations, experiments, and judicious guessing based on experience, one can usually determine the probable configuration of any given molecule that does not contain too many atoms.

It should be observed that most of the experimental methods, as well as the simplifying assumptions which make these methods useful in determining the structure of molecules, are restricted to the vapor state

Thus, the molecular energy levels can be divided into rotational, vibrational, and electronic levels whose relative order of magnitude can be roughly estimated in the following way. Suppose the molecule has a length of the order l. Therefore if an electron moves throughout an entire molecule with a characteristic length l then

$$\Delta p l \sim \frac{h}{2\pi}$$

$$\Delta p \sim \frac{h}{2\pi l}$$

$$E_e \sim \frac{\overline{\Delta p}^2}{2m} \sim \frac{h^2}{8\pi^2 l^2 m} \tag{13-5}$$

For l = a few angstroms, $E_e \sim$ transitions in the visible and ultraviolet spectrum. The energy associated with a normal vibration of a molecule can be estimated using Eq. 8-10

$$E_v{}' = h \left(n + \frac{1}{2} \right) \nu \sim h\nu$$

but $\nu = \sqrt{K/M}$ where K is the stiffness constant and M is of the order of the mass of a nucleus. If the displacement of the nuclei in a vibration were of the order of magnitude l, the electronic wave function would be seriously distorted and this would require

$$E_e \sim K_0 l^2 \quad \text{or} \quad K_0 \sim \frac{E_e}{l^2} \tag{13-6}$$

Thus

$$E_v \sim h \sqrt{\frac{E_e}{Ml^2}} \sim \left(\frac{m}{M} \right)^{\frac{1}{2}} E_e \tag{13-7}$$

The rotational energy can be estimated from Eq. 13-4 and 13-5:

$$E_r \sim \frac{h^2}{8\pi M a^2} \sim \frac{m}{M} E_r, \quad \left(\frac{m}{M} \right)^{\frac{1}{2}} \sim 10^{-2} \quad \text{and} \quad \frac{m}{M} \sim 10^{-4}$$

thus the vibrational energy is about $\frac{1}{100}$ of the electronic energy and the rotational energy is about $\frac{1}{100}$ of the vibrational energy. It is this different order of magnitude of the energies that makes it possible to consider the different internal degrees of freedom separately. However, the electronic spectra show not only electronic states but have superposed on the electronic states, the vibrational and rotational energies. This is the reason why the electronic spectra of molecules are wide bands while the electronic spectra of atoms which have no rotational or vibrational degrees of freedom are sharp line spectra.

CHAPTER 2. BOND ENERGIES
KARL F. HERZFELD
VIRGINIA GRIFFING

B,14. Introduction. Spectroscopic and Thermal Methods. With the knowledge that the atoms consist of positively charged nuclei surrounded by electrons it was first believed that molecules were held together by simple electrostatic forces between positively and negatively charged ions (polar bonds). It was assumed that certain elements had a tendency to gain extra electrons while others lost electrons easily and these combined to form stable molecules. Although this picture was adequate to explain the stability of many molecules, it gave no explanation for the existence of molecules consisting of two or more like atoms held together by strong chemical bonds (covalent bonds). It was in the development of quantum mechanics and the explanation of the periodic table of the elements that chemistry and physics merged their points of view in an attempt to understand more completely the structure of molecules. Quantum mechanics shows that chemical bond formation is the result of a profound rearrangement of electronic structure when two or more atoms are brought together, and gives a qualitative understanding of valency and bond formation; similarly, quantum mechanics has shown that molecules may exist only in certain permitted energy states and the transition from one to another is accompanied by the absorption or emission of energy. Ideally, a theory of molecular structure would enable one to determine the energy of formation of a molecule as a function of all variations in size and shape. Then, the coordinates for which this function has a minimum would give the stable configuration of the molecule. The difference between the value of this function at the minimum and the value for the atoms infinitely separated from one another would give the binding energy. Quantum mechanics, in principle, enables one to calculate this, but in practice, as has already been shown, the mathematical difficulties are too great and one must turn to experimental methods for the quantitative determination of bond energies and binding energies in molecules. The two primary sources of experimental data used in the determination of bond energies are spectroscopic and thermodynamic data. The sources of these data and their use in estimating bond energies are discussed in this chapter.

Thermal methods differ from spectroscopic methods in that thermochemical measurements are made on substances in bulk, at room temperature, or higher, and are then reduced to a standard temperature, usually 25°C. Since spectroscopy deals almost entirely with atoms and molecules in the free gaseous state, the energies determined in this way are at 0°K and zero pressure. Thermochemical measurements ordinarily involve matter in the liquid and solid state as well as the gaseous state. It is customary to reduce all thermochemical data to give energies for reactions between chemical substances in the "standard state." The "standard state" is defined as the state in which a substance normally exists at 25°C and one atmosphere pressure; e.g. nitrogen (N_2) and oxygen (O_2) are gases and water (H_2O) is a liquid. In some cases it is necessary to specify the allotropic form used as standard state if the substance exists in more than one form at the reference temperature. Carbon is one of the important substances for which a choice must be made as it exists as both diamond and graphite at 1 atmosphere and 25°C.[14] Thus in order to compare bond energies determined by thermochemical means with those determined from spectroscopic data, it is necessary to determine the energy needed to change a substance from a free gas at 0°K to its standard state at 25°C. Usually, spectroscopic values refer to the energy per molecule and must be multiplied by the Avogadro number to determine the energy per mole. Thermal measurements are usually made on arbitrarily chosen samples and must also be calculated for a mole. One can change the thermochemical value of the dissociation energy of a substance in its solid state at temperature T_1, to the value one would obtain for one mole of gaseous molecules at zero pressure and 0°K by the following thermodynamic relationship (see Sec. A)

$$H^g (0°K) = H^s_{T_1} \text{ (experimental value)} + \int_{T_1}^{T_f} C^s_p dT$$
$$+ \int_{T_f}^{T_v} C^l_p dT + \int_{T_v}^{0°K} C^g_p dT + L_f + L_v \quad (14\text{-}1)$$

where C^s_p, C^l_p, C^g_p are the molar specific heats at constant pressure for the solid, liquid, and gas, respectively; L_f and L_v are the latent heats of fusion and vaporization respectively and T_f and T_v are the freezing points and boiling points; $H^s_{T_1}$ is the experimentally determined heat of dissociation at constant pressure and temperature T_1.

Dissociation energies are large compared to specific heat terms; one need not have very accurate values of C_p but latent heats are of the same order of magnitude as the quantities being measured and thus accurate values are necessary when the reaction involves a change of phase. If the reaction does not involve a change of phase, one can use, for a change in H from 0° to 298°K, 5 kcal/mole for a monatomic gas and up to about 8 kcal/mole for a polyatomic gas. Since bond energies are of the order of 100 kcal/mole, the errors introduced by using these values are relatively insignificant. For this discussion, it is convenient to consider diatomic molecules and polyatomic molecules separately.

---

[14] References [16] are very useful compendiums of numerical results of thermochemical measurements and are invaluable in making thermochemical calculations.

B,15. Diatomic Molecules. In diatomic molecules, it is possible to give a rigorous definition of bond energy in terms of quantities that can often be determined experimentally. The bond energy of a diatomic molecule A—B is the energy that must be supplied to the molecule A—B in order to dissociate it completely into two neutral atoms A and B in their ground electronic states; both the molecule and the atoms should be at zero pressure and 0°K.

The most direct way of determining the bond energy is from the dissociation limits of the characteristic spectra of the molecule. The absorption spectrum is obtained when light possessing a continuous spectrum is passed through the substance, usually in the gaseous state. The molecule absorbs the characteristic frequencies of the molecule. The molecules may be excited by some other means, such as an electric discharge, and the excitation energy is emitted in the form of an emission spectrum. As has already been shown, the energy associated with the absorbed or emitted radiations can be obtained from the measured frequencies by the following relation

$$E_2 - E_1 = h\nu \tag{15-1}$$

The characteristic spectra of a diatomic molecule are simple band series which can be completely described in terms of three quantum numbers, namely, the rotational quantum number j, the vibrational quantum number v, and the electronic quantum number n. The bonding energy of a molecule is different for different electronic states of the molecule but at ordinary temperatures all the molecules are in the ground electronic state. Hence this is the state for which the bond energy is most important. The equilibrium internuclear distance can be determined from the rotational spectrum as shown in Chap. 1. The vibrational energy of a diatomic molecule can be represented in a potential energy curve such as that plotted in Fig. B,15 for H_2. If one assumes simple harmonic forces, the vibrational energy levels are given by

$$E = (n + \tfrac{1}{2})h\nu \tag{15-2}$$

However, as the molecule is stretched far from its equilibrium position, the frequency ν changes, the levels are no longer spaced equally, and Eq. 15-2 must be replaced by

$$E_n = (n + \tfrac{1}{2})h\nu - (n + \tfrac{1}{2})^2\alpha h\nu \tag{15-3}$$

where α is called the anharmonicity constant and must be experimentally determined from the vibration-rotation spectrum of the molecule. There have been many attempts to represent this type of potential energy-internuclear distance relationships by analytic expressions. The most satisfactory, because of its relative simplicity combined with a fairly good representation of the dependence of the potential energy of binding on the internuclear distance, is the following equation due to Morse:

$$V = D_e[1 - e^{-2\beta(r-r_e)}]^2 \tag{15-4}$$

where

$$\beta = \omega_e \sqrt{\frac{\pi^2 c \mu}{2hD_e}}$$

ω_e is the characteristic vibration frequency in cm^{-1}, μ is the reduced mass in atomic weight units, c and h are the velocity of light and Planck's constant. D_e is the dissociation energy measured from the minimum of

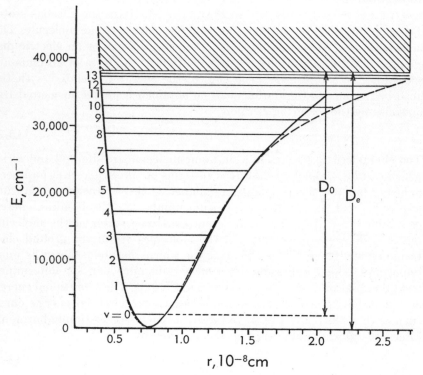

Fig. B,15. Potential curve of the H_2 ground state with vibrational levels and continuous term spectrum. The broken curve is the Morse curve. After [17] by permission.

the potential energy curve in cm^{-1}. In Fig. B,15 the full curve is drawn from spectroscopic data and the broken curve is the Morse curve. The cross-hatched space above the curve represents the continuous spectrum that results from the translational kinetic energy of the atoms which is no longer quantized once the bond is broken. Thus the dissociation energy is the energy necessary to just separate the molecule into free atoms and leave them with zero velocity at the asymptote of the converging vibrational levels. This is the same energy that was defined above as the bond energy. The spectra of over two hundred and fifty diatomic molecules have been studied and this material has been thoroughly reviewed and critically evaluated in two recently published books [17,18]. Although spectroscopic data are very important, it should be emphasized that they are often difficult to interpret and there is considerable disagreement among various observers for some important molecules. Thus according to recent evaluations [17,18] the dissociation energies of only about fifty diatomic molecules have been unambiguously determined.

The most direct thermochemical method of measuring the dissociation energy is to determine the equilibrium conditions for the dissociation

$$AB \rightleftharpoons A + B$$

Then, the equilibrium constant K, which is a function of the temperature only, is given by

$$K = \frac{p_A p_B}{p_{AB}} \qquad (15\text{-}5)$$

where p_A, p_B, and p_{AB} are the partial pressures of the three gases assumed ideal. If K is determined as a function of temperature, one can calculate the dissociation energy according to the following thermodynamic equation due to Van't Hoff (see Sec. A),

$$\frac{d \ln K}{dT} = -\frac{\Delta H}{R} \qquad (15\text{-}6)$$

This value must then be converted to 0°K as discussed above.

The equilibrium constant, instead of its change with temperature, can be used directly for the determination of ΔH at 0°K if sufficient data are available. ΔH can be calculated according to the following equation from statistical mechanics

$$\ln K = \frac{\Delta H_0}{RT} + \ln \left[\mu_A^{\frac{3}{2}} \frac{\sigma}{10^{40} I} \left(\frac{T}{100} \right)^{\frac{3}{2}} \right] - \ln (1 - e^{-\theta/T})$$
$$+ \ln \frac{\nu_A \nu_B}{\nu_{AB}} + 6.94 \qquad (15\text{-}7)$$

where K is the equilibrium constant in atmospheres; μ_A is the reduced mass in atomic weight units; I is the moment of inertia of the molecule AB in g/cm²; $\theta = \omega h c / k$ is the characteristic temperature related to the fundamental vibration frequency; ν_A, ν_B, and ν_{AB} are the electronic statistical weights; σ is the symmetry number which is 2 for homonuclear diatomic molecules and 1 otherwise. I, θ, and the electronic statistical weights are determined from spectroscopic data. Eq. 15-6 and 15-7 both assume ideal gases; since these experiments are often conducted at high temperatures it is usually satisfactory to make this assumption. In addition, Eq. 15-7 assumes:

1. Temperature high enough to neglect effects of nuclear spin
2. Temperature high enough for rotational degrees of freedom to be treated classically
3. Neglect of interaction between vibrational and rotational degrees of freedom
4. The molecule to be a harmonic oscillator, i.e. anharmonic terms are neglected
5. The energy difference between the ground and first excited electronic state to be large compared to kT

The errors introduced by the first three assumptions are slight and Eq. 15-7 can be modified to take 4 and 5 into consideration if sufficient experimental data are available. The principles upon which Eq. 15-7 depends are discussed in the chapter on statistical mechanics (Chap. 5). In some cases, due to experimental difficulties, K may be the equilibrium constant for some reaction other than the direct dissociation of the molecule. In this case, Eq. 15-7 is replaced by a more complicated expression for the partition functions in order to determine the dissociation energy.

The dissociation energy of some diatomic molecule can be determined calorimetrically by combining thermochemical measurements of heats of formation with known values of other dissociation energies. For example, from the calorimetric determination of the heat of formation of NO from N_2 and O_2, combined with dissociation energy of N_2 and O_2 from spectroscopic measurements, one can calculate the dissociation energy of NO. The dissociation energy of NO is equal to the heat of formation of NO from N_2 and O_2, under standard conditions, minus the dissociation energies of N_2 and O_2. It is much simpler if all the substances are gases but this method can still be used for substances in the liquid or solid state if latent heats are known. For example, consider one of the alkali halides such as sodium chloride (NaCl). One would use the following Born-Fajans-Haber cycle:

$$\mathrm{Na + Cl} \longleftarrow L_s(\mathrm{Na}) + \tfrac{1}{2}D(\mathrm{Cl_2}) \longrightarrow \mathrm{Na_{solid}} + \tfrac{1}{2}\mathrm{Cl_2}$$

$$D(\mathrm{NaCl}) \uparrow \qquad\qquad\qquad\qquad\qquad Q(\text{formation NaCl}) \downarrow$$

$$\mathrm{NaCl_{gas}} \longleftarrow L_s(\mathrm{NaCl}) \longrightarrow \mathrm{NaCl_{solid}}$$

where $L_s(\mathrm{X})$ means heat of sublimation of atoms or molecules X, and Q is a measured heat of formation; $D(\mathrm{NaCl})$ is the dissociation energy of NaCl. Thus

$$D(\mathrm{NaCl})_{gas} = L_s(\mathrm{Na}) + \tfrac{1}{2}D(\mathrm{Cl_2}) + Q(\mathrm{NaCl}) - L_s(\mathrm{NaCl})$$

This value would, of course, have to be reduced to zero pressure and 0°K. This method is dependent on the principle (conservation of energy) that any arbitrarily chosen path of reaction which leads to dissociation must give the same value for the dissociation energy. In Table B,15 is given a list of dissociation energies of common diatomic molecules. In general, for diatomic molecules, when it is possible to determine the dissociation energy spectroscopically, this value is more accurate than dissociation energies of molecules determined by thermal methods. Of course, it is better if one can determine these dissociation energies by thermal and spectroscopic methods and use the thermal method simply as a check.

Table B,15

Molecule	D, kcal	Molecule	D, kcal
H—H	104.1	O—O	117.20
F—F	63.5	N—N	225.1*
Cl—Cl	58.1	C—O	256.1*
Br—Br	46.3	C—C	83*
I—I	36.4	C—N	175*
Li—Li	27.2	N—O	150
Na—Na	18.5	S—S	101
K—K	12.8		

    * Doubtful.

B,16. Polyatomic Molecules. There are several different quantities which have in the past been called bond energies; some confusion has been caused by the failure to distinguish between them. Szwarc and Evans [19] have pointed out that two quantities should be considered, the bond dissociation energy and the average bond energy (the two are identical in diatomic molecules). In polyatomic molecules the bond dissociation energy is susceptible to direct experimental measurement, whereas the average bond energy is a calculated quantity obtained from the heat of atomization. This latter is the heat necessary to dissociate completely the molecule into the atoms, all in their electronic ground state, at 0°K.

This heat of atomization may be found in the following manner: Assume the tables give the heat of formation of a molecule A_2B from the elements as $-\Delta H^{(1)}$

$$(A_2B)_{gas} \rightarrow (A_2)_{gas} + (B)_{solid} - \Delta H^{(1)} \qquad (16\text{-}1)$$

To atomize A_2B one has also to write

$$(A_2)_{gas} \rightarrow 2(A)_{gas} - \Delta H^{(2)} \qquad (16\text{-}2)$$

$\Delta H^{(2)}$ is the heat of dissociation of gaseous A_2.

$$(B)_{solid} \rightarrow (B)_{gas} - \Delta H^{(3)} \qquad (16\text{-}3)$$

$\Delta H^{(3)}$ is the heat of sublimation. Then

$$\text{heat of atomization} = \Delta H^{(1)} + \Delta H^{(2)} + \Delta H^{(3)} \qquad (16\text{-}4)$$

⟨ 153 ⟩

While the heats of formation are often measured accurately, those of dissociation and particularly those of sublimation (particularly in the case of carbon) are often uncertain.

The bond dissociation energy may be defined for a bond between two fragments of a polyatomic molecule M—N in an analogous fashion to the dissociation energy of a diatomic molecule. Thus the energy in the bond between the fragment M and the fragment N is the energy necessary to separate the two fragments if one assumes that the original molecule MN and the fragments M and N are in the gaseous phase at zero pressure and 0°K. However, during this process, other bonds may be weakened or strengthened, new bonds may be formed, and electronic states of the atoms may be changed. All these effects are included in the bond dissociation energy.

The sum of the bond dissociation energies must be equal to the heat of atomization of the molecule. This relationship between these quantities can be best illustrated by an example. Consider the water molecule which has a heat of atomization per mole of 218 kcal. Since the reaction

$$H_2O \rightarrow O + 2H$$

requires the breaking of two O—H bonds, the "average bond energy" (see below) of the O—H bond in water is 109 kcal/mole. However, the bond dissociation energy of the first O—H bond in water is 118 kcal/mole, i.e.

$$H_2O \rightarrow H + OH - [D(H—OH) = 118 \text{ kcal/mole}]$$

$$OH \rightarrow O + H - [D(O—H) = 100 \text{ kcal/mole}]$$

This means that the removal of the first H atom has weakened the remaining OH bond. Thus it is obvious that like bonds do not have the same dissociation energy but are dependent on the fragments of the dissociation process. In general in a molecule ABC (e.g. HCN) the bond energy for the AB bond, i.e. the process $ABC \rightarrow A + BC$, may be D_1 that for the bond BC in that fragment, i.e. for $BC \rightarrow B + C$, is D_2. D_2 may be different from D_3, the energy of the process $ABC \rightarrow AB + C$, $AB \rightarrow A + B$ needs D_4, different from D_1. But

$$D_1 + D_2 = D_3 + D_4 = \text{heat of atomization}$$

if the atoms end up in the same state in both procedures.

The bond dissociation energy may in principle be determined as follows:

1. Spectroscopically. This, however, is in general impossible at present, due to the complexity of the spectra of polyatomic molecules.

2. Thermodynamically. If the equilibrium concentration (and its temperature dependence) of the fragments can be measured, then Eq. 15-6 applies here also.

3. Rate measurements. As shown in Art. 18, the temperature coefficient of a rate constant is determined by the so-called heat of activation which can be found from the measurement of the rate.

Furthermore, from the first law of thermodynamics

heat of activation (decomposition) − heat of activation
$$\text{(recombination)} = \text{bond dissociation energy}$$

If one assumes that the heat of activation for the recombination is zero, then the bond dissociation energy is equal to the heat of activation of the decomposition. An example is given in a paper by Szwarc [20]. Szwarc studies the rate of decomposition of a molecule into two radicals. The principal experimental problem is to eliminate the radicals formed in the decomposition before they have time to recombine or initiate other reactions making the kinetics complicated. He solves this problem by using a large excess of toluene as a carrier gas. Many radicals react instantly with the toluene according to the equation

$$C_6H_5CH_3 + R \rightarrow C_6H_5CH_2 + RH \qquad (16\text{-}5$$

and resulting benzyl radicals survive long enough to escape from the zone of reaction, eventually forming dibenzyl. Thus the rate of the unimolecular decomposition $R_1R_2 \rightarrow R_1 + R_2$ can be measured by the rate of formation of either R_1H, R_2H, or dibenzyl. This technique has been used for measuring the heats of the following bond dissociations:

(i) $C_6H_5CH_2CH_3 \rightarrow C_6H_5CH_2 + CH_3$ (63.0 kcal/mole)
(ii) $C_6H_5CH_2Br \quad \rightarrow C_6H_5CH_2 + Br \quad$ (50.0 "   ")
(iii) $C_6H_5CH_3 \qquad \rightarrow C_6H_5CH_2 + H \quad$ (77.5 "   ")
(iv) $N_2H_4 \qquad\qquad \rightarrow 2NH_2 \qquad\qquad$ (60   "   ")

In the first three of these reactions the heats of formation of the species concerned, except the benzyl radical, are all known from other sources. Therefore, the heat of formation of the benzyl radical can be calculated from any one of the three bond dissociation energies, and the concordance of the results provides a valuable cross check on the measured bond dissociation energies.

Similarly, if the heat of formation of the radicals is known from an independent experiment, one can calculate the bond dissociation energy, if the heat of formation of the compound is also known, e.g. the dissociation energy of the N—N bond in hydrazine (N_2H_4) is 60 kcal. The heat of formation of gaseous hydrazine from the elements in their standard state is 22 kcal/mole; thus one obtains the heat of formation of NH_2 radical as 41 kcal/mole, i.e.

$$\Delta H_f(NH_2) = \tfrac{1}{2}\{[\Delta H_f(N_2H_4) + D(NH_2\text{—}NH_2)]\}$$
$$= 41 \text{ kcal/mole} \qquad (16\text{-}6)$$

Szwarc [20] shows how, by using this value for the heat of formation of hydrazine, the dissociation energy of hydrogen (H_2), and the heat of formation of NH_3, one can calculate the bond dissociation energy of the first N—H bond in NH_3. This bond energy can be calculated according to the following equation which is simply an application of the first law of thermodynamics:

$$D(NH_2\text{—}H) = \Delta H_f(NH_2) + \tfrac{1}{2}D(H\text{—}H) - \Delta H_f(NH_3)$$

$$D(NH_2\text{—}H) = 41 + 52 + 11 = 104 \text{ kcal/mole} \qquad (16\text{-}7)$$

One can calculate, according to this method, bond dissociation energies even if the rate of breaking the bond cannot be measured directly.[15]

The relationships between the bond dissociation energy and the heat of reaction have been used ingeniously by Kistiakowsky and Van Artsdalen [*21*] to determine the bond dissociation energy of the first C—H bond in methane (CH_4). The principle involved is again an application of the first law of thermodynamics. Given a reaction of the type,

$$RA + B \rightarrow R + AB$$

then

$$\sum \text{dissociation energies of bonds formed} - \sum \text{dissociation}$$

energies of bonds broken is equal to heat of reaction

Thus

$$D(R\text{—}A) = D(A\text{—}B) - \text{heat of the reaction}$$

Kistiakowsky determined the heat of reaction:

$$CH_4 + Br \rightarrow CH_3 + HBr - 16 \text{ kcal/mole}$$

at 453°K. Recalculating the value of ΔH to 0°K, he obtained $\Delta H_0^0 = 15$ kcal/mole. Then applying the above principle and using a value for $D(H\text{—}Br)$ as 85.8 kcal/mole he concluded:

$$D(CH_3\text{—}H) = D(H\text{—}Br) + 15 \text{ kcal/mole} = 101 \text{ kcal/mole}$$

The average bond energy is most directly defined for molecules which have only one kind of bond, e.g. in a molecule AX_n where all the atoms X are in symmetric positions, the heat of atomization refers to the process:

$$AX_n \rightarrow A + nX$$

and is set equal to n times the average energy of the A—X bond. Or the heat of atomization of $H_3C\text{—}(CH_2)_2\text{—}CH_3$ is set equal to 3 times the average bond energy of a C—C bond plus 10 times the average bond energy of a C—H bond.

The calculation of the average bond energy is therefore based entirely on the experimental determination of the heat of atomization, discussed previously.

---

[15] Other examples of the measurement of bond dissociation energies are discussed in [*20*].

The average bond energy is usually not equal to the bond dissociation energy of any particular bond in the molecule as exemplified in the above by H_2O. The average bond energy would be the energy required to rupture an A—X bond in an idealized experiment in which all the other bonds are extended to infinity while the molecule maintains its original geometric form. However, the sum of the average bond energies and the sum of the bond dissociation energies are equal to each other and are equal to the heats of atomization of the molecule.

The concept of average bond energy is particularly useful for groups of molecules for which one can assume (1) that the bond energy of a given bond is the same in all molecules in which the same combination of atoms appears and (2) that bond energies are additive.

The validity of these assumptions can be experimentally established for molecules which contain only normal single bonds, i.e. a bond localized between two atoms in which the wave functions of two-paired electrons[16] —one from each atom—thoroughly overlap. To find the average bond energies in molecules which contain two different kinds of bonds, one has to assume that these have the same values in at least two molecules of a homologous series, e.g.

heat of atomization of C_2H_6 = 1 average bond energy of a C—C bond plus 6 average bond energies of C—H bond

heat of atomization of C_3H_8 = 2 average bond energies of C—C bonds plus 8 average bond energies of C—H bond

The assumption may be tested by using the data for more than two molecules and has been confirmed by Prosen, Johnson, and Rossini [*22*]. The increment per CH_2 group becomes constant after the second or third member of a number of homologous series.

Even for single bonds there are significant deviations from the constant value for a given bond if that bond exists in a markedly different environment such that the angles are different from the normal configuration. In such cases, also, the bond lengths differ appreciably. This is particularly evident in the consideration of isomers, which are molecules containing the same number of like bonds but the chains are now branched rather than straight, e.g. the experimentally determined heat of formation of butane,

$$
\begin{array}{ccccc}
 & H & H & H & H \\
 & | & | & | & | \\
H- & C- & C- & C- & C- H \\
 & | & | & | & | \\
 & H & H & H & H
\end{array}
$$

[16] If the resultant spin of two electrons is zero, they are called "paired electrons."

is 1044.8 kcal/mole while the heat of formation of isobutane

$$
\begin{array}{ccc}
 & \mathrm{H} & \\
 & | & \\
\mathrm{H} & \mathrm{H-\!C-\!H} & \\
| & | & \\
\mathrm{H-\!C} & \quad\quad \mathrm{C-\!H} & \\
| & | & \\
\mathrm{H} & \mathrm{H-\!C-\!H} & \\
 & | & \\
 & \mathrm{H} &
\end{array}
$$

is 1046.4 kcal/mole.

These deviations are probably due primarily to a difference in the C—H bond energies since it has long been known in hydrocarbon chemistry that there is a difference in the reactivity of C—H bonds depending on the position in the chain. For example, it has been shown by E. W. R. Steacie [23] that the relative attack of alkyl radicals on primary, secondary, and tertiary hydrogen atoms is 1:3:4. Primary, secondary, and tertiary hydrogen atoms are hydrogen atoms attached to carbon atoms which are also bonded, respectively, to two, one, or no additional hydrogen atoms. However, these bonds can be treated as different bonds in order to allow for these deviations in numerical calculations.

Table B,16. After [24] by permission.

Molecule	C—C—C bond angle, degrees	C—C bond energy, kcal
Straight chain hydrocarbon	111	62.8
	(Normal tetrahedral angle)	
Cyclopropane	60	50.8
Cyclobutane	90	51.8
Cyclopentane	108	60.0
Cyclohexane	111	61.0

Another significant deviation from single bond constancy is exhibited by so-called "strained molecules," i.e. molecules for which the usual valence bond angles are distorted. These deviations are illustrated in Table B,16 and are due to the fact that the bonding orbitals do not overlap to the maximum extent.

Next, one must also consider multiple bonds.

Isolated double and triple bonds are bonds consisting of four and six electrons, respectively, overlapping entirely between two adjacent atoms. The average energies of these bonds are approximately constant as long as they are localized between two atoms; however, the energy in multiple bonds is not simply a multiple of the energy in the analogous single bonds, because the additional electrons are not in the same types of orbitals as those forming single bonds. For example, one finds a normal C—C single bond in ethane

$$
\begin{array}{c}
\;\;\text{H}\;\;\;\text{H}\\
\;\;|\;\;\;\;|\\
\text{H—C—C—H}\\
\;\;|\;\;\;\;|\\
\;\;\text{H}\;\;\;\text{H}
\end{array}
$$

which is due to the overlap between two p electrons directed along the C—C bond—one from each carbon atom—and this bond has an average bond energy of 62.8 kcal or 79.1 kcal depending upon whether one uses $L_s = 124$ kcal/mole or $L_s = 170$ kcal/mole for the heat of sublimation of graphite.[17] The C—C double bond, such as occurs in ethylene

$$
\begin{array}{c}
\;\;\text{H}\;\;\;\text{H}\\
\;\;|\;\;\;\;|\\
\text{C}=\text{C}\\
\;\;|\;\;\;\;|\\
\;\;\text{H}\;\;\;\text{H}
\end{array}
$$

consists of the normal single bond and a second bond due to the overlap of two π electrons. These electrons are in approximately unexcited p orbitals with an axis normal to the single bond. Using the value $L_s = 124$ kcal/mole, the average bond energy of the C=C bond is 101.16 kcal/mole. The triple bond, as in acetylene

$$
\begin{array}{c}
\;\;\text{H}\;\;\;\text{H}\\
\;\;|\;\;\;\;|\\
\text{C}\equiv\text{C}
\end{array}
$$

is 128.15 kcal/mole.

In molecules containing multiple bonds the average bond energy of the multiple bonds can be assumed constant if there is no ambiguity in the localization of the electrons between two atoms (isolated multiple bonds) and only one valence bond structure can be written. However, there are many molecules in which more than one equivalent valence bond structure can be written or in the language of molecular orbitals, there are certain "unsaturation" or "mobile electrons" which cannot be localized between any two adjacent atoms but rather move throughout the field of the entire molecule producing additional stabilization of the structure. This energy of stabilization has often been called resonance energy and is defined by the following relation:

$$\sum \text{ average bond energies} - \text{heat of atomization} = \text{resonance energy}$$

[17] The determination of the heat of sublimation of graphite is experimentally difficult and authorities are sharply divided as to which of these two values is correct. However, even though the choice of this value affects the value of the bond energies it cancels out in prediction of heats of combustion which are more important in practical problems. For convenience, because this value has been more widely used in the literature we use the value $L_s = 124$ kcal/mole.

where the first term is obtained by assuming a certain valence bond structure and using numerical values for the average bond energies obtained from analogous molecules having localized multiple bonds. Benzene is the classical example for illustrating resonance.

Assuming a hypothetical structure for benzene, namely

and using experimentally determined values one finds for benzene

6(C—H) bond energy + 3(C—C) bond energy

+ 3(C=C) bond energy − heat of atomization of benzene

$$\cong 34 \text{ kcal/mole}$$

Thus resonance energy can be given a value if one knows the heat of atomization accurately. There have been many semiempirical and some theoretical calculations made to determine resonance energy and some progress has been made. However, the exact nature of these deviations from additivity in bond energy is much more significant in the understanding of molecular structure and chemical properties than in the assignment of values which enable one to predict heats of formation or heats of combustion.

B,17. Use of Average Bond Energies for Calculating Heats of Combustion. If the combustion of a molecule M can be represented by the following balanced chemical equation

$$nM + mO_2 \rightarrow aP_1 + bP_2 \qquad (17\text{-}1)$$

then the relationship between the heat of formation of a molecule and the heat of combustion of the molecule is given in the following equation

$$n\Delta H_f \text{ (molecule)} + mD = a\Delta H_f(P_1) + b\Delta H_f(P_2) + Q \qquad (17\text{-}2)$$

where $\Delta H_f(M)$ = heat of formation of the molecule M in its gaseous state from the constituent atoms in their gaseous state, D = dissociation energy of O_2, $\Delta H_f[(P_1), (P_2)]$ = heats of formation of the products in their gaseous state, Q = heat of combustion of the molecule. However, the heats of formation of the products and the heats of combustion are usually measured in their standard state so that Eq. 17-2 has to be modified in order to use the usual experimental data. However, if one calculates the heat of formation of a molecule from the average bond energies one obtains the heat of formation of the molecule in its gaseous state. The calculation of the heat of combustion of a molecule from average bond energies and the necessary thermochemic data is now illustrated for the normal hydrocarbon C_nH_{2n+2} where the process of combustion can be represented by the following set of chemical equations:

$$C_nH_{2n+2} + \frac{3n + 1}{2} O_2 \rightarrow nCO_2 + (n + 1)H_2O + Q(C_nH_{2n+2})$$

$$nCO_2 \rightarrow nC_{\text{solid}} + nO_2 - nQ(C)$$

$$(n + 1)H_2O \rightarrow (n + 1)H_2 + \frac{n + 1}{2} O_2 - nQ(H_2)$$

$$(n + 1)H_2 \rightarrow (2n + 2)H_{\text{gas}} - D(H_2) \tag{17-3}$$

$$nC_{\text{solid}} + nL_s \rightarrow nC_{\text{gas}}$$

$$nC_{\text{gas}} + (2n + 2)H_{\text{gas}} \rightarrow C_nH_{2n+2} + \Delta H_f(C_nH_{2n+2})$$

where $Q(M)$ = heat of formation of molecule M in its standard state
$\quad\quad D$ = dissociation energy of molecular H_2
$\quad\quad L_s$ = heat of sublimation of carbon
$\quad\quad \Delta H_f$ = heat of formation of C_nH_{2n+2}
From this cycle one can write the following thermochemical equation

$$\Delta H_f = nQ(C) + (n + 1)Q(H_2) + nL_s + (n + 1)D_{H_2} - QC_nH_{2n+2} \tag{17-4}$$

Since the other quantities except L_s are known from accurate experimental data, one may calculate the heat of combustion $Q(C_nH_{2n+2})$ if the heat of formation ΔH_f (or vice versa) is known and one chooses[18] a value for L_s which is either 124.1 kcal/mole (Herzberg) or 170 kcal/mole (Gaydon and Penny). However, if neither ΔH_f nor $Q(C_nH_{2n+2})$ are known one can estimate $\Delta H_f(C_nH_{2n+2})$ according to the following equation

$$\Delta H_f(C_nH_{2n+2}) = (n - 1)E_{C-C} + (2n + 2)E_{C-H} \tag{17-5}$$

using the values in Table B,17. In this case the calculated value of the heat of combustion is independent of L_s since L_s has been used to calculate the bond energies and thus cancels out if one uses the same value of L_s in Eq. 17-4 as is used in Table B,17. This method can be used for molecules other than hydrocarbons as long as the necessary experimental data are available and the molecules in question do not possess any appreciable resonance energy which cannot be estimated. Resonance energies for many characteristic structures have been experimentally determined and are discussed extensively in [6,24]. Another experimental value that is often important in such calculations and is also not settled is the dissociation energy of molecular N_2.

The validity of this method for n saturated hydrocarbons and n alco-

[18] See [17] and [18] for difficulties in determining L_s and for references to the now extensive literature relevant to the interpretation of these measurements.

hols has been established. As would be expected, the agreement is very good for the higher members of the series where the number of secondary hydrogen atoms is large.

The previous considerations have dealt largely with molecules made up of electron pair bonds for which the additivity assumption was approximately valid. However, there are a large number of molecules

Table B,17. Bond energies in organic molecules.*

Bond	Energy, kcal	Bond	Energy, kcal
C—H	85.56	C—F	104†
C—C	62.77	C—Cl	69
C=C	101.16	C—Br	57
C≡C (acetylene)	128.15	C—I	43
O—H	110.	N—H (NH_3)	83
C—O (alcohols)	75	N—C	53.5
C—O (ethers)	75	C≡N (HCN)	146
C=O (ketones)	155–157	C≡N (nitriles)	149
C=O (CH_2O)	144	N≡C (isonitriles)	139
C=O (aldehydes)	149.5	C≡N	84†
		N=N	80†
		N—N	27 ± 3
C⟋O ＼OH (HCOOH)	348	N—O	61†
		N=O	108†
C⟋O ＼OH (acids)	360†	N⁺⟋O ＼O⁻	169 < E < 186
		C=S (CS_2)	107.5
C⟋O ＼OC (formates)	313	C—S	54
		S—H	82
C⟋O ＼OC (esters)	327		

* Taken from [24, p. 240] by permission. This is based on the heat of sublimation of graphite = 124 kcal/mole.
† Approximate values.

which contain bonds called ionic bonds; these are formed in an entirely different way. In an ionic bond between AB the electron from atom B is transferred to the other atom A forming two ions A and B and these are then held together by the Coulombic attraction between the two charges of opposite sign. If this simple description were adequate it might be possible to devise some fairly simple scheme for determining bond energies and using these to calculate heats of formation of ionic compounds, but there are bonds which can be represented as a combination of ionic and covalent bonding in almost all proportions. However, this proportion depends very much on the other atoms present in the molecule. Accordingly, the whole scheme of bond energies is not very suitable for inorganic compounds. Thus, if one wishes to predict heats of formation or heats of combustion of organic molecules and is satisfied with an accuracy of ± 10 per cent, one can use average bond energies to estimate these quantities. As more experimental data are accumulated, and in particular, more bond dissociation energies are measured and better spectroscopic data are obtained, it should be possible to determine more accurately the heats of formation of molecules for which measurements do not exist. These also will contribute much to an understanding of both molecular structure and chemical reaction rate theory.

A recent volume, *A Discussion on Bond Energies and Bond Lengths* [25], gives an excellent up-to-date discussion of the various factors affecting bond strengths. Many more quantities than we have considered in this chapter are discussed. The authors are concerned with small differences in bond energies, 1 or 2 kilocalories. These factors have little effect in the prediction of heats of combustion as discussed here, but are exceedingly valuable in a better understanding of molecular structure.

CHAPTER 3. ACTIVATION ENERGIES

KARL F. HERZFELD
VIRGINIA GRIFFING

B,18. Introduction. The Arrhenius Equation. It has long been known that stable molecules react with one another to form new molecules; old bonds are broken, new bonds are formed, and atoms are rearranged. Furthermore, these reactions often take place with a finite measureable rate. If one reviews the experimentally determined rate data, accumulated in the past sixty years, two striking generalizations become evident: (1) the rate of a chemical reaction is strongly dependent on temperature, e.g. the rate of a reaction ordinarily doubles for each $10°$ rise in temperature, while the number of collisions between molecules varies scarcely at all (proportional to $T^{\frac{1}{2}}$) over a small temperature range; (2) the number of molecules reacting in unit time is usually much smaller than the number of collisions per unit time. These two facts suggest that only a restricted number of molecules present in an aggregate at a given time fulfill the requisite conditions for reaction.

Arrhenius was the first to formulate and explain these generalizations in terms of the following mechanism. He assumed that chemical reactions take place according to the following scheme:

$$\text{average molecules} \underset{k_2}{\overset{k_1}{\rightleftarrows}} \text{energetic molecules} \qquad (18\text{-}1a)$$

$$\text{energetic molecules} \rightarrow \text{products of chemical reaction} \qquad (18\text{-}1b)$$

If one makes the assumption that the forward reaction goes with a velocity constant k_1 and the back reaction k_2, and that the equilibrium between average molecules and "energetic molecules" is essentially maintained, the temperature variation of the equilibrium constant $K = k_1/k_2$ is given by the Van't Hoff equation

$$\frac{d \ln K}{dT} = \frac{q}{RT^2}$$

where q is the heat necessary to convert 1 mole of average molecules into energetic molecules. Then

$$\frac{d \ln k_1}{dT} - \frac{d \ln k_2}{dT} = \frac{q}{RT^2} \qquad (18\text{-}2)$$

Now if

$$\frac{d \ln k_1}{dT} = \frac{E_{a1}}{RT^2} + B \qquad (18\text{-}3\text{a})$$

and E_{a2} is defined by $E_{a1} - E_{a2} = q$

$$\frac{d \ln k_2}{dT} = \frac{E_{a2}}{RT^2} + B \qquad (18\text{-}3\text{b})$$

If B is taken as zero then

$$\frac{d \ln k}{dT} = \frac{E_a}{RT^2} \qquad (18\text{-}4)$$

or if E_a is temperature independent one obtains

$$k = Ce^{-\frac{E_a}{RT}} \qquad (18\text{-}5)$$

which has the same form as the equation proposed empirically by Arrhenius as early as 1889. This equation can naively be interpreted as the product of the total number of collisions multiplied by the fraction of collisions resulting in chemical reaction. This interpretation is based upon the assumption that activation is due to collision between molecules. E_a is called the activation energy of the reaction and was considered by Arrhenius to be the energy that must be supplied to average molecules to change them into "energetic molecules" which could then react according to Eq. 18-1b. Even though the detailed notions of Arrhenius are erroneous, the fundamental idea with its later modifications is now almost universally accepted. It is now believed that any chemical process which goes at a finite rate requires an energy of activation which is the minimum energy the system must acquire before the process takes place. Examples of such processes which follow the Arrhenius law are

$$\frac{\text{number of molecules evaporating}}{\text{second}} = C_1 e^{-\frac{L}{RT}}$$

where L = molar latent heat, and

$$\frac{\text{number of electrons emitted by an incandescent solid}}{\text{second}} = C_2 e^{-\frac{W}{RT}}$$

where W = thermionic work function per electron.

Experimental rate data can be used to calculate the activation energy according to Eq. 18-3a if it can be shown experimentally that the constant B is zero. If $\ln k$ is plotted against $1/T$, a straight line with slope $-E_a/R$ is observed. Even though the constant C, usually called the "frequency factor" of the reaction, were proportional to T^n (where n is a small number) over the small range of temperatures for which it is practicable to measure k, the deviation from linearity is not significant. In fact, any marked deviation from linearity when $\ln k$ is plotted against $1/T$ can safely be attributed to complicated kinetics, such as consecutive reactions, chain reactions, etc. However, if the temperature dependence of the frequency factor is known, the experimental energy of activation, E_a, should be determined by plotting $\ln k/T^n$ against $1/T$.

B,19. Formal Theory of Reaction Kinetics. In order to give a more exact formulation of the concept of energy of activation it is convenient to classify chemical reactions according to the number of molecules taking part in each elementary step leading to chemical change. Since many elementary reactions take place according to a first order (unimolecular) or second order (bimolecular) mechanism, only these two mechanisms are considered. Most chemical reactions do not follow these simple kinetic laws but are due to a series of such elementary reactions taking place successively and simultaneously. For such reactions one can calculate an over-all energy of activation.

First order, unimolecular reactions. A reaction which follows a unimolecular mechanism can be described as follows: A normal molecule A is converted to an energetic molecule A′ which subsequently spontaneously decomposes or rearranges itself to form the product. A first order reaction is one for which the rate constant is defined by

$$-\frac{d[A]}{dt} = k_1[A] \tag{19-1}$$

Consider a first order, unimolecular reaction in which the rate of activation is sufficiently fast to maintain the equilibrium concentration of activated molecules. Then, according to the Maxwell-Boltzmann distribution law (see Art. 26) the number of molecules in the activated state, $N_{A'}$, is given by

$$N_{A'} = \frac{N_A p_A e^{-\frac{\epsilon_A}{kT}}}{\sum_i p_i e^{-\frac{\epsilon_i}{kT}}} \tag{19-2}$$

⟨ 165 ⟩

N_A = total number of molecules

p_A = a priori probability of the state A

ϵ_A = energy of the molecule in state A

Now assign to the molecules in state A the probability k_A of undergoing spontaneous reaction in unit time, the total rate of reaction is given by

$$-\frac{dN}{dt} = \frac{N\sum k_A p_A e^{-\frac{\epsilon_A}{kT}}}{\sum p_i e^{-\frac{\epsilon_i}{kT}}} \tag{19-3}$$

If the reaction is known to be first order, then

$$-\frac{dN}{dt} = k_1 N$$

and the specific rate is given by

$$k_1 = \frac{\sum k_A p_A e^{-\frac{\epsilon_A}{kT}}}{\sum p_i e^{-\frac{\epsilon_i}{kT}}} \tag{19-4}$$

and the temperature coefficient of the specific reaction rate is

$$\frac{d \ln k_1}{dT} = \frac{\sum k_A p_A e^{-\frac{\epsilon_A}{kT}} \frac{\epsilon_A}{kT^2} - \sum p_i e^{-\frac{\epsilon_i}{kT}} \frac{\epsilon_i}{kT^2}}{\sum p_i e^{-\frac{\epsilon_i}{kT^2}}}$$

or more simply

$$\frac{d \ln k_1}{dT} = \frac{\bar{\bar{\epsilon}} - \bar{\epsilon}}{kT^2} \tag{19-5}$$

and

$$\bar{\bar{\epsilon}} - \bar{\epsilon} = \text{energy of activation}$$

where $\bar{\bar{\epsilon}}$ = average energy of the molecules that react

$\bar{\epsilon}$ = average energy of all the molecules.

In most cases $\bar{\epsilon}$ will not differ appreciably from the average energy of the unactivated molecules, and thus $(\bar{\bar{\epsilon}} - \bar{\epsilon})$ will be the average energy that must be supplied to the molecules that react and is identical with the energy of activation proposed by Arrhenius.

Now if one examines the case where the rate of activation is not necessarily fast enough to maintain the equilibrium concentration of activated molecules, one obtains [26] for the temperature coefficient of the specific first order rate constant

$$\frac{d \ln k_1}{dT} = \frac{\overline{d \ln \theta_A}}{dT} + \frac{\overline{d \ln A_{A-i}}}{dT} + \frac{\bar{\bar{\epsilon}}_A - \bar{\epsilon}_i}{kT^2} \tag{19-6}$$

where θ = fraction of activated molecules that return to the unactivated state

A_{A-i} = specific rate of deactivation back to any initial state i.

Since the process of deactivation can occur only by collisions or by the
emission of radiation, the temperature coefficient of deactivation must
be small; then for reactions of interest where the temperature coefficient
is large, Eq. 19-6 becomes identical with Eq. 19-5 and $N_0(\bar{\bar{\epsilon}} - \bar{\epsilon}) = E_A$,
the energy of activation that occurs in the Arrhenius equation.

Second order, bimolecular reactions. A bimolecular mechanism can
be described as follows:

$$A \rightarrow A' \quad \text{(activated molecule)}$$
$$B \rightarrow B' \quad \text{(activated molecule)}$$
$$A' + B' \rightarrow AB^*$$

or

$$A' + B \rightarrow AB^*$$
$$AB^* \rightarrow \text{products}$$

where AB^*, called the reacting complex, represents the pair of molecules
A' and B' at the instant that A' is at the point of decomposing. B may
or may not decompose. Such a reaction follows a second order law where
the rate constant is given by

$$-\frac{d[A]}{dt} = k_2[A][B] \tag{19-7}$$

The species A may be the same as, or different from B.

Consider a second order bimolecular reaction in which it is assumed
that the fraction of the two kinds of molecules A and B in the activated
states A' and B' has the equilibrium value. This assumption will be
valid only for reactions that remain second order over a range of concentrations. Then, using the Maxwell-Boltzmann equation, the number of
activated molecules $N_{A'}$ and $N_{B'}$ is given by

$$N_{A'} = \frac{N_A p_{A'} e^{-\frac{\epsilon_{A'}}{kT}}}{\sum p_A e^{-\frac{\epsilon_A}{kT}}} \quad \text{and} \quad N_{B'} = \frac{N_B p_{B'} e^{-\frac{\epsilon_{B'}}{kT}}}{\sum p_B e^{-\frac{\epsilon_B}{kT}}} \tag{19-8}$$

where N_A and N_B are the number of molecules of A and B per cm³, in the
original state and p_A is the a priori probability of the state. Furthermore
it can be shown from kinetic theory that the number of collisions between
molecules depends on $T^{\frac{1}{2}}$; thus the rate of the bimolecular second order
reaction is given by

$$-\frac{dN_A}{dt} = T^{\frac{1}{2}} \sum_{A',B'} k_{A'B'} N_{A'} N_{B'} \tag{19-9}$$

where $k_{A'B'}$ is a constant for each pair of activated molecules and is discussed in greater detail in Art. 20. Substituting Eq. 19-8 in Eq. 19-9 and solving for the second order rate constant

$$k_2 = -\frac{1}{N_A N_B}\frac{d(N_A)}{dt}$$

i.e.

$$k_2 = \frac{T^{\frac{1}{2}}\sum_{A'}\sum_{B'}k_{A'B'}p_{A'B'}e^{-\frac{\epsilon_{A'}+\epsilon_{B'}}{kT}}}{(\sum p_A e^{-\frac{\epsilon_A}{kT}})(\sum p_B e^{-\frac{\epsilon_B}{kT}})} \tag{19-10}$$

One can calculate the temperature coefficient and obtain

$$\frac{d\ln k_2}{dT} = \frac{1}{2T} + \frac{\overline{\epsilon_{A'}+\epsilon_{B'}} - \overline{\epsilon_A + \epsilon_B}}{kT^2} \tag{19-11}$$

where $\overline{\epsilon_{A'}+\epsilon_{B'}}$ = average energy of the molecules that react
$\overline{\epsilon_A + \epsilon_B}$ = average energy of all the molecules
Thus

$$N_0(\overline{\epsilon_{A'}+\epsilon_{B'}} - \overline{\epsilon_A + \epsilon_B}) = E_a$$

the energy of activation in the Arrhenius equation.

The frequency factor for bimolecular reactions. The interpretation of the frequency factor, i.e. C, in the integrated form of the Arrhenius equation is more difficult. The process can be divided into two steps, the process of forming the activated complex AB*, and the process of decomposition of AB* into the products. Two extreme situations are as follows: In the first, the reaction AB* → products occurs almost immediately after the formation of AB*, before the complex can fly apart again into A' + B, and before part of the energy of AB*, sufficient to make it inactive, can be removed by a further collision. In that case, all the AB* formed gives the products, and the rate of formation of the products is equal to the rate of formation of AB*. Accordingly, one can, in this case, interpret the frequency factor as the number of collisions between an A, and a B.

The other extreme occurs if most of the AB* complexes formed are destroyed before decomposing into the products after concentrating the necessary energy into a particular bond. The destruction might occur either by the flying apart of A' and B or by the removal of sufficient energy through collision with another molecule. In this case, the rate at which the products are formed is determined by the rate of the decomposition of the complex AB*, and this rate may be calculated by the "absolute rate theory." The second case requires that the rate calculated by the absolute rate theory is *less* than would be given by the number of collisions forming the complex AB* (first extreme).

In the first case, the factor C can be interpreted in terms of the elementary collision theory of the kinetic theory of gases for a simple second order bimolecular reaction

$$A + B \rightarrow C + D$$

If one writes the rate in molecular units

$$v = kN_A N_B = ze^{-\frac{E_a}{RT}} \quad \frac{\text{molecules}}{\text{cm}^3 \text{ sec}} \qquad (19\text{-}12)$$

then z can be interpreted as the number of collisions per cm³ per second and according to kinetic theory is

$$z = N_A N_B \sigma_{AB}^2 \left(\frac{8\pi kT}{\mu_{AB}}\right)^{\frac{1}{2}} \qquad (19\text{-}13)$$

where N_A and N_B are the concentrations of reactants in number of molecules per cm³, σ_{AB} is the average molecular diameter of A and B, and $\mu_{AB} = m_A m_B/(m_A + m_B)$, the reduced mass of the molecules A and B. Thus

$$k = \sigma_{AB}^2 \left(\frac{8\pi kT}{\mu_{AB}}\right)^{\frac{1}{2}} e^{-\frac{E_a}{RT}} \qquad (19\text{-}14)$$

Since σ_{AB} can be determined from viscosity data and E_a can be determined from rate data, the validity can be tested. It does, in fact, give good agreement for many simple reactions in both the gaseous and liquid states as shown by the values given in Tables B,19a and B,19b.

Table B,19a. Gaseous reactions.*

Reaction	E_a, calories	T^0, abs	$\sigma_{AB} \times 10^8$, cm	k_{obs},	k_{calc}, liters/g molecule sec	$\dfrac{k_{obs}}{k_{calc}}$
$2N_2O \rightarrow 2N_2 + O_2$	58,500	1001	3.3	3.80×10^{-1}	3.15×10^{-2}	12
$CH_3CHO \rightarrow CH_4 + CO$	45,500	800	5.0	5.15×10^{-1}	1.38×10^{-1}	3.7
$2HI \rightarrow H_2 + I_2$	43,800	666	3.5	2.20×10^{-4}	4.68×10^{-4}	0.47
$C_2H_4 + H_2 \rightarrow C_2H_6$	42,400	787	2.0	1.77×10^{-2}	3.53×10^{-1}	0.05
$H_2 + I_2 \rightarrow 2HI$	38,800	660	2.0	1.63×10^{-2}	3.46×10^{-2}	0.47
$2NO_2 \rightarrow 2NO + O_2$	26,500	610	3.3	2.06×10^{0}	6.93×10^{1}	0.03

* Table taken by permission from Moelwyn-Hughes, E. A., *The Kinetics of Reactions in Solution*, p. 74. Clarendon Press, Oxford, 1933.

However, there are many bimolecular reactions whose experimental rates deviate widely from the rate calculated according to the simple collision theory; for some reactions the calculated rates are larger and for others smaller than the observed rate. In order to account for these low values it has been observed that the number of collisions effective for reaction may be considerably smaller than the total number of collisions, since some critical orientation of even energetic molecules before the collision would be required to bring about reaction. In order to take this effect into account, Eq. 19-12 is modified thus

$$v = Pze^{-\frac{E_a}{RT}} \tag{19-15}$$

where P is called the steric factor and is the probability that a sufficiently energetic collision would be geometrically oriented to bring about reaction. This factor must be estimated for individual reactions and there is no a priori method for determining it.

Table B,19b. Liquid reactions.*

Reaction	Solvent	E_a, calories	$z \times 10^{-11}$ Observed	$z \times 10^{-11}$ Calculated	$\frac{k_{calc}}{k_{obs}}$
$CH_3ONa + 1{:}2{:}4\text{-}$ $ClC_6H_3(NO_2)_2$	CH_3OH	17,450	1.91	2.42	1.3
$C_2H_5ONa + CH_3I$	C_2H_5OH	19,490	2.42	1.93	0.8
$C_2H_5ONa + C_2H_5I$	C_2H_5OH	20,650	1.49	2.23	1.5
$C_6H_5CH_2ONa + C_4H_9I$	C_2H_5OH	21,560	2.92	2.43	0.8
$C_6H_5CH_2ONa + iso\ C_4H_9I$	C_2H_5OH	21,350	2.45	2.43	1.0
$C_6H_5CH_2ONa + C_{16}H_{33}I$	C_2H_5OH	21,090	1.26	3.12	2.5
$\beta\text{-}C_{10}H_7ONa + C_2H_5I$	C_2H_5OH	19,840	0.11	2.21	20.1
$(CH_3)_2SO_4 + NaCNS$	CH_3OH	17,360	0.19	1.91	10.0
$NH_4CNO \rightarrow (NH_2)_2CO$	H_2O	23,170	42.7	4.05	0.1
$C_6H_4\overset{CH_2}{\underset{CO}{\diagup\diagdown}}O + OH^-$	H_2O	12,500	41.7	2.93	0.07
$C_6H_5CO[CH_2]_2Cl + I^-$	$(CH_3)_2CO$	22,160	10.5	1.88	0.2
$CH_3S[CH_2]_2Cl + I^-$	$(CH_3)_2CO$	20,740	0.085	1.57	18.5
$C_2H_5Br + OH^-$	C_2H_5OH	21,400	4.30	3.86	0.9
$C_3H_6Br_2 + I^-$	CH_3OH	25,100	1.07	1.39	1.3

* Table taken by permission from Moelwyn-Hughes, E. A., *The Kinetics of Reactions in Solution*, p. 79. Clarendon Press, Oxford, 1933.

However, it is even more probable that in the case where C is found too small, the second case is present and one has to use the absolute rate theory. In case of values of C large compared to $z/N_A N_B$ one must consider, with Lindemann and Polanyi, that more than one degree of freedom may be involved as the source of the activation energy. If the activation energy E_a may be distributed over s classical degrees of freedom in molecule A, then

$$\frac{N_{A'}}{N_A} = \left(\frac{E_A}{kT}\right)^{s-1} \frac{1}{(s-1)!} e^{-\frac{E}{kT}} \tag{19-16}$$

and Eq. 19-13 should be replaced by

$$z = N_A N_B \sigma_{AB}^2 \left(\frac{8\pi kT}{\mu_{AB}}\right)^{\frac{1}{2}} \left(\frac{E_A}{kT}\right)^{s-1} \frac{1}{(s-1)!} \tag{19-17}$$

If, e.g. $E_A/kT = 20$, $s = 5$, the increase in z is by a factor of more than 6,000.

The difficulty in interpretation lies in the fact that in general, s is unknown. If s is sufficiently large, the rate of supply of activated complexes may be so large that the decomposition of the complex into the products (absolute rate theory) may be determining, even if that rate is larger than the simple collision theory, with $s = 1$, would give.

The idea of entropy of activation, associated with the steric factor, was developed by Rodebush, La Mer, and others. However, this concept is more precise from the point of view of the absolute reaction rate theory discussed in Art. 20.

Frequency factor in unimolecular reactions. Here also, the energy supply must occur through collisions which are bimolecular. To give a resultant monomolecular reaction, the decomposition of the activated complex must be slow compared to the energy supply. Originally, this provided a difficulty, since according to the forerunners of the absolute rate theory (Herzfeld), and according to experiment, C is of the order 10^{12} to 10^{13}, while the simple collision factor under standard conditions is 10^9. Actually, in diatomic molecules decomposition is not unimolecular, but bimolecular in consequence of the recombination being termolecular. For polyatomic molecules, the solution lies, as Lindemann and Polanyi have shown, in an increase of the collision factor according to Eq. 19-17.

In Lindemann's picture the energy of activation is accumulated in the internal degrees of freedom of the molecule before reaction can occur. Since this energy is distributed among all the vibrational degrees of freedom and must get into one bond before reaction can occur (i.e. probably a particular linear combination of the normal modes of the molecule) there would be a time lag between activation and reaction which would be proportional to the reciprocal of the frequency factor. Unimolecular reactions become second order at low pressures for which the rate of deactivation due to collisions is much smaller than the rate of decomposition.

For termolecular reactions, i.e. a reaction which requires the simultaneous collision of three particles, the energy of activation must be very small or the reaction would not go at all since the probability of the occurrence of a triple collision is so small. Only a few reactions following third order kinetics have been observed and in all these cases the energy of activation is small (see [27]). However, ternary collisions are important in the recombination of atoms and seem to be a relatively efficient process. It is now a well-established fact that in the recombination of atoms, a third body is required to carry off the excess energy or the two atoms would again separate. Since many atoms do recombine with a measureable rate, one can conclude that the recombination of atoms does not require an energy of activation.

B,20. Theory of Absolute Reaction Rates. More recently, Eyring and Polanyi [*28*], and others have given the following general picture of the process of decomposition of the activated complex. Assume a reaction goes according to the relationship

$$\text{reactants} \rightarrow \text{products}$$

with a finite rate. Then if one plots the potential energy as a function of all the coordinates of the constituent atoms one would obtain a potential energy surface which would contain at least two minima. However, since the reaction goes at a finite rate these two minima must be

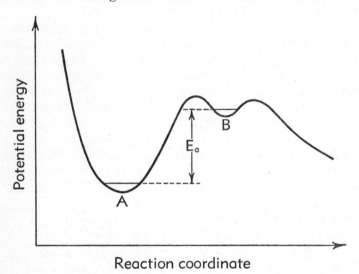

Fig. B,20. A = stable molecule; B = activated complex; E_a = activation energy (for the formation of the activated complex); i.e. difference between the zero point energies of the stable configuration A and the activated complex B.

separated by potential barriers. If one connects the point representing the stable configuration of the reactants with that representing the stable products by a continuous curve on the potential energy surface choosing as the reaction coordinate the path that surmounts the minimum barrier, one obtains the one-dimensional potential energy curve given in Fig. B,20.

According to this picture, the energy of activation is the minimum energy which must be supplied to the reactant molecules at 0°K to raise them to the point B, i.e. zero point energy of the activated complex. The molecular complex at this point is called the "activated complex." Then, using this concept, the reaction rate is the number of activated complexes passing over the potential energy barrier per second. This rate is equal to the concentration of the activated complex multiplied by the average speed with which the complex moves. In order to calculate the concentration of activated complexes for a simple bimolecular reaction, consider the reaction

$$A + B \rightleftarrows (AB)^{\ddagger} \rightarrow \text{products}$$

Assume $(AB)^{\ddagger}$ in equilibrium with the reactants; then the equilibrium constant for the formation of $(AB)^{\ddagger}$ is given by

$$K^{\ddagger} = \frac{[(AB)^{\ddagger}]}{[A][B]}$$

where [A] means concentration of A, etc.; then

$$\frac{d[A]}{dt} = K^{\ddagger}[A][B] \times \text{rate of passage over the barrier}$$

According to this theory, one then assumes that the complex spontaneously decomposes into its products when one of its vibrations has its classical energy $\epsilon = kT$ and becomes a translation, or the rate of passage over the barrier becomes kT/h. Then the reaction rate becomes

$$\frac{d[A]}{dt} = K^{\ddagger}[A][B] \times \frac{kT}{h} \tag{20-1}$$

(For a unimolecular reaction, $K^{\ddagger}$ would be the equilibrium constant for the equilibrium $A \rightarrow A^{\ddagger}$.) According to statistical mechanics, the equilibrium constant $K^{\ddagger}$ is

$$K^{\ddagger} = \frac{Q^{\ddagger}}{Q_A Q_B} e^{-\frac{E_a}{RT}} \tag{20-2}$$

where $Q^{\ddagger}$, Q_A, and Q_B are the partition functions of the activated complex and of the molecules A and B respectively (or $A^{\ddagger}$ in unimolecular reactions) and E_a is the difference in the zero point energy of the activated complex and the reactants, i.e. the energy of activation shown in Fig. B,20. In $Q^{\ddagger}$ the vibration which has become a translation is to be omitted.

$$k_2 = \frac{kT}{h} \frac{Q^{\ddagger}}{Q_A Q_B} e^{-\frac{E_a}{RT}} \tag{20-3}$$

Thermodynamically

$$\Delta F = -RT \ln K^{\ddagger}$$

and

$$\Delta F^{\ddagger} = \Delta H^{\ddagger} - T\Delta S^{\ddagger}$$

and Eq. 20-3 becomes

$$k_2 = \frac{kT}{h} e^{+\frac{\Delta S^{\ddagger}}{R}} e^{-\frac{\Delta H^{\ddagger}}{RT}} \tag{20-4}$$

According to the definition of the experimental activation energy calculated according to the Arrhenius equation (i.e. Eq. 18-5)

$$\frac{d \ln k}{dT} = \frac{E_a}{RT^2} = \frac{\Delta H^{\ddagger} + (\Delta n^{\ddagger} - 1)RT}{RT^2}$$

⟨ 173 ⟩

where $\Delta n^{\ddagger}$ = the number of moles of "activated complex" − number of moles of reactants. Thus the "entropy of activation" can be calculated from the experimental rate constant and activation energy.

In comparing Eq. 20-3 with Eq. 19-10 one has

$$\frac{kT}{h}\frac{Q^{\ddagger}}{Q_A Q_B} = \frac{T^{\frac{1}{2}}\sum\sum k'_{AB}p_{A'B'}e^{\frac{\frac{1}{N_0}E_a - \epsilon_{A'} - \epsilon_{B'}}{kT}}}{(\sum p_A e^{-\frac{\epsilon_A}{kT}})(\sum p_B e^{-\frac{\epsilon_B}{kT}})}$$

From Eq. 20-4, the frequency factor, according to this theory, is

$$C = \frac{kT}{h} \cdot \frac{\text{product of the partition functions for the activated complex}}{\text{product of the partition functions of the reactant molecules}}$$

B,21. Theoretical Calculation of the Structure of the Activated Complex. The activated complex can be treated as a definite molecular species. Thus the structure of the activated complex can be calculated, in principle, according to the methods of quantum mechanics. Just as in other problems of molecular structure, one can write the Schrödinger equation as a function of the coordinates of all the electrons and nuclei of the reactants. Then, this wave equation must be solved as a function of all the coordinates, without any assumptions of electron pairs or minimum energy. The energy of the activated state would then be the highest energy through which the system must pass in going from the initial configuration (reactants) to the final configuration (products). The results of such a calculation would be a many-dimensional potential energy surface. In practice, such a calculation is not feasible for even the simplest molecules and reactions. Wigner [29] and Evans and Polanyi [30] have discussed the inherent difficulties of calculating such potential energy surfaces by anything approaching rigorous methods.

B,22. Semiempirical Calculations on Activation Energies.[19] Eyring and his collaborators have used a semiempirical method for calculating the structure of the activated complex for a simple reaction

$$AB + C \rightarrow BC + A$$

where A, B, and C are all monatomic. One can show that the atom C will approach the molecule AB with the minimum energy along a line formed by the extension of a straight line connecting the atoms A and B. Call the distance between A and B, r_{AB} and the distance between B and C, r_{BC}. Then when r_{BC} is large, r_{AB} will be the interatomic distance of the stable molecule AB; similarly, after reaction, r_{BC} will be the interatomic

[19] This method is discussed in detail in [31]. Literature reference for applications to individual reactions is also found in this book.

distance of BC and r_{AB} will be large. If one plots the energy as a function of these two coordinates, one will obtain a potential energy surface along which the chemical reaction must take place. The reaction coordinate will be a continuous path along which a particle can move with a minimum expenditure of energy from the stable well representing reactants to the stable configuration of the products. The height of the potential hill between the two low points will be the energy of activation. Eyring and his collaborators have empirically calculated potential energy surfaces for a few reactions. It is assumed that all directional valence effects can be neglected; a Morse (see Art. 15) potential energy curve for each pair of atoms is constructed (i.e. energy as a function of distance). This energy can be divided into two parts, the electrostatic Coulomb energy and a quantum mechanical form of energy called exchange energy. Since these energies depend on the coordinates differently, Eyring quite arbitrarily assumes a ratio of 14/86 for Coulomb energy/exchange energy. This value was chosen to give agreement between experimental and calculated activation energies for ortho-para hydrogen conversion. He then uses this same ratio in considering all nonmetallic electron pair bonds. The quantitative agreement with experiment which Eyring obtains is surprisingly good considering the radical assumptions that have been made. In fact, the agreement is destroyed when less drastic assumptions are made. Slater [3] suggests that the agreement may be due to the fact that it is really a method-of-interpolation formula between the energies of the final and initial states. Furthermore, direct computations show that the assumed energy ratio between Coulombic and exchange energy varies considerably from atom to atom (for p electrons the exchange energy sometimes becomes negative). However, Eyring's calculations have been useful in giving a general concept of the activated complex as a problem of molecular structure and of the energy of activation as the difference in the binding energy of this complex and that of the stable reactants.

B,23. Discussion. In general, one can conclude that reactions which require a high energy of activation will proceed slowly. In practice, the only dependable method at present of determining the energy of activation of a reaction is to measure its rate as a function of temperature, to attempt to estimate the temperature dependence of the frequency factor, and to calculate the energy of activation from the experimental rate data. If one can calculate the energy of activation in this way, one can then get an independent check by calculating, e.g. the collision cross section σ_{AB} (collision theory) and comparing this with an experimental value of σ_{AB} from viscosity data. However, certain general statements can be made. For endothermic reactions, the activation energy is of the same order of magnitude as the heat of reaction plus the energy of activation of the reverse process. Szwarc has used this conclusion and makes the assumption that the recombination of radicals does not require an energy of activation in determining the bond dissociation energy of a molecule into free radicals (usually defined as electrically neutral fragments of a molecule with an odd number of electrons). His values of bond dissociation energies seem to be in agreement with those determined by other methods [*20*]. For exothermic reactions of the type

$$AB + C \rightarrow BC + A$$

where AB is a diatomic molecule and C is a single atom, the energy of activation is almost zero, e.g.

$$Na + Cl_2 \rightarrow NaCl + Cl$$

The recombination of atoms does not require an appreciable energy of activation. For exothermic reactions in which diatomic molecules exchange partners, i.e.

$$AB + CD \rightarrow AC + BD + heat$$

it has been found that the activation energy is approximately one-fourth the sum of the dissociation energies of the reactant molecules, e.g.

$$H_2 + I_2 \rightarrow 2HI \qquad E_a \text{ (exptl)} = 40 \text{ kcal/mole}$$

$$\tfrac{1}{4}(D_{H_2} + D_{I_2}) = 40 \text{ kcal/mole}$$

$$H_2 + H_2 \rightarrow H_2 + H_2 \qquad E_a \text{ (exptl)} > 57 \text{ kcal/mole}$$

$$\tfrac{1}{2}(D_{H_2}) = 52 \text{ kcal/mole}$$

One would expect that often the activation energy would be less than the energy required to break bonds since new bonds are formed in the formation of the activated complex while old bonds are only weakened. In semiempirical calculations [*31*] it has been found that a bond length increases in the activated state about 10 per cent of its normal value.

CHAPTER 4. STATISTICAL MECHANICS[20]

J. O. HIRSCHFELDER   C. F. CURTISS
R. B. BIRD   E. L. SPOTZ

The methods of classical and quantum mechanics have been highly successful in the analysis of the behavior of simple systems involving only a few degrees of freedom. It is clearly impractical, however, to apply these principles to the examination of the behavior of a very

[20] This chapter is based upon material given in Chapter 2 of *Molecular Theory of Gases and Liquids*, by J. O. Hirschfelder, C. F. Curtiss, and R. B. Bird (John Wiley & Sons, Inc., 1954). The authors wish to thank the publishers for permission to use this material.

complex system, such as a gas containing 6.023×10^{23} molecules. Furthermore a knowledge of the microscopic behavior thus provided is not particularly of interest. When the knowledge of the initial state of the system is limited to the results of measurements of the bulk properties, statistical mechanics may be used to predict the change of the macroscopic state of the system with time.

B,24. The Fundamentals of Statistical Thermodynamics. Statistical mechanics may be thought of as being made up of two important branches: *equilibrium* and *nonequilibrium* statistical mechanics. The former is well understood from the standpoint of the fundamental principles and the formal development of the theory. The important results of the theory are summarized in this chapter. Although progress in this direction has thus far been seriously handicapped by the numerical difficulties encountered, much has been learned about the properties of matter and their dependence on the forces between the molecules.

The nonequilibrium statistical mechanics is of more recent development and is one of the frontier fields of research today. A general discussion of the formal treatment of nonequilibrium statistical mechanics is presented in Chap. 5 and the applications to hydrodynamics and transport properties are discussed in Sec. D.

In this article we discuss the statistical mechanical relations between the thermodynamic quantities (such as the internal energy, entropy, and temperature) and the properties of molecules. The relationship between statistical mechanics and thermodynamics is usually discussed in terms of the "partition function." Hence we preface the treatment of statistical thermodynamics by a brief discussion of the partition function in quantum and classical statistics.

The partition function. The quantum mechanical partition function[21] (which is sometimes referred to as the "sum over states" or "Zustandssumme") for a system of N molecules, Q_{N_q}, is defined by either of the two equivalent relations:

$$Q_{N_q} = \sum_{\substack{\text{Sum over all} \\ \text{energy } states}} e^{-\beta E_i} = \sum_{\substack{\text{Sum over all} \\ \text{energy } levels}} g_j e^{-\beta E_i} \qquad (24\text{-}1)$$

In the first expression E_j represents the energy of the system in the jth quantum state. On the other hand, in the second expression E_j is the energy associated with the jth energy level, and the degeneracy of the level is indicated by g_j (that is, the jth level is composed of g_j states). Both forms for the partition function are in common use in the literature.

---

[21] Both the classical and quantum mechanical partition functions are designated by Q_N. When it is desired to distinguish between the two quantities, a subscript q serves to indicate the quantum mechanical partition function.

The partition function is a function of β (which is shown presently to be $1/kT$) and also of any mechanical properties of the system which influence the energy levels. Usually the only mechanical parameter of the system which enters is the volume. In Art. 25 the explicit nature of the volume dependence of the E_j is discussed in connection with practical thermodynamical calculations.

The quantum mechanical partition function may also be written as an integral over configuration space, involving the quantum mechanical Hamiltonian operator, $\mathcal{H}$:

$$Q_{N_q} = \int \sum_{\rho} \phi_{\rho}^*(\mathbf{r}^N) e^{-\beta\mathcal{H}} \phi_{\rho}(\mathbf{r}^N) d\mathbf{r}^N \qquad (24\text{-}2)$$

In this expression the $\phi_{\rho}(\mathbf{r}^N)$ form a complete set of orthonormal functions with quantum numbers $\{\rho\} \equiv \rho_1, \rho_2, \rho_3 \cdots$. The symbol $\mathbf{r}^N \equiv \mathbf{r}_1, \mathbf{r}_2, \mathbf{r}_3, \cdots$ is a vector in $3N$-dimensional configuration space which gives the positions of the N particles in the system. When the partition function is written in this fashion, the volume dependence manifests itself in the limits of the integration over configuration space, and also in the boundary conditions which the expansion functions satisfy.

In the correspondence limit, where classical behavior is approached, it may be shown[22] that the partition function given in Eq. 24-2 becomes an integral over the classical phase space involving the classical Hamiltonian $H(\mathbf{r}^N, \mathbf{p}^N)$:

$$Q_N = [N!h^{3N}]^{-1} \iint e^{-\beta H(\mathbf{r}^N, \mathbf{p}^N)} d\mathbf{r}^N d\mathbf{p}^N \qquad (24\text{-}3a)$$

or in terms of the potential energy of the system $\Phi(\mathbf{r}^N)$,

$$Q_N = \frac{(2\pi m k T)^{3N/2}}{N!h^{3N}} \int e^{-\beta\Phi(\mathbf{r}^N)} d\mathbf{r}^N \qquad (24\text{-}3b)$$

These expressions for the classical partition function[23] are valid only for the case of a system of N identical particles. The factor $N!$, which appears in the denominator, is due to the Pauli exclusion principle. Because of the identity of the particles certain regions of phase space are equivalent in that they correspond to a simple renumbering of the particles. Since there are $N!$ permutations of the set of N particles, the factor $(1/N!)$ "corrects" for this equivalence. Such corrections must always be made in classical formulas. In the remainder of this article the quantum mechanical form of the partition function is used.

The internal energy and the first law of thermodynamics. Let us consider a large number of identical systems in weak energy contact with one another. This "ensemble" of systems represents a single system

---

[22] See for example the very excellent review article by J. de Boer [*32*].

[23] The classical partition function is sometimes called the "phase integral." This terminology should not be confused with the Sommerfeld-Wilson phase integrals of old quantum theory.

bathed in a thermostat at a particular temperature. It may be shown that the probable number of systems in such an ensemble which are in state j is proportional to $e^{-\beta E_j}$. Hence the average energy of the members of the ensemble which is the thermodynamic internal energy U is

$$U = \frac{\sum E_j e^{-\beta E_j}}{\sum e^{-\beta E_j}} \qquad (24\text{-}4)$$

The internal energy may also be expressed directly as a derivative of the natural logarithm of the partition function:

$$U = -\left(\frac{\partial \ln Q_N}{\partial \beta}\right)_V \qquad (24\text{-}5)$$

where the subscript V indicates that the external mechanical parameters (such as the volume) of the system are held fixed.

The first law of thermodynamics may be written in the differential form

$$dU = \delta q - \delta w \qquad (24\text{-}6)$$

in which δq is the small quantity of heat absorbed by the system and δw is the work done by the system while undergoing a small change in state. Here, dU is an *exact* differential, while δq and δw are both *inexact* differentials. It is also possible to write an expression for dU in terms of the energy levels of the system. Letting $\bar{a}_j = Q_N^{-1} e^{-\beta E_j}$ we may write Eq. 24-4 as

$$U = \sum \bar{a}_j E_j \qquad (24\text{-}7)$$

whence

$$dU = \sum E_j d\bar{a}_j + \sum \bar{a}_j dE_j \qquad (24\text{-}8)$$

The first term on the right-hand side represents the change in energy due to a redistribution of the total energy over the various quantum states of the system. The second term gives the change in energy which results from the shift in the energy levels of the system caused by the alteration of the volume (or other external parameters). This latter term may clearly be associated with δw and the former with δq:

$$\delta q = \sum E_j d\bar{a}_j \qquad (24\text{-}9)$$

$$\delta w = -\sum \bar{a}_j dE_j \qquad (24\text{-}10)$$

Eq. 24-8 may then be regarded as giving a microscopic interpretation of the first law of thermodynamics.

Temperature and entropy and the second law of thermodynamics. It is now necessary to introduce the concepts of temperature and entropy. In the axiomatic thermodynamics the reciprocal of temperature is defined as the integrating factor of the heat change, and entropy is defined in terms of the perfect differential so obtained. The statistical definition of entropy is based on an analogy with this approach. We have obtained expressions which are intuitively related to the concepts of infinitesimal heat and work terms. The reciprocal of the temperature is defined as the integrating factor for this infinitesimal heat change and the entropy is defined by the perfect differential which results.

Let us define a function, the "entropy," by the relation

$$S = S(E_1, E_2, \cdots, \beta) = k(\ln Q_N + \beta U) + S_0 \qquad (24\text{-}11)$$

in which k is Boltzmann's constant and S_0 is a constant. It is now possible to define a perfect differential dS as

$$dS = \left(\frac{\partial S}{\partial \beta}\right)_{E_1 E_2 \ldots} d\beta + \sum \left(\frac{\partial S}{\partial E_j}\right)_\beta dE_j$$

$$= kd(\ln Q_N + \beta U) \qquad (24\text{-}12)$$

Using the definition of the partition function and the relations in Eq. 24-9 and 24-10 for δq and δw, we get:

$$dS = -\frac{k}{Q_N} \sum (\beta dE_j + E_j d\beta)e^{-\beta E_j} + k\beta dU + kU d\beta$$

$$= k\beta \left[dU - \sum \bar{a}_j dE_j \right]$$

$$= k\beta \delta q \equiv \frac{1}{T}\, \delta q \qquad (24\text{-}13)$$

This demonstrates that $k\beta$, or $1/T$, is an integrating factor for the heat change. That is, multiplication of the inexact differential δq by $1/T$ yields an exact differential dS.

This in itself does not define the temperature T uniquely. However, if in addition it be required that the entropy be an extensive property then it can be shown that the choice is unique except for a multiplicative constant (the scale factor). An empirical temperature is often defined by the perfect gas thermometer. This temperature is related to the equation of state of a perfect gas by the equation $pV = NkT$. The thermodynamic temperature just defined is identical with this temperature since, as may easily be shown, the present treatment leads to the same equation of state. We may hence rewrite the expression for the entropy as

$$S = k\left[\ln Q_N + \frac{U}{kT} \right] + S_0 \qquad (24\text{-}14)$$

In this way it is possible to introduce temperature and entropy by a method analogous to thermodynamics. Clearly S and T are both state functions.

To complete the statistical proof of the second law of thermodynamics it would be necessary to show that the entropy of an isolated system never decreases. This is the content of the famous H-theorem, the proof of which is much too lengthy to be included here.[24]

Entropy at absolute zero and the third law of thermodynamics. The constant S_0, which occurs in the definition of entropy just given, is independent of the temperature and the mechanical properties of the system. In the limit as the temperature goes to absolute zero

$$\lim_{T \to 0} S = \lim_{T \to 0} k \left[\ln \sum g_j e^{-E_i/kT} + \frac{\partial \ln \sum g_j e^{-E_i/kT}}{\partial \ln T} \right] + S_0$$

$$= k[\ln g_0] + S_0 \tag{24-15}$$

in which g_0 is the degeneracy of the ground state of the system.

Let us now consider two states of the same system: One state consists of the chemical AB in a vessel at absolute zero; the other state consists of two vessels—one of A and one of B—both at absolute zero. It is possible to conceive of a reversible process by which the system may be transferred from one state to the other. Hence the two states AB and $A + B$ are really two states of the same system, differing only in the mechanical parameters describing the state. Since S_0 is the same for both states, the entropy difference in the states of the system is

$$S_{AB} - S_{A+B} = k \ln (g_{AB}/g_A g_B) \tag{24-16}$$

If all three materials, A, B, and AB are such that their ground states are nondegenerate, then $g_A = g_B = g_{AB} = 1$ and

$$\Delta S = S_{AB} - (S_A + S_B) = 0 \tag{24-17}$$

For many systems the lowest state is normally considered to be multiply degenerate. However, there is usually a small separation of the energy levels due to small perturbations which are ordinarily neglected. As kT approaches zero, these very small separations become effectively large compared with kT. Hence it is probable that, strictly speaking, the ground state is always nondegenerate and Eq. 24-17 is valid.

Inasmuch as S_0 always cancels out, it is convenient to let it be exactly zero and define the entropy as

$$S = k \ln Q_N + \frac{U}{T} \tag{24-18}$$

With this definition, the third law of thermodynamics assumes the form

$$\lim_{T \to 0} S = k \ln g_0 \tag{24-19}$$

and if the ground state of the system is nondegenerate

$$\lim_{T \to 0} S = 0 \tag{24-20}$$

---

[24] See for example R. H. Tolman [*33*] for a summary of the proofs of this theorem in classical and quantum statistics.

The quantity g_0 is the true degeneracy of the lowest quantum state of the system. However, in making comparisons with calorimetrically measured entropies it may be necessary to modify somewhat the meaning of this quantity. For if the separation of the lowest levels of the system is small compared with kT_0, where T_0 is the lowest measurable temperature, there would be a small hump in the specific heat curve at a lower temperature. The contribution of this hump to the entropy would be ignored in the integration of experimental C_p/T data. For this purpose it is necessary to consider as degenerate the group of levels separated by energies small compared to kT_0, where T_0 is the lowest temperature attained in the experimental measurements.

The thermodynamic properties in terms of the partition function. We have thus seen how the fundamental thermodynamic functions, energy and entropy, can be expressed in terms of the partition function which in turn depends upon the energy levels of the system. Therefore, if detailed information about the energy levels of a system is available, it is possible to calculate all of the thermodynamic properties from the partition function. The relations needed for this may be summarized as follows:

$$U = kT^2 \left(\frac{\partial \ln Q_N}{\partial T} \right) \tag{24-21}$$

$$C_V = \frac{\partial}{\partial T} \left(kT^2 \frac{\partial \ln Q_N}{\partial T} \right) \tag{24-22}$$

$$S = k \ln Q_N + \frac{U}{T} \tag{24-23}$$

$$A = U - TS = -kT \ln Q_N \tag{24-24}$$

For systems in which the only external mechanical parameter is the volume V, we have the additional relations

$$p = - \left(\frac{\partial A}{\partial V} \right)_T = kT \left(\frac{\partial \ln Q_N}{\partial V} \right)_T \tag{24-25}$$

$$H = U + pV = kT^2 \left(\frac{\partial \ln Q_N}{\partial T} \right)_V + kTV \left(\frac{\partial \ln Q_N}{\partial V} \right)_T \tag{24-26}$$

$$F = H - TS = -kT \ln Q_N + kTV \left(\frac{\partial \ln Q_N}{\partial V} \right)_T \tag{24-27}$$

The first of these last three relations is used in the derivation of the equation of state from statistical mechanics.[25]

[25] See J. de Boer [*32*]; see also J. O. Hirschfelder, C. F. Curtiss, and R. B. Bird [*34*].

B,25. The Evaluation of the Thermodynamic Properties of Ideal Gases. In this article we discuss in detail an important application of the principles of statistical thermodynamics, namely the calculation of the thermodynamic properties of gases at sufficiently low densities that their behavior can be considered to be ideal. It is first shown that the symmetry restrictions imposed on the wave functions for systems made up of identical particles lead to two types of distributions of energy among the molecules in the gas: one for Fermi-Dirac gases and another for Bose-Einstein gases. At high temperatures, the two distribution functions approach one another, and the thermodynamic properties of the two kinds of gases become the same. This limiting form for the two types of statistics is referred to as "Boltzmann Statistics." In the latter portion of this article, the thermodynamic properties of Boltzmann gases are calculated and the contributions due to the internal degrees of freedom are discussed.

The partition function for an ideal gas. If the density of a gaseous system of N molecules is sufficiently low and if the intermolecular forces are short range (compared to Coulombic), the amount of time any molecule spends in collisions is negligible compared with the time between collisions. Under such conditions one may say that the intermolecular potential energy is negligible with respect to the total energy of the system and hence that the total energy is just the sum of the energies of the individual molecules. Each of the molecules may be in any one of the quantum states of the free molecule. However, since the molecules are identical, the state of the gas is specified by the number of molecules in each state, and it is meaningless to specify which molecules are in which states. That is, the kth state of the gas with energy E_k is specified by a set of occupation numbers, n_j^k, which give the number of molecules in the jth molecular quantum state.

Let the energy of a molecule in the jth state be ϵ_j. Then since the energy of the gas is the sum of that of the individual molecules, the energy of the gas in the kth state is

$$E_k = \sum_j n_j^k \epsilon_j \qquad (25\text{-}1)$$

Clearly, the n_j^k satisfy the relation

$$N = \sum n_j^k \qquad (25\text{-}2)$$

There is in addition a possible restriction on the n_j^k due to statistics. The occupation numbers are restricted to 0 and 1 for Fermi-Dirac statistics. However, for Bose-Einstein particles the symmetry requirements on the wave function of the gas do not limit the number of molecules in any state.

The partition function for the entire gas may be written as

$$Q_N = \sum_k e^{-E_k/kT}$$

$$= \sum_k e^{-(\Sigma_j n_j^k \epsilon_j)/kT}$$

$$= \sum_k w_1^{n_1^k} w_2^{n_2^k} w_3^{n_3^k} \cdots \qquad (25\text{-}3)$$

in which

$$w_j = e^{-\epsilon_j/kT} \qquad (25\text{-}4)$$

It is understood that the sum k is taken only over those sets of n_j^k which are consistent with the statistics of the individual molecules, and the constraint Eq. 25-2.

Let us now define a generating function $f(\zeta)$ by

$$f(\zeta) = \prod_j (1 \pm \zeta w_j)^{\pm 1} \qquad (25\text{-}5)$$

In this expression and those which follow, the upper sign corresponds to Fermi-Dirac statistics and lower sign to Bose-Einstein statistics. The partition function, Q_N, is then just the coefficient of ζ^N in the expansion of $f(\zeta)$. If ζ is now taken to be a complex variable, we can divide $f(\zeta)$ by ζ^{N+1} and use the method of residues (or Cauchy's theorem) to obtain Q_N:

$$Q_N = \frac{1}{2\pi i} \oint_C \zeta^{-N-1} f(\zeta) d\zeta \qquad (25\text{-}6)$$

The closed contour, C, selected for the integration in the complex domain must be chosen in such a way as to enclose $\zeta = 0$. This integral can be evaluated by the "method of steepest descents" and the result is

$$\ln Q_N = -N \ln \zeta_0 \pm \sum_j \ln (1 \pm \zeta_0 e^{-\epsilon_j/kT}) \qquad (25\text{-}7)$$

in the limit that N is large (i.e. a large sample with negligible surface effects). The auxiliary relation

$$N = \sum_j (\zeta^{-1}_0 e^{\epsilon_j/kT} \pm 1)^{-1} \qquad (25\text{-}8)$$

serves to define the parameter ζ_0 which is a positive real number.

Distribution of energy among the molecules of an ideal gas. Let us now consider the energy distribution among the molecules of a Fermi-Dirac and Bose-Einstein gas. As mentioned above, the probability that the system is in state k is proportional to $e^{-E_k/kt}$. Hence the probable number of molecules in state j is given by

⟨ 184 ⟩

$$\overline{n}_j = \frac{\sum_k n_j^k e^{-E_k/kT}}{\sum_k e^{-E_k/kT}} \tag{25-9}$$

When the quantities E_k are expressed by means of Eq. 25-1

$$\overline{n}_j = \frac{\sum_k n_j^k e^{-(\sum_i n_i^k \epsilon_i)/kT}}{Q_N} \tag{25-10}$$

so that one finally obtains

$$\overline{n}_j = -\frac{kT}{Q_N}\left(\frac{\partial Q_N}{\partial \epsilon_j}\right) \tag{25-11}$$

Care must be exercised in obtaining $(\partial Q_N/\partial \epsilon_j)$ from Eq. 25-7 for ζ_0 is a function of the quantities ϵ_j. The result of the differentiation is[26]

$$\overline{n}_j = (\zeta_0^{-1} e^{\epsilon_j/kT} \pm 1)^{-1} \quad \begin{matrix} + \text{ sign: Fermi-Dirac} \\ - \text{ sign: Bose-Einstein} \end{matrix} \tag{25-12}$$

This describes the manner in which the energy in a Fermi-Dirac or Bose-Einstein gas is distributed among the individual molecules. The parameter ζ_0 may easily be shown to be related to the Gibbs free energy by $F = NkT \ln \zeta_0$.

For most actual systems $\zeta_0^{-1} \gg 1$, the main exceptions being electrons in metals and substances at extremely low temperatures or very high densities. To a good approximation $\zeta_0^{-1} = 3.122 \times 10^{-4} V_0(\mathfrak{M}T)^{\frac{3}{2}}$, where V_0 is the volume in cm³ per mole and $\mathfrak{M}$ is the molecular weight. For a perfect gas at standard conditions $\zeta_0^{-1} = 31{,}590\mathfrak{M}^{\frac{3}{2}}$. Systems which have a value of ζ_0^{-1} small enough so that the ± 1 cannot be neglected are sometimes referred to as "degenerate" systems or are said to be "in a state of degeneracy." For most applications we can use the distribution

$$\overline{n}_j \cong \zeta_0 e^{-\epsilon_j/kT} \tag{25-13}$$

We see thus that the Fermi-Dirac and Bose-Einstein distributions approach as a limit the Maxwell-Boltzmann distribution. Furthermore, in this limit the partition function for the gas as given by Eq. 25-7 becomes

$$Q_N = \frac{Q^N}{N!} \tag{25-14}$$

where Q is the partition function for one molecule in the vessel

$$Q = \sum_j e^{-\epsilon_j/kT} \tag{25-15}$$

The $N!$ which appears here is of course due fundamentally to the indistinguishability of the molecules. Systems whose partition functions are given by Eq. 25-14 are said to obey Boltzmann statistics. The problem

[26] The distribution functions for Fermi-Dirac and Bose-Einstein gases may also be obtained by combinatorial analysis. See, for example, R. H. Tolman, [*33*, Chap. 10].

of calculating the thermodynamic properties for the Boltzmann gas has thus been reduced to that of determining the partition function for one molecule in the vessel. The computation of the partition function for a single molecule is considered in the remaining part of this article.

Contributions to the thermodynamic properties due to the translational and internal motions of the molecules. For an accurate calculation of the partition function for complex molecules it is necessary to know all of the energy levels of the system. Because of the large number of degrees of freedom this is very difficult, and a great deal of information is required which is ordinarily not available. For most practical purposes, however, it suffices to idealize the situation and to neglect the weak couplings between various degrees of freedom.

Let $\mathcal{H}$ be the quantum mechanical Hamiltonian of a complex molecule, and let the wave function and energy corresponding to the jth quantum state be ψ_j and ϵ_j respectively, so that

$$\mathcal{H}\psi_j = \epsilon_j\psi_j \tag{25-16}$$

For present purposes, the set of energy levels ϵ_j is taken relative to the ground state as zero. (In considering mixtures of different chemical species it is necessary to refer the energy of the ground states of chemical species to a consistent set of standard states chosen for the elements. This is discussed below under the subheading: *Ideal gas mixtures.*) The motions executed by polyatomic molecules are very complex. In general, however, it is possible to consider the motion as being made up of six types of motion: the over-all translation of the molecule (tr); the various stretching and bending vibrations (vib); the rotational motion of the entire molecule (rot); the various rotations or restricted rotations of groups within the molecule (int rot); the electronic motion (elec); and the nuclear spin (nucl). These several motions are to various extents independent of one another. For example, the rotational motion is nearly independent of the electronic motion but frequently rather strongly linked to the vibrational motion. Nevertheless as a first approximation we may assume that these motions are completely independent so that

$$\mathcal{H} = \mathcal{H}^{(\text{tr})} + \mathcal{H}^{(\text{rot})} + \sum \mathcal{H}^{(\text{vib})} + \sum \mathcal{H}^{(\text{int rot})} + \sum \mathcal{H}^{(\text{elec})} + \sum \mathcal{H}^{(\text{nucl})} \tag{25-17}$$

$$= \mathcal{H}^{(\text{tr})} + \sum \mathcal{H}^{(\text{i})} \tag{25-18}$$

Here we designate the various internal (nontranslational) motions by superscript (i). This assumption then enables one to separate the Schrödinger equation (25-16) into component parts:

$$\mathcal{H}^{(\text{tr})}\phi_j^{(\text{tr})} = \epsilon_j^{(\text{tr})}\phi_j^{(\text{tr})} \tag{25-19}$$

$$\mathcal{H}^{(\text{i})}\phi_j^{(\text{i})} = \epsilon_j^{(\text{i})}\phi_j^{(\text{i})} \tag{25-20}$$

The solution of these individual Schrödinger equations gives the energy levels necessary to obtain partition functions for the various types of motions

$$Q^{(\text{tr})} = \sum_j e^{-\epsilon_j^{(\text{tr})}/kT} \tag{25-21}$$

$$Q^{(\text{i})} = \sum_j e^{-\epsilon_j^{(\text{i})}/kT} \tag{25-22}$$

Since the energy of the molecule in any state is assumed to be simply the sum of the energies associated with the several types of motion, we write the molecular partition function as

$$Q = Q^{(\text{tr})} \prod_i Q^{(\text{i})} \tag{25-23}$$

Now according to Eq. 25-14, the partition function for the entire gas of N molecules may be written as

$$Q_N = \frac{Q^N}{N!} = \frac{[Q^{(\text{tr})}]^N}{N!} \left[\prod_i Q^{(\text{i})} \right]^N \tag{25-24}$$

As it is always $\ln Q_N$ which appears in the expressions for the thermodynamic functions, these may be written as a sum of the contributions from the translational and various internal motions

$$X = X^{(\text{tr})} + \sum_i X^{(\text{i})} \tag{25-25}$$

in which X can be internal energy, specific heats, free energy, etc. It is customary to include the $N!$ in the translational contribution as indicated; the latter is the predominant contribution in most cases. Accordingly, the various contributions are given by[27]

$$U^{(\text{tr})} = NkT^2 \left(\frac{\partial \ln Q^{(\text{tr})}}{\partial T} \right) \qquad U^{(\text{i})} = NkT^2 \left(\frac{\partial \ln Q^{(\text{i})}}{\partial T} \right)$$

$$S^{(\text{tr})} = \frac{U^{(\text{tr})}}{T} + Nk \left[\ln \left(\frac{Q^{(\text{tr})}}{N} \right) + 1 \right] \qquad S^{(\text{i})} = \frac{U^{(\text{i})}}{T} + Nk \ln Q^{(\text{i})}$$

$$A^{(\text{tr})} = -NkT \ln \left(\frac{Q^{(\text{tr})}}{N} \right) - NkT \qquad A^{(\text{i})} = -NkT \ln Q^{(\text{i})}$$

$$H^{(\text{tr})} = U^{(\text{tr})} + NkT \qquad H^{(\text{i})} = U^{(\text{i})}$$

$$F^{(\text{tr})} = A^{(\text{tr})} + NkT \qquad F^{(\text{i})} = A^{(\text{i})}$$

$$C_v^{(\text{tr})} = (\partial U^{(\text{tr})}/\partial T)_v \qquad C_v^{(\text{i})} = (\partial U^{(\text{i})}/\partial T)_v$$

$$C_p^{(\text{tr})} = C_v^{(\text{tr})} + Nk \qquad C_p^{(\text{i})} = C_v^{(\text{i})} \tag{25-26}$$

[27] In the translational contributions, Stirling's formula for $\ln N!$ has been used:

$$\ln N! \cong N \ln N - N$$

Thus to calculate the thermodynamic functions of an ideal gas, one simply adds together the contributions for the various types of motion which are active within the molecules. A complete description of the methods for calculating these various contributions for complex molecules would require a discussion of great length and the inclusion of many tabulated functions. Inasmuch as such complete treatments of the subject are readily available in several standard references,[28] the discussion here is confined to several simple calculations for monatomic and diatomic molecules.

Translational contributions. Unless the gas is at a temperature very close to absolute zero, the translational contributions to the thermodynamic properties may be computed from the classical partition function. The molecule is considered to be confined to a volume V and its classical Hamiltonian is simply $(p_x^2 + p_y^2 + p_z^2)/2m$. Then the phase integral for the translational motion is

$$Q^{(\text{tr})} = \frac{V}{h^3} \int_{-\infty}^{+\infty} \int_{-\infty}^{+\infty} \int_{-\infty}^{+\infty} e^{-\frac{p_x^2 + p_y^2 + p_z^2}{2mkT}} dp_x dp_y dp_z \qquad (25\text{-}27)$$

in which the factor V results from the triple integration over the spatial coordinates x, y, z. The integration over the momenta is a standard integral, giving

$$Q^{(\text{tr})} = \frac{V}{h^3} (2\pi mkT)^{\frac{3}{2}} \qquad (25\text{-}28)$$

This shows explicitly how the partition function can depend on certain mechanical parameters of the system—in this case, the volume. From formulas relating the thermodynamic functions to the partition function the familiar relations for the quantities per mole,

$$U^{(\text{tr})} = \tfrac{3}{2}RT; \qquad C_V^{(\text{tr})} = \tfrac{3}{2}R; \qquad C_p^{(\text{tr})} = \tfrac{5}{2}R \qquad (25\text{-}29)$$

can be easily verified. It may also be shown that the entropy per mole is

$$S^{(\text{tr})} = R(\tfrac{3}{2} \ln M + \tfrac{3}{2} \ln T + \ln V) + 2.6546$$
$$= R(\tfrac{3}{2} \ln M + \tfrac{5}{2} \ln T - \ln p) - 2.3141 \qquad (25\text{-}30)$$

in which the constants are just combinations of various universal constants.[29] This expression for the entropy is the Sackur-Tetrode equation. For a monatomic gas, the translational contributions are the sole con-

---

[28] The most usable treatment is that given by J. E. Mayer and M. G. Mayer [*36*].

[29] These values for the constants are correct if R is in cal/mole degree, T is degrees K, V is liters, and p is atmospheres. Throughout the section we use the defined calorie, 4.1833 international Joules or 4.18401 absolute Joules as recommended by the National Bureau of Standards. Here we take $R = 1.98718$ cal/mole deg.

tributions to the thermodynamic properties. For gases composed of polyatomic molecules these are generally the primary contributions.

Rotational contributions in diatomic molecules. If a diatomic molecule is pictured as a rigid dumbbell with moment of inertia I rotating in space, solution of the Schrödinger equation for the system gives the energy and degeneracy of the Jth level, where J is the rotational quantum number

$$\epsilon_J^{(\text{rot})} = J(J+1)(\hbar^2/2I) \qquad (25\text{-}31)$$

$$g_J^{(\text{rot})} = 2J+1 \qquad (25\text{-}32)$$

Thus the partition function is

$$Q^{(\text{rot})} = \sum_{J=0}^{\infty} (2J+1)e^{-\frac{\hbar^2 J(J+1)}{2IkT}} \qquad (25\text{-}33)$$

The moment of inertia can be obtained from spectroscopic data. The Euler-Maclaurin summation formula is very useful for the evaluation of such expressions

$$\sum_{J=J_0}^{J=J_1} f(J) = \int_{J_0}^{J_1} f(J)dJ + \frac{1}{2}[f(J_0) + f(J_1)]$$

$$+ \sum_{k=1}^{\infty} (-1)^k \frac{B_k}{(2k)!} \left[\left(\frac{d^{2k-1}f}{dJ^{2k+1}}\right)_{J_0} - \left(\frac{d^{2k-1}f}{dJ^{2k-1}}\right)_{J_1} \right] \qquad (25\text{-}34)$$

Here the B_k are the Bernoulli numbers: $B_1 = \frac{1}{6}$, $B_2 = \frac{1}{30}$, $B_3 = \frac{1}{42}$, $B_4 = \frac{1}{30}$, $B_5 = \frac{5}{66}$, $\cdots$. Substituting

$$(2J+1)e^{-\hbar^2 J(J+1)/2IkT}$$

for $f(J)$ and letting $J_0 = 0$ and $J_1 = \infty$ we obtain

$$Q^{(\text{rot})} = \frac{2IkT}{\hbar^2} + \frac{1}{3} + \frac{1}{15}\left(\frac{\hbar^2}{2IkT}\right) + \cdots \qquad (25\text{-}35)$$

But for diatomic molecules at normal temperatures $(2IkT/\hbar^2) \gg 1$, so that only the first term is important.

It is usual to include in the denominator of the rotational partition function a symmetry number σ, which is 1 for heteronuclear and 2 for homonuclear diatomic molecules. This factor arises from the restrictions on the number of allowed quantum states imposed by the Pauli exclusion principle.

The first term of Eq. 25-35 (aside from the symmetry number) may be obtained from the evaluation of the classical phase integral. From these results one can obtain the following expressions for the thermodynamic properties per mole:

$$U^{(\text{rot})} = H^{(\text{rot})} = RT \tag{25-36}$$

$$C_p^{(\text{rot})} = C_V^{(\text{rot})} = R \tag{25-37}$$

$$S^{(\text{rot})} = R\left[1 + \ln\frac{2IkT}{\sigma\hbar^2}\right] \tag{25-38}$$

Vibrational contributions in diatomic molecules. If in a diatomic molecule the stretching of the bond is assumed to obey Hooke's law (the force tending to restore the molecule to its equilibrium position is directly proportional to the distortion of the bond) then the problem reduces itself to the solution of the Schrödinger equation for the one-dimensional simple harmonic oscillator. The energy level of the nth vibrational state is

$$\epsilon_n^{(\text{vib})} = h\nu(n + \tfrac{1}{2}) \tag{25-39}$$

These vibrational states are all nondegenerate. The vibrational partition function is usually defined in terms of energy above the zero-point energy, so that

$$Q^{(\text{vib})} = \sum_{n=0}^{\infty} e^{-nh\nu/kT} = \frac{1}{1 - e^{-h\nu/kT}} \tag{25-40}$$

The last step is achieved by using the formula for the sum of a geometric series. The associated thermodynamic contributions per mole are then

$$U^{(\text{vib})} = H^{(\text{vib})} = Nh\nu(e^{h\nu/kT} - 1)^{-1} \tag{25-41}$$

$$S^{(\text{vib})} = \frac{U^{(\text{vib})}}{T} - R\ln(1 - e^{-h\nu/kT}) \tag{25-42}$$

The frequency ν is the natural vibration frequency of the molecule and is obtained from vibration spectra. At high temperatures, corrections for the increasing anharmonicity of the oscillations must be applied.

Electronic contributions. In most molecules, rather high temperatures are required for the activation of the higher electronic levels. Consequently, in most cases $Q^{(\text{elec})}$ is simply the degeneracy of the electronic ground state. The electronic degeneracy for monatomic, diatomic, and polyatomic gases may be obtained from the spectroscopist's "term values" in the following manner:

1. Monatomic Molecules. In the term symbols for the electronic state of the atom (e.g. $^3P_3$, $^1S_2$, $^4F_0$), the right subscript indicates the total (orbital + spin) angular momentum J of all the electrons in the atom. The electronic degeneracy is given by:

$$g^{(\text{elec})} = 2J + 1 \tag{25-43}$$

2. Diatomic Molecules. In the term symbols for the electronic states of the diatomic molecules (e.g. $^3\Sigma_g^-$, $^2\Pi_u$, $^1\Delta_g$), the left superscript indicates the "spin multiplicity," $2S + 1$. The electronic degeneracy is then:

$$(2S + 1) \quad \text{for } \Sigma \text{ states}$$
$$2(2S + 1) \quad \text{for } \Pi, \Delta, \text{ etc. states}$$

3. Polyatomic Molecules. In polyatomic valence-saturated molecules, $g^{(\text{elec})} = 1$ or 2 according to whether there are an even or odd number of electrons (since for an even number of electrons there is no resultant spin angular momentum, but for an odd number of electrons there is a resultant spin of $\frac{1}{2}$).

Nuclear spin contributions. The nuclear spin partition function is simply the product of the nuclear spin multiplicities for all the atoms in the molecule

$$Q^{(\text{nucl})} = g^{(\text{nucl})} = \prod_j (2S_j^{(\text{nucl})} + 1) \tag{25-44}$$

where $S_j^{(\text{nucl})}$ is the nuclear spin of the jth atom. However, since this contribution affects only the additive constant on the entropy and always cancels out (except in processes involving transmutation of the elements) it is usually ignored. The result is "virtual" entropies rather than "absolute" entropies.

Ideal gas mixtures. It can be shown that for an ideal gas mixture containing N_A molecules of substance A and N_B molecules of B, $(N = N_A + N_B)$, the partition function is

$$Q_N = \frac{Q_A^{N_A} Q_B^{N_B}}{N_A! N_B!} e^{-\frac{N_A(\epsilon_0)_A + N_B(\epsilon_0)_B}{kT}} \tag{25-45}$$

Here the Q_A and Q_B are the molecular partition functions discussed above in which all the energies are referred to the ground states of the respective molecules. The factors $N_A!$ and $N_B!$ arise because of the indistinguishability of molecules of the same species in the same way that the $N!$ arises in the corresponding expression for the partition function of a pure substance. The $(\epsilon_0)_A$ and $(\epsilon_0)_B$ are the energies of the ground states of molecules A and B referred to a consistent set of standard states for the elements. Thus $(\epsilon_0)_A$ is the energy of formation of a molecule of A in the ground state from the elements of which it is composed, each being in its own standard state. The standard states of the elements are usually taken to be the elements in the form in which they naturally occur at zero degrees centigrade.

From the above expression (Eq. 25-45) for the partition function it is possible to calculate the various thermodynamic properties for mixtures of ideal gases. It is thus found that

$$U_{\text{mixture}} = \sum X_j U_j \qquad (25\text{-}46)$$

$$H_{\text{mixture}} = \sum X_j H_j \qquad (25\text{-}47)$$

$$C_{p_{\text{mixture}}} = \sum X_j C_{p_j} \qquad (25\text{-}48)$$

This last expression is valid only for nonreacting mixtures. The entropy for a mixture of gases is not simply the sum of contributions from the individual components. Substitution of the partition function for a mixture into Eq. 24-18 for the entropy shows that the entropy of a mixture is given by

$$S_{\text{mixture}} = \sum X_j S_j - Nk \sum X_j \ln X_j \qquad (25\text{-}49)$$

The quantity $-Nk\sum X_j \ln X_j$ is referred to as the entropy of mixing. Similar contributions due to mixing arise in the expressions for the free energy F and the work function A.

In treating the temperature dependence of the thermodynamical properties of a mixture, consideration must be given as to whether chemical reactions can be ignored or whether chemical equilibrium is maintained between specified molecular species. In the first case, the numbers N_A and N_B remain constant, whereas in the second case they vary in accordance with the equilibrium constants.

CHAPTER 5. THE KINETIC THEORY OF GASES[30]

J. O. HIRSCHFELDER   C. F. CURTISS

R. B. BIRD   E. L. SPOTZ

The preceding chapter is concerned with the properties of systems in equilibrium. In this chapter the statistical methods are applied to the description of the nonequilibrium properties—in particular the transport phenomena. In this chapter we arrive at expressions for the hydrodynamical equations and formulas for the transport coefficients. Sec. D deals with the evaluation and the practical computation of the transport coefficients.

We begin by showing that the properties of a dilute gas are completely described by the distribution function $f(\mathbf{r}, \mathbf{v}, t)$, defined so that $f(\mathbf{r}, \mathbf{v}, t)d\mathbf{r}d\mathbf{v}$ is the probable number of molecules which at time t have position coordinates $\mathbf{r}$ between $\mathbf{r}$ and $\mathbf{r} + d\mathbf{r}$ and have a velocity $\mathbf{v}$ be-

---

[30] This chapter is based upon material given in Chapter 7 of *Molecular Theory of Gases and Liquids*, by J. O. Hirschfelder, C. F. Curtiss, and R. B. Bird (John Wiley & Sons, Inc., 1954). The authors wish to thank the publisher for permission to use this material.

tween v and $v + dv$. This distribution function is given as the solution of an integro-differential equation, known as the Boltzmann equation. This equation is valid at densities sufficiently low that the effect of collisions involving more than two molecules is negligible. If the mean free path of the molecules in the gas is short compared with all of the macroscopic dimensions, the gas behaves as a continuum. Under such conditions the Boltzmann equation leads to the Navier-Stokes equations of hydrodynamics and expressions for the flux vectors. The transport coefficients are defined in terms of the flux vectors. Expressions for the transport coefficients are obtained in terms of integrals involving the intermolecular potential function.

B,26. The Distribution Functions. The kinetic theory in this chapter is based on the Boltzmann equation which specifies the distribution function $f(r, v, t)$. We give here two derivations of the Boltzmann equation. The first, a simple physical derivation, gives physical interpretation to the various terms. The second, a more rigorous derivation, is based on the integration of the Liouville equation. Before presenting these derivations, we discuss some of the properties of the various kinetic theory distribution functions and their use in describing nonequilibrium systems.

Physical description of nonequilibrium systems.[31] The exact dynamical state of a system of particles is given by specifying the complete set of position and momentum coordinates of all the individual particles. According to the laws of classical mechanics a knowledge of the exact dynamical state at a particular time permits an exact prediction of the state at any future time.

It is virtually impossible to give a complete description of the state of a complex macroscopic system. We must content ourselves with descriptions of the system which are considerably less than complete. The problem of predicting the probable behavior of a system from incomplete information about the system at some specified time is a statistical one. It is useful to employ the technique of representing the system by means of an ensemble consisting of a large number of replicas of the single system. The state of the ensemble is then described by a distribution function $f^{(N)}(r^N, p^N, t)$ in the phase space of a single system. This distribution function is so chosen that averages over the ensemble are in exact agreement with the incomplete (macroscopic) knowledge of the state of the system at some specified time. Then the probable behavior of the system at subsequent times is taken to be the average behavior of members of the representative ensemble. There are, of course, many different ways in which the ensemble could be formed, and therefore the distribution function is not uniquely specified. In the equilibrium case, the ensemble is specified by the ergodic theorem of Birkhoff. Such

[31] The discussion presented here is similar to that of H. Grad [37].

a theorem has not yet been developed in the nonequilibrium case. However, this offers no difficulties, since the study of nonequilibrium statistical mechanics is principally concerned with the lower order distribution functions, $f^{(1)}$ and $f^{(2)}$. Equations for the lower order distribution functions are derived by introducing restrictions, such as the concept of "molecular chaos," which effectively restrict the consideration to certain types of distribution functions $f^{(N)}$.

The variation of the distribution function $f^{(N)}(\mathbf{r}^N, \mathbf{p}^N, t)$ with time is described by the Liouville equation. This equation, involving $6N$ variables, is difficult to solve. Fortunately, one is usually not interested in a description of the system as complete as that afforded by $f^{(N)}$. Rather, one is satisfied with the less complete description given by one of the lower order distribution functions, $f^{(h)}(\mathbf{r}^h, \mathbf{p}^h, t)$. These functions are obtained by integrating $f^{(N)}$ over the coordinates of the $N - h$ molecules not included in the group $1, 2, 3, \ldots, h$. Of particular interest are the distribution functions with $h = 1$ and $h = 2$.

In this chapter we are concerned primarily with the function $f^{(1)}(\mathbf{r}, \mathbf{p}, t)$ which gives the probability of finding one particular molecule with the specified position and momentum. The configuration and momenta of the other $N - 1$ molecules remain unspecified. In considering a system made up of identical molecules, the distribution function $f^{(N)}$ is symmetric in the coordinates of all the molecules, inasmuch as no physical experiment differentiates among them. Consequently, in obtaining $f^{(1)}$ it is immaterial which molecule is singled out as special. Clearly, $f^{(1)}$ is adequate for the description of all of the physical properties of gases which do not depend upon the relative positions of two or more molecules. This means that the level of information corresponding to $f^{(1)}$ is sufficient for studying the behavior of moderately dilute gases.

For gases at higher density, a knowledge of higher order distribution functions is required. If, however, two-body forces can be assumed (i.e. $\Phi(\mathbf{r}^N) = \frac{1}{2}\sum_{i,j} \phi_{ij}$), the distribution function of order $h = 2$ is sufficient to determine all of the macroscopic properties of the system. The distribution function $f^{(2)}(\mathbf{r}_1, \mathbf{r}_2, \mathbf{p}_1, \mathbf{p}_2, t)$ is the distribution in the phase space of pairs. This pair distribution function is used in the study of the behavior of dense gases.

Let us now consider the time-dependence of the various distribution functions. As already mentioned, the manner in which $f^{(N)}$ changes with time is given by the Liouville equation. That is, to each $f^{(N)}$ at an initial time t_0 there corresponds uniquely a function $f^{(N)}$ at a later time t_1. However, for the lower order distribution functions, it is not possible to predict from a knowledge of $f^{(h)}(t_0)$ a unique value of $f^{(h)}(t_1)$. For example, at t_0 it is possible that there are a number of functions $f^{(N)}(t_0)$, $f^{(N)'}(t_0)$, $f^{(N)''}(t_0)$, $\ldots$ which, when integrated over the variables corresponding to $N - 1$ molecules, all give the same function $f^{(1)}(t_0)$. Later on the group of Nth order functions becomes $f^{(N)}(t_1)$, $f^{(N)\prime}(t_1)$, $f^{(N)\prime\prime}(t_1)$, . . . , and there correspond to these functions the singlet distribution functions $f^{(1)}(t_1)$, $f^{(1)\prime}(t_1)$, $f^{(1)\prime\prime}(t_1)$, . . . which are in general different from one another. This means that no unique integro-differential equation exists for $f^{(1)}$. In order to remove this ambiguity it is necessary to invoke an additional condition which restricts the possible functions $f^{(N)}$. This is the condition of *molecular chaos*, which is introduced into the derivation of the Boltzmann equation for $f^{(1)}$.

A physical derivation of the Boltzmann equation. Let us consider a monatomic gas mixture in a nonequilibrium state. The gas is assumed to be sufficiently dilute that two-body but not three-body collisions are important. For generality we suppose that the molecules of the ith species are subject to an external force, $\mathbf{X}_i$. In this treatment $\mathbf{X}_i$ may be a function of position and time, but not of velocity. The effect of velocity-dependent forces is considered in a somewhat different manner [*38*]. The external force is assumed to be much smaller than the forces which act on the molecules during an encounter. The intermolecular forces are generally of the order of many powers of ten times the force of gravity and act only during the very short time of encounter.

As discussed above we are interested in the description of the gas in terms of the distribution function in the phase space of a single molecule (μ space). In the case of a mixture there is a distribution function $f_i^{(1)}(\mathbf{r}, \mathbf{p}_i, t)$ for each component such that the probable number of molecules of kind i with position coordinates in the range $d\mathbf{r}$ about $\mathbf{r}$ and with momentum coordinates in the range $d\mathbf{p}_i$ about $\mathbf{p}_i$ is $f_i^{(1)}(\mathbf{r}, \mathbf{p}_i, t)d\mathbf{r}d\mathbf{p}_i$. According to equilibrium statistical mechanics the function $f_i^{(1)}$ at equilibrium is independent of time and space and the velocity distribution is Maxwellian. Now it is desired to ascertain the manner in which $f_i^{(1)}(\mathbf{r}, \mathbf{p}_i, t)$ depends upon the variables in nonequilibrium situations. That is, we wish to determine the nature of the flow of phase points through a six-dimensional phase space, where each phase point represents one molecule and the molecules interact with one another. If there were no interaction between the individual molecules, the behavior of the function $f_i^{(1)}(\mathbf{r}, \mathbf{p}_i, t)$ would be given by a Liouville equation for points in μ space. We shall find, in fact, that the assumption of interaction simply modifies the Liouville equation by the addition of terms which account for molecular collisions.

We visualize a region of volume $d\mathbf{r}d\mathbf{p}_i$ located about a point $\mathbf{r}, \mathbf{p}_i$. In this element of volume there are $f_i^{(1)}d\mathbf{r}d\mathbf{p}_i$ phase points associated with particles of the ith kind. In the absence of collisions in the gas, the molecules corresponding to these phase points move in such a way that at time $t + dt$, their position vectors[32] are $[\mathbf{r} + (\mathbf{p}_i/m_i)dt]$ and their momentum vectors are $[\mathbf{p}_i + \mathbf{X}_idt]$. No other phase points arrive at this

[32] Here we use explicitly the properties of Cartesian coordinate systems.

latter position (in absence of collisions), so that

$$f_i^{(1)}(\mathbf{r}, \mathbf{p}_i, t)d\mathbf{r}d\mathbf{p}_i = f_i^{(1)}\left[\left(\mathbf{r} + \frac{\mathbf{p}_i}{m_i}\,dt\right), (\mathbf{p}_i + \mathbf{X}_idt), (t + dt)\right]d\mathbf{r}d\mathbf{p}_i \quad (26\text{-}1)$$

But since collisions are taking place in the gas, not all of the phase points at [$\mathbf{r}$, $\mathbf{p}_i$] arrive at

$$\left[\left(\mathbf{r} + \frac{\mathbf{p}_i}{m_i}\,dt\right), (\mathbf{p}_i + \mathbf{X}_idt)\right]$$

after the interval dt, for the molecules associated with these phase points which are deflected from their course by collisions suffer changes in momentum. There are also some phase points which did not begin at $\mathbf{p}$, $\mathbf{r}_i$ but which, as a result of colliding with other molecules, arrive at

$$\left[\left(\mathbf{r} + \frac{\mathbf{p}_i}{m_i}\,dt\right), (\mathbf{p}_i + \mathbf{X}_idt)\right]$$

Let the number of molecules of the ith kind, lost from the momentum range $\mathbf{p}_i$ to $\mathbf{p}_i + d\mathbf{p}_i$ in the position range $\mathbf{r}$ and $\mathbf{r} + d\mathbf{r}$ because of collisions with molecules of type j during the time interval dt, be $\Gamma_{ij}^{(-)}d\mathbf{r}d\mathbf{p}_idt$. Similarly, the number of molecules of the ith kind which in a time dt join the group of points which started from [$\mathbf{r}$, $\mathbf{p}_i$] because of collision with molecules of type j is denoted by $\Gamma_{ij}^{(+)}d\mathbf{r}d\mathbf{p}_idt$. When the equation for the flow of phase points takes into account the effects of collisions, it becomes

$$f_i^{(1)}\left[\left(\mathbf{r} + \frac{\mathbf{p}_i}{m_i}\,dt\right), (\mathbf{p}_i + \mathbf{X}_idt), (t + dt)\right]d\mathbf{r}d\mathbf{p}_i$$
$$= f_i^{(1)}(\mathbf{r}, \mathbf{p}_i, t)d\mathbf{r}d\mathbf{p}_i + \sum_j [\Gamma_{ij}^{(+)} - \Gamma_{ij}^{(-)}]d\mathbf{r}d\mathbf{p}_idt \quad (26\text{-}2)$$

The term on the left-hand side of this equation may be expanded in a Taylor series about the point $\mathbf{r}$, $\mathbf{p}_i$, t,

$$f_i^{(1)}\left[\left(\mathbf{r} + \frac{\mathbf{p}_i}{m_i}\,dt\right), (\mathbf{p}_i + \mathbf{X}_idt), (t + dt)\right]d\mathbf{r}d\mathbf{p}_i$$
$$= \left[f_i^{(1)}(\mathbf{r}, \mathbf{p}_i, t) + \frac{1}{m_i}\,(\mathbf{p}_i \cdot \nabla f_i^{(1)})dt + (\mathbf{X}_i \cdot \nabla_{p_i}f_i^{(1)})dt\right.$$
$$\left. + \left(\frac{\partial f_i^{(1)}}{\partial t}\right)dt + \cdots\right]d\mathbf{r}d\mathbf{p}_i \quad (26\text{-}3)$$

These two equations may be combined to give the Boltzmann equation:

$$\frac{\partial f_i^{(1)}}{\partial t} + \frac{1}{m_i}\,(\mathbf{p}_i \cdot \nabla f_i^{(1)}) + (\mathbf{X}_i \cdot \nabla_{p_i}f_i^{(1)}) = \sum_j (\Gamma_{ij}^{(+)} - \Gamma_{ij}^{(-)}) \quad (26\text{-}4)$$

which describes the time rate of change of the function $f_i^{(1)}$. It has the same general form as the Liouville equation except for the addition of the collision terms on the right-hand side.

It should be mentioned that the quantities $\Gamma_{ij}^{(+)}$ and $\Gamma_{ij}^{(-)}$ do not include the contributions resulting from the molecules colliding with the walls. These contributions are taken into account in the boundary conditions which are imposed on the hydrodynamical equations.

An explicit expression for the terms on the right-hand side of the Boltzmann equation—the "collision integrals"—can be found from the following arguments: First we examine $\Gamma_{ij}^{(-)}$, the number of molecules of type i which are removed from the volume element $d\mathbf{r} d\mathbf{p}_i$ by collisions with the molecules of type j during an element of time dt. Let us consider

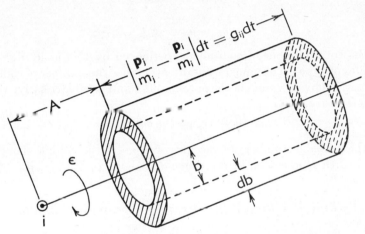

Fig. B,26. Collisions of molecules of type "j" with one molecule of type "i."

a molecule of type i, located at the position $\mathbf{r}$, and having a momentum $\mathbf{p}_i$. We wish to find the probability that this molecule will experience a collision with a molecule of type j, in the time interval dt, with the impact parameter[33] in a range db about b. If molecule "i" is considered to be fixed, then molecule "j" approaches it with a relative velocity $[(\mathbf{p}_j/m_j) - (\mathbf{p}_i/m_i)]$. This way of looking at the collision is pictured in Fig. B,26. It is assumed that the intermolecular force is negligible for distances of separation greater than a distance A, which is small compared to the mean free path.

From Fig. B,26 it is seen that any molecule of type j within the cylindrical shell will undergo an encounter with molecule i during the time interval dt—an encounter characterized by an impact parameter b

---

[33] The impact parameter b is the distance of closest approach of the two molecules if they continued to move in straight lines with their initial velocities and were not acted upon by intermolecular forces.

and an initial relative velocity

$$g_{ji} = \frac{\mathbf{p}_j}{m_j} - \frac{\mathbf{p}_i}{m_i} \tag{26-5}$$

This picture is useful for visualizing collisions with molecule i by molecules of type j under conditions where the impact parameter is b, and the relative velocity is $\mathbf{g}_{ij}$. The distance A is essentially the intermolecular distance at which the potential begins to "take hold." During a short time interval dt any molecule of type j, which is located in the cylinder of base $b\,db\,d\epsilon$ and height $g_{ij}dt$, will begin to undergo a collision with the molecule i. The probable number of molecules of type j within this cylinder is

$$f_j^{(1)}(\mathbf{r},\ \mathbf{p}_j,\ t)g_{ij}b\,db\,d\epsilon\,dt \tag{26-6}$$

where

$$g_{ij} = g_{ji} = |\mathbf{g}_{ji}| \tag{26-7}$$

Now the total number of collisions experienced by this molecule i with molecules of type j is obtained by adding together the number of collisions characterized by all values of the parameters b and ϵ and all relative velocities $\mathbf{g}_{ji}$. The result is

$$dt \iiint f_j^{(1)}(\mathbf{r},\ \mathbf{p}_j,\ t)g_{ij}b\,db\,d\epsilon\,d\mathbf{p}_j \tag{26-8}$$

Since the probable number of molecules of type i in the volume element $d\mathbf{r}$ about $\mathbf{r}$ with momentum in the range $d\mathbf{p}_i$ about $\mathbf{p}_i$ is $f_i^{(1)}(\mathbf{r},\ \mathbf{p}_i,\ t)d\mathbf{r}d\mathbf{p}_i$, it follows that

$$\Gamma_{ij}^{(-)}d\mathbf{r}d\mathbf{p}_idt = d\mathbf{r}d\mathbf{p}_idt \iiint f_j^{(1)}(\mathbf{r},\ \mathbf{p}_j,\ t)f_i^{(1)}(\mathbf{r},\ \mathbf{p}_i,\ t)g_{ij}b\,db\,d\epsilon\,d\mathbf{p}_j \tag{26-9}$$

Hence

$$\Gamma_{ij}^{(-)} = \iiint f_i^{(1)}f_j^{(1)}g_{ij}b\,db\,d\epsilon\,d\mathbf{p}_j \tag{26-10}$$

represents the contribution to $\partial f_i^{(1)}/\partial t$ due to the removal from the group of molecules i by collisions with molecules of j. (In the last equation $f_i^{(1)}$ and $f_j^{(1)}$ are abbreviations for $f_i^{(1)}(\mathbf{r},\ \mathbf{p}_i,\ t)$ and $f_j^{(1)}(\mathbf{r},\ \mathbf{p}_j,\ t)$.)

The remaining portion of the collision integral $\Gamma_{ij}^{(+)}$ may be evaluated in a similar manner. Let us consider a collision between molecules with momenta $\mathbf{p}_i$ and $\mathbf{p}_j$ characterized by an impact parameter b. The momenta of the molecules after collision are denoted by $\mathbf{p}_i'$ and $\mathbf{p}_j'$. The values of the momenta after the collision are determined by the values of the momenta before the collision, the collision parameters, and the nature of the intermolecular force. For potential functions which are spherically symmetric it follows from the conservation of energy that the absolute values of the relative velocity before and after the collision are equal,

$$g_{ij} = g_{ij}' \tag{26-11}$$

And from the conservation of angular momentum the impact parameters before and after the collisions are equal,

$$b = b' \tag{26-12}$$

Because of the symmetry of the dynamical equations, a collision, with impact parameter b, between molecules with momenta $\mathbf{p}'_i$ and $\mathbf{p}'_j$ leaves the molecules with momenta $\mathbf{p}_i$ and $\mathbf{p}_j$.

By arguments identical with those above it follows that the probable number of collisions in the range $d\mathbf{r}$ about $\mathbf{r}$ in the time interval dt which result in molecules with momenta in the range $d\mathbf{p}_i$ about $\mathbf{p}_i$ is

$$\Gamma_{ij}^{(+)}d\mathbf{r}d\mathbf{p}_idt = d\mathbf{r}d\mathbf{p}'_idt \iiint f_i^{(1)}(\mathbf{r}, \mathbf{p}'_i, t)f_j^{(1)}(\mathbf{r}, \mathbf{p}'_j, t)g'_{ij}b'db'd\epsilon d\mathbf{p}'_j \tag{26-13}$$

Here the primed quantities are functions of the unprimed quantities, the functional relationship being determined by the nature of the intermolecular force. It is a direct consequence of the Liouville theorem that

$$d\mathbf{p}'_id\mathbf{p}'_j = d\mathbf{p}_id\mathbf{p}_j \tag{26-14}$$

This fact may be used, along with the equivalence before and after collision of both g_{ij} and b, to obtain $\Gamma_{ij}^{(+)}$

$$\Gamma_{ij}^{(+)} = \iiint f_i^{(1)'}f_j^{(1)'}g_{ij}bdbd\epsilon d\mathbf{p}_j \tag{26-15}$$

where $f_i^{(1)'}$ and $f_j^{(1)'}$ represent $f_i^{(1)}(\mathbf{r}, \mathbf{p}'_i, t)$ and $f_j^{(1)}(\mathbf{r}, \mathbf{p}'_j, t)$. This expression gives the contribution to $\partial f_i^{(1)}/\partial t$ due to additions to the group of molecules by collision processes.

Now the expressions for $\Gamma_{ij}^{(+)}$ and $\Gamma_{ij}^{(-)}$ are substituted into the Boltzmann equation as it appears in Eq. 26-4, and the following equation for $f_i^{(1)}(\mathbf{r}, \mathbf{p}_i, t)$ results:

$$\frac{\partial f_i^{(1)}}{\partial t} + \frac{1}{m_i}(\mathbf{p}_i \cdot \nabla f_i^{(1)}) + (\mathbf{X}_i \cdot \nabla_{p_i}f_i^{(1)})$$

$$= \sum_j \iiint (f_i^{(1)'}f_j^{(1)'} - f_i^{(1)}f_j^{(1)})g_{ij}bdbd\epsilon d\mathbf{p}_j \tag{26-16}$$

This is the important Boltzmann integro-differential equation for the distribution function. Such an equation may be written for all the components in the gas mixture. In each of these equations, the distribution functions for all of the components appear on the right-hand side of the equation under the integral sign. It should be kept in mind that the law of force enters these integrals implicitly. The functions $f_i^{(1)'}$ and $f_j^{(1)'}$ are functions of $\mathbf{p}'_i$ and $\mathbf{p}'_j$ which can be calculated from dynamical principles when $\mathbf{p}_i$, $\mathbf{p}_j$, b, and ϵ are given, along with the intermolecular potential energy.

This derivation of the Boltzmann equation has the advantage of simplicity and direct physical interpretation. However, some aspects of this treatment present logical difficulties, because of the finite extension of the molecules and because of the finite duration of a collision. To put the Boltzmann equation on a firmer foundation, Kirkwood [39] has derived it directly from the Liouville theorem.

The Boltzmann equation derived from the Liouville theorem. The state of a gas made up of N molecules is described by the distribution function $f^{(N)}(\mathbf{r}^N, \mathbf{p}^N, t)$ in the γ space of $6N$ dimensions. According to the Liouville equation, the time variation of the distribution function $f^{(N)}$ is given by the equation

$$\frac{\partial f^{(N)}}{\partial t} + \sum_i (\nabla_{p_i}H) \cdot (\nabla_{r_i}f^{(N)}) - \sum_i (\nabla_{r_i}H) \cdot (\nabla_{p_i}f^{(N)}) = 0 \quad (26\text{-}17)$$

or

$$\frac{\partial f^{(N)}}{\partial t} + \sum_{i=1}^N \left\{ \frac{1}{m_i} (\mathbf{p}_i \cdot \nabla_{r_i}f^{(N)}) + [(\mathbf{F}_i + \mathbf{X}_i) \cdot \nabla_{p_i}f^{(N)}] \right\} = 0 \quad (26\text{-}18)$$

where m_i is the mass of molecule i, $\mathbf{F}_i$ is the force on molecule i due to all of the other molecules, $\mathbf{X}_i$ is the force on molecule i due to an external field, and H is the Hamiltonian.

As stated earlier in this article, the macroscopic behavior of a gas is usually described with sufficient accuracy by a distribution function of lower order. For example, the macroscopic behavior of a gas at sufficiently low densities is described by the set of distribution functions $f_i^{(1)}$. These functions are defined as the integral of $f^{(N)}$ over the coordinates and momenta of all but one of the molecules. Because of the symmetry of $f^{(N)}$, this function depends only upon the species of the remaining molecule, indicated by the subscript i, and does not depend upon which molecule of the particular kind is chosen as special.

An equation for $f_i^{(1)}$ may be obtained from the Liouville equation (26-18) by integrating over the coordinates of $(N - 1)$ molecules. When such an integration is performed and use is made of the fact that $f_i^{(1)}$ vanishes when $|\mathbf{p}_i| \to \infty$ and also at the walls of the containing vessel, one obtains

$$\frac{\partial f_i^{(1)}}{\partial t} + \frac{1}{m_i} (\mathbf{p}_i \cdot \nabla f_i^{(1)}) + (\mathbf{X}_i \cdot \nabla_{p_i}f_i^{(1)})$$

$$= - \frac{1}{(N-1)!} \iint (\mathbf{F}_i \cdot \nabla_{p_i}f^{(N)})d\mathbf{r}^{N-1}d\mathbf{p}^{N-1} \quad (26\text{-}19)$$

This equation does not in itself define the behavior of $f_i^{(1)}$. As discussed above, whenever one lowers the level of description it is necessary to introduce a condition which effectively restricts the nature of the systems under consideration. In this case, in order to obtain the Boltzmann equation it is necessary to introduce the concept of "molecular chaos."

Kirkwood [*39*] showed that in the derivation of the Boltzmann equation, the assumption is made implicitly that the distribution functions, $f_i^{(1)}(t)$, do not change appreciably during the time of a collision. This may be seen in the following way: For the case of a gas containing a single component and having only two-body forces between the molecules, Eq. 26-19 reduces to

$$\frac{\partial f_1^{(1)}}{\partial t} + \frac{1}{m}(\mathbf{p}_1 \cdot \nabla f_1^{(1)}) + (\mathbf{X}_1 \cdot \nabla_{p_1} f_1^{(1)}) = -\iint (\mathbf{F}_{12} \cdot \nabla_{p_1} f_{12}^{(2)}) d\mathbf{r}_2 d\mathbf{p}_2 \quad (26\text{-}20)$$

where $\mathbf{F}_{12}$ is the force on molecule 1 due to molecule 2. If the intermolecular forces are short range, we can define a collision diameter r_0, such that $\mathbf{F}_{12}$ is effectively zero when $|\mathbf{r}_1 - \mathbf{r}_2| \geqq r_0$. All of the contributions to the integral of Eq. 26-20 come from regions where $|\mathbf{r}_1 - \mathbf{r}_2| < r_0$. The principle of molecular chaos assumes that outside this interaction sphere,

$$f_{12}^{(2)}(t) = f_1^{(1)}(t) f_2^{(1)}(t) \qquad |\mathbf{r}_1 - \mathbf{r}_2| \geqq r_0 \qquad (26\text{-}21)$$

But inside of the interaction sphere, the pair distribution function, $f_{12}^{(2)}(t)$, is not known explicitly. Let us propose a scheme by which $f_{12}^{(2)}(t)$ could be calculated in principle.

If we neglect the possibility of three-body collisions, there is only one trajectory in two-particle phase space passing through the point $\mathbf{r}_1$, $\mathbf{p}_1$; $\mathbf{r}_2$, $\mathbf{p}_2$. Thus following the trajectory backward in time, if the system is at $\mathbf{r}_1$, $\mathbf{p}_1$; $\mathbf{r}_2$, $\mathbf{p}_2$ at the time t, it must have been at a well-defined point $\mathbf{r}_1'$, $\mathbf{r}_2'$; $\mathbf{p}_1'$, $\mathbf{p}_2'$ at time $t - \delta t$. Let us define the time $\delta t(\mathbf{r}_1, \mathbf{r}_2; \mathbf{p}_1, \mathbf{p}_2; t)$ as the interval of time such that $|\mathbf{r}_1' - \mathbf{r}_2'| = r_0$. At this time, $f_{12}^{(2)}(\mathbf{r}_1', \mathbf{r}_2'; \mathbf{p}_1', \mathbf{p}_2', t - \delta t) = f_1^{(1)}(\mathbf{r}_1', \mathbf{p}_1', t - \delta t) f_2^{(1)}(\mathbf{r}_2', \mathbf{p}_2', t - \delta t)$. Thus it follows that,

$$f_{12}^{(2)}(\mathbf{r}_1, \mathbf{r}_2; \mathbf{p}_1, \mathbf{p}_2, t) = f_1^{(1)}(\mathbf{r}_1', \mathbf{p}_1', t - \delta t) f_2^{(1)}(\mathbf{r}_2', \mathbf{p}_2', t - \delta t) \quad (26\text{-}22)$$

Thus for every point $\mathbf{r}_2$, $\mathbf{p}_2$ in the integral of Eq. 26-20 the pair distribution function is related to one particle distribution function at a time $t - \delta t$ and for each point there is a different δt. The magnitude of δt is of the order of the duration of a collision and is small compared with the times involved in macroscopic measurements.

Kirkwood corrected for the existence of the various δt corresponding to different points $\mathbf{r}_2$, $\mathbf{p}_2$ by time averaging Eq. 26-19 over an interval somewhat longer than the duration of a collision. This time-averaging is denoted by a bar so that the time-averaged distribution function is $\bar{f}_i^{(1)}$. In this manner he obtained

$$\frac{\partial \bar{f}_i^{(1)}}{\partial t} + \frac{1}{m_i}(\mathbf{p}_i \cdot \nabla \bar{f}_1^{(1)}) + (\mathbf{X}_i \cdot \nabla_{p_i} \bar{f}_1^{(1)})$$

$$= 2\pi \sum_j \iiint (\overline{f_i^{(1)'} f_j^{(1)'}} - \overline{f_i^{(1)} f_j^{(1)}}) g_{ij} b \, db \, d\epsilon \, d\mathbf{p}_j \quad (26\text{-}23)$$

This equation would be the same as the simple Boltzmann equation derived in the previous subarticle if $\overline{f_i^{(1)}f_j^{(1)}} = \bar{f}_i^{(1)}\bar{f}_j^{(1)}$. This condition is satisfied provided the distribution functions do not change appreciably in the interval of time τ_0 (comparable to the duration of a collision) over which they are time-averaged. This may be seen in the following way:

$$\overline{f_i^{(1)}f_j^{(1)}} = \frac{1}{\tau_0} \int_{-\tau_0/2}^{\tau_0/2} f_i(t+\tau)f_j(t+\tau)d\tau$$

$$= f_i^{(1)}(t)f_j^{(1)}(t) + \frac{\tau_0^2}{24}\left(f_i^{(1)}\frac{\partial^2 f_j^{(1)}}{\partial t^2} + 2\frac{\partial f_i^{(1)}}{\partial t}\frac{\partial f_j^{(1)}}{\partial t} + f_j^{(1)}\frac{\partial^2 f_i^{(1)}}{\partial t^2}\right) \quad (26\text{-}24)$$

$$\bar{f}_i^{(1)}\bar{f}_j^{(1)} = \left(\frac{1}{\tau_0}\int_{-\tau_0/2}^{\tau_0/2} f_i^{(1)}(t+\tau)d\tau\right)\left(\frac{1}{\tau_0}\int_{-\tau_0/2}^{\tau_0/2} f_j^{(1)}(t+\tau)d\tau\right)$$

$$= f_i^{(1)}(t)f_j^{(1)}(t) + \frac{\tau_0^2}{24}\left(f_i^{(1)}\frac{\partial^2 f_j^{(1)}}{\partial t^2} + f_j^{(1)}\frac{\partial^2 f_i^{(1)}}{\partial t^2}\right)$$

In the usual derivations of the Boltzmann equation δt is neglected, and it is argued that the error introduced thereby is comparable to the error introduced by neglecting in the distribution function the distance between the centers of the molecules on collision. Both errors should be negligible provided the distribution functions do not change appreciably in times of the order of the collision duration nor in distances of the order of a molecular diameter.

The distribution in velocities. In most kinetic theory problems it is more convenient to work in terms of velocities rather than momenta. Hence in the remainder of this chapter we shall use the distribution function in coordinate-velocity space $f_i(\mathbf{r}, \mathbf{v}_i\ t)$, rather than the distribution function in coordinate momentum space $f_i^{(1)}(\mathbf{r}, \mathbf{p}_1, t)$. In terms of this function the Boltzmann equation is[34]

$$\frac{\partial f_i}{\partial t} + (\mathbf{v}_i \cdot \nabla f_i) + \frac{1}{m_i}(\mathbf{X}_i \cdot \nabla_{v_i} f_i) = 2\pi \sum_j \iiint (f_i'f_j' - f_if_j)g_{ij}b\,db\,d\epsilon\,d\mathbf{v}_j \quad (26\text{-}25)$$

This equation forms the basis for the discussion of the transport properties of gases.

B,27. The Equations of Change. The hydrodynamic equations of change, the equations of conservation of mass, momentum, and energy, may be derived directly from the Boltzmann equation. Certain expressions involving the distribution functions appear in the derivation of these equations. These expressions may be shown to represent the flux of mass,

---

[34] We omit the superscript (1) when the distribution function is written in terms of the velocities rather than the momenta.

momentum, and energy and are directly related to the diffusion velocity, the pressure tensor, and the heat flux. These relations are derived in the present article. The approximate solutions of the Boltzmann equation and evaluation of the fluxes are discussed in subsequent articles. We begin this article by presenting a set of definitions of the various velocities which are needed to discuss the hydrodynamic equations.

Molecular velocities and stream velocities. The *linear velocity* of a molecule of species j with respect to a coordinate system fixed in space is denoted by v_j, with components v_{jx}, v_{jy}, v_{jz}. Its magnitude $|v_j|$, or simply v_j, is called the molecular speed. For a chemical species j present at a number density n_j we define an *average velocity* $\bar{v}_j$ by

$$\bar{v}_j(\mathbf{r}, t) = \frac{1}{n_j} \int v_j f_j(\mathbf{r}, v_j, t) dv_j \qquad (27\text{-}1)$$

The average velocity is a function of position and time, and represents the macroscopic rate of flow of the chemical species j. The bar denotes, in general, the average value of a function of the velocity, e.g.

$$\bar{\alpha}(\mathbf{r}, t) = \frac{1}{n_j} \int \alpha(v_j) f_j(\mathbf{r}, v_j, t) dv_j \qquad (27\text{-}2)$$

is the average value of $\alpha(v_j)$.

The *mass average velocity* is defined by

$$v_0(\mathbf{r}, t) = \frac{1}{\rho} \sum n_j m_j \bar{v}_j \qquad (27\text{-}3)$$

in which $\rho(\mathbf{r}, t)$ is the over-all density of the gas at a particular point

$$\rho(\mathbf{r}, t) = \sum n_j m_j \qquad (27\text{-}4)$$

The mass average velocity is then a weighted mean, with each molecule being given a weight proportional to its mass. The momentum of the gas per unit volume is the same as if all the molecules were moving with the mass average velocity v_0. This velocity is also referred to as the *stream velocity* or the *flow velocity*.

The *peculiar velocity* of a molecule of species j is defined as the velocity of the molecule with respect to an axis moving with the mass average velocity v_0

$$V_j(v_j, \mathbf{r}, t) = v_j - v_0 \qquad (27\text{-}5)$$

The *diffusion velocity* of chemical species j is the rate of flow of molecules of j with respect to the mass average velocity of the gas,

$$\bar{V}_j(\mathbf{r}, t) = \bar{v}_j - v_0 \qquad (27\text{-}6)$$

Clearly, the diffusion velocity is also the average of the peculiar velocity and may be written in the form

$$\overline{\mathbf{V}}_j(\mathbf{r},\ t) = \frac{1}{n_j} \int (\mathbf{v}_j - \mathbf{v}_0) f_j(\mathbf{r},\ \mathbf{v}_j,\ t) d\mathbf{v}_j \qquad (27\text{-}7)$$

as a consequence of the definitions of $\bar{\mathbf{v}}_j$ and $\mathbf{V}_j$. (Note that $\mathbf{v}_0$ is a function of position and time, but not of the velocities $\mathbf{v}_j$.) It follows from the definitions of the diffusion velocity and the mass average velocity that

$$\sum n_j m_j \overline{\mathbf{V}}_j = \sum n_j m_j(\bar{\mathbf{v}}_j - \mathbf{v}_0) = 0 \qquad (27\text{-}8)$$

For the sake of simplicity in writing certain expressions in subsequent articles, a *reduced velocity* $\mathbf{W}_j$ is used frequently. It is defined by

$$\mathbf{W}_j = \sqrt{\frac{m_j}{2kT}}\ \mathbf{V}_j \qquad (27\text{-}9)$$

and its magnitude is designated by W_j.

We define the *kinetic theory temperature* in terms of the mean peculiar kinetic energy, averaged over all types of molecules

$$\frac{3}{2} kT = \frac{1}{n} \sum n_j \left(\frac{1}{2}\ m_j \overline{V_j^2} \right) \qquad (27\text{-}10)$$

where

$$n = \sum n_j \qquad (27\text{-}11)$$

is the total number density of the mixture. The concept of temperature was introduced in Art. 24 through thermodynamic arguments. It is of course necessary that the present definition be consistent with the earlier one. Since, however, the earlier discussion was restricted to equilibrium conditions, the previous definition has meaning only under these conditions. That the present more general definition reduces correctly in this limit is evident from the fact that the equilibrium distribution function (the Maxwellian distribution, given by Eq. 28-7) is a special case of the Boltzmann distribution function of Art. 25.

The flux vectors. In a gas under nonequilibrium conditions, gradients exist in one or more of the macroscopic physical properties of the system: composition, mass average velocity, and temperature. The gradients of these properties are the cause of the molecular transport of mass (m_j), momentum $(m_j\mathbf{V}_j)$, and kinetic energy $(\frac{1}{2}m_j\mathbf{V}_j^2)$ through the gas. Since the mechanism of the transport of each of these molecular properties can be treated similarly, they are designated collectively by ψ_j.

Let us now examine the transport of these properties ψ_j on the microscopic level. Imagine in the gas a small element of surface, dS, moving with the mass average velocity $\mathbf{v}_0$. The orientation of the surface is designated by a unit vector $\mathbf{n}$ normal to the surface. Then the velocity of molecules of the jth species with respect to the surface element dS is $\mathbf{V}_j$, according to the definition in Eq. 27-5. All those molecules of the jth species which have velocity[35] $\mathbf{V}_j$ and which cross dS during a time interval dt must at the beginning of this time interval be located in a cylinder with dS as its base and with generators parallel to $\mathbf{V}_j$ and of length $|\mathbf{V}_j|dt$ (see Fig. B,27a). This cylinder has a volume $(\mathbf{n}dS \cdot \mathbf{V}_j dt)$.

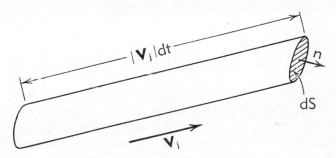

Fig. B,27a.   Elemental cylinder.

Since there are $f_j d\mathbf{V}_j$ molecules per unit volume which have a velocity $\mathbf{V}_j$, the number of molecules which cross dS during a time interval dt is

$$(\mathbf{n} \cdot \mathbf{V}_j) f_j d\mathbf{V}_j dS dt \qquad (27\text{-}12)$$

If associated with each molecule there is some property ψ_j, the magnitude of which depends on $\mathbf{V}_j$, then

$$(\mathbf{n} \cdot \mathbf{V}_j) \psi_j f_j d\mathbf{V}_j dS dt \qquad (27\text{-}13)$$

is the amount of this property transported across dS during the time interval dt by molecules with velocities in the range $d\mathbf{V}_j$ about $\mathbf{V}_j$. The flux of this property (that is, the amount which crosses per unit area per unit time) is then

$$\psi_j f_j (\mathbf{n} \cdot \mathbf{V}_j) d\mathbf{V}_j \qquad (27\text{-}14)$$

The total flux across the elementary surface is obtained by adding the contributions from molecules within all velocity ranges, and is accordingly:

$$\int \psi_j f_j (\mathbf{n}_j \cdot \mathbf{V}_j) d\mathbf{V}_j = (\mathbf{n} \cdot \quad \psi_j f_j \mathbf{V}_j d\mathbf{V}_j) \equiv (\mathbf{n} \cdot \mathbf{\Psi}_j) \qquad (27\text{-}15)$$

The vector

$$\mathbf{\Psi}_j = \int \psi_j f_j \mathbf{V}_j d\mathbf{V}_j \qquad (27\text{-}16)$$

is called the "flux vector" associated with the property ψ_j. This vector has the physical significance that the component of the vector in any direction $\mathbf{n}$ is the flux of the associated physical property across a surface normal to $\mathbf{n}$.

[35] Or more precisely those molecules whose velocities lie in a small range $d\mathbf{V}_j$ about $\mathbf{V}_j$.

Let us now examine the flux vectors related to the transport of mass, momentum, and kinetic energy:

1. Transport of Mass

If $\psi_j = m_j$, then[36]

$$\mathbf{\Psi}_j = m_j \int f_j \mathbf{V}_j d\mathbf{V}_j = n_j m_j \overline{\mathbf{V}}_j \tag{27-17}$$

is the flux vector associated with the transport of mass.

2. Transport of Momentum

If $\psi_j = m_j (\mathbf{v}_j - \mathbf{v}_0)_x = m_j V_{jx}$, then

$$\mathbf{\Psi}_j = m_j \int V_{jx} \mathbf{V}_j f_j d\mathbf{V}_j = n_j m_j \overline{V_{jx} \mathbf{V}_j} \tag{27-18}$$

is the flux vector associated with the transport of the x component of momentum (relative to $\mathbf{v}_0$). This vector has components proportional to $\overline{V_{jx} V_{jx}}$, $\overline{V_{jx} V_{jy}}$, and $\overline{V_{jx} V_{jz}}$. Similar flux vectors can be obtained for the y and z components of the momentum, making a total of three flux vectors associated with momentum transfer. The nine components of these three vectors form a symmetric second order tensor, $\mathbf{p}$,

$$(p_j)_{xx} = m_j \int f_j V_{jx} V_{jx} d\mathbf{V}_j = n_j m_j \overline{V_{jx} V_{jx}}$$

$$(p_j)_{xy} = (p_j)_{yx} = n_j m_j \overline{V_{jx} V_{jy}}$$

$$\cdots \tag{27-19}$$

Symbolically,

$$\mathbf{p}_j = n_j m_j \overline{\mathbf{V}_j \mathbf{V}_j} \tag{27-20}$$

is the tensor associated with the partial pressure of the jth chemical species in the gas. The sum of the partial pressure tensors over all the species in the gas gives the pressure tensor for the mixture:

$$\mathbf{p} = \sum \mathbf{p}_j = \sum n_j m_j \overline{\mathbf{V}_j \mathbf{V}_j} \tag{27-21}$$

The pressure tensor has the physical significance that it represents the flux of momentum through the gas. The individual components have the following meaning: The diagonal elements, p_{xx}, p_{yy}, p_{zz} are *normal stresses;* that is, p_{xx} is the force per unit area in the x direction exerted on a plane surface in the gas which is perpendicular to the x direction. The nondiagonal elements are *shear stresses;* that is, p_{yx} represents the force per unit area in the x direction exerted on a plane surface which is perpendicular to the y direction. The significance of the components, p_{yx}, p_{yy}, p_{yz}, which when combined together give a resultant force, $\mathbf{p}_y$, on a unit area perpendicular to the y direction, is shown in Fig. B,27b. The pressure tensor represents stresses or pressures measured by an instru-

[36] It is to be noted that in computing average quantities, integration over V_j is equivalent to integration over $\mathbf{v}_j$ since the two differ by a constant and the integration is over the entire range.

ment moving with the stream velocity v_0. The pressure as measured by a stationary gauge depends upon v_0 and the orientation of the gauge.

It is shown in Art. 29 that at equilibrium the shear stresses are zero and the normal stresses are equal. In this case the force on any surface element in the gas is constant and normal to the surface regardless of its orientation; that is

$$p_{xx} = p_{yy} = p_{zz} = p \qquad (27\text{-}22)$$

where p is the equilibrium hydrostatic pressure.

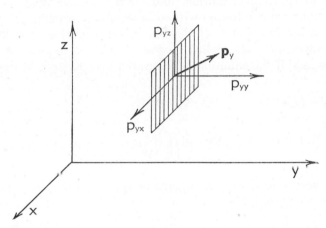

Fig. B,27b. Significance of the components of the pressure tensor. In this figure is shown a small element of surface whose normal is in the y direction. On this element, located in the body of a system of gas, there is a total force per unit area, $\mathbf{p}_y$. The components of this force are p_{yy} (a normal stress) and p_{yx} and p_{yz} (shear stresses). The nine components of this type make up the "pressure tensor."

3. Transport of Kinetic Energy

If $\psi_j = \frac{1}{2}m_j(\mathbf{v}_j - \mathbf{v}_0)^2 = \frac{1}{2}m_j V_j^2$, then

$$\boldsymbol{\Psi}_j = \tfrac{1}{2}m_j \int V_j^2 \mathbf{V}_j f_j d\mathbf{V}_j = \tfrac{1}{2}n_j m_j \overline{V_j^2 \mathbf{V}_j} \qquad (27\text{-}23)$$

is the flux vector associated with the transport of kinetic energy for molecules of the jth species. The sum of such vectors over all the components in the gas mixture is the "heat flux vector" $\mathbf{q}$:

$$\mathbf{q} = \sum \tfrac{1}{2}n_j m_j \overline{V_j^2 \mathbf{V}_j} \qquad (27\text{-}24)$$

This vector has the physical significance that its components q_x, q_y, and q_z represent the flux of kinetic energy in the x, y, and z directions respectively.

It should be noted that these are the correct expressions for the flux vectors in a dilute gas only. In a more dense gas there are additional terms due to "collisional transfer." When two molecules undergo a collision, a certain amount of momentum and energy is transferred almost instantaneously from the center of one molecule to that of the other. Now if in Fig. B,27a the centers of two molecules should be on the opposite sides of the surface element dS, the resulting collisional transfer provides a contribution to the fluxes which is not included in the above expressions.[37] This limitation will not be of importance in this chapter inasmuch as the effect of collisional transfer is negligible under conditions for which the Boltzmann equation which we use is valid.

The general equation of change.[38] The fundamental hydrodynamic equations of continuity, motion, and energy balance may be derived from the Boltzmann equation without actually determining the form of the distribution function f_i. If the Boltzmann equation (Eq. 26-25) for the ith component is multiplied by the quantity ψ_i associated with the ith species, and if the equation is integrated over $\mathbf{v}_i$, one obtains

$$\int \psi_i \left[\frac{\partial f_i}{\partial t} + (\mathbf{v}_i \cdot \nabla f_i) + \frac{1}{m_i} (\mathbf{X}_i \cdot \nabla_{v_i} f_i) \right] d\mathbf{v}_i$$

$$= \sum_j \iiiint \psi_i (f_i' f_j' - f_i f_j) g_{ij} b \, db \, d\epsilon \, d\mathbf{v}_i d\mathbf{v}_j \quad (27\text{-}25)$$

The three terms on the left-hand side of Eq. 27-25 may be transformed by simple manipulations:

$$\int \psi_i \frac{\partial f_i}{\partial t} \, d\mathbf{v}_i = \frac{\partial}{\partial t} \int \psi_i f_i d\mathbf{v}_i - \int f_i \frac{\partial \psi_i}{\partial t} \, d\mathbf{v}_i = \frac{\partial (n_i \overline{\psi_i})}{\partial t} - n_i \overline{\frac{\partial \psi_i}{\partial t}} \quad (27\text{-}26)$$

$$\int \psi_i v_{ix} \frac{\partial f_i}{\partial x} \, d\mathbf{v}_i = \frac{\partial}{\partial x} \int \psi_i v_{ix} f_i d\mathbf{v}_i - \int f_i v_{ix} \frac{\partial \psi_i}{\partial x} \, d\mathbf{v}_i$$

$$= \frac{\partial}{\partial x} (n_i \overline{\psi_i v_{ix}}) - n_i \overline{v_{ix} \frac{\partial \psi_i}{\partial x}} \quad (27\text{-}27)$$

$$\int \psi_i \frac{\partial f_i}{\partial v_{ix}} \, d\mathbf{v}_i = \iint [\psi_i f_i]_{v_{ix}=-\infty}^{v_{ix}=+\infty} dv_{iy} dv_{iz} - \int f_i \frac{\partial \psi_i}{\partial v_{ix}} \, d\mathbf{v}_i$$

$$= -n_i \overline{\frac{\partial \psi_i}{\partial v_{ix}}} \quad (27\text{-}28)$$

The last two equations have been written for only the x components.[39] In Eq. 27-28 the first term produced by the partial integration vanishes because the product $f_i \psi_i$ is assumed to diminish sufficiently rapidly for

[37] A detailed discussion of this has been given by Kirkwood [40]. Collisional transfer is very important in the theory of dense gases and liquids; see [34, Chap. 9].

[38] Although the derivation given here is valid only for dilute gases, the forms of the equations of change as derived in this article are valid even for dense gases and liquids.

[39] The quantity ψ_i may depend on $\mathbf{r}$ and t through $\mathbf{v}_0(\mathbf{r}, t)$. The quantities $\mathbf{r}$, $\mathbf{v}_i$, and t are taken as independent variables.

large v_i. We may use these last three equations to obtain

$$\frac{\partial n_i \overline{\psi_i}}{\partial t} + (\nabla \cdot n_i \overline{\psi_i v_i}) - n_i \left[\overline{\frac{\partial \psi_i}{\partial t}} + (\overline{v_i \cdot \nabla \psi_i}) + \left(\frac{X_i}{m_i} \cdot \overline{\nabla_{v_i} \psi_i} \right) \right]$$

$$= \sum_j \iiiint \psi_i (f_i' f_j' - f_i f_j) g_{ij} b \, db \, d\epsilon \, dv_i \, dv_j \quad (27\text{-}29)$$

This is known as Enskog's general "equation of change" for a physical quantity ψ_i associated with the ith kind of molecule. Summation over i gives the equation of change for the property ψ for the entire gas.

The vanishing of the collision integrals for the summational invariants. The equations of the type shown in Eq. 27-29 are not particularly useful for a general ψ_i because of the very complex integrals which occur on the right side. However, if ψ_i is the mass of the ith molecule, then because the masses of the individual molecules are unchanged in a collision,

$$\iiiint m_i (f_i' f_j' - f_i f_j) g_{ij} b \, db \, d\epsilon \, dv_i \, dv_j = 0 \quad (27\text{-}30)$$

Since mass, momentum, and energy are conserved during a collision, it follows that if ψ_i is m_i, $m_i V_i$, or $\frac{1}{2} m_i V_i^2$ then

$$\sum_{i,j} \iiiint \psi_i (f_i' f_j' - f_i f_j) g_{ij} b \, db \, d\epsilon \, dv_i \, dv_j = 0 \quad (27\text{-}31)$$

These equations enable one to simplify the general equation of change.

The validity of these last two equations may be justified by the following arguments: The integral,

$$\iiiint \psi_i (f_i' f_j' - f_i f_j) g_{ij} b \, db \, d\epsilon \, dv_i \, dv_j \quad (27\text{-}32)$$

is equal to the integral

$$\iiiint \psi_i' (f_i f_j - f_i' f_j') g_{ij}' b' \, db' \, d\epsilon \, dv_i' \, dv_j' \quad (27\text{-}33)$$

which is written in terms of inverse encounters, i.e. different symbols are used to indicate the integration variables. In Art. 26 it is stated that

$$g_{ij} = g_{ij}', \quad b = b', \quad \text{and} \quad dv_i \, dv_j = dv_i' \, dv_j' \quad (27\text{-}34)$$

so that Eq. 27-33 may be rewritten as

$$- \iiiint \psi_i' (f_i' f_j' - f_i f_j) g_{ij} b \, db \, d\epsilon \, dv_i \, dv_j \quad (27\text{-}35)$$

Since the integrals of Eq. 27-32 and 27-35 are equal, they are also each equal to one-half the sum of the two. The result of this "symmetrizing" operation is that

$$\iiiint \psi_i (f_i' f_j' - f_i f_j) g_{ij} b \, db \, d\epsilon \, dv_i \, dv_j$$

$$= \frac{1}{2} \iiiint (\psi_i - \psi_i')(f_i' f_j' - f_i f_j) g_{ij} b \, db \, d\epsilon \, dv_i \, dv_j \quad (27\text{-}36)$$

For the case that $\psi_i = m_i$ this equation shows immediately the validity of Eq. 27-30; for $(\psi_i - \psi_i') = 0$ expresses the fact that the masses of the individual molecules are not changed during an encounter.

Eq. 27-36 may be summed over both i and j; then the dummy indices may be interchanged to give the two equivalent expressions

$$\frac{1}{2}\sum_{i,j} \iiiint (\psi_i - \psi_i')(f_i'f_j' - f_if_j)g_{ij}bdbd\epsilon d\mathbf{v}_i d\mathbf{v}_j$$

$$= \frac{1}{2}\sum_{i,j} \iiiint (\psi_j - \psi_j')(f_i'f_j' - f_if_j)g_{ij}bdbd\epsilon d\mathbf{v}_i d\mathbf{v}_j \quad (27\text{-}37)$$

so that

$$\sum_{i,j} \iiiint \psi_i(f_i'f_j' - f_if_j)g_{ij}bdbd\epsilon d\mathbf{v}_i d\mathbf{v}_j$$

$$= \frac{1}{4}\sum_{i,j} \iiiint (\psi_i + \psi_j - \psi_i' - \psi_j')(f_i'f_j' - f_if_j)g_{ij}bdbd\epsilon d\mathbf{v}_i d\mathbf{v}_j \quad (27\text{-}38)$$

The vanishing of the expression $(\psi_i + \psi_j - \psi_i' - \psi_j')$ is used to define the invariants of the encounter. Consequently, Eq. 27-31 is valid for the properties m_i, $m_i\mathbf{V}_i$, and $\frac{1}{2}m_iV_i^2$.

Explicit expressions for the equations of change. Now that the validity of Eq. 27-30 and 27-31 has been demonstrated, this information may be used to derive the equations of change for specific molecular properties. This is done by letting ψ_i in Eq. 27-29 be m_i, $m_i\mathbf{V}_i$, and $\frac{1}{2}m_iV_i^2$ and then summing over the index i.

When $\psi_i = m_i$ we may follow this procedure and use the vanishing of the collision integrals just established to obtain

$$\frac{\partial n_i}{\partial t} + (\nabla \cdot n_i\bar{\mathbf{v}}_i) = 0 \quad (27\text{-}39)$$

which, in terms of the diffusion velocity, becomes

$$\frac{\partial n_i}{\partial t} + (\nabla \cdot n_i(\mathbf{v}_0 + \bar{\mathbf{V}}_i)) = 0 \quad (27\text{-}40)$$

These last two equations represent two forms of the "equation of continuity for the ith chemical species." If in the last expression each of the equations is multiplied by m_i and the equations added, then (since $\sum n_i m_i\bar{\mathbf{V}}_i = 0$)

$$\frac{\partial \rho}{\partial t} + (\nabla \cdot \rho\mathbf{v}_0) = 0 \quad (27\text{-}41)$$

This is the *equation of continuity* for the gas as a whole.

If we put $\psi_i = m_i\mathbf{V}_i$ in Eq. 27-29 and sum over i, the collision integrals on the right side of the equation vanish so that we obtain

$$\sum_i m_i \left[\frac{\partial n_i \overline{\mathbf{V}}_i}{\partial t} + (\nabla \cdot n_i \overline{\mathbf{v}_i \mathbf{V}_i}) - n_i \frac{\overline{\partial \mathbf{V}_i}}{\partial t} - n_i (\overline{\mathbf{v}_i \cdot \nabla \mathbf{V}_i}) - \frac{n_i}{m_i} (\mathbf{X}_i \cdot \overline{\nabla_{v_i} \mathbf{V}_i}) \right] = 0$$

(27-42)

This equation may be simplified by using the relation among the diffusion velocities (Eq. 27-8), the definition of the pressure tensor (Eq. 27-21), and the definition of the diffusion velocities (Eq. 27-6). It should be noted that in the differentiations $\mathbf{r}$ and $\mathbf{v}_i$ are considered as the independent variables. Then one obtains for the *equation of motion of the gas*

$$\frac{\partial \mathbf{v}_0}{\partial t} + (\mathbf{v}_0 \cdot \nabla \mathbf{v}_0) = -\frac{1}{\rho} (\nabla \cdot \mathbf{p}) + \frac{1}{\rho} \sum_i n_i \mathbf{X}_i \qquad (27\text{-}43)$$

If $\psi_i = \frac{1}{2} m_i V_i^2$ is used in the general equation of change, we may perform the manipulations just described to obtain

$$\sum_i \frac{1}{2} m_i \left[\frac{\partial n_i \overline{V_i^2}}{\partial t} + (\nabla \cdot n_i \overline{V_i^2 \mathbf{v}_i}) - n_i \frac{\overline{\partial V_i^2}}{\partial t} \right.$$

$$\left. - n_i (\overline{\mathbf{v}_i \cdot \nabla V_i^2}) - \left(\frac{\mathbf{X}_i}{m_i} \cdot \overline{\nabla_{v_i} V_i^2} \right) \right] = 0 \quad (27\text{-}44)$$

This equation may be transformed using the same methods as in the treatment of the equation of motion. If one introduces the pressure tensor, defined by Eq. 27-21, and the heat flux vector, defined by Eq. 27-24, one obtains the *equation of energy balance*

$$\frac{\partial}{\partial t} (\rho \hat{U}^{(\text{tr})}) + (\nabla \cdot \rho \hat{U}^{(\text{tr})} \mathbf{v}_0) + (\nabla \cdot \mathbf{q}) + (\mathbf{p} : \nabla \mathbf{v}_0)$$

$$- \sum_i n_i (\mathbf{X}_i \cdot \overline{\mathbf{V}}_i) = 0 \quad (27\text{-}45)$$

in which the notation $(\mathbf{p} : \nabla \mathbf{v}_0)$ means $\sum_i \sum_j p_{ij} (\partial V_{0i} / \partial x_j)$, and $\hat{U}^{(\text{tr})}$ is the translational contribution to the internal energy per unit mass defined by:[40]

$$\hat{U}^{(\text{tr})} = \frac{1}{\rho} \sum_i \frac{1}{2} n_i m_i \overline{V_i^2} \qquad (27\text{-}46)$$

This quantity represents the total energy of unit mass of gas in a coordinate frame moving with the mass average velocity $\mathbf{v}_0$ (that is, the kinetic energy of the over-all flow is not included), excluding the potential energy due to the external field.[41] If one uses the equation of continuity

---

[40] For molecules without internal degrees of freedom this is the only contribution to the internal energy. In general, however, there are other contributions.

[41] Some authors have written the energy balance equation in terms of an energy which includes either the kinetic energy associated with $\mathbf{v}_0$ or the potential energy associated with the external force, or both.

(Eq. 27-41), the equation of energy balance (Eq. 27-45) may be written in a somewhat different form:

$$\rho \frac{\partial \hat{U}^{(\mathrm{tr})}}{\partial t} + \rho(\mathbf{v}_0 \cdot \nabla \hat{U}^{(\mathrm{tr})}) = -(\nabla \cdot \mathbf{q}) - (\mathbf{p}:\nabla \mathbf{v}_0) + \sum n_i(\mathbf{X}_i \cdot \overline{\mathbf{V}}_i) \quad (27\text{-}47)$$

This may be restated in terms of the temperature by using the definitions of $\hat{U}^{(\mathrm{tr})}$ and T

$$\frac{3}{2} nk \left[\frac{\partial T}{\partial t} + (\mathbf{v}_0 \cdot \nabla T) \right] = -(\nabla \cdot \mathbf{q}) - (\mathbf{p}:\nabla \mathbf{v}_0)$$

$$+ \sum n_i(\mathbf{X}_i \cdot \overline{\mathbf{V}}_i) + \frac{3}{2} kT \left(\nabla \cdot \sum n_i \overline{\mathbf{V}}_i \right) \quad (27\text{-}48)$$

These last two equations are two forms of the energy balance equation. It may be shown that Eq. 27-47 is quite general and applies even in the case of a reacting mixture of polyatomic molecules, if $\hat{U}^{(\mathrm{tr})}$ is replaced by total internal energy per gram. However, Eq. 27-48 applies only to a non-reacting mixture of particles which have no internal degrees of freedom.

B,28. Enskog's Solution of the Boltzmann Equation. Various attempts have been made to obtain approximate solutions to the Boltzmann equation. We consider here the perturbation technique of Enskog, which is a modification of a method due to Hilbert. This method of successive approximations can, in principle, be extended to systems in which the gradients of the thermodynamic quantities are quite large. In the zeroeth approximation, the distribution function is locally Maxwellian, and one obtains the Eulerian equations of change. The first order perturbation leads to the Navier-Stokes[42] equations; the second order perturbation gives the Burnett equations. From the higher approximations there result more complicated equations in which the flux vectors depend progressively on higher derivatives of the thermodynamic quantities and higher powers of the lower derivatives. The results of the higher order perturbations are seldom used.

A gas in any initial state which is permitted to remain undisturbed for a sufficient length of time approaches a stationary state. If the gas is isolated adiabatically and not subject to an external force, the stationary state is a uniform condition in which all of the distribution functions are Maxwellian. The proof that the equilibrium distribution functions are Maxwellian (the H-theorem) is discussed below. The remaining portion of the article is devoted to a discussion of Enskog's solution of the Boltzmann equation, and includes a detailed consideration of the results of

---

[42] The Navier-Stokes equations apply to systems in which the gradients in the physical properties are small, i.e. in which the physical properties do not change appreciably in a distance of mean free path.

the first order perturbation. This method involves the solution of a set of integral equations by a variational procedure which leads to a rapidly converging series.

The H-theorem. The distribution functions describing the behavior of a gaseous mixture are the solutions of the set of Boltzmann equations, one for each component. From these equations, which are derived in Art. 26 and are given in final form in Eq. 26-25, we find that in the absence of external forces and under uniform conditions the time rate of change of the distribution functions f_i is given by

$$\frac{\partial f_i}{\partial t} = \sum_j \iiint (f_i' f_j' - f_i f_j) g_{ij} b\, db\, d\epsilon\, d\mathbf{v}_j \qquad (28\text{-}1)$$

That these functions approach a limiting form which is the Maxwellian distribution function is evident from the treatment of equilibrium statistical mechanics of Chap. 4. It is, however, of interest to show that the Boltzmann equations lead to an identical set of equilibrium distribution functions.

In order to examine the equilibrium solution it is convenient to introduce a function $H(t)$ defined by

$$H(t) = \sum_i \int f_i(\mathbf{v}_i, t) \ln f_i(\mathbf{v}_i, t) d\mathbf{v}_i \qquad (28\text{-}2)$$

This function is a generalization of the entropy defined in Chap. 4 and the proof of the H-theorem given here is a special case of the general statistical proof of the second law of thermodynamics. Differentiating $H(t)$ and making use of the Boltzmann equation for $\partial f_i/\partial t$, we obtain

$$\frac{dH}{dt} = 2\pi \sum_{i,j} \iiiint (1 + \ln f_i)(f_i' f_j' - f_i f_j) g_{ij} b\, db\, d\epsilon\, d\mathbf{v}_i\, d\mathbf{v}_j \qquad (28\text{-}3)$$

The integral on the right-hand side of this equation may be symmetrized by the method explained in the previous article to give

$$\frac{dH}{dt} = -\frac{1}{4} \sum_{i,j} \iiiint \left[\ln \frac{f_i' f_j'}{f_i f_j} \right] (f_i' f_j' - f_i f_j) g_{ij} b\, db\, d\epsilon\, d\mathbf{v}_i\, d\mathbf{v}_j \qquad (28\text{-}4)$$

Each of the integrands is of the form $(x - y) \ln (x/y)$ where in each case $x = f_i' f_j'$ and $y = f_i f_j$. If $x > y$ then both $(x - y)$ and $\ln (x/y)$ are positive; if $x < y$ then both $(x - y)$ and $\ln (x/y)$ are negative. Therefore the integrand of each of the integrals on the right of this equation is always positive or zero. Hence dH/dt is negative or zero so that $H(t)$ can never increase. From the definition of H it follows that it is bounded, and thus approaches a limit[43] for large values of t. In this limit the distribution functions are such that integrands of each of the integrals on the right of Eq. 28-4 are identically zero. Thus, at equilibrium,

$$\ln f_i + \ln f_j = \ln f'_i + \ln f'_j \tag{28-5}$$

which states that the logarithms of the distribution functions are summational invariants of a molecular collision.

It can be shown that the only summational invariants are linear combinations of the three (five scalar) invariants: the mass m_i, the momentum $m_i \mathbf{v}_i$, and the kinetic energy $\frac{1}{2}m_i v_i^2$. Thus at equilibrium the most general expression for $\ln f_i$ is of the form

$$\ln f_i = a_i m_i + [\mathbf{b}_i \cdot (m_i \mathbf{v}_i)] + c_i(\tfrac{1}{2}m_i v_i^2) \tag{28-6}$$

where a_i, $\mathbf{b}_i$, and c_i are constants depending (through the initial distribution functions) on the total number of molecules of kind i, the total momentum, and the total energy of the system. It is convenient to write this expression in terms of the physical parameters: n_i, the number density of molecules of kind i; $\mathbf{v}_0$, the mass average velocity, defined by Eq. 27-3; and the temperature T, defined by Eq. 27-10. In terms of these quantities the equilibrium distribution is

$$f_i = n_i \left(\frac{m_i}{2\pi kT}\right)^{\frac{3}{2}} e^{-m_i V_i^2/2kT} \tag{28-7}$$

where $\mathbf{V}_i = (\mathbf{v}_i - \mathbf{v}_0)$ is the peculiar velocity defined in Eq. 27-5.

At equilibrium, f_i is independent of time and hence the term on the right of Eq. 28-1 is zero. This constitutes a state of over-all balance in the collision processes: The number of molecules of kind i in a particular velocity range which are lost due to collisions is exactly compensated by the number created by the collision processes. However, the H-theorem states that the only equilibrium solution[44] to the Boltzmann equations is one in which not only the term on the right of Eq. 28-1 is zero but also the integrand of each integral is identically zero. This is proof of the statistical principle of "detailed balance." That is, at equilibrium the number of molecules of kind i in a particular velocity range which are lost due to collisions of a particular kind with molecules of kind j is exactly balanced by the number of reverse collisions.

[43] For simplicity consider a single pure component rather than a mixture. The function H can equal $-\infty$ only if the integral, $(a) = \int f \ln f dv$ fails to converge. Now, in any case the integral, $(b) = \int \frac{1}{2}mv^2 f dv$ which corresponds to the total kinetic energy of the molecules, must converge. A comparison of the integrals (a) and (b) indicates that (a) must converge provided that $\ln f$ does not approach infinity faster than v^2. However, if $\ln f$ approached infinity faster than v^2 it would imply that f itself decreased faster than $e^{-\frac{1}{2}(mv^2)}$ in which case the integral (a) would surely converge. Chapman and Cowling [38, p. 70] consider this problem carefully.

[44] The proof of this rests basically on the proof that the only summational invariants are linear combinations of the five scalars mentioned above.

The Enskog series [41]. The Boltzmann equations (26-25) may be written as

$$\frac{\partial f_i}{\partial t} + (\mathbf{v}_i \cdot \nabla f_i) + \frac{1}{m_i}(\mathbf{X}_i \cdot \nabla_{v_i} f_i) = \sum_j J(f_i, f_j) \tag{28-8}$$

where $J(f_i, f_j)$ is the "bilinear form"

$$J(f_i, f_j) = \iiint (f_i' f_j' - f_i f_j) g_{ij} b \, db \, d\epsilon \, d\mathbf{v}_j \tag{28-9}$$

representing the collision integrals.

The series solutions to the Boltzmann equations are obtained by introducing a perturbation parameter ζ into the Boltzmann equation in such a manner that the frequency of collisions can be varied in an arbitrary manner without affecting the relative number of collisions of a particular kind. Thus we consider a hypothetical problem in which the Boltzmann equation is

$$\frac{\partial f_i}{\partial t} + (\mathbf{v}_i \cdot \nabla f_i) + \frac{1}{m_i}(\mathbf{X}_i \cdot \nabla_{v_i} f_i) = \frac{1}{\zeta}\sum_j J(f_i, f_j) \tag{28-10}$$

and $1/\zeta$ measures the frequency of collisions. If ζ were small, collisions would be very frequent and the gas would behave like a continuum in which local equilibrium is everywhere maintained. The distribution function is expanded in a series in ζ,

$$f_i = f_i^{(0)} + \zeta f_i^{(1)} + \zeta^2 f_i^{(2)} + \cdots \tag{28-11}$$

If this series is introduced into the modified Boltzmann equation (28-10) and the coefficients of equal powers of ζ equated, one obtains the following set of equations for the functions, $f_i^{(0)}, f_i^{(1)}, f_i^{(2)}, \ldots$:

$$\sum_j J(f_i^{(0)}, f_j^{(0)}) = 0$$

$$\frac{\partial f_i^{(0)}}{\partial t} + (\mathbf{v}_i \cdot \nabla f_i^{(0)}) + \frac{1}{m_i}(\mathbf{X}_i \cdot \nabla_{v_i} f_i^{(0)}) = \sum_j [J(f_i^{(0)}, f_j^{(1)}) + J(f_i^{(1)}, f_j^{(0)})]$$

$$\frac{\partial f_i^{(1)}}{\partial t} + (\mathbf{v}_i \cdot \nabla f_i^{(1)}) + \frac{1}{m_i}(\mathbf{X}_i \cdot \nabla_{v_i} f_i^{(1)}) = \sum_j \left[\begin{array}{l} J(f_i^{(0)}, f_j^{(2)}) + J(f_i^{(1)}, f_j^{(1)}) \\ + J(f_i^{(2)}, f_j^{(0)}) \end{array} \right]$$

$$\cdots \tag{28-12}$$

These equations for the $f_i^{(r)}$ serve to determine the distribution function uniquely in the manner described below.

The first expression of Eq. 28-12 is the set of coupled integral equations considered in the discussion of the equilibrium solution of the

Boltzmann equation and the H-theorem. From the arguments presented there, it is clear that the most general solution of these equations is

$$f_i^{(0)} = n_i \left(\frac{m_i}{2\pi kT}\right)^{\frac{3}{2}} e^{-m_i(\mathbf{v}_i - \mathbf{v}_0)^2/2kT} \qquad (28\text{-}13)$$

The quantities

$$n_i = n_i(\mathbf{r},\, t), \qquad \mathbf{v}_0 = \mathbf{v}_0(\mathbf{r},\, t), \qquad T = T(\mathbf{r},\, t) \qquad (28\text{-}14)$$

are arbitrary functions of space and time insofar as this set of equations is concerned. In order for these functions to represent the local values of the physical quantities, i.e. number density, mass average velocity, and temperature, it is necessary that the solutions of the remaining equations be such that

$$\int f_i d\mathbf{v}_i = n_i \qquad (28\text{-}15)$$

$$\sum_{i,j} m_i \int \mathbf{v}_i f_i d\mathbf{v}_i = \rho \mathbf{v}_0 \qquad (28\text{-}16)$$

$$\tfrac{1}{2} \sum_i m_i \int (\mathbf{v}_i - \mathbf{v}_0)^2 f_i d\mathbf{v}_i = \tfrac{3}{2} nkT \qquad (28\text{-}17)$$

It may be shown [38] that the remaining integral equations of Eq. 28-12, along with the auxiliary conditions,

$$\int f_i^{(r)} d\mathbf{v}_i = 0 \quad r = 1, 2, 3, \cdots \qquad (28\text{-}18)$$

$$\sum_{i,j} m_i \int \mathbf{v}_i f_i^{(r)} d\mathbf{v}_i = 0 \quad r = 1, 2, 3, \cdots \qquad (28\text{-}19)$$

$$\tfrac{1}{2} \sum_i m_i \int (\mathbf{v}_i - \mathbf{v}_0)^2 f_i^{(r)} d\mathbf{v}_i = 0 \quad r = 1, 2, 3, \cdots \qquad (28\text{-}20)$$

specify uniquely a set of functions $f_i^{(r)}$. Since the set of distribution functions so defined satisfies the conditions of Eq. 28-15, 16, and 17, it is used as the solution to the Boltzmann equation.

The first order perturbation solution. The equation for the $f_i^{(1)}$ may be written in terms of a perturbation function ϕ_i, defined such that

$$f_i^{(1)}(\mathbf{r},\, \mathbf{v}_i,\, t) = f_i^{(0)}(\mathbf{r},\, \mathbf{v}_i,\, t)\phi_i(\mathbf{r},\, \mathbf{v}_i,\, t) \qquad (28\text{-}21)$$

In terms of this function the second of Eq. 28-12 becomes

$$\frac{\partial f_i^{(0)}}{\partial t} + (\mathbf{v}_i \cdot \nabla f_i^{(0)}) + \frac{1}{m_i}(\mathbf{X}_i \cdot \nabla_{v_i} f_i^{(0)})$$

$$= \sum_j \iiint f_i^{(0)} f_j^{(0)}(\phi_i' + \phi_j' - \phi_i - \phi_j) g_{ij} b\, db\, d\epsilon\, d\mathbf{v}_j \qquad (28\text{-}22)$$

The preceding auxiliary conditions, in terms of ϕ_i are:

$$\int f_i^{(0)} \phi_i d\mathbf{v}_i = 0 \qquad (28\text{-}23)$$

$$\sum_i m_i \int \mathbf{v}_i f_i^{(0)} \phi_i d\mathbf{v}_i = 0 \qquad (28\text{-}24)$$

$$\tfrac{1}{2} \sum_i m_i \int (\mathbf{v}_i - \mathbf{v}_0)^2 f_i^{(0)} \phi_i d\mathbf{v}_i = 0 \qquad (28\text{-}25)$$

As stated above this set of equations is just sufficient to define the perturbation functions ϕ_i uniquely.

The differentiations of the function $f_i^{(0)}$ indicated in Eq. 28-22 may be carried out. The resulting expressions involve space and time derivatives of the functions, $n_i(\mathbf{r}, t)$, $\mathbf{v}_0(\mathbf{r}, t)$, and $T(\mathbf{r}, t)$. The time derivatives are eliminated by means of the equations of change (27-40, 43, 48). It is consistent with this approximation to replace f_i by $f_i^{(0)}$ in the integrals for the flux vectors which occur in the equations of change (that is, we use $\overline{\mathbf{V}}_i = 0$, $\mathbf{p} = p\mathbf{1}$, $\mathbf{q} = 0$). The resulting equation for the perturbation function ϕ_i is

$$f_i^{(0)} \left[\frac{n}{n_i} (\mathbf{V}_i \cdot \mathbf{d}_i) + (\mathbf{b}_i : \nabla \mathbf{v}_0) - \left(\frac{5}{2} - W_i^2 \right) (\mathbf{V}_i \cdot \nabla \ln T) \right]$$

$$= \sum_j \iiint f_i^{(0)} f_j^{(0)} (\phi_i' + \phi_j' - \phi_i - \phi_j) g_{ij} b \, db \, d\epsilon \, d\mathbf{v}_j \qquad (28\text{-}26)$$

The quantities $\mathbf{d}_i$ and $\mathbf{b}_i$ are defined by

$$\mathbf{d}_i = \nabla \left(\frac{n_i}{n} \right) + \left(\frac{n_i}{n} - \frac{n_i m_i}{\rho} \right) \nabla \ln p - \left(\frac{n_i m_i}{p\rho} \right) \left[\frac{\rho}{m_i} \mathbf{X}_i - \sum_j n_j \mathbf{X}_j \right] \qquad (28\text{-}27)$$

$$\mathbf{b}_i = 2[\mathbf{W}_i \mathbf{W}_i - \tfrac{1}{3} W_i^2 \mathbf{1}] \qquad (28\text{-}28)$$

The dimensionless velocity $\mathbf{W}_i$ is defined by Eq. 27-9.

The integral equations. The perturbation function ϕ_i depends upon space and time only through the quantities n_i, $\mathbf{v}_0$, and T and their space derivatives. It is clear from the form of the integral equation for ϕ_i that this quantity is linear in the derivatives and has the form

$$\phi_i = -(\mathbf{A}_i \cdot \nabla \ln T) - (\mathbf{B}_i : \nabla \mathbf{v}_0) + n \sum_j (\mathbf{C}_i^{(j)} \cdot \mathbf{d}_j) \qquad (28\text{-}29)$$

where the $\mathbf{A}_i$, $\mathbf{B}_i$, and $\mathbf{C}_i^{(j)}$ are functions of the dimensionless velocity $\mathbf{W}_i$, the local composition, and the local temperature. If there are ν components to the chemical mixture, there are only $(\nu - 1)$ independent vectors $\mathbf{d}_i$, since according to the definition of the $\mathbf{d}_i$

$$\sum_i \mathbf{d}_i = 0 \qquad (28\text{-}30)$$

This fact enables us to set one of the $\mathbf{C}_i^{(j)}$ equal to zero for each i. To retain the symmetry we let

$$\mathbf{C}_i^{(i)} = 0 \qquad (28\text{-}31)$$

When the expression for ϕ_i in Eq. 28-29 is inserted into Eq. 28-26 and the coefficients of similar gradients are equated, there result separate integral equations for the functions $\mathbf{C}_i^{(j)}$, $\mathbf{B}_i$, and $\mathbf{A}_i$,[45]

$$\frac{1}{n_i} f_i^{(0)} (\delta_{ih} - \delta_{ik}) \mathbf{V}_i = \sum_j \cdot \iiint \ (\mathbf{C}_i^{(h)\prime} + \mathbf{C}_j^{(h)\prime} - \mathbf{C}_i^{(k)\prime}$$
$$- \mathbf{C}_j^{(k)\prime} - \mathbf{C}_i^{(h)} - \mathbf{C}_j^{(h)} + \mathbf{C}_i^{(k)} + \mathbf{C}_j^{(k)}) f_i^{(0)} f_j^{(0)} g_{ij} b \, db \, d\epsilon \, d\mathbf{v}_j \qquad (28\text{-}32)$$

$$f_i^{(0)} \mathbf{b}_i = - \sum_j \iiint \ (\mathbf{B}_i' + \mathbf{B}_j' - \mathbf{B}_i - \mathbf{B}_j) f_i^{(0)} f_j^{(0)} g_{ij} b \, db \, d\epsilon \, d\mathbf{v}_j \qquad (28\text{-}33)$$

$$f_i^{(0)} (\tfrac{5}{2} - W_i^2) \mathbf{V}_i = \sum_j \iiint \ (\mathbf{A}_i' + \mathbf{A}_j' - \mathbf{A}_i - \mathbf{A}_j) f_i^{(0)} f_j^{(0)} g_{ij} b \, db \, d\epsilon \, d\mathbf{v}_j \qquad (28\text{-}34)$$

---

[45] Eq. 28-32 is obtained in the following way: We have by inserting from Eq. 28-29 into Eq. 28-26

$$\frac{1}{n_i} f_i^{(0)} (\mathbf{V}_i \cdot \mathbf{d}_i) = \sum_{j,h} \iiint \ [(\mathbf{C}_i^{(h)\prime} + \mathbf{C}_j^{(h)\prime} - \mathbf{C}_i^{(h)} - \mathbf{C}_j^{(h)}) \cdot \mathbf{d}_h] f_i^{(0)} f_j^{(0)} g_{ij} b \, db \, d\epsilon \, d\mathbf{v}_j$$

Then making use of the fact that

$$\sum_j \mathbf{d}_j = 0$$

and making algebraic rearrangements,

$$\frac{1}{n_i} f_i^{(0)} \left(\mathbf{V}_i \cdot \sum_h \delta_{ih} \mathbf{d}_h \right)$$

$$= \sum_{h \neq k} \mathbf{d}_h \sum_j \iiint \left[\begin{matrix} \mathbf{C}_i^{(h)\prime} + \mathbf{C}_j^{(h)\prime} - \mathbf{C}_i^{(k)\prime} - \mathbf{C}_j^{(k)\prime} \\ -\mathbf{C}_i^{(h)} - \mathbf{C}_j^{(h)} + \mathbf{C}_{i_d}^{(k)} + \mathbf{C}_j^{(k)} \end{matrix} \right] f_i^{(0)} f_j^{(0)} g_{ij} b \, db \, d\epsilon \, d\mathbf{v}_j$$

The left-hand side may now be rewritten as

$$\frac{1}{n_i} f_i^{(0)} \left(\mathbf{V}_i \cdot \sum_{h \neq k} (\delta_{ih} - \delta_{ik}) \mathbf{d}_h \right)$$

and coefficients of $\mathbf{d}_h$ may now be equated to give Eq. 28-32.

In these equations the only variables involved are $n_i(\mathbf{r}, t)$, $T(\mathbf{r}, t)$, and $\mathbf{V}_i(\mathbf{r}, t)$. (Actually we choose to work with $\mathbf{W}_i(\mathbf{r}, t)$ rather than $\mathbf{V}_i(\mathbf{r}, t)$.) The spatial coordinates (or derivatives) do not occur explicitly. Consequently, $\mathbf{A}_i$, $\mathbf{B}_i$, and $\mathbf{C}_i^{(j)}$ are functions of the space coordinates only through the variables mentioned above. It may be shown that any vector function of $\mathbf{W}_i$, the only vector variable, is the vector itself multiplied by some scalar function of the absolute value of the vector $\mathbf{W}_i$. Hence $\mathbf{A}_i$ and $\mathbf{C}_i^{(j)}$ are of the form

$$\mathbf{C}_i^{(j)} = \mathbf{W}_i C_i^{(j)}(W_i) \qquad (28\text{-}35)$$

$$\mathbf{A}_i = \mathbf{W}_i A_i(W_i) \qquad (28\text{-}36)$$

It may also be shown that the only tensor $\mathbf{B}_i$, which is consistent with the form of the integral equation for $\mathbf{B}_i$, Eq. 28-33, is of the form

$$\mathbf{B}_i = [\mathbf{W}_i\mathbf{W}_i - \tfrac{1}{3}W_i^2\mathbf{1}]B_i(W_i) \qquad (28\text{-}37)$$

The integral equations for the $\mathbf{A}_i$, $\mathbf{B}_i$, and $\mathbf{C}_i^{(j)}$ (28-32, 33, and 34), are, of course, to be solved in conjunction with the auxiliary conditions imposed by Eq. 28-23, 24, and 25. In terms of these quantities the auxiliary relations become

$$\sum_i \sqrt{m_i} \int [(\mathbf{C}_i^{(j)} - \mathbf{C}_i^{(k)}) \cdot \mathbf{W}_i] f_i^{(0)} d\mathbf{v}_i = 0 \qquad (28\text{-}38)$$

$$\sum_i \sqrt{m_i} \int (\mathbf{A}_i \cdot \mathbf{W}_i) f_i^{(0)} d\mathbf{v}_i = 0 \qquad (28\text{-}39)$$

There is no auxiliary equation for the $\mathbf{B}_i$ analogous to these equations inasmuch as the functions of the form defined by Eq. 28-37 automatically satisfy the constraints given in Eq. 28-23, 24, and 25 for any arbitrary function $B_i(W_i)$.

Solutions to these integral equations have been obtained by two equivalent methods, that of Chapman and Cowling [38] and a variational method [42]. In both methods the scalar functions $C_i^{(j)}(W_i)$, $B_i(W_i)$, and $A_i(W_i)$ are expanded in a series of Sonine polynomials.[46] Chapman and Cowling used an *infinite series of these polynomials* with the result that the transport coefficients are expressed in terms of ratios of infinite determinants. To get numerical values it is necessary to consider only a few elements of these determinants since the convergence of the ratios of determinants is quite rapid as additional rows and columns are included. Here we discuss the problem from the standpoint of the variational method.

Because the integral equations given in Eq. 28-32, 33, and 34 are quite similar in form, it is possible to write one general equation for a

[46] See Eq. 28-57 for the definition of these polynomials.

tensor $T_i^{(h,k)}$, which includes all three of these equations,[47]

$$R_i^{(h,k)} = \sum_j \iiint [T_i^{(h,k)\prime} + T_j^{(h,k)\prime} - T_i^{(h,k)} - T_j^{(h,k)}]f_i^{(0)}f_j^{(0)}g_{ij}bdbd\epsilon d\mathbf{v}_j \quad (28\text{-}40)$$

The correspondence between the symbols $R_i^{(h,k)}$ and $T_i^{(h,k)}$, and their counterparts in Eq. 28-32, 33, and 34 is given in the following table:

Equation	$R_i^{(h,k)}$	$T_i^{(h,k)}$
(28-32)	$\dfrac{1}{n_i}f_i^{(0)}(\delta_{ih} - \delta_{ik})\mathbf{V}_i$	$\mathbf{C}_i^{(h)} - \mathbf{C}_i^{(k)}$
(28-33)	$-2f_i^{(0)}(\mathbf{W}_i\mathbf{W}_i - \tfrac{1}{3}W_i^2\mathbf{1})$	$\mathbf{B}_i$
(28-34)	$f_i^{(0)}(\tfrac{5}{2} - W_i^2)\mathbf{V}_i$	$\mathbf{A}_i$

It should be kept in mind that the subscript i in the symbol $T_i^{(h,k)}$ indicates that the tensor is a function of the velocity vector $\mathbf{W}_i$. The subscripts on the other symbols, $\mathbf{R}$, $\mathbf{A}$, $\mathbf{B}$, $\mathbf{C}$, have the same significance. We shall seek an approximate solution to the integral equation for $T_i^{(h,k)}$, Eq. 28-40, by a variational method. This equation, together with the auxiliary equation

$$\sum_i \sqrt{m_i} \int (T_i^{(h,k)} \cdot \mathbf{W}_i)f_i^{(0)}dv_i = 0 \quad (28\text{-}41)$$

(which is equivalent to Eq. 28-38 and 39) serves to specify $T_i^{(h,k)}$ uniquely.

Several important integral theorems. In the following development, several abbreviations in the notation will be useful. Let $\mathbf{G}_{ij}$ and $\mathbf{H}_{ij}$ be any two tensors, in general functions of both $\mathbf{W}_i$ and $\mathbf{W}_j$. Then let us define $[\mathbf{G}_{ij}; \mathbf{H}_{ij}]_{ij}$ by[48]

$$[\mathbf{G}_{ij}; \mathbf{H}_{ij}]_{ij} = -\frac{1}{n_i n_j} \iiiint (\mathbf{G}_{ij}:(\mathbf{H}_{ij}' - \mathbf{H}_{ij}))f_i^{(0)}f_j^{(0)}g_{ij}bdbd\epsilon d\mathbf{v}_i d\mathbf{v}_j \quad (28\text{-}42)$$

From symmetry arguments similar to those introduced in Art. 27 it follows that

$$[\mathbf{G}_{ij}; \mathbf{H}_{ij}]_{ij} = \frac{1}{2n_i n_j} \iiiint ((\mathbf{G}_{ij}' - \mathbf{G}_{ij}):(\mathbf{H}_{ij}' - \mathbf{H}_{ij}))$$
$$f^{(0)}f_j^{(0)}g_{ij}bdbd\epsilon d\mathbf{v}_i d\mathbf{v}_j \quad (28\text{-}43)$$

Hence the bracket is symmetrical with respect to the interchange of $\mathbf{G}_{ij}$ and $\mathbf{H}_{ij}$ and also of the i and j subscripts on the bracket

$$[\mathbf{G}_{ij}; \mathbf{H}_{ij}]_{ij} = [\mathbf{H}_{ij}; \mathbf{G}_{ij}]_{ij} = [\mathbf{G}_{ij}; \mathbf{H}_{ij}]_{ji} = [\mathbf{H}_{ij}; \mathbf{G}_{ij}]_{ji} \quad (28\text{-}44)$$

[47] Two of the equations involve the vector quantities (tensors of order 1) $\mathbf{A}_i$ and $\mathbf{C}_i^{(h)} - \mathbf{C}_i^{(k)}$.

[48] The subscript ij on the bracket indicates an integration over the variables $\mathbf{v}_i$ and $\mathbf{v}_j$.

This "square bracket" is a linear operator. If G_{ij} and H_{ij} have the form

$$G_{ij} = K_i + L_j, \qquad H_{ij} = M_i + N_j \tag{28-45}$$

where K_i and M_i depend only on W_i, and L_j and N_j depend only on W_j, then it is clear that

$$[K_i + L_j; M_i + N_j]_{ij} = [K_i; M_i + N_j]_{ij} + [L_j; M_i + N_j]_{ij}$$

$$= [K_i; M_i]_{ij} + [K_i; N_j]_{ij}$$

$$+ [L_j; M_i]_{ij} + [L_j; N_j]_{ij} \tag{28-46}$$

It should be noted that the subscripts on the symbols within the bracket indicate the functional dependence of the tensors on the velocities W_i and W_j. The subscript ij on the bracket itself indicates that the integral is evaluated for collisions between molecules i and j.

Let us consider two sets of tensor functions K_i and L_i and define an additional quantity in terms of these sets by

$$\{K; L\} = \sum_{i,j} n_i n_j [K_i + K_j; L_i + L_j]_{ij} \tag{28-47}$$

These "curly brackets" satisfy the following relations:

$$\{K; L\} = \{L; K\} \tag{28-48}$$

$$\{K; L + M\} = \{K; L\} + \{K; M\} \tag{28-49}$$

Inasmuch as $\{K; K\}$ represents a sum of integrals, all of which have non-negative integrands, it follows that

$$\{K; K\} \geqq 0 \tag{28-50}$$

It can easily be shown that the curly bracket $\{K; K\}$ vanishes if and only if K_i is a linear combination of the constants of motion. The only linear combination of the constants of motion which satisfies the auxiliary condition, Eq. 28-41, is identically zero. Hence, if we restrict the consideration to sets of tensor functions K_i which satisfy the auxiliary condition, it follows that the curly bracket $\{K; K\}$ vanishes if and only if each of the K_i are identically zero.

A variational principle. A variational principle may be employed now to obtain approximate solutions to the integral equations, Eq. 28-40. Let us use as trial functions a set of functions $t_i^{(h,k)}$, which satisfy the equations

$$\int (t_i^{(h,k)} : R_i^{(h,k)}) dv_i = - \sum_j n_i n_j [t_i^{(h,k)}; t_i^{(h,k)} + t_j^{(h,k)}]_{ij} \tag{28-51}$$

and which contain as many arbitrary parameters as is convenient.

If $t_i^{(h,k)}$ is "double-dotted" into the integral equation for $T_i^{(h,k)}$ (Eq.

28-40) and an integration carried out over $\mathbf{v}_i$, one obtains

$$\int (\mathbf{t}_i^{(h,k)} : \mathbf{R}_i^{(h,k)}) d\mathbf{v}_i = -\sum_j n_i n_j [\mathbf{t}_i^{(h,k)}; \mathbf{T}_i^{(h,k)} + \mathbf{T}_j^{(h,k)}]_{ij} \qquad (28\text{-}52)$$

where the $\mathbf{t}_i^{(h,k)}$ are the trial functions and the $\mathbf{T}_i^{(h,k)}$ are the exact solutions to the integral equations. Equating the right sides of the last two equations and summing over i, one obtains (after making use of the symmetry relations, Eq. 28-44 and the definition of the curly bracket, Eq. 28-47),

$$\{\mathbf{t}^{(h,k)}; \mathbf{T}^{(h,k)}\} = \{\mathbf{t}^{(h,k)}; \mathbf{t}^{(h,k)}\} \qquad (28\text{-}53)$$

Since the curly bracket of identical sets of functions is non-negative (Eq. 28-50),

$$\{\mathbf{T}^{(h,k)} - \mathbf{t}^{(h,k)}; \mathbf{T}^{(h,k)} - \mathbf{t}^{(h,k)}\} \geqq 0 \qquad (28\text{-}54)$$

Then making use of the linear operator property of the curly brackets, Eq. 28-49, and the relation between the trial functions and the exact solutions, Eq. 28-53, we find that,

$$\{\mathbf{t}^{(h,k)}; \mathbf{t}^{(h,k)}\} \leqq \{\mathbf{T}^{(h,k)}; \mathbf{T}^{(h,k)}\} \qquad (28\text{-}55)$$

This is the statement of the variational method of obtaining approximations to the solutions $\mathbf{T}_i^{(h,k)}$. Specifically, the method of solution is as follows: One begins by choosing a set of trial functions, $\mathbf{t}_i^{(h,k)}$, which contain a number of arbitrary parameters. Then if only those trial functions are considered which satisfy the auxiliary condition, Eq. 28-41, the equality sign in Eq. 28-55 applies only when $\mathbf{T}_i^{(h,k)}$ and $\mathbf{t}_i^{(h,k)}$ are identical. Thus the best approximation to the true solution of the integral equation is obtained by maximizing the curly bracket on the left of Eq. 28-55 with respect to all of the available parameters in the set of trial functions. That is, for the best approximation

$$\delta\{\mathbf{t}^{(h,k)}; \mathbf{t}^{(h,k)}\} = -2\delta \sum_i \int (\mathbf{t}_i^{(h,k)} : \mathbf{R}_i^{(h,k)}) d\mathbf{v}_i = 0 \qquad (28\text{-}56)$$

This, along with Eq. 28-51, which restricts the choice of the trial functions, forms the basis of the variational method of solution of the integral equations, Eq. 28-40.

The application of the variational principle. Let us now consider the implications of the variational principle discussed above when the trial functions are taken to be finite series of polynomials in the square of the velocity, W_i^2. It is convenient to make use of the Sonine polynomials, $S_n^{(m)}$, defined by[49]

[49] Except for the normalization these polynomials are the same as the associated Laguerre polynomials. The first two Sonine polynomials are

$$S_m^{(0)}(x) = 1$$
$$S_m^{(1)}(x) = m + 1 - x$$

$$S_n^{(m)}(x) = \sum_j \frac{(-1)^i (m+n)!}{(n+j)!(m-j)!j!} x^j \qquad (28\text{-}57)$$

These polynomials satisfy the orthogonality condition,

$$\int_0^\infty x^n e^{-x} S_n^{(m)}(x) S_n^{(m')}(x) dx = \frac{(n+m)!}{m!} \delta_{mm'} \qquad (28\text{-}58)$$

and are convenient, for as two special cases of this orthogonality relation we have

$$\int f_i^{(0)} S_{\frac{3}{2}}^{(m)}(W_i^2) V_i^2 d\mathbf{V}_i = \frac{3n_i kT}{m_i} \delta_{m0} \qquad (28\text{-}59)$$

$$\int f_i^{(0)} S_{\frac{5}{2}}^{(m)}(W_i^2) V_i^4 d\mathbf{V}_i = 15n_i \left(\frac{kT}{m_i}\right)^2 \delta_{m0} \qquad (28\text{-}60)$$

As the trial functions, $\mathbf{t}_i^{(h,k)}$, we now take a *finite* linear combination of the Sonine polynomials, $S_n^{(m)}(W_i^2)$,

$$\mathbf{t}_i^{(h,k)}(\mathbf{W}_i) = \mathbf{W}_i \sum_{m=0}^{\xi-1} \mathbf{t}_{im}^{(h,k)}(\xi) S_n^{(m)}(W_i^2) \qquad (28\text{-}61)$$

in which the values of the index, n, and the meaning of the tensor $\mathbf{W}_i$ are as follows:

When $\mathbf{T}_i^{(h,k)}$ is	The value of the index, n is	The quantity $\mathbf{W}_i$ is	The Sonine expansion coefficients $t_{im}^{(h,k)}$ will be designated by
$\mathbf{A}_i$	$\frac{3}{2}$	$\mathbf{W}_i$	$a_{im}(\xi)$
$\mathbf{B}_i$	$\frac{5}{2}$	$\mathbf{W}_i \mathbf{W}_i - \frac{1}{3} W_i^2 \mathbf{1}$	$b_{im}(\xi)$
$\mathbf{C}_i^{(h)} - \mathbf{C}_i^{(k)}$	$\frac{3}{2}$	$\mathbf{W}_i$	$c_{im}^{(h,k)}(\xi)$

For reasons which will become apparent later we have indicated the dependence of the expansion coefficients on the number of terms, ξ, used in the finite series trial function. These coefficients are *not* coefficients in an *infinite series* expansion and therefore do depend upon the number of terms used.

Let us define

$$R_{im}^{(h,k)} = \int (\mathbf{R}_i^{(h,k)} : \mathbf{W}_i) S_n^{(m)}(W_i^2) d\mathbf{V}_i \qquad (28\text{-}62)$$

and

$$g^{(h,k)} = \sum_{i,m} t_{im}^{(h,k)} R_{im}^{(h,k)} \qquad (28\text{-}63)$$

In terms of these quantities the constraints on the trial functions, Eq. 28-51, become

$$w_i^{(h,k)} = 0 \qquad (28\text{-}64)$$

where

$$w_i^{(h,k)} = \sum_{m=0}^{\xi-1} t_{im}^{(h,k)} R_{im}^{(h,k)}$$

$$+ \sum_j \sum_{m=0}^{\xi-1} \sum_{m'=0}^{\xi-1} n_i n_j t_{im}^{(h,k)} \left[\begin{array}{l} t_{im'}^{(h,k)} [\mathbf{W}_i S_n^{(m)}(W_i^2); \mathbf{W}_i S_n^{(m')}(W_i^2)]_{ij} \\ + t_{jm'}^{(h,k)} [\mathbf{W}_i S_n^{(m)}(W_i^2); \mathbf{W}_j S_n^{(m')}(W_j^2)]_{ij} \end{array} \right] \quad (28\text{-}65)$$

and the statement of the variational criterion, Eq. 28-56, becomes

$$\delta g^{(h,k)} = 0 \quad (28\text{-}66)$$

The problem then is to find the extremum of $g^{(h,k)}$ subject to the constraints of Eq. 28-64. This extremum is determined by the method of the Lagrangian multipliers. Let $\lambda_i^{(h,k)}$ be the multipliers. Then Eq. 28-64 and the equations,

$$\left(\frac{\partial g^{(h,k)}}{\partial t_{im}^{(h,k)}} \right) + \sum_r \lambda_r^{(h,k)} \left(\frac{\partial w_r^{(h,k)}}{\partial t_{im}^{(h,k)}} \right) = 0 \quad (28\text{-}67)$$

are sufficient to determine the $\lambda_i^{(h,k)}$ and the expansion coefficients $t_{im}^{(h,k)}(\xi)$. Performing the indicated differentiations, we get

$$[1 + \lambda_i^{(h,k)}] R_{im}^{(h,k)}$$

$$+ \sum_j \sum_{m'=0}^{\xi-1} n_i n_j \left[\begin{array}{l} 2\lambda_i^{(h,k)} t_{im'}^{(h,k)} [\mathbf{W}_i S_n^m(W_i^2); \mathbf{W}_i S_n^{(m')}(W_i^2)]_{ij} \\ + (\lambda_i^{(h,k)} + \lambda_j^{(h,k)}) t_{jm'}^{(h,k)} [\mathbf{W}_i S_n^{(m)}(W_i^2); \mathbf{W}_j S_n^{(m')}(W_j^2)]_{ij} \end{array} \right] = 0$$

$$i = 1, 2, \cdots, \nu \quad (28\text{-}68)$$

$$m = 0, 1, \cdots, \xi - 1$$

The only solution to this set of equations together with Eq. 28-64 is

$$\lambda_i^{(h,k)} = 1 \quad i = 1, 2, 3, : \cdots, \nu \quad (28\text{-}69)$$

with the constants $t_{im}^{(h,k)}(\xi)$ determined by Eq. 28-68, with $\lambda_i^{(h,k)} = 1$. The equations may be rewritten in the form,

$$\sum_j \sum_{m'=0}^{\xi-1} Q_{ij}^{mm'} t_{jm'}^{(h,k)}(\xi) = -R_{im}^{(h,k)} \quad (28\text{-}70)$$

where

$$Q_{ij}^{mm'} = \sum_l n_i n_l \left[\begin{array}{l} \delta_{ij} [\mathbf{W}_i S_n^{(m)}(W_i^2); \mathbf{W}_i S_n^{(m')}(W_i^2)]_{il} \\ + \delta_{jl} [\mathbf{W}_i S_n^{(m)}(W_i^2); \mathbf{W}_l S_n^{(m')}(W_i^2)]_{il} \end{array} \right] \quad (28\text{-}71)$$

For the case where $\mathbf{T}_i^{(h,k)}$ is $\mathbf{B}_i$ (and $t_{im}^{(h,k)}$ is $b_{im}^{(h,k)}$) Eq. 28-70 are all linearly independent, and hence all the $b_{im}^{(h,k)}$ can be determined from these equations. However, when $\mathbf{T}_i^{(h,k)}$ is either $\mathbf{A}_i$ or $(\mathbf{C}_i^{(h)} - \mathbf{C}_i^{(k)})$ then it may be shown that the set of equations for $m = 0$ includes one redundant equation. For these cases we make use of the auxiliary relation (Eq. 28-41) which in terms of the $t_{im}^{(h,k)}$ is

$$\sum_i \sum_{m=0}^{\xi-1} \sqrt{m_i}\, t_{im}^{(h,k)}(\xi) \int W_i^2 S_{\frac{3}{2}}^{(m)}(W_i^2) f_i^{(0)} d\mathbf{V}_i = 0 \qquad (28\text{-}72)$$

Because of the orthogonality relation (Eq. 28-59) the terms in this sum are zero for m other than zero. Thus the auxiliary condition becomes

$$\sum_i \sqrt{m_i}\, t_{i0}^{(h,k)}(2n_i/\sqrt{\pi})\Gamma(\tfrac{5}{2}) = 0 \qquad (28\text{-}73)$$

Consequently, when $\mathbf{T}_i^{(h,k)}$ is either $\mathbf{A}_i$ or $(\mathbf{C}_i^{(h)} - \mathbf{C}_i^{(k)})$, the trial function must be chosen so that

$$\sum_i n_i \sqrt{m_i}\, t_{i0}^{(i,k)} = 0 \qquad (28\text{-}74)$$

This supplies the additional information needed for the specification of all the coefficients $t_{im}^{(h,k)}(\xi)$. Eq. 28-70 may be modified to include this statement. The result is

$$\sum_j \sum_{m'=0}^{\xi-1} \tilde{Q}_{ij}^{mm'} t_{jm'}^{(h,k)}(\xi) = -R_{im}^{(h,k)} \qquad (28\text{-}75)$$

where

$$\tilde{Q}_{ij}^{mm'} = \begin{cases} Q_{ij}^{mm'}, & \text{when } t_{jm'}^{(h,k)} = b_{jm'} \\[2mm] Q_{ij}^{mm'} - \dfrac{n_j \sqrt{m_j}}{n_i \sqrt{m_i}} Q_{ii}^{mm'} \delta_{m0}\delta_{m'0}, & \text{when } t_{jm'}^{(h,k)} = a_{jm'} \text{ or } c_{jm'}^{(h,k)} \end{cases} \qquad (28\text{-}76)$$

From Eq. 28-75 one can obtain the $t_{im}^{(h,k)}(\xi)$, which give the functions $\mathbf{A}_i$, $\mathbf{B}_i$, and $\mathbf{C}_i^{(j)}$. These in turn give the function ϕ_i and the distribution function f_i correct to the first order. The knowledge of the nonequilibrium distribution function f_i then provides the information needed for the evaluation of the transport coefficients. Fortunately it turns out that only a few terms in the Sonine expansion are needed. For viscosity and diffusion, one term gives a good approximation—the result of using two terms differs by only a few per cent. For diffusion, the use of one term alone does not describe the dependence of the diffusion coefficient on concentration; the slight concentration-dependence is brought out when the first two terms in the Sonine expansion are used. The transfer of mass due to a temperature gradient (i.e. thermal diffusion) does not appear at all in the expression for the diffusion velocity if only one term in the Sonine polynomial expansion is used; thus the fact that thermal diffusion is a small effect compared with mass transfer due to a concentration gradient manifests itself in the mathematical formulation of the physical processes.

B,29. The Formulation of the Transport Coefficients. The integral expressions for the flux vectors, which describe the flux of mass, momentum, and energy are derived in Art. 27. The evaluation of these integrals requires a knowledge of the distribution function f_i. An approximation to the distribution function in the form $f_i = f_i^{(0)}(1 + \phi_i)$ is derived in the previous article. If the expression for ϕ_i (given by Eq. 28-29) is used in the integrals for the flux vectors, one obtains expressions for the diffusion velocity, the pressure tensor, and the heat flux vector in terms of integrals of the functions $A_i(W_i)$, $B_i(W_i)$, and $C_i^{(j)}(W_i)$. It is these relations for the flux vectors which we shall now derive and discuss.

Diffusion coefficients and thermal diffusion coefficients in terms of Sonine expansion coefficients. The integral for the diffusion velocity (27-17) rewritten in terms of ϕ_i is

$$\overline{\mathbf{V}}_i = \frac{1}{n_i} \int \mathbf{V}_i f_i d\mathbf{V}_i = \frac{1}{n_i} \int \mathbf{V}_i \phi_i f_i^{(0)} d\mathbf{V}_i \tag{29-1}$$

Using Eq. 28-29 and noting that the term involving $\mathbf{B}_i$ vanishes on integration, we may write $\overline{\mathbf{V}}_i$ as

$$\overline{\mathbf{V}}_i = \frac{1}{n_i} \int \left\{ n \sum_j (\mathbf{C}_i^{(j)} \cdot \mathbf{d}_j) - (\mathbf{A}_i \cdot \nabla \ln T) \right\} \mathbf{V}_i f_i^{(0)} d\mathbf{V}_i \tag{29-2}$$

Then making use of the form of the functions $\mathbf{A}_i$ and $\mathbf{C}_i^{(j)}$ indicated in Eq. 28-35 and 28-36, we obtain[50]

$$\overline{\mathbf{V}}_i = \left(\frac{n^2}{n_i \rho}\right) \sum_j m_j D_{ij} \mathbf{d}_j - \frac{1}{n_i m_i} D_i^T \nabla \ln T \tag{29-3}$$

In this expression $\mathbf{d}_j$ is defined in Eq. 28-27 and

$$D_{ij} = \frac{\rho}{3n m_j} \sqrt{\frac{2kT}{m_i}} \int C_i^{(j)}(W_i) W_i^2 f_i^{(0)} d\mathbf{V}_i \tag{29-4}$$

$$D_i^T = \tfrac{1}{3} m_i \sqrt{\frac{2kT}{m_i}} \int A_i(W_i) W_i^2 f_i^{(0)} d\mathbf{V}_i \tag{29-5}$$

are the "multicomponent diffusion coefficients" and the "multicomponent thermal diffusion coefficients" respectively.[51]

[50] Here we use a theorem which may be proved by symmetry arguments: If $F(r)$ is any function of the absolute value of $\mathbf{r}$, then

$$\int F(r) \mathbf{r} \mathbf{r} d\mathbf{r} = \tfrac{1}{3} \mathbf{1} \int F(r) r^2 d\mathbf{r}$$

[51] There is a considerable variation among authors in the nomenclature and definition of these quantities. The D_{ij} defined here are such that for a two-component mixture the D_{ij} reduce to the usual "binary diffusion coefficient" $\mathfrak{D}_{ij}$. The quantities D_i^T have not been previously defined. In the case of two components, the D_i^T defined here do *not* reduce to the "binary thermal diffusion coefficients" as defined in Chapman and Cowling.

Thus we see that the diffusion velocity $\overline{\mathbf{V}}_i$ contains terms proportional to the concentration gradient, the pressure gradient, the difference in the external forces acting on the various species of molecules, and the gradient in the temperature. Before the work of Chapman and Enskog, discussed in the previous article, the latter had been unknown theoretically and unobserved experimentally. Subsequent experiments of Chapman and coworkers revealed that the theoretical prediction of the phenomenon of thermal diffusion was quite correct. This is one of a number of historically interesting instances of the prediction of experimentally observable phenomena by rigorous theoretical analysis. Experiments for the measurement of D_{ij} are usually arranged so that the contributions to the diffusion velocity resulting from pressure gradients, external forces, and thermal gradients are negligible.

By means of the Sonine polynomial expansions (Eq. 28-61) the expressions for the diffusion coefficients become

$$D_{ij}(\xi) = \left(\frac{\rho}{3nm_j}\right)\sqrt{\frac{m_i}{2kT}} \sum_{m=0}^{\xi-1} c_{im}^{(j,i)}(\xi) \int V_i^2 S_{\frac{3}{2}}^{(m)}(W_i^2) f_i^{(0)} d\mathbf{V}_i \quad (29\text{-}6)$$

$$D_i^T(\xi) = \frac{m_i}{3}\sqrt{\frac{m_i}{2kT}} \sum_{m=0}^{\xi-1} a_{im}(\xi) \int V_i^2 S_{\frac{3}{2}}^{(m)}(W_i^2) f_i^{(0)} d\mathbf{V}_i \quad (29\text{-}7)$$

the argument ξ of $D_{ij}(\xi)$ and $D_i^T(\xi)$ being the number of terms used in the Sonine expansions. Subsequent use of Eq. 28-59 to evaluate the integrals then gives

$$D_{ij}(\xi) = \frac{\rho n_i}{2nm_j}\sqrt{\frac{2kT}{m_i}}\, c_{i0}^{(j,i)}(\xi) \quad (29\text{-}8)$$

$$D_i^T(\xi) = \frac{n_i m_i}{2}\sqrt{\frac{2kT}{m_i}}\, a_{i0}(\xi) \quad (29\text{-}9)$$

We have thus expressed D_{ij} and D_i^T in terms of the *zeroeth* Sonine expansion coefficient alone. No matter how many terms are used in the expansion (i.e. regardless of the value of ξ), it is only the zeroeth coefficient which remains after the integrations have been performed. However, the values of the coefficients $c_{i0}^{(j,i)}(\xi)$ and $a_{i0}(\xi)$ which are determined by Eq. 28-75 depend upon the number of terms considered in the polynomial.

In the case of D_{ij} letting $\xi = 1$ gives quite good results; if $\xi = 2$, one obtains a small correction term. Except in very unusual cases, it is unnecessary to use any approximations beyond $\xi = 2$. However, when $\xi = 1$ the coefficients D_i^T vanish identically. This arises because the function, $\mathbf{R}_i^{(h,k)} = f_i^{(0)}[\frac{5}{2} - W_i^2]\mathbf{V}_i$, when used in Eq. 28-62 with $n = \frac{3}{2}$, causes this integral to vanish since $(\frac{5}{2} - W_i^2)$ is the same as $S_{\frac{3}{2}}^{(1)}(W_i^2)$ and is therefore orthogonal to $S_{\frac{3}{2}}^{(0)}(W_i^2)$. Hence in order to get the coefficient of thermal diffusion, it is necessary to take at least two terms in the Sonine expansion (i.e. $\xi = 2$). For realistic potential functions, this approximation is in error by about 5 to 10 per cent.

The coefficient of viscosity in terms of the Sonine expansion coefficients. The integral for the pressure tensor (Eq. 27-21) in terms of the perturbation function ϕ_i is

$$\mathbf{p} = \sum_j m_j \int \mathbf{V}_j \mathbf{V}_j f_j d\mathbf{V}_j \tag{29-10}$$

$$= \sum_j m_j \left\{ \int \mathbf{V}_j \mathbf{V}_j f_j^{(0)} d\mathbf{V}_j + \int \mathbf{V}_j \mathbf{V}_j f_j^{(0)} \phi_j d\mathbf{V}_j \right\} \tag{29-11}$$

$$= p\mathbf{1} + \sum_j m_j \int \mathbf{V}_j \mathbf{V}_j f_j^{(0)} \phi_j d\mathbf{V}_j \tag{29-12}$$

where

$$p = nkT \tag{29-13}$$

is the equilibrium hydrostatic pressure at the local temperature and density. Then using the form of the perturbation function ϕ_i as given by Eq. 28-29 we find that

$$\mathbf{p} = p\mathbf{1} - \sum_j m_j \int \mathbf{V}_j \mathbf{V}_j (\mathbf{B}_j : \nabla \mathbf{v}_0) f_j^{(0)} d\mathbf{V}_j \tag{29-14}$$

The terms in $\mathbf{A}_i$ and $\mathbf{C}_i^{(j)}$ can be shown to be zero on the basis of symmetry arguments. Then using the form of the tensor $\mathbf{B}_i$ as given in Eq. 28-37 and further symmetry arguments we obtain

$$\mathbf{p} = p\mathbf{1} - \left[\frac{2}{15} \sum_j \frac{m_j^2}{2kT} \int B_j(W_j) V_j^4 f_j^{(0)} d\mathbf{V}_j \right] \mathbf{S} \tag{29-15}$$

where $\mathbf{S}$ is the "rate of shear tensor," defined by

$$S_{\alpha\beta} = \frac{1}{2} \left[\frac{\partial v_{0\beta}}{\partial x_\alpha} + \frac{\partial v_{0\alpha}}{\partial x_\beta} \right] - \frac{1}{3} \delta_{\alpha\beta} (\nabla \cdot \mathbf{v}_0) \tag{29-16}$$

The coefficient of viscosity μ is defined by the relation

$$\mathbf{p} = p\mathbf{1} - 2\mu \mathbf{S} \tag{29-17}$$

From Eq. 29-15 it follows that the coefficient of viscosity is

$$\mu = \frac{1}{15} \sum_j \frac{m_j^2}{2kT} \int B_j(W_j) V_j^4 f_j^{(0)} d\mathbf{V}_j \tag{29-18}$$

Then making use of the Sonine polynomial expansion (Eq. 28-61) we obtain

$$\mu(\xi) = \frac{1}{15} \sum_j \frac{m_j^2}{2kT} \sum_{m=0}^{\xi-1} b_{jm}(\xi) \int S_{\frac{5}{2}}^{(m)}(W_j^2) V_j^4 f_j^{(0)} d\mathbf{V}_j \qquad (29\text{-}19)$$

Again the argument of $\mu(\xi)$ indicates the order of the approximation. The orthogonality relation, Eq. 28-60, can now be employed to evaluate the integral and one obtains

$$\mu(\xi) = \tfrac{1}{2}kT \sum_j n_j b_{j0}(\xi) \qquad (29\text{-}20)$$

as the coefficient of viscosity of a mixture in terms of the Sonine expansion coefficients $b_{j0}(\xi)$. As in the case of ordinary diffusion, the first approximation is the predominant contribution. Actual calculations show that there is very little change in μ when additional terms in the expansion are used.

Thermal conductivity. The integral for the energy or heat flux vector $\mathbf{q}$ (Eq. 27-24) is given in terms of the perturbation function ϕ_i by

$$\mathbf{q} = \tfrac{1}{2} \sum_i m_j \int V_j^2 \mathbf{V}_j f_j^{(0)} \phi_j d\mathbf{V}_j \qquad (29\text{-}21)$$

When the expression for ϕ_i (Eq. 28-29) is used in this equation, the term containing $\mathbf{B}_j$ does not contribute and we have

$$\mathbf{q} = \tfrac{1}{2} \sum_j m_j \int \left\{ n \sum_k (\mathbf{C}_j^{(k)} \cdot \mathbf{d}_k) - (\mathbf{A}_j \cdot \nabla \ln T) \right\} V_j^2 \mathbf{V}_j f_j^{(0)} d\mathbf{V}_j \qquad (29\text{-}22)$$

The energy flux may be separated into two parts—that due to the flux of molecules relative to the mass velocity and that due to other causes. Using the forms of the functions $\mathbf{A}_i$ and $\mathbf{C}_i^{(j)}$ given by Eq. 28-35 and 28-36, we obtain

$$\mathbf{q} = \tfrac{5}{2}kT \sum_j n_j \overline{\mathbf{V}}_j$$

$$- kT \sum_j \int \left\{ n \sum_k C_j^{(k)}(W_j)(\mathbf{W}_j \cdot \mathbf{d}_j) - A_j(W_j)(\mathbf{W}_j \cdot \nabla \ln T) \right\}$$

$$\times (\tfrac{5}{2} - W_j^2) \mathbf{V}_j f_j^{(0)} d\mathbf{V}_j \qquad (29\text{-}23)$$

Then according to the symmetry arguments discussed above it follows that

$$\mathbf{q} = \tfrac{5}{2}kT \sum_j n_j \overline{\mathbf{V}}_j - \lambda' \nabla T$$

$$- \frac{\sqrt{2}}{3} n(kT)^{\frac{3}{2}} \sum_k \mathbf{d}_k \sum_j \frac{1}{\sqrt{m_j}} \int C_j^{(k)}(W_j) \left(\frac{5}{2} - W_j^2 \right) W_j^2 f_j^{(0)} d\mathbf{V}_j \qquad (29\text{-}24)$$

where

$$\lambda' = -\frac{\sqrt{2}}{3}\bar{k}\sqrt{kT}\sum_j \frac{1}{\sqrt{m_j}}\int A_j(W_j)\left(\frac{5}{2}-W_j^2\right)W_j^2 f_j^{(0)} d\mathbf{V}_j \quad (29\text{-}25)$$

The first term represents the flux of energy incident to mass transport; the second, that due to a temperature gradient; and the third, an additional effect due directly to the concentration gradients. The last term is analogous to the effect of temperature gradients on diffusion, i.e. thermal diffusion.

The expression for $\mathbf{q}$ can be rearranged as follows: From the integral equation for the A_i (Eq. 28-34) we may obtain the relation

$$\sqrt{\frac{2kT}{m_j}}\int C_j^{(k)}(W_j)\left(\frac{5}{2}-W_j^2\right)W_j^2 f_j^{(0)} d\mathbf{V}_j$$

$$= \sum_i \iiiint ([\mathbf{A}_i' + \mathbf{A}_j' - \mathbf{A}_i - \mathbf{A}_j]\cdot\mathbf{C}_j^{(k)})f_i^{(0)}f_j^{(0)}g_{ij}bdbd\epsilon d\mathbf{V}_i d\mathbf{V}_j \quad (29\text{-}26)$$

which can be used to rewrite the expression for $\mathbf{q}$ (Eq. 29-24). Then "symmetrizing" the sum over "i" and "j" and making use of the fact that $\sum_k \mathbf{d}_k = 0$, one obtains

$$\mathbf{q} = \tfrac{5}{2}kT\sum_j n_j\overline{\mathbf{V}}_j - \lambda'\nabla T$$

$$-\tfrac{1}{6}nkT\sum_k \mathbf{d}_k\sum_{i,j}\iiiint ([\mathbf{A}_i' + \mathbf{A}_j' - \mathbf{A}_i - \mathbf{A}_j]\cdot[\mathbf{C}_i^{(k)} + \mathbf{C}_j^{(k)} - \mathbf{C}_i^{(h)} - \mathbf{C}_j^{(h)}])$$

$$f_i^{(0)}f_j^{(0)}g_{ij}bdbd\epsilon d\mathbf{V}_i d\mathbf{V}_j \quad (29\text{-}27)$$

But from the integral equation for $\mathbf{C}_i^{(k)}$ (Eq. 28-32) it follows that

$$(\delta_{ih} - \delta_{ik})\frac{1}{n_i}\sqrt{\frac{2kT}{m_i}}\int A_i(W_i)W_i^2 f_i^{(0)} d\mathbf{V}_i$$

$$= \sum_j \iiiint \left(\mathbf{A}_i\cdot\begin{bmatrix}\mathbf{C}_i^{(h)\prime} + \mathbf{C}_j^{(h)\prime} - \mathbf{C}_i^{(k)\prime} - \mathbf{C}_j^{(k)\prime} \\ -\,\mathbf{C}_i^{(h)} - \mathbf{C}_j^{(h)} + \mathbf{C}_i^{(k)} + \mathbf{C}_j^{(k)}\end{bmatrix}\right)f_i^{(0)}f_j^{(0)}g_{ij}bdbd\epsilon d\mathbf{V}_i d\mathbf{V}_j$$

$$(29\text{-}28)$$

Summing Eq. 29-28 over i and symmetrizing results in

$$\sum_i (\delta_{ih} - \delta_{ik})\frac{1}{n_i}\sqrt{\frac{2kT}{m_i}}\int A_i(W_i)W_i^2 f_i^{(0)} d\mathbf{V}_i$$

$$= -\tfrac{1}{2}\sum_{i,j}\iiiint \left(\begin{bmatrix}\mathbf{A}_i' + \mathbf{A}_j' \\ -\,\mathbf{A}_i - \mathbf{A}_j\end{bmatrix}\cdot\begin{bmatrix}\mathbf{C}_i^{(k)} + \mathbf{C}_j^{(k)} \\ -\,\mathbf{C}_i^{(h)} - \mathbf{C}_j^{(h)}\end{bmatrix}\right)f_i^{(0)}f_j^{(0)}g_{ij}bdbd\epsilon d\mathbf{V}_i d\mathbf{V}_j$$

$$(29\text{-}29)$$

Then with the definition of D_j^T (Eq. 29-5) and the fact that $\sum_k \mathbf{d}_k = 0$, the energy flux becomes

$$\mathbf{q} = \frac{5}{2} kT \sum_j n_j \overline{\mathbf{V}}_j - \lambda' \nabla T - nkT \sum_j \frac{1}{n_j m_j} D_j^T \mathbf{d}_j \qquad (29\text{-}30)$$

The coefficient λ' is not the coefficient of thermal conductivity as it is usually defined. It is conventional to eliminate the gradients $\mathbf{d}_j$ from the expression for $\mathbf{q}$ by means of the equation for the diffusion velocities (Eq. 29-3). The energy flux is then given in terms of the diffusion velocities and the temperature gradient. Because of the thermal diffusion term in the expression for the diffusion velocity, a small term adds to λ' to result in the quantity λ which is the usual coefficient of thermal conductivity. The final expression for λ (Eq. 29-65) is derived later in this article.

If the functions $A_i(W_i)$ are expressed as a series of Sonine polynomials as in Eq. 28-61 the expression for λ' (Eq. 29-25) becomes

$$\lambda'(\xi) =$$

$$-\frac{\sqrt{2}}{3} k \sqrt{kT} \sum_j \sum_{m=0}^{\xi-1} \frac{1}{\sqrt{m_j}} a_{jm}(\xi) \int S_{\frac{3}{2}}^{(m)}(W_j^2) \left(\frac{5}{2} - W_j^2 \right) W_j^2 f_j^{(0)} d\mathbf{V}_j;$$

$$(29\text{-}31)$$

Then since

$$S_{\frac{3}{2}}^{(1)}(W_j^2) = \tfrac{5}{2} - W_j^2 \qquad (29\text{-}32)$$

one obtains from the condition of orthogonality of the polynomials, (Eq. 28-58),

$$\lambda'(\xi) = -\frac{5}{4} k \sum_j n_j \sqrt{\frac{2kT}{m_j}} a_{j1}(\xi) \qquad (29\text{-}33)$$

The integrals, $\Omega^{(l)}(s)$. The transport coefficients have been expressed in terms of the Sonine polynomial expansion coefficients. It will be recalled that these expansion coefficients are obtained by the solution of sets of simultaneous equations, Eq. 28-75. It can be seen that the expansion coefficients $t_{jm}^{(h,k)}(\xi)$, are complicated combinations of the square bracket integrals, which were defined by Eq. 28-42. Chapman and Cowling [38] have shown that these integrals may be written as linear combinations of a set of integrals $\Omega^{(l)}(s)$. For collisions between molecules of type i and type j, these integrals (which are average collision cross sections) are defined by

$$\Omega_{ij}^{(l)}(s) = \sqrt{\pi} \left(\frac{m_{ij}}{2kT} \right)^{\frac{2s+3}{2}} \int_0^\infty \int_0^\infty e^{-\frac{m_{ij} g_{ij}^2}{2kT}} g_{ij}^{2s+3} (1 - \cos^l \chi) b\,db\,dg_{ij} \qquad (29\text{-}34)$$

In these integrals m_{ij} is the reduced mass of colliding molecules, i and j,

g_{ij} is the initial relative speed of the colliding molecules, χ is the angle by which the molecules are deflected in the center of gravity coordinate system, and b is the impact parameter. A tabulation of the most frequently needed square brackets in terms of the $\Omega^{(l)}(s)$ has been given by Chapman and Cowling [38]. With these tables and Eq. 28-75 any of the Sonine expansion coefficients $t_{im}^{(h,k)}$ may be calculated.

The dynamics of the collisions enter into the description of the transport coefficients through the collision integrals defined by Eq. 29-34. For, in order to evaluate $\Omega^{(l)}(s)$, one must know χ as a function of the initial relative velocity g_{ij} and the impact parameter b. This relation depends on the form of the potential energy of interaction $\varphi(r)$. Thus given the interaction potential, one can calculate the $\Omega^{(l)}(s)$ integrals and hence the expansion coefficients $t_{im}^{(h,k)}(\xi)$.

The formulas for the transport coefficients in terms of the $\Omega^{(l)}(s)$ integrals are discussed in the next subarticle. The actual evaluation of the angles $\chi(g, b)$, the integrals $\Omega^{(l)}(s)$, and the transport coefficients for several intermolecular laws of force are discussed in Sec. D. The most satisfactory and usable calculations are those made on the basis of the Lennard-Jones potential, which describes reasonably well the interaction between spherical nonpolar molecules. Equations and tables are given in Sec. D which enable one to make practical applications of the theory. It is shown that the agreement between calculated and experimental results is quite satisfactory.

The transport coefficients in terms of the collision integrals. The method of obtaining formulas for the transport coefficients in terms of the intermolecular forces and the dynamics of binary collisions has been discussed in this and the preceding articles. The algebraic detail is rather lengthy and will be omitted, except to indicate briefly how the results obtained thus far may be used to obtain the lowest approximation to the various transport coefficients.

1. The Coefficient of Diffusion. The coefficient of diffusion in a multicomponent mixture can be obtained to a very good approximation by considering only one term in the Sonine polynomial expansion. The equations specifying the $c_{j0}^{(h,k)}(1)$ (Eq. 28-75) are then,

$$\sum_j \bar{Q}_{ij}^{00} c_{j0}^{(h,k)}(1) = -R_{i0}^{(h,k)} \qquad (29\text{-}35)$$

In terms of the $\Omega^{(l)}(s)$ these equations become

$$\sum_j c_{j0}^{(h,k)}(1) \sum_l \frac{n_l m_l}{(m_i + m_l)\sqrt{m_j}} [n_i m_i(\delta_{ij} - \delta_{jl}) - n_j m_j(1 - \delta_{il})]\Omega_{il}^{(1)}(1)$$

$$= -(\delta_{ih} - \delta_{ik})\frac{3}{16}\sqrt{2kT} \qquad (29\text{-}36)$$

For a binary mixture one immediately obtains from this equation,

$$c_{i0}^{(h,k)}(1) = (\delta_{jh} - \delta_{jk}) \frac{3}{16} \frac{(m_i + m_j)}{n_i\rho} \sqrt{\frac{2kT}{m_i}} \frac{1}{\Omega_{ij}^{(1)}(1)} \qquad (29\text{-}37)$$

so that the first approximation to the coefficient of diffusion of a binary mixture[52] is (from Eq. 29-8)

$$\mathfrak{D}_{ij}(1) = \frac{3(m_i + m_j)}{16nm_im_j} \frac{kT}{\Omega_{ij}^{(1)}(1)} \qquad (29\text{-}38)$$

From the definitions (or from the form of Eq. 29-37),

$$c_{j0}^{(h,k)} = c_{j0}^{(h,i)} - c_{j0}^{(k,i)} \qquad (29\text{-}39)$$

Using this result, the expressions for the diffusion constants, and the above relation for the binary diffusion constants, we get for the equation for the general diffusion constants (Eq. 29-36)

$$\sum_j F_{ij}\{m_h D_{jh}(1) - m_k D_{jk}(1)\} = (\delta_{ih} - \delta_{ik}) \qquad (29\text{-}40)$$

where

$$F_{ij} = \left\{\frac{n_i}{\rho\mathfrak{D}_{ij}(1)} + \sum_{l \neq i} \frac{n_l m_j}{\rho m_i \mathfrak{D}_{il}(1)}\right\} (1 - \delta_{ij}) \qquad (29\text{-}41)$$

A formal solution of this set of equations can be obtained easily. Let us define F^{ii} as the cofactor of F_{ij} in the determinant $|F|$ of the F_{ij} so that

$$F^{ii} = (-1)^{i+i} \begin{vmatrix} F_{11} & \cdots & F_{1,j-1} & F_{1,j+1} & \cdots & F_{1\nu} \\ \cdot & & \cdot & \cdot & & \cdot \\ \cdot & & \cdot & \cdot & & \cdot \\ \cdot & & \cdot & \cdot & & \cdot \\ F_{i-1,1} & \cdots & F_{i-1,j-1} & F_{i-1,j+1} & \cdots & F_{i-1,\nu} \\ F_{i+1,1} & \cdots & F_{i+1,j-1} & F_{i+1,j+1} & \cdots & F_{i+1,\nu} \\ \cdot & & \cdot & \cdot & & \cdot \\ \cdot & & \cdot & \cdot & & \cdot \\ \cdot & & \cdot & \cdot & & \cdot \\ F_{\nu,1} & \cdots & F_{\nu,j-1} & F_{\nu,j+1} & \cdots & F_{\nu,\nu} \end{vmatrix} \qquad (29\text{-}42)$$

Then solving Eq. 29-40,

$$m_h D_{ih}(1) - m_k D_{ik}(1) = \frac{F^{hi} - F^{ki}}{|F|} \qquad (29\text{-}43)$$

Thus since $D_{ii} \equiv 0$, it follows that

$$D_{ij}(1) = \frac{F^{ii} - F^{ii}}{m_j|F|} \qquad (29\text{-}44)$$

The set of Eq. 29-44 relates the generalized diffusion coefficients of a mixture to the binary diffusion coefficients of the various pairs. The form of the result, however, is usually difficult to handle in actual problems. For this reason it is often advantageous to make use of an alternate

[52] In a binary mixture, we denote D_{ij} by $\mathfrak{D}_{ij}$.

formulation. From Eq. 29-3, one finds that

$$\sum_j \frac{n_i n_j}{\mathfrak{D}_{ij}(1)} (\overline{\mathbf{V}}_i - \overline{\mathbf{V}}_j) = \frac{n^2}{\rho} \sum_{\substack{j,k \\ j \neq i}} \frac{m_k}{\mathfrak{D}_{ij}(1)} [n_j D_{ik} - n_i D_{jk}] \mathbf{d}_k$$

$$- (\nabla \ln T) \sum_j \frac{1}{\mathfrak{D}_{ij}(1)} \left[\frac{n_j}{m_i} D_i^T - \frac{n_i}{m_j} D_j^T \right] \quad (29\text{-}45)$$

This expression can be simplified considerably by making use of a special form of Eq. 29-40. The auxiliary conditions on the coefficients, $c_{i0}^{(h,k)}$ (Eq. 28-74) can be written in terms of the diffusion coefficients. The result is

$$\sum_i \{ m_i m_h D_{ih}(1) - m_i m_k D_{ik}(1) \} = 0 \quad (29\text{-}46)$$

Making use of this, we find that Eq. 29-40 becomes[53]

$$\sum_{j \neq i} \frac{1}{\mathfrak{D}_{ij}(1)} \{ n_i m_h D_{jh}(1) - n_i m_k D_{jk}(1) - n_j m_h D_{ih}(1) + n_j m_k D_{ik}(1) \}$$

$$= (\delta_{ih} - \delta_{ik})\rho \quad (29\text{-}47)$$

This set of equations is not linearly independent and hence could not be used without Eq. 29-46 to obtain the coefficients. Nevertheless they are valid relations. Because of Eq. 29-47 and the fact that $\sum_k \mathbf{d}_k = 0$, Eq. 29-45 becomes

$$\sum_j \frac{n_i n_j}{\mathfrak{D}_{ij}(1)} (\overline{\mathbf{V}}_i - \overline{\mathbf{V}}_j) = -n^2 \mathbf{d}_i - (\nabla \ln T) \sum_j \frac{1}{\mathfrak{D}_{ij}(1)} \left[\frac{n_j}{m_i} D_i^T - \frac{n_i}{m_j} D_j^T \right]$$

$$(29\text{-}48)$$

This is a set of $(\nu - 1)$ independent equations which are often directly applicable to hydrodynamic problems.

2. The Coefficient of Thermal Diffusion. To obtain the coefficients of thermal diffusion, it is necessary to evaluate the functions $\mathbf{A}_i$. In this case two terms in the Sonine polynomial expansion must be considered. Use of a single term results in a zero thermal diffusion coefficient; for this reason thermal diffusion is frequently referred to as a "second order" effect. In this case, Eq. 28-75 becomes

$$\sum_j \sum_{m'=0}^{1} \tilde{Q}_{ij}^{mm'} a_{jm'}(2) = -R_{im} \quad (29\text{-}49)$$

In terms of the $\Omega^{(l)}(s)$

$$\tilde{Q}_{ij}^{00} = 8 \sum_k \frac{n_k m_k}{\sqrt{m_i m_j} (m_i + m_k)} [n_i m_i(\delta_{ij} - \delta_{jk}) - n_j m_j(1 - \delta_{ik})]\Omega_{ik}^{(1)}(1)$$

$$(29\text{-}50)$$

[53] This set of equations is a special case of the general relations (Eq. 28-70).

$$\tilde{Q}_{ij}^{01} = -8 \left(\frac{m_i}{m_j}\right)^{\frac{3}{2}} \sum_k \frac{n_i n_k m_k^2}{(m_i + m_k)^2} (\delta_{ij} - \delta_{kj}) \left[\Omega_{ik}^{(1)}(2) - \frac{5}{2} \Omega_{ik}^{(1)}(1)] \right] \quad (29\text{-}51)$$

$$\tilde{Q}_{ij}^{10} = \frac{m_j}{m_i} \tilde{Q}_{ij}^{01} \quad (29\text{-}52)$$

$$\tilde{Q}_{ij}^{11} = 8 \left(\frac{m_i}{m_j}\right)^{\frac{3}{2}} \sum_k \frac{n_i n_k m_k}{(m_i + m_k)^3} \left[(\delta_{ij} - \delta_{jk}) \left[\begin{array}{l} \frac{5}{4}(6m_j^2 + 5m_k^2)\Omega_{ik}^{(1)}(1) \\ - 5m_k^2 \Omega_{ik}^{(1)}(2) \\ + m_k^2 \Omega_{ik}^{(1)}(3) \end{array} \right] + (\delta_{ij} + \delta_{jk})2m_j m_k \Omega_{ik}^{(2)}(2) \right]$$

$$(29\text{-}53)$$

$$R_{im} = \delta_{m1} \frac{15}{4} n_i \sqrt{\frac{2kT}{m_i}} \quad (29\text{-}54)$$

The expressions in Eq. 29-49 form a set of linear equations for the coefficients a_{j0} and a_{j1}, which can be solved by Cramer's rule.[54] Then from Eq. 29-9 one obtains the expression for the coefficient of thermal diffusion:

$$D_i^T(2) = n_i \sqrt{\frac{m_i kT}{2}} \frac{\left| \begin{matrix} \tilde{Q}_{11}^{00} & \tilde{Q}_{11}^{00} & \cdots & \tilde{Q}_{1\nu}^{00} & \tilde{Q}_{11}^{01} & \tilde{Q}_{12}^{01} & & \tilde{Q}_{1\nu}^{01} & 0 \\ \tilde{Q}_{21}^{00} & \tilde{Q}_{22}^{00} & \cdots & \tilde{Q}_{2\nu}^{00} & \tilde{Q}_{21}^{01} & \tilde{Q}_{22}^{01} & \cdots & \tilde{Q}_{2\nu}^{01} & 0 \\ \cdot & \cdot & & \cdot & \cdot & \cdot & & \cdot & \cdot \\ \cdot & \cdot & & \cdot & \cdot & \cdot & & \cdot & \cdot \\ \cdot & \cdot & & \cdot & \cdot & \cdot & & \cdot & \cdot \\ \tilde{Q}_{\nu 1}^{00} & \tilde{Q}_{\nu 2}^{00} & \cdots & \tilde{Q}_{\nu\nu}^{00} & \tilde{Q}_{\nu 1}^{01} & \tilde{Q}_{\nu 2}^{01} & \cdots & \tilde{Q}_{\nu\nu}^{01} & 0 \\ \tilde{Q}_{11}^{10} & \tilde{Q}_{12}^{10} & \cdots & \tilde{Q}_{1\nu}^{10} & \tilde{Q}_{11}^{11} & \tilde{Q}_{12}^{11} & \cdots & \tilde{Q}_{1\nu}^{11} & R_{11} \\ \tilde{Q}_{21}^{10} & \tilde{Q}_{22}^{10} & \cdots & \tilde{Q}_{2\nu}^{10} & \tilde{Q}_{21}^{11} & \tilde{Q}_{22}^{11} & \cdots & \tilde{Q}_{2\nu}^{11} & R_{21} \\ \cdot & \cdot & & \cdot & \cdot & \cdot & & \cdot & \cdot \\ \cdot & \cdot & & \cdot & \cdot & \cdot & & \cdot & \cdot \\ \tilde{Q}_{\nu 1}^{10} & \tilde{Q}_{\nu 2}^{10} & \cdots & \tilde{Q}_{\nu\nu}^{10} & \tilde{Q}_{\nu 1}^{11} & \tilde{Q}_{\nu 2}^{11} & \cdots & \tilde{Q}_{\nu\nu}^{11} & R_{\nu 1} \\ \delta_{i1} & \delta_{i2} & \cdots & \delta_{i\nu} & 0 & 0 & \cdots & 0 & 0 \end{matrix} \right|}{\left| \begin{matrix} \tilde{Q}_{11}^{00} & \cdots & \tilde{Q}_{1\nu}^{00} & \tilde{Q}_{11}^{01} & \cdots & \tilde{Q}_{1\nu}^{01} \\ \cdot & & \cdot & \cdot & & \cdot \\ \cdot & & \cdot & \cdot & & \cdot \\ \tilde{Q}_{\nu 1}^{00} & \cdots & \tilde{Q}_{\nu\nu}^{00} & \tilde{Q}_{\nu 1}^{01} & \cdots & \tilde{Q}_{\nu\nu}^{01} \\ \tilde{Q}_{11}^{10} & \cdots & \tilde{Q}_{1\nu}^{10} & \tilde{Q}_{11}^{11} & \cdots & \tilde{Q}_{1\nu}^{11} \\ \cdot & & \cdot & \cdot & & \cdot \\ \cdot & & \cdot & \cdot & & \cdot \\ \tilde{Q}_{\nu 1}^{10} & \cdots & \tilde{Q}_{\nu\nu}^{10} & \tilde{Q}_{\nu 1}^{11} & \cdots & \tilde{Q}_{\nu\nu}^{11} \end{matrix} \right|}$$

$$(29\text{-}55)$$

[54] Cramer's rule states that the solution of a set of linear equations can be expressed as the ratio of determinants of the coefficients in the usual manner.

3. The Coefficient of Viscosity.   For a ν component mixture, the first approximation to the multicomponent viscosity is (according to Eq. 29-20)

$$\mu(1) = \tfrac{1}{2}kT \sum_j n_j b_{j0}(1) \tag{29-56}$$

The $b_{j0}(1)$ are then determined by the ν equations (according to Eq. 28-75)

$$\sum_j \left(\frac{Q_{ij}^{00}}{R_{i0}} \right) b_{j0}(1) = -1, \qquad i = 1, 2, 3, \cdots, \nu \tag{29-57}$$

with

$$Q_{ij}^{00} = \sum_l n_i n_l \{ \delta_{ij}[\mathbf{W}_i; \mathbf{W}_i]_{il} + \delta_{jl}[\mathbf{W}_i; \mathbf{W}_l]_{il} \} \tag{29-58}$$

In this case $\mathbf{W}_i$ and R_{i0} are

$$\mathbf{W}_i = \mathbf{W}_i \mathbf{W}_i - \tfrac{1}{3}W_i^2 \mathbf{1} \tag{29-59}$$

$$R_{i0} = \int 2(\mathbf{W}_i : \mathbf{W}_i) f_i^{(0)} d\mathbf{V}_i$$

$$= -\tfrac{4}{3} \int W_i^4 f_i^{(0)} d\mathbf{V}_i = -5n_i \tag{29-60}$$

From Eq. 29-57 one can, of course, obtain the $b_{j0}(1)$ as ratios of two determinants of order ν by Cramer's rule. However, the only quantity which appears in the expression for the coefficient of viscosity is $\sum_j n_j b_{j0}(1)$. This can be written as a ratio of two determinants—the one in the numerator being of order $(\nu + 1)$, and that in the denominator of order ν. Specifically, one obtains,

$$[\mu]_1 = \frac{\begin{vmatrix} J_{11} & J_{12} & \cdots & J_{1\nu} & 1 \\ J_{21} & J_{22} & \cdots & J_{2\nu} & 1 \\ \cdot & \cdot & & \cdot & \\ \cdot & \cdot & & \cdot & \\ \cdot & \cdot & & \cdot & \\ J_{\nu 1} & J_{\nu 2} & \cdots & J_{\nu\nu} & 1 \\ 1 & 1 & \cdots & 1 & 0 \end{vmatrix}}{|J_{ij}|} \tag{29-61}$$

with

$$J_{ij} = \frac{2Q_{ij}^{00}}{n_j kT R_{i0}} = -\frac{2}{5}\frac{1}{kT} \sum_l \frac{n_l}{n_j} \{ \delta_{ij}[\mathbf{W}_i; \mathbf{W}_i]_{il} + \delta_{jl}[\mathbf{W}_i; \mathbf{W}_l]_{il} \} \tag{29-62}$$

In terms of the $\Omega_{ij}^{(l)}(s)$

$$J_{ij} = -\frac{32}{15}\frac{m_i}{n_j m_j kT} \sum_l \frac{n_l m_l}{(m_i + m_l)^2} \left[\begin{array}{l} 5m_j(\delta_{ij} - \delta_{jl}) \Omega_{il}^{(1)}(1) \\ + \tfrac{3}{2}m_l(\delta_{ij} + \delta_{jl}) \Omega_{il}^{(2)}(2) \end{array} \right] \tag{29-63}$$

This result can easily be extended to include the effect of more terms in the Sonine polynomial expansion. The formal results can be simplified considerably in the case of binary mixtures and pure gases. (See Sec. D.)

4. The Coefficient of Thermal Conductivity. The expression for the energy flux is usually written in terms of the diffusion velocities and the temperature gradient. Combining Eq. 29-30 and 29-48 gives

$$\mathbf{q} = -\lambda \nabla T + \frac{5}{2} kT \sum_i n_i \bar{\mathbf{V}}_i + \frac{kT}{n} \sum_{i,j} \frac{n_j D_i^T}{m_i \mathfrak{D}_{ij}} (\bar{\mathbf{V}}_i - \bar{\mathbf{V}}_j) \quad (29\text{-}64)$$

In this expression

$$\lambda = \lambda' - \frac{k}{2n} \sum_{i,j} \frac{n_i n_j}{\mathfrak{D}_{ij}} \left[\frac{D_i^T}{n_i m_i} - \frac{D_j^T}{n_j m_j} \right]^2 \quad (29\text{-}65)$$

is the usual coefficient of thermal conductivity. The quantity λ' is expressed in terms of the Sonine expansion coefficients by Eq. 29-33 from which, on applying the methods and results described above, we obtain

$$\lambda'(2) = -\tfrac{75}{8}k^2T \frac{\begin{vmatrix} q_{11}^{00} & \cdots & q_{1\nu}^{00} & q_{11}^{01} & \cdots & q_{1\nu}^{01} & 0 \\ & & & & & & \\ q_{\nu 1}^{00} & \cdots & q_{\nu\nu}^{00} & q_{\nu 1}^{01} & \cdots & q_{\nu\nu}^{01} & 0 \\ q_{11}^{10} & \cdots & q_{1\nu}^{10} & q_{11}^{11} & \cdots & q_{1\nu}^{11} & 1 \\ & & & & & & \\ q_{\nu 1}^{10} & \cdots & q_{\nu\nu}^{10} & q_{\nu 1}^{11} & \cdots & q_{\nu\nu}^{11} & 1 \\ 0 & \cdots & 0 & 1 & \cdots & 1 & 0 \end{vmatrix}}{\begin{vmatrix} q_{11}^{00} & \cdots & q_{1\nu}^{00} & q_{11}^{01} & \cdots & q_{1\nu}^{01} \\ & & & & & \\ q_{\nu 1}^{00} & \cdots & q_{\nu\nu}^{00} & q_{\nu 1}^{01} & \cdots & q_{\nu\nu}^{01} \\ q_{11}^{10} & \cdots & q_{1\nu}^{10} & q_{11}^{11} & \cdots & q_{1\nu}^{11} \\ & & & & & \\ q_{\nu 1}^{10} & \cdots & q_{\nu\nu}^{10} & q_{\nu 1}^{11} & \cdots & q_{\nu\nu}^{11} \end{vmatrix}} \quad (29\text{-}66)$$

Here

$$q_{ij}^{mm'} = \frac{\sqrt{m_i m_j}}{n_i n_j} \tilde{Q}_{ij}^{mm'} \tag{29-67}$$

where the $\tilde{Q}_{ij}^{mm'}$ are those given by Eq. 29-50, 51, 52, and 53.

B,30. Cited References and Bibliography.

Cited References

1. Born, M. *Atomic Physics*, 4th ed. Blackie, 1947.
2. Darwin, C. G. *The New Conceptions of Matter*. Macmillan, 1931.
3. Slater, J. C., and Frank, N. H. *Introduction to Theoretical Physics*. McGraw-Hill, 1933.
4. Uhlenbeck, G. E., and Goudsmit, S. *Naturwiss. 13*, 953 (1925); *Nature 117*, 264 (1926).
5. Mott, N. F., and Sneddon, I. N. *Wave Mechanics and Its Applications*. Oxford Univ. Press, 1948.
6. Pauling, L. *The Nature of the Chemical Bond*. Cornell, 1948.
7. Craig, D. P. *Proc. Roy. Soc. London A200*, 272 (1950a); *A200*, 390 (1950b); *A200*, 401 (1950c); *A200*, 474 (1950d).
8. Coulson, C. A. *Quart. Revs. London 1*, 144 (1947). See also the bibliography in *Proc. Roy. Soc. London A207*, 1951.
9. Mulliken, R. S. *J. chim. phys. 46*, 497 (1949). Annual Reports of the Spectroscopic Laboratory, University of Chicago.
10. Lennard-Jones, J. *Proc. Roy. Soc. London A198*, 14 (1949). *Trans. Faraday Soc. 25*, 668 (1929).
11. Sherman, A., and Van Vleck, J. H. *Revs. Mod. Phys. 7*, 167–228 (1935).
12. Mulligan, J. *J. Chem. Phys. 19*, 347–362 (1951).
13. Roothaan, C. C. J. *Ph.D. Thesis*, Univ. of Chicago, 1950; published in *ONR Technical Report from the Univ. of Chicago* for the period Sept. 1, 1948 to May 31, 1949, Part Two; Report for the period June 1, 1949 to March 31, 1950, Part Two.
14. Herzberg, G. *Infrared and Raman Spectra*. Van Nostrand, 1945.
15. Gordy, W. *Revs. Mod. Phys. 20*, 668–717 (1948).
16. Bichowsky, F. R., and Rossini, F. D. *Thermochemistry of the Chemical Substances*. Reinhold, 1936. Also: Rossini, F. D., Wagman, D. D., Evans, W. H., Levine, S., and Jaffe, I. *Selected Values of Chemical Thermodynamic Properties*. Natl. Bur. Standards Circ. 500 U. S. Government Printing Office, 1952.
17. Herzberg, G. *Spectra of Diatomic Molecules*, 2nd ed. Van Nostrand, 1950.
18. Gaydon, A. G. *Dissociation Energies*. Dover, 1950.
19. Szwarc, M., and Evans, M. G. *J. Chem. Phys. 18*, 618–622 (1950).
20. Szwarc, M. *Chem. Revs. 47*, 75 (1950).
21. Kistiakowsky, G. B., and Van Artsdalen, E. R. *J. Chem. Phys. 12*, 469 (1944).
22. Prosen, E., Johnson, W., and Rossini, F. *J. Research Natl. Bur. Standards 37*, 51 (1946).
23. Steacie, E. W. R. *Atomic and Free Radical Reactions*. Reinhold, 1946.
24. Syrkin, Y. K., and Dyatkina, M. E. *Structure of Molecules*. Interscience, 1950.
25. A discussion on bond energies and bond lengths. *Proc. Roy. Soc. London A207 (A1088)*, 1–136 (1951).
26. Tolman, R. C. *Statistical Mechanics with Applications to Chemistry and Physics*. Chemical Catalog, 1927.
27a. Hinshelwood, C. N. *The Kinetics of Chemical Change*. Oxford Univ. Press, 1940.
27b. Laidler, K. J. *Chemical Kinetics*. McGraw-Hill, 1950.
28. Eyring, H., and Polanyi, M. *Z. physik. Chem. B12*, 279 (1931).
29. Wigner, E. *Trans. Faraday Soc. 34*, 29 (1938).
30. Evans, M. G., and Polanyi, M. *Trans. Faraday Soc. 34*, 11 (1938).
31. Glasstone, S., Laidler, K. J., and Eyring, H. *Theory of Rate Processes*. McGraw-Hill, 1941.

32. de Boer, J. *Repts. Progr. in Phys. 12*, 305 (1949).
33. Tolman, R. H. *Principles of Statistical Mechanics.* Oxford Univ. Press, 1938.
34. Hirschfelder, J. O., Curtiss, C. F., and Bird, R. B. *The Molecular Theory of Gases and Liquids.* Wiley, 1954.
35. Fowler, R. H., and Guggenheim, E. A. *Statistical Thermodynamics.* Cambridge Univ. Press, 1939.
36. Mayer, J. E., and Mayer, M. G. *Statistical Mechanics.* Wiley, 1940.
37. Grad, H. *Commun. on Pure and Appl. Math. 2*, 331 (1949).
38. Chapman, S., and Cowling, T. G. *The Mathematical Theory of Non-Uniform Gases.* Cambridge Univ. Press, 1939, 1952.
39. Kirkwood, J. G. *J. Chem. Phys. 15*, 72 (1947).
40. Kirkwood, J. G. *J. Chem. Phys. 18*, 817 (1950).
41. Enskog, D. *Arkiv Mat., Astron. Fysik Stockholm 16*, 16 (1922); *Kinetische Theorie der Vorgänge in mässig verdünnten Gasen.* (*Inaugural Disseration.*) Uppsala, Sweden. Almquist and Wiksell, 1917.
42. Curtiss, C. F., and Hirschfelder, J. O. *J. Chem. Phys. 17*, 550 (1949).

Bibliography

Eyring, H., Walter, J., and Kimball, G. E. *Quantum Chemistry.* Wiley, 1944.
Pauling, L. C., and Wilson, E. B., Jr. *Introduction to Quantum Mechanics*, 1st ed. McGraw-Hill, 1935.
Rice, F. O., and Teller, E. *The Structure of Matter.* Wiley, 1949.
Rojanski, V. B. *Introductory Quantum Mechanics.* Prentice-Hall, 1938.
Schiff, L. I. *Quantum Mechanics.* McGraw-Hill, 1949.
Tolman, R. C. *The Principles of Statistical Mechanics.* Oxford, 1938.

SECTION C

THERMODYNAMIC PROPERTIES OF REAL GASES AND MIXTURES OF REAL GASES

JAMES A. BEATTIE

The relations derived from the laws of perfect gases have the advantage of simplicity, which is sufficient justification for use of the expressions so obtained even under circumstances beyond their applicability. The laws themselves are strictly valid only in the limit of vanishing density, but some of the consequences of the laws are not true in this region. Even at atmospheric pressure the laws of perfect gases must be amended to attain high precision in the description of gaseous behavior, and, at the much higher pressures encountered in industrial syntheses and fractionation, the laws represent only the crudest sort of approximation and not even this in some respects. There is thus a clear, practical reason for studying the properties of real gases over a wide range of conditions. A second and equally cogent reason for such studies lies in their theoretical value. Our present knowledge of the nature and magnitude of intermolecular forces, which are a prime factor in almost all chemical phenomena, has been derived to a considerable extent from investigations of the gaseous state.

In this section[1] the properties of gases *at equilibrium* are discussed. First the experimental pressure-volume-temperature relationships of pure and mixed real gases are described, and semiempirical methods of correlation are treated.

Then a general thermodynamic theory of pure gases is presented, and three important methods for treating gas mixtures of variable composition, including mixtures in which chemical reaction may occur, are discussed. In this section the aim is to state explicitly the assumptions on which the thermodynamic theory rests and not to include statistical methods at this stage of the argument.

---

[1] This section is taken with some additions to and deletions from the first part of Chapter II (The Thermodynamics and Statistical Mechanics of Real Gases by J. A. Beattie and W. H. Stockmayer) of H. S. Taylor and S. Glasstone, *A Treatise on Physical Chemistry*, Vol. II, *States of Matter* (New York: D. Van Nostrand Company, Inc., 1951); and is reproduced with the consent of the D. Van Nostrand Company.

There follows an application of the results to a variety of physico-chemical problems. In view of the widespread usefulness of these relations, they have been given in considerable detail.

CHAPTER 1. COMPRESSIBILITIES AND EQUATIONS OF STATE FOR GASEOUS SYSTEMS

C,1. Methods of Representation. The relation among the pressure p, the molar volume v (the ratio of the total volume V to the number of moles n), and the absolute thermodynamic temperature T of a pure gas

$$f(p, v, T) = 0 \tag{1-1s}$$

may be represented graphically or given by an equation. The latter is called the equation of state of the gas and contains a number of parameters known as the equation of state constants or simply the constant) of the gas.

The quantities plotted in the graphical method depend on the problem to be solved. Frequently, use is made of the relation (1-1) for an ideal gas

$$pv = RT \tag{1-2}$$

where R is the universal gas constant. We may plot the deviation of some state property of a real gas from that given by Eq. 1-2 as one of the coordinates or we may use Eq. 1-2 as a guide to the choice of the quantities to be plotted.

With very few exceptions, practical equations of state give the pressure as an explicit function of the molar volume and temperature:

$$p = \phi(v, T) \tag{1-3}$$

The equation explicit in the volume

$$v = \psi(p, T) \tag{1-4}$$

is less successful in representing the behavior of gaseous systems over the same range of temperature and pressure than the form explicit in the pressure when the same number of constants is used in each.

The expression corresponding to Eq. 1-1 for a gas mixture composed of the constituents 1, 2, . . . at the mole numbers $n_1, n_2, . . .$ is

$$F(p, v, T, X_1, X_2, \cdot \cdot \cdot) = 0 \tag{1-5}$$

where v is the molar volume of the mixture and X_i is the mole fraction of the gas i, $n_i/(\sum_i n_i)$.

Graphical methods for gas mixtures are not particularly useful except for mixtures of constant composition. When the composition is variable, the number of independent variables is too great for simple representation.

Theoretical and practical considerations indicate that, for a gas mixture of constant composition, Eq. 1-5 has the same form as Eq. 1-1, the equation of state constants of the pure gas being replaced by parameters that are functions of the composition. The functions must contain the constants of the pure constituent gases in order that Eq. 1-5 reduce to 1-1 for each $X_i = 1$, but will include other constants arising from the interaction of unlike molecules. The interaction constants can be evaluated with sufficient accuracy for many purposes from the corresponding constants of the constituent gases by a method called "combination of constants." The term *equation of state of a gas mixture* denotes such an equation: one that permits computation of the pressure (volume) of a gas mixture from the volume (pressure), temperature, and mole numbers of the gases composing the mixture and the equation of state constants of the pure constituent gases. Thus the volumetric behavior of mixtures may be computed to a certain degree of approximation from data on the pure gases only.

For those regions in which an equation of state gives a sufficiently accurate representation of the compressibility, the analytic method would seem to be superior to the graphical method both for pure gases and mixtures of constant composition. The graphical method is hardly applicable to gas mixtures of variable composition.

C,2. Graphical Methods. The computation of certain thermodynamic properties of pure gases is facilitated and the accuracy is increased by use of plots of the deviation functions [1, p. 195; 2]:

$$\alpha = \mathrm{v} - \frac{RT}{p} \tag{2-1}$$

$$\Delta = \mathrm{v}\left(\frac{p\mathrm{v}}{RT} - 1\right) \tag{2-2}$$

against the pressure or temperature.

Plots [3] of isothermals in the pressure-volume plane and of the compressibility factor Z,

$$Z = \frac{p\mathrm{v}}{RT} \tag{2-3}$$

against pressure or density at constant temperature have been used for certain purposes. Such plots for different gases have a similar general appearance but cannot be superimposed.

A graphical method that has found considerable use in engineering calculations especially when compressibility data for a gas are lacking but the critical pressure and temperature are known is based on the following considerations.

The discovery of the critical point between the liquid and gaseous states by Andrews [4] and the work of van der Waals [5] led to the law of corresponding states according to which all gases have the same value of the reduced pressure p_r for the same reduced molar volume v_r and reduced temperature T_r. The reduced quantities are the dimensionless ratios

$$p_r = \frac{p}{p_c}, \qquad v_r = \frac{v}{v_c}, \qquad T_r = \frac{T}{T_c} \qquad (2\text{-}4)$$

where the subscript c denotes the value of a quantity at the critical state. Thus a single surface in p_r, v_r, T_r space would represent the state behavior of all gases.

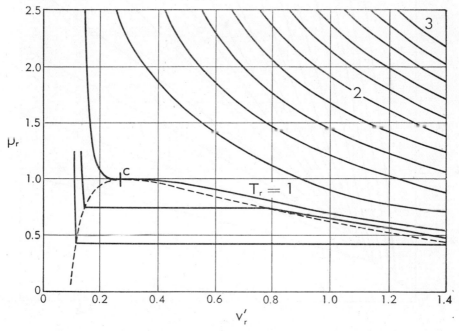

Fig. C,2a. Plot of the reduced pressure p_r against the pseudo-reduced volume v_r' for the reduced isotherms T_r from 1 to 3 in steps of 0.2. The critical point is marked c. The two-phase region is beneath the dotted curve. Two isotherms below the critical are sketched. (From [8].)

The law of corresponding states is only a rough approximation for real gases. It fell into disrepute, but more recently has returned to favor in a somewhat modified form [6,7]. One modification is based on the fact that the critical pressure and temperature of a substance are more readily determined and are known for more substances than the critical volume. Furthermore, the critical ratio $RT_c/p_c v_c$ is fairly constant for nonpolar gases and has a value of about 3.42 for the monatomic and diatomic gases (except hydrogen and helium) and a value of about 3.65 when a large number of nonpolar gases are included in the average. For these reasons the reduced volume v_r has been replaced by the pseudo-reduced volume v_r'

$$v_r' = \frac{v}{RT_c/p_c} = \frac{v_r}{RT_c/p_cv_c} \tag{2-5}$$

in certain graphical methods.

The contour lines[2] of the reduced pressure-volume-temperature surface are drawn for several values of the reduced temperature T_r in

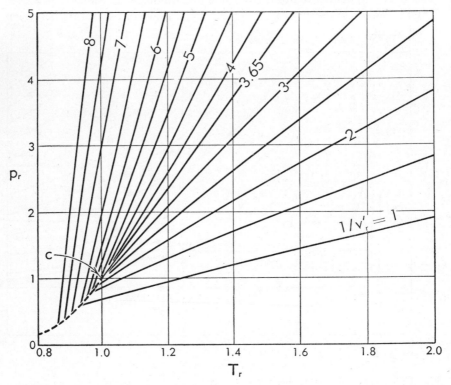

Fig. C,2b. Plot of the reduced pressure p_r against the reduced temperature T_r for the pseudo-reduced densities $1/v_r'$ from 1 to 8 in steps of 0.5. The critical point is marked c and 3.65 is the critical pseudo-density. The vapor pressure curve is dotted. (From [8].)

Fig. C,2a.[2] The coordinates are the reduced pressure p_r and pseudo-reduced volume v_r'. If the law of corresponding states were exact, the plot would represent the behavior of all gaseous substances. Qualitatively the features to be noted are (1) at high temperatures the isotherms approximate rectilinear hyperbolas except at small molar volumes, and at all temperatures the isotherms approach rectilinear hyperbolas at large molar volumes; (2) at lower temperatures (starting at about

[2] This and the three following plots are taken from [8].

$T_r = 1.1$) two inflection points become evident; (3) at one temperature, called the critical, the inflection point at the smaller molar volume has a horizontal tangent so that both the first and second derivatives of pressure with respect to volume are zero; (4) below the critical temperature each isotherm has a horizontal portion where the liquid and gas are in equilibrium, to the left of which the liquid curve rises steeply and to the right of which the gas curve starts concave downward so that an inflection point must occur, since at large molar volumes the curve is concave

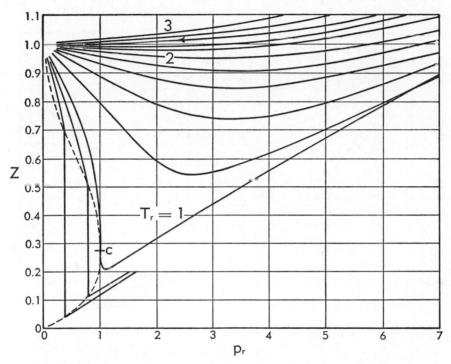

Fig. C,2c. Plot of the compressibility factor Z against the reduced pressure p_r for the reduced isotherms T_r from 1 to 3 in steps of 0.2. The critical point is marked c and the Boyle temperature (taken to be at $T_r = 2.6$) denoted by an arrow. The two-phase region is to the left of the dotted curve. Two isotherms below the critical are sketched. (From [8].)

upward. The dotted curve separating the region of two phases from the regions of one phase is sometimes called the steam dome.

In Fig. C,2b the reduced isometrics [9] showing the variation of p_r with T_r for a series of pseudo-reduced densities ($1/v'_r$) are drawn. The isometrics have negative curvature (concave downward) from low reduced densities to about the critical where the curvature changes sign. At about twice the critical density the curvature becomes negative again.

According to the law of corresponding states, the compressibility factor depends only on the reduced state of a gas and is independent of the particular gas:

$$Z = \frac{pv}{RT} = \left(\frac{p_r v_r}{RT_r}\right)\left(\frac{p_c v_c}{T_c}\right) = \frac{p_r v_r'}{T_r} \tag{2-6}$$

In Fig. C,2c is given a plot of Z against the reduced pressure p_r for several reduced temperatures T_r, and in Fig. C,2d a plot of Z against the pseudo-reduced density $(1/v_r')$ for several reduced temperatures. The isotherms of Fig. C,2c below a temperature somewhat greater than the critical have a point of inflection, whereas the isotherms of Fig. C,2d are

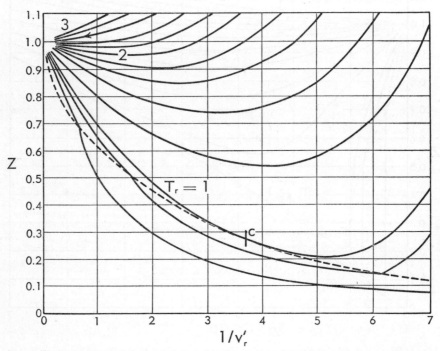

Fig. C,2d. Plot of the compressibility factor Z against the pseudo-reduced density $1/v_r'$ for the reduced isotherms T_r from 1 to 3 in steps of 0.2. The critical point is marked c and the Boyle temperature denoted by an arrow. The two-phase region is beneath the dotted curve. Two isotherms below the critical are sketched. (From [8].)

always concave upward, down to temperatures considerably below the critical. When Z is plotted against the reduced pressure, the curves are vertical straight lines in the two-phase region; when plotted against the pseudo-reduced density, the curves are rectilinear hyperbolas in this region.

The foregoing four plots were made from an average of the properties of the lower hydrocarbons [10,11]. They represent the properties of these gases and the nonpolar gases except hydrogen and helium with an over-all accuracy of several per cent. Deviations for polar gases are larger.

Hydrogen and helium are notable exceptions to the law of corresponding states; but the generalized reduced curves can be used for these gases, provided we use fictitious values [10,11,12] for the critical pressure and temperature rather than the true values.

The compressibility factor for a gas mixture of constant composition can be determined from Fig. C,2c and 2d. The true critical constants of the mixture are not used, but fictitious [13] ones are computed from the relations

$$p_c \text{ (mixture)} = \sum_i X_i p_{ci}$$

$$T_c \text{ (mixture)} = \sum_i X_i T_{ci}$$

(2-7)

where p_{ci} and T_{ci} are the critical constants of the constituent i, and X_i its mole fraction in the mixture.

C,3. Empirical Equations of State. Virial Coefficients. Empirical equations of state expressing the pressure-volume product of a gas as an expansion in the density [14] or pressure [15,16] have been extensively used. These are usually written:

$$pv = A \left(1 + \frac{B}{v} + \frac{C}{v^2} + \frac{D}{v^4} + \cdots \right)$$

(3-1)

$$pv = A + B'p + C'p^2 + D'p^4 + \cdots$$

(3-2)

where

$$A = A_0 \frac{T}{T_0}$$

(3-3)

and the coefficients $B, C, \ldots, B', C', \ldots$ are functions of temperature. Theoretical considerations based on the virial theorem of Clausius would yield a relation similar to Eq. 3-1 but containing all powers of $1/v$. As a practical matter of curve fitting, fewer terms are required if the odd powers of the density except the first are omitted.

It is evident that the function A must equal RT. But, in general, the investigators using these equations expressed density of gases in terms of the Amagat unit: the density of the gas at 0°C and 1 atm; or a similar unit: the density of the gas at 0°C and 1 meter of mercury. Thus the number of moles of gas in the system was not independently known.

The parameters B and C are called the second and third virial coefficients. Definite relations should exist between them and the corresponding parameters B' and C' of the infinite series (3-2):

$$B' = B$$

(3-4)

$$C' = \frac{C - B^2}{A}, \qquad C = AC' + B'^2$$

(3-5)

However, if the two equations (3-1 and 3-2), each with a finite number of terms, are fitted to the same observations, the relations (3-4 and 3-5) hold only approximately, because of the failure of each equation written in closed form to give an exact representation of the data and of experimental errors in the data themselves. In general, for a given pressure

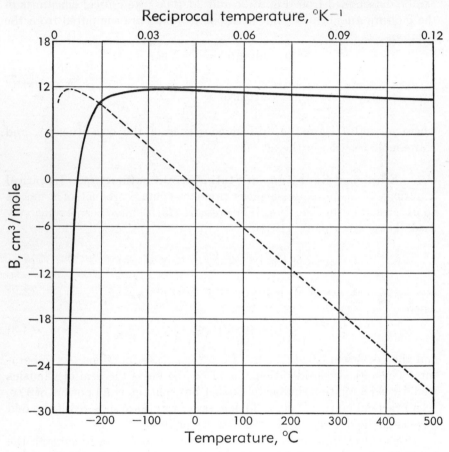

Fig. C,3. Plot of the second virial coefficient B of helium against the Centigrade temperature (full line) and against the reciprocal Kelvin temperature (dashed line).

range, Eq. 3-1 fits the observations better than Eq. 3-2 when the same number of terms is used in each.

Fig. C,3 shows a plot of the second virial coefficient B against the temperature and against the reciprocal Kelvin temperature for helium.[3] The coefficient is negative at low reduced temperatures, passes through zero somewhat above the critical temperature, rises to a maximum, and then decreases as the temperature is further increased. The second virial

[3] For the values of B used, see [17, p. 45; 18].

coefficients of other gases exhibit the same general trends, but the temperature of maximum B is above the region of compressibility measurements for all gases except hydrogen, helium, and neon.

The temperature at which the second virial coefficient is zero is called the Boyle temperature.

Two other temperatures of importance are connected with the second virial coefficient. These are the inversion temperature of the Joule-Thomson effect at zero pressure and the inversion temperature of the Joule effect in the region of low density.

In the Joule-Thomson experiment, a fluid flows through a porous plug in such a manner that its heat content H remains constant. The Joule-Thomson coefficient μ_{JT} is defined as

$$\mu_{JT} = \left(\frac{\partial T}{\partial p}\right)_H \tag{3-6}$$

whence from general thermodynamic relations we find

$$\mu_{JT}C_p = -\left(\frac{\partial H}{\partial p}\right)_T = T\left(\frac{\partial V}{\partial T}\right)_p - V$$

$$= -\left[\frac{\partial(V/T)}{\partial(1/T)}\right]_p = T^2\left[\frac{\partial(V/T)}{\partial T}\right]_p \tag{3-7}$$

where C_p is the heat capacity at constant pressure. Evaluation of the last derivative from Eq. 3-2 gives, when we pass to the limit of zero pressure,

$$\lim_{p\to 0} \mu_{JT}C_p = -\frac{d(B/T)}{d(1/T)} = T^2\frac{d(B/T)}{dT} \tag{3-8}$$

Since C_p remains finite, the zero-pressure Joule-Thomson coefficient passes through zero at the temperature at which B/T is a maximum. This is called the zero-pressure inversion temperature. Inversion temperatures at higher pressures evidently depend on the third and higher virial coefficients as well as on B. Eq. 3-8 affords a means of computing [17, p. 45] the change of the second virial coefficient with temperature from measurements of μ_{JT} and C_p in the region of low pressures. The latter is usually computed from spectroscopic data. One value of B must be given, and this is taken from a well-studied isotherm, as 0°C.

In the Joule or free expansion experiment the energy E of a fluid remains constant. The Joule coefficient η is defined as

$$\eta = -\left(\frac{\partial T}{\partial V}\right)_E \tag{3-9}$$

whence:

$$\eta C_V = \left(\frac{\partial E}{\partial V}\right)_T = T\left(\frac{\partial p}{\partial T}\right)_V - p = -\left[\frac{\partial(p/T)}{\partial(1/T)}\right]_V = T^2\left[\frac{\partial(p/T)}{\partial T}\right]_V \tag{3-10}$$

where C_V is the heat capacity at constant volume. From Eq. 3-1 we find for the region of low pressures:

$$\eta C_V = \frac{RT^2}{\mathbf{v}^2}\frac{dB}{dT} + O\left(\frac{1}{\mathbf{v}^3}\right) \qquad (3\text{-}11)$$

where $O(1/\mathbf{v}^3)$ represents terms of the order of the cube of the density. As C_V remains finite, the Joule coefficient becomes zero at zero pressure. But at a density so small that terms of higher order may be neglected, the Joule coefficient has an inversion temperature, at the maximum of the second virial coefficient. Above this temperature free expansion causes an increase rather than a decrease in the temperature of a gas. The experimental determination of Joule coefficients presents extraordinary difficulties and accurate values have never been measured [19]. They may be computed [20, p. 60] from other measurements through the relation

$$\eta C_V = - \left[\mu_{JT} C_p + \left(\frac{\partial(pV)}{\partial p}\right)_T \right]\left(\frac{\partial p}{\partial V}\right)_T \qquad (3\text{-}12)$$

Keyes [17, p. 45] finds the following values of the three characteristic temperatures for helium, hydrogen, and nitrogen from his correlation of all of the data available for determination of B. Some of the values are derived by extrapolation of the equations expressing B as a function of temperature and must be considered as estimates only.

Gas	Boyle temperature $B = 0$	Low density Joule inversion B = maximum	Zero-pressure Joule-Thomson inversion $\frac{B}{T}$ = maximum
He	−249°C	− 77°C	−228°C
H$_2$	−166	+ 443	− 72
N$_2$	+ 51	+1867	+327

The third virial coefficient C is positive down to temperatures well below the critical; but the corresponding parameter C' though positive at higher temperatures passes through zero between the Boyle and critical temperatures.

From a kinetic viewpoint the second virial coefficient arises from binary encounters of molecules, and the third virial coefficient from ternary encounters. The general statistical theory of the kth virial coefficient (the kth term in the expansion of pv containing all powers of $1/\mathbf{v}$) has been worked out.

When the molecular model is the rigid sphere of diameter σ with the attractive energy varying inversely as some power of the separation, say the theoretically correct inverse sixth power, we find for the second virial coefficient:

$$B = b - \frac{a}{RT} - O\left(\frac{1}{T^2}\right) \tag{3-13}$$

where $O(1/T^2)$ represents terms of the order of $1/T^2$ and

$$b = \frac{2\pi N\sigma^3}{3}, \qquad a = Nb\epsilon \tag{3-14}$$

In these relations N is the Avogadro number, and ϵ the mutual potential energy of a pair of molecules on contact, that is, of separation σ. According to Eq. 3-13, B increases with increasing temperature and has the limit b at infinite temperature. Thus the hard-sphere molecular model does not lead to a maximum in the second virial coefficient.

A special form of the potential introduced by Lennard-Jones [21], based on a soft-sphere molecular model, represents the attractive potential energy of a pair of molecules by an inverse sixth power dependence on the separation, and the repulsive energy by an inverse twelfth power. The rather complicated expression for the second virial coefficient fits almost all data within experimental accuracy and predicts a maximum in B. The equation may be approximated very closely in the range θ/T equal to 0.20 to 1.00 by the expression [22]

$$\frac{B}{\beta} = 0.71875 - 2.131899\,\frac{\theta}{T} - 1.120795\left(\frac{\theta}{T}\right)^2 \tag{3-15}$$

and in the same range to within the accuracy that B is known for most gases by the simpler relation

$$\frac{B}{\beta} = \left(\frac{\theta}{T}\right)^{\frac{1}{4}}\left(1.064 - 3.602\,\frac{\theta}{T}\right) \tag{3-16}$$

Here,

$$\left.\begin{aligned}\beta &= \frac{2\pi N\sigma^3}{3}\\[2mm] \theta &= \frac{\epsilon}{k}\end{aligned}\right\} \tag{3-17}$$

where σ is the separation of a pair of molecules for zero potential energy, ϵ the magnitude of the potential energy minimum, and k Boltzmann's constant.

The third virial coefficient for the Lennard-Jones potential has been evaluated numerically by two groups of investigators [23,24] with somewhat discordant results.

C,4. Early Semiempirical Equations of State. A great number of equations of state with a more or less rational basis has been proposed. In order to be useful, an equation of state must be of such a form that evaluation of the constants from experimental data can be readily accomplished and mathematical manipulation easily executed.

Three classical equations of state have received considerable attention:

$$p = \frac{nRT}{V - nb} - \frac{n^2a}{V^2} \quad \text{(van der Waals [5])} \tag{4-1}$$

$$p = \frac{nRT}{V - nb} \, e^{-na/VRT} \quad \text{(Dieterici [25])} \tag{4-2}$$

$$p = \frac{nRT}{V - nb} - \frac{n^2a}{TV^2} \quad \text{(Berthelot [26])} \tag{4-3}$$

None of these equations gives a good representation of the compressibility of gases over a wide range of pressure and temperature, yet the leading features of the pressure-volume-temperature surface are qualitatively represented; and the equations, especially that of van der Waals, have inspired much theoretical and experimental work.

All of the equations give isothermals similar to those plotted in Fig. C,2a, with one pressure-volume curve having a horizontal inflection point at which there are three real coincident values of v. Below this temperature the equations give continuous isothermal curves with continuous first derivatives. In the region of equilibrium between liquid and vapor phases the isothermals have a maximum and a minimum similar to the continuous isotherm postulated by Thomson [27] on the basis of a study of Andrew's data on the compressibility of carbon dioxide. Thus all three equations of state provide for a liquid-gas critical point.

In regard to pressure-temperature curves at constant molar volume, van der Waals' equation requires linear isometrics; Dieterici's, isometrics of positive curvature; and Berthelot's, isometrics with negative curvature. Berthelot was primarily interested in a low pressure equation of state for the permanent gases to be used in the correction of gas thermometric measurements for the imperfection of the gas. His equation gives the correct sign of the curvature of the isometrics in this region.

The equations of van der Waals and Dieterici give for the second virial coefficient

$$B = b - \frac{a}{RT} \tag{4-4}$$

while that of Berthelot gives

$$B = b - \frac{a}{RT^2} \tag{4-5}$$

All predict a Boyle temperature, but none requires a maximum in B. The relation (4-4) is the first two terms of Eq. 3-13, which was derived for a hard-sphere molecular model.

Three conditions hold at the critical point of a substance: the equation of state $f(p, v, T) = 0$, the condition of a horizontal tangent to the critical isotherm $(\partial p/\partial v)_T = 0$, and the condition of a point of inflection $(\partial^2 p/\partial v^2)_T = 0$. These are sufficient to permit evaluation of the three critical constants in terms of R, a, and b; or conversely to express R, a, and b in terms of p_c, v_c, and T_c. When the resulting values of R and the two equation of state constants are substituted into the original equation

Table C,4. Reduced forms of equations of state.

Van der Waals' Equation

$$p = \frac{RT}{v - b} - \frac{a}{v^2}$$

$$pv = RT + \left(b - \frac{a}{RT} \right) p + O(p^2)$$

$$p_c = \frac{a}{27b^2} \qquad v_c = 3b \qquad T_c = \frac{8a}{27Rb}$$

$$b = \frac{v_c}{3} = \frac{1}{8} \frac{RT_c}{p_c} \qquad a = 3p_c v_c^2 = \frac{27}{64} \frac{R^2 T_c^2}{p_c} \qquad R = \frac{8}{3} \frac{p_c v_c}{T_c} \qquad \frac{RT_c}{p_c v_c} = \frac{8}{3} = 2.67$$

$$p_r = \frac{8T_r}{3v_r - 1} - \frac{3}{v_r^2}$$

$$p_r v_r = \frac{8}{3} T_r + \left(\frac{1}{3} - \frac{9}{8T_r} \right) p_r + O(p_r^2)$$

$$pv = RT + \left[\frac{RT_c}{p_c} \left(\frac{1}{8} - \frac{27}{64T_r} \right) \right] p + O(p^2)$$

Dieterici's Equation

$$p = \frac{RT}{v - b} e^{-a/vRT}$$

$$pv = RT + \left(b - \frac{a}{RT} \right) p + O(p^2)$$

$$p_c = \frac{a}{4e^2 b^2} \qquad v_c = 2b \qquad T_c = \frac{a}{4Rb}$$

$$b = \frac{v_c}{2} = \frac{1}{e^2} \frac{RT_c}{p_c} \qquad a = e^2 p_c v_c^2 = \frac{4}{e^2} \frac{R^2 T_c^2}{p_c} \qquad R = \frac{e^2 p_c v_c}{2T_c} \qquad \frac{RT_c}{p_c v_c} = \frac{e^2}{2} = 3.69$$

$$p_r = \frac{T_r}{2v_r - 1} e^{2 - 2/T_r v_r}$$

$$p_r v_r = \frac{e^2}{2} T_r + \left(\frac{1}{2} - \frac{2}{T_r} \right) p_r + O(p_r^2)$$

$$pv = RT + \left[\frac{RT_c}{p_c} \left(\frac{1}{e^2} - \frac{4}{e^2 T_r} \right) \right] p + O(p^2)$$

Table C,4 (continued)

Berthelot's Equation

$$p = \frac{RT}{v - b} - \frac{a}{Tv^2}$$

$$pv = RT + \left(b - \frac{a}{RT^2} \right) p + O(p^2)$$

$$p_c^2 = \frac{aR}{216b^3} \qquad v_c = 3b \qquad T_c^2 = \frac{8a}{27Rb}$$

$$b = \frac{v_c}{3} = \frac{1}{8} \frac{RT_c}{p_c} \qquad a = 3p_c v_c^2 T_c = \frac{27}{64} \frac{R^2 T_c^3}{p_c} \qquad R = \frac{8}{3} \frac{p_c v_c}{T_c} \qquad \frac{RT_c}{p_c v_c} = \frac{8}{3} = 2.67$$

$$p_r = \frac{8T_r}{3v_r - 1} - \frac{3}{T_r v_r^2}$$

$$p_r v_r = \frac{8}{3} T_r + \left(\frac{1}{3} - \frac{9}{8T_r^2} \right) p_r + O(p_r^2)$$

$$pv = RT + \left[\frac{RT_c}{p_c} \left(\frac{1}{8} - \frac{27}{64T_r^2} \right) \right] p + O(p^2)$$

Berthelot's Equation with Empirical Value of Critical Ratio

$$b = \frac{v_c}{4} = \frac{9}{128} \frac{RT_c}{p_c} \qquad a = \frac{16}{3} p_c v_c^2 T_c = \frac{27}{64} \frac{R^2 T_c^3}{p_c} \qquad R = \frac{32}{9} \frac{p_c v_c}{T_c} \qquad \frac{RT_c}{p_c v_c} = \frac{32}{9} = 3.56$$

$$p_r = \frac{128}{9} \frac{T_r}{4v_r - 1} - \frac{16}{3T_r v_r^2}$$

$$p_r v_r = \frac{32}{9} T_r + \left(\frac{1}{4} - \frac{3}{2T_r^2} \right) p_r + O(p_r^2)$$

$$pv = RT + \left[\frac{RT_c}{p_c} \left(\frac{9}{128} - \frac{27}{64T_r^2} \right) \right] p + O(p^2)$$

of state, there results a relation among the reduced pressure, reduced volume, and reduced temperature that contains no constants characteristic of the gas. Written in terms of the pressure, volume, and temperature the equation of state contains the three critical constants as parameters.

In Table C,4 is given under the heading of "Van der Waals' Equation," "Dieterici's Equation," and "Berthelot's Equation" a group of relations peculiar to each: the first line gives the equation of state written for one mole of gas; the second gives the virial form of each equation to terms of the order of p^2, the coefficient of p being the second virial coefficient B as defined by Eq. 3-1 or 3-2; the third and fourth lines give the values of R, a, and b in terms of p_c, v_c, and T_c, and the converse relations; the fifth and sixth lines give the reduced equations of state corresponding to the forms written in the first and second lines; and the last line gives the virial equation of state in terms of p, v, and T but with the second virial coefficient (the expression in brackets) stated in terms of the critical pressure and temperature and the reduced temperature. This relation may be compared with that in the second line.

Dieterici's equation gives a critical ratio 3.69 close to the average 3.65 for a large number of non-polar gases; the other two give critical ratios far below this average. Berthelot proposed an empirical set of values of R, a, and b in terms of critical constants, not consistent with his equation of state, but yielding a critical ratio of 3.56—closer to the average value 3.4 for the simpler gases. Substitution of these empirical values into his equation yields the relation given in the second line of the last section of Table C,4. The last two lines are approximations of this to terms of the order of p^2. The last equation has been used frequently for correction of thermodynamic results for gas imperfection in the region of low pressure. Only the critical pressure and temperature need be known.

It was a cardinal point of the earlier workers that the equation of state constants be determined from critical data alone and not from the actual compressibility of a gas. As a result the compilations of van der Waals' constants found in various handbooks are utterly worthless for computing the volumetric behavior of gases.

C,5. Later Semiempirical Equations of State. The following equations of state are more successful in representing the compressibility of gases:

$$p = \frac{nRT}{V - n\delta} - \frac{n^2A}{(V + nl)^2} \qquad \delta = \beta e^{-n\alpha/V} \quad \text{(Keyes [28])} \quad \text{(5-1)}$$

$$p = \frac{nRT(1 - \epsilon)}{V^2}(V + nB) - \frac{n^2A}{V^2} \qquad \left. \begin{array}{l} B = B_0\left(1 - \dfrac{nb}{V}\right) \\[2mm] \text{(Beattie-Bridgeman [29])} \\[2mm] A = A_0\left(1 - \dfrac{na}{V}\right) \\[2mm] \epsilon = \dfrac{nc}{VT^3} \end{array} \right\} \quad \text{(5-2a)}$$

or

$$p = T\psi(d) - \phi(d) - \frac{\Gamma(d)}{T^2} \qquad \left. \begin{array}{l} \psi(d) = Rd(1 + B_0d - B_0bd^2) \\[2mm] \phi(d) = A_0d^2 - A_0ad^3 \\[2mm] \Gamma(d) = Rcd^2(1 + B_0d - B_0bd^2) \\[2mm] d \equiv \dfrac{n}{V} \end{array} \right\} \quad \text{(5-2b)}$$

$$p = T\psi(d) - \phi(d) - \frac{\Gamma(d)}{T^2} \quad \left.\begin{array}{l} \psi(d) = Rd(1 + B_0d + bd^2) \\[6pt] \text{(Benedict-Webb-Rubin [30])} \\[6pt] \phi(d) = A_0d^2 + ad^3 - a\alpha d^6 \\[6pt] \Gamma(d) = C_0d^2 - cd^3(1 + \gamma d^2)e^{-\gamma d^2} \end{array}\right\} \quad (5\text{-}3)$$

These equations have four, five, and eight adjustable constants, respectively. The representation of gas compressibility is increasingly better as the number of constants increase. Eq. 5-2 is fairly satisfactory to the critical density for temperatures above the critical; Eq. 5-3 to about twice the critical density and down to temperatures well below the critical.

Each of the equations predicts a critical isotherm with a horizontal inflection point. Below this temperature the isotherms are of the type postulated by Thomson, the liquid and vapor isotherms of the same temperature being connected by a smooth curve with a maximum and a minimum in the two-phase region. Since the free energies of a pure liquid and its vapor in isothermal equilibrium are equal, the two areas in the two-phase region enclosed between the continuous isotherm and the vapor pressure line must be equal. Application of this principle to the Benedict-Webb-Rubin equation permits calculation of vapor pressures and saturated liquid and vapor volumes with satisfactory accuracy. The actual method of calculation consists in computing both the pressure (from the equation of the state) and the fugacity (from the integration of the general thermodynamic relation for fugacity by means of the equation of state) for a series of molar volumes at a constant temperature in the vapor and in the liquid region. The fugacity is plotted against the pressure for each phase. The intersection of the curves gives the vapor pressure, from which the saturated liquid and **vapor** volumes can be determined.

Eq. 5-1 requires linear isometrics; Eq. 5-2, isometrics with negative curvature throughout the entire density range; while Eq. 5-3 permits negative curvature at low densities, positive at intermediate densities, and negative again at high densities in agreement with the observed behavior of gases. The sign of the curvature is determined by the sign of $\Gamma(d)$:

$$\left(\frac{\partial^2 p}{\partial T^2}\right)_V = -\frac{6\Gamma(d)}{T^4} \tag{5-4}$$

The Keyes equation of state gives for the second virial coefficient

$$B = \beta - \frac{A}{RT} \tag{5-5}$$

while the other two give a relation of the type

$$B = B_0 - \frac{A_0}{RT} - \frac{c}{T^3} \tag{5-6}$$

where c is replaced by C_0 in the Benedict-Webb-Rubin equation. Thus all three equations of state are based on a hard-sphere molecular model. They do not provide for a maximum in the second virial coefficient. This deficiency is not serious from the standpoint of representing compressibility data except for helium and possibly hydrogen and neon.

All three equations of state have too many constants to be determined uniquely in terms of the three critical constants of a gas, and reduced equations of the type of those discussed in the last article cannot be derived. One method of introducing the critical constants and writing a reduced equation of state is given in a later article.

For polar gases Keyes [31,32] writes

$$p = \frac{RT}{v - B'}, \qquad B' = B + f(p, T)$$

$$B = B_0 - \frac{A}{RT} e^{D/T^2} \tag{5-7}$$

where $f(p, T)$ contains six constants for water vapor. This gives for the second virial coefficient B

$$B = B_0 - \frac{A}{RT} e^{D/T^2} \tag{5-8}$$

For nonpolar gases at not too low temperatures D/T^2 is small, and the exponential may be expanded to give

$$B = B_0 - \frac{A}{RT} - \frac{AD}{RT^3} - \cdots \tag{5-9}$$

in agreement with Eq. 5-6 to the first three terms.

C,6. The Beattie-Bridgeman Equation of State. The equation of state (5-2) can be written in the virial form

$$\frac{pV}{n} = RT + \frac{n\beta}{V} + \frac{n^2\gamma}{V^2} + \frac{n^3\delta}{V^3} \tag{6-1}$$

$$\beta = RTB_0 - A_0 - \frac{Rc}{T^2}$$

$$\gamma = -RTB_0 b + A_0 a - \frac{RB_0 c}{T^2}$$

$$\delta = \frac{RB_0 bc}{T^2}$$

Pressure and temperature are the usual independent variables employed for reporting experimental results. For the integration of the equations stating the thermodynamic properties of gases in terms of these independent variables, we desire an equation of state expressing the density as a function of pressure and temperature. Such an equation of manageable form and with relatively few parameters does not exist. We may make several approximations to Eq. 6-1 that give reasonably good representation of the density over certain restricted ranges.

In the first and most exact approximation [*33*], Eq. 6-1 is expanded in terms of itself:

$$\frac{V}{n} = \frac{RT}{p} + \frac{\beta}{RT} + \left[\frac{\gamma}{(RT)^2} - \frac{\beta^2}{(RT)^3}\right] p$$

$$+ \left[\frac{\delta}{(RT)^3} - \frac{3\beta\gamma}{(RT)^4} + \frac{2\beta^3}{(RT)^5}\right] p^2 \quad (6\text{-}2)$$

This equation gives pV/n to terms of the order of p^3. A less exact form would be obtained by replacing n/V by p/RT in each term on the right-hand side of Eq. 6-1:

$$\frac{V}{n} = \frac{RT}{p} + \frac{\beta}{RT} + \frac{\gamma}{(RT)^2} p + \frac{\delta}{(RT)^3} p^2 \quad (6\text{-}3)$$

The equation [*34*] would probably give a better representation of the density of gases than Eq. 6-2, provided we redetermined the values of the parameters A_0, a, B_0, b, and c for this form of equation. To do this we would need to resmooth all of the compressibility data to give densities at each temperature for an evenly spaced set of values of p/RT. Then in place of Eq. 5-2 we would write

$$\frac{V}{n} = \left(\frac{RT}{p} + B\right)(1 - \epsilon) - \frac{A}{RT} \qquad A = A_0\left(1 - \frac{ap}{RT}\right)$$

$$B = B_0\left(1 - \frac{bp}{RT}\right) \quad (6\text{-}4)$$

$$\epsilon = \frac{c}{T^3}\frac{p}{RT}$$

Thus we would have two sets of the equation of state parameters: one for Eq. 5-2 or 6-1 and one for Eq. 6-3 or 6-4. Unfortunately the values of the parameters for Eq. 6-3 have not yet been determined, and we are forced to use those determined for Eq. 6-1.

Sufficient accuracy is obtained in many thermodynamic calculations if we drop the last two terms of Eq. 6-3 and write

$$\frac{V}{n} = \frac{RT}{p} + \frac{\beta}{RT} \quad (6\text{-}5)$$

Table C,6. Values of the constants of the Beattie-Bridgeman
equation of state for several gases.

$$p = [RT(1 - \epsilon)/v^2][v + B] - A/v^2$$
$$A = A_0(1 - a/v), \qquad B = B_0(1 - b/v), \qquad \epsilon = c/vT^3$$

Units: normal atmospheres; liters per mole; °K ($T°K = t°C + 273.13$); $R = 0.08206$

Gas	A_0	a	B_0	b	$10^{-4} \times c$	Molecular weight
He..........	0.0216	0.05984	0.01400	0.0	0.0040	4.00
Ne..........	0.2125	0.02196	0.02060	0.0	0.101	20.2
A...........	1.2907	0.02328	0.03931	0.0	5.99	39.91
H_2..........	0.1975	−0.00506	0.02096	−0.04359	0.0504	2.0154
N_2..........	1.3445	+0.02617	0.05046	−0.00691	4.20	28.016
O_2..........	1.4911	0.02562	0.04624	+0.004208	4.80	32
Air.........	1.3012	0.01931	0.04611	−0.01101	4.34	28.964
I_2........	17.0		0.325		4000	253.864
CO_2........	5.0065	0.07132	0.10476	+0.07235	66.00	44.000
NH_3........	2.3930	0.17031	0.03415	+0.19112	476.87	17.0311
CH_4........	2.2769	0.01855	0.05587	−0.01587	12.83	16.0308
C_2H_4........	6.1520	0.04964	0.12156	+0.03597	22.68	28.0308
C_2H_6........	5.8800	0.05861	0.09400	+0.01915	90.00	30.0462
C_3H_8........	11.9200	0.07321	0.18100	+0.04293	120.00	44.0616
1-C_4H_8.......	16.6979	0.11988	0.24046	+0.10690	300.00	56.0616
iso-C_4H_8.....	16.9600	0.10860	0.24200	+0.08750	250.00	56.0616
n-C_4H_{10}......	17.7940	0.12161	0.24620	+0.09423	350.00	58.077
iso-C_4H_{10}.....	16.6037	0.11171	0.23540	+0.07697	300.00	58.077
n-C_5H_{12}......	28.2600	0.15099	0.39400	+0.13960	400.00	72.0924
neo-C_5H_{12}....	23.3300	0.15174	0.33560	+0.13358	400.00	72.0924
n-C_7H_{16}......	54.520	0.20066	0.70816	+0.19179	400.00	100.1232
CH_3OH......	33.309	0.09246	0.60362	+0.09929	32.03	32.0308
$(C_2H_5)_2O$.....	31.278	0.12426	0.45446	+0.11954	33.33	74.077

Gas	$A_0^{\frac{1}{2}}$	$B_0^{\frac{1}{3}}$	$10^{-2} \times c^{\frac{1}{3}}$	Gas	$A_0^{\frac{1}{2}}$	$B_0^{\frac{1}{3}}$	$10^{-2} \times c^{\frac{1}{3}}$
He........	0.14697	0.241014	0.0632	C_2H_6.......	2.42487	0.454684	9.4868
Ne........	0.46098	0.274129	0.3178	C_3H_8.......	3.45254	0.565665	10.9545
A.........	1.13609	0.340017	2.4474	1-C_4H_8.....	4.08631	0.621843	17.3205
H_2.........	0.44441	0.275717	0.2245	iso-C_4H_8...	4.11825	0.623168	15.8114
N_2.........	1.15953	0.369529	2.0494	n-C_4H_{10}.....	4.21829	0.626752	18.7083
O_2.........	1.22111	0.358927	2.1909	iso-C_4H_{10}...	4.07476	0.617451	17.3205
Air........	1.14070	0.358590	2.0833	n-C_5H_{12}.....	5.31601	0.733104	20.0000
I_2.........	4.12311	0.687534	63.2456	neo-C_5H_{12}...	4.83011	0.694929	20.0000
CO_2........	2.23752	0.471410	8.1240	n-C_7H_{16}.....	7.38377	0.891341	20.0000
NH_3........	1.54693	0.324437	21.8374	CH_3OH.....	5.77139	0.845126	5.6595
CH_4........	1.50894	0.382290	3.5819	$(C_2H_5)_2O$...	5.59267	0.768833	5.7732
C_2H_4........	2.48032	0.495371	4.7624				

using the values of the parameters A_0, B_0, and c determined for use in Eq. 6-1. This very approximate equation is entirely inadequate for computation of the density of a gas but gives excellent results in the calculation of the effect of pressure on the mass action constant, doubtless through a compensation of errors.

The constants of the equation explicit in the pressure are given for several gases in Table C,6. When the constants are not known, they may be approximated by the method given in the next paragraph.

C,7. Approximate Reduced Equation of State. Computation of the Constants from Critical Data. Other Relations Among the Constants. The equation of state (5-2 or 6-1) contains too many constants—six including the gas constant R—to be expressed uniquely in terms of the three critical constants of a gas through the three conditions at the critical point. We may, however, proceed as follows. In Eq. 6-1 each molal volume v can be written in terms of the pseudo-critical volume defined in Eq. 2-5:

$$v = \frac{RT_c}{p_c} v'_r \tag{7-1}$$

Then Eq. 6-1 becomes

$$p_r v'_r = T_r + \frac{\beta_r}{v'_r} + \frac{\gamma_r}{v'^2_r} + \frac{\delta_r}{v'^3_r}$$

$$\beta_r = \frac{p_c}{(RT_c)^2} \beta = T_r B_{0r} - A_{0r} - \frac{c_r}{T_r^2}$$

$$\gamma_r = \frac{p_c^2}{(RT_c)^3} \gamma = -T_r B_{0r} b_r + A_{0r} a_r - \frac{B_{0r} c_r}{T_r^2} \tag{7-2}$$

$$\delta_r = \frac{p_c^3}{(RT_c)^4} \delta = \frac{B_{0r} b_r c_r}{T_r^2}$$

The dimensionless ratios β_r, γ_r, δ_r may be considered the reduced virial parameters; and the dimensionless ratios

$$A_{0r} = \frac{A_0}{R^2 T_c^2/p_c}, \qquad B_{0r} = \frac{B_0}{RT_c/p_c}, \qquad c_r = \frac{c}{RT_c^4/p_c}$$

$$a_r = \frac{a}{RT_c/p_c}, \qquad b_r = \frac{b}{RT_c/p_c} \tag{7-3}$$

may be considered the reduced equation of state constants of a gas.

The ratios A_{0r}, B_{0r}, and c_r were found by Keyes [32] to be fairly constant for a number of nonpolar gases. We might employ the relations (7-3) in any one of a number of ways in order to obtain the equation of state constants for use in Eq. 6-1 when compressibility data on a gas are lacking but its critical pressure and temperature are known: (1) Compute [35,36] values of the reduced constants from some one gas, say nitrogen, and then use these to compute the equation of state constants for the gas whose compressibility has not been measured; (2) use the same procedure but use as a reference gas one whose structure is similar to the gas of unknown constants; (3) resmooth the compressibility data on a number of gases to give reduced pressures in terms of reduced temperatures for a series of pseudo-reduced isometrics, average the resulting reduced pressures, and determine a single set of reduced equation of state constants. The latter has been done [10] from the compressibility data on seven hydrocarbons, and the reduced constants so obtained were used to calculate the pressures of nine other gases, not hydrocarbons, over a range of density and temperature with satisfactory results. The values of the reduced constants determined in this way are

$$A_{0r} = 0.4758 \qquad a_r = 0.1127$$

$$B_{0r} = 0.18764 \qquad b_r = 0.03833 \qquad (7\text{-}4)$$

$$c_r = 0.05$$

Thus for the equation of state constants of a gas expressed in terms of its critical pressure and temperature we find

$$A_0 = 0.4758 \left(\frac{RT_c}{p_c}\right)^2 p_c \qquad a = 0.1127 \left(\frac{RT_c}{p_c}\right)$$

$$B_0 = 0.18764 \left(\frac{RT_c}{p_c}\right) \qquad b = 0.03833 \left(\frac{RT_c}{p_c}\right) \qquad (7\text{-}5)$$

$$c = 0.05 \left(\frac{RT_c}{p_c}\right) T_c^3$$

The approximate equation (6-5) can be written

$$pv = RT + \frac{RT_c}{p_c}\left(B_{0r} - \frac{A_{0r}}{T_r} - \frac{c_r}{T_r^3}\right)p$$

$$= RT + \frac{RT_c}{p_c}\left(0.18764 - \frac{0.4758}{T_r} - \frac{0.05}{T_r^3}\right)p \qquad (7\text{-}6)$$

This equation is preferable to Berthelot's equation given in Table C,4 for the approximate correction of low pressure thermodynamic data for the imperfection of the gas.

From a corresponding states study of the equation of state constants as determined from experimental data Keyes [32] found empirically

$$c = 0.023 \frac{A_0^3}{R^3 B_0^2} \qquad (7\text{-}7)$$

for nonpolar gases. Hirschfelder and Roseveare [37] found 0.024 for the coefficient on theoretical grounds by use of a (6, 12) Lennard-Jones potential, and Corner [38] found 0.013 when a (6, 9) potential was used. Corner also extended the method to the third virial coefficient and gave the theoretical relations

$$a = 0.45B_0 \qquad b = 0.1B_0 \tag{7-8}$$

The constants of many of the nonpolar gases are in fair agreement with these relations.

C,8. Dalton's Law and Amagat's Law for Gas Mixtures. The usual statement of Dalton's law [39] is: The pressure of a mixture of gases is equal to the sum of the pressures of the different gases as existing each by itself at the same temperature and in a volume equal to the total volume of the mixture. This may be called the law of the additivity of pressures at constant volume and temperature. As stated here, the law is simply a prescription for writing the equation of state of a gas mixture given the equations of the constituent gases. Recently the suggestion [40] has been made that Gibbs' [41] formulation of Dalton's law, which does contain the idea of equilibrium required as a basis for the thermodynamic treatment of gas mixtures, was implied by Dalton. Dalton did state that the same amount of a liquid would evaporate into air as into a vacuum. But his discussion was a kinetic one based on "no attractive or repulsive power" between the particles of different substances composing a gas mixture, so that the foregoing statement of his law, although not given in exactly his terms, seems to summarize Dalton's conclusion.

Consider a series of vessels, one containing a gas mixture and the others containing the pure constituent gases subject to the conditions:

$$\left. \begin{aligned} T \text{ (each pure gas)} &= T \text{ (mixture)} \\ V \text{ (each pure gas)} &= V \text{ (mixture)} \\ n_k = n_i, \quad \text{that is,} \quad C_k &= C_i \quad i \equiv k = 1, 2, \cdots \end{aligned} \right\} \tag{A}$$

Here the subscript i denotes one of the gases in the mixture, k the same gas when pure, and C the concentration, (n/V). Dalton's law states

$$p = \sum_k p_{ck} \tag{8-1}$$

where p is the total pressure of the mixture and p_{ck} that of the constituent gas k measured pure and subject to the conditions (A). The subscript c indicates that concentration of the gas is the same in the pure state as in the mixture.

Dalton's law can be applied to real as well as ideal gases. It requires that the equation of state of a gas mixture be the sum

$$p = f_1(V, T, n_1) + f_2(V, T, n_2) + \cdots \qquad (8\text{-}2)$$

where p is the pressure of the mixture, and

$$p_{ck} = f_k(V, T, n_k) \qquad (8\text{-}3)$$

is the equation of state of the pure gas k. Applied to Eq. 6-1 Dalton's law gives

$$p = \frac{(\sum_i n_i)RT}{V} + (\sum_i x_i^2 \beta_i)\frac{(\sum_i n_i)^2}{V^2} + (\sum_i x_i^3 \gamma_i)\frac{(\sum_i n_i)^3}{V^3} + (\sum_i x_i^4 \delta_i)\frac{(\sum_i n_i)^4}{V^4} \quad (8\text{-}4)$$

where β_i, γ_i, δ_i are the virial parameters for the pure gas k. At low pressures the law gives good results, but at higher pressures the errors may become very large.

From a study of his measurements of the compressibilities of oxygen, nitrogen, and air, Amagat [42] concluded that: The volume of a mixture of gases is equal to the sum of the volumes of the different gases as existing each by itself at the temperature and under the total pressure of the mixture. This is the law of the additivity of volumes at constant pressure and temperature.

Consider a gas mixture and the pure constituents each measured under the conditions

$$\left.\begin{array}{l} T \text{ (each pure gas)} = T \text{ (mixture)} \\ p \text{ (each pure gas)} = p \text{ (mixture)} \\ n_k = n_i \quad i \equiv k = 1, 2, \cdots \end{array}\right\} \qquad (\text{B})$$

Amagat's law requires

$$V = \sum_k V_{Pk} \qquad (8\text{-}5)$$

where V is the volume of the mixture and V_{Pk} that of the pure gas k measured under the conditions (B).

Amagat's law gives for the volume V of a mixture the relation

$$V = F_1(p, T, n_1) + F_2(p, T, n_2) + \cdots \qquad (8\text{-}6)$$

where

$$V_k = F_k(p, T, n_k) \qquad (8\text{-}7)$$

is the equation of state of the pure gas k. Thus for a gas mixture obeying Amagat's law Eq. 6-3 becomes

$$V = \frac{\sum_i n_i RT}{p} + \frac{\sum_i n_i \beta_i}{RT} + \frac{\sum_i n_i \gamma_i}{(RT)^2}p + \frac{\sum_i n_i \delta_i}{(RT)^3}p^2 \qquad [(8\text{-}8)$$

Amagat's law gives, in general, a better representation of the properties of gas mixtures than Dalton's law, although there are some notable exceptions. At least Amagat's law gives the correct result for the mixing of a gas with itself whereas Dalton's law does not.

C,9. Equation of State of Gas Mixtures. The nth virial coefficient of the complete expansion of pv for a binary gas mixture has been shown [43] from statistical mechanics to be a polynomial of the nth degree in the mole fractions, the coefficients being function of the temperature. Thus the second, third, and fourth virial coefficients of a binary mixture would be written

$$\beta_m = \sum_i \sum_j X_i X_j \beta_{ij} \tag{9-1}$$

$$\gamma_m = \sum_i \sum_j \sum_k X_i X_j X_k \gamma_{ijk} \tag{9-2}$$

$$\delta_m = \sum_i \sum_j \sum_k \sum_l X_i X_j X_k X_l \delta_{ijkl} \tag{9-3}$$

The subscript m denotes the value of a quantity for the mixture. Quantities on the right with all subscripts the same refer to the pure components, otherwise to interaction parameters arising from collisions of unlike molecules. For a binary mixture the second virial coefficient becomes

$$\beta_m = X_1^2 \beta_{11} + 2X_1 X_2 \beta_{12} + X_2^2 \beta_{22} \tag{9-4}$$

since the two interaction constants are obviously equal, that is,

$$\beta_{12} = \beta_{21} \tag{9-5}$$

We might well generalize Eq. 9-1 to 9-3 and apply them to a mixture of any number of components [44]. Thus for a ternary gas mixture Eq. 9-4 would be written

$$\beta_m = X_1^2 \beta_{11} + X_2^2 \beta_{22} + X_3^2 \beta_{33} + 2X_1 X_2 \beta_{12} + 2X_1 X_3 \beta_{13} + 2X_2 X_3 \beta_{23} \tag{9-6}$$

From the relation between the second virial coefficients and the equation of state constants, Eq. 6-1, we would conclude that Eq. 9-1 gives the dependence of the constants A_{0m}, B_{0m}, and c_m of a gas mixture on the composition, and we might extend the same method of computation to the less important parameters a_m and b_m. The interaction coefficients, as A_{0ij}, are now constants characteristic of the pair of gases i and j. The foregoing method does not yet yield an equation of state of gas mixtures as defined in Art. 1 since the method of computing the interaction constants, except from data on gas mixtures, is not defined.

Several methods of computing the values of the interaction constants from the corresponding constants of the pure gases have been proposed. Let B represent any one of the equation of state constants. Then the most used relations [5,45,46,47] for combination of constants are

$$B_{ij} = \tfrac{1}{2}(B_{ii} + B_{jj}) \quad \text{(linear combination)} \tag{9-7}$$

$$B_{ij} = B_{ii}^{\frac{1}{3}} B_{jj}^{\frac{1}{3}} \qquad \text{(square-root combination)} \qquad (9\text{-}8)$$

$$B_{ij} = \left(\frac{B_{ii}^{\frac{1}{3}} + B_{jj}^{\frac{1}{3}}}{2} \right)^{3} \quad \text{(Lorentz combination)} \qquad (9\text{-}9)$$

The first relation gives the largest value of B_{ij}, and the second the smallest. The following tabulation gives an idea of the magnitudes of the differences encountered for several ratios of B_{jj} to B_{ii}.

Values of B_{ij}

	Linear B_{ij}	Square-root B_{ij}	Lorentz B_{ij}
$B_{jj} = 1.1 B_{ii}$	$1.0500 B_{ii}$	$1.0488 B_{ii}$	$1.0492 B_{ii}$
$B_{jj} = 2.0 B_{ii}$	$1.5000 B_{ii}$	$1.4142 B_{ii}$	$1.4427 B_{ii}$
$B_{jj} = 4.0 B_{ii}$	$2.5000 B_{ii}$	$2.0000 B_{ii}$	$2.1652 B_{ii}$
$B_{jj} = 10.0 B_{ii}$	$5.500 B_{ii}$	$3.162 B_{ii}$	$3.924 B_{ii}$

General physical considerations indicate square-root combination for the attractive constant A_0 (a of van der Waals' equation) and Lorentz combination for the repulsive constant B_0 (b in van der Waals' equation). The latter corresponds to averaging the radii of the molecules. The best reproduction of the compressibilities of gas mixture is obtained [48] by square-root combination for c, provided Lorentz combination is used for B_0; but the much simpler linear combination for both B_0 and c gives quite satisfactory results.

Thus we shall write for the interaction constants

$$
\left.
\begin{aligned}
A_{0ij} &= A_{0ii}^{\frac{1}{2}} A_{0jj}^{\frac{1}{2}} & a_{ij} &= \frac{a_{ii} + a_{jj}}{2} \\[2ex]
B_{0ij} &= \left(\frac{B_{0ii}^{\frac{1}{3}} + B_{0jj}^{\frac{1}{3}}}{2} \right)^{3} & b_{ij} &= \frac{b_{ii} + b_{jj}}{2} \\[2ex]
c_{ij} &= c_{ii}^{\frac{1}{2}} c_{jj}^{\frac{1}{2}}
\end{aligned}
\right\}
\qquad (9\text{-}10)
$$

The parameters for a gas mixture are

$$
\left.
\begin{aligned}
A_{0m} &= \sum_i \sum_j X_i X_j A_{0ii}^{\frac{1}{2}} A_{0jj}^{\frac{1}{2}} \\[2ex]
a_m &= \sum_i \sum_j X_i X_j \frac{a_{ii} + a_{jj}}{2} \\[2ex]
B_{0m} &= \sum_i \sum_j X_i X_j \left(\frac{B_{0ii}^{\frac{1}{3}} + B_{0jj}^{\frac{1}{3}}}{2} \right)^{3} \\[2ex]
b_m &= \sum_i \sum_j X_i X_j \left(\frac{b_{ii} + b_{jj}}{2} \right) \\[2ex]
c_m &= \sum_i \sum_j X_i X_j c_{ii}^{\frac{1}{2}} c_{jj}^{\frac{1}{2}}
\end{aligned}
\right\}
\qquad (9\text{-}11)
$$

We can now write Eq. 6-1 as an equation of state for gas mixtures.

$$p = \frac{(\sum_i n_i)RT}{V} + \frac{(\sum_i n_i)^2 \beta_m}{V^2} + \frac{(\sum_i n_i)^3 \gamma_m}{V^3} + \frac{(\sum_i n_i)^4 \delta_m}{V^4} \qquad (9\text{-}12)$$

where

$$\left.\begin{aligned}
\beta_m &= RTB_{0m} - A_{0m} - \frac{Rc_m}{T^2} \\[2mm]
\gamma_m &= -RTB_{0m}b_m + A_{0m}a_m - \frac{RB_{0m}c_m}{T^2} \\[2mm]
\delta_m &= \frac{RB_{0m}b_m c_m}{T^2}
\end{aligned}\right\} \qquad (9\text{-}13)$$

and

$$\left.\begin{aligned}
A_{0m} &= (\sum_i X_i A_{0i}^{\frac{1}{2}})^2 \\[2mm]
B_{0m} &= \tfrac{1}{8}\sum_i\sum_j X_i X_j (B_{0i}^{\frac{1}{3}} + B_{0j}^{\frac{1}{3}})^3 \\[2mm]
&= \tfrac{1}{4}\sum_i X_i B_{0i} + \tfrac{3}{4}(\sum_i X_i B_{0i}^{\frac{1}{3}})(\sum_i X_i B_{0i}^{\frac{2}{3}}) \\[2mm]
c_m &= (\sum_i X_i c_i^{\frac{1}{3}})^2 \\[2mm]
a_m &= (\sum_i X_i a_i) \\[2mm]
b_m &= (\sum_i X_i b_i)
\end{aligned}\right\} \qquad (9\text{-}14)$$

In the foregoing equations A_{0i} has been written for A_{0ii} and similarly for the other constants since no confusion is introduced.

The equation of state for gas mixtures explicit in the volume is

$$\frac{V}{\sum_i n_i} = \frac{RT}{p} + \frac{\beta_m}{RT} + \frac{\gamma_m}{(RT)^2}p + \frac{\delta_m}{(RT)^3}p^2 \qquad (9\text{-}15)$$

and the approximate mixture relation similar to Eq. 6-5 for pure gases becomes

$$\frac{V}{\sum_i n_i} = \frac{RT}{p} + \frac{\beta_m}{RT} \qquad (9\text{-}16)$$

The combination of constants rules of Eq. 9-11 violates in two instances the relations (9-2) and (9-3). In γ_m the term $RB_{0m}c_m/T^2$ is of the fourth degree in the mole fractions; and the term δ_m, $RB_{0m}b_m c_m/T^2$, is of the fifth degree. To overcome this difficulty we might consider $B_{0m}c_m$ as a single rather than a composite constant and write

$$B_{0m}c_m = \left[\sum_i X_i (B_{0i}c_i)^{\frac{1}{3}}\right]^3 \tag{9-17}$$

However, the difference between this and the method of Eq. 9-14 is unimportant in the calculation of p or $(\partial p/\partial n_i)_{V,T,n}$ from Eq. 9-12, or of V or $(\partial V/\partial n_i)_{p,T,n}$ from Eq. 9-15.

C,10. Derivatives of the Equation of State Parameters. The temperature derivatives of the virial parameters β, γ, δ of Eq. 6-1 are

$$
\left.\begin{aligned}
\frac{d\beta}{dT} &= RB_0 + \frac{2Rc}{T^3} & \frac{d^2\beta}{dT^2} &= -\frac{6Rc}{T^4} \\[2mm]
\frac{d\gamma}{dT} &= -RB_0 b + \frac{2RB_0 c}{T^3} & \frac{d^2\gamma}{dT^2} &= -\frac{6RB_0 c}{T^4} \\[2mm]
\frac{d\delta}{dT} &= -\frac{2RB_0 bc}{T^3} & \frac{d^2\delta}{dT^2} &= \frac{6RB_0 bc}{T^4}
\end{aligned}\right\} \tag{10-1}
$$

The temperature derivatives at constant composition of the parameters of Eq. 9-12, 9-15, and 9-16 for gas mixtures are given by the rela tions (10-1) with the constants of the pure gas replaced by the parameters of the particular mixture: β_m, γ_m, δ_m, and A_{0m}, B_{0m}, c_m, a_m, b_m.

The derivatives of the equation of state parameters of a mixture with respect to one of the mole numbers n_i with all of the other mole numbers held constant (denoted by a subscript n to the partial derivative) are

$$
\left.\begin{aligned}
\left(\frac{\partial B_{0m}}{\partial n_i}\right)_n &= \frac{1}{\sum_i n_i}[B_{0i} + D_i(B_0) - B_{0m}], \\[2mm]
& D_i(B_0) = -\tfrac{3}{4}(B_{0i}^{\frac{1}{3}} - \sum_i X_i B_{0i}^{\frac{1}{3}})(B_{0i}^{\frac{2}{3}} - \sum_i X_i B_{0i}^{\frac{2}{3}}) \\[2mm]
\left(\frac{\partial A_{0m}}{\partial n_i}\right)_n &= \frac{1}{\sum_i n_i}[A_{0i} + D_i(A_0) - A_{0m}], \\[2mm]
& D_i(A_0) = -(A_{0i}^{\frac{1}{2}} - \sum_i X_i A_{0i}^{\frac{1}{2}})^2 \\[2mm]
\left(\frac{\partial c_m}{\partial n_i}\right)_n &= \frac{1}{\sum_i n_i}[c_i + D_i(c) - c_m], \\[2mm]
& D_i(c) = -(c_i^{\frac{1}{3}} - \sum_i X_i c_i^{\frac{1}{3}})^2 \\[2mm]
\left(\frac{\partial a_m}{\partial n_i}\right)_n &= \frac{1}{\sum_i n_i}[a_i - a_m] \\[2mm]
\left(\frac{\partial b_m}{\partial n_i}\right)_n &= \frac{1}{\sum_i n_i}[b_i - b_m]
\end{aligned}\right\} \tag{10-2}
$$

The derivatives of the virial parameters with respect to n_i for use in Eq. 9-12, 9-15, and 9-16 are

$$\left(\frac{\partial \beta_m}{\partial n_i}\right)_{T,n} = \frac{2}{\sum_i n_i} [\sum_j X_j \beta_{ij} - \beta_m]$$

$$= \frac{1}{\sum_i n_i} [\beta_i + D_i(\beta) - \beta_m]$$

$$\left(\frac{\partial \gamma_m}{\partial n_i}\right)_{T,n} = \frac{3}{\sum_i n_i} [\sum_j \sum_k X_j X_k \gamma_{ijk} - \gamma_m]$$

$$= \frac{1}{\sum_i n_i} [\gamma_i + D_i(\gamma) - 2\gamma_m]$$

$$\left(\frac{\partial \delta_m}{\partial n_i}\right)_{T,n} = \frac{4}{\sum_i n_i} [\sum_j \sum_k \sum_l X_j X_k X_l \delta_{ijkl} - \delta_m]$$

$$= \frac{1}{\sum_i n_i} [\delta_i + D_i(\delta) - 3\delta_m]$$

$$D_i(\beta) = RTD_i(B_0) - D_i(A_0) - \frac{R}{T^2} D_i(c) \tag{10-3}$$

$$= -\frac{3RT}{4} (B_{0i}^{\frac{1}{3}} - \sum_i X_i B_{0i}^{\frac{1}{3}})(B_{0i}^{\frac{2}{3}} - \sum_i X_i B_{0i}^{\frac{2}{3}})$$

$$+ (A_{0i}^{\frac{1}{2}} - \sum_i X_i A_{0i}^{\frac{1}{2}})^2 + \frac{R}{T^2} (c_i^{\frac{1}{2}} - \sum_i X_i c_i^{\frac{1}{2}})^2$$

$$D_i(\gamma) = - RT\{b_m[B_{0i} + D_i(B_0)] + b_i[B_{0m} - B_{0i}]\}$$

$$+ \{a_m[A_{0i} + D_i(A_0)] + a_i[A_{0m} - A_{0i}]\}$$

$$- \frac{R}{T^2} \{c_m[B_{0i} + D_i(B_0)] + c_i[B_{0m} - B_{0i}] + B_{0m}D_i(c)\}$$

$$D_i(\delta) = \frac{R}{T^2} \{B_{0m}b_m[c_i + D_i(c)] + b_m c_m[B_{0i} + D_i(B_0)]$$

$$+ b_i[B_{0m}c_m - B_{0i}c_i]\}$$

To determine the derivative with respect to n_i of the product of any parameter (say β_m) into $(\sum_i n_i)$ raised to any power q, we can use

$$\left(\frac{\partial[(\sum_i n_i)^q \beta_m]}{\partial n_i}\right)_{T,n} = (\sum_i n_i)^q \left(\frac{\partial \beta_m}{\partial n_i}\right)_{T,n} + q(\sum_i n_i)^{q-1}\beta_m \tag{10-4}$$

The arrangement of the computation of the foregoing derivatives for ethane in one mixture of ethane and n-butane is given in Table C,10. This pair of substances was chosen because the equation of state constants of n-butane are about two to four times as large as those of ethane. The method is evidently applicable to mixtures of any number of constituents.

Two quantities of importance in the theory of gas mixtures are the

Table C,10. Computation of the derivatives of the virial parameters with respect to mole numbers for a gas mixture.
See Eq. 10-3 and 10-4.

Units: atmosphere, liter per mole, degree Kelvin. $R = 0.08206$.

The calculation is made for ethane in a gas mixture 50 mole per cent ethane and 50 mole per cent n-butane at 500°K.

Y represents any parameter in the columns following.

	A_0	B_0	$c \times 10^{-4}$	a	b	$A_0^{\frac{1}{2}}$	$B_0^{\frac{1}{3}}$	$B_0^{\frac{2}{3}}$	$c^{\frac{1}{2}} \times 10^{-2}$
Y_1(ethane)	5.8800	0.09400	90.00	0.05861	0.01015	2.42487	0.454684	0.206738	9.4868
Y_2(n-butane)	17.7940	0.24620	350.00	0.12161	0.09423	4.21829	0.626752	0.392818	18.7083
$\Sigma_i X_i Y_i$		0.170100		0.0901100	0.0556900				
Y_m(mixture)	11.03289	0.164097	198.742	0.0901100	0.0556900	3.32158	0.540718	0.299778	14.0976
$Y_1 - \Sigma_i X_i Y_i$	−0.80409	−0.006003	− 21.259						
$D_1(Y)$	+5.07591	+0.087997	+ 68.741			−0.89671	−0.086034	−0.093040	−4.6108
$Y_1 + D_1(Y)$	+5.15289	+0.070097	+108.742						
$Y_m - Y_1$									

	β	γ	$\delta \times 10^4$
Y_1(ethane)	−2.31860	+0.24300	+ 5.3178
Y_m(mixture)	−4.95234	+0.50544	+ 60.6860
$D_1(Y)$	+0.62757	+0.43298	+ 68.7150
$Y_1 + D_1(Y)$	−1.69103	+0.67598	+ 74.0328
$Y_1 + D_1(Y) + Y_m$	−6.64337	+1.18142	+134.7188

Pressure of ethane at $V = 1$ liter/mole from Eq. 6-1 = 38.95 atm

Pressure of mixture at $V = 1$ liter/mole from Eq. 9-12 = 36.59 atm partial molar volume, $(\partial V/\partial n_i)_{p,T,n}$, and the corresponding quantity $(\partial p/\partial n_i)_{V,T,n}$.

From the equation of state of gas mixtures (9-15) explicit in the volume and the relations (10-3 and 10-4) we find

$$\left(\frac{\partial V}{\partial n_i}\right)_{p,T,n} = \frac{RT}{p} + \frac{[\beta_i + D_i(\beta)]}{RT} + \frac{[\gamma_i + D_i(\gamma) - \gamma_m]}{(RT)^2} p$$

$$+ \frac{[\delta_i + D_i(\delta) - 2\delta_m]}{(RT)^3} p^2 \quad (10\text{-}5)$$

$$= \frac{V_{Pk}}{n_k} + \frac{D_i(\beta)}{RT} + \frac{[D_i(\gamma) - \gamma_m]}{(RT)^2} p + \frac{[D_i(\delta) - 2\delta_m]}{(RT)^3} p^2$$

$$(i \equiv k = 1, 2, \cdots) \quad (10\text{-}6)$$

The term V_{Pk}/n_k is molar volume of gas i measured pure at the total pressure and the temperature of the mixture. It is the value of the partial molar volume predicted by Amagat's law, see Eq. 8-5 and 8-8. For the gas mixture considered in Table C,10 we find for the ethane in the mixture

$$\left(\frac{\partial V}{\partial n_i}\right)_{p,T,n} - \frac{V_{Pk}}{n_k} = 0.01530 - 4.30 \times 10^{-5}p - 7.6 \times 10^{-8}p^2 \quad (10\text{-}7)$$

where p is in atmospheres and V in liters, and the values of the constants appropriate for the equation of state explicit in the pressure were used. The calculated value of the right-hand side of Eq. 10-7 is 0.014 liter per mole, for a volume of 1 liter per mole. The computed error of Amagat's law is 1.4 per cent, a small error for this pressure, 36.59 atm.

Eq. 9-12 and the partial derivatives listed above give

$$\left(\frac{\partial p}{\partial n_i}\right)_{V,T,n} = \frac{RT}{V} + [\beta_i + D_i(\beta) + \beta_m]\frac{\sum_i n_i}{V^2}$$

$$+ [\gamma_i + D_i(\gamma) + \gamma_m]\frac{(\sum_i n_i)^2}{V^3}$$

$$+ [\delta_i + D_i(\delta) + \delta_m]\frac{(\sum_i n_i)^3}{V^4} \quad (10\text{-}8)$$

$$= \left(\frac{\partial p_{ck}}{\partial n_k}\right)_{V,T,n_k} + [\beta_i(1 - 2x_i) + D_i(\beta) + \beta_m]\frac{\sum_i n_i}{V^2}$$

$$+ [\gamma_i(1 - 3X_i^2) + D_i(\gamma) + \gamma_m]\frac{(\sum_i n_i)^2}{V^3}$$

$$+ [\delta_i(1 - 4x_i^3) + D_i(\delta) + \delta_m]\frac{(\sum_i n_i)^3}{V^4}$$

$$(i \equiv k = 1, 2, \cdots) \quad (10\text{-}9)$$

The term $(\partial p_{ck}/\partial n_k)_{V,T,n_k}$ is the value of $(\partial p/\partial n_i)_{V,T,n}$ given by Dalton's law, (see Eq. 8-1 and 8-4), and the sum of the remaining terms on the right-hand side of Eq. 10-9 is the error of the Dalton law calculation. For the ethane in the mixture considered in Table C,10 at 500°K and a volume of 1 liter per mole, the value of $(\partial p/\partial n_i)_{V,T,n}$ computed from Eq. 10-8 is 35.58 atm per mole of ethane, and the Dalton value, $(\partial p_{ck}/\partial n_k)_{V,T,n_k}$, is 38.89 atm per mole of ethane, an error of 9.3 per cent. For this mixture and under the specified conditions, Amagat's law is considerably better than Dalton's law.

C,11. Other Rules for Combination of Constants. Application [49,37] of the relation for the second virial coefficient given by the Lennard-Jones potential to gas mixtures indicates that the interaction constants σ_{12} and θ_{12} of Eq. 3-17 should be combined according to the rules:

$$\sigma_{12} = \tfrac{1}{2}(\sigma_{11} + \sigma_{22})$$

$$\theta_{12} = \theta_{11}^{\frac{1}{2}}\theta_{22}^{\frac{1}{2}} \qquad (11\text{-}1)$$

Since B_0 of the equation of state is analogous to $2\pi N\sigma^3/3$ and A_0/RB_0 to θ, the foregoing methods for the computation of the interaction constants suggest [50] that the second virial coefficient of a gas mixture be written

$$\frac{\beta_m}{RT} = B_{0m}\left[1 - \left(\frac{A_0}{B_0}\right)_m \frac{1}{RT} - \left(\frac{c}{B_0}\right)_m \frac{1}{T^3}\right] \qquad (11\text{-}2)$$

and that B_{0m} be computed by Lorentz combination as in Eq. 9-11, but that the ratios $(A_0/B_0)_m$ and $(c/B_0)_m$ be combined by square-root combination, as for A_{0m} in Eq. 9-11.

Eq. 5-8 gives a relation for the second virial coefficient B of a highly polar gas, such as water vapor:

$$B = B_0 - \frac{A}{RT} e^{D/T^2} \qquad (11\text{-}3)$$

In the application [51] of this relation to mixtures containing polar gases, the constants A and D are each written as the sum of two terms: one, A_0 and D_0, depending on the type of intermolecular force common to all kinds of molecules; and the second, A_p and D_p, on the dipole moment μ and differing from zero only if the molecules are polar:

$$\left.\begin{array}{l} A = A_0 + A_p \\ D = D_0 + D_p \end{array}\right\} \qquad (11\text{-}4)$$

$$\left.\begin{array}{l} A_0 = \tfrac{1}{2}[A + (A^2 - 0.756\mu^4)^{\frac{1}{2}}] \\ A_p = \tfrac{1}{2}[A - (A^2 - 0.756\mu^4)^{\frac{1}{2}}] \end{array}\right\} \qquad (11\text{-}5)$$

$$\left.\begin{array}{l} D_0 = D - D_p \\ D_p = 13.6\mu^4/B_0^2 \end{array}\right\} \qquad (11\text{-}6)$$

In case the form (11-3) has not been fitted to the experimental data for nonpolar gases in the mixture, we can write $D_0 = Rc/A_0$ for these gases (compare Eq. 5-9 and 5-6). For gas mixtures, B_{0m} is computed by Lorentz combination, and A_{0m}, A_{pm}, D_{0m}, and D_{pm} by square-root combination. In the above relations the units of the equation of state are atmosphere, liter per mole, °K, and μ is in Debye units.

CHAPTER 2. THERMODYNAMIC TREATMENT OF PURE GASES

C,12. The General Limit Method. The first and second laws of thermodynamics define the increase in the energy and entropy of a system that has undergone a change in state, but not the absolute values of these quantities. We are at liberty to assign any value to the energy and entropy integration constants consistent with the particular problem to be solved. Some one state of each of the substances composing a system may be selected, and appropriate values may be assigned to the energy and entropy of the substance in this state. The state is called the standard state, and each substance has at each temperature a series of standard states.

One method applicable to gases is to select a single standard state for each substance, say the state of one mole at the pressure p_0 and temperature T_0, the corresponding molar volume being v_0. Let the molar energy and entropy of the substance be $E(p_0, T_0)$ and $S(p_0, T_0)$ in this state. The problem of computing the energy and entropy of the pure gas in any other state $(p, T$ or $v, T)$ relative to the values in the standard state $(p_0, T_0$ or $v_0, T_0)$ is a simple one involving a two-step process: first integrating dE and dS from T_0 to T at the constant pressure p_0 (or the corresponding constant volume v_0) and then integrating from p_0 to p (or from v_0 to v) at the constant temperature T.

The only data required for carrying out the calculations to a numerical solution are: the value of the constant pressure heat capacity at p_0 (or the constant volume heat capacity at v_0) as a function of temperature; the compressibility of the gas at the temperature T, which may be given in the form of an equation of state or an equivalent table or graph; and the values of the integration constants $E(p_0, T_0)$ and $S(p_0, T_0)$. Thus the problem is completely solved without the necessity of making any assumptions.

We cannot even get a start on a general thermodynamic theory of gas mixtures including mixtures in which chemical reactions may occur without some assumption regarding equilibrium between a gas mixture and its pure constituents. Amagat's law, Dalton's law, and an equation of state for gas mixtures do not contain the fundamental idea of equilibrium and hence are of no help. A number of approaches to the solution of the problem have been suggested and will be considered later. Of these the general limit method [52] yields equations for the thermodynamic properties of mixtures of real gases that may be considered exact. The method assumes [53,54,55] that as the pressure on a gaseous mixture approaches zero a certain property of the mixture approaches that of mixtures of ideal gases in a specified manner. The resulting equations express the thermodynamic properties of gas mixtures in terms of definite integrals that can be evaluated from an equation of state of mixtures as defined in Art. 1 and from relations for the temperature variation of the constant volume heat capacity at zero pressure for the pure constituent gases. Thus no data on mixtures are required, although when available they may be employed in principle to evaluate the definite integrals by graphical means.

A similar method may be used to derive general relations for the thermodynamic properties of pure gases. The resulting equations contain a definite integral that can be evaluated by an equation of state or an equivalent graphical method. Two basic assumptions suffice for both pure gases and gas mixtures; but for clarity of presentation we shall separate the discussion of pure gases from that for mixtures. In this case we need three assumptions, two for pure gases and one for mixtures, one of the former being derivable from the other two.

C,13. Assumptions for Pure Gases. We shall consider two pressure regions:[4]

1. The region of low pressure, in which terms of the order of p^2 are negligible in comparison with terms of the order of p or of unity.
2. The region of very low pressure, in which terms of the order of p are negligible in comparison with unity. Thermodynamic quantities in the region of very low pressure will be denoted by a superscript asterisk, as p^*.

The two assumptions for pure gases are:

1. At all temperatures[5] the pressure-volume product pV of a fixed mass m of a real gas at a constant temperature T and in the region of low pressure can be represented by the expression

$$pV = F(T, m) + A(T, m)p + O(p^2) \quad (T, m \text{ const}) \qquad (13\text{-}1)$$

where the functions of temperature and mass, $F(T, m)$ and $A(T, m)$, and their derivatives with respect to temperature are bounded, and $O(p^2)$ represents terms of the order of p^2.

[4] Much of the following treatment is taken from [56] and is reproduced with the permission of the publisher, The Williams and Wilkins Company, Baltimore.
[5] The region in the neighborhood of 0°K is to be excluded.

2. At all temperatures the heat content H of a fixed mass of a gas at constant temperature and in the region of low pressure can be represented by the expression:

$$H = f(T, m) + B(T, m)p + O(p^2) \quad (T, m \text{ const}) \qquad (13\text{-}2)$$

where $f(T, m)$ and $B(T, m)$ and their derivatives with respect to temperature are bounded.

C,14. Results Derivable from the Assumptions. Substitution from Eq. 13-1 and 13-2 into the general thermodynamic relation

$$\left(\frac{\partial H}{\partial p}\right)_T = V - T\left(\frac{\partial V}{\partial T}\right)_p \quad (m \text{ const})$$

gives

$$B + O(p) = \frac{1}{p}\left[F - T\left(\frac{\partial F}{\partial T}\right)_m\right] + \left[A - T\left(\frac{\partial A}{\partial T}\right)_m\right] + O(p)$$

$$(m \text{ const}) \quad (14\text{-}1)$$

for a fixed mass of gas in the region of low pressure. Eq. 14-1 can hold for all values of the pressure in the region of low pressure only when

$$F - T\left(\frac{\partial F}{\partial T}\right)_m = 0 \qquad (14\text{-}2)$$

Integration gives

$$F = r(m)T \qquad (14\text{-}3)$$

where T is absolute thermodynamic temperature and $r(m)$ depends only on the mass for any given gas. Thus Eq. 13-1 becomes

$$pV = r(m)T + A(T, m)p + O(p^2) \quad (m \text{ const}) \qquad (14\text{-}4)$$

and in the region of very low pressure

$$(pV)^* = r(m)T \quad (m \text{ const}) \qquad (14\text{-}5)$$

The volume is an extensive state property of a system. At constant pressure and temperature it is a homogeneous function of the first degree in the mass. If we replace V in Eq. 14-5 by V/m, the volume per unit mass, the quantity $r(m)$ will be a constant characteristic of each gas. Furthermore, let m be expressed in terms of the mass unit: the mole. One mole of any gas is defined as the mass that occupies at a very low pressure and at each temperature the same volume as 32 grams of gaseous oxygen measured at the same pressure and temperature. When the mass of gas is expressed in moles, r is a universal constant independent of the kind of gas and is denoted by R. Thus for low pressures we may write Eq. 14-4 in the form:

$$pV = nRT + \frac{n\beta p}{RT} + O(p^2) \qquad (14\text{-}6)$$

and to the same degree of approximation

$$pV = nRT + \frac{n^2\beta}{V} + O\left(\frac{n}{V}\right)^2 \qquad (14\text{-}7)$$

where n is the number of moles of gas in the volume V, β is a pure temperature function and has the value

$$\beta = RTA(T, 1) \qquad (14\text{-}8)$$

if $A(T, 1)$ is taken for one mole of gas. The particular form used for β is chosen to conform to the usual method of writing equations of state.

C,15. The Path of Integration. The standard state of each pure gaseous substance is one mole at any arbitrarily chosen pressure p_0 and temperature T_0, the corresponding volume of n moles being V_0.

The thermodynamic functions in which we are interested are all state variables and hence we can proceed from the standard state (p_0, T_0 or V_0, T_0) to any other state (p, T or V, T) along any path. We shall use a three-step path involving the region of very low pressure p^* where the corresponding volume is V^*. Let the number of moles n of gas remain constant and:

1. Change the pressure from p_0 to p^* (or the volume from the corresponding values V_0 to V^*) at the temperature T_0.
2. Change the temperature from T_0 to T with the pressure held constant at p^* (or the volume at V^*).
3. Change the pressure from p^* to p (or the volume from V^* to V) at the temperature T.

C,16. Derivations for the Independent Variables p and T. The total differentials of the heat content H and entropy S of a constant mass of n moles of a real gas are:

$$dH = C_p dT + \left[V - T\left(\frac{\partial V}{\partial T}\right)_p\right] dp \qquad (16\text{-}1)$$

$$dS = \frac{C_p}{T} dT - \left(\frac{\partial V}{\partial T}\right)_p dp \qquad (16\text{-}2)$$

where C_p is the constant pressure heat capacity of n moles. We can integrate these relations along the three-step path just described from the standard state p_0, T_0 where the heat content and entropy have the values $H(p_0, T_0)$ and $S(p_0, T_0)$ to the variable state p, T and the corresponding values $H(p, T)$ and $S(p, T)$:

$$H(p, T) - H(p_0, T_0) = \int_{T_0, p_0}^{p^*} \left[V - T\left(\frac{\partial V}{\partial T}\right)_p\right] dp$$

$$+ \int_{p^*, T_0}^{T} nc_p^* dT + \int_{T, p^*}^{p} \left[V - T\left(\frac{\partial V}{\partial T}\right)_p\right] dp \quad (16\text{-}3)$$

$$S(p, T) - S(p_0, T_0) = -\int_{T_0}^{p^*}\!\!\int_{p_0} \left(\frac{\partial V}{\partial T}\right)_p dp$$

$$+ \int_{p^*}^{T}\!\!\int_{T_0} \frac{nc_p^*}{T}\, dT - \int_{T}^{p}\!\!\int_{p^*} \left(\frac{\partial V}{\partial T}\right)_p dp \quad (16\text{-}4)$$

Here c_p^* is the molar constant pressure heat capacity of the gas in the region of very low pressure. Addition and subtraction of the term $nR \ln (p/p_0)$ to the right-hand side of Eq. 16-4 gives

$$S(p, T) - S(p_0, T_0) = \int_{T_0}^{p^*}\!\!\int_{p_0} \left[\frac{nR}{p} - \left(\frac{\partial V}{\partial T}\right)_p\right] dp + \int_{p^*}^{T}\!\!\int_{T_0} \frac{nc_p^*}{T}\, dT$$

$$+ \int_{T}^{p}\!\!\int_{p^*} \left[\frac{nR}{p} - \left(\frac{\partial V}{\partial T}\right)_p\right] dp - nR \ln \frac{p}{p_0} \quad (16\text{-}5)$$

These expressions can be simplified. From Eq. 14-6 we find

$$\lim_{p^*\to 0} \int_{p^*}^{0} \left[V - T\left(\frac{\partial V}{\partial T}\right)_p\right] dp$$

$$= \lim_{p^*\to 0}\left[\left(T\frac{d\beta}{dT} - 2\beta\right)\frac{np^*}{RT} + O(p^{*2})\right] = 0 \quad (16\text{-}6)$$

$$\lim_{p^*\to 0} \int_{p^*}^{0} \left[\frac{nR}{p} - \left(\frac{\partial V}{\partial T}\right)_p\right] dp$$

$$= \lim_{p^*\to 0}\left[\left(\frac{d\beta}{dT} - \frac{\beta}{T}\right)\frac{np^*}{RT} + O(p^{*2})\right] = 0 \quad (16\text{-}7)$$

so that the limits p^* in Eq. 16-3 and 16-5 can be replaced by zero.
From Eq. 13-2 we see that

$$nc_p = \left(\frac{\partial H}{\partial T}\right)_{p,n} = \left(\frac{\partial f}{\partial T}\right)_m + \left(\frac{\partial B}{\partial T}\right)_m p + O(p^2) \quad (16\text{-}8)$$

whence

$$nc_p^* = \left(\frac{\partial f}{\partial T}\right)_m \quad (16\text{-}9)$$

a pure temperature function.
Let us define the following quantities:

$$H^0 = H_0^0 + \int_{T_0}^{T} c_p^* dT \quad (16\text{-}10)$$

$$nH_0^0 = H(p_0, T_0) + \int_{T_0}^{p^*}\!\!\int_{p_0} \left[V - T\left(\frac{\partial V}{\partial T}\right)_p\right] dp \quad (16\text{-}11)$$

$$s^0 = s_0^0 + \int_{T_0}^{T} \frac{c_p^*}{T}\, dT \quad (16\text{-}12)$$

$$ns_0^0 = S(p_0, T_0) + \int_{T_0}^{p^*}\!\!\int_{p_0} \left[\frac{nR}{p} - \left(\frac{\partial V}{\partial T}\right)_p\right] dp + nR \ln p_0 \quad (16\text{-}13)$$

Eq. 16-3 and 16-5 can now be written

$$H(p, T) = \int_0^p \left[V - T\left(\frac{\partial V}{\partial T}\right)_p \right] dp + n\text{H}^0 \qquad (16\text{-}14)$$

$$S(p, T) = \int_0^p \left[\frac{nR}{p} - \left(\frac{\partial V}{\partial T}\right)_p \right] dp - nR \ln p + n\text{S}^0 \qquad (16\text{-}15)$$

In view of Eq. 16-14 we may interpret the parameter H^0 in either of the following ways:

1. H^0 is the molar heat content of the gas at the temperature T and a very low pressure:

$$\text{H}^0 = \frac{1}{n} H(p^*, T) \qquad (16\text{-}16)$$

2. H^0 is the molar heat content the gas would have at the temperature T and any pressure, say 1 atmosphere, if it behaved as an ideal gas, i.e. if $V - T(\partial V/\partial T)_p = 0$.

The corresponding interpretations of S^0 from Eq. 16-15 are:

1. S^0 is the molar entropy of the gas at the temperature T and a very low pressure increased by $R \ln p^*$:

$$\text{S}^0 = \frac{1}{n} S(p^*, T) + R \ln p^* \qquad (16\text{-}17)$$

2. S^0 is the molar entropy the gas would have at the temperature T and 1 atmosphere pressure if it behaved as an ideal gas.

The quantities H_0^0 and S_0^0 have a similar interpretation for the standard state temperature T_0. They are constants characteristic of each gas. Their evaluation will be considered later.

We can now write the relations for the energy E, work content A, free energy F, chemical potential μ, and fugacity f of a gas from the usual thermodynamic relations:

$$H = E + pV \qquad (16\text{-}18)$$

$$A = E - TS \qquad (16\text{-}19)$$

$$F = H - TS \qquad (16\text{-}20)$$

$$\mu = \left(\frac{\partial A}{\partial n}\right)_{VT} = \left(\frac{\partial F}{\partial n}\right)_{pT} \qquad (16\text{-}21)$$

$$\mu = RT \ln f + \text{H}^0 - T\text{S}^0 \qquad (16\text{-}22)$$

The thermodynamic relation between the heat capacity at constant pressure C_p and the heat capacity at constant volume C_V is

$$C_p = C_V - T \frac{(\partial V/\partial T)_p^2}{(\partial V/\partial p)_T} \qquad (16\text{-}23)$$

Evaluation of the partial derivatives from Eq. 14-6 gives

$$C_p - C_V = nR + O(p) \qquad (16\text{-}24)$$

whence

$$c_p^* = c_V^* + R \qquad (16\text{-}25)$$

where c_p^* and c_V^* are the molar quantities in the region of very low pressure.

The relation

$$dC_p = -T\left(\frac{\partial^2 V}{\partial T^2}\right)_p dp \quad (T, n \text{ const}) \qquad (16\text{-}26)$$

can be integrated at constant temperature and mass from p^* to p:

$$C_p(p, T) - C_p^*(p^*, T) = -T\int_{p^*}^{p}\left(\frac{\partial^2 V}{\partial T^2}\right)_p dp \qquad (16\text{-}27)$$

From Eq. 14-6 we find that the limit p^* can be replaced by zero. Also $C_p^*(p^*, T)$ is simply nc_p^*. Hence

$$C_p = nc_p^* - T\int_{0}^{p}\left(\frac{\partial^2 V}{\partial T^2}\right)_p dp \qquad (16\text{-}28)$$

The corresponding relation for the variation of C_V with pressure is more complicated. This can be obtained, however, by computing C_p from Eq. 16-28, then applying the relations (16-23 and 16-25) to convert C_p to C_V and c_p^* to c_V^*.

In the expression for the Joule-Thomson coefficient μ_{JT}

$$\mu_{JT}C_p = T^2\left[\frac{\partial(V/T)}{\partial T}\right]_p \qquad (16\text{-}29)$$

C_p is to be computed from Eq. 16-28 and the partial derivative evaluated from an equation of state explicit in the volume, as Eq. 6-2 or 6-3. The relation for the Joule coefficient η may be written

$$\eta C_V = T\left(\frac{\partial p}{\partial T}\right)_V - p$$

$$= -\left[p + T\frac{(\partial V/\partial T)_p}{(\partial V/\partial p)_T}\right] \qquad (16\text{-}30)$$

All of the foregoing relations are collected in Art. 18.

C,17. Derivations for the Independent Variables V and T. The total differentials of the energy E and the entropy S of a constant mass of n moles of a real gas are

⟨ 278 ⟩

$$dE = C_V dT + \left[T \left(\frac{\partial p}{\partial T} \right)_V - p \right] dV \qquad (17\text{-}1)$$

$$dS = \frac{C_V}{T} dT + \left(\frac{\partial p}{\partial T} \right)_V dV \qquad (17\text{-}2)$$

Integration from the standard state V_0, T_0 to the variable state V, T along the three-step path gives

$$E(V, T) - E(V_0, T_0) = \int_{T_0, V_0}^{V^*} \left[T \left(\frac{\partial p}{\partial T} \right)_V - p \right] dV$$
$$+ \int_{V^*, T_0}^{T} n c_V^* dT + \int_{T, V^*}^{V} \left[T \left(\frac{\partial p}{\partial T} \right)_V - p \right] dV \qquad (17\text{-}3)$$

$$S(V, T) - S(V_0, T_0) = \int_{T_0, V_0}^{V^*} \left(\frac{\partial p}{\partial T} \right)_V dV$$
$$+ \int_{V^*, T_0}^{T} \frac{n c_V^*}{T} dT + \int_{T, V^*}^{V} \left(\frac{\partial p}{\partial T} \right)_V dV \qquad (17\text{-}4)$$

where c_V^* is the molar constant volume heat capacity in the region of very low pressures. Addition and subtraction of the term $nR \ln (V/V_0)$ gives for Eq. 17-4,

$$S(V, T) - S(V_0, T_0) = \int_{T_0, V_0}^{V^*} \left[\left(\frac{\partial p}{\partial T} \right)_V - \frac{nR}{V} \right] dV + \int_{V^*, T_0}^{T} \frac{n c_V^*}{T} dT$$
$$+ \int_{T, V^*}^{V} \left[\left(\frac{\partial p}{\partial T} \right)_V - \frac{nR}{V} \right] dV + nR \ln \frac{V}{V_0} \qquad (17\text{-}5)$$

We can simplify these expressions as before. Use of Eq. 14-7 shows that

$$\lim_{V^* \to \infty} \int_{V^*}^{\infty} \left[T \left(\frac{\partial p}{\partial T} \right)_V - p \right] dV$$
$$= \lim_{V^* \to \infty} \int_{V^*}^{\infty} \left[\left(\frac{\partial p}{\partial T} \right)_V - \frac{nR}{V} \right] dV = 0 \qquad (17\text{-}6)$$

so that the limit V^* can be replaced by infinity.

From Eq. 16-9 and 16-25 we find that c_V^* is a pure temperature function.

Let us define the following quantities:

$$E^0 = E_0^0 + \int_{T_0}^{T} c_V^* dT \qquad (17\text{-}7)$$

$$n E_0^0 = E(V_0, T_0) + \int_{T_0, V_0}^{V^*} \left[T \left(\frac{\partial p}{\partial T} \right)_V - p \right] dV \qquad (17\text{-}8)$$

Now E^0 and E_0^0 can be related to H^0 and H_0^0. From Eq. 16-11, 17-8, and

14-6 we find

$$nH_0^0 - nE_0^0 = H(p_0, T_0) - E(V_0, T_0) + \int_{T_0, p_0}^{p^*} \left[V - T\left(\frac{\partial V}{\partial T}\right)_p \right] dp$$

$$- \int_{T_0, V_0}^{V^*} \left[T\left(\frac{\partial p}{\partial T}\right)_V - p \right] dV$$

$$= p_0 V_0 + \int_{T_0, p_0 V_0}^{p^* V^*} d(pV)$$

$$= nRT_0 \tag{17-9}$$

This expression together with Eq. 16-25, 16-10, and 17-7 gives

$$H^0 - E^0 = RT \tag{17-10}$$

Since $S(V_0, T)$ refers to the same standard state as $S(p_0, T_0)$, we can replace the former in Eq. 17-5 by the value of $S(p_0, T_0)$ given by Eq. 16-13. Thus on simplification we find for the following three terms of Eq. 17-5:

$$S(V_0, T_0) + \int_{T_0, V_0}^{V^*} \left[\left(\frac{\partial p}{\partial T}\right)_V - \frac{nR}{V} \right] dV - nR \ln V_0$$

$$= -nR \ln p_0 V_0 - nR \int_{T_0, p_0 V_0}^{p^* V^*} d \ln (pV) + ns_0^0$$

$$= -nR \ln nRT_0 + ns_0^0 \tag{17-11}$$

Note that we can express s^0 in terms of c_V^* rather than in terms of c_p^*:

$$s^0 = s_0^0 + \int_{T_0}^{T} \frac{c_V^*}{T} dT + R \ln \frac{T}{T_0} \tag{17-12}$$

Introduction of these simplifications into Eq. 17-3 and 17-5 gives

$$E(V, T) = \int_V^\infty \left[p - T\left(\frac{\partial p}{\partial T}\right)_V \right] dV + nE^0 \tag{17-13}$$

$$S(V, T) = \int_V^\infty \left[\frac{nR}{V} - \left(\frac{\partial p}{\partial T}\right)_V \right] dV + nR \ln \frac{V}{nRT} + ns^0 \tag{17-14}$$

These, together with Eq. 16-18 through 16-22, yield expressions for the thermodynamic properties H, A, F, μ, and f in terms of the independent variables V and T.

In terms of the independent variables V and T, Eq. 16-23 becomes

$$C_p = C_V - T \frac{(\partial p/\partial T)_V^2}{(\partial p/\partial V)_T} \tag{17-15}$$

The relation

$$dC_V = T \left(\frac{\partial^2 p}{\partial T^2}\right)_V dV \quad (T, n \text{ const}) \tag{17-16}$$

can be integrated at constant temperature from V^* to V. The resulting definite integral can be shown to be a proper integral from Eq. 14-7; and the limit V^* can be replaced by infinity. Then

$$C_V = nc_V^* - T \int_V^\infty \left(\frac{\partial^2 p}{\partial T^2}\right)_V dV \tag{17-17}$$

In a manner similar to that used in Art. 16 we can express C_p as a function of V, T, n.

The Joule-Thomson and Joule coefficients become in terms of the independent variables V and T

$$\mu_{JT} C_p = - \left[V + T \frac{(\partial p/\partial T)_V}{(\partial p/\partial V)_T} \right] \tag{17-18}$$

$$\eta C_V = T^2 \left[\frac{\partial (p/T)}{\partial T} \right]_V \tag{17-19}$$

All of the foregoing expressions are collected in Art. 19.

C,18. General Equations for the Thermodynamic Properties of Pure Gases in Terms of p and T. The following relations whose derivations are given in Art. 16 may be considered general thermodynamic relations for pure gases. The only assumptions are those relating to the region of very low pressure.

$$E = \int_0^p \left[V - T\left(\frac{\partial V}{\partial T}\right)_p \right] dp - pV + n\text{H}^0 \tag{18-1}$$

$$H = \int_0^p \left[V - T\left(\frac{\partial V}{\partial T}\right)_p \right] dp + n\text{H}^0 \tag{18-2}$$

$$S = \int_0^p \left[\frac{nR}{p} - \left(\frac{\partial V}{\partial T}\right)_p \right] dp - nR \ln p + n\text{s}^0 \tag{18-3}$$

$$A = \int_0^p \left[V - \frac{nRT}{p} \right] dp + nRT \ln p - pV + n(\text{H}^0 - T\text{s}^0) \tag{18-4}$$

$$F = \int_0^p \left[V - \frac{nRT}{p} \right] dp + nRT \ln p + n(\text{H}^0 - T\text{s}^0) \tag{18-5}$$

$$\mu = \int_0^p \left[\frac{V}{n} - \frac{RT}{p} \right] dp + RT \ln p + \text{H}^0 - T\text{s}^0 \tag{18-6}$$

$$RT \ln f = \int_0^p \left[\frac{V}{n} - \frac{RT}{p} \right] dp + RT \ln p \tag{18-7}$$

$$C_p = nc_p^* - T \int_0^p \left(\frac{\partial^2 V}{\partial T^2}\right)_p dp \tag{18-8}$$

$$C_V = nc_V^* + nR + T \frac{(\partial V/\partial T)_p^2}{(\partial V/\partial p)_T} - T \int_0^p \left(\frac{\partial^2 V}{\partial T^2}\right)_p dp \tag{18-9}$$

$$C_p - C_V = -T \frac{(\partial V/\partial T)_p^2}{(\partial V/\partial p)_T} \tag{18-10}$$

$$\mu_{JT} C_p = T^2 \left[\frac{\partial(V/T)}{\partial T} \right]_p \tag{18-11}$$

$$\eta C_V = - \frac{T(\partial V/\partial T)_p + p(\partial V/\partial p)_T}{(\partial V/\partial p)_T} \tag{18-12}$$

In the foregoing equations the definite integrals are to be evaluated at the temperature T. The integration constants are given by the expressions:

$$\mathrm{H}^0 = \mathrm{H}_0^0 + \int_{T_0}^{T} c_p^* dT \tag{18-13}$$

$$\mathrm{s}^0 = \mathrm{s}_0^0 + \int_{T_0}^{T} \frac{c_p^*}{T} dT \tag{18-14}$$

where the integrals are to be evaluated along the zero pressure curve and H_0^0 and s_0^0 are the molar heat content and entropy constants for the gas at T_0.

C,19. General Equations for the Thermodynamic Properties of Pure Gases in Terms of V and T. The derivation of the following relations are given in Art. 17.

$$E = \int_{V}^{\infty} \left[p - T \left(\frac{\partial p}{\partial T} \right)_v \right] dV + n\mathrm{E}^0 \tag{19-1}$$

$$H = \int_{V}^{\infty} \left[p - T \left(\frac{\partial p}{\partial T} \right)_v \right] dV + pV + n\mathrm{E}^0 \tag{19-2}$$

$$S = \int_{V}^{\infty} \left[\frac{nR}{V} - \left(\frac{\partial p}{\partial T} \right)_v \right] dV + nR \ln \frac{V}{nRT} + n\mathrm{s}^0 \tag{19-3}$$

$$A = \int_{V}^{\infty} \left[p - \frac{nRT}{V} \right] dV - nRT \ln \frac{V}{nRT} + n(\mathrm{E}^0 - T\mathrm{s}^0) \tag{19-4}$$

$$F = \int_{V}^{\infty} \left[p - \frac{nRT}{V} \right] dV - nRT \ln \frac{V}{nRT} + pV + n(\mathrm{E}^0 - T\mathrm{s}^0) \tag{19-5}$$

$$\mu = \int_{V}^{\infty} \left[\left(\frac{\partial p}{\partial n} \right)_{V,T} - \frac{RT}{V} \right] dV - RT \ln \frac{V}{nRT} + RT + \mathrm{E}^0 - T\mathrm{s}^0 \tag{19-6}$$

$$= \int_{V}^{\infty} \left[\frac{p}{n} - \frac{RT}{V} \right] dV - RT \ln \frac{V}{nRT} + \frac{pV}{n} + \mathrm{E}^0 - T\mathrm{s}^0 \tag{19-7}$$

$$RT \ln f = \int_{V}^{\infty} \left[\left(\frac{\partial p}{\partial n} \right)_{V,T} - \frac{RT}{V} \right] dV - RT \ln \frac{V}{nRT} \tag{19-8}$$

$$= \int_{V}^{\infty} \left[\frac{p}{n} - \frac{RT}{V} \right] dV - RT \ln \frac{V}{nRT} + \frac{pV - nRT}{n} \tag{19-9}$$

$$C_p = nc_p^* - nR - T\frac{(\partial p/\partial T)_V^2}{(\partial p/\partial V)_T} - T\int_V^\infty \left(\frac{\partial^2 p}{\partial T^2}\right)_V dV \quad (19\text{-}10)$$

$$C_V = nc_V^* - T\int_V^\infty \left(\frac{\partial^2 p}{\partial T^2}\right)_V dV \quad (19\text{-}11)$$

$$C_p - C_V = -T\frac{(\partial p/\partial T)_V^2}{(\partial p/\partial V)_T} \quad (19\text{-}12)$$

$$\mu_{JT}C_p = -\frac{T(\partial p/\partial T)_V + V(\partial p/\partial V)_T}{(\partial p/\partial V)_T} \quad (19\text{-}13)$$

$$\eta C_V = T^2\left[\frac{\partial(p/T)}{\partial T}\right]_V \quad (19\text{-}14)$$

In these relations the definite integrals are to be evaluated at the temperature T, and

$$E^0 = E_0^0 + \int_{T_0}^T c_V^* dT; \qquad E_0^0 = H_0^0 - RT_0 \quad (19\text{-}15)$$

$$s^0 = s_0^0 + \int_{T_0}^T \frac{c_V^*}{T} dT + R\ln\frac{T}{T_0} \quad (19\text{-}16)$$

The temperature integral is to be evaluated along the zero pressure curve.

C,20. Integrated Equations for the Thermodynamic Properties of Pure Gases in Terms of p and T. The general relations of Art. 18 can be expressed in terms of the virial parameters of the equation of state (6-3) explicit in the volume:

$$V = \frac{nRT}{p} + \frac{n\beta}{RT} + \frac{n\gamma}{(RT)^2}p + \frac{n\delta}{(RT)^3}p^2$$

The derivatives of the virial parameters are given in Art. 10. The values of the equation of state constants determined for this form of equation of state should be used in the following relations. The order of magnitude of the error introduced by using the constants for the equation explicit in the pressure, as listed in Table C,6, can be estimated by a comparison of Eq. 6-2 and 6-3. More accurate values can be obtained by replacing γ and δ in the following expressions by the coefficients of p and p^2 of Eq. 6-2. For better results the equations of Art. 21 must be used, the thermodynamic quantities being computed at the temperature in question for a series of densities and the corresponding pressure computed from the equation of state explicit in the pressure.

$$E = \left(\beta - T\frac{d\beta}{dT}\right)\frac{np}{RT} + \left(\gamma - T\frac{d\gamma}{dT}\right)\frac{np^2}{2(RT)^2}$$

$$+ \left(\delta - T\frac{d\delta}{dT}\right)\frac{np^3}{3(RT)^3} - nRT + nH^0 \quad (20\text{-}1)$$

$$H = \left(2\beta - T\frac{d\beta}{dT}\right)\frac{np}{RT} + \left(3\gamma - T\frac{d\gamma}{dT}\right)\frac{np^2}{2(RT)^2}$$

$$+ \left(4\delta - T\frac{d\delta}{dT}\right)\frac{np^3}{3(RT)^3} + nH^0 \quad (20\text{-}2)$$

$$S = -nR\ln p + \left(\frac{\beta}{T} - \frac{d\beta}{dT}\right)\frac{np}{RT} + \left(2\frac{\gamma}{T} - \frac{d\gamma}{dT}\right)\frac{np^2}{2(RT)^2}$$

$$+ \left(3\frac{\delta}{T} - \frac{d\delta}{dT}\right)\frac{np^3}{3(RT)^3} + ns^0 \quad (20\text{-}3)$$

$$A = nRT\ln p - \gamma\frac{np^2}{2(RT)^2} - 2\delta\frac{np^3}{3(RT)^3}$$

$$- nRT + nH^0 - nTs^0 \quad (20\text{-}4)$$

$$F = nRT\ln p + \beta\frac{np}{RT} + \gamma\frac{np^2}{2(RT)^2} + \delta\frac{np^3}{3(RT)^3}$$

$$+ nH^0 - nTs^0 \quad (20\text{-}5)$$

$$\mu = RT\ln p + \beta\frac{p}{RT} + \gamma\frac{p^2}{2(RT)^2} + \delta\frac{p^3}{3(RT)^3} + H^0 - Ts^0 \quad (20\text{-}6)$$

$$RT\ln f = RT\ln p + \beta\frac{p}{RT} + \gamma\frac{p^2}{2(RT)^2} + \delta\frac{p^3}{3(RT)^3} \quad (20\text{-}7)$$

$$C_p = nc_p^* - \left(2\frac{\beta}{T} - 2\frac{d\beta}{dT} + T\frac{d^2\beta}{dT^2}\right)\frac{np}{RT}$$

$$- \left(6\frac{\gamma}{T} - 4\frac{d\gamma}{dT} + T\frac{d^2\gamma}{dT^2}\right)\frac{np^2}{2(RT)^2}$$

$$- \left(12\frac{\delta}{T} - 6\frac{d\delta}{dT} + T\frac{d^2\delta}{dT^2}\right)\frac{np^3}{3(RT)^3} \quad (20\text{-}8)$$

$$C_V = nc_V^* + nR$$

$$- \frac{nT\left[R - \left(\frac{\beta}{T} - \frac{d\beta}{dT}\right)\frac{p}{RT} - \left(2\frac{\gamma}{T} - \frac{d\gamma}{dT}\right)\frac{p^2}{(RT)^2} - \left(3\frac{\delta}{T} - \frac{d\delta}{dT}\right)\frac{p^3}{(RT)^3}\right]^2}{RT - \gamma\frac{p^2}{(RT)^2} - 2\delta\frac{p^3}{(RT)^3}}$$

$$- \left(2\frac{\beta}{T} - 2\frac{d\beta}{dT} + T\frac{d^2\beta}{dT^2}\right)\frac{np}{RT}$$

$$- \left(6\frac{\gamma}{T} - 4\frac{d\gamma}{dT} + T\frac{d^2\gamma}{dT^2}\right)\frac{np^2}{2(RT)^2}$$

$$- \left(12\frac{\delta}{T} - 6\frac{d\delta}{dT} + T\frac{d^2\delta}{dT^2}\right)\frac{np^3}{3(RT)^3} \quad (20\text{-}9)$$

$$C_p - C_v = \cfrac{nT\left[R - \left(\dfrac{\beta}{T} - \dfrac{d\beta}{dT}\right)\dfrac{p}{RT} - \left(2\dfrac{\gamma}{T} - \dfrac{d\gamma}{dT}\right)\dfrac{p^2}{(RT)^2} - \left(3\dfrac{\delta}{T} - \dfrac{d\delta}{dT}\right)\dfrac{p^3}{(RT)^3}\right]^2}{RT - \gamma\dfrac{p^2}{(RT)^2} - 2\delta\dfrac{p^3}{(RT)^3}} \tag{20-10}$$

$$\mu_{JT}C_p = -\left(2\beta - T\frac{d\beta}{dT}\right)\frac{n}{RT} - \left(3\gamma - T\frac{d\gamma}{dT}\right)\frac{np}{(RT)^2} - \left(4\delta - T\frac{d\delta}{dT}\right)\frac{np^2}{(RT)^3} \tag{20-11}$$

$$\eta C_V = \cfrac{-\left(\beta - T\dfrac{d\beta}{dT}\right)\dfrac{p^2}{RT} - \left(\gamma - T\dfrac{d\gamma}{dT}\right)\dfrac{p^3}{(RT)^2} - \left(\delta - T\dfrac{d\delta}{dT}\right)\dfrac{p^4}{(RT)^3}}{RT - \gamma\dfrac{p^2}{(RT)^2} - 2\delta\dfrac{p^3}{(RT)^3}} \tag{20-12}$$

C,21. Integrated Equations for The Thermodynamic Properties of Pure Gases in Terms of V and T. The general thermodynamic relations of Art. 19 can be expressed in terms of the virial parameters of the equation of state (6-1):

$$p = \frac{nRT}{V} + \frac{n^2\beta}{V^2} + \frac{n^3\gamma}{V^3} + \frac{n^4\delta}{V^4}$$

The derivatives of the parameters expressed as a function of temperature and the equation of state constants are given in Art. 10.

$$E = \left(\beta - T\frac{d\beta}{dT}\right)\frac{n^2}{V} + \left(\gamma - T\frac{d\gamma}{dT}\right)\frac{n^3}{2V^2} + \left(\delta - T\frac{d\delta}{dT}\right)\frac{n^4}{3V^3} + n_E^0 \tag{21-1}$$

$$H = \left(2\beta - T\frac{d\beta}{dT}\right)\frac{n^2}{V} + \left(3\gamma - T\frac{d\gamma}{dT}\right)\frac{n^3}{2V^2} + \left(4\delta - T\frac{d\delta}{dT}\right)\frac{n^4}{3V^3} + nRT + n_E^0 \tag{21-2}$$

$$S = nR\ln\frac{V}{nRT} - \frac{d\beta}{dT}\frac{n^2}{V} - \frac{d\gamma}{dT}\frac{n^3}{2V^2} - \frac{d\delta}{dT}\frac{n^4}{3V^3} + n_S^0 \tag{21-3}$$

$$A = -nRT\ln\frac{V}{nRT} + \beta\frac{n^2}{V} + \gamma\frac{n^3}{2V^2} + \delta\frac{n^4}{3V^3} + n_E^0 - nT_S^0 \tag{21-4}$$

$$F = -nRT \ln \frac{V}{nRT} + 2\beta \frac{n^2}{V} + 3\gamma \frac{n^3}{2V^2}$$

$$+ 4\delta \frac{n^4}{3V^3} + nRT + n\mathrm{E}^0 - nT\mathrm{s}^0 \quad (21\text{-}5)$$

$$\mu = -RT \ln \frac{V}{nRT} + 2\beta \frac{n}{V} + 3\gamma \frac{n^2}{2V^2}$$

$$+ 4\delta \frac{n^3}{3V^3} + RT + \mathrm{E}^0 - T\mathrm{s}^0 \quad (21\text{-}6)$$

$$RT \ln f = -RT \ln \frac{V}{nRT} + 2\beta \frac{n}{V} + 3\gamma \frac{n^2}{2V^2} + 4\delta \frac{n^3}{3V^3} \quad (21\text{-}7)$$

$$C_p = nc_p^* - nR + \frac{nT \left[R + \frac{d\beta}{dT}\frac{n}{V} + \frac{d\gamma}{dT}\frac{n^2}{V^2} + \frac{d\delta}{dT}\frac{n^3}{V^3} \right]^2}{RT + 2\beta \frac{n}{V} + 3\gamma \frac{n^2}{V^2} + 4\delta \frac{n^3}{V^3}}$$

$$- T\frac{d^2\beta}{dT^2}\frac{n^2}{V} - T\frac{d^2\gamma}{dT^2}\frac{n^3}{2V^2} - T\frac{d^2\delta}{dT^2}\frac{n^4}{3V^3} \quad (21\text{-}8)$$

$$C_V = nc_V^* - T\frac{d^2\beta}{dT^2}\frac{n^2}{V} - T\frac{d^2\gamma}{dT^2}\frac{n^3}{2V^2} - T\frac{d^2\delta}{dT^2}\frac{n^4}{3V^3} \quad (21\text{-}9)$$

$$C_p - C_V = \frac{nT \left[R + \frac{d\beta}{dT}\frac{n}{V} + \frac{d\gamma}{dT}\frac{n^2}{V^2} + \frac{d\delta}{dT}\frac{n^3}{V^3} \right]^2}{RT + 2\beta \frac{n}{V} + 3\gamma \frac{n^2}{V^2} + 4\delta \frac{n^3}{V^3}} \quad (21\text{-}10)$$

$$\mu_{\mathrm{JT}}C_p = \frac{-\left(2\beta - T\frac{d\beta}{dT}\right)n - \left(3\gamma - T\frac{d\gamma}{dT}\right)\frac{n^2}{V} - \left(4\delta - T\frac{d\delta}{dT}\right)\frac{n^3}{V^2}}{RT + 2\beta \frac{n}{V} + 3\gamma \frac{n^2}{V^2} + 4\delta \frac{n^3}{V^3}}$$

$$(21\text{-}11)$$

$$\eta C_V = -\left(\beta - T\frac{d\beta}{dT}\right)\frac{n^2}{V^2} - \left(\gamma - T\frac{d\gamma}{dT}\right)\frac{n^3}{V^3} - \left(\delta - T\frac{d\delta}{dT}\right)\frac{n^4}{V^4}$$

$$(21\text{-}12)$$

C,22. Integrated Approximate Equations for the Thermodynamic Properties of Pure Gases in Terms of p and T. The relations given in this article are a sufficiently good approximation for many purposes. They are derived from the equations of Art. 20 by dropping terms of higher order in the pressure and are expressed in terms of the equation of state constants rather than the virial parameters. The values of the constants to be employed are those listed in Table C,6 determined for the equation explicit in the pressure. For the most part the expression given here may be derived from the general relations of Art. 18 and Eq. 6-5:

$$V = \frac{nRT}{p} + \frac{n\beta}{RT}$$

$$E = -\left[\frac{A_0}{RT} + \frac{3c}{T^3}\right] np - nRT + n\text{H}^0 \tag{22-1}$$

$$H = \left[B_0 - \frac{2A_0}{RT} - \frac{4c}{T^3}\right] np + n\text{H}^0 \tag{22-2}$$

$$S = -nR \ln p - \left[\frac{A_0}{RT^2} + \frac{3c}{T^4}\right] np + n\text{s}^0 \tag{22-3}$$

$$A = nRT \ln p - nRT + n\text{H}^0 - nT\text{s}^0 \tag{22-4}$$

$$F = nRT \ln p + \left[B_0 - \frac{A_0}{RT} - \frac{c}{T^3}\right] np + n\text{H}^0 - nT\text{s}^0 \tag{22-5}$$

$$\mu = RT \ln p + \left[B_0 - \frac{A_0}{RT} - \frac{c}{T^6}\right] p + \text{H}^0 - T\text{s}^0 \tag{22-6}$$

$$RT \ln f = RT \ln p + \left[B_0 - \frac{A_0}{RT} - \frac{c}{T^3}\right] p \tag{22-7}$$

$$C_p = nc_p^* + \left[\frac{2A_0}{RT^2} + \frac{12c}{T^4}\right] np \tag{22-8}$$

$$C_V = nc_V^* + \frac{6c}{T^4} np \tag{22-9}$$

$$C_p - C_V = nR + \left[\frac{2A_0}{RT^2} + \frac{6c}{T^4}\right] np \tag{22-10}$$

$$\mu_{JT} C_p = -\left[B_0 - \frac{2A_0}{RT} - \frac{4c}{T^3}\right] n + \left[\frac{2B_0 b}{RT} - \frac{3A_0 a}{(RT)^2} + \frac{5B_0 c}{RT^4}\right] np \tag{22-11}$$

$$\eta C_V = \left[\frac{A_0}{(RT)^2} + \frac{3c}{RT^4}\right] p^2 \tag{22-12}$$

C,23. General Equations for the Thermodynamic Properties of Pure Gases in Terms of p_r and T_r, and the Compressibility Factor. The thermodynamic properties of gases are derived in many engineering calculations from plots of the compressibility factor $Z(= pV/nRT)$ against the reduced pressure p_r for a series of reduced isotherms T_r. The general thermodynamic equations of Art. 18 can be expressed in these variables. The integrals and partial derivatives are evaluated graphically from the generalized Z chart.

$$\frac{E}{nRT_c} = -T_r^2 \int_0^{p_r} \left(\frac{\partial Z}{\partial T_r}\right)_{p_r} d\ln p_r - T_r Z + \mathrm{H}_r^0 \tag{23-1}$$

$$\frac{H}{nRT_c} = -T_r^2 \int_0^{p_r} \left(\frac{\partial Z}{\partial T_r}\right)_{p_r} d\ln p_r + \mathrm{H}_r^0 \tag{23-2}$$

$$\frac{S}{nR} = \int_0^{p_r} \left[1 - Z - T_r\left(\frac{\partial Z}{\partial T_r}\right)_{p_r}\right] d\ln p_r - \ln p_r + \mathrm{s}_r^0 \tag{23-3}$$

$$\frac{A}{nRT_c} = T_r \int_0^{p_r} (Z-1)d\ln p_r + T_r \ln p_r - T_r Z + \mathrm{H}_r^0 - T_r \mathrm{s}_r^0 \tag{23-4}$$

$$\frac{F}{nRT_c} = T_r \int_0^{p_r} (Z-1)d\ln p_r + T_r \ln p_r + \mathrm{H}_r^0 - T_r \mathrm{s}_r^0 \tag{23-5}$$

$$\frac{\mu}{RT_c} = T_r \int_0^{p_r} (Z-1)d\ln p_r + T_r \ln p_r + \mathrm{H}_r^0 - T_r \mathrm{s}_r^0 \tag{23-6}$$

$$\ln \frac{f}{p} = \int_0^{p_r} (Z-1)d\ln p_r \tag{23-7}$$

$$\frac{C_p}{nR} = \frac{\mathrm{c}_p^*}{R} - \int_0^{p_r} \left[2T_r\left(\frac{\partial Z}{\partial T_r}\right)_{p_r} + T_r^2\left(\frac{\partial^2 Z}{\partial T_r^2}\right)_{p_r}\right] d\ln p_r \tag{23-8}$$

$$\frac{C_V}{nR} = \frac{\mathrm{c}_V^*}{R} + 1 - \int_0^{p_r} \left[2T_r\left(\frac{\partial Z}{\partial T_r}\right)_{p_r} + T_r^2\left(\frac{\partial^2 Z}{\partial T_r^2}\right)_{p_r}\right] d\ln p_r$$
$$- \frac{[Z + T_r(\partial Z/\partial T_r)_{p_r}]^2}{Z - p_r(\partial Z/\partial p_r)_{T_r}} \tag{23-9}$$

$$\frac{C_p}{nR} - \frac{C_V}{nR} = \frac{[Z + T_r(\partial Z/\partial T_r)_{p_r}]^2}{Z - p_r(\partial Z/\partial p_r)_{T_r}} \tag{23-10}$$

$$\frac{p_c}{nRT_c}\mu_{JT}C_p = \frac{T_r^2}{p_r}\left(\frac{\partial Z}{\partial T_r}\right)_{p_r} \tag{23-11}$$

$$\frac{1}{p_c}\eta C_V = \left[\frac{T_r(\partial Z/\partial T_r)_{p_r} + p_r(\partial Z/\partial p_r)_{T_r}}{Z - p_r(\partial Z/\partial p_r)_{T_r}}\right] p_r \tag{23-12}$$

In the foregoing equations the definite integrals are to be evaluated at the reduced temperature T_r. The integration constants are given by the expressions:

$$\mathrm{H}_r^0 = \frac{\mathrm{H}_0^0}{RT_c} + \frac{1}{R}\int_{T_{0r}}^{T_r} \mathrm{c}_p^* dT_r \tag{23-13}$$

$$\mathrm{s}_r^0 = \frac{\mathrm{s}_0^0}{R} + \frac{1}{R}\int_{T_{0r}}^{T_r} \frac{\mathrm{c}_p^*}{T_r} dT_r - \ln p_c \tag{23-14}$$

Here H_0^0 and s_0^0 are the heat content and entropy constants of the substance at the standard temperature T_0 as in the earlier equations; and c_p^* is to be given as a function of the reduced temperature T_r.

C,24. General Relations for the Thermodynamic Properties of Pure Gases in Terms of p and T, and the Compressibility Factor. Eq. 23-1 to 23-12 can be written to express the properties of pure gases in terms of p and T, and the compressibility factor $Z(= pV/nRT)$ by making the following changes:

1. Write p for p_r and T for T_r.
2. Place $T_c = p_c = 1$.
3. Write H^0/RT_c for H_r^0 and s^0/R for s_r^0, and use Eq. 18-13 and 18-14 to express the temperature variation of the parameters H^0 and s^0.

C,25. General Equations for the Thermodynamic Properties of Pure Gases in Terms of C and T. The relations of Art. 19 are expressed below in terms of the concentration (or density) C

$$C \equiv \frac{n}{V} \tag{25-1}$$

and the temperature T. The relations corresponding to Eq. 19-6 and 19-8 are omitted.

$$E = n \int_0^C \left[p - T \left(\frac{\partial p}{\partial T} \right)_c \right] \frac{dC}{C^2} + n\mathrm{E}^0 \tag{25-2}$$

$$H = n \int_0^C \left[p - T \left(\frac{\partial p}{\partial T} \right)_c \right] \frac{dC}{C^2} + \frac{np}{C} + n\mathrm{E}^0 \tag{25-3}$$

$$S = n \int_0^C \left[RC - \left(\frac{\partial p}{\partial T} \right)_c \right] \frac{dC}{C^2} - nR \ln RTC + n\mathrm{s}^0 \tag{25-4}$$

$$A = n \int_0^C [p - RTC] \frac{dC}{C^2} + nRT \ln RTC + n(\mathrm{E}^0 - T\mathrm{s}^0) \tag{25-5}$$

$$F = n \int_0^C [p - RTC] \frac{dC}{C^2} + nRT \ln RTC + \frac{np}{C}$$
$$+ n(\mathrm{E}^0 - T\mathrm{s}^0) \tag{25-6}$$

$$\mu = \int_0^C [p - RTC] \frac{dC}{C^2} + RT \ln RTC + \frac{p}{C} + \mathrm{E}^0 - T\mathrm{s}^0 \tag{25-7}$$

$$RT \ln f = \int_0^C [p - RTC] \frac{dC}{C^2} + RT \ln RTC + \frac{p}{C} - RT \tag{25-8}$$

$$C_p = n\mathrm{c}_p^* - nR + \frac{nT}{C^2} \frac{(\partial p/\partial T)_C^2}{(\partial p/\partial C)_T} - n \int_0^C T \left(\frac{\partial^2 p}{\partial T^2} \right)_c \frac{dC}{C^2} \tag{25-9}$$

$$C_V = n\mathrm{c}_V^* - n \int_0^C T \left(\frac{\partial^2 p}{\partial T^2} \right)_c \frac{dC}{C^2} \tag{25-10}$$

⟨ 289 ⟩

$$C_p - C_v = \frac{nT}{C^2} \frac{(\partial p/\partial T)_c^2}{(\partial p/\partial C)_T} \tag{25-11}$$

$$\mu_{JT} C_p = \frac{n}{C^2} \frac{T(\partial p/\partial T)_c - C(\partial p/\partial C)_T}{(\partial p/\partial C)_T} \tag{25-12}$$

$$\eta C_V = T^2 \left[\frac{\partial(p/T)}{\partial T} \right]_c \tag{25-13}$$

In the above expressions the definite integrals are to be evaluated at the temperature T, and E^0 and s^0 are given by Eq. 19-15 and 19-16.

When the above relations are expressed in terms of the virial parameters of Eq. 6-1, which may be written

$$p = RTC + \beta C^2 + \gamma C^3 + \delta C^4 \tag{25-14}$$

we obtain the equations given in Art. 21.

C,26. General Equations for the Thermodynamic Properties of Pure Gases in Terms of C and T, and the Compressibility Factor. The relations given below are derived from those of Art. 25 and are designed for use when the compressibility factor $Z(= pV/nRT)$ is given as a function of the concentration $C(= n/V)$ and the temperature T.

$$E = -nRT \int_0^C T \left(\frac{\partial Z}{\partial T} \right)_c d \ln C + n\mathrm{E}^0 \tag{26-1}$$

$$H = -nRT \int_0^C T \left(\frac{\partial Z}{\partial T} \right)_c d \ln C + nRTZ + n\mathrm{E}^0 \tag{26-2}$$

$$S = nR \int_0^C \left[1 - Z - T \left(\frac{\partial Z}{\partial T} \right)_c \right] d \ln C$$
$$- nR \ln RTC + n\mathrm{s}^0 \tag{26-3}$$

$$A = nRT \int_0^C (Z - 1) d \ln C + nRT \ln RTC$$
$$+ n(\mathrm{E}^0 - T\mathrm{s}^0) \tag{26-4}$$

$$F = nRT \int_0^C (Z - 1) d \ln C + nRT \ln RTC$$
$$+ nRTZ + n(\mathrm{E}^0 - T\mathrm{s}^0) \tag{26-5}$$

$$\mu = RT \int_0^C (Z - 1) d \ln C + RT \ln RTC$$
$$+ RTZ + \mathrm{E}^0 - T\mathrm{s}^0 \tag{26-6}$$

$$\ln \frac{f}{p} = \int_0^C (Z - 1) d \ln C - \ln Z + (Z - 1) \tag{26-7}$$

$$C_p = nc_p^* - nR + nR \frac{[Z + T(\partial Z/\partial T)_c]^2}{Z + C(\partial Z/\partial C)_T}$$
$$- nR \int_0^C \left[2T \left(\frac{\partial Z}{\partial T} \right)_c + T^2 \left(\frac{\partial^2 Z}{\partial T^2} \right)_c \right] d \ln C \tag{26-8}$$

$$C_V = nc_V^* - nR \int_0^C \left[2T \left(\frac{\partial Z}{\partial T} \right)_c + T^2 \left(\frac{\partial^2 Z}{\partial T^2} \right)_c \right] d \ln C \quad (26\text{-}9)$$

$$C_p - C_V = nR \frac{[Z + T(\partial Z/\partial T)_c]^2}{Z + C(\partial Z/\partial C)_T} \quad (26\text{-}10)$$

$$\mu_{JT} C_p = \frac{n}{C} \frac{T(\partial Z/\partial T)_c - C(\partial Z/\partial C)_T}{Z + C(\partial Z/\partial C)_T} \quad (26\text{-}11)$$

$$\eta C_V = RCT^2 \left(\frac{\partial Z}{\partial T} \right)_c \quad (26\text{-}12)$$

In the above relations the definite integrals are to be evaluated at the temperature T, and E^0 and s^0 are given by Eq. 19-15 and 19-16.

These expressions were used by Woolley, Scott, and Brickwedde [57] to compute the thermodynamic properties of hydrogen, c_V^* being determined from spectroscopic data and Z from the existing compressibility measurements.

CHAPTER 3. THERMODYNAMIC TREATMENT OF GAS MIXTURES

C,27. General Considerations. In order to give a general thermodynamic treatment of gas mixtures including mixtures in which chemical reaction may occur, we need one assumption that permits expressing the chemical potential of a gas in a mixture in terms of the chemical potential of the pure gas. The resulting equations contain, in general, definite integrals that can be evaluated from an equation of state of gas mixtures or, in some cases, from an equation of state for pure gases, or an equivalent graphical method. Three proposals as a starting point for gas mixtures have received considerable attention:

1. The general limit method for gas mixtures. An equation of state for gas mixtures is required for evaluation of the definite integrals appearing in the general relations.

2. The Lewis and Randall rule [58]. The properties of gas mixtures are expressed in terms of the properties of pure gases. An equation of state for pure gases explicit in the volume or an equivalent graphical method is needed.

3. The Gibbs-Dalton law [40; 41, pp. 155–158]. The properties of gas mixtures are given in terms of the properties of pure gases. An equation of state for pure gases explicit in the pressure or an equivalent graphical method is required.

The general relations given by the first procedure may be considered exact, approximations being introduced by use of an equation of state of gas mixtures. The general relations of the other two procedures are approximate.

C,28. Notation. Let p, V, T be the total pressure, total volume, and Kelvin temperature; and E, S, H, A, F, C_V, and C_p be the total energy, entropy, heat content, work content, free energy, and constant-volume and constant-pressure heat capacities, respectively, of $\sum_i n_i$ moles of a gas mixture consisting of n_1, n_2, . . . moles of the gases 1, 2, ... Let μ_i be the chemical potential of gas i in a mixture.

Let $C = \sum_i n_i/V$ be the concentration of the mixture; and let $C_i = n_i/V$, $X_i = n_i/\sum_i n_i$, and f_i be, respectively, the concentration, mole fraction, and fugacity of gas i in the mixture.

Small capital letters used for an extensive quantity denote the value for one mole.

If it is necessary to distinguish between a pure gas and the same gas in a mixture, the subscript k will denote the value of a quantity for the pure gas and i that for the gas in the mixture.

The subscript e denotes the value of a thermodynamic quantity for a pure gas having the same total volume, temperature, and chemical potential as in a gas mixture. Under these conditions the pure gas would evidently be in thermodynamic equilibrium with the mixture through a membrane permeable to that gas alone; and, since the volume is specified, the values of all extensive as well as intensive properties of the gas would be fixed. Such quantities will be called equilibrium quantities [53], e.g. equilibrium pressure, p_e.

The subscript C denotes the value of a thermodynamic quantity for a pure gas having the same total volume, temperature, and number of moles as in a mixture. The concentration (moles per liter) of the pure gas is the same as its concentration in the mixture. Thus p_C is the pressure exerted by a gas that has been separated from a mixture and has the total volume and temperature of the mixture.

The subscript p denotes the value of a thermodynamic quantity for a pure gas having the same total pressure, temperature, and number of moles as in a mixture. Thus V_p is the volume of a pure gas that has been separated from a mixture and is at the total pressure and temperature of the mixture.

Let ν_i be the stoichiometric coefficient of a constituent i in the equation representing a chemical reaction, being a negative number for a reactant and positive for a product. The exact mass action law is

$$\sum_i \nu_i \mu_i = 0 \tag{28-1}$$

The mass action "constants" or functions in terms of partial pressures, K_p, and concentrations, K_C, are defined through the relations

$$\ln K_p = \sum_i \nu_i \ln p X_i \tag{28-2}$$

$$\ln K_C = \sum_i \nu_i \ln \frac{n_i}{V} \qquad (28\text{-}3)$$

In the discussion of equilibrium between condensed and gaseous solutions, we shall let y_i be the mole fraction of the ith constituent of the condensed phase, and p_{0i} the vapor pressure of the pure constituent at the temperature T and under its own vapor pressure.

The term partial pressure of a gas i in a mixture is reserved for the product pX_i where p is the total pressure of the mixture.

Thermodynamic relations among certain of the variables are

$$E = TS - pV + \sum_i \mu_i n_i \qquad (28\text{-}4)$$

$$H = E + pV = TS + \sum_i \mu_i n_i \qquad (28\text{-}5)$$

$$A = E - TS = -pV + \sum_i \mu_i n_i \qquad (28\text{-}6)$$

$$F = H - TS = \sum_i \mu_i n_i \qquad (28\text{-}7)$$

$$C_V = (\partial E/\partial T)_{V,n} \qquad (28\text{-}8)$$

$$C_p = (\partial H/\partial T)_{p,n} \qquad (28\text{-}9)$$

where the subscript n denotes constant composition as well as constant total number of moles if for a gas mixture.

C,29. General Limit Method Assumption for Gas Mixtures. We shall make the following assumption [55] as a starting point for the thermodynamic treatment of gas mixtures:

At all temperatures the ratio of the equilibrium pressure of each gas in a mixture to the product of the mole fraction of that gas in the mixture into the total pressure of the mixture can be represented in the region of low pressure by the expression:

$$\frac{p_{ek}}{pX_i} = 1 + D_i(T, X_1, X_2, \cdots)p + O(p^2) \quad (i \equiv k = 1, 2, \cdots) \quad (29\text{-}1)$$

where D_i depends only on the temperature and composition of the mixture, and D_i and its derivatives with respect to T, n_1, n_2, . . . are bounded.

C,30. Relations for Gas Mixtures in the Region of Low Pressure. Consider a system of $\sum_i n_i$ moles of a gas mixture and k systems each containing n_{ek} moles of one of the constituent gases. In all variations let

$$T \text{ (each pure gas)} = T \text{ (mixture)}$$
$$V \text{ (each pure gas)} = V \text{ (mixture)} \left.\begin{array}{c} \\ \\ \\ \end{array}\right\} \quad \text{(C)}$$
$$\mu_k = \mu_i \quad (i \equiv k = 1, 2, \cdots)$$

Each pure gas would be in equilibrium with the mixture if separated from it by a membrane permeable to that gas alone. Hence the properties of the pure gases may be called equilibrium properties of the mixture.

Subject to the condition (C) the general limit method, Eq. 29-1, gives the following results for the region of low pressure:

(i)
$$\sum_k p_{ek} = p(1 + D_m p), \qquad \text{(30-1)}$$

where D_m is a function of temperature and composition ($= \sum_i X_i D_i$).

(ii)
$$\frac{n_{ek}}{V} = \frac{n_i}{V}(1 + 2D_m p) \quad (i \equiv k = 1, 2, \cdots)$$
$$C_{ek} = C_i(1 + 2D_m p)$$
$$= Cx_i(1 + 2D_m p) \qquad \text{(30-2)}$$
$$n_{ek} = n_i(1 + 2D_m p)$$

(iii)
$$\sum_k S_{ek} = S(1 + 2D_m p) \qquad \text{(30-3)}$$

(iv)
$$pV = \sum_i n_i RT + \frac{\sum_i (_i n_i)\beta_m}{RT} p$$
$$pV = \sum_i n_i RT + \frac{(\sum_i n_i)^2 \beta_m}{V} \qquad \text{(30-4)}$$

where β_m is a bounded function of temperature and the composition of the gas mixture.

(v)
$$\sum_k E_{ek} = E(1 + 2D_m p) + (D_m p V)p$$
$$\sum_k H_{ek} = H(1 + 2D_m P)$$
$$\sum_k A_{ek} = A(1 + 2D_m p) + (D_m p V)p$$
$$\sum_k F_{ek} = F(1 + 2D_m p) \qquad \text{(30-5)}$$
$$\sum_k C_{Vek} = C_V(1 + 2D_m p) + \alpha p$$
$$\sum_k C_{p_{ek}} = C_p(1 + 2D_m p) + \alpha' p$$

where α and α' are bounded functions of temperature and the composition of the gas mixture.

To prove these relations we take as independent variables T, μ_1, μ_2, . . . for the gas mixture and T, μ_k for each pure gas. Eq. 30-1 follows from Eq. 29-1 which may be written for the region of low pressure

$$p_{ek} = pX_i(1 + D_i p) \tag{30-6}$$

The thermodynamic relation having T, μ_1, μ_2, . . . as independent variables is Gibbs' Equation (97) [*41*, p. 88]. Written for the gas mixture this equation is

$$dp = (S/V)dT + \sum_i (n_i/V)d\mu_i \tag{30-7}$$

and for each pure gas,

$$dp_{ek} = (S_{ek}/V)dT + (n_{ek}/V)d\mu_k \quad (k = 1, 2, \cdots) \tag{30-8}$$

Thus

$$\left(\frac{\partial p}{\partial \mu_i}\right)_{T,\mu} = \frac{n_i}{V} \equiv C_i, \qquad \left(\frac{\partial p}{\partial T}\right)_{\mu} = \frac{S}{V} \quad (i = 1, 2, \cdots) \tag{30-9}$$

$$\left(\frac{\partial p_{ek}}{\partial \mu_k}\right)_T = \frac{n_{ek}}{V} \equiv C_{ek}, \qquad \left(\frac{\partial p_{ek}}{\partial T}\right)_{\mu_k} = \frac{S_{ek}}{V} \quad (k = 1, 2, \cdots) \tag{30-10}$$

The subscript μ in Eq. 30-9 denotes that all of the μ's are constant unless the differentiation is with respect to one of the μ's, in which case all of the other μ's are constant.

Differentiating Eq. 30-1 first with respect to one of the μ's with T and all of the other μ's constant, and then with respect to T with all of the μ's constant, we find for the region of low pressure

$$\left(\frac{\partial p_{ek}}{\partial \mu_k}\right)_T = \left(\frac{\partial p}{\partial \mu_i}\right)_{T,\mu} (1 + 2D_m p) \quad (i \equiv k = 1, 2, \cdots) \tag{30-11}$$

$$\sum_k \left(\frac{\partial p_{ek}}{\partial T}\right)_{\mu_k} = \left(\frac{\partial p}{\partial T}\right)_{\mu} (1 + 2D_m p) \tag{30-12}$$

Use of Eq. 30-9 and 30-10 gives the first of Eq. 30-2 and 30-3. The remainder of the Eq. 30-2 follow from the definitions given in Art. 28 and the second of the conditions (C).

Division of Eq. 30-6 by the first of Eq. 30-2 gives for the region of low pressure

$$\frac{p_{ek}V}{n_{ek}} = \frac{pV}{\sum_i n_i} [1 + (D_i - 2D_m)p] \tag{30-13}$$

Now the left-hand side of this equation refers to the pure gas k existing by itself, and hence Eq. 14-6 applies. Thus in the region of low pressure

$$\frac{pV}{\sum_i n_i}[1 + (D_i - 2D_m)p] = RT + \frac{\beta p_{ek}}{RT}$$

$$= RT + \frac{\beta}{RT}pX_i(1 + D_i p) \qquad (30\text{-}14)$$

where T is thermodynamic absolute temperature. This can be written in the form of the first of Eq. 30-4 where β_m is a function of T, X_1, X_2, $\cdots$; the second Eq. 30-4 follows from the first to terms of the order of the density.

The relation

$$E = TS - pV + \sum_i \mu_i n_i \qquad (30\text{-}15)$$

holds for the gas mixture, and

$$E_{ek} = TS_{ek} - p_{ek}V + \mu_k n_{ek} \quad (k = 1, 2, \cdots) \qquad (30\text{-}16)$$

for each of the pure gases. The first of Eq. 30-5 follows from these relations, the conditions (C), and Eq. 30-1, 30-2, and 30-3. The remaining relations (30-5) come from the definitions of H, A, F, C_p, and C_V, Eq. 28-5 to 28-9.

C,31. Relations for Gas Mixtures in the Region of Very Low Pressures. As the pressure p on a pure gas becomes very small at constant temperature, the relations of Art. 14 and 18 show that the functions pV, E, H, C_p, and C_V approach constant values while S, A, and F increase or decrease in the same manner as $\pm \ln p$. The same must be true of a gas mixture of constant composition. But

$$\lim_{p \to 0} p \ln p = 0 \qquad (31\text{-}1)$$

Hence we have for the region of very low pressure the following relations which may be derived by dropping the terms of the order of p from the relations of Art. 30:

(i) Equilibrium relationships

$$\left.\begin{array}{l}\left(\dfrac{p_{ek}}{pX_i}\right)^* = 1, \qquad \left(\dfrac{C_{ek}}{C_i}\right)^* = 1, \qquad \left(\dfrac{C_{ek}}{CX_i}\right)^* = 1 \\[3mm] \left(\dfrac{n_{ek}}{n_i}\right)^* = 1 \quad (i \equiv k = 1, 2, \cdots)\end{array}\right\} \qquad (31\text{-}2)$$

(ii) Additive relationships

$$\left(\frac{\sum_k p_{ek}}{p}\right)^* = 1, \qquad \left(\frac{\sum_k C_{ek}}{C}\right)^* = 1 \qquad (31\text{-}3)$$

$$S^* = \sum_k S_{ek}^* \qquad (31\text{-}4)$$

$$E^* = \sum_k E_k^*, \qquad H^* = \sum_k H_k^*, \qquad F^* = \sum_k F_{ek}^* \left.\vphantom{\begin{array}{c}1\\1\end{array}}\right\}$$
$$A^* = \sum_k A_{ek}^*, \qquad C_V^* = \sum_k C_{Vk}^*, \qquad C_p^* = \sum_k C_{p_k}^* \quad (31\text{-}5)$$

(iii) The equation of state, independent of the conditions (C)

$$(pV)^* = \left(\sum_i n_i\right) RT$$

The designation e can be omitted in the relations for E, H, C_V, and C_p, since these quantities are essentially constant in the region of very low pressure at constant temperature and mole numbers.

C,32. Derivations for the Independent Variables p and T. Corresponding to Eq. 16-3 and 16-5 for the heat content and entropy of a pure gas, we have for $\sum_i n_i$ moles of a gas mixture of constant composition

$$H(p, T) - H(p_0, T_0) = {}_{T_0}\!\!\int_{p_0}^{p^*} \left[V - T\left(\frac{\partial V}{\partial T}\right)_{p,n} \right] dp$$

$$+ {}_{p^*}\!\!\int_{T_0}^{T} C_p^* dT + {}_{T}\!\!\int_{p^*}^{p} \left[V - T\left(\frac{\partial V}{\partial T}\right)_{p,n} \right] dp \quad (32\text{-}1)$$

$$S(p, T) - S(p_0, T_0) = {}_{T_0}\!\!\int_{p_0}^{p^*} \left[\frac{(\sum_i n_i)R}{p} - \left(\frac{\partial V}{\partial T}\right)_{p,n} \right] dp + {}_{p^*}\!\!\int_{T_0}^{T} \frac{C_p^*}{T} dT$$

$$+ {}_{T}\!\!\int_{p^*}^{p} \left[\frac{(\sum_i n_i)R}{p} - \left(\frac{\partial V}{\partial T}\right)_{p,n} \right] dp - \left(\sum_i n_i\right)R \ln \frac{p}{p_0} \quad (32\text{-}2)$$

where the subscript n denotes constant mole numbers and C_p^* is the heat capacity of $\sum_i n_i$ moles of gas mixture at a very low pressure.

Now from Eq. 31-5, 18-2, and 31-2

$$H(p^*, T_0) = [\sum_k H_k(p^*, T_0)] = (\sum_k n_{ek} \text{H}_{0k}^0) = (\sum_i n_i \text{H}_{0i}^0) \quad (32\text{-}3)$$

where for convenience H_{0i}^0 is written for H_{0k}^0, since this will lead to no confusion. And from Eq. 31-4, 18-3, and 31-2

$$S(p^*, T_0) = [\sum_k S_{ek}(p_{ek}^*, T_0)] = (\sum_k n_{ek} \text{s}_{0k}^0) - (\sum_k n_{ek} R \ln p_{ek}^*)$$

$$= (\sum_i n_i \text{s}_{0i}^0) - (\sum_i n_i R \ln p^* X_i) \quad (32\text{-}4)$$

Also from Eq. 31-5 and 31-2

$$C_p^* = (\sum_k C_{pk}^*) = (\sum_k n_{ek} \text{c}_{pk}^*) = (\sum_i n_i \text{c}_{pi}^*) \quad (32\text{-}5)$$

Thus from Eq. 32-1 and 32-3

$$H(p_0, T_0) + {}_{T_0}\!\!\int_{p_0}^{p^*} \left[V - T\left(\frac{\partial V}{\partial T}\right)_{p,n} \right] dp = H(p^*, T_0) = (\sum_i n_i \text{H}_{0i}^0) \quad (32\text{-}6)$$

and from Eq. 32-2 and 32-4

$$S(p_0, T_0) + {}_{T_0}\!\!\int_{p_0}^{p^*} \left[\frac{(\sum_i n_i)R}{p} - \left(\frac{\partial V}{\partial T} \right)_{p,n} \right] dp + (\sum_i n_i)R \ln p_0$$

$$= S(p^*, T_0) + (\sum_i n_i)R \ln p^*$$

$$= (\sum_i n_i s_{0i}^0) - (\sum_i n_i R \ln X_i) \quad (32\text{-}7)$$

We can now substitute from Eq. 32-5, 32-6, and 32-7 into Eq. 32-1 and 32-2. Then use of Eq. 30-4 shows that we can replace the limit p^* by 0 (compare Eq. 16-6 and 16-7) and obtain

$$H(p, T) = \int_0^p \left[V - T \left(\frac{\partial V}{\partial T} \right)_{p,n} \right] dp + (\sum_i n_i H_i^0) \quad (32\text{-}8)$$

$$S(p, T) = \int_0^p \left[\frac{(\sum_i n_i)R}{p} - \left(\frac{\partial V}{\partial T} \right)_{p,n} \right] dp - (\sum_i n_i R \ln pX_i)$$

$$+ (\sum_i n_i s_i^0) \quad (32\text{-}9)$$

where H_i^0 and s_i^0 are given by Eq. 18-13 and 18-14.

The other thermodynamic properties can now be written as was done for the pure gases. These are collected in Art. 34.

C,33. Derivations for the Independent Variables V and T. The relations for the energy and entropy of a gas mixture of constant composition corresponding to Eq. 17-3 and 17-5 for pure gases are

$$E(V, T) - E(V_0, T_0) = {}_{T_0}\!\!\int_{V_0}^{V^*} \left[T \left(\frac{\partial p}{\partial T} \right)_{v,n} - p \right] dV + {}_{V^*}\!\!\int_{T_0}^{T} C_V^* dT$$

$$+ {}_{T}\!\!\int_{V^*}^{V} \left[T \left(\frac{\partial p}{\partial T} \right)_{v,n} - p \right] dV \quad (33\text{-}1)$$

$$S(V, T) - S(V_0, T_0) = {}_{T_0}\!\!\int_{V_0}^{V^*} \left[\left(\frac{\partial p}{\partial T} \right)_{v,n} - \frac{(\sum_i n_i)R}{V} \right] dV + {}_{V^*}\!\!\int_{T_0}^{T} \frac{C_V^*}{T} dT$$

$$+ {}_{T}\!\!\int_{V^*}^{V} \left[\left(\frac{\partial p}{\partial T} \right)_{v,n} - \frac{(\sum_i n_i)R}{V} \right] dV + (\sum_i n_i)R \ln \frac{V}{V_0} \quad (33\text{-}2)$$

From Eq. 31-5, 19-1, and 31-2 we find

$$E(V^*, T_0) = [\sum_k E_k(V^*, T_0)] = (\sum_k n_{ek} E_{0k}^0) = (\sum_i n_i E_{0i}^0) \quad (33\text{-}3)$$

and from Eq. 31-4, 19-3, and 31-2

$$S(V^*, T_0) = [\sum_k S_{ek}(V^*, T_0)] = (\sum_k n_{ek} s_{0k}^0) + \left(\sum_k n_{ek} R \ln \frac{V^*}{n_{ek} RT} \right)$$

$$= (\sum_i n_i s_{0i}^0) + \left(\sum_i n_i R \ln \frac{V^*}{n_i RT} \right) \quad (33\text{-}4)$$

Also from Eq. 31-5 and 31-2

$$C_V^* = \left(\sum_k C_{Vk}^*\right) = \left(\sum_k n_{ek} c_{Vk}^*\right) = \left(\sum_i n_i c_{Vi}^*\right) \tag{33-5}$$

From Eq. 33-1 and 33-3 we find

$$E(V_0, T_0) + \int_{T_0}^{V^*}\int_{V_0}^{} \left[T\left(\frac{\partial p}{\partial T}\right)_{V,n} - p\right] dV = E(V^*, T_0) = \left(\sum_i n_i E_{0i}^0\right) \tag{33-6}$$

and from Eq. 33-2 and 33-4

$$S(V_0, T_0) + \int_{T_0}^{V^*}\int_{V_0}^{} \left[\left(\frac{\partial p}{\partial T}\right)_{V,n} - \frac{(\sum_i n_i)R}{V}\right] dV - \left(\sum_i n_i\right)R \ln V_0$$

$$= S(V^*, T_0) - \left(\sum_i n_i\right)R \ln V^* = \left(\sum_i n_i s_{0i}^0\right) - \left(\sum_i n_i R \ln n_i RT\right) \tag{33-7}$$

Substitution from Eq. 33-6 and 33-7 into Eq. 33-1 and 33-2, and replacement of V^* by infinity (compare Eq. 17-13 and 17-14) give

$$E = \int_V^\infty \left[p - T\left(\frac{\partial p}{\partial T}\right)_{V,n}\right] dV + \left(\sum_i n_i E_i^0\right) \tag{33-8}$$

$$S = \int_V^\infty \left[\frac{(\sum_i n_i)R}{V} - \left(\frac{\partial p}{\partial T}\right)_{V,n}\right] dV + \left(\sum_i n_i R \ln \frac{V}{n_i RT}\right) + \left(\sum_i n_i s_i^0\right) \tag{33-9}$$

Here E_i^0 and s_i^0 are given by Eq. 19-15 and 19-16.

The other thermodynamic equations can be written as before. They are collected in Art. 35.

C,34. General Equations for the Thermodynamic Properties of Gas Mixtures in Terms of p and T. The equations derived in Art. 32 follow:

$$E = \int_0^p \left[V - T\left(\frac{\partial V}{\partial T}\right)_{p,n}\right] dp - pV + \left(\sum_i n_i H_i^0\right) \tag{34-1}$$

$$H = \int_0^p \left[V - T\left(\frac{\partial V}{\partial T}\right)_{p,n}\right] dp + \left(\sum_i n_i H_i^0\right) \tag{34-2}$$

$$S = \int_0^p \left[\frac{(\sum_i n_i)R}{p} - \left(\frac{\partial V}{\partial T}\right)_{p,n}\right] dp - \left(\sum_i n_i R \ln pX_i\right)$$

$$+ \left(\sum_i n_i s_i^0\right) \tag{34-3}$$

$$A = \int_0^p \left[V - \frac{(\sum_i n_i)RT}{p}\right] dp$$

$$+ \left(\sum_i n_i RT \ln pX_i\right) - pV + \left[\sum_i n_i(H_i^0 - Ts_i^0)\right] \tag{34-4}$$

$$F = \int_0^p \left[V - \frac{(\sum_i n_i) RT}{p} \right] dp + (\sum_i n_i RT \ln pX_i)$$
$$+ [\sum_i n_i (\mathrm{H}_i^0 - T\mathrm{s}_i^0)] \quad (34\text{-}5)$$

$$\mu_i = \int_0^p \left[\left(\frac{\partial V}{\partial n_i} \right)_{p,T,n} - \frac{RT}{p} \right] dp + RT \ln pX_i + \mathrm{H}_i^0 - T\mathrm{s}_i^0 \quad (34\text{-}6)$$

$$RT \ln f_i = \int_0^p \left[\left(\frac{\partial V}{\partial n_i} \right)_{p,T,n} - \frac{RT}{p} \right] dp + RT \ln pX_i \quad (34\text{-}7)$$

$$C_p = (\sum_i n_i \mathrm{c}_{pi}^*) - T \int_0^p \left(\frac{\partial^2 V}{\partial T^2} \right)_{p,n} dp \quad (34\text{-}8)$$

$$C_V = (\sum_i n_i \mathrm{c}_{Vi}^*) + (\sum_i n_i) R + T \frac{(\partial V/\partial T)_{p,n}^2}{(\partial V/\partial p)_{T,n}} - T \int_0^p \left(\frac{\partial^2 V}{\partial T^2} \right)_{p,n} dp$$
$$(34\text{-}9)$$

$$C_p - C_V = -T \frac{(\partial V/\partial T)_{p,n}^2}{(\partial V/\partial p)_{T,n}} \quad (34\text{-}10)$$

$$\mu_{JT} C_p = T^2 \left[\frac{\partial(V/T)}{\partial T} \right]_{p,n} \quad (34\text{-}11)$$

$$\eta C_V = - \frac{T(\partial V/\partial T)_{p,n} + p(\partial V/\partial p)_{T,n}}{(\partial V/\partial p)_{T,n}} \quad (34\text{-}12)$$

In the foregoing expressions the definite integrals are to be evaluated at the temperature T and at constant composition, and

$$\mathrm{H}_i^0 = \mathrm{H}_{0i}^0 + \int_{T_0}^T \mathrm{c}_{pi}^* dT \quad (34\text{-}13)$$

$$\mathrm{s}_i^0 = \mathrm{s}_{0i}^0 + \int_{T_0}^T \frac{\mathrm{c}_{pi}^*}{T} dT \quad (34\text{-}14)$$

C,35. General Equations for the Thermodynamic Properties of Gas Mixtures in Terms of V and T. The relations derived in Art. 33 follow:

$$E = \int_V^\infty \left[p - T \left(\frac{\partial p}{\partial T} \right)_{V,n} \right] dV + (\sum_i n_i \mathrm{E}_i^0) \quad (35\text{-}1)$$

$$H = \int_V^\infty \left[p - T \left(\frac{\partial p}{\partial T} \right)_{V,n} \right] dV + pV + (\sum_i n_i \mathrm{E}_i^0) \quad (35\text{-}2)$$

$$S = \int_V^\infty \left[\frac{(\sum_i n_i) R}{V} - \left(\frac{\partial p}{\partial T} \right)_{V,n} \right] dV$$
$$+ \left(\sum_i n_i R \ln \frac{V}{n_i RT} \right) + (\sum_i n_i \mathrm{s}_i^0) \quad (35\text{-}3)$$

$$A = \int_V^\infty \left[p - \frac{(\sum_i n_i) RT}{V} \right] dV - \left(\sum_i n_i RT \ln \frac{V}{n_i RT} \right)$$
$$+ \left[\sum_i n_i(\mathrm{E}_i^0 - T\mathrm{s}_i^0) \right] \quad (35\text{-}4)$$

$$F = \int_V^\infty \left[p - \frac{(\sum_i n_i) RT}{V} \right] dV - \left(\sum_i n_i RT \ln \frac{V}{n_i RT} \right)$$
$$+ pV + \left[\sum_i n_i(\mathrm{E}_i^0 - T\mathrm{s}_i^0) \right] \quad (35\text{-}5)$$

$$\mu_i = \int_V^\infty \left[\left(\frac{\partial p}{\partial n_i} \right)_{V,T,n} - \frac{RT}{V} \right] dV - RT \ln \frac{V}{n_i RT}$$
$$+ RT + \mathrm{E}_i^0 - T\mathrm{s}_i^0 \quad (35\text{-}6)$$

$$RT \ln f_i = \int_V^\infty \left[\left(\frac{\partial p}{\partial n_i} \right)_{V,T,n} - \frac{RT}{V} \right] dV - RT \ln \frac{V}{n_i RT} \quad (35\text{-}7)$$

$$C_p = (\sum_i n_i \mathrm{c}_{pi}^*) - (\sum_i n_i) R - T \frac{(\partial p/\partial T)_{V,n}^2}{(\partial p/\partial V)_{T,n}} - T \int_V^\infty \left(\frac{\partial^2 p}{\partial T^2} \right)_{V,n} dV$$
$$(35\text{-}8)$$

$$C_V = (\sum_i n_i \mathrm{c}_{Vi}^*) - T \int_V^\infty \left(\frac{\partial^2 p}{\partial T^2} \right)_{V,n} dV \quad (35\text{-}9)$$

$$C_p - C_V = -T \frac{(\partial p/\partial T)_{V,n}^2}{(\partial p/\partial V)_{T,n}} \quad (35\text{-}10)$$

$$\mu_{JT} C_p = - \frac{T(\partial p/\partial T)_{V,n} + V(\partial p/\partial V)_{T,n}}{(\partial p/\partial V)_{T,n}} \quad (35\text{-}11)$$

$$\eta C_V = T^2 \left[\frac{\partial (p/T)}{\partial T} \right]_{V,n} \quad (35\text{-}12)$$

In the foregoing expressions

$$\mathrm{E}_i^0 = \mathrm{E}_{0i}^0 + \int_{T_0}^T \mathrm{c}_{Vi}^* dT \quad (35\text{-}13)$$

$$\mathrm{s}_i^0 = \mathrm{s}_{0i}^0 + \int_{T_0}^T \frac{\mathrm{c}_{Vi}^*}{T} dT + R \ln \frac{T}{T_0} \quad (35\text{-}14)$$

C,36. Integrated Equations for the Thermodynamic Properties of Gas Mixtures in Terms of p and T. The relations of Art. 34 can be expressed in terms of the virial parameters of the equation of state (9-15) for gas mixtures:

$$V = \frac{(\sum_i n_i) RT}{p} + \frac{(\sum_i n_i) \beta_m}{RT} + \frac{(\sum_i n_i) \gamma_m}{(RT)^2} p + \frac{(\sum_i n_i) \delta_m}{(RT)^3} p^2$$

The derivatives of the virial parameters are given in Art. 10.

$$E = \left[\beta_m - T\left(\frac{\partial\beta_m}{\partial T}\right)_n\right]\frac{(\sum_i n_i)p}{RT} + \left[\gamma_m - T\left(\frac{\partial\gamma_m}{\partial T}\right)_n\right]\frac{(\sum_i n_i)p^2}{2(RT)^2}$$

$$+ \left[\delta_m - T\left(\frac{\partial\delta_m}{\partial T}\right)_n\right]\frac{(\sum_i n_i)p^3}{3(RT)^3} - (\sum_i n_i)RT + (\sum_i n_i H_i^0) \quad (36\text{-}1)$$

$$H = \left[2\beta_m - T\left(\frac{\partial\beta_m}{\partial T}\right)_n\right]\frac{(\sum_i n_i)p}{RT}$$

$$+ \left[3\gamma_m - T\left(\frac{\partial\gamma_m}{\partial T}\right)_n\right]\frac{(\sum_i n_i)p^2}{2(RT)^2}$$

$$+ \left[4\delta_m - T\left(\frac{\partial\delta_m}{\partial T}\right)_n\right]\frac{(\sum_i n_i)p^3}{3(RT)^3} + (\sum_i n_i H_i^0) \quad (36\text{-}2)$$

$$S = -(\sum_i n_i R \ln pX_i) + \left[\frac{\beta_m}{T} - \left(\frac{\partial\beta_m}{\partial T}\right)_n\right]\frac{(\sum_i n_i)p}{RT}$$

$$+ \left[2\frac{\gamma_m}{T} - \left(\frac{\partial\gamma_m}{\partial T}\right)_n\right]\frac{(\sum_i n_i)p^2}{2(RT)^2}$$

$$+ \left[3\frac{\delta_m}{T} - \left(\frac{\partial\delta_m}{\partial T}\right)_n\right]\frac{(\sum_i n_i)p^3}{3(RT)^3} + (\sum_i n_i S_i^0) \quad (36\text{-}3)$$

$$A = (\sum_i n_i RT \ln pX_i) - \gamma_m\frac{(\sum_i n_i)p^2}{2(RT)^2}$$

$$- 2\delta_m\frac{(\sum_i n_i)p^3}{3(RT)^3} - (\sum_i n_i)RT + (\sum_i n_i H_i^0) - T(\sum_i n_i S_i^0) \quad (36\text{-}4)$$

$$F = (\sum_i n_i RT \ln pX_i) + \beta_m\frac{(\sum_i n_i)p}{RT} + \gamma_m\frac{(\sum_i n_i)p^2}{2(RT)^2}$$

$$+ \delta_m\frac{(\sum_i n_i)p^3}{3(RT)^3} + (\sum_i n_i H_i^0) - T(\sum_i n_i S_i^0) \quad (36\text{-}5)$$

$$\mu_i = RT \ln pX_i + \left[\beta_m + (\sum_i n_i)\left(\frac{\partial\beta_m}{\partial n_i}\right)_{T,n}\right]\frac{p}{RT}$$

$$+ \left[\gamma_m + (\sum_i n_i)\left(\frac{\partial\gamma_m}{\partial n_i}\right)_{T,n}\right]\frac{p^2}{2(RT)^2}$$

$$+ \left[\delta_m + (\sum_i n_i)\left(\frac{\partial\delta_m}{\partial n_i}\right)_{T,n}\right]\frac{p^3}{3(RT)^3} + H_i^0 - T S_i^0 \quad (36\text{-}6)$$

$$RT \ln f_i = RT \ln pX_i + \left[\beta_m + (\sum_i n_i)\left(\frac{\partial\beta_m}{\partial n_i}\right)_{T,n}\right]\frac{p}{RT}$$

$$+ \left[\gamma_m + (\sum_i n_i)\left(\frac{\partial\gamma_m}{\partial n_i}\right)_{T,n}\right]\frac{p^2}{2(RT)^2}$$

$$+ \left[\delta_m + (\sum_i n_i)\left(\frac{\partial\delta_m}{\partial n_i}\right)_{T,n}\right]\frac{p^3}{3(RT)^3} \quad (36\text{-}7)$$

$$C_p = \left(\sum_i n_i c_{pi}^*\right) - \left[2\frac{\beta_m}{T} - 2\left(\frac{\partial\beta_m}{\partial T}\right)_n + T\left(\frac{\partial^2\beta_m}{\partial T^2}\right)_n\right]\frac{(\sum_i n_i)p}{RT}$$

$$- \left[6\frac{\gamma_m}{T} - 4\left(\frac{\partial\gamma_m}{\partial T}\right)_n + T\left(\frac{\partial^2\gamma_m}{\partial T^2}\right)_n\right]\frac{(\sum_i n_i)p^2}{2(RT)^2}$$

$$- \left[12\frac{\delta_m}{T} - 6\left(\frac{\partial\delta_m}{\partial T}\right)_n + T\left(\frac{\partial^2\delta_m}{\partial T^2}\right)_n\right]\frac{(\sum_i n_i)p^3}{3(RT)^3} \quad (36\text{-}8)$$

$$C_V = \left(\sum_i n_i c_{Vi}^*\right) + \left(\sum_i n_i\right)R$$

$$\frac{\left(\sum_i n_i\right)T\left\{R - \left[\dfrac{\beta_m}{T} - \left(\dfrac{\partial\beta_m}{\partial T}\right)_n\right]\dfrac{p}{RT} - \left[2\dfrac{\gamma_m}{T} - \left(\dfrac{\partial\gamma_m}{\partial T}\right)_n\right]\dfrac{p^2}{(RT)^2} - \left[3\dfrac{\delta_m}{T} - \left(\dfrac{\partial\delta_m}{\partial T}\right)_n\right]\dfrac{p^3}{(RT)^3}\right\}^2}{RT - \gamma_m\dfrac{p^2}{(RT)^2} - 2\delta_m\dfrac{p^3}{(RT)^3}}$$

$$- \left[2\frac{\beta_m}{T} - 2\left(\frac{\partial\beta_m}{\partial T}\right)_n + T\left(\frac{\partial^2\beta_m}{\partial T^2}\right)_n\right]\frac{(\sum_i n_i)p}{RT}$$

$$- \left[6\frac{\gamma_m}{T} - 4\left(\frac{\partial\gamma_m}{\partial T}\right)_n + T\left(\frac{\partial^2\gamma_m}{\partial T^2}\right)_n\right]\frac{(\sum_i n_i)p^2}{2(RT)^2}$$

$$- \left[12\frac{\delta_m}{T} - 6\left(\frac{\partial\delta_m}{\partial T}\right)_n + T\left(\frac{\partial^2\delta_m}{\partial T^2}\right)_n\right]\frac{(\sum_i n_i)p^3}{3(RT)^3} \quad (36\text{-}9)$$

$$C_p - C_V = \frac{\left(\sum_i n_i\right)T\left\{R - \left[\dfrac{\beta_m}{T} - \left(\dfrac{\partial\beta_m}{\partial T}\right)_n\right]\dfrac{p}{RT} - \left[2\dfrac{\gamma_m}{T} - \left(\dfrac{\partial\gamma_m}{\partial T}\right)_n\right]\dfrac{p^2}{(RT)^2} - \left[3\dfrac{\delta_m}{T} - \left(\dfrac{\partial\delta_m}{\partial T}\right)_n\right]\dfrac{p^3}{(RT)^3}\right\}^2}{RT - \gamma_m\dfrac{p^2}{(RT)^2} - 2\delta_m\dfrac{p^3}{3(RT)^3}}$$

$$(36\text{-}10)$$

$$\mu_{JT}C_p = -\left[2\beta_m - T\left(\frac{\partial\beta_m}{\partial T}\right)_n\right]\frac{(\sum_i n_i)}{RT}$$

$$- \left[3\gamma_m - T\left(\frac{\partial\gamma_m}{\partial T}\right)_n\right]\frac{(\sum_i n_i)p}{(RT)^2}$$

$$- \left[4\delta_m - T\left(\frac{\partial\delta_m}{\partial T}\right)_n\right]\frac{(\sum_i n_i)p^2}{(RT)^3} \quad (36\text{-}11)$$

$$\eta C_V = \frac{-\left[\beta_m - T\left(\dfrac{\partial\beta_m}{\partial T}\right)_n\right]\dfrac{p^2}{RT} - \left[\gamma_m - T\left(\dfrac{\partial\gamma_m}{\partial T}\right)_n\right]\dfrac{p^3}{(RT)^2} - \left[\delta_m - T\left(\dfrac{\partial\delta_m}{\partial T}\right)_n\right]\dfrac{p^4}{(RT)^3}}{RT - \gamma_m\dfrac{p^2}{(RT)^2} - 2\delta_m\dfrac{p^3}{(RT)^3}} \quad (36\text{-}12)$$

C,37. Integrated Equations for the Thermodynamic Properties of Gas Mixtures in Terms of V and T. The general relations of Art. 35 can be expressed in terms of the virial parameters of Eq. 9-12 for gas mixtures:

$$p = \frac{(\sum_i n_i)RT}{V} + \frac{(\sum_i n_i)^2 \beta_m}{V^2} + \frac{(\sum_i n_i)^3 \gamma_m}{V^3} + \frac{(\sum_i n_i)^4 \delta_m}{V^4}$$

The derivatives of the virial parameters are given in Art. 10.

$$E = \left[\beta_m - T\left(\frac{\partial \beta_m}{\partial T}\right)_n \right] \frac{(\sum_i n_i)^2}{V}$$

$$+ \left[\gamma_m - T\left(\frac{\partial \gamma_m}{\partial T}\right)_n \right] \frac{(\sum_i n_i)^3}{2V^2}$$

$$+ \left[\delta_m - T\left(\frac{\partial \delta_m}{\partial T}\right)_n \right] \frac{(\sum_i n_i)^4}{3V^3} + (\sum_i n_i E_i^0) \quad (37\text{-}1)$$

$$H = \left[2\beta_m - T\left(\frac{\partial \beta_m}{\partial T}\right)_n \right] \frac{(\sum_i n_i)^2}{V}$$

$$+ \left[3\gamma_m - T\left(\frac{\partial \gamma_m}{\partial T}\right)_n \right] \frac{(\sum_i n_i)^3}{2V^2}$$

$$+ \left[4\delta_m - T\left(\frac{\partial \delta_m}{\partial T}\right)_n \right] \frac{(\sum_i n_i)^4}{3V^3}$$

$$+ (\sum_i n_i)RT + (\sum_i n_i E_i^0) \quad (37\text{-}2)$$

$$S = \left(\sum_i n_i R \ln \frac{V}{n_i RT} \right) - \left(\frac{\partial \beta_m}{\partial T}\right)_n \frac{(\sum_i n_i)^2}{V}$$

$$- \left(\frac{\partial \gamma_m}{\partial T}\right)_n \frac{(\sum_i n_i)^3}{2V^2} - \left(\frac{\partial \delta_m}{\partial T}\right)_n \frac{(\sum_i n_i)^4}{3V^3} + (\sum_i n_i S_i^0) \quad (37\text{-}3)$$

$$A = - \left(\sum_i n_i RT \ln \frac{V}{n_i RT} \right) + \beta_m \frac{(\sum_i n_i)^2}{V}$$

$$+ \gamma_m \frac{(\sum_i n_i)^3}{2V^2} + \delta_m \frac{(\sum_i n_i)^4}{3V^3} + (\sum_i n_i E_i^0) - T(\sum_i n_i S_i^0) \quad (37\text{-}4)$$

$$F = - \left(\sum_i n_i RT \ln \frac{V}{n_i RT} \right) + 2\beta_m \frac{(\sum_i n_i)^2}{V} + 3\gamma_m \frac{(\sum_i n_i)^3}{2V^2}$$

$$+ 4\delta_m \frac{(\sum_i n_i)^4}{3V^3} + (\sum_i n_i)RT + (\sum_i n_i E_i^0) - T(\sum_i n_i S_i^0) \quad (37\text{-}5)$$

$$\mu_i = -RT \ln \frac{V}{n_i RT} + \left[2\beta_m + (\textstyle\sum_i n_i) \left(\frac{\partial \beta_m}{\partial n_i}\right)_{T,n} \right] \frac{(\sum_i n_i)}{V}$$

$$+ \left[3\gamma_m + (\textstyle\sum_i n_i) \left(\frac{\partial \gamma_m}{\partial n_i}\right)_{T,n} \right] \frac{(\sum_i n_i)^2}{2V^2}$$

$$+ \left[4\delta_m + (\textstyle\sum_i n_i) \left(\frac{\partial \delta_m}{\partial n_i}\right)_{T,n} \right] \frac{(\sum_i n_i)^3}{3V^3} + \mathrm{E}_i^0 - T\mathrm{s}_i^0 \quad (37\text{-}6)$$

$$RT \ln f_i = -RT \ln \frac{V}{n_i RT} + \left[2\beta_m + (\textstyle\sum_i n_i) \left(\frac{\partial \beta_m}{\partial n_i}\right)_{T,n} \right] \frac{(\sum_i n_i)}{V}$$

$$+ \left[3\gamma_m + (\textstyle\sum_i n_i) \left(\frac{\partial \gamma_m}{\partial n_i}\right)_{T,n} \right] \frac{(\sum_i n_i)^2}{2V^2}$$

$$+ \left[4\delta_m + (\textstyle\sum_i n_i) \left(\frac{\partial \delta_m}{\partial n_i}\right)_{T,n} \right] \frac{(\sum_i n_i)^3}{3V^3} \quad (37\text{-}7)$$

$$C_p = (\textstyle\sum_i n_i \mathrm{c}_{pi}^*) - (\textstyle\sum_i n_i)R$$

$$+ \frac{(\sum_i n_i)T \left[R + \left(\frac{\partial \beta_m}{\partial T}\right)_n \frac{(\sum_i n_i)}{V} + \left(\frac{\partial \gamma_m}{\partial T}\right)_n \frac{(\sum_i n_i)^2}{V^2} + \left(\frac{\partial \delta_m}{\partial T}\right)_n \frac{(\sum_i n_i)^3}{V^3} \right]^2}{RT + 2\beta_m \frac{(\sum_i n_i)}{V} + 3\gamma_m \frac{(\sum_i n_i)^2}{V^2} + 4\delta_m \frac{(\sum_i n_i)^3}{V^3}}$$

$$- T\left(\frac{\partial^2 \beta_m}{\partial T^2}\right)_n \frac{(\sum_i n_i)^2}{V} - T\left(\frac{\partial^2 \gamma_m}{\partial T^2}\right)_n \frac{(\sum_i n_i)^3}{2V^2}$$

$$- T\left(\frac{\partial^2 \delta_m}{\partial T^2}\right)_n \frac{(\sum_i n_i)^4}{3V^3} \quad (37\text{-}8)$$

$$C_v = (\textstyle\sum_i n_i \mathrm{c}_{\mathrm{V}i}^*) - T\left(\frac{\partial^2 \beta_m}{\partial T^2}\right)_n \frac{(\sum_i n_i)^2}{V}$$

$$- T\left(\frac{\partial^2 \gamma_m}{\partial T^2}\right)_n \frac{(\sum_i n_i)^3}{2V^2} - T\left(\frac{\partial^2 \delta_m}{\partial T^2}\right)_n \frac{(\sum_i n_i)^4}{3V^3} \quad (37\text{-}9)$$

$$C_p - C_v = \frac{(\sum_i n_i)T \left[R + \left(\frac{\partial \beta_m}{\partial T}\right)_n \frac{(\sum_i n_i)}{V} + \left(\frac{\partial \gamma_m}{\partial T}\right)_n \frac{(\sum_i n_i)^2}{V^2} + \left(\frac{\partial \delta_m}{\partial T}\right)_n \frac{(\sum_i n_i)^3}{V^3} \right]^2}{RT + 2\beta_m \frac{(\sum_i n_i)}{V} + 3\gamma_m \frac{(\sum_i n_i)^2}{V^2} + 4\delta_m \frac{(\sum_i n_i)^3}{V^3}} \quad (37\text{-}10)$$

$$\mu_{\mathrm{JT}} C_p = \cfrac{ - \left[2\beta_m - T\left(\frac{\partial \beta_m}{\partial T} \right)_n \right] (\sum_i n_i) - \left[3\gamma_m - T\left(\frac{\partial \gamma_m}{\partial T} \right)_n \right] \frac{(\sum_i n_i)^2}{V} - \left[4\delta_m - T\left(\frac{\partial \delta_m}{\partial T} \right)_n \right] \frac{(\sum_i n_i)^3}{V^2} }{ RT + 2\beta_m \frac{(\sum_i n_i)}{V} + 3\gamma_m \frac{(\sum_i n_i)^2}{V^2} + 4\delta_m \frac{(\sum_i n_i)^3}{V^3} } \qquad (37\text{-}11)$$

$$\eta C_V = - \left[\beta_m - T\left(\frac{\partial \beta_m}{\partial T} \right)_n \right] \frac{(\sum_i n_i)^2}{V^2}$$

$$- \left[\gamma_m - T\left(\frac{\partial \gamma_m}{\partial T} \right)_n \right] \frac{(\sum_i n_i)^3}{V^3}$$

$$- \left[\delta_m - T\left(\frac{\partial \delta_m}{\partial T} \right)_n \right] \frac{(\sum_i n_i)^4}{V^4} \qquad (37\text{-}12)$$

C,38. Integrated Approximate Equations for the Thermodynamic Properties of Gas Mixtures in Terms of p and T. The following approximate equations for gas mixtures correspond to those given for pure gases in Art. 22. The values of the parameters A_{0m}, B_{0m}, c_m for the mixture are

$$A_{0m} = (\sum_i X_i A_{0i}^{\frac{1}{2}})^2$$

$$B_{0m} = \tfrac{1}{8} \sum_i \sum_j X_i X_j (B_{0i}^{\frac{1}{3}} + B_{0j}^{\frac{1}{3}})^3 = \tfrac{1}{4}(\sum_i X_i B_{0i}) + \tfrac{3}{4}(\sum_i X_i B_{0i}^{\frac{1}{3}})(\sum_i X_i B_{0i}^{\frac{2}{3}})$$

$$c_m = (\sum_i X_i c_i^{\frac{1}{2}})^2$$

$$E = - \left[\frac{A_{0m}}{RT} + \frac{3c_m}{T^3} \right] (\sum_i n_i)p - (\sum_i n_i)RT + (\sum_i n_i \mathrm{H}_i^0) \qquad (38\text{-}1)$$

$$H = \left[B_{0m} - \frac{2A_{0m}}{RT} - \frac{4c_m}{T^3} \right] (\sum_i n_i)p + (\sum_i n_i \mathrm{H}_i^0) \qquad (38\text{-}2)$$

$$S = -(\sum_i n_i R \ln pX_i) - \left[\frac{A_{0m}}{RT^2} + \frac{3c_m}{T^4} \right] (\sum_i n_i)p + (\sum_i n_i \mathrm{S}_i^0) \qquad (38\text{-}3)$$

$$A = (\sum_i n_i RT \ln pX_i) - (\sum_i n_i)RT + (\sum_i n_i \mathrm{H}_i^0) - T(\sum_i n_i \mathrm{S}_i^0) \qquad (38\text{-}4)$$

$$F = (\sum_i n_i RT \ln pX_i) + \left[B_{0m} - \frac{A_{0m}}{RT} - \frac{c_m}{T^3} \right] (\sum_i n_i)p$$

$$+ (\sum_i n_i \mathrm{H}_i^0) - T(\sum_i n_i \mathrm{S}_i^0) \qquad (38\text{-}5)$$

$$\mu_i = RT \ln pX_i + \left[\frac{\beta_i}{RT} + \frac{D_i(\beta)}{RT}\right] p + \mathrm{H}_i^0 - T\mathrm{s}_i^0$$

$$= RT \ln pX_i + \left\{\left[B_{0i} - \frac{A_{0i}}{RT} - \frac{c_i}{T^3}\right]\right.$$

$$- \left[\tfrac{3}{4}(B_{0i}^{\frac{1}{4}} - \sum_i X_i B_{0i}^{\frac{1}{4}})(B_{0i}^{\frac{3}{4}} - \sum_i X_i B_{0i}^{\frac{3}{4}})\right.$$

$$\left. - \frac{(A_{0i}^{\frac{1}{2}} - \sum_i X_i A_{0i}^{\frac{1}{2}})^2}{RT} - \frac{(c_i^{\frac{1}{2}} - \sum_i X_i c_i^{\frac{1}{2}})^2}{T^3}\right]\right\} p$$

$$+ \mathrm{H}_i^0 - T\mathrm{s}_i^0 \quad (38\text{-}6)$$

$$RT \ln f_i = RT \ln pX_i + \left[\frac{\beta_i}{RT} + \frac{D_i(\beta)}{RT}\right] p \quad (38\text{-}7)$$

$$C_p = \left(\sum_i n_i c_{pi}^*\right) + \left[\frac{2A_{0m}}{RT^2} + \frac{12c_m}{T^4}\right]\left(\sum_i n_i\right)p \quad (38\text{-}8)$$

$$C_V = \left(\sum_i n_i c_{Vi}^*\right) + \frac{6c_m}{T^4}\left(\sum_i n_i\right)p \quad (38\text{-}9)$$

$$C_p - C_V = \left(\sum_i n_i\right)R + \left[\frac{2A_{0m}}{RT^2} + \frac{6c_m}{T^4}\right]\left(\sum_i n_i\right)p \quad (38\text{-}10)$$

$$\mu_{\mathrm{JT}} C_p = -\left[B_{0m} - \frac{2A_{0m}}{RT} - \frac{4c_m}{T^3}\right]\left(\sum_i n_i\right)$$

$$+ \left[\frac{2B_{0m}b_m}{RT} - \frac{3A_{0m}a_m}{(RT)^2} + \frac{5B_{0m}c_m}{RT^4}\right]\left(\sum_i n_i\right)p \quad (38\text{-}11)$$

$$\eta C_V = -\left[\frac{A_{0m}}{(RT)^2} + \frac{3c_m}{RT^4}\right] p^2 \quad (38\text{-}12)$$

C,39. Equilibrium Pressure and Equilibrium Concentration of a Gas in a Mixture. When a pure gas is in isothermal equilibrium with a gas mixture through a membrane permeable to that gas alone, the chemical potential of the substance is the same in both phases. Let the gas in the mixture be distinguished by the subscript i and the same gas when pure by k. The pressure and concentration of the pure gas under these circumstances are actually properties of the gas in the mixture and may be called the equilibrium pressure p_{ek} and equilibrium concentration C_{ek} of the gas i in the mixture.

Eq. 18-6 and 34-6 express the chemical potential of a pure gas and of a gas in a mixture in terms of pressure as one of the independent variables, whereas Eq. 19-6 and 35-6 are the corresponding equations with volume as one of the independent variables. Equating the two expressions for the chemical potentials in terms of the same set of independent variables, we find the expression (39-1) given below for the ratio of the equilibrium pressure p_{ek} of a gas in a mixture to its partial pressure pX_i and Eq. 39-5 for the ratio of the equilibrium concentration C_{ek} of a gas in a mixture to its concentrations C_i ($= CX_i = X_i(\sum_i n_i)/V$) in the mixture. In each expression the first integral on the right-hand side is to be evaluated for the gas mixture at the temperature T of the calculation; and the second for the pure gas.

In Eq. 39-2 and 39-6 the integrals have been expressed in terms of the virial parameters of the equation of state (6-1) or (6-3) for the pure gas and (9-12) or (9-15) for the gas mixture. Eq. 39-3 and 39-7 express the derivatives in terms of the quantities defined in Art. 10. In general the equilibrium pressure or concentration is not computed for its own sake but as an intermediate step in the calculation of the mass-action function of a chemical reaction or of the equilibrium conditions among two or more phases. In these cases we obtain very accurate results if we drop all terms on the right-hand sides of Eq. 39-3 and 39-7, except those enclosed in the first pairs of braces, which give expressions exact to terms of the order of p or C. Then the equation of state constants listed in Table C,6 may be used in either relation, and the calculation may be systematized in the manner indicated in Table C,10. Eq. 39-4 and 39-8 give these approximate expressions for p_{ek}/pX_i and C_{ek}/C_i in terms of the equation of state constants.

$$RT \ln \frac{p_{ek}}{pX_i} = \int_0^p \left[\left(\frac{\partial V}{\partial n_i} \right)_{p,T,n} - \frac{RT}{p} \right] dp - \int_0^{p_{ek}} \left[\frac{V_k}{n_k} - \frac{RT}{p_k} \right] dp_k$$

$$(i \equiv k = 1, 2, \cdots) \quad (39\text{-}1)$$

$$\ln \frac{p_{ek}}{pX_i} = \left\{ \left[\frac{\beta_m}{RT} + \frac{(\sum_i n_i)}{RT} \left(\frac{\partial \beta_m}{\partial n_i} \right)_{T,n} \right] \frac{p}{RT} - \frac{\beta_k}{RT} \frac{p_{ek}}{RT} \right\}$$

$$+ \left\{ \left[\frac{\gamma_m}{RT} + \frac{(\sum_i n_i)}{RT} \left(\frac{\partial \gamma_m}{\partial n_i} \right)_{T,n} \right] \frac{p^2}{2(RT)^2} - \frac{\gamma_k}{RT} \frac{p_{ek}^2}{2(RT)^2} \right\}$$

$$+ \left\{ \left[\frac{\delta_m}{RT} + \frac{(\sum_i n_i)}{RT} \left(\frac{\partial \delta_m}{\partial n_i} \right)_{T,n} \right] \frac{p^3}{3(RT)^3} - \frac{\delta_k}{RT} \frac{p_{ek}^3}{3(RT)^3} \right\} \quad (39\text{-}2)$$

$$\ln \frac{p_{ek}}{pX_i} = \left\{ \frac{\beta_k}{RT} \left(\frac{p - p_{ek}}{RT} \right) + \frac{D_i(\beta)}{RT} \frac{p}{RT} \right\}$$

$$+ \left\{ \frac{\gamma_k}{RT} \left(\frac{p^2 - p_{ek}^2}{2(RT)^2} \right) + \frac{[D_i(\gamma) - \gamma_m]}{RT} \frac{p^2}{2(RT)^2} \right\}$$

$$+ \left\{ \frac{\delta_k}{RT} \left(\frac{p^3 - p_{ek}^3}{3(RT)^3} \right) + \frac{[D_i(\delta) - 2\delta_m]}{RT} \frac{p^3}{3(RT)^3} \right\} \quad (39\text{-}3)$$

$$\ln \frac{p_{ek}}{pX_i} = \left[B_{0k} - \frac{A_{0k}}{RT} - \frac{c_k}{T^3} \right] \left(\frac{p - p_{ek}}{RT} \right)$$

$$- \left[\tfrac{3}{4}(B_{0k}^{\frac{1}{3}} - \sum_i X_i B_{0i}^{\frac{1}{3}})(B_{0k}^{\frac{2}{3}} - \sum_i X_i B_{0i}^{\frac{2}{3}}) \right.$$

$$\left. - \frac{(A_{0k}^{\frac{1}{2}} - \sum_i X_i A_{0i}^{\frac{1}{2}})^2}{RT} - \frac{(c_k^{\frac{1}{2}} - \sum_i X_i c_i^{\frac{1}{2}})^2}{T^3} \right] \frac{p}{RT} \quad (39\text{-}4)$$

$$RT \ln \frac{C_{ek}}{C_i} = \int_V^\infty \left[\left(\frac{\partial p}{\partial n_i} \right)_{V,T,n} - \frac{RT}{V} \right] dV - \int_V^\infty \left[\left(\frac{\partial p_k}{\partial n_k} \right)_{V_k,T} - \frac{RT}{V_k} \right] dV_k$$

$$(i \equiv k = 1, 2, \cdots) \quad (39\text{-}5)$$

$$\ln \frac{C_{ek}}{C_i} = \left\{ \left[\frac{2\beta_m}{RT} + \frac{(\sum_i n_i)}{RT} \left(\frac{\partial \beta_m}{\partial n_i} \right)_{T,n} \right] C - \frac{2\beta_k}{RT} C_{ek} \right\}$$

$$+ \left\{ \left[\frac{3\gamma_m}{RT} + \frac{(\sum_i n_i)}{RT} \left(\frac{\partial \gamma_m}{\partial n_i} \right)_{T,n} \right] \frac{C^2}{2} - \frac{3\gamma_k}{RT} \frac{C_{ek}^2}{2} \right\}$$

$$+ \left\{ \left[\frac{4\delta_m}{RT} + \frac{(\sum_i n_i)}{RT} \left(\frac{\partial \delta_m}{\partial n_i} \right)_{T,n} \right] \frac{C^3}{3} - \frac{4\delta_k}{RT} \frac{C_{ek}^3}{3} \right\} \quad (39\text{-}6)$$

$$\ln \frac{C_{ek}}{C_i} = \left\{ \frac{\beta_k}{RT} (C - 2C_{ek}) + \frac{[D_i(\beta) + \beta_m]}{RT} C \right\}$$

$$+ \left\{ \frac{\gamma_k}{RT} \left(\frac{C^2 - 3C_{ek}^2}{2} \right) + \frac{[D_i(\gamma) + \gamma_m]}{RT} \frac{C^2}{2} \right\}$$

$$+ \left\{ \frac{\delta_k}{RT} \left(\frac{C^3 - 4C_{ek}^3}{3} \right) + \frac{[D_i(\delta) + \delta_m]}{RT} \frac{C^3}{3} \right\} \quad (39\text{-}7)$$

$$\ln \frac{C_{ek}}{C_i} = \left[B_{0k} - \frac{A_{0k}}{RT} - \frac{c_k}{T^3} \right] (C - 2C_{ek})$$

$$- \left[\tfrac{1}{4}(B_{0k} - \sum_i X_i B_{0i}) + \tfrac{1}{4} B_{0k}^{\frac{2}{3}}(B_{0k}^{\frac{1}{3}} - 3 \sum_i X_i B_{0i}^{\frac{1}{3}}) \right.$$

$$\left. + \tfrac{1}{4} B_{0k}^{\frac{1}{3}}(B_{0k}^{\frac{2}{3}} - 3 \sum_i X_i B_{0i}^{\frac{2}{3}}) - \frac{A_{0k}^{\frac{1}{2}}(A_{0k}^{\frac{1}{2}} - 2\sum_i X_i A_{0i}^{\frac{1}{2}})}{RT} \right.$$

$$\left. - \frac{c_k^{\frac{1}{2}}(c_k^{\frac{1}{2}} - 2\sum_i X_i c_i^{\frac{1}{2}})}{T^3} \right] C \quad (39\text{-}8)$$

To compute the equilibrium pressure p_{ek} of a gas in a mixture given the total pressure p and the composition $X_1, X_2, \ldots$ of the mixture, place p_{ek} on the right-hand side of any one of the Eq. 39-2 to 39-4 equal to its ideal gas value, pX_i, for the first approximation. Then repeat the calculation with the provisional value of p_{ek} resulting from the first approximation. Usually a third approximation is unnecessary. The equilibrium concentration C_{ek} can now be calculated from the equation of state (6-3) of the pure gas.

To compute the composition of a mixture of m gases given the total pressure and $(m - 1)$ equilibrium pressures, use the ideal gas values $X_i = p_{ek}/p$ for the mole fractions occurring on the right-hand side of Eq. 39-2 to 39-4. Then repeat with the resulting provisional values.

Similarly, given the concentration C and composition of the mixture, we can evaluate the equilibrium concentration C_{ek} from any one of the Eq. 39-6 to 39-8. If desired, the complete equation can be used with the equation of state constants given in Table C,6. For the first approximation, place C_{ek} equal to CX_i. The equilibrium pressure can then be found from the equation of state (6-1) of the pure gas.

Also, given the concentration C of the mixture and $(m - 1)$ equilibrium concentrations, we can place X_i on the right-hand side of the equation equal to C_{ek}/C for the first approximation.

C,40. Effect of Hydrostatic Pressure and of an Inert Gas on a Univariant Equilibrium Involving a Pure Gaseous Phase. In a univariant equilibrium between a pure gaseous substance S_1 and one or more condensed phases, as

$$\text{NH}_3 \text{ (l)} = \text{NH}_3 \text{ (g)} \qquad\qquad (p_{01}, T)$$

$$\tfrac{1}{8}\text{BaCl}_2 \cdot 8\text{NH}_3 \text{ (s)} = \text{NH}_3 \text{ (g)} + \tfrac{1}{8}\text{BaCl}_2 \text{ (s)} \qquad (p_{01}, T)$$

$$\frac{1}{a} \text{ sat. soln. (l, } S_2 \cdot a\text{NH}_3) = \text{NH}_3 \text{ (g)} + \frac{1}{a} S_2 \text{ (s)} \quad (p_{01}, T)$$

the pressure p_{01} is a function of temperature alone. We can define [59] the chemical potential μ_{S_1} and the partial molar volume v_{S_1} of S_1 in the condensed complex by the relations

$$\mu_{S_1} = \Delta F_j, \qquad v_{S_1} = \Delta V_j \qquad\qquad (40\text{-}1)$$

where ΔF_j is the increase in free energy, and ΔV_j the increase in volume of the condensed complex when one mole of S_1 is absorbed from the gas phase. When only one condensed phase is present, μ_{S_1} is its molar free energy and v_{S_1} is its molar volume.

Now let the condensed phases be subjected to the hydrostatic pressure p, say by a piston permeable to the gas alone, whereby the equilibrium pressure p_{01} is increased to p_{e1}. For the chemical potential of S_1 in the condensed complex we find

$$\mu_{S_1}(p, T) = \mu_{S_1}(p_{01}, T) + \int_{p_{01}}^{p} v_{S_1} dp \qquad\qquad (40\text{-}2)$$

where $\mu_{S_1}(p_{01}, T)$ is equal to the chemical potential of the vapor of S_1 at the vapor pressure p_{01} and is given by Eq. 18-6 with p replaced by p_{01}.

The chemical potential of S_1 in the gas phase when the condensed complex is under the pressure p is the equilibrium pressure p_{e1} given by Eq. 18-6 with p replaced by p_{e1}. Equating the two values of the chemical potential of S_1 gives Eq. 40-4 written below.

Let

$$v_{S_1}(p, T) = v_{S_1}^*(0, T)(1 - \kappa_1 p) \tag{40-3}$$

where $v_{S_1}^*$ is the (extrapolated) value of v_{S_1} at zero pressure and κ_1 is the isothermal compressibility of this quantity.

Introduction of the equation of state (6-3) and the relation (40-3) into Eq. 40-4 gives 40-5. In general, terms of higher order than the first in pressure may be dropped, and the equation of state constants of Table C,6 or those derived from critical data used. Eq. 40-6 expresses p_{e1}/p_{01} in terms of the equation of state constants: here v_{S_1} may as well be taken for a pressure of one atmosphere or for p_{01}.

$$RT \ln \frac{p_{e1}}{p_{01}} = - \int_{p_{01}}^{p_{e1}} \left[\frac{V_1}{n_1} - \frac{RT}{p_1} \right] dp_1 + \int_{p_{01}}^{p} v_{S_1} dp \tag{40-4}$$

$$\ln \frac{p_{e1}}{p_{01}} = - \frac{\beta_1}{RT} \left(\frac{p_{e1} - p_{01}}{RT} \right) - \frac{\gamma_1}{RT} \left(\frac{p_{e1}^2 - p_{01}^2}{2(RT)^2} \right)$$

$$- \frac{\delta_1}{RT} \left(\frac{p_{e1}^3 - p_{01}^3}{3(RT)^3} \right) + \frac{v_{S_1}^*}{RT} (p - p_{01}) - \frac{v_{S_1}^* \kappa_1}{2RT} (p^2 - p_{01}^2) \tag{40-5}$$

$$\ln \frac{p_{e1}}{p_{01}} = - \left[B_{01} - \frac{A_{01}}{RT} - \frac{c_1}{T^3} \right] \left(\frac{p_{e1} - p_{01}}{RT} \right) + \frac{v_{S_1}}{RT} (p - p_{01}) \tag{40-6}$$

In using these equations, we can place p_{e1} equal to p_{01} on the right-hand side for the first approximation which yields the usual ideal gas integration of the Poynting relation.

Now let a univariant system be in equilibrium under its vapor pressure p_{01}, and let an inert gas that does not react chemically with the vapor S_1 and is insoluble in the condensed complex be introduced into the system until the total pressure becomes p, the mole fraction of S_1 in the gas phase being X_1. The chemical potential of S_1 in the condensed complex is given by Eq. 40-2 and in the gas phase by Eq. 34-6. The resulting relation for the ratio of the partial pressure pX_1 of S_1 in the gas mixture to the vapor pressure p_{01} before the introduction of the inert gas is (40-7). The first integral of this expression refers to the gas mixture, the second to pure gaseous S_1, and the third to the condensed complex. The two following equations correspond to (40-5) and (40-6). Eq. 40-8 was derived by Gerry and Gillespie [60] and applied to the calculation of the normal vapor pressure of iodine from measurements made by the gas current method.

⟨ 311 ⟩

$$RT \ln \frac{pX_1}{p_{01}} = - \int_0^p \left[\left(\frac{\partial V}{\partial n_1} \right)_{p,T,n} - \frac{RT}{p} \right] dp$$

$$+ \int_0^{p_{01}} \left[\frac{V_1}{n_1} - \frac{RT}{p_1} \right] dp_1 + \int_{p_{01}}^p v_{S_1} dp \quad (40\text{-}7)$$

$$\ln \frac{pX_1}{p_{01}} = \left\{ \left(v_{S_1}^* - \frac{\beta_1}{RT} \right) \left(\frac{p - p_{01}}{RT} \right) - \frac{D_1(\beta)}{RT} \frac{p}{RT} \right\}$$

$$- \left\{ \left(RTv_{S_1}^* \kappa_1 + \frac{\gamma_1}{RT} \right) \left(\frac{p^2 - p_{01}^2}{2(RT)^2} \right) + \frac{[D_1(\gamma) - \gamma_m]}{RT} \frac{p^2}{2(RT)^2} \right\}$$

$$- \left\{ \frac{\delta_1}{RT} \left(\frac{p^3 - p_{01}^3}{3(RT)^3} \right) + \frac{[D_1(\delta) - 2\delta_m]}{RT} \frac{p^3}{3(RT)^3} \right\} \quad (40\text{-}8)$$

$$\ln \frac{pX_1}{p_{01}} = \left[v_{S_1} - \left(B_{01} - \frac{A_{01}}{RT} - \frac{c_1}{T^3} \right) \right] \left(\frac{p - p_{01}}{RT} \right)$$

$$+ \left[\tfrac{3}{4} (B_{01}^{\frac{1}{2}} - \sum_i X_i B_{0i}^{\frac{1}{2}})(B_{01}^{\frac{2}{3}} - \sum_i X_i B_{0i}^{\frac{2}{3}}) \right.$$

$$\left. - \frac{(A_{01}^{\frac{1}{2}} - \sum_i X_i A_{0i}^{\frac{1}{2}})^2}{RT} - \frac{(c_1^{\frac{1}{2}} - \sum_i X_i c_i^{\frac{1}{2}})^2}{T^3} \right] \frac{p}{RT} \quad (40\text{-}9)$$

C,41. Chemical Potential of a Volatile Constituent of a Condensed Phase. For the discussion of the equilibrium between condensed and gaseous phases we need a relation for the chemical potential of a constituent of a condensed phase. The activity coefficient α_i of the constituent i at a mole fraction Y_i in a solution (liquid or solid) at the pressure p and temperature T is defined by the relation

$$\mu_{S_i}(p,\, T,\, Y_i) = RT \ln Y_i + RT \ln \alpha_i(p,\, T,\, Y_i) + \mu_{S_i}^0(p,\, T) \quad (41\text{-}1)$$

where $\mu_{S_i}(p,\, T,\, Y_i)$ is the chemical potential of i in the state p, T, Y_i, and $\mu_{S_i}^0(p,\, T)$ is an integration constant determined by the statement that $\alpha_i = 1$ in the arbitrarily selected reference state. In the following treatment p is always the vapor pressure of the solution.

The most convenient choice of reference state for the present problem is the following. Irrespective of the designation of the substance S_i as solvent or solute, we may select the pure condensed substance ($Y_i = 1$) under the vapor pressure p of the solution at each temperature T as the reference state of unit activity coefficient ($\alpha_i = 1$). In this state its chemical potential by Eq. 41-1 is $\mu_{S_i}^0(p,\, T)$, and this is given for any pressure p by the expression

$$\mu_{S_i}^0(p,\, T) = \mu_{S_i}^0(p_{0i},\, T) + \int_{p_{0i}}^p v_{S_i} dp \quad (41\text{-}2)$$

where $\mu_{S_i}^0(p_{0i},\, T)$ is the chemical potential of the pure substance under its vapor pressure p_{0i} at T, and v_{Si} is its molar volume. But $\mu_{Si}^0(p_{0i}, T)$ is equal to the chemical potential of the vapor at p_{0i} and T; and this is given by Eq. 18-6 with p replaced by p_{0i}. Making this substitution in Eq. 41-2 and inserting the resulting relation for $\mu_{Si}^0(p, T)$ into Eq. 41-1, we find

$$\mu_{Si}(p, T, Y_i) = RT \ln p_{0i}Y_i + RT \ln \alpha_i$$
$$+ \int_{p_{0i}}^p v_{Si}dp + \int_0^{p_{0i}} \left[\frac{V}{n} - \frac{RT}{p}\right] dp + \text{H}_i^0 - T\text{s}_i^0 \quad (41\text{-}3)$$

where H_i^0 and s_i^0 are temperature functions for the gas given in Art. 18. The first integral refers to the pure condensed substance i, and the second to the pure gaseous substance i.

In view of Eq. 18-7 we can write Eq. 41-3 in the form

$$\mu_{Si}(p, T, Y_i) = RT \ln f_{0i}Y_i + RT \ln \alpha_i + \int_{p_{0i}}^p v_{Si}dp + \text{H}_i^0 - T\text{s}_i^0 \quad (41\text{-}4)$$

where f_{0i} is the fugacity of the constituent i of p_{0i} and T.

We can express v_{Si} by Eq. 40-3 for evaluation of the integral of Eq. 41-3 and Eq. 41-4.

C,42. Chemical Potentials of Pure Condensed Phases. If the condensed phase is a pure substance S_j we can select as the standard state the same pressure p_0 and temperature T_0 as for a gas. At any other pressure p and temperature T we find for the chemical potential μ_j,

$$\mu_j(p, T) = {}_T\!\int_{p_0}^p v_{Sj}dp + \text{H}_j^0 - T\text{s}_j^0 \quad (42\text{-}1)$$

$$\text{H}_j^0 = \text{H}_{0j}^0 + {}_{p_0}\!\int_{T_0}^T c_{pj}dT$$
$$\quad (42\text{-}2)$$
$$\text{s}_j^0 = \text{s}_{0j}^0 + {}_{p_0}\!\int_{T_0}^T c_{pj}\frac{dT}{T}$$

where v_{Sj} is the molar volume of S_j at T, c_{pj} its heat capacity at constant pressure p_0, and H_{0j}^0 and s_{0j}^0 its heat content and entropy at p_0 and T_0.

C,43. Equilibrium between Condensed and Gaseous Solutions. When equilibrium subsists with respect to the passage of a component i from a condensed to a gaseous phase, the chemical potential $\mu_{Si}(p, T, Y_i)$ of i in the condensed phase equals the potential $\mu_i(p, T, X_i)$ in the gaseous phase. A relation for the former is given in Eq. 41-3, and for the latter in Eq. 34-6. Equating the two values of the potential and solving for the ratio of the partial pressure pX_i in the gas phase (p, total pressure; X_i, mole fraction in gas phase) to the Raoult's law pressure $p_{0i}Y_i$ computed for the condensed phase (p_{0i}, vapor pressure of pure i; Y_i, mole fraction in the condensed phase), we obtain Eq. 43-1 given below. The first integral of the expression is to be evaluated at T for the gas mixture, the second for pure gaseous i, and the third for pure condensed i.

In Eq. 43-2 the integrals of Eq. 43-1 are expressed in terms of the virial parameters of Eq. 9-15 for the gas mixture and of Eq. 6-3 for the pure gas, see Art. 10, and of the compressibility of pure condensed i as defined in Eq. 40-6. In Eq. 43-3 terms of higher order than the pressure are dropped, and the parameters β_{0m} and β_k are expressed in terms of the equation of state constants.

Eq. 43-2 has been applied to many systems by Scatchard [61,62,63] and his collaborators.

$$RT \ln \frac{pX_i}{p_{0i}Y_i} = - \int_0^p \left[\left(\frac{\partial V}{\partial n_i} \right)_{p,T,n} - \frac{RT}{p} \right] dp + \int_0^{p_{0i}} \left[\frac{V_k}{n_k} - \frac{RT}{p_k} \right] dp_k$$

$$+ \int_{p_{0i}}^p \mathrm{v}_{8i} dp + RT \ln \alpha_i \quad (i \equiv k = 1, 2, \cdots) \quad (43\text{-}1)$$

$$\ln \frac{pX_i}{p_{0i}Y_i} = \left\{ \left(\mathrm{v}_{8i}^* - \frac{\beta_i}{RT} \right) \left(\frac{p - p_{0i}}{RT} \right) - \frac{D_i(\beta)}{RT} \frac{p}{RT} \right\}$$

$$- \left\{ \left(RT \mathrm{v}_{8i}^* \kappa_i + \frac{\gamma_i}{RT} \right) \left(\frac{p^2 - p_{0i}^2}{2(RT)^2} \right) + \frac{[D_i(\gamma) - \gamma_m]}{RT} \frac{p^2}{2(RT)^2} \right\}$$

$$- \left\{ \frac{\delta_i}{RT} \left(\frac{p^3 - p_{0i}^3}{3(RT)^3} \right) + \frac{[D_i(\delta) - 2\delta_m]}{RT} \frac{p^3}{3(RT)^3} \right\} + \ln \alpha_i \quad (43\text{-}2)$$

$$\ln \frac{pX_i}{p_{0i}Y_i} = \left[\mathrm{v}_{8i} - \left(B_{0i} - \frac{A_{0i}}{RT} - \frac{c_i}{T^3} \right) \right] \left(\frac{p - p_{0i}}{RT} \right)$$

$$+ \left[\tfrac{3}{4} (B_{0i}^{\frac{1}{3}} - \sum_i X_i B_{0i}^{\frac{1}{3}})(B_{0i}^{\frac{2}{3}} - \sum_i X_i B_{0i}^{\frac{2}{3}}) \right.$$

$$\left. - \frac{(A_{0i}^{\frac{1}{2}} - \sum_i X_i A_{0i}^{\frac{1}{2}})^2}{RT} - \frac{(c_i^{\frac{1}{2}} - \sum_i X_i c_i^{\frac{1}{2}})^2}{T^3} \right] \frac{p}{RT} + \ln \alpha_i \quad (43\text{-}3)$$

C,44. Mass Action Function for a Homogeneous Gaseous Reaction. Eq. 34-6 expresses the chemical potential of a gas in a mixture in terms of p, T, X_1, X_2, ... Application of the general equilibrium condition (28-1) gives a relation containing the logarithm of the mass action function K_p as defined in (28-2). In a similar manner from (35-6), which expresses the chemical potential in terms of C, T, X_1, X_2, . . . , we find a relation for the logarithm of K_C as defined in (28-3). These expressions are given below: K_p being given in terms of p, T, X_1, X_2, . . . and K_C in terms of C, T, X_1, X_2, ... Either equilibrium function may be expressed in terms of the other set of independent variables. Thus, to find K_p as a function of C, T, X_1, X_2, we add and subtract the

term $RT \ln pX_i$ to and from the right-hand side of (35-6) before applying the general equilibrium condition; and to find K_C as a function of p, T,
X_1, X_2, . . . we add and subtract the term $RT \ln (RTn_i/V)$ to and
from the right-hand side of (34-6) before applying the general equilibrium
condition.

The quantities K_p^* and K_C^* are the values of K_p and K_C, respectively,
at a very low pressure and are functions of temperature alone and contain
the heat content (or energy) and entropy constants of the gases at T_0.

The integrals of Eq. 44-1 are evaluated in Eq. 44-7 in terms of the
virial parameters and their derivatives given in Art. 10. In Eq. 44-8,
terms of higher order than the first in pressure are dropped, and the
equation of state constants are used.

$$\ln \frac{K_p}{K_p^*} = -\frac{1}{RT} \left\{ \sum_i \nu_i \left[\int_0^p \left[\left(\frac{\partial V}{\partial n_i}\right)_{p,T,n} - \frac{RT}{p} \right] dp \right] \right\} \tag{44-1}$$

$$= -\frac{1}{RT} \left\{ \sum_i \nu_i \left[\int_V^\infty \left[\left(\frac{\partial p}{\partial n_i}\right)_{V,T,n} - \frac{RT}{V} \right] dV \right] \right\}$$

$$+ (\sum_i \nu_i) \ln \frac{pV}{(\sum_i n_i)RT} \tag{44-2}$$

$$\ln K_p^* = -\frac{1}{RT} [\sum_i \nu_i(\mathrm{H}_i^0 - T\mathrm{s}_i^0)] \tag{44-3}$$

$$\ln \frac{K_C}{K_C^*} = -\frac{1}{RT} \left\{ \sum_i \nu_i \left[\int_V^\infty \left[\left(\frac{\partial p}{\partial n_i}\right)_{V,T,n} - \frac{RT}{p} \right] dV \right] \right\} \tag{44-4}$$

$$= -\frac{1}{RT} \left\{ \sum_i \nu_i \left[\int_0^p \left[\left(\frac{\partial V}{\partial n_i}\right)_{p,T,n} - \frac{RT}{p} \right] dp \right] \right\}$$

$$- (\sum_i \nu_i) \ln \frac{pV}{(\sum_i n_i)RT} \tag{44-5}$$

$$\ln K_C^* = -\frac{1}{RT} [\sum_i \nu_i(\mathrm{E}_i^0 + RT - T\mathrm{s}_i^0 + RT \ln RT)] \tag{44-6}$$

$$\ln \frac{K_p}{K_p^*} = -\frac{\{\sum_i\nu_i[\beta_i + D_i(\beta)]\}}{RT} \frac{p}{RT} - \frac{\{\sum_i\nu_i[\gamma_i + D_i(\gamma) - \gamma_m]\}}{RT} \frac{p^2}{2(RT)^2}$$

$$- \frac{\{\sum_i\nu_i[\delta_i + D_i(\delta) - 2\delta_m]\}}{RT} \frac{p^3}{3(RT)^3} \tag{44-7}$$

$$= -\left\{ (\sum_i \nu_iB_{0i}) - \frac{(\sum_i\nu_iA_{0i})}{RT} - \frac{(\sum_i\nu_ic_i)}{T^3} \right\} \frac{p}{RT}$$

$$+ \left\{ \tfrac{3}{4}[\sum_i \nu_i(B_{0i}^{\frac{1}{3}} - \sum_i X_iB_{0i}^{\frac{2}{3}})(B_{0i}^{\frac{2}{3}} - \sum_i X_iB_{0i}^{\frac{2}{3}})] \right.$$

$$\left. - \frac{[\sum_i\nu_i(A_{0i}^{\frac{1}{3}} - \sum_iX_iA_{0i}^{\frac{1}{3}})^2]}{RT} - \frac{[\sum_i\nu_i(c_i^{\frac{1}{3}} - \sum_iX_ic_i^{\frac{1}{3}})^2]}{T^3} \right\} \frac{p}{RT} \tag{44-8}$$

$$\ln K_p^* = \frac{1}{R}\left[\int_{T_0}^{T} \frac{(\sum_i \nu_i C_{pi}^*)}{T}\, dT\right] - \frac{1}{RT}\left[\int_{T_0}^{T} (\sum_i \nu_i C_{pi}^*)dT\right]$$

$$- \frac{1}{RT}(\sum_i \nu_i \mathrm{H}_{0i}^0) + \frac{1}{R}(\sum_i \nu_i \mathrm{S}_{0i}^0) \quad (44\text{-}9)$$

$$= \frac{1}{R}\int_{T_0}^{T}\left[\int_{T_0}^{T} (\sum_i \nu_i C_{pi}^*)dT\right]\frac{dT}{T^2} - \frac{1}{RT}(\sum_i \nu_i \mathrm{H}_{0i}^0) + \frac{1}{R}(\sum_i \nu_i \mathrm{S}_{0i}^0)$$

$$(44\text{-}10)$$

In the foregoing equations all summations extend over all species in the gas mixture, the stoichiometric coefficient ν_i being zero for a gas i that does not enter into the chemical reaction, but X_i is not zero.

Eq. 44-8 and 44-10 express the mass action function K_p in terms of the pressure, temperature, composition of the equilibrium mixture, the equation of state constants of all gases present, the heat capacities of the gases entering into the reaction, and the heat content and entropy constants at the standard temperature of the gases entering into the reaction. The ideal gas law gives K_p equal to K_p^*, a function of temperature only. The Lewis and Randall rule gives the first term enclosed in braces on the right-hand side of Eq. 44-8 and thus predicts that K_p is a function of pressure and temperature but not of the composition of the equilibrium mixture.

The last two sums of Eq. 44-10 may be considered adjustable in the absence of heat content and entropy data on the gases entering into the chemical reaction, but these are the only adjustable constants in the complete expression for K_p.

All of the measurements of the ammonia synthesis equilibrium to 1,000 atm, including equilibrium mixtures containing argon and those containing no argon, have been correlated [64] by the approximate Eq. 44-8, with K_p^* given by Eq. 44-10. In this calculation the less exact linear combination for B_{0m} and c_m were used. The ΔH for the reaction computed for 0°C from the sum $(\sum_i \nu_i \mathrm{H}_{0i}^0)$ was in good agreement with that derived by other methods, and the predicted compositions of the equilibrium mixtures agreed within experimental accuracy with the measured values.

Eq. 44-8 indicates that the optimum mixture [64] of gases to use in order to produce the largest mole fraction of some product in the equilibrium mixture is not necessarily the stoichiometric proportions, and the optimum composition of the initial mixture will vary with the amounts and kinds of inert gases present.

To compute the composition of an equilibrium mixture from Eq. 44-8 given the initial composition, pressure, temperature, and the necessary constants of the pure gases, we first compute K_p^* (the ideal gas value of K_p). From this we compute a provisional value of the composition of the equilibrium mixture which, inserted into the right-hand side of Eq. 44-8, gives a provisional value of K_p from which a second approximation to the equilibrium composition can be found. In general, two approximations are sufficient even at high pressures. Faster convergence is obtained if we use the first term in braces on the right-hand side of Eq. 44-8, which does not contain any composition terms, to find K_p for the first approximation.

C,45. Mass Action Function for a Gaseous Reaction in a System Containing Pure Condensed Phases. Eq. 42-1 and 42-2 give the chemical potential of a pure condensed substance as a function of pressure and temperature. When such substances enter into a reaction, the relations of Art. 44 must be modified by the addition to the right-hand side of the equations for $\ln K_p/K_p^*$ and $\ln K_c/K_c^*$ of the sum:

$$- \frac{1}{RT} \left\{ \sum_j \nu_j \left[\int_{p_0}^{p} \mathrm{v}_{sj} dp \right] \right\} \qquad (45\text{-}1)$$

and to the right-hand side of the equations for K_p^* and K_c^*, the sum

$$- \frac{1}{RT} \left[\sum_j \nu_j (\mathrm{H}_j^0 - T\mathrm{s}_j^0) \right] \qquad (45\text{-}2)$$

where H_j^0 and s_j^0 are given by Eq. 42-2 and the sums extend over all pure condensed phases entering into the chemical reaction.

C,46. Determination of the Energy, Heat Content, and Entropy Constants. The interpretation of the heat content and entropy constants H_0^0 and s_0^0 of a gas are given in Art. 16, and the energy constant E_0^0 is discussed in Art. 17. The evaluation of these constants depends on what changes in state are to be studied and may be made on the basis of the following considerations.

1. When no chemical reaction may occur, we can assign arbitrary values to the molar heat content and entropy of each individual substance or indeed to a gas mixture of constant composition. If the temperature is to be considered variable, arbitrary values are assigned only at p_0, T_0, but if the temperature is to be constant in all variations, we can assign an arbitrary value at p_0 and the temperature in question.

The usual practice is to take the pressure of the standard state as one atmosphere. Eq. 22-2 and 22-3 are sufficiently accurate at this pressure to permit computation of H^0 and s^0 from the assigned values of H and S at one atmosphere pressure and a temperature T.

2. When chemical reactions may occur among the constituent gases of a system, arbitrary values, say zero, may be assigned to the molar

heat content and entropy of all elementary substances in the standard state (p_0, T_0). The constants H_0^0 and S_0^0 of those elements that are gases under these conditions may be computed from Eq. 22-2 and 22-3; and those of elements that are not gases and of compounds can be calculated from these equations and other thermodynamic data. Thus to determine the heat content and entropy constants of a volatile element that is, however, condensed at one atmosphere and T_0, we can add to the value zero the small change in these properties for the change in state from one atmosphere to the vapor pressure, then add ΔH and ΔS of vaporization to give the corresponding quantities for the vapor at the vapor pressure and T_0, and finally compute H_0^0 and S_0^0 for the vapor from Eq. 22-2 and 22-3. For a gaseous compound we can compute $\sum_i \nu_i H_{0i}^0$ and $\sum_i \nu_i S_{0i}^0$ from Eq. 44-8 and 44-10. This requires equilibrium measurements of a reaction in which the compound is formed from its elements or of some reaction involving the compound with other substances whose constants are known.

When interested only in the effect of pressure on chemical equilibrium at constant temperature, we can use Eq. 44-8 with K_p^* treated as an adjustable parameter.

C,47. Units in the Equations Given by the General Limit Method.

Units of mass. Any consistent unit of mass may be employed. Then V, E, H, S, A, F, C_p, C_v, and η refer to the total number of units of mass in the system under consideration, and μ, E, H, s, c_p^*, and c_v^* to a unit mass. The gas constant R, the virial parameters β, γ, and δ, and the equation of state constants must be expressed in the appropriate unit of mass.

Units of energy. The quantities E, H, s, c_p^*, and c_v^* will ordinarily be expressed in an energy unit (for example, calorie, BTU), that differs from the energy unit (liter-atmosphere, foot-pound) employed in the numerical evaluation of the remaining terms. Conversion of a quantity from one set of energy units to another can be accomplished by dividing by the value of R in the units employed and multiplying by the value of R in the desired units.

Units of pressure. The equations for S, A, F, μ, K_p^*, and K_c^* contain one or more terms of the type $\ln p$ or $\ln (V/nRT)$ together with a corresponding number of terms each having as a factor the quantity S_0^0. We find in Eq. 16-13 that the relation for S_0^0 of a pure substance contains the quantity $R \ln p_0$, where p_0 is the pressure of the standard state. In tables of standard thermodynamic functions the pressure of the standard state is always taken to be 1 atm, so that $\ln p_0 = 0$. Therefore in all of the foregoing equations the pressure p in the factor $\ln p$ *must be expressed in atmospheres* and V/nRT in the factor $\ln V/nRT$ *must be expressed in reciprocal atmospheres*, whatever units of pressure are used elsewhere in the calculation. This is equivalent to writing $\ln (p/p_0)$ for $\ln p$ and $\ln (p_0 V/nRT)$ for $\ln (V/nRT)$ throughout, and deleting the term $nR \ln p_0$ in Eq. 16-13.

C,48. Reexamination of the Assumptions of the General Limit Method.

Of the three assumptions made as a basis for the thermodynamic treatment of real gases and gas mixtures, one can be derived, as stated earlier, from the other two. In particular the assumption regarding the isothermal compressibility of a gas, Eq. 13-1, can be derived from the assumption (13-2) concerning the isothermal variation of the heat content of a pure gas with pressure and that (29-1) for the ratio of the equilibrium pressure to the partial pressure of a gas in a mixture.

From Eq. 13-2 we find for the region of low pressure

$$-T^2 \left[\frac{\partial (V/T)}{\partial T}\right]_p = \left(\frac{\partial H}{\partial p}\right)_T = B(T, m) + O(p) \quad (T, m \text{ const}) \quad (48\text{-}1)$$

We can write the integral of Eq. 48-1 in the form

$$V = T\psi(p, m) + A(T, m) + O(p) \quad (T, m \text{ const}) \quad (48\text{-}2)$$

or

$$pV = T\phi(p, m) + A(T, m)p + O(p^2) \quad (T, m \text{ const}) \quad (48\text{-}3)$$

where Eq. 48-3 is in the form of Eq. 13-1 except for the first term which is $F(T, m)$ in Eq. 13-1.

The derivations given in Art. 30 depend only on the assumption (29-1) for gas mixtures as far as Eq. 30-13 which may be written

$$\frac{p_{ek}V}{n_{ek}} \frac{1}{1 + D_i p} = \frac{pV}{(\sum_i n_i)} \frac{1}{1 + 2D_m p} \quad (i \equiv k = 1, 2, \cdots) \quad (48\text{-}4)$$

Consider that $n_{e1}, n_{e2}, \ldots$ moles of the pure gases $1, 2, \ldots$ and $(\sum_i n_i)$ moles of the gas mixture are placed in separate compartments each of volume V and at the temperature T, and that the chemical potential of each of the pure gases has the same value during all variations as that which it has in the gas mixture. Let the independent variables for each pure gas k be T and μ_k, and those for the mixture be $T, \mu_1, \mu_2, \ldots$ as in Eq. 30-7 and 30-8. Let all variations be in the region of low pressure and at constant temperature and mass. With μ_1 held constant for both the pure gas 1 and the gas 1 in the mixture, we can vary $\mu_2, \mu_3, \ldots$, thus causing the pressures and concentrations of the gases $2, 3, \ldots$ and of the gas mixture to vary. From Eq. 30-8 we see that the left-hand side of Eq. 48-4 for gas 1 cannot vary except through the factor $(1 + D_i p)^{-1}$, but the effect of this variation can be made as small as desired by carrying out all of the variations at sufficiently low pressure. In particular when all variations are carried out at a very low pressure, $p_{e1}V/n_{e1}$ remains constant, and hence $pV/(\sum_i n_i)$ for the gas mixture and $p_{ek}V/n_{ek}$ for each of the other pure gases must have remained constant although V, p, and p_{ek} ($k = 2, 3, \cdots$) varied. Hence

$$\left(\frac{p_1V_1}{n_1}\right)^* = \left(\frac{p_2V_2}{n_2}\right)^* = \cdots = \left(\frac{pV}{\sum_i n_i}\right)^* = F(T) \qquad (48\text{-}5)$$

The subscript e was omitted since the ratios of Eq. 48-5 are each individually constant at constant temperature for the gases and gas mixture each confined in a cylinder.

Thus for any one gas we find

$$(pV)^* = F(T, m) \quad (T, m \text{ const}) \qquad (48\text{-}6)$$

for the region of very low pressure. Hence $T\phi(p, m)$ of Eq. 48-3 must equal $F(T, m)$ and

$$pV = F(T, m) + A(T, m)p + O(p^2) \quad (T, m \text{ const}) \qquad (48\text{-}7)$$

which is the assumption (13-1).

CHAPTER 4. THE LEWIS AND RANDALL RULE

C,49. The Lewis and Randall Assumption for Gas Mixtures.
Lewis and Randall [1, pp. 225–227] proposed as a basis for the thermodynamic treatment of gas mixtures the rule: The fugacity f_i of a gas i in a mixture is equal to the product of its mole fraction X_i and the fugacity f_{pk} of the pure gas at the total pressure p and temperature T of the mixture:

$$f_i = f_{pk}X_i \quad (i \equiv k = 1, 2, \cdots) \qquad (49\text{-}1)$$

The fugacity f of a pure gas is defined [1, p. 191] through the relations

$$\mu = RT \ln f + \psi(T), \qquad \lim_{p \to 0} \frac{f}{p} = 1 \text{ at all temperatures} \qquad (49\text{-}2)$$

and the fugacity f_i of a gas i in a mixture may be defined by the relation

$$\mu_i = RT \ln f_i + \psi_k(T) \quad (i \equiv k = 1, 2, \cdots) \qquad (49\text{-}3)$$

where $\psi_k(T)$ is the temperature function of Eq. 49-2 for the pure gas. Now f_i is evidently equal to the fugacity of the pure gas k at its equilibrium pressure p_{ek} and at the temperature of the mixture. According to the Lewis and Randall rule we can write

$$\mu_i = RT \ln f_{pk}X_i + \psi_k(T) \quad (i \equiv k = 1, 2, \cdots) \qquad (49\text{-}4)$$

The pure gas in the state to which f_{pk} refers is, of course, not in equilibrium with the gas mixture since it is under the total pressure of the mixture and not its equilibrium pressure.

The Lewis and Randall rule gives immediately the thermodynamic relations of gas mixtures in terms of the independent variables p, T, n_1, n_2, . . . , which are those usually employed in experimental work.

C,50. Deductions from the Lewis and Randall Rule. The following results may be derived from the rule:

1. Subject to the conditions

$$T \text{ (each pure gas)} = T \text{ (mixture)}$$
$$p \text{ (each pure gas)} = p \text{ (mixture)} \qquad \text{(B)}$$
$$n_k = n_i \quad (i \equiv k = 1, 2, \cdot \cdot \cdot)$$

the following relations hold:

$$\mu_i = \mu_{pk} + RT \ln X_i \quad (i \equiv k = 1, 2, \cdot \cdot \cdot) \qquad \text{(50-1)}$$

$$V = (\sum_k V_{pk}) \qquad \text{(50-2)}$$

$$S = (\sum_k S_{pk}) - (\sum_i n_i R \ln X_i) \qquad \text{(50-3)}$$

$$\left. \begin{array}{l} E - (\sum_k E_{pk}) \quad H = (\sum_k H_{pk}) \quad A = (\sum_k A_{pk}) + (\sum_i n_i RT \ln X_i) \\ F = (\sum_k F_{pk}) + (\sum_i n_i RT \ln X_i) \quad C_V = (\sum_k C_{Vpk}) \quad C_p = (\sum_k C_{pvk}) \end{array} \right\} \quad \text{(50-4)}$$

where the subscript p denotes that the conditions (B) apply. Eq. 50-2 is Amagat's law.

2. Subject to conditions (B) the partial molar volume of a gas in a mixture equals the molar volume of the pure gas:

$$\left(\frac{\partial V}{\partial n_i} \right)_{p,T,n} = \frac{V_{pk}}{n_k} \quad (i \equiv k = 1, 2, \cdot \cdot \cdot) \qquad \text{(50-5)}$$

3. The Lewis and Randall rule leads to a complete solution of the problem of the determination of the thermodynamic properties of gas mixtures from measurements on pure gases only.

The quantity μ_{pk} can be computed from Eq. 49-2 by substitution of f_{pk} in the right-hand side. Comparison with Eq. 49-4 yields Eq. 50-1. Differentiation of Eq. 50-1 subject to conditions (B) gives

$$\left(\frac{\partial \mu_i}{\partial p} \right)_{T,n} = \left(\frac{\partial \mu_{pk}}{\partial p} \right)_T \qquad (i \equiv k = 1, 2, \cdot \cdot \cdot) \qquad \text{(50-6)}$$

$$\left(\frac{\partial \mu_i}{\partial T} \right)_{p,n} = \left(\frac{\partial \mu_{pk}}{\partial T} \right)_p + R \ln X_i \quad (i \equiv k = 1, 2, \cdot \cdot \cdot) \qquad \text{(50-7)}$$

where the subscript n denotes constant composition. From general thermodynamic theory the left-hand sides of Eq. 50-6 and 50-7 are equal, respectively, to the partial molar volume and the negative partial molar entropy of the gas i in the mixture, and the partial derivatives on the right-hand sides are the corresponding molar quantities for the pure gas. Thus

$$\left(\frac{\partial V}{\partial n_i}\right)_{p,T,n} = \frac{V_{pk}}{n_k} \qquad (i \equiv k = 1, 2, \cdots) \qquad (50\text{-}8)$$

$$\left(\frac{\partial S}{\partial n_i}\right)_{p,T,n} = \frac{S_{pk}}{n_k} - R \ln X_i \quad (i \equiv k = 1, 2, \cdots) \qquad (50\text{-}9)$$

The first is Eq. 50-5. By Euler's theorem

$$V = \left[\sum_i n_i \left(\frac{\partial V}{\partial n_i}\right)_{p,T,n}\right] = (\sum_k V_{pk}) \qquad (i \equiv k = 1, 2, \cdots) \quad (50\text{-}10)$$

$$S = \left[\sum_i n_i \left(\frac{\partial S}{\partial n_i}\right)_{p,T,n}\right] = (\sum_k S_{pk}) - (\sum_i n_i R \ln X_i)$$

$$(i \equiv k = 1, 2, \cdots) \quad (50\text{-}11)$$

Thus Eq. 50-2 and 50-3 are proved. Substitution from Eq. 50-1, 50-2, and 50-3 into the general thermodynamic relations (28-4) to (28-9) and use of the conditions (B) give the relations (50-4).

Statement 3 follows directly from Eq. 50-1 through 50-4.

C,51. General Thermodynamic Relations for Gas Mixtures from the Lewis and Randall Rule.

Substitution of the relations for the thermodynamic properties of pure gases derived from the general limit method and given in Art. 18 into the Eq. 50-1 to 50-4 yields the expressions written below that are derived from the Lewis and Randall rule for gas mixtures.

Eq. 51-1 to 51-12 can be expressed in terms of the virial parameters β_k, γ_k, and δ_k of the pure gases through the relations of Art. 20; and approximate expressions in terms of the equation of state constants A_0, B_0, and c through the use of the relations of Art. 22.

$$E = \sum_k \left\{ \int_0^p \left[V_k - T\left(\frac{\partial V_k}{\partial T}\right)_{p_k} \right] dp_k - pV_k + n_k H_k^0 \right\} \qquad (51\text{-}1)$$

$$H = \sum_k \left\{ \int_0^p \left[V_k - T\left(\frac{\partial V_k}{\partial T}\right)_{p_k} \right] dp_k + n_k H_k^0 \right\} \qquad (51\text{-}2)$$

$$S = \sum_k \left\{ \int_0^p \left[\frac{n_k R}{p_k} - \left(\frac{\partial V_k}{\partial T}\right)_{p_k} \right] dp_k + n_k s_k^0 \right\}$$

$$- (\sum_i n_i R \ln pX_i) \quad (51\text{-}3)$$

$$A = \sum_k \left\{ \int_0^p \left[V_k - \frac{n_k RT}{p_k} \right] dp_k - pV_k + n_k(H_k^0 - Ts_k^0) \right\}$$
$$+ \left(\sum_i n_i RT \ln pX_i \right) \quad (51\text{-}4)$$

$$F = \sum_k \left\{ \int_0^p \left[V_k - \frac{n_k RT}{p_k} \right] dp_k + n_k(H_k^0 - Ts_k^0) \right\}$$
$$+ \left(\sum_i n_i RT \ln pX_i \right) \quad (51\text{-}5)$$

$$\mu_i = \int_0^p \left[\frac{V_k}{n_k} - \frac{RT}{p_k} \right] dp_k + RT \ln pX_i + H_k^0 - Ts_k^0 \quad (51\text{-}6)$$

$$RT \ln f_i = \int_0^p \left[\frac{V_k}{n_k} - \frac{RT}{p_k} \right] dp_k + RT \ln pX_i \quad (51\text{-}7)$$

$$C_p = \sum_k \left[n_k C_{pk}^* - T \int_0^p \left(\frac{\partial^2 V_k}{\partial T^2} \right)_{p_k} dp_k \right] \quad (51\text{-}8)$$

$$C_V = \sum_k \left[n_k C_{Vk}^* + n_k R + T \frac{(\partial V_k/\partial T)_{p_k}^2}{(\partial V_k/\partial p_k)_T} - T \int_0^p \left(\frac{\partial^2 V_k}{\partial T^2} \right)_{p_k} dp_k \right] \quad (51\text{-}9)$$

$$C_p - C_V = -T \sum_k \left[\frac{(\partial V_k/\partial T)_{\mu_k}^2}{(\partial V_k/\partial p_k)_T} \right] \quad (51\text{-}10)$$

$$\mu_{JT} C_p = T^2 \sum_k \left\{ \left[\frac{\partial(V_k/T)}{\partial T} \right]_{p_k} \right\} \quad (51\text{-}11)$$

$$\eta C_V = - \sum_k \left[\frac{T(\partial V_k/\partial T)_{p_k} + p_k(\partial V_k/\partial p_k)_T}{(\partial V_k/\partial p_k)_T} \right] \quad (51\text{-}12)$$

In the foregoing relations the summations extend over all gases in the mixture, and

$$H_k^0 = \int_{T_0}^T C_{pk}^* dT + H_{0k}^0 \quad (51\text{-}13)$$

$$s_k^0 = \int_{T_0}^T \frac{C_{pk}^*}{T} dT + s_{0k}^0 \quad (51\text{-}14)$$

The left-hand sides of Eq. 51-1 to 51-5 and 51-8 to 51-12 refer to the gas mixture at p, T, and the mole numbers n_i ($i \equiv k = 1, 2, \cdots$). The terms enclosed in braces are to be computed for each pure gas k with p_k, T, and n_k having the values p, T, and n_i respectively of the mixture, and the sum taken for all gases composing the mixture. The terms not enclosed in braces are to be computed for the gas mixture. In Eq. 51-6 and 51-7 the left-hand side refers to a gas in a mixture, and the right-hand side is to be computed for the pure gas as just described except for the term pX_i which refers to the mixture.

C,52. Compressibilities of Gas Mixtures According to the Lewis and Randall Rule. The Lewis and Randall rule requires Amagat's law to hold at all pressures and temperatures. Thus it places a definite restriction on the equation of state of a gas mixture. Let

$$\frac{V_k}{n_k} = F_k(p, T) \tag{52-1}$$

be the equation of state of a pure gas. The rule gives for the equation of state of a gas mixture

$$V = \left[\sum_k n_k F_k(p, T) \right] \tag{52-2}$$

where conditions (B) apply and the summation extends over all species in the mixture. The functions $F_k(p, T)$ may be different for the different gases, and some or all of the functions may be evaluated graphically. The implications of Eq. 52-2 in regard to combination of constants in an equation of state are indicated in Eq. 8-8.

C,53. Equilibrium Pressure and Equilibrium Concentration of a Gas in a Mixture. If we proceed as in Art. 39 but use the value of the chemical potential of a gas in a mixture given by the Lewis and Randall rule, Eq. 51-6, we find the relations given below for the ratio of the equilibrium pressure p_{ek} of a gas in a mixture to its partial pressure pX_i. These expressions are to be compared with Eq. 39-1 to 39-4. No composition terms appear in the expression given by the Lewis and Randall rule.

Once the equilibrium pressure of a gas has been found, we can compute the corresponding equilibrium concentration from the equation of state (52-1) of the pure gas.

$$RT \ln \frac{p_{ek}}{pX_i} = \int_{p_{ek}}^{p} \left[\frac{V_k}{n_k} - \frac{RT}{p_k} \right] dp_k \quad (i \equiv k = 1, 2, \cdots) \tag{53-1}$$

$$\ln \frac{p_{ek}}{pX_i} = \frac{\beta_k}{RT} \left(\frac{p - p_{ek}}{RT} \right) + \frac{\gamma_k}{RT} \left(\frac{p^2 - p_{ek}^2}{2(RT)^2} \right) + \frac{\delta_k}{RT} \left(\frac{p^3 - p_{ek}^3}{3(RT)^3} \right) \tag{53-2}$$

$$\ln \frac{p_{ek}}{pX_i} = \left[B_{0k} - \frac{A_{0k}}{RT} - \frac{c_k}{T^3} \right] \left(\frac{p - p_{ek}}{RT} \right) \tag{53-3}$$

C,54. Effect of an Inert Gas on a Univariant Equilibrium. In place of the relations (40-7) to (40-9) given by the general limit method, the Lewis and Randall rule leads to the Eq. 54-1 to 54-3, given below, for the ratio of the partial pressure pX_1 of a vapor 1 to the vapor pressure p_{01} in a system originally univariant into which an inert gas is introduced. Here p_{01} is the vapor pressure in the univariant system at the temperature T, and p is the total pressure resulting on the addition of an inert gas that is insoluble in the condensed phase or phases. Strictly, the application of these equations is limited to the vapor pressure of the pure substance 1 since the integrand refers not to the gas mixture but to substance 1. In their application of the Lewis and Randall rule to the system $BaCl_2 \cdot 8NH_3(s)$, $BaCl_2(s)$, $NH_3(g) + N_2(g)$, Lurie and Gillespie [65] used the relations only to the vapor pressure of liquid ammonia, with fair results. In other applications [66] of the Lewis and Randall rule the calculations were carried to pressures far above the vapor pressure of the liquid where it is difficult to determine what part of the disagreement is caused by failure of the equation of state extrapolation. Gerry[6] found the Lewis and Randall rule extremely bad for cases of condensible vapors at small mole fraction.

The equations given by the Lewis and Randall rule follow.

$$RT \ln \frac{pX_1}{p_{01}} = - \int_{p_{01}}^{p} \left[\frac{V_1}{n_1} - \frac{RT}{p_1} \right] dp_1 + \int_{p_{01}}^{p} \mathrm{v}_{s_1} dp \tag{54-1}$$

$$\ln \frac{pX_1}{p_{01}} = \left(\mathrm{v}_{s_1}^* - \frac{\beta_1}{RT} \right) \left(\frac{p - p_{01}}{RT} \right)$$
$$- \left(RT \mathrm{v}_{s_1}^* \kappa_1 + \frac{\gamma_1}{RT} \right) \left(\frac{p^2 - p_{01}^2}{2(RT)^2} \right) - \frac{\delta_1}{RT} \left(\frac{p^3 - p_{01}^3}{3(RT)^3} \right) \tag{54-2}$$

$$\ln \frac{pX_1}{p_{01}} = \left[\mathrm{v}_{s_1} - \left(B_{01} - \frac{A_{01}}{RT} - \frac{c_1}{T^3} \right) \right] \left(\frac{p - p_{01}}{RT} \right) \tag{54-3}$$

C,55. Equilibrium Between Condensed and Gaseous Solutions.

The Lewis and Randall rule has been used extensively for the vapor phase of a multicomponent system of two phases: liquid and vapor. These computations were in general for industrial use, and approximations were made for the liquid phase also.

Consider the equilibrium between the liquid and vapor phases of a multicomponent system at a total pressure p and temperature T. If the liquid were a perfect solution, the fugacity of a substance i in the liquid phase would be $f_{Li}Y_i$ where f_{Li} is the fugacity of the pure liquid i at p and T, and Y_i is its mole fraction in the solution. The Lewis and Randall rule gives for the fugacity of i in the vapor $f_{pk}X_i$, where f_{pk} is the fugacity of the pure vapor i at p and T, and X_i is its mole fraction in the vapor. At equilibrium

$$f_{Li}Y_i = f_{pk}X_i \quad (i \equiv k = 1, 2, \cdots) \tag{55-1}$$

The application of this equation to the design of high pressure hydrocarbon equipment has been discussed by Brown and his collaborators [67,68] and by Lewis and Luke [69] who introduced the further approximation that f_{Li} may be replaced by the fugacity of the pure liquid i at its own vapor pressure and T, which is equal to the fugacity of the vapor of i at the vapor pressure and T.

[6] H. T. Gerry, quoted in [52].

In general the evaluation of f_{pk} for use in Eq. 55-1 requires extrapolation to pressures above the condensation pressure of the pure vapor k, that is, into the region of supercompressed vapor which has not been investigated experimentally. The extrapolation can be made by use of Eq. 18-7 and 6-3, or from a generalized fugacity chart [70,71,72]. The latter involves the use of the law of corresponding states and consists of curves of the ratio f/p of the fugacity to the pressure of a pure gas plotted against the reduced pressure p_r for a series of reduced temperatures T_r. The chart can be prepared from Eq. 23-7 and a generalized chart of the compressibility factor, in which Z is plotted against reduced coordinates.

Although the approximations made in the use of Eq. 55-1 are more severe than those of the Lewis and Randall rule, the results are sufficiently accurate for the design of high-pressure hydrocarbon equipment.

We can apply the Lewis and Randall rule to the calculation of equilibrium conditions between a gaseous and a condensed solution, using the argument of Art. 43, but evaluating the chemical potential of a gas in a mixture by the rule. The equations for the ratio of the partial pressure pX_i of constituent i in the vapor phase to the Raoult's law pressure $p_{0i}Y_i$ are given below. They are to be compared with Eq. 43-1 to 43-3.

$$RT \ln \frac{pX_i}{p_{0i}Y_i} = -\int_{p_{0i}}^{p}\left[\frac{V_k}{n_k} - \frac{RT}{p_k}\right] dp_k + \int_{p_{0i}}^{p} \mathrm{v}_{si} dp + RT \ln \alpha_i \qquad (55\text{-}2)$$

$$(i \equiv k = 1, 2, \cdots)$$

$$\ln \frac{pX_i}{p_{0i}Y_i} = \left(\mathrm{v}_{si}^* - \frac{\beta_i}{RT}\right)\left(\frac{p - p_{0i}}{RT}\right) - \left(RT\mathrm{v}_{si}^*\kappa_i + \frac{\gamma_i}{RT}\right)\left(\frac{p^2 - p_{0i}^2}{2(RT)^2}\right)$$

$$- \frac{\delta_i}{RT}\left(\frac{p^3 - p_{0i}^3}{3(RT)^3}\right) + \ln \alpha_i \qquad (55\text{-}3)$$

$$\ln \frac{pX_i}{p_{0i}Y_i} = \left[\mathrm{v}_{si} - \left(B_{0i} - \frac{A_{0i}}{RT} - \frac{c_i}{T^3}\right)\right]\left(\frac{p - p_{0i}}{RT}\right) + \ln \alpha_i \qquad (55\text{-}4)$$

C,56.   Mass Action Function for a Homogeneous Gaseous Reaction.   Applying the general equilibrium relation $(\sum_i \nu_i \mu_i)$ to the chemical potential of a gas in a mixture expressed in terms of fugacity, Eq. 16-22, we find

$$\left(\sum_i \nu_i \ln f_i\right) = \ln K_f = -\frac{1}{RT}\left[\sum_i \nu_i(\mathrm{H}_i^0 - T\mathrm{s}_i^0)\right] = K_p^* \qquad (56\text{-}1)$$

for the condition of chemical equilibrium. The Lewis and Randall rule gives

$$f_i = f_{pk}X_i = (f_{pk}/p)(pX_i) \quad (i \equiv k = 1, 2, \cdots)$$

where pX_i is the partial pressure of gas i in the mixture. Thus

$$\left(\sum_i \nu_i \ln f_i\right) = \left(\sum_k \nu_k \ln \frac{f_{pk}}{p}\right) + \left(\sum_i \nu_i \ln pX_i\right) \quad (i \equiv k = 1, 2, \cdots) \quad (56\text{-}2)$$

or

$$\ln \frac{K_p}{K_f} = \ln \frac{K_p}{K_p^*} = -\left(\sum_k \nu_k \ln \frac{f_{pk}}{p}\right) \quad (56\text{-}3)$$

Newton and Dodge [73] used this equation to correlate the data on the ammonia synthesis equilibrium evaluating f_{pk}/p from generalized fugacity charts. The agreement between observed and calculated values of K_p was good at 300 atm, fair at 600 atm, but poor at 1000 atm.

Another method of deriving the relation for K_p from the Lewis and Randall rule is to apply the general equilibrium condition to the relation (51-6) given by the rule for the chemical potential of a gas in a mixture. This gives Eq. 56-4 first derived by Gillespie [74]. This equation (56-6) and (56-7) are to be compared with the general limit relations (44-1), (44-7), and (44-8). The Lewis and Randall relation does not require K_p to vary with the composition of the equilibrium mixture, as it should, yet the expression does hold to quite high pressures.

The effect of the presence of pure solid phases that take part in the chemical reaction can be included by the method of Art. 45.

$$\ln \frac{K_p}{K_p^*} = -\frac{1}{RT} \left\{ \sum_k \nu_k \left[\int_0^p \left[\frac{V_k}{n_k} - \frac{RT}{p_k} \right] dp_k \right] \right\} \quad (56\text{-}4)$$

$$\ln K_p^* = -\frac{1}{RT} \left[\sum_i \nu_i (\mathrm{H}_i^0 - T\mathrm{s}_i^0) \right] \quad (56\text{-}5)$$

$$\ln \frac{K_p}{K_p^*} = -\frac{(\sum_i \nu_i \beta_i)}{RT} \frac{p}{RT} - \frac{(\sum_i \nu_i \gamma_i)}{RT} \frac{p^2}{2(RT)^2} - \frac{(\sum_i \nu_i \delta_i)}{RT} \frac{p^3}{3(RT)^3} \quad (56\text{-}6)$$

$$\ln \frac{K_p}{K_p^*} = -\left[\left(\sum_i \nu_i B_{0i}\right) - \frac{(\sum_i \nu_i A_{0i})}{RT} - \frac{(\sum_i \nu_i C_i)}{T^3} \right] \frac{p}{RT} \quad (56\text{-}7)$$

C,57. Error of the Lewis and Randall Rule. One of the requirements of the Lewis and Randall rule is that Amagat's law of the additivity of volumes at constant pressure and temperature hold for a gas mixture. This determines how the constants of an equation of state are to be combined to form the corresponding equation for a gas mixture. As indicated in Eq. 8-8 we must write

$$\frac{V}{(\sum_i n_i)} = \frac{RT}{p} + \frac{(\sum_i X_i \beta_i)}{RT} + \frac{(\sum_i X_i \gamma_i)}{(RT)^2} p + \frac{(\sum_i X_i \delta_i)}{(RT)^3} p^2 \quad (57\text{-}1)$$

that is, linear combination must be employed for each virial parameter.

Eq. 57-1 may be compared with the relations (9-13) to (9-15) resulting from combination of constants in an equation of state.

Amagat's law and hence the Lewis and Randall rule require that the partial molar volume of a gas in a mixture be equal to the molar volume of the pure gas measured at the total pressure and temperature of the mixture. The error of this as compared with combination of constants in an equation of state is given in Eq. 10-6, and is

$$\left(\frac{\partial V}{\partial n_i}\right)_{p,T,n} - \frac{V_{pk}}{n_k} = \frac{D_i(\beta)}{RT} + O(p) \quad (i \equiv k = 1, 2, \cdots) \quad (57\text{-}2)$$

The left-hand side of this equation is the increase in volume of a system consisting of a large quantity of a gas mixture together with a quantity of the pure gas k at the same pressure and temperature when one mole of substance is removed from the pure gas and combined with the mixture. It was called the expansion of the gas on mixing by Gillespie [75], who studied this property for several different mixtures. In general this quantity is positive except at high pressures and it does not approach zero as the pressure is decreased. Eq. 10-3 states the value of $D_i(\beta)$ in terms of the equation of state constants, temperature, and composition of the mixture.

The error of the Lewis and Randall rule in the computation of fugacity can be determined by comparison of the general limit method relation (34-7) for the fugacity f_i of a gas in a mixture with the corresponding Lewis and Randall expression $f_{pk}X_i$. The error expressed as a ratio is

$$\ln \frac{f_i}{f_{pk}X_i} = \frac{1}{RT} \int_0^p \left[\left(\frac{\partial V}{\partial n_i}\right)_{p,T,n} - \frac{V_k}{n_k} \right] dp \quad (57\text{-}3)$$

Since the integrand of Eq. 57-3 is, in general, positive, the fugacity computed from the rule is too small.

The relations for the equilibrium properties of a gas mixture given by the general limit method all contain terms depending on the composition of the mixture which are missing from the equations derived from the Lewis and Randall rule. Thus the general limit method gives for the equilibrium pressure p_{ek} of a gas in a mixture

$$\ln \frac{p_{ek}}{pX_i} = \frac{\beta_i}{RT}\left(\frac{p - p_{ek}}{RT}\right) + \frac{D_i(\beta)}{RT}\frac{p}{RT} + O(p^2) \quad (57\text{-}4)$$

whereas in the Lewis and Randall expression the term containing $D_i(\beta)$ is missing. Since this is, in general, positive, the equilibrium pressure computed from the rule is too small; or if the equilibrium pressure is given, the corresponding mole fraction X_i given by the rule is too large.

The results of a number of comparisons of calculations from the Lewis and Randall rule with experiment may be summarized as follows:

(1) When all gases in the mixture are far above their critical temperatures, the rule gives good results up to 100 atm and fair results to several hundred atmospheres. (2) When one of the gases in the mixture is close to or below its critical point, the rule may fail badly even at moderate pressures. (3) So far as the calculation of the partial molar volume of a gas in a mixture is concerned the absolute error of the rule does not approach zero as the pressure approaches zero, although the fractional error does.

CHAPTER 5. THE GIBBS-DALTON LAW

C,58. The Gibbs-Dalton Assumption for Gas Mixtures. As a starting point for the discussion of the thermodynamic properties of gas mixtures, Gibbs [*41*, pp. 155–158] proposed the following law: The pressure of a mixture of different gases is equal to the sum of the pressures of the different gases as existing each by itself at the same temperature and with the same value of its (chemical) potential. In commenting on the results derivable from this law Gibbs remarks: "It is in this sense that we should understand the law of Dalton, that every gas is as a vacuum to every other gas."

Gillespie [*40*] called the foregoing assumption the Gibbs-Dalton law. He pointed out that it contained the essential idea of equilibrium necessary for a general thermodynamic treatment of gas mixtures and derived the various consequences of the law.

The Gibbs-Dalton law leads to relations for the thermodynamic properties of gas mixtures in terms of the independent variables V, T, n_1, n_2, $\cdots$ which are those of the great majority of equations of state.

C,59. Deductions from the Gibbs-Dalton Law. The different gases "existing each by itself at the same temperature and with the same value of its potential" would evidently each be in equilibrium with the gas mixture through a membrane permeable to that gas alone. The pressure of each gas under these conditions is its equilibrium pressure p_e and the Gibbs-Dalton law states that, subject to the conditions

$$\left. \begin{array}{l} T \text{ (each pure gas)} = T \text{ (mixture)} \\ V \text{ (each pure gas)} = V \text{ (mixture)} \\ \mu_k = \mu_i \quad (i \equiv k = 1, 2, \cdots) \end{array} \right\} \quad \text{(C)}$$

the pressure p of the gas mixture is

$$p = \left(\sum_k p_{ek} \right) \quad (59\text{-}1)$$

The second condition is unnecessary for Eq. 59-1 but is required to fix the value of any extensive property of the pure gases.

The results derivable from the Gibbs-Dalton law may be summarized as follows:

1. The concentration of a gas is the same at equilibrium on each side of a membrane permeable to it alone; and under conditions (C) the number of moles of each pure gas is the same as in the mixture:

$$C_{ek} = C_i \quad (i \equiv k = 1, 2, \cdots) \tag{59-2}$$

$$n_{ek} = n_i \quad (i \equiv k = 1, 2, \cdots) \tag{59-3}$$

2. When conditions (C) apply the following quantities are additive:

$$S = (\sum_k S_{ek}) \tag{59-4}$$

$$\left.\begin{array}{ccc} E = (\sum_k E_{ek}) & H = (\sum_k H_{ek}) & A = (\sum_k A_{ek}) \\ F = (\sum_k F_{ek}) & C_V = (\sum_k C_{Vek}) & C_p = (\sum_k C_{pek}) \end{array}\right\} \tag{59-5}$$

3. When conditions (C) apply the following are also true:

$$\left.\begin{array}{c} T \text{ (each pure gas)} = T \text{ (mixture)} \\ V \text{ (each pure gas)} = V \text{ (mixture)} \\ n_k = n_i, \text{ that is, } C_k = C_i \quad (i \equiv k = 1, 2, \cdots) \end{array}\right\} \tag{A}$$

and

$$p = (\sum_k p_{ck}) \tag{59-6}$$

$$\mu_i = \mu_{ck} \tag{59-7}$$

$$S = (\sum_k S_{ck})$$

$$\left.\begin{array}{ccc} E = (\sum_k E_{ck}) & H = (\sum_k H_{ck}) & A = (\sum_k A_{ck}) \\ F = (\sum_k F_{ck}) & C_V = (\sum_k C_{Vck}) & C_p = (\sum_k C_{pck}) \end{array}\right\} \tag{59-8}$$

where the subscript c denotes that conditions (A) apply. Eq. 59-6 is the usual statement of Dalton's law. Although Dalton's law is a consequence of the Gibbs-Dalton law, the converse cannot be proved, since the idea of equilibrium is lacking in Dalton's law.

4. Subject to conditions (A):

$$\left(\frac{\partial p}{\partial n_i}\right)_{V,T,n} = \left(\frac{\partial p_{ck}}{\partial n_k}\right)_{V,T} \quad (i \equiv k = 1, 2, \cdots) \tag{59-9}$$

5. The Gibbs-Dalton law leads to a complete solution of the problem of the determination of the thermodynamic properties of gas mixtures from information on the behavior of pure gases only.

Consider a number of systems, one consisting of a gas mixture and each of the others of one of the pure constituent gases. Let the conditions (C) apply for all variations. From Eq. 59-1 we find

$$\left(\frac{\partial p}{\partial \mu_i}\right)_{T,\mu} = \left(\frac{\partial p_{ek}}{\partial \mu_k}\right)_T \quad (i \equiv k = 1, 2, \cdots) \tag{59-10}$$

$$\left(\frac{\partial p}{\partial T}\right)_\mu = \left[\sum_k \left(\frac{\partial p_{ek}}{\partial T}\right)_{\mu_k}\right] \tag{59-11}$$

Substitution from the foregoing equations into (30-9) and (30-10) gives

$$\frac{n_i}{V} = \frac{n_{ek}}{V} \quad (i \equiv k = 1, 2, \cdots) \tag{59-12}$$

$$\frac{S}{V} = \left[\sum_k \frac{S_{ek}}{V}\right] \tag{59-13}$$

Since n/V is the concentration C, Eq. 59-2 is proved; and since V has the same value for the gas mixture and each pure gas, (59-3) and (59-4) are true. To prove the Eq. 59-5 we substitute from (59-1), (59-3), and (59-4) into the general thermodynamic relations for pure gases and mixtures, Eq. 28-4 to 28-9, making use of conditions (C).

From Eq. 59-2 and 59-3 it is evident that the conditions (C) imply the conditions (A), provided the Gibbs-Dalton law is true. Now conditions (A) and (C) each define the same state of each pure gas as regards both intensive and extensive thermodynamic properties. Hence when conditions (A) apply, the chemical potential of each pure gas has the same value as in the mixture, Eq. 59-7, and Eq. 59-1, 59-4, and 59-5 become Eq. 59-6 and 59-8.

Differentiation of Eq. 59-6 with respect to n_i ($= n_k$), ($i \equiv k = 1$, 2, $\cdots$), subject to the conditions (A) gives Eq. 59-9.

The relations (59-6) to (59-8) state the properties of a gas mixture in terms of those of the pure constituent gases without requiring any measurements on the mixture.

C,60. General Thermodynamic Relations for Gas Mixtures from the Gibbs–Dalton Law.

In terms of the relations for the thermodynamic properties of pure gases derived by the general limit method and listed in Art. 19, the Gibbs-Dalton law yields the relations written below for a gas mixture. They follow immediately from Eq. 59-6 to 59-8.

$$E = \sum_k \left\{ \int_V^\infty \left[p_k - T \left(\frac{\partial p_k}{\partial T}\right)_{V_k} \right] dV_k + n_k E_k^0 \right\} \tag{60-1}$$

$$H = \sum_k \left\{ \int_V^\infty \left[p_k - T \left(\frac{\partial p_k}{\partial T}\right)_{V_k} \right] dV_k + p_k V + n_k E_k^0 \right\} \tag{60-2}$$

$$S = \sum_k \left\{ \int_V^\infty \left[\frac{n_k R}{V_k} - \left(\frac{\partial p_k}{\partial T} \right)_{V_k} \right] dV_k \right.$$
$$\left. + n_k R \ln \frac{V}{n_k RT} + n_k s_k^0 \right\} \quad (60\text{-}3)$$

$$A = \sum_k \left\{ \int_V^\infty \left[p_k - \frac{n_k RT}{V_k} \right] dV_k - n_k RT \ln \frac{V}{n_k RT} \right.$$
$$\left. + n_k (E_k^0 - T s_k^0) \right\} \quad (60\text{-}4)$$

$$F = \sum_k \left\{ \int_V^\infty \left[p_k - \frac{n_k RT}{V_k} \right] dV_k - n_k RT \ln \frac{V}{n_k RT} \right.$$
$$\left. + p_k V + n_k (E_k^0 - T s_k^0) \right\} \quad (60\text{-}5)$$

$$\mu_i = \int_V^\infty \left[\left(\frac{\partial p_k}{\partial n_k} \right)_{V_k, T} - \frac{RT}{V_k} \right] dV_k - RT \ln \frac{V}{n_k RT}$$
$$+ RT + (E_k^0 - T s_k^0) \quad (60\text{-}6)$$

$$RT \ln f_i = \int_V^\infty \left[\left(\frac{\partial p_k}{\partial n_k} \right)_{V_k, T} - \frac{RT}{V_k} \right] dV_k - RT \ln \frac{V}{n_k RT} \quad (60\text{-}7)$$

$$C_p = \sum_k \left\{ n_k C_{pk}^* - n_k R - T \frac{(\partial p_k / \partial T)_{V_k}^2}{(\partial p_k / \partial V_k)_T} - T \int_V^\infty \left(\frac{\partial^2 p_k}{\partial T^2} \right)_{V_k} dV_k \right\} \quad (60\text{-}8)$$

$$C_V = \sum_k \left\{ n_k C_{Vk}^* - T \int_V^\infty \left(\frac{\partial^2 p_k}{\partial T^2} \right)_{V_k} dV_k \right\} \quad (60\text{-}9)$$

$$C_p - C_V = -T \sum_k \left\{ \frac{(\partial p_k / \partial T)_{V_k}^2}{(\partial p_k / \partial V_k)_T} \right\} \quad (60\text{-}10)$$

$$\mu_{JT} C_p = - \sum_k \left\{ \frac{T(\partial p_k / \partial T)_{V_k} + V_k (\partial p_k / \partial V_k)_T}{(\partial p_k / \partial V_k)_T} \right\} \quad (60\text{-}11)$$

$$\eta C_V = T^2 \sum_k \left\{ \left[\frac{\partial (p_k / T)}{\partial T} \right]_{V_k} \right\} \quad (60\text{-}12)$$

In these relations the summations extend over all of the gases in the mixture, and:

$$E_k^0 = \int_{T_0}^T C_{Vk}^* dT + E_{0k}^0 \quad (60\text{-}13)$$

$$s_k^0 = \int_{T_0}^T \frac{C_{Vk}^*}{T} dT + R \ln \frac{T}{T_0} + s_{0k}^0 \quad (60\text{-}14)$$

The quantities E_{0k}^0 and S_{0k}^0 are the molar energy and entropy constants for the pure gas k at the temperature T_0, and c_{vk}^* the molar constant volume heat capacity at zero pressure.

In each of the Eq. 60-1 to 60-5 and 60-8 to 60-12 the left-hand side is the value of a thermodynamic quantity of a gas mixture at V, T, and the mole numbers n_i ($i \equiv k = 1, 2, \cdots$). The terms enclosed in the braces on the right-hand side are to be computed for each pure gas k with V, T, n_k, or V, T, n_k/V having the same values for each pure gas as in the gas mixture, and the sum taken for all of the gases composing the mixture. In Eq. 60-6 and 60-7 the left-hand side is the value of a quantity for gas i in the mixture, and the right-hand side is computed for the pure gas as just described.

C,61. Compressibility of Gas Mixtures According to the Gibbs-Dalton Law. Let

$$p_k = \phi_k(T, n_k/V) \tag{61-1}$$

be the equation of state of a pure gas. The Gibbs-Dalton law gives for the total pressure p of the gas mixture the relation

$$p = \left(\sum_k p_k \right) = \left[\sum_k \phi_k(T, n_k/V) \right] \tag{61-2}$$

where the conditions (A) apply and the summation extends over all species in the mixture. Eq. 61-2 is Dalton's law as stated in Art. 8. The same form of the function ϕ_k need not be used for all of the gases and indeed ϕ_k can be evaluated graphically for some or all of the gases involved.

The error of Dalton's law is discussed in Art. 10. The implications of the law in regard to combination of constants in an equation of state are indicated in Eq. 8-4.

C,62. Equilibrium Pressure and Equilibrium Concentration of a Gas in a Mixture. The Gibbs-Dalton law is particularly well suited to the calculation of the equilibrium pressure and concentration of a gas in a mixture [40,65].

1. Given the volume V, temperature T, and mole numbers $n_1, n_2, \cdots$ of the gas mixture, to find the equilibrium concentrations and pressures of the constituent gases: The equilibrium concentration C_{ek} of gas i is simply its concentration n_i/V in the mixture

$$C_{ek} = C_i \quad (i \equiv k = 1, 2, \cdots) \tag{62-1}$$

The equilibrium pressure of each gas at T and C_{ek} can now be computed from its equation of state (61-1).

2. Given the total pressure p, temperature T, and composition X_1, X_2, $\ldots$ of the gas mixture, to find the equilibrium pressures and concen-

trations of the individual gases: By successive approximations we can compute the molar volume v of the mixture from Eq. 61-2, which may be written

$$p = \phi_1(T, X_1/\text{v}) + \phi_2(T, X_2/\text{v}) + \cdots \qquad (62\text{-}2)$$

the desired equilibrium pressures, $p_{ek} \equiv \phi_k(T, X_k/\text{v})$, being evaluated at the same time. The equilibrium concentrations are then X_k/v.

3. Given the total pressure p, the temperature T, and the equilibrium pressures p_{ek} of $m - 1$ of the m substances in the gas phase, to calculate the equilibrium concentrations of the individual gases and the composition of the mixture: Compute the equilibrium pressure of the mth substance by difference. From the m equations of state (61-1) of the pure gases, $p_{ek} = \phi_k(T, n_k/V)$, we can compute the equilibrium concentration $n_k/V (\equiv n_{ek}/V)$ of each gas which is also the concentration n_i/V of gas k in the mixture. Whence

$$X_i = \frac{n_i/V}{[\sum_i(n_i/V)]} \qquad (62\text{-}3)$$

C,63. Effect of an Inert Gas on a Univariant Equilibrium. The equilibrium vapor pressure of the substance 1 over the condensed complex is, by Eq. 40-4,

$$RT \ln \frac{p_{e1}}{p_{01}} = -\int_{p_{01}}^{p_{e1}} \left[\frac{V_1}{n_1} - \frac{RT}{p_1} \right] dp_1 + \int_{p_{01}}^{p} \text{v}_{s_1} dp \qquad (63\text{-}1)$$

This equation depends on the general limit assumptions for pure gases but not on that for gas mixtures, so that p_{e1} is the true equilibrium vapor pressure of substance 1 over the condensed complex.

The data on the system may be given in either of the two alternate forms considered in Art. 62, and the computation is carried out as outlined there. The equilibrium pressure of substance 1 should satisfy Eq. 63-1 if the method of 2 is used, and is given by Eq. 63-1 for the method of 3.

In some cases the Gibbs-Dalton law may require extrapolation of the equation of state or a plot of p against V for a vapor into the region of supersaturation. Since the effect of hydrostatic pressure on vapor pressure is small, the extrapolation is, in general, not severe. In this particular the Gibbs-Dalton law is superior to the Lewis and Randall rule which requires extrapolation to the total pressure of the system.

In their application of the Gibbs-Dalton law to the system $BaCl_2 \cdot 8NH_3(s)$, $BaCl_2(s)$, $NH_3(g) + N_2(g)$, Lurie and Gillespie computed the equilibrium pressure of ammonia in the gas phase from the known total pressure, temperature, and composition of the mixture. The equilibrium pressure of ammonia so determined should agree with the vapor pressure of the univariant system $BaCl_2 \cdot 8NH_3(s)$, $BaCl_2(s)$, $NH_3(g)$ when the solid phases are under a hydrostatic pressure equal to the total gas pressure, as computed from Eq. 63-1. The Gibbs-Dalton law gave too high an equilibrium pressure of ammonia, the deviations being in the same direction as those of the ideal gas computation, $p_{ek} = pX_i$, and up to moderate pressure roughly one half as large. There is an indication that the deviations of the equilibrium pressures computed from the Gibbs-Dalton law may pass through zero and change sign at higher pressures. When the mole fraction of the vapor is very small, as in the system $I_2(s)$, $I_2(g) + N_2(g)$, the Gibbs-Dalton law may give no better results than does the ideal gas approximation [60].

C,64. Equilibrium Between Condensed and Gaseous Solutions. Eq. 41-3 is the relation for the chemical potential of a constituent i of a condensed solution. The chemical potential of a constituent of a gaseous solution is equal to that of the pure gas at its equilibrium pressure p_{ek} and the temperature of the mixture, and is given by Eq. 18-6 with p replaced by p_{ek}. Equating these two expressions, we find at equilibrium

$$RT \ln \frac{p_{ek}}{p_{0i}Y_i} = - \int_{p_{0i}}^{p_{ek}} \left[\frac{V_k}{n_k} - \frac{RT}{p_k} \right] dp_k + \int_{p_{0i}}^{p} v_{s_i} dp + RT \ln \alpha_i$$

$$(\iota \equiv k = 1, 2, \cdots) \quad (64\text{-}1)$$

This equation depends on the general limit assumptions for pure gases but not on that for gas mixtures.

The method of application of the Gibbs-Dalton law is similar to that of Art. 63, with p_{ek} given by Eq. 64-1.

C,65. Mass Action Function for a Homogeneous Gas Reaction. Application of the general equilibrium condition ($\sum_i \nu_i \mu_i$) to the relation (60-6) yields immediately a relation for K_C. To find K_p we add and subtract a term $RT \ln pX_i$ before applying the general equilibrium condition. The following relations result.

$$\ln \frac{K_C}{K_C^*} = - \frac{1}{RT} \left\{ \sum_k \nu_k \left[\int_V^\infty \left[\left(\frac{\partial p_k}{\partial n_k} \right)_{V_k, T} - \frac{RT}{V_k} \right] dV_k \right] \right\} \quad (65\text{-}1)$$

$$\ln K_C^* = - \frac{1}{RT} \left\{ \sum_k \nu_k \left[E_k^0 + RT - Ts_k^0 + RT \ln RT \right] \right\} \quad (65\text{-}2)$$

$$\ln \frac{K_p}{K_p^*} = - \frac{1}{RT} \left\{ \sum_k \nu_k \left[\int_V^\infty \left[\left(\frac{\partial p_k}{\partial n_k} \right)_{V_k, T} - \frac{RT}{V_k} \right] dV_k \right] \right\}$$

$$+ \left(\sum_i \nu_i \right) \ln \frac{pV}{(\sum_i n_i)RT} \quad (65\text{-}3)$$

$$\ln K_p^* = - \frac{1}{RT} \left\{ \sum_k \nu_k [E_k^0 + RT - Ts_k^0] \right\} \quad (65\text{-}4)$$

In these equations the terms enclosed in braces are evaluated for each pure gas k in the mixture, with V, T, and n_k/V having the same values for each pure gas as in the mixture. The summation extends over all gases in the mixture with $\nu_k = 0$ for gases that do not take part in the chemical reaction. The last term in Eq. 65-3 is to be computed for the gas mixture, the sum $(\sum_i n_i)$ being taken for all gases in the mixture. It will be noticed that both K_C and K_p are functions of the composition of the equilibrium mixture as well as of temperature and volume or pressure.

To compute K_C for a given chemical reaction at a given molar volume V and temperature T: (1) Calculate K_C^* for the given temperature and as a first approximation set $K_C = K_C^*$ (the ideal gas relation), from which a provisional set of equilibrium mole fractions can be obtained. (2) These mole fractions are the n_k's which together with V and T permit an approximate evaluation of the right-hand side of Eq. 65-1 and hence a second approximation to K_C and the equilibrium mole fractions. The process can be repeated until no further change in composition results. The convergence of the calculation to the final equilibrium composition is rapid.

To compute K_p for a given pressure p and temperature T from Eq. 65-3 and 65-4, the same method is employed. However, the volume of the mixture must be calculated at each stage of the computation from Eq. 61-2.

C,66. Error of the Gibbs-Dalton Law. The Gibbs-Dalton law requires Dalton's law of the additivity of pressure at constant volume and temperature to hold for a gas mixture. The implications of this as regards the equation of state for mixtures are indicated in Eq. 8-4: the nth virial parameter A_m of the mixture is a homogeneous function of the nth degree in the mole fractions, $A_m = (\sum_i X_i^n A_i)$.

As a result of this the quantity $(\partial p/\partial n_i)_{V,T,n}$ for a gas mixture is found to be equal to $(\partial p_{ck}/\partial n_k)_{V,T}$ for each pure gas measured at the temperature and the concentration of that gas in the mixture, Eq. 59-9. The experimentally determined compressibilities of gases and gas mixtures have not been studied directly with a view to determining how well this condition is obeyed, as has been done for the partial molar volume and molar volume. If we consider that the equation of state (9-12 to 9-14) for gas mixtures gives a satisfactory representation of these derivatives, the error of the Gibbs-Dalton result is, from Eq. 10-9,

$$\left(\frac{\partial p}{\partial n_i}\right)_{V,T,n} - \left(\frac{\partial p_{ck}}{\partial n_k}\right)_{V,T} = [\beta_i(1 - 2X_i) + D_i(\beta) + \beta_m]\frac{(\sum_i n_i)}{V^2}$$
$$+ O\left(\frac{1}{V^3}\right) \quad (i \equiv k = 1, 2, \cdots) \quad (66\text{-}1)$$

The right-hand side of (66-1) may be either positive, zero, or negative.

The general limit method for gas mixtures gives for the ratio of the equilibrium concentration C_{ek} of a gas in a mixture to its concentration C_i in the mixture

$$\ln \frac{C_{ek}}{C_i} = [\beta_i + D_i(\beta) + \beta_m] \frac{C}{RT} - 2\beta_i \frac{C_{ek}}{RT} + O(C^2)$$

$$(i \equiv k = 1, 2, \cdots) \quad (66\text{-}2)$$

where C is the concentration, $(\sum_i n_i)/V$, of the mixture. The Gibbs-Dalton law requires that the right-hand side of this expression be zero.

Up to moderate pressures the equilibrium pressure of a gas in a mixture computed from the Gibbs-Dalton law is too large. Since the Lewis and Randall rule gives too small a value for this quantity in the same pressure range, the true value lies somewhere between those given by these two assumptions for gas mixtures.

C,67. Cited References.

1. Lewis, G. N., and Randall, M. *Thermodynamics*. McGraw-Hill, 1923.
2. Deming, W. E., and Shupe, L. E. *Phys. Rev. 37*, 638 (1931).
3. Sage, B. H., Webster, D. C., and Lacey, W. N. *Ind. Eng. Chem. 00*, 660 (1937).
4. Andrews, T. *Phil. Trans. Roy. Soc. London 159*, 575 (1869).
5. van der Waals, J. D. *Die Continuität der gasförmigen und flüssigen Zustandes*. Barth, Leipzig, 1899–1900.
6. Cope, J. Q., Lewis, W. K., and Weber, H. C. *Ind. Eng. Chem. 23*, 887 (1931).
7. Brown, G. G., Souders, M., Jr., and Smith, R. L. *Ind. Eng. Chem. 24*, 513 (1932).
8. Beattie, J. A., and Stockmayer, W. H. *Repts. Progr. in Phys. 7*, 195 (1940).
9. Lewis, W. K. *Ind. Eng. Chem. 28*, 257 (1936).
10. Su, G. J., and Chang, C. H. *J. Am. Chem. Soc. 68*, 1080 (1946).
11. Su, G. J. *Ind. Eng. Chem. 38*, 803 (1946).
12. Newton, R. H. *Ind. Eng. Chem. 27*, 302 (1935).
13. Kay, W. B. *Ind. Eng. Chem. 28*, 1014 (1936).
14. Onnes, H. K. *Leiden Commun. 71* (1901).
15. Holborn, L. *Ann. Physik (4) 63*, 674 (1920).
16. Holborn, L., and Otto, J. *Z. Physik 33*, 1 (1925).
17. Keyes, F. G. *Temperature*. Reinhold, 1941.
18. Schneider, W. G., and Duffie, J. A. H. *J. Chem. Phys. 17*, 751 (1949).
19. Keyes, F. G., and Sears, F. W. *Proc. Natl. Acad. Sci. U. S. 11*, 38 (1925).
20. Roebuck, J. R., and Murrell, T. A. *Temperature*. Reinhold, 1941.
21. Lennard-Jones, J. E. *Proc. Roy. Soc. London A106*, 463 (1924).
22. Stockmayer, W. H., and Beattie, J. A. *J. Chem. Phys. 7*, 476 (1942).
23. de Boer, J., and Michels, A. *Physica 6*, 97 (1939).
24. Mayer, J. E., and Montroll, E. *J. Chem. Phys. 9*, 626 (1941).
25. Dieterici, C. *Ann. Physik 69*, 685 (1899).
26. Berthelot, D. *Trav. bur. int. poids mes. 13*, 113 (1907).
27. Thomson, J. *Proc. Roy. Soc. London 20*, 1 (1871).
28. Keyes, F. G. *J. Amer. Soc. Refrig. Engrs. 1*, 9 (1914); *Proc. Natl. Acad. Sci. U. S. 3*, 323 (1917).
29. Beattie, J. A., and Bridgeman, O. C. *J. Am. Chem. Soc. 49*, 1665 (1927); *Proc. Amer. Acad. Arts Sci. 63*, 229 (1928).
30. Benedict, M., Webb, G. B., and Rubin, L. C. *J. Chem. Phys. 8*, 334 (1940).
31. Keyes, F. G., Smith, L. B., and Gerry, H. T. *Proc. Amer. Acad. Arts Sci. 70*, 319 (1936).
32. Keyes, F. G. *J. Am. Chem. Soc. 60*, 1761 (1938); *J. Chem. Phys. 17*, 923 (1949).

33. Scatchard, G. *Proc. Natl. Acad. Sci. U. S. 16*, 811 (1930).
34. Beattie, J. A. *Proc. Natl. Acad. Sci. U. S. 16*, 14 (1930).
35. Maron, S. H., and Turnbull, D. *Ind. Eng. Chem. 33*, 408 (1941).
36. Brown, F. W. *Ind. Eng. Chem. 33*, 1536 (1941).
37. Hirschfelder, J. O., and Roseveare, W. E. *J. Phys. Chem. 43*, 15 (1939).
38. Corner, J. *Trans. Faraday Soc. 37*, 358 (1941).
39. Dalton, J. *Nicholson's J. of Natural Phil. 5*, 241 (1801); *Gilbert's Ann. Phys. 12*, 385 (1802); *15*, 1 (1803).
40. Gillespie, L. J. *Phys. Rev. 36*, 121 (1930).
41. Gibbs, J. W. *Scientific Papers*, Vol. I, 155–57. Longmans, Green & Co., 1906.
42. Amagat, E. H. *Ann. chem. phys.* (5) *19*, 384 (1880); *Compt. rend. 127*, 88 (1898).
43. Mayer, J. E. *J. Phys. Chem. 43*, 71 (1939).
44. Fuchs, K. *Proc. Roy. Soc. London A179*, 408 (1941).
45. Lorentz, H. A. *Ann. Physik 12*, 127, 660 (1881).
46. Galitzine, B. *Ann. Physik 41*, 770 (1890).
47. Berthelot, D. *Compt. rend. 126*, 1703, 1857 (1898).
48. Beattie, J. A., Stockmayer, W. H., and Ingersoll, H. G. *J. Chem. Phys. 9*, 871 (1941).
49. Lennard-Jones, J. E., and Cook, W. R. *Proc. Roy. Soc. London A115*, 334 (1927).
50. Beattie, J. A., and Stockmayer, W. H. *J. Chem. Phys. 10*, 473 (1942).
51. Stockmayer, W. H. *J. Chem. Phys. 9*, 863 (1941).
52. Gillespie, L. J. *Chem. Revs. 18*, 359 (1936).
53. Gillespie, L. J. *J. Am. Chem. Soc. 47*, 305 (1925).
54. de Donder, T. *Compt. rend. 180*, 1922 (1925).
55. Beattie, J. A. *Phys. Rev. 36*, 132 (1930).
56. Beattie, J. A. *Chem. Revs. 44*, 141–92 (1949).
57. Woolley, H. W., Scott, R. B., and Brickwedde, F. G. *J. Research Natl. Bur. Standards 41*, 379 (1948).
58. Lewis, G. N., and Randall, M. *Thermodynamics*, 225–227. McGraw-Hill, 1923.
59. Gillespie, L. J. *Proc. Amer. Acad. Arts Sci. 66*, 153 (1930).
60. Gerry, H. T., and Gillespie, L. J. *Phys. Rev. 40*, 269 (1932).
61. Scatchard, G. *Chem. Revs. 8*, 321 (1931).
62. Scatchard, G., and Raymond, C. L. *J. Am. Chem. Soc. 60*, 1278 (1938).
63. Scatchard, G., Wood, S. E., and Mochel, J. M. *J. Am. Chem. Soc. 62*, 712 (1940).
64. Gillespie, L. J., and Beattie, J. A. *Phys. Rev. 36*, 743, 1008 (1930); *37*, 655 (1931); *J. Am. Chem. Soc. 52*, 4239 (1930).
65. Lurie, E., and Gillespie, L. J. *J. Am. Chem. Soc. 49*, 1146 (1927).
66. Randall, M., and Sosnick, B. *J. Am. Chem. Soc. 50*, 967 (1928).
67. Selheimer, C. W., Souders, M., Jr., Smith, L. R., and Brown, G. G. *Ind. Eng. Chem. 24*, 515 (1932).
68. Souders, M., Jr., Selheimer, C. W., and Brown, G. G. *Ind. Eng. Chem. 24*, 517 (1932).
69. Lewis, W. K., and Luke, C. D. *Trans. Am. Soc. Mech. Engrs. 54*, PME-8, 55 (1932); *Ind. Eng. Chem. 25*, 725 (1933).
70. Brown, G. G., and collaborators. *Ind. Eng. Chem. 24*, 515 (1932).
71. Lewis, W. K. *Ind. Eng. Chem. 28*, 257 (1936).
72. Newton, R. H. *Ind. Eng. Chem. 27*, 302 (1935).
73. Newton, R. H., and Dodge, B. F. *J. Am. Chem. Soc. 56*, 1287 (1934).
74. Gillespie, L. J. *J. Am. Chem. Soc. 48*, 28 (1926).
75. Gillespie, L. J. *Phys. Rev. 34*, 352, 1605 (1929).

SECTION D

THE TRANSPORT PROPERTIES OF GASES AND GASEOUS MIXTURES

J. O. HIRSCHFELDER   C. F. CURTISS
R. B. BIRD   E. L. SPOTZ

The macroscopic properties of a system may be related to the properties of the constituent molecules by the methods of statistical mechanics.[1] The application of these methods to the study of the equilibrium properties is well understood, and much success has been obtained in the study of many problems, particularly the interpretation of the thermodynamic properties of various types of systems. The nonequilibrium statistical mechanics is of more recent development and is one of the frontier fields of research today. The special case of dilute gases was investigated about a century ago by Maxwell, Boltzmann, and others, using somewhat special methods. The term "kinetic theory" is customarily associated with these later techniques. In the view of recent work the validity of some of the general results is open to serious question. This is particularly true of the application of the early methods to the solution of problems involving gases in states far removed from equilibrium. Nevertheless the "classical" results as applied to the study of gases in states only slightly removed from equilibrium seem to remain well justified. The detailed numerical results discussed here are based on the early results of Boltzmann, Chapman, Enskog, and others [1,2].

D,1. The Equations of Change. The dynamics of a fluid may be expressed compactly by the equations of change. These equations describe the behavior of the fluid in terms of the diffusion velocity, the pressure tensor, and the heat flux vector. They may be derived by very general statistical mechanical arguments [3], based on the following concepts: The exact dynamical state of the gas may be represented by a point in the multidimensional phase space of the gas. Hence, statistically,

---

[1] A more complete treatment of this subject may be found in *The Molecular Theory of Gases and Liquids*, by J. O. Hirschfelder, C. F. Curtiss, and R. B. Bird; John Wiley & Sons, New York (1954): Chapter 7, Kinetic Theory of Gases; Chapter 8, Calculation of Transport Coefficients of Dilute Gases; Chapter 9, Transport Coefficients of Dense Gases and Liquids; Chapter 10, Quantum Effects in Transport-Phenomena; Chapter 11, Hydrodynamic Applications.

the properties of the gas may be described by means of a distribution of points in this phase space representing an ensemble of systems. The time dependence of the distribution function is described by the Liouville equation. The laws of conservation of mass, momentum, and energy in the collision process then lead to the three equations of change: the equation of continuity, the equation of motion, and the equation of energy balance. For a mixture of gases there is an equation of continuity for each chemical species.

In the derivation of the equations of change certain integrals appear which may be interpreted as representing the rate of transport of energy, momentum, and molecules of a particular species with respect to the average rate of flow of the gas. These are the flux vectors, and the representation in terms of the integrals of the distribution function provides, in principle, an exact method of evaluating the transport coefficients. The problem is reduced to obtaining the distribution function.

Let n_i be the number of moles of species i per cm³ and $\mathfrak{M}_i$ be the molecular weight of i. Then the mass density of the gas is

$$\rho = \sum_i n_i \mathfrak{M}_i \tag{1-1}$$

Let $\mathbf{v}_i$ be the average velocity of molecules of i, defined in such a manner that $n_i \mathbf{v}_i$ is the average flux of component i in moles per cm² sec. with respect to space-fixed coordinates. Then the mass average velocity of the fluid is defined by

$$\mathbf{v}_0 = \frac{1}{\rho} \sum_i n_i \mathfrak{M}_i \mathbf{v}_i \tag{1-2}$$

The velocity $\mathbf{v}_0$ is the macroscopically observed stream velocity. The diffusion velocity of component i is defined as the difference,

$$\mathbf{V}_i = \mathbf{v}_i - \mathbf{v}_0 \tag{1-3}$$

Because of this definition the $\mathbf{V}_i$'s satisfy the relation

$$\sum_i n_i \mathfrak{M}_i \mathbf{V}_i = 0 \tag{1-4}$$

In terms of the diffusion velocity, the molar flux of chemical species i with respect to the mass average velocity is $n_i \mathfrak{M}_i \mathbf{V}_i$.

The basic equations of the fluid mechanics of multicomponent systems are the differential equations of change. We summarize these equations here in their most general form in terms of the flux vectors and including the effects of chemical reactions:

THE EQUATIONS OF CONTINUITY.

$$\frac{\partial n_i}{\partial t} + [\nabla \cdot n_i(\mathbf{v}_0 + \mathbf{V}_i)] = K_i \tag{1-5}$$

Here K_i is the rate of formation of molecules of i due to chemical reactions in moles per cm³ sec. The expressions for the diffusion velocity, $\mathbf{V}_i$, and K_i are discussed later. Because of the conservation of mass,

$$\sum_i \mathfrak{M}_i K_i = 0 \qquad (1\text{-}6)$$

Making use of this relation and Eq. 1-4 we obtain the usual equation of continuity from Eq. 1-5 by multiplying each by $\mathfrak{M}_i$ and summing:

$$\frac{\partial \rho}{\partial t} + (\nabla \cdot \rho \mathbf{v}_0) = 0 \qquad (1\text{-}7)$$

Here ρ is the local density of the gas, defined by Eq. 1-1.

THE EQUATION OF MOTION.

$$\frac{\partial \mathbf{v}_0}{\partial t} + (\mathbf{v}_0 \cdot \nabla \mathbf{v}_0) = -\frac{1}{\rho}(\nabla \cdot \mathbf{p}) + \frac{1}{\rho}\sum_i n_i \mathbf{X}_i \qquad (1\text{-}8)$$

Here $\mathbf{p}$ is the pressure tensor and $\mathbf{X}_i$ is an external force on molecules of species i. The effects of viscosity are included in the expressions for the pressure tensor. The exact form of $\mathbf{p}$ is discussed in Art. 2 (Eq. 2-18).

THE EQUATION OF ENERGY BALANCE.

$$\rho \left[\frac{\partial u}{\partial t} + (\mathbf{v}_0 \cdot \nabla u) \right] = -(\nabla \cdot \mathbf{q}) - (\mathbf{p}:\nabla \mathbf{v}_0) + \sum_i n_i(\mathbf{V}_i \cdot \mathbf{X}_i) \qquad (1\text{-}9)$$

Here, u is the thermodynamic internal energy of the gas per unit mass, and $\mathbf{q}$ is the heat flux, i.e. the flux of energy, discussed in Art. 2 (Eq. 2-21). The quantity u does not include the kinetic energy associated with the macroscopic flow $\mathbf{v}_0$, or the potential energy associated with the external forces $\mathbf{X}_i$.

The equations of change, Eq. 1-7, 1-8, and 1-9, apply over a large range of conditions to all fluids, i.e. liquids and gases. In fact these equations apply under all conditions for which it is meaningful to discuss point properties. That is, whenever one can define a local density, temperature, etc., the equations of change discussed above hold. Exceptions are to be found when there are large differences in the macroscopic properties over distances of the order of a mean free path. This may occur when the gas is exceedingly dilute. Under these conditions, the dimensions of the vessel or an immersed object may be of the order of a mean free path, and it is meaningless to speak of point properties of the macroscopic variables—the gas no longer behaves at all like a continuous medium. Another possible exception is associated with shock-wave phenomena. In passing through a shock wave, the macroscopic properties change abruptly within a few mean free paths, and the usual equations of change, i.e. the concepts of a continuum break down (see III,E,1).

Turbulent motion is another case, often met in engineering practice, in which one might question the applicability of the equations of change. A fluid flowing slowly through a pipe flows laminarly, that is the streamlines are nearly straight and the motion takes place in parallel layers. However, as the rate of flow is increased the flow changes into turbulent flow; small eddies appear, and there is superimposed on the over-all flow a complex pattern of more or less random motions. However, the scale of turbulence is always large compared to the mean free path so that the phenomenon is macroscopic rather than molecular. Thus, the concept of the fluid as a continuous medium is still valid and the ordinary equations of change still apply. In the equations of change, the variables refer to instantaneous values at a point. However, for most practical purposes only the values of these quantities averaged over a time long compared to the period of fluctuations are physically significant. Thus, for turbulent flows the equations of change must be modified by time averaging to obtain relations among the average macroscopic variables (see V,B and C).

While the equations of change have a wide range of applicability, no simple expressions for the irreversibility factors V_i, p, q, and K_i can be given. Irving and Kirkwood [3] in their derivation of the equations of change obtained general integral expressions for these quantities. The expressions involve the usual gaslike terms and the liquidlike terms due to the "collisional" transfers. The gaslike terms are integrals of the "singlet" distribution function $f(r, v, t)$, the distribution function in the phase space of a single molecule. In the limit of low densities this distribution function is obtained as the solution of the Boltzmann equation. If one assumes that the forces between molecules are two-body forces, i.e. that the potential energy is a sum of terms each depending on the coordinates of a pair of molecules, then the liquidlike terms become integrals of the "pair" distribution function. The pair distribution function is the distribution function in the phase space of two molecules. Whereas the liquidlike terms play a dominant role in the theory of transport processes in liquids, they are completely missing from the expressions for a dilute gas.

The Boltzmann equation is an integro-differential equation. An analytical solution is out of the question, but for small gradients a perturbation technique may be used. The application of such a method is suggested by the fact that for states near equilibrium the distribution function at any point in the gas is only slightly different from a Maxwellian distribution. The resulting expression for the distribution function and hence the flux vectors is in terms of the thermodynamic variables n_i, v_0, and T and is linear in the first derivatives of these variables. The corresponding equations of change are the first approximations of Enskog and lead to the Navier-Stokes equations.

Enskog carried out a series of higher approximations leading to expressions involving higher derivatives of thermodynamic quantities. The next approximation leads to the Burnett equations. However, at present there are serious doubts as to the validity of the method. First, there is some doubt as to the convergence of the series. Then there is the question of causality. Is the specification of the density, velocity, and temperature of a gas at all points at a single time sufficient to specify the whole future of the gas? A complete specification requires a knowledge of the entire distribution function at a particular time. The density, velocity, and temperature correspond to the first three moments of the distribution function with respect to velocity. Surely the values of the higher moments must affect the hydrodynamic behavior. However, Grad [5] has shown that under normal conditions an arbitrary distribution function changes very rapidly into one in which the higher moments are specified by values of the first three. Another possible source of error arises from the fact that Enskog's series is based on the older form of Boltzmann's equation rather than on Kirkwood's recent statistical mechanical modification [4]. The difference does not affect Enskog's derivation of the Navier-Stokes equations, but it is important in the higher approximations.

The final result of Enskog's first approximation is a set of expressions for the transport coefficients in terms of a set of integrals, $\Omega^{(l)}(n)$. These integrals involve explicitly the dynamics of a molecular encounter and hence the intermolecular force law. The present incomplete knowledge of the nature of intermolecular forces limits to some extent the applicability of the results to practical problems. On the other hand, the relation between the transport coefficients and intermolecular forces leads indirectly to important information about the nature of these forces.

There are several assumptions which are introduced into the derivation of the integrals for the transport coefficients, and to some extent these affect the usability of the final results. For convenience of reference these assumptions may be summarized as follows:

1. Classical mechanics is employed. For all but the light gases at very low temperatures this restriction is unimportant.

2. Only binary collisions are included. This limits the applicability of the results to pressures not too far removed from atmospheric pressure. Deviations are to be expected when the density becomes sufficiently great so that three-body collisions are frequent.

3. The dimensions of the containing vessel are very large compared to the mean free path. At very low densities, where the molecules collide more frequently with the walls of the containing vessel than with one another, marked deviations in the transport properties are observed. A gas in such a rarefied state is sometimes referred to as a "Knudsen gas."

The method of solving the Boltzmann equation which we shall describe here does not apply to this case. Hence the interesting phenomena associated with very rare gases are not discussed in this section.

4. The gradients of the physical quantities are small. This assumption is introduced by the perturbation technique and is closely related physically to assumption 3 above.

5. Monatomic gases are considered. The treatment is restricted to monatomic gases. However, for diffusion and viscosity the results are generally applicable to any gases composed of molecules which have approximately spherically symmetric potential fields. Pronounced discrepancies between calculated and observed properties can be expected when the molecules in the gas have very unsymmetric force fields. The theoretical results are totally unsatisfactory in the case of thermal conductivity of polyatomic molecules because of the possibility of an exchange of energy between translational and internal motion during an encounter. A discussion of the effect of the internal degrees of freedom is presented in Art. 11.

An awareness of the fact that these assumptions have been made should enable one to estimate better the reliability and applicability of the results calculated on the basis of the theory. Generally speaking, the agreement between the results of this theoretical work and the experimental measurements is highly satisfactory.

D,2.   The Flux Vectors.   In this article we present the kinetic-theory expressions for the flux vectors of a dilute gas. First we discuss the diffusion velocity, associated with flux of mass, which is expressed in terms of the diffusion coefficients. Then the pressure tensor, associated with the flux of momentum, is related to the coefficient of shear viscosity. Finally the heat flux vector is expressed in terms of the thermal conductivity coefficient.

The mutual diffusion in a mixture of gases may be due to gradients in any of the thermodynamic variables. It is convenient to consider the diffusion velocity as the sum of two terms,

$$\mathbf{V}_i = \mathbf{V}_i^{(p)} + \mathbf{V}_i^{(t)} \tag{2-1}$$

$\mathbf{V}_i^{(p)}$, the ordinary diffusion velocity, and $\mathbf{V}_i^{(t)}$, the thermal diffusion velocity. The ordinary diffusion velocity is due to three causes: gradients in the pressure, gradients in the concentration, and external forces. The diffusion velocity represents a mean velocity of molecules of species i with respect to a mass average rate of flow of all molecules. The ordinary diffusion velocity may be written in the form

$$\mathbf{V}_i^{(p)} = \frac{n^2}{n_i \rho} \sum_{j \neq i} \mathfrak{M}_j D_{ij} \mathbf{d}_j \tag{2-2}$$

in which the D_{ij} are the multicomponent diffusion coefficients (not to be confused with the binary diffusion coefficients $\mathfrak{D}_{ij}$), and the diagonal elements D_{ii} are identically zero. The $\mathbf{d}_j$ are the vectors representing the gradients:

$$\mathbf{d}_j = \nabla\left(\frac{n_j}{n}\right) + \left[\left(\frac{n_j}{n}\right) - \left(\frac{n_j\mathfrak{M}_j}{\rho}\right)\right] \nabla \ln p$$

$$- \frac{n_j\mathfrak{M}_j}{\rho p}\left(\frac{\rho}{\mathfrak{M}_j}\mathbf{X}_j - \sum_k n_k\mathbf{X}_k\right) \quad (2\text{-}3)$$

In the case of a binary mixture, the D_{ij} are nearly independent of the composition. In the case of more complicated mixtures, the D_{ij} depend, in general, upon the entire composition of the mixture. The thermal diffusion velocity may be written in the form

$$\mathbf{V}_i^{(t)} = -\frac{1}{n_i\mathfrak{M}_i}\alpha_i\nabla \ln T \quad (2\text{-}4)$$

where the α_i are the thermal diffusion constants of the mixture.

In the case of two components we have

$$\mathbf{V}_1 = \frac{n^2}{n_1\rho}\mathfrak{M}_2\mathfrak{D}_{12}\mathbf{d}_2 - \frac{1}{n_1\mathfrak{M}_1}\alpha_1\nabla \ln T \quad (2\text{-}5)$$

The values of the D_{ij} for a binary mixture are denoted $\mathfrak{D}_{ij}$ for later convenience. Then since $\mathbf{d}_1 = -\mathbf{d}_2$, and using Eq. 1-4,

$$\mathfrak{D}_{12} = \mathfrak{D}_{21} \quad (2\text{-}6)$$

and

$$\alpha_1 = -\alpha_2 \quad (2\text{-}7)$$

The difference in the diffusion velocities for the two species is

$$\mathbf{V}_1 - \mathbf{V}_2 = -\frac{n^2}{n_1 n_2}\mathfrak{D}_{12}(\mathbf{d}_1 + k_T\nabla \ln T) \quad (2\text{-}8)$$

where the quantity,

$$k_T = \frac{\alpha_1\rho}{n^2\mathfrak{M}_1\mathfrak{M}_2\mathfrak{D}_{12}} \quad (2\text{-}9)$$

is termed the thermal diffusion ratio. In the case of a multicomponent mixture, it is possible to generalize the relation (2-8) to obtain a useful set of relations[2]

$$\sum_j \frac{n_i n_j}{n^2\mathfrak{D}_{ij}}(\mathbf{V}_j - \mathbf{V}_i) = \mathbf{d}_i - \nabla \ln T \sum_j \frac{(n_i\mathfrak{M}_i\alpha_j - n_j\mathfrak{M}_j\alpha_i)}{n^2\mathfrak{M}_i\mathfrak{M}_j\mathfrak{D}_{ij}} \quad (2\text{-}10)$$

[2] The $\mathfrak{D}_{ij}$ in these equations are binary diffusion coefficients at the temperature and *over-all* density of the system.

Let us consider the diffusion of a nonreacting gas mixture under conditions such that the pressure and temperature are independent of space and time. Adding together the equations of continuity, Eq. 1-5, for all of the chemical species i, and making use of the fact that $n = \sum_i n_i$ is constant, it follows that

$$(\nabla \cdot n\omega) = 0 \qquad (2\text{-}11)$$

where

$$\omega = \frac{1}{n} \sum_i n_i(\mathbf{v}_0 + \mathbf{V}_i) \qquad (2\text{-}12)$$

is a new kind of average velocity—the molar average. In the one-dimensional case, Eq. 2-11 implies that ω is a function of time only and is independent of the position coordinate. In the general three-dimensional case it is usually reasonable to assume that ω is irrotational, i.e. that the curl of ω is zero. When this assumption is made, Eq. 2-11 implies that ω is a function of time only. From Eq. 2-12 it follows that the mass average velocity is

$$\mathbf{v}_0 = \omega - \sum_i{}' \frac{n_i}{n} \mathbf{V}_i \qquad (2\text{-}13)$$

Eq. 2-13 may be used to eliminate $\mathbf{v}_0$ from one of the equations of continuity,

$$\frac{\partial n_i}{\partial t} + \left\{ \nabla \cdot n_i \left[\omega + \sum_j \left(\delta_{ij} - \frac{n_j}{n} \right) \mathbf{V}_j \right] \right\} = 0 \qquad (2\text{-}14)$$

Then making use of Eq. 2-2 for the diffusion velocity (since T is constant, the thermal diffusion velocity is zero), it follows that:

$$\frac{\partial n_i}{\partial t} = - \left\{ \nabla \cdot \sum_k \left[\sum_j \left(\delta_{ij} - \frac{n_j}{n} \right) \frac{n n_i}{n_j \rho} \mathfrak{M}_k \mathfrak{D}_{jk} \right] \nabla n_k \right\} - (\omega \cdot \nabla n_i) \qquad (2\text{-}15)$$

Eq. 2-15 is a generalization of the well-known Fick law. In the special case of two components, it reduces to

$$\frac{\partial n_1}{\partial t} = (\nabla \cdot \mathfrak{D}_{12} \nabla n_1) - (\omega \cdot \nabla n_1) \qquad (2\text{-}16)$$

This equation applies to any nonreacting binary mixture under conditions of constant temperature and pressure. For a dilute gas system in a closed, stationary container, the molar average velocity $\omega(t)$ is identically zero, and one obtains the more usual form of Fick's law,

$$\frac{\partial n_1}{\partial t} = (\nabla \cdot \mathfrak{D}_{12} \nabla n_1) \qquad (2\text{-}17)$$

However, it should be mentioned that there are many practical cases such as problems involving evaporation in which ω is not zero and the more general form of Fick's law is required.

The pressure tensor for a dilute gas in which the velocity gradients are not too large can be written in the form

$$\mathbf{p} = p\mathbf{1} - \mu[\nabla \mathbf{v}_0 + (\nabla \mathbf{v}_0)^\dagger - \tfrac{2}{3}(\nabla \cdot \mathbf{v}_0)\mathbf{1}] \qquad (2\text{-}18)$$

where p is the usual static pressure, $\mathbf{1}$ is the unit tensor, and the $\dagger$ indicates the transpose tensor obtained by interchanging rows and columns. From Eq. 2-18 it follows that a typical diagonal element of the pressure tensor is

$$p_{xx} = p - \frac{2\mu}{3}\left(2\frac{\partial v_{0x}}{\partial x} - \frac{\partial v_{0y}}{\partial y} - \frac{\partial v_{0z}}{\partial z}\right) \qquad (2\text{-}19)$$

and a typical nondiagonal element is

$$p_{xy} = -\mu\left(\frac{\partial v_{0y}}{\partial x} + \frac{\partial v_{0x}}{\partial y}\right) \qquad (2\text{-}20)$$

The coefficient of viscosity μ is a function of temperature and depends upon the nature of the gas or gas mixture.

The heat flux vector $\mathbf{q}$ for a dilute gas may be written in the form

$$\mathbf{q} = -\lambda\nabla T + \sum_{i} n_i H_i \mathbf{V}_i - \frac{kT}{n}\sum_{i,k}\frac{n_k}{\mathfrak{M}_i\mathfrak{D}_{ik}}\alpha_i(\mathbf{V}_k - \mathbf{V}_i) \qquad (2\text{-}21)$$

in which H_i is the enthalpy per mole of species i. Here the first term is the heat transferred by thermal conductivity and λ is the thermal conductivity coefficient. The second term represents the flux of energy due to diffusion processes. The third term, which is small, depends upon the coefficients of thermal diffusion.

The term K_i, which appears in the equation of continuity, is the rate of production of species i by chemical reaction. The function K_i can usually be taken as the reaction rate which would prevail in a static reaction vessel under the same local conditions of temperature, pressure, and composition.[3] It is always possible to represent the kinetics of a reacting mixture in terms of a set of stoichiometric equations of the form

$$\beta_{1j}[1] + \beta_{2j}[2] + \cdots \rightleftarrows \eta_{1j}[1] + \eta_{2j}[2] + \cdots \qquad (2\text{-}22)$$

the β_{ij} and η_{ij} being integers and $[i]$ indicating the chemical formula for the ith species. Denoting the rate constant for the forward reaction by k_j and the constant for the backward reaction by k_j', the rate of the forward reaction is

$$k_j n_1^{\beta_{1j}} n_2^{\beta_{2j}} \cdots \qquad (2\text{-}23)$$

[3] In flames, the rapid flow through regions of large temperature gradients and the excited states of the molecules produced in various stages of the reaction chain may result in modifications of the function K_i.

and similarly the backward reaction is

$$k'_j n_1^{\eta_{1j}} n_2^{\eta_{2j}} \cdots \tag{2-24}$$

Here the k_j and k'_j are functions only of the temperature. Then the total rate of formation of molecules of i by chemical reaction is

$$K_i = \sum_j (\eta_{ij} - \beta_{ij})(k_j n_1^{\beta_{1j}} n_2^{\beta_{2j}} \cdots - k' n_1^{\eta_{1j}} n_2^{\eta_{2j}} \cdots) \tag{2-25}$$

D,3. The Collision Cross Sections. The expressions for the transport coefficients obtained by Enskog's first approximation are given in terms of a set of integrals, $\Omega_{ij}^{(l)}(n)$. These integrals depend on the potential of interaction between a pair of molecules, and, for a multicomponent mixture, integrals appear involving the law of force between all pairs of molecules. The integral depending on the dynamics of a collision between a molecule of type i and one of type j may be written as

$$\Omega_{ij}^{(l)}(n) = \sqrt{\pi} \int_0^\infty e^{-\frac{m_{ij} g_{ij}^2}{2kT}} \left(\frac{m_{ij} g_{ij}^2}{2kT}\right)^{\frac{2n+3}{2}} \phi^{(l)}(g_{ij}) dg_{ij} \tag{3-1}$$

where the function $\phi^{(l)}(g_{ij})$ is[4]

$$\phi^{(l)}(g_{ij}) = \int_0^\infty [1 - \cos^l \chi(g_{ij}, b)] b \, db \tag{3-2}$$

In these formulas m_{ij} is the reduced mass of the two colliding molecules:

$$\frac{1}{m_{ij}} = \frac{1}{m_i} + \frac{1}{m_j} \tag{3-3}$$

g_{ij} is the relative speed of molecules i and j before a collision, b is the so-called collision parameter or impact parameter, and $\chi(g_{ij}, b)$ is the angle of deflection for a collision characterized by the values of g_{ij} and b. The quantity b is shown in Fig. D,3.

The expressions for the transport coefficients in terms of the collision integrals are described below. However, to make actual calculations of viscosity, thermal conductivity, and diffusion coefficients, one must first introduce into the $\Omega^{(l)}(n)$ integrals an explicit expression for the potential energy of interaction between two molecules. A brief review is given of the various calculations which have been made of the $\Omega^{(l)}(n)$ integrals. Then calculations of the transport properties based on the Lennard-Jones potential are described. Specific formulas are given and the applicability and reliability of the calculations made with these formulas are discussed. The determination of the parameters (force constants) in the Lennard-Jones potential from the experimental data for viscosity and

---

[4] This definition of $\phi^{(l)}$ differs from that given in [1, p. 157] by a factor of g_{ij}.

diffusion are illustrated. Numerical values for these parameters are provided for most of the common gases. The intermolecular fields thus determined are compared with those obtained from measurements of other physical properties.

In the simplified kinetic theory, the cross section πr_0^2 of the rigid spherical molecules of diameter r_0 occurs in all of the expressions for the transport coefficients. This quantity enters into the treatment because as one molecule moves through the gas, a cylinder of cross section πr_0^2 can be constructed such that any other molecule whose center lies within this cylinder will be hit. The cross section is thus a measure of the target area as seen by an oncoming molecule. Now the integrals $\phi^{(l)}(g_{ij})$ have the dimensions of area, and a posteriori may be associated with the concept of cross section. That they are functions of the initial relative velocity is quite logical, for in an encounter where the molecules come together slowly, they will effectively see a larger potential field (target area) than in the case where the relative velocity is large. To some extent, then, the $\phi^{(l)}(g_{ij})$ are a measure of the effective range of the potential function.

Before the development of modern kinetic theory, experimental transport measurements were used along with simple kinetic theory formulas to calculate molecular diameters and hence cross sections. It was observed that the cross section for viscosity measurements was larger than that for diffusion measurements. Thus it is gratifying to find that in the elaborate kinetic theory several different cross sections (corresponding to various values of the index l) appear quite naturally by virtue of a more exact consideration of the collision processes involved.

The functions $\sqrt{m_{ij}kT}\ \Omega_{ij}^{(l)}(n)$ also have dimensions of a cross section and correspond to a weighted average of $\phi^{(l)}(g_{ij})$ over the relative initial velocity g_{ij}. The weighting factor depends primarily upon the temperature T through the Boltzmann factor $e^{-m_{ij}g_{ij}^2/2kT}$. Consequently, at low temperatures, low energy collisions, i.e. small g_{ij}, are weighted heavily, while at high temperatures the high energy collisions are emphasized. In the expression for the transport properties derived using the rigorous kinetic theory, there always appears a $\sqrt{m_{ij}/kT}\ \Omega_{ij}^{(l)}(n)$ where there was previously a $\pi(r_0)_{ij}^2$ in a simple kinetic theory.

It can easily be shown [6] by simple dynamic arguments that the dependence of the angle of deflection χ on the relative velocity of approach g_{ij} and the impact parameter b is related to the intermolecular potential function $E(r_{ij})$ in the following manner:

$$\chi(g_{ij}, b) = \pi - 2b \int_{(r_{ij})_m}^{\infty} \frac{dr_{ij}/r_{ij}^2}{\sqrt{1 - \dfrac{b^2}{r_{ij}^2} - \dfrac{2E(r_{ij})}{m_{ij}g_{ij}^2}}} \tag{3-4}$$

Here $(r_{ij})_m$ is the distance between the two particles at the point of closest approach (see Fig. D,3). The form of this relation is such that if the potential energy of the interacting systems can be written as

$$E(r_{ij}) = \epsilon_{ij} f\left(\frac{r_{ij}}{(r_0)_{ij}}\right) \tag{3-5}$$

where ϵ_{ij} and $(r_0)_{ij}$ are characteristic parameters depending on the particular interacting pair and f is a universal function, then χ can be obtained as a general function of certain reduced parameters. The

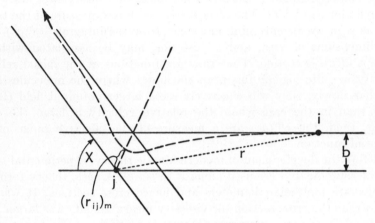

[Fig. D,3. Angle of deflection χ.

dimensionless parameters are (1) a parameter representing the relative kinetic energy involved in the collision,

$$K_{ij} = \frac{1}{2} m_{ij} \frac{g_{ij}^2}{\epsilon_{ij}} \tag{3-6}$$

and (2) a parameter measuring the impact parameter in units of the characteristic length $(r_0)_{ij}$,

$$\beta = \frac{b}{(r_0)_{ij}} \tag{3-7}$$

In terms of these quantities and a dimensionless separation,

$$r_{ij}^* = \frac{r_{ij}}{(r_0)_{ij}} \tag{3-8}$$

the angle of deflection may be written as

$$\chi(K_{ij}, \beta) = \pi - 2\beta \int_{(r_{ij})_m}^{\infty} \frac{dr_{ij}^*/r_{ij}^{*2}}{\sqrt{1 - \frac{\beta^2}{r_{ij}^{*2}} - \frac{f(r_{ij}^*)}{K_{ij}}}} \tag{3-9}$$

where $(r_{ij}^*)_m$ is the distance of closest approach in units of $(r_0)_{ij}$. Since most of the potential functions which we will consider here are of the form indicated by Eq. 3-5, we will henceforth employ these reduced variables. An important result of this dependence of χ on K and β is the fact that the $\Omega_{ij}^{(l)}(n)$ integrals become universal functions of the reduced temperature $\tau_{ij} = kT/\epsilon_{ij}$ and the collision diameter $(r_0)_{ij}$, the nature of the universal function depending only on the shape of the potential function f. This is analogous to and is an extension of the ordinary law of corresponding state as applied to the equation of state of gases.

Since calculations of transport properties can be made easily for rigid spheres, and because of the simple physical interpretation of the results, it seems convenient to "reduce" the ϕ and Ω functions by dividing them by their corresponding rigid sphere values:[5]

$$S^{(l)}(K_{ij}) = \frac{\phi^{(l)}(g_{ij})}{[\phi^{(l)}(g_{ij})]_{\text{rig. sph.}}} = \frac{\phi^{(l)}(g_{ij})}{\frac{1}{4}\left[2 - \frac{1 + (-1)^l}{1 + l}\right](r_0)_{ij}^2} \tag{3-10}$$

$$= \frac{4\int_0^\infty [1 - \cos^l \chi]\beta d\beta}{\left[2 - \frac{[1 + (-1)^l]}{1 + l}\right]}$$

$$Y(l, n; \tau_{ij}) = \frac{\Omega_{ij}^{(l)}(n)}{[\Omega_{ij}^{(l)}(n)]_{\text{rig. sph.}}}$$

$$= \frac{\Omega_{ij}^{(l)}(n)}{\sqrt{\pi}\,\frac{(n+1)!}{8}\left[2 - \frac{1 + (-1)^l}{1 + l}\right]\sqrt{\frac{2kT}{m_{ij}}}(r_0)_{ij}^2} \tag{3-11}$$

$$= \frac{\tau_{ij}^{-(n+2)}}{(n+1)!}\int_0^\infty e^{-K_{ij}/\tau_{ij}}S^{(l)}(K_{ij})K_{ij}^{(n+1)}dK_{ij}$$

The "reduced collision cross section" $S^{(l)}(K_{ij})$ and the "average reduced collision of cross section" $Y(l, n; \tau_{ij})$ are thus expressed as integrals over the reduced variables K_{ij} and β. These functions have the physical significance that they indicate the deviation of any arbitrary molecular model from the idealized rigid sphere model. Hence the $\pi(r_0)_{ij}^2$ of simple kinetic theory is replaced, in the first approximation by $\pi(r_0)_{ij}^2 Y(l, n; \tau_{ij})$, the particular values of l and n depending upon the transport property under consideration:

$$\begin{bmatrix} \text{First approximation to coef-} \\ \text{ficient of viscosity for a pure} \\ \text{gas } i \end{bmatrix} = [\mu_i]_1 = \frac{\frac{5}{16}\sqrt{m_i kT/\pi}}{(r_0)_i^2 Y(2, 2; \tau_i)} \tag{3-12}$$

[5] Here we make use of a result in Art. 4: the value of $\phi^{(l)}(g_{ij})$ for rigid spheres (see Eq. 4-7).

$$\begin{bmatrix} \text{First approximation to coef-} \\ \text{ficient of thermal conductivity} \\ \text{for pure } i \end{bmatrix} = [\lambda_i]_1 = \frac{[C_v + \frac{9}{4}R][\mu_i]_1}{\mathfrak{M}_i} \tag{3-13}$$

$$\begin{bmatrix} \text{First approximation to coef-} \\ \text{ficient of diffusion in a binary} \\ \text{mixture of gases } i \text{ and } j \end{bmatrix} = [\mathfrak{D}_{ij}]_1 = \frac{\frac{3}{16}\sqrt{2k^3T^3/\pi m_{ij}}}{p(r_0)_{ij}^2 Y(1,1;\tau_{ij})} \tag{3-14}$$

In higher approximations, other $Y(l, n; \tau_{ij})$ enter into the formulas in complex combinations, there being no parallel to this in the simplified kinetic theory. This emphasizes the fact that it is rather artificial to think of the S and Y functions as cross sections. While simple kinetic theory is built upon the concepts of the cross section and mean free path, these ideas are not used explicitly in the more rigorous development.

Certain combinations of the collision integrals appear frequently in the formulas for the higher approximation to the transport coefficients. These quantities are defined as follows:

$$A(\tau_{ij}) = \frac{2Y(2,2;\tau_{ij})}{5Y(1,1;\tau_{ij})} \tag{3-15}$$

$$B(\tau_{ij}) = \frac{15Y(1,2;\tau_{ij}) - 12Y(1,3;\tau_{ij})}{5Y(1,1;\tau_{ij})} \tag{3-16}$$

$$C(\tau_{ij}) = \frac{6Y(1,2;\tau_{ij})}{5Y(1,1;\tau_{ij})} \tag{3-17}$$

In addition, there are two other quantities, $\mathfrak{g}$ and $\mathfrak{K}$, which serve as correction factors for viscosity and thermal conductivity, respectively, of pure components. The expressions for these quantities in terms of the $Y(l, n; \tau)$ are quite lengthy and are given elsewhere [1,9d]. The quantities $\mathfrak{g}$ and $\mathfrak{K}$ are discussed further below in connection with Eq. 6-1 and 10-1.

D,4. Evaluation of the Reduced Average Collision Cross Sections for Several Simple Potentials. In addition to the assumptions outlined in Art. 1, the results of Art. 3 are restricted by the assumption that the general form of the interaction potential is of the form indicated in Eq. 3-5. To make further application of the theory, it is necessary to assume an explicit force law for the molecular interaction. The five models used here, which are shown in Fig. D,4, are as follows:

Rigid elastic spheres. This is the simplest molecular model and gives the transport properties in a simple analytic form. It is a convenient starting point for making calculations in the rigorous kinetic theory.

Point centers of repulsion. This model, which accounts only for the strong repulsive forces between molecules, allows a reasonably easy numerical calculation of the collision integrals. The transport properties may then be expressed as constants multiplied by adjustable powers of the temperature.

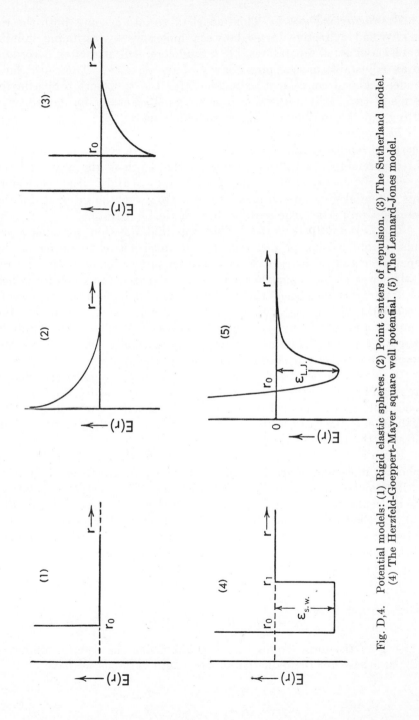

Fig. D,4. Potential models: (1) Rigid elastic spheres. (2) Point centers of repulsion. (3) The Sutherland model. (4) The Herzfeld-Goeppert-Mayer square well potential. (5) The Lennard-Jones model.

The Sutherland model. This model takes into account both the repulsive and attractive forces between molecules by assuming infinite repulsion at small separations, i.e. a rigid core, and attraction according to an adjustable inverse power law at large distances. The Sutherland model leads to convenient expressions for the transport properties in terms of two easily adjustable parameters. Because of its flexibility in fitting experimental data, it has been widely used.

The square well potential. This model takes into account both the energy of repulsion and the energy of attraction in collisions. It involves three parameters: a collision diameter, the depth of the well, and the range of the energy of attraction. For second and third virial coefficients this potential gives analytic expressions. However, the integrals for the transport properties require difficult numerical integrations.

The Lennard-Jones model. This potential function contains a repulsive contribution proportional to the inverse twelfth power of the separation and an attractive contribution proportional to the inverse sixth power of the separation. Of all the potential functions for which the Ω integrals have been evaluated, the Lennard-Jones model represents most faithfully the true interaction for molecules which are reasonably nonpolar and spherically symmetric. For those molecules which definitely cannot be included in this category, it is generally better to use the simpler models for purposes of empirical interpolation.

In this article, the results for the first four of these molecular models are summarized. In the subsequent articles, we present for the Lennard-Jones potential a detailed discussion of the dynamics of collisions, the evaluation of the reduced collision cross sections, and the practical calculation of the transport properties.

RIGID ELASTIC SPHERES. Let us consider impenetrable nonattracting spherical molecules of species i with diameter $(r_0)_i$ and those of species j with diameter $(r_0)_j$. Accordingly the distance r_{ij} between the centers of the molecules can never be less than $(r_0)_{ij} = \frac{1}{2}[(r_0)_i + (r_0)_j]$. The quantity $(r_0)_{ij}$ is called the collision diameter of the system. For gases consisting of but one component i, the collision diameter is just equal to the diameter of the molecule, $(r_0)_{ii} = (r_0)_i$. In collisions between molecules i and j the potential energy in terms of the collision diameter is:

$$\begin{aligned} E(r_{ij}) &= \infty, & r_{ij} &\leqq (r_0)_{ij} \\ E(r_{ij}) &= 0, & r_{ij} &> (r_0)_{ij} \end{aligned} \tag{4-1}$$

which is of the form required by Eq. 3-5. Using the collision diameter $(r_0)_{ij}$ as a basis for the reduction of the length variable, we have

$$\begin{aligned} E(r_{ij}) &= f(r_{ij}^*) = \infty, & r_{ij}^* &\leqq 1 \\ E(r_{ij}) &= f(r_{ij}^*) = 0, & r_{ij}^* &> 1 \end{aligned} \tag{4-2}$$

The distance of closest approach for two colliding molecules, $(r_{ij}^*)_m$, is 1 if $\beta \leq 1$ and is β if $\beta > 1$. Hence the insertion of Eq. 4-2 into the expression for $\chi(K_{ij}, \beta)$ given in Eq. 3-9 gives immediately for $\beta \leq 1$

$$\chi(K_{ij}, \beta) = \pi - 2\beta \int_1^\infty \frac{dr_{ij}^*/r_{ij}^*}{\sqrt{r_{ij}^{*2} - \beta^2}}$$

$$= \pi - 2\beta \left[\frac{1}{\beta} \cos^{-1} \left(\beta/r_{ij}^* \right) \right]_1^\infty = 2 \cos^{-1} \beta \quad (4\text{-}3)$$

or

$$\cos \chi = 2\beta^2 - 1 \quad (4\text{-}4)$$

And for $\beta > 1$,

$$\chi = \pi - 2\beta \int_\beta^\infty \frac{dr_{ij}^*/r_{ij}^*}{\sqrt{r_{ij}^{*2} - \beta^2}} = 0 \quad (4\text{-}5)$$

These last two results (Eq. 4-4 and 4-5) may be verified easily by simple geometrical considerations. That the angle of deflection for this model is independent of the initial relative kinetic energy K_{ij} is indeed what one would expect for the collisions of perfectly impenetrable "billiard balls."

The reduced collision cross sections $S^{(l)}(K_{ij})$ may be obtained by substituting Eq. 4-4 and 4-5 into Eq. 3-10

$$S^{(l)}(K_{ij}) = \frac{4}{\left[2 - \dfrac{1 + (-1)^l}{1 + l} \right]} \int_0^1 [1 - (2\beta^2 - 1)^l]\beta d\beta = 1 \quad (4\text{-}6)$$

the integral from $\beta = 1$ to $\beta = \infty$ not contributing because for this range of β, $(1 - \cos^l \chi)$ is zero. The $S^{(l)}(K_{ij})$ are unity because of the definition of these quantities in Eq. 3-10; however, Eq. 4-6 shows the origin of the factor

$$\frac{4}{\left[2 - \dfrac{1 + (-1)^l}{1 + l} \right]}$$

The average reduced collision cross sections $Y(l, n; \tau_{ij})$ have also been defined to be unity for rigid spheres; hence

$$Y(l, n; \tau_{ij}) = \frac{1}{(n + 1)!} \tau_{ij}^{-(n+2)} \int_0^\infty e^{-K_{ij}/\tau_{ij}} K_{ij}^{n+1} dK_{ij} = 1 \quad (4\text{-}7)$$

Setting the Y integrals equal to unity in Eq. 3-12, 3-13, and 3-14, we then get for rigid nonattracting spheres,

$$\begin{bmatrix} \text{First approximation to} \\ \text{coefficient of viscosity for} \\ \text{a pure gas } i \end{bmatrix} = [\mu_i]_1^{\text{rig.sph.}} = \frac{\dfrac{5}{16} \sqrt{\dfrac{m_i kT}{\pi}}}{(r_0)_i^2} \quad (4\text{-}8)$$

$$\begin{bmatrix} \text{First approximation to} \\ \text{coefficient of thermal con-} \\ \text{ductivity for a pure gas } i \end{bmatrix} = [\lambda_i]_1^{\text{rig.sph.}} = \left[\frac{15}{4} R\right] \frac{[\mu_i]_0}{\mathfrak{M}_i} \qquad (4\text{-}9)$$

$$\begin{bmatrix} \text{First approximation to} \\ \text{coefficient of diffusion for} \\ \text{mixture of } i \text{ and } j \end{bmatrix} = [\mathfrak{D}_{ij}]_1^{\text{rig.sph.}} = \frac{3\sqrt{2k^3T^3/\pi m_{ij}}}{16p(r_0)_{ij}^2} \qquad (4\text{-}10)$$

It is seen that for rigid spherical molecules the dependence of the transport coefficients upon temperature, pressure, mass of the molecules, and the collision diameter is the same as obtained in simple kinetic theory; the results differ from any simple treatment only in the constant factors which appear in the expressions. The expression for the thermal conductivity does *not* include the Eucken correction for internal degrees of freedom; this correction is discussed in Art. 11.

POINT CENTERS OF REPULSIVE FORCES. At very high temperatures where repulsive forces are large in comparison with attractive forces, molecules have been considered as point centers with a potential energy of repulsion given by

$$E(r_{ij}) = a_{ij}r_{ij}^{-\nu_{ii}} \qquad (4\text{-}11)$$

Here ν_{ij} gives an indication of the hardness or softness of the molecules. Small values of ν_{ij}, e.g. 5, correspond to soft molecules, while large values of ν_{ij}, e.g. 16, correspond to hard molecules. In the limit as ν_{ij} goes to infinity, this model becomes identical with the rigid sphere model. The formula for the $Y(l, n; \tau_{ij})$, obtained by substituting this potential function into the expression for the angle of deflection and the reduced collision cross section, is

$$Y(l, n; \tau_{ij}) = \frac{4(\nu_{ij})^{2/\nu_{ij}}\Gamma\left(n + 2 - \dfrac{2}{\nu_{ij}}\right) A_l(\nu_{ij})}{(n+1)!\left[2 - \dfrac{1 + (-1)^l}{1 + l}\right](2\tau_{ij})^{2/\nu_{ij}}} \qquad (4\text{-}12)$$

where

$$A_l(\nu_{ij}) = \int_0^\infty (1 - \cos^l \chi)\beta d\beta \qquad (4\text{-}13)$$

The $A_l(\nu_{ij})$, which depend only on l and ν_{ij}, must be evaluated numerically. The transport properties then have the following dependence upon temperature and pressure

$$[\mu_i]_1 \sim T^{s_{ii}}, \qquad [\lambda_i]_1 \sim T^{s_{ii}}, \qquad [\mathfrak{D}_{ij}]_1 \sim T^{s_{ij}+1}p^{-1} \qquad (4\text{-}14)$$

where the temperature index s_{ij} is

$$s_{ij} = \frac{1}{2} + \frac{2}{\nu_{ij}} \qquad (4\text{-}15)$$

Two special cases of this type of interaction deserve mention. Molecules which obey a repulsion law with $\nu_{ij} = 4$ are referred to as Maxwellian molecules. It is interesting that Maxwell, long before the time of Enskog and Chapman, realized that it is possible to develop the rigorous kinetic theory for such molecules without actually solving the integral equation which determines the Boltzmann function. Maxwellian molecules, though very satisfactory from the standpoint of mathematical development, are physically highly unreal—so bad, indeed, that Maxwellian molecules do not show the phenomenon of thermal diffusion.

The Coulomb law of interaction is also a special case, where $\nu_{ij} = 1$. Here the angle of deflection can be found analytically but the integrals for the S functions do not converge. The physical explanation for this mathematical difficulty is that the force field falls off so slowly that it is difficult to define a binary encounter. Although this problem can be solved satisfactorily, it is not discussed here.[6]

THE SUTHERLAND MODEL.[7] The potential function for this model embodies both the idea of strong, short range repulsive forces and long range attractive forces. It is assumed that molecules attract one another according to an inverse power law but that the centers of the molecules can never come closer than a distance equal to the collision diameter $(r_0)_{ij}$. Hence the potential function is written

$$E(r_{ij}) = \infty, \qquad r_{ij} \leqq (r_0)_{ij} \qquad (4\text{-}16)$$

$$E(r_{ij}) = -a'_{ij}r_{ij}^{-\nu'_{ij}}, \qquad r_{ij} > (r_0)_{ij} \qquad (4\text{-}17)$$

where a'_{ij} and ν'_{ij} are constants which serve to describe the interaction between a molecule of the ith species and one of the jth. For a gas at high temperatures, where the majority of collisions involve large relative kinetic energies, the colliding systems will scarcely "see" the attractive portion of the potential and the various properties of the gas become rigid sphere properties in the limit as T goes to ∞.

Accordingly the average reduced cross sections $Y(l, n; \tau_{ij})$ for the Sutherland model are unity plus a correction factor which becomes smaller as the temperature increases. For moderately high temperatures where the effect of the attractive part of the potential is small,

$$Y(l, n; \tau_{ij}) = 1 + \frac{C(l, \nu'_{ij})}{T} \qquad (4\text{-}18)$$

The Sutherland constant C depends upon the value of l and the index of attraction ν'_{ij}. Its value may be calculated in the usual manner by getting the cross section from the dynamics of an individual encounter. How-

[6] For a discussion of this topic see [1, p. 177].

[7] For a more detailed treatment of this subject see [1, p. 182]; extensive numerical work has been done by Kotani, M. *Proc. Physico-Math. Soc. Japan* 24, 76 (1942).

ever, numerical values of $C(l, \nu'_{ij})$ are usually obtained by curve-fitting viscosity data for $l = 2$, and diffusion data for $l = 1$.

The transport coefficients for the Sutherland model are

$$[\mu_i]_1^{\text{Suth}} = \frac{[\mu_i]_1^{\text{rig.sph.}}}{1 + \dfrac{C(2, \nu'_i)}{T}} \tag{4-19}$$

$$[\mathfrak{D}_{ij}]_1^{\text{Suth}} = \frac{[\mathfrak{D}_{ij}]_1^{\text{rig.sph.}}}{1 + \dfrac{C(1, \nu'_{ij})}{T}} \tag{4-20}$$

Equations such as Eq. 4-19 and 4-20 are frequently convenient for interpolating experimental data but cannot be recommended for extrapolation beyond the range of the experimental data.

THE SQUARE WELL POTENTIAL. The square well potential is characterized by the behavior:

$$
\begin{aligned}
E(r) &= \infty, & r &< r_0 \\
E(r) &= -\epsilon, & r_0 &< r < r_1 \\
E(r) &= 0, & r_1 &< r
\end{aligned}
\tag{4-21}
$$

Holleran and Hulburt [7] have evaluated the collision integrals for this potential by numerical methods to obtain the results shown in Table D,4a. The transport properties can then be obtained by the use of Eq. 3-12, 3-13, and 3-14. Using the parameters listed in Table D,4b and

Table D,4a. The $Y(l, n)$ for the square well model.

$\tau = kT/\epsilon$		∞	5.000	2.500	1.667	1.250	1.000	0.833	0.500
$1/\tau$		0	0.200	0.400	0.600	0.800	1.000	1.200	2.000
r_0/r_1	l, n								
0.4	1, 1	1.0000	1.1513	1.3388	1.5263	1.7038	1.8713	2.0300	2.5638
	1, 2	1.0000	1.0925	1.2113	1.3421	1.4725	1.5996	1.7233	2.1804
	1, 3	1.0000	1.0654	1.1483	1.2431	1.3429	1.4418	1.5396	1.9183
	2, 2	1.0000	1.1833	1.4333	1.7100	1.9817	2.2417	2.4908	3.3688
0.6	1, 1	1.0000	1.0911	1.1894	1.2794	1.3578	1.4267	1.4872	1.6578
	1, 2	1.0000	1.0581	1.1257	1.1944	1.2593	1.3191	1.3746	1.5535
	1, 3	1.0000	1.0418	1.0916	1.1440	1.1966	1.2467	1.2944	1.4629
	2, 2	1.0000	1.0996	1.2335	1.3687	1.4933	1.6052	1.7057	2.0037
0.8	1, 1	1.0000	1.0491	1.0947	1.1281	1.1519	1.1700	1.1844	1.2234
	1, 2	1.0000	1.0315	1.0688	1.1001	1.1244	1.1432	1.1583	1.1977
	1, 3	1.0000	1.0217	1.0515	1.0792	1.1029	1.1222	1.1379	1.1796
	2, 2	1.0000	1.0573	1.1259	1.1823	1.2231	1.2520	1.2723	1.3093

Table D,4b. Parameters of the square well model for
various gases as found from viscosity.

	ϵ/k (°K)	r_0 (A)	r_1 (A)	r_0/r_1
N_2	80	3.36	7.00	0.480
CO	91	3.29	7.48	0.440
H_2	94	2.57	3.67	0.700
O_2	94	3.16	6.72	0.470
Ne	101	2.38	3.66	0.650
A	167	2.98	5.84	0.510
CH_4	174	3.35	6.57	0.510
He	232	1.90	2.64	0.720
Air	87	3.30	6.88	0.480

Table D,4c. Viscosity and compressibility parameters.

Gas	ϵ/k	Compressibility		Viscosity	
		r_0	r_1	r_0	r_1
Ethane	244	3.54	5.84	3.81	8.71
Propane	347	4.42	6.47	4.21	8.77
n-butane	387	4.82	7.11	4.50	9.78
Ethene	222	3.35	5.61	3.73	8.48
Propene	339	4.32	6.31	4.02	8.93

D,4c, Holleran and Hulburt obtained excellent agreement with experimental measurements of viscosity. In Table D,4c the square well parameters [8] obtained from fitting second virial coefficient data are compared with those obtained from viscosity. The fact that the equation of state and the viscosity potential wells are quite different corresponds to a different emphasis on the relative importance of different parts of the potential energy function. Holleran and Hulburt were able to predict accurately diffusion, self-diffusion, and thermal-diffusion using the parameters which they had determined from viscosity. Because the result of the square well treatment is not simple, because the square well involves three rather than two parameters, and because the shape of the square well is unrealistic, we prefer to place the emphasis on the Lennard-Jones potential.

These simple potential functions give rather good results for the viscosity of many gases over limited temperature ranges. However, their use for purposes of calculating the other transport properties, which are more sensitive to the potential function used, is not generally satisfactory—particularly if an extrapolation of the available data is desired.

D,5. Evaluation of the Averaged Reduced Cross Sections Using the Lennard-Jones Potential. The evaluation of the transport coefficients for molecules described by the Lennard-Jones potential is carried out in much the same manner as those discussed in the preceding articles. However, the calculations for the Lennard-Jones potential are more difficult and can be accomplished only by numerical methods. The potential function for this model is

$$E(r_{ij}) = 4\epsilon_{ij} \left\{ \left[\frac{(r_0)_{ij}}{r_{ij}} \right]^{12} - \left[\frac{(r_0)_{ij}}{r_{ij}} \right]^6 \right\} \tag{5-1}$$

The two parameters characteristic of the interaction are ϵ_{ij}, the absolute value of the maximum energy of attraction, and $(r_0)_{ij}$, that value of the separation for which the potential is zero. Using these parameters to reduce the variables, we can write the potential in the form of Eq. 3-5 where the universal function is

$$f(r_{ij}^*) = 4(r_{ij}^{*-12} - r_{ij}^{*-6}) \tag{5-2}$$

The calculations for this potential function have been carried out independently by four groups of workers [9], and extremely good agreement among the numerical results has been found. The details of the calculations may be found in the original publications; only the results are given here.

Dynamics of the collision. An effective potential energy curve for the equivalent one-dimensional problem is obtained when the centrifugal energy $K_{ij}\beta^2 r_{ij}^{*-2}$ is added to the potential energy:

$$V_{\text{eff}}(r_{ij}^*) = K_{ij}\beta^2 r_{ij}^{*-2} - 4r_{ij}^{*-6} + 4r_{ij}^{*-12} \tag{5-3}$$

In Fig. D,5a effective potential energy curves are shown for several values of the product $K_{ij}\beta^2$. The humps in the curves occur roughly at the point where the attractive van der Waals forces balance the centrifugal repulsion. Above the critical value $K_{ij}\beta^2 = 2.462$, the effective potential curves are monotone decreasing.

If a pair of colliding molecules has an initial relative kinetic energy K_{ij} less than 0.8, then several types of collisions are dynamically possible, depending upon the initial relative kinetic energy and the collision parameter β. These possibilities may be illustrated by the specific case where K_{ij} is approximately 0.2. Then (1) if β is such that $K_{ij}\beta^2 = 10$, there will be only a gradual deflection of one molecule with respect to the other, i.e. a grazing collision, the repulsive part of the potential having a negligible effect on the collision. (2) If β is such that $K_{ij}\beta^2 = 0.008$, i.e. nearly head-on, then both the attractive forces at large separations and the repulsive forces at small separations influence the trajectory. (3) If β is such that the system cannot quite get over the hump in the energy, then the phenomenon of "orbiting" takes place, for the system spends a great deal of time in the vicinity of the separation corresponding to the hump, the molecules meanwhile spinning around one another. The molecules finally separate under the influence of the centrifugal

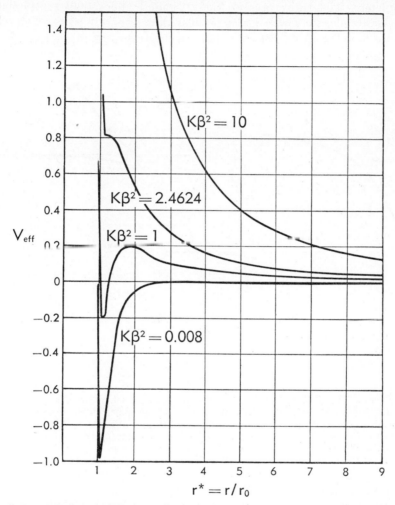

Fig. D,5a. Effective potential curves for several values of $K\beta^2$. The combination of the original potential and the centrifugal energy leads to effective potential energy curves exhibiting humps when $K\beta^2$ is less than the critical value 2.4624. No orbiting is possible for collisions in which K is greater than 0.8.

repulsion, but are never close enough to feel the effect of the strong quantum mechanical repulsion. Collisions of types (1), (2), and (3) are shown in Fig. D,5b.

For collisions taking place with $K_{ij} \leqq 0.8$, there is for each K_{ij} one value of β for which the energy of the top of the hump coincides precisely with the energy of the system—we designate this value of β as β_0. For this special case the angle of deflection χ is infinite.

Kirkwood [4] has considered the effect of interactions in which the relative kinetic energy is not sufficient to permit the molecules to separate completely. The trajectories of these "bound molecules" are periodic with orbits large compared to molecular dimensions. Kirkwood showed that such collisions do not contribute to the transport properties. In an ionic gas in which the energy of interaction varies as the inverse first

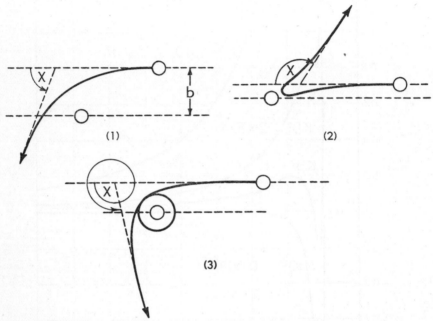

(1)

(2)

(3)

Fig. D,5b. Types of collisions: (1) Type of collision where repulsive forces are essentially not involved. (2) Type of collision where short range repulsive forces come into play. (3) Type of collision in which "orbiting" takes place; this phenomenon results from the hump in the effective potential curve caused by the counter-balancing of van der Waals' attractive forces and the centrifugal force.

power of the separation, there are a large number of bound molecules. Since the number of molecules in a spherical shell of thickness dr at a distance r varies as r^2, if $E(r)$ decreases more rapidly than r^{-2} the fraction of bound molecules is small. In the case here under consideration, at large distances, $E(r)$ varies as r^{-6} and the number of bound molecules is negligible. However, the very low energy encounters in which two molecules circle about each other for a few times at a distance of a few angstroms and then separate of their own accord differ from Kirkwood's bound molecules, which require the influence of a third molecule to effect the separation. Such examples of close orbiting correspond to well-defined collisions and contribute to the transport coefficients. Since collisions involving orbiting do not occur frequently, the net effect on the transport properties is slight.

The angle of deflection. The angle of deflection χ for the Lennard-Jones model may be calculated by substituting Eq. 5-2 into Eq. 3-9; this substitution gives

$$\chi(K_{ij}, \beta) = \pi - 2\beta \int_0^{y_m} \frac{dy}{\sqrt{1 - \beta^2 y^2 - (4/K_{ij})(y^{12} - y^6)}} \quad (5\text{-}4)$$

where $y = 1/r_{ij}^*$ and y_m is the reciprocal of the distance of closest approach. By taking the lowest root for which the radical in the integrand vanishes, y_m may be found. For large values of β, the angle of deflection may be expressed in the series:

$$\frac{\chi}{\pi} = -0.9375 y_m^6 \left(\frac{4}{K_{ij}}\right) - 0.5713 y_m^{12} \left(\frac{4}{K_{ij}}\right)^2 + 1.3535 y_m^{12} \left(\frac{4}{K_{ij}}\right) \quad (5\text{-}5)$$

However, for small values of β, the integral must be evaluated numerically.

The general form of the results may be seen pictorially in Fig. D,5c, where $(1 - \cos \chi)$ vs β^2 is plotted for four values of K_{ij}. The area under this curve is then $S^{(1)}(K_{ij})$. For $K_{ij} = 0.4$ and 0.8, rapid oscillations in the curve near $\beta = \beta_0$ give evidence of the phenomenon of orbiting—if β is just slightly larger than β_0, collisions of type (3) occur. For $\beta > \beta_0$ the curve represents collisions of type (1). Similarly, for $\beta < \beta_0$ the collisions are of type (2). The region between $\beta^2 \cong 2$ and $\beta^2 = \beta_0^2$ is that range of β for which the molecules attract one another during most of their collision time. For the region below $\beta^2 \cong 2$, the molecules attract one another only during about half their collision time.

It is not surprising then to see the hump between $\beta^2 = 2$ and $\beta^2 = 3$ in the $(1 - \cos \chi)$ curve gradually disappear because, as previously stated, the colliding system feels the dip in the potential curve less and less as the kinetic energy becomes greater. When $K_{ij} = 10$, the "attractive loop" in the $(1 - \cos \chi)$ curve has almost completely disappeared.

At $K_{ij} = 10$, the $(1 - \cos \chi)$ curve very nearly approximates the curve which one would get for rigid spheres, i.e. $(1 - \cos \chi) = 2 - 2\beta^2$. However, for $K_{ij} = 10$ and higher energies, the Lennard-Jones curve falls more and more beneath the rigid sphere line. The integral of the curve is associated with the cross section. The Lennard-Jones molecules appear to have smaller cross sections than the rigid spheres, since the Lennard-Jones r^{-12} term allows for the natural interpenetration of the molecules.

Reduced collision cross sections and average reduced collision cross sections. Using values of χ obtained numerically, the $S^{(1)}(K_{ij})$ integrals may be evaluated. Several of the cross sections which are needed for transport property calculations are shown in Fig. D,5d: $S^{(1)}$, which is

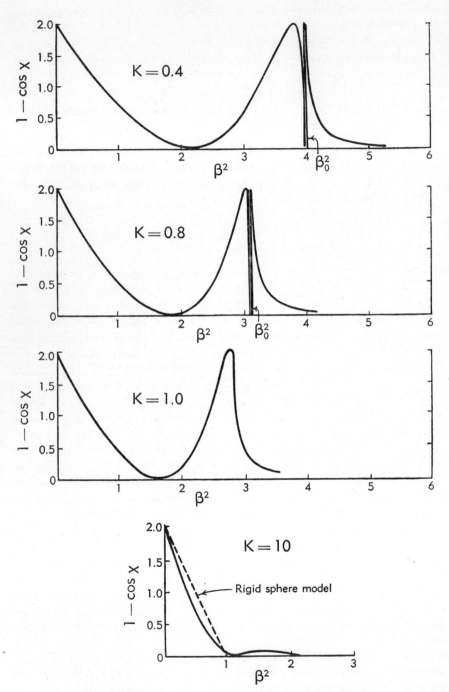

Fig. D,5c. $(1 - \cos \chi)$ versus β^2 for several values of K_{ij}.

used to calculate diffusion and thermal diffusion; $S^{(2)}$, which is needed for viscosity and thermal conductivity; and $S^{(4)}$, which is needed for the calculation of higher approximations to viscosity and heat conductivity.

Numerical integration of Eq. 3-11 then yields the reduced average collision cross sections, $Y(l, n; \tau_{ij})$, which are functions of only the reduced

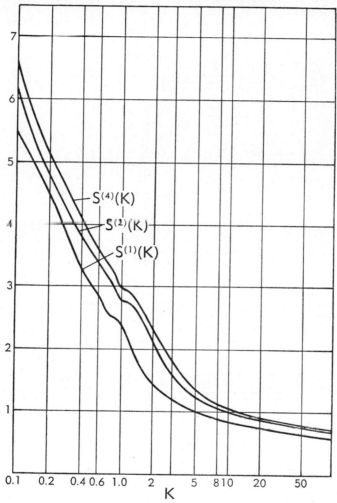

Fig. D,5d.   The reduced collision cross sections $S^{(l)}(K_{ij})$.

temperature $\tau_{ij} = kT/\epsilon_{ij}$. The values of these integrals are given in Table D,5a. The integrals have been evaluated for enough values of n and l to permit the calculation of all of the transport properties of both pure gases and their mixtures with reasonable accuracy, i.e. within the accuracy of the potential function used. The mechanical accuracy of the entries in Table D,5a is about one part in one thousand.

Table D,5a. The $Y(l, n; \tau)$ for the Lennard-Jones potential.

$\tau = kT/\epsilon$	$Y(1,1)$	$Y(1,2)$	$Y(1,3)$	$Y(2,2)$	$Y(2,3)$	$Y(2,4)$	$Y(2,5)$	$Y(2,6)$	$Y(4,4)$
0.30	2.662	2.256	1.962	2.785	2.535	2.333	2.152	1.990	2.557
0.35	2.476	2.078	1.795	2.628	2.375	2.163	1.978	1.819	2.378
0.40	2.318	1.931	1.663	2.492	2.232	2.016	1.833	1.682	2.223
0.45	2.184	1.808	1.556	2.368	2.105	1.889	1.713	1.574	2.090
0.50	2.066	1.705	1.468	2.257	1.992	1.781	1.614	1.486	1.975
0.55	1.966	1.618	1.396	2.156	1.893	1.689	1.532	1.415	1.875
0.60	1.877	1.543	1.336	2.065	1.806	1.610	1.463	1.356	1.788
0.65	1.798	1.479	1.285	1.982	1.729	1.542	1.406	1.307	1.712
0.70	1.729	1.423	1.242	1.908	1.661	1.484	1.357	1.267	1.645
0.75	1.667	1.375	1.205	1.841	1.602	1.434	1.315	1.231	1.587
0.80	1.612	1.332	1.172	1.780	1.549	1.389	1.278	1.201	1.535
0.85	1.562	1.295	1.144	1.725	1.502	1.350	1.247	1.175	1.488
0.90	1.517	1.261	1.119	1.675	1.460	1.316	1.219	1.152	1.447
0.95	1.476	1.231	1.096	1.629	1.422	1.286	1.194	1.131	1.410
1.00	1.439	1.204	1.076	1.587	1.388	1.258	1.172	1.113	1.377
1.05	1.406	1.179	1.058	1.549	1.357	1.234	1.152	1.097	1.347
1.10	1.375	1.157	1.041	1.514	1.329	1.212	1.135	1.082	1.319
1.15	1.346	1.137	1.027	1.482	1.304	1.192	1.119	1.068	1.294
1.20	1.320	1.119	1.013	1.452	1.280	1.174	1.104	1.056	1.272
1.25	1.296	1.102	1.000	1.424	1.259	1.157	1.091	1.045	1.251
1.30	1.273	1.086	0.9887	1.399	1.239	1.142	1.078	1.035	1.232
1.35	1.253	1.072	0.9780	1.375	1.221	1.128	1.067	1.025	1.215
1.40	1.233	1.059	0.9680	1.353	1.205	1.115	1.057	1.016	1.198
1.45	1.215	1.046	0.9588	1.333	1.189	1.103	1.047	1.008	1.183
1.50	1.198	1.034	0.9502	1.314	1.175	1.092	1.037	1.000	1.169
1.55	1.182	1.023	0.9420	1.296	1.162	1.081	1.029	0.9929	1.156
1.60	1.167	1.013	0.9345	1.279	1.149	1.072	1.022	0.9860	1.144
1.65	1.153	1.004	0.9272	1.264	1.137	1.063	1.014	0.9795	1.133
1.70	1.140	0.9947	0.9205	1.248	1.126	1.054	1.007	0.9735	1.122
1.75	1.128	0.9860	0.9142	1.234	1.116	1.046	1.000	0.9677	1.112
1.80	1.116	0.9780	0.9082	1.221	1.106	1.038	0.9942	0.9623	1.103
1.85	1.105	0.9707	0.9023	1.209	1.097	1.031	0.9875	0.9569	1.094
1.90	1.094	0.9633	0.8968	1.197	1.088	1.024	0.9825	0.9520	1.085
1.95	1.084	0.9567	0.8917	1.186	1.080	1.018	0.9767	0.9473	1.078
2.0	1.075	0.9500	0.8867	1.175	1.073	1.012	0.9717	0.9427	1.070
2.1	1.057	0.9380	0.8775	1.156	1.055	1.000	0.9617	0.9343	1.056
2.2	1.041	0.9267	0.8688	1.138	1.045	0.9895	0.9525	0.9261	1.043
2.3	1.026	0.9167	0.8612	1.122	1.033	0.9800	0.9450	0.9190	1.032
2.4	1.012	0.9073	0.8538	1.107	1.022	0.9710	0.9375	0.9120	1.021
2.5	0.9996	0.8987	0.8470	1.093	1.012	0.9630	0.9300	0.9058	1.012

2.6	1.003	0.8996	0.9233	0.9555	1.002	1.081	0.8407	0.8907	0.9878
2.7	0.9942	0.8940	0.9175	0.9485	0.9933	1.069	0.8347	0.8833	0.9770
2.8	0.9863	0.8887	0.9117	0.9415	0.9855	1.058	0.8290	0.8767	0.9672
2.9	0.9792	0.8836	0.9058	0.9355	0.9780	1.048	0.8237	0.8700	0.9576
3.0	0.9721	0.8788	0.9008	0.9295	0.9708	1.039	0.8187	0.8640	0.9490
3.1	0.9658	0.8742	0.8958	0.9240	0.9643	1.030	0.8138	0.8580	0.9406
3.2	0.9596	0.8698	0.8908	0.9185	0.9578	1.022	0.8093	0.8520	0.9328
3.3	0.9538	0.8656	0.8867	0.9135	0.9518	1.014	0.8048	0.8473	0.9256
3.4	0.9483	0.8617	0.8825	0.9085	0.9463	1.007	0.8007	0.8420	0.9186
3.5	0.9433	0.8577	0.8783	0.9040	0.9408	0.9999	0.7967	0.8373	0.9120
3.6	0.9383	0.8539	0.8742	0.8995	0.9358	0.9932	0.7928	0.8327	0.9058
3.7	0.9333	0.8504	0.8700	0.8955	0.9308	0.9870	0.7892	0.8287	0.8998
3.8	0.9288	0.8469	0.8667	0.8915	0.9263	0.9811	0.7857	0.8240	0.8942
3.9	0.9246	0.8436	0.8633	0.8875	0.9218	0.9755	0.7822	0.8200	0.8888
4.0	0.9204	0.8404	0.8592	0.8840	0.9175	0.9700	0.7790	0.8167	0.8836
4.1	0.9167	0.8371	0.8558	0.8805	0.9133	0.9649	0.7758	0.8127	0.8788
4.2	0.9125	0.8342	0.8533	0.8770	0.9093	0.9600	0.7727	0.8093	0.8740
4.3	0.9088	0.8312	0.8500	0.8735	0.9055	0.9553	0.7697	0.8060	0.8694
4.4	0.9054	0.8283	0.8467	0.8705	0.9018	0.9507	0.7668	0.8027	0.8652
4.5	0.9021	0.8256	0.8442	0.8670	0.8985	0.9464	0.7640	0.7993	0.8610
4.6	0.8988	0.8229	0.8408	0.8640	0.8950	0.9422	0.7613	0.7960	0.8568
4.7	0.8954	0.8202	0.8383	0.8610	0.8918	0.9382	0.7585	0.7933	0.8530
4.8	0.8925	0.8176	0.8358	0.8585	0.8885	0.9343	0.7560	0.7907	0.8492
4.9	0.8892	0.8152	0.8332	0.8555	0.8855	0.9305	0.7535	0.7873	0.8456
5	0.8863	0.8127	0.8307	0.8530	0.8823	0.9269	0.7510	0.7847	0.8422
6	0.8613	0.7912	0.8083	0.8295	0.8565	0.8963	0.7295	0.7607	0.8124
7	0.8413	0.7736	0.7902	0.8105	0.8360	0.8727	0.7120	0.7420	0.7896
8	0.8246	0.7587	0.7749	0.7945	0.8193	0.8538	0.6973	0.7260	0.7712
9	0.8108	0.7458	0.7617	0.7810	0.8048	0.8379	0.6847	0.7127	0.7556
10	0.7988	0.7345	0.7501	0.7690	0.7923	0.8242	0.6735	0.7013	0.7424
20	0.7242	0.6643	0.6783	0.6950	0.7160	0.7432	0.6048	0.6293	0.6640
30	0.6842	0.6264	0.6396	0.6555	0.6750	0.7005	0.5680	0.5909	0.6232
40	0.6571	0.6007	0.6135	0.6285	0.6475	0.6718	0.5432	0.5651	0.5960
50	0.6367	0.5817	0.5940	0.6085	0.6268	0.6504	0.5248	0.5459	0.5756
60	0.6208	0.5664	0.5784	0.5930	0.6105	0.6335	0.5100	0.5307	0.5596
70	0.6075	0.5539	0.5657	0.5795	0.5970	0.6194	0.4980	0.5181	0.5464
80	0.5963	0.5433	0.5548	0.5685	0.5855	0.6076	0.4878	0.5075	0.5352
90	0.5867	0.5342	0.5454	0.5590	0.5755	0.5973	0.4790	0.4984	0.5256
100	0.5779	0.5261	0.5371	0.5505	0.5670	0.5882	0.4713	0.4903	0.5170
200	0.5246	0.4757	0.4857	0.4978	0.5128	0.5320	0.4233	0.4403	0.4644
300	0.4954	0.4486	0.4580	0.4694	0.4835	0.5016	0.3975	0.4135	0.4360
400	0.4758	0.4302	0.4393	0.4502	0.4638	0.4811	0.3802	0.3955	0.4170

Table D,5b. Constants for determination of transport properties of gaseous mixtures.

$\tau_{ij} = kT/\epsilon_{ij}$	A	B	C
0.30	0.4185	0.7739	1.017
0.35	0.4246	0.7779	1.007
0.40	0.4300	0.7772	0.9995
0.45	0.4337	0.7742	0.9934
0.50	0.4370	0.7698	0.9901
0.55	0.4387	0.765	0.9877
0.60	0.4402	0.759	0.9869
0.65	0.4409	0.752	0.9868
0.70	0.4415	0.746	0.9880
0.75	0.4418	0.740	0.9896
0.80	0.4418	0.734	0.9918
0.85	0.4418	0.729	0.9947
0.90	0.4417	0.725	0.9978
0.95	0.4413	0.720	1.001
1.00	0.4410	0.715	1.004
1.05	0.4408	0.711	1.007
1.10	0.4406	0.707	1.010
1.15	0.4404	0.705	1.014
1.20	0.4399	0.701	1.017
1.25	0.4396	0.696	1.021
1.30	0.4395	0.695	1.023
1.35	0.4391	0.694	1.027
1.40	0.4389	0.692	1.030
1.45	0.4388	0.689	1.033
1.50	0.4387	0.687	1.036
1.55	0.4384	0.684	1.039
1.60	0.4382	0.683	1.042
1.65	0.4384	0.682	1.045
1.70	0.4378	0.679	1.047
1.75	0.4377	0.677	1.049
1.80	0.4376	0.676	1.052
1.85	0.4377	0.676	1.054
1.90	0.4376	0.674	1.056
1.95	0.4376	0.673	1.059
2.00	0.4374	0.671	1.061
2.1	0.4375	0.670	1.065
2.2	0.4374	0.670	1.069
2.3	0.4375	0.666	1.072
2.4	0.4375	0.665	1.076
2.5	0.4374	0.664	1.079
2.6	0.4377	0.663	1.082
2.7	0.4377	0.662	1.085
2.8	0.4376	0.662	1.088
2.9	0.4378	0.661	1.090
3.0	0.4379	0.661	1.093
3.1	0.4380	0.660	1.095
3.2	0.4383	0.658	1.096
3.3	0.4382	0.659	1.099
3.4	0.4385	0.658	1.100
3.5	0.4386	0.658	1.102
3.6	0.4386	0.657	1.103
3.7	0.4388	0.658	1.105
3.8	0.4389	0.656	1.106

Table D,5b (continued)

$\tau_{ij} = kT/\epsilon_{ij}$	A	B	C
3.9	0.4389	0.656	1.107
4.0	0.4391	0.657	1.109
4.1	0.4392	0.655	1.110
4.2	0.4393	0.656	1.111
4.3	0.4395	0.656	1.112
4.4	0.4395	0.656	1.113
4.5	0.4396	0.656	1.114
4.6	0.4398	0.655	1.115
4.7	0.4399	0.656	1.116
4.8	0.4400	0.656	1.117
4.9	0.4402	0.655	1.117
5.0	0.4402	0.655	1.118
6	0.4413	0.656	1.125
7	0.4421	0.655	1.128
8	0.4428	0.657	1.131
9	0.4435	0.655	1.132
10	0.4441	0.657	1.134
20	0.4477	0.6569	1.137
30	0.4496	0.6569	1.138
40	0.4508	0.6574	1.138
50	0.4520	0.6567	1.138
60	0.4528	0.6569	1.138
70	0.4535	0.6574	1.138
80	0.4540	0.6573	1.138
90	0.4546	0.6575	1.138
100	0.4551	0.6569	1.138
200	0.4582	0.6568	1.138
300	0.4602	0.6573	1.138
400	0.4615	0.6571	1.138

Table D,5c. Viscosity and thermal conductivity correction factors.

$\tau_{ij} = kT/\epsilon_{ij}$	$\mathfrak{I}$	$\mathfrak{K}$
0.30	1.0014	1.0022
0.50	1.0002	1.0003
0.75	1.0000	1.0000
1.00	1.0000	1.0001
1.25	1.0001	1.0002
1.5	1.0004	1.0006
2.0	1.0014	1.0021
2.5	1.0025	1.0038
3.0	1.0034	1.0052
4.0	1.0049	1.0076
5.0	1.0058	1.0090
10.0	1.0075	1.0116
50.0	1.0079	1.0124
100.0	1.0080	1.0125
400.0	1.0080	1.0125

When the quantities $Y(l, n; \tau_{ij})$ were defined, it was pointed out that these functions indicate the degree of deviation for the model under consideration from the idealized rigid sphere model. We may now examine the dependence of $Y(1, 1; \tau_{ij})$ and $Y(2, 2; \tau_{ij})$ on τ_{ij} for the Lennard-Jones potential and show how this dependence is related to the nature of the collision. Fig. D,5e shows these two reduced average collision cross sections plotted as functions of the reduced temperature. For low values of τ_{ij} the Y are greater than unity; this corresponds to the fact that in low energy collisions, the molecules spend a relatively large part of the collision time in the attractive region of the potential. Thus the collision cross section as seen by a molecule about to undergo a

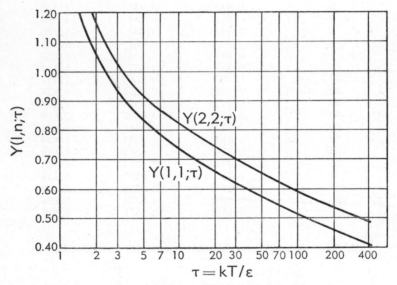

Fig. D,5e. The average reduced cross sections $Y(l, n; \tau)$.

collision is larger than $\pi(r_0)_{ij}^2$. Similarly for high values of τ_{ij} the repulsive region of the potential is more important. Consequently, the colliding molecules see a cross section smaller than $\pi(r_0)_{ij}^2$, due to the penetration afforded by the r^{-12} term in the potential.

For convenience in making technical calculations, the functions given in Eq. 3-15, 3-16, 3-17 (also $\mathcal{G}$ and $\mathcal{K}$) are tabulated here for the Lennard-Jones potential as functions of τ_{ij}. The quantities A, B, and C which are used in calculating the transport coefficients for gaseous mixtures are given in Table D,5b. The correction factor for viscosity, $\mathcal{G}$, and the correction factor for thermal conductivity, $\mathcal{K}$, are in Table D,5c.

D,6. The Coefficient of Viscosity for Pure Gases. We shall begin the discussion of the various transport phenomena by considering the viscosity of pure gases, its calculation, and its use in determining force fields between like molecules.

FORMULA FOR THE COEFFICIENT OF VISCOSITY FOR PURE GASES. The first approximation to the viscosity of mixtures is given in terms of the average collision cross sections in Art. 3. For a pure gas the third approximation is

$$[\mu_i]_3 = \frac{5}{16} \left(\frac{m_i kT}{\pi} \right)^{\frac{1}{2}} \frac{\mathcal{J}(\tau_i)}{(r_0)_i^2 Y(2,2;\tau_i)} \tag{6-1}$$

where $\mathcal{J}(\tau_i)$, the correction factor is a slowly varying function of τ_i differing by at most 0.8 per cent from unity in the case of the Lennard-Jones potential. For purposes of practical calculations Eq. 6-1 may be rewritten:

$$[\mu_i]_3 \times 10^7 = 266.93 (\mathfrak{M}_i T)^{\frac{1}{2}} \frac{\mathcal{J}(\tau_i)}{(r_0)_i^2 Y(2,2;\tau_i)} \tag{6-2}$$

in which

$[\mu_i]_3$ = viscosity of gas of species i, in g cm^{-1} sec^{-1}

$\mathfrak{M}_i$ = molecular weight of the ith species

$(r_0)_i$, ϵ_i/k = force constants (in angstroms and °K, respectively) presented in Table D,6a

$\tau_i = kT/\epsilon_i$ = reduced temperature

Y, $\mathcal{J}$ = tabulated functions of τ_i in Tables D,5a and D,5c

The theory on which Eq. 6-1 and 6-2 are based is valid only for pressures low enough so that three-body collisions are not important and high enough so that the gas behaves as a continuous medium. Over this range, the viscosity is independent of the pressure. Of course, it is true that experimental measurements have been made which demonstrate the pressure dependence of viscosity. For nitrogen, for example, as the pressure is increased from 15 atm to 1,000 atm, the viscosity more than doubles its value. But within the pressure range for which this theory is valid, the change in viscosity with pressure is generally small.

The viscosity depends on the temperature through the factor $T^{\frac{1}{2}}$ and to some extent through the factor $\mathcal{J}(\tau_i)/Y(2,2;\tau_i)$. The fact that viscosity increases with temperature was discovered by Maxwell, during his pioneer work in kinetic theory. Subsequent experiments proved the truth of this fact, which at the time seemed illogical since the viscosity of liquids decreases with increasing temperature.

CALCULATION OF INTERMOLECULAR FORCES FROM VISCOSITY MEASUREMENTS. The two "force constants" $(r_0)_i$ and ϵ_i/k which are the parameters in the Lennard-Jones interaction potential appear in Eq. 6-2. There is no way at present to calculate a priori the values of these parameters. For collisions between like molecules the force constants may

D · TRANSPORT PROPERTIES

Table D,6a. Force constants between similar molecules for the Lennard-Jones potential. The letters in columns R_1 and R_2 indicate the literature references for the viscosity and second virial data respectively; these references are given at the end of this table.

Gas	Force constants from viscosity data		Force constants from second virial coefficient data			R_1	R_2
	ϵ/k (°K)	r_0 (A)	ϵ/k (°K)	r_0 (A)	b_0 (cm³/mole)		
Air	97.0	3.617	99.2	3.522	55.11	a	m
H_2	33.3	2.968	36.77*	2.92*	31.409*	a	n
D_2	39.27	2.948				bb	
N_2	91.46	3.681	95.05	3.698	63.78	a	p
CO_2	190	3.996	189	4.486	113.9	a	q
N_2O	220	3.879	189	4.59	122	a	r
NO	119	3.470	131	3.17	40	a	r
CH_4	136.5	3.882	148.2	3.817	70.16	a	s
O_2	113.2	3.433	117.5	3.58	57.75	a	t
CO	110.3	3.590	95.33	3.65	61.47	a	u
A	124.0	3.418	119.75	3.405	49.804	b	v
Ne	35.7	2.80	35.7	2.74	25.95	b	x
He	6.03	2.70	10.16*	2.56*	21.165*	b	n
Kr	190	3.61	158	3.597	58.7	d	y
Xe	230	4.051	217	3.963	78.5	d	y
			225	4.064	84.65		cc
CH≡CH	185	4.221				e	
CH_2=CH_2	205	4.232	199.2	4.523	116.7	d	w
C_2H_6	230	4.418	243	3.954	78	d	y
C_3H_8	254	5.061	242	5.637	226	d	y
n-C_4H_{10}	410	4.997	297	4.971	155	e	y
i-C_4H_{10}	313	5.341				e	
n-C_5H_{12}	345	5.769				f	
n-C_6H_{14}	413	5.909				f	
n-C_7H_{16}			282	8.88	884		y
n-C_8H_{18}	320	7.451				d	
n-C_9H_{20}	240	8.448				d	
Cyclohexane	324	6.093				f	
C_6H_6	440	5.270				d	
CH_3OH	507	3.585				f	
C_2H_5OH	391	4.455				f	
C_2N_2	339	4.38				d	
AsH_3	281	4.06				d	
CH_2Cl_2	406	4.759				c	
F_2	112	3.653				z	
Cl_2	357	4.115				c	
Br_2	520	4.268				g,aa	
COS	335	4.13				d	
I_2	550	4.982				c	

* These force constants were obtained by fitting the experimental data with the theoretical expression which includes the quantum effects.

⟨ 372 ⟩

Table D,6a (continued)

Gas	Force constants from viscosity data		Force constants from second virial coefficient data			R_1	R_2
	ϵ/k (°K)	r_0 (A)	ϵ/k (°K)	r_0 (A)	b_0 (cm³/mole)		
CCl_4	327	5.881				d	
HgI_2	698	5.625				c	
$SnBr_4$	465	6.666				c	
CS_2	488	4.438				f	
$HgBr_2$	530	5.414				c	
CH_3Cl	855	3.375				c	
$CHCl_3$	327	5.430				d	
HCl	360	3.305				h	
SO_2	252	4.290				j	
$SnCl_4$	1550	4.540				c	

Table References.

a. Johnston, H. L., and McKloskey, K. E.   *J. Chem. Phys.* *44*, 1038 (1939).
b. Johnston, H. L., and Grilly, E. R.   *J. Phys. Chem.* *46*, 938 (1942).
c. Braune, H., and Linke, R.   *Z. physik. Chem. A148*, 195 (1930).
d. Landolt-Börnstein.   *Physikalisch-Chemische Tabellen.*
e. Titani, T.   *Bull. Chem. Soc. Japan 5*, 98 (1930).
f. Titani, T.   *Bull. Chem. Soc. Japan 8*, 255 (1933).
g. Rankine, A. O.   *Proc. Roy. Soc. London A88*, 582 (1913).
h. Trautz, M., and Narath, A.   *Ann. Physik (4)79*, 637 (1926).
j. Trautz, M., and Zink, R.   *Ann. Physik (5)7*, 427 (1930).
m. Holborn, L., and Schultze, H.   *Ann. Physik 47*, 1089 (1915).
n. de Boer, J., and Michels, A.   *Physica 5*, 945 (1938).
p. Michels, A., Wouters, H., and de Boer, J.   *Physica 1*, 587 (1934).
q. Michels, A., and Michels, C.   *Proc. Roy. Soc. London A153*, 201 (1936).
r. Hirschfelder, J. O., McClure, F. T., Curtiss, C. F., and Osborne, D. W.   *Natl. Defense Research Comm. Rept. A116*, Nov. 1942.
s. Michels, A., and Nederbragt, G. W.   *Physica 3*, 569 (1936).
t. Hirschfelder, J. O., and Roseveare, W. E.   *J. Phys. Chem. 43*, 15 (1939).
u. Corner, J.   *Proc. Roy. Soc. London A58*, 737 (1946).
v. Michels, A., Wijker, Hub., and Wijker, Hk.   *Physica 15*, 627 (1949).
w. Michels, A., and Geldermans, M.   *Physica 9*, 967 (1942).
x. Buckingham, R. A.   *Proc. Roy. Soc. London A168*, 264 (1938).
y. Newitt, D. M.   *The Design of High Pressure Plants and the Properties of Fluids at High Pressures.* Oxford Univ. Press, 1940.
z. Kanda, E.   *Bull. Chem. Soc. Japan 12*, 465 (1937).
aa. Braune, H., Basch, R., and Wentzel, W.   *Z. physik. Chem. A137*, 176, 447 (1928).
bb. van Itterbeek, A., and Claes, A.   *Physica 5*, 938 (1938).
cc. Beattie, J. A., Barriault, R. J., and Brierley, J. S.   *J. Chem. Phys. 19*, 1222 (1951).

be obtained from viscosity or from second virial coefficients. For collisions between unlike molecules, diffusion measurements give the desired information most accurately.

The two parameters $(r_0)_i$ and ϵ_i/k may be obtained by writing Eq. 6-2 for two temperatures, T and T', for which experimental values are

Table D,6b. Viscosity of pure gases (in units 10^{-7} g/cm sec).

T (°K)	Air ε/k = 97.0, r₀ = 3.617		H₂ ε/k = 33.3, r₀ = 2.968		N₂ ε/k = 91.46, r₀ = 3.681		CO₂ ε/k = 190, r₀ = 3.996		N₂O ε/k = 220, r₀ = 3.879		NO ε/k = 119, r₀ = 3.470	
	$\mu_{exptl}^{[a]}$	μ_{calc}	$\mu_{exptl}^{[a]}$	μ_{calc}	$\mu_{exptl}^{[a]}$	μ_{calc}	$\mu_{exptl}^{[a]}$	μ_{calc}	$\mu_{exptl}^{[a]}$	μ_{calc}	$\mu_{exptl}^{[a]}$	μ_{calc}
80												
100	713	702	421	416	698	687						
120	846	840	481	477	826	820					844	841
140	975	972	535	533	948	947					981	980
160	1101	1099	585	586	1068	1070					1115	1116
180	1221	1221	634	635	1183	1186			898	898	1245	1246
200	1336	1337	681	683	1295	1296	1015	1014	999	998	1371	1371
220	1448	1447	727	728	1403	1402	1112	1114	1099	1100	1493	1492
240	1556	1554	771	773	1505	1503	1209	1212	1198	1199	1610	1608
260	1659	1657	814	815	1603	1600	1303	1308	1296	1297	1711	1719
280	1756	1756	856	856	1696	1693	1400	1402	1393	1394	1838	1828
293.16	1819[b]	1819										
300	1851	1851	896	896	1786	1785	1495	1495	1489	1489	1934	1935
400	2294[d]	2290	1073	1073		2202		1923				
500	2680[d]	2678	1237	1237		2570		2309				
800	3613[d]	3680	1689	1689	3493[d]	3528	3391[d]	3285				
1000	4165[d]	4257	1958	1958	4011[d]	4068	3935[d]	3839				
1200	4631[d]	4761	2199	2199	4452[d]	4554	4453[d]	4348				
1500	5262[d]	5494	2542	2542	5050[d]	5268	5139[d]	5052				
5000		12080										
10000		18870										

Table D,6b (continued)

T (°K)	CH₄ $\epsilon/k = 136.5$, $r_0 = 3.822$		O₂ $\epsilon/k = 113.2$, $r_0 = 3.433$		CO $\epsilon/k = 110.3$, $r_0 = 3.590$		Argon $\epsilon/k = 124.0$, $r_0 = 3.418$		Neon $\epsilon/k = 35.7$, $r_0 = 2.80$		Helium $\epsilon/k = 6.03$, $r_0 = 2.70$	
	μ_{exptl}[a]	μ_{calc}	μ_{exptl}[a]	μ_{calc}	μ_{exptl}[a]	μ_{calc}	μ_{exptl}[c]	μ_{calc}	μ_{exptl}[c]	μ_{calc}	μ_{exptl}[c]	μ_{calc}
80					533	523	688	649	1198	1212	821	827
100	403	393	768	757	669	657	839	814	1435	1451	947	957
120	478	472	917	910	796	788	993	979	1646	1665	1068	1086
140	560	553	1061	1059	919	916	1146	1142	1841	1867	1182	1197
160	629	630	1202	1203	1038	1040	1298	1300	2026	2054	1290	1305
180	703	707	1341	1342	1154	1160	1447	1454	2204	2231	1395	1413
200	778	780	1476	1474	1268	1274	1594	1601	2376	2396	1496	1509
220	850	852	1604	1602	1379	1384	1739	1744	2544	2558	1595	1605
240	919	921	1728	1726	1486	1489	1878	1882	2708	2713	1692	1700
260	986	987	1845	1845	1589	1591	2014	2014	2867	2862	1789	1789
280	1053	1052	1958	1959	1688	1689	2145	2143	3021	3008	1888	1877
300	1116	1116	2071	2070	1785	1784	2270	2269	3173	3149	1987	1964
400		1405		2578		2219						
500		1661		3031		2607						
800		2312	4115[e]	4183		3595	4621[d]	4641	5918[e]	5945	3840[e]	3665
1000		2687	4720[e]	4853		4168	5302[d]	5391	6800[e]	6872	4455[e]	4237
1200		3034		5457		4681	5547[d]	6083				
1500		3498		6264		5380	6678[d]	6983				

Table References.

a. Johnston, H. L., and McCloskey, K. E. *J. Phys. Chem. 44*, 1038 (1939).
b. Bearden, J. A. *Phys. Rev. 56*, 1023 (1939).
c. Johnston, H. L., and Grilly, E. R. *J. Phys. Chem. 46*, 948 (1942).
d. Vasilesco, V. *Ann. physique 20*, 292 (1945).
e. Trautz, M., and Zink, R. *Ann. Physik 7*, 427 (1930).

known. Taking a ratio of the two equations, one gets

$$\frac{[\mu_i(T)]_{\text{exptl}}}{[\mu_i'(T')]_{\text{exptl}}} = \left(\frac{T}{T'}\right)^{\frac{1}{2}} \left[\frac{\mathcal{G}(\tau_i)/Y(2,\,2;\,\tau_i)}{\mathcal{G}(\tau_i')/Y(2,\,2;\,\tau_i')}\right] \qquad (6\text{-}3)$$

This equation may be solved by trial and error for ϵ_i/k. One can begin the numerical solution by estimating ϵ_i/k from the critical temperature or from the boiling point, using the approximate relations, $\epsilon_i/k \cong 0.77T_{\text{cr}}$ and $\epsilon_i/k \cong 1.15T_{\text{b}}$, which follow from the Lennard-Jones and Devonshire theory of gases and liquids [10,11]. The value of $(r_0)_i$ is then obtained from Eq. 6-2, at either T or T'.

If the molecules really interacted according to the Lennard-Jones potential, the force constants thus obtained would permit an exact reproduction of the entire viscosity-temperature curve. But since this potential is approximate, there is a small amount of uncertainty in the force constants determined from Eq. 6-2. Nevertheless, these calculations based on the Lennard-Jones potential provide the best method yet available for the determination of intermolecular force fields from viscosity data.

Values of $(r_0)_i$ and ϵ_i/k which represent good fits of the observed viscosity data are given in Table D,6a. The best fits of the data were of course obtained for those molecules which are chemically simple and which have negligible dipole moments. For such molecules, the accuracy of the curve fit may be seen in the calculations of viscosity shown in Table D,6b. There are included in Table D,6a, however, a number of chemically complex molecules which are polar and/or nonspherical in nature, and which, strictly speaking, do not conform to the restrictions outlined in Art. 1.

Table D,6a also shows the values of the force constants calculated from second virial coefficient data. These values agree quite well with those obtained from viscosity measurements. However, any real differences between the two sets of force constants can be regarded as resulting from the fact that the second virial coefficient and the viscosity formula emphasize different regions of the intermolecular potential curve.

EXPERIMENTAL OBSERVATION OF QUANTUM EFFECTS IN VISCOSITY. The importance of quantum effects in collisional processes may be estimated by comparing the wavelength,[8] λ_{ij}, associated with the particles with their collision diameter, $(r_0)_{ij}$; that is, when the quantity

$$Q = \lambda_{ij}/(r_0)_{ij} = (\hbar/m_{ij}g_{ij})/(r_0)_{ij} \cong \hbar/[(r_0)_{ij}(2m_{ij}kT)^{\frac{1}{2}}] \qquad (6\text{-}4)$$

is not small compared with unity, deviations from classical behavior may be expected. Several values of this quantity Q are shown in Table D,6c. These values show that for the light gases, only very small quantum effects exist at room temperatures; but it is apparent that considerable

[8] The symbol λ refers to the true wavelength divided by 2π.

deviations from classical behavior are to be expected for all gases at very low temperature.

Because of the appreciable quantum corrections for He, H_2, and D_2, the force constants for these gases should be obtained by fitting the viscosity data in the high temperature region where these effects do not contribute. This is difficult because there are such few data available. Alternately, the data in the range 100°K to 300°K can be fitted to a theoretical curve, which accounts for the slight quantum corrections in that range. This too is difficult, as the theory has not yet been fully developed to include the quantum corrections for this intermediate temperature range. Hence, until the necessary experimental and theoretical work has been carried out, we simply fit Eq. 6-2 to the experimental data in the temperature range 100 to 300°K and arrive at a provisional set of force constants for these gases. The resulting force constants cannot be wholeheartedly recommended for extrapolation purposes because of the inherent inclusion of the quantum effects in the low

Table D,6c.   Values of Q.

	10°K	100°K	300°K	500°K
He	0.408	0.129	0.074	0.058
H_2	0.523	0.165	0.095	0.074
D_2	0.374	0.118	0.068	0.052
Ne	0.175	0.055	0.032	0.025
A	0.102	0.032	0.019	0.014

temperature range. However, these force constants should be quite satisfactory for calculations of transport properties in the range 50 to 400°K.

The use of a classical formula to fit the experimental data in a region where quantum mechanical effects are noticeable results in an $(r_0)_i$ which is somewhat too large and an ϵ_i/k which is slightly small. In Table D,6a, the collision diameters from viscosity for He, H_2, and D_2 are consistently larger than those from the second virial coefficient where quantum effects have been taken into account, and the ϵ_i/k are consistently smaller.

To get a graphical idea of the situation, we show in Fig. D,6a the calculated and experimental values of the reduced viscosity μ^* which is defined as

$$\mu^* = \frac{\mu r_0^2}{\sqrt{m\epsilon}} = \left(\frac{5}{16\sqrt{\pi}}\right) \frac{\sqrt{\tau}}{Y(2,2;\tau)} \qquad (6\text{-}5)$$

Experimental μ^* are given for He, H_2, and D_2 calculated on the basis of the viscosity coefficient force constants. There is also shown the very low temperature quantum calculation of de Boer for He[4]. From this plot[9]

[9] This method of comparing the results was first suggested by de Boer and van Kranendonk [9b].

three points are rather clear: (1) that the deviation from classical behavior is greatest for He and least for D_2 in accordance with Table D,6c; (2) that the experimental points have the classical curve as a limit at high temperatures; and (3) that the experimental points for He seem to tie in with the very low temperature quantum calculations of de Boer.

In conclusion, then, it is seen that the available experimental measurements are reasonably consistent with the available theoretical calculations, but that there is certainly some work yet to be done before this phase of the study of transport phenomena is complete.[10]

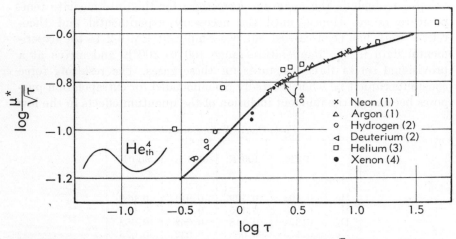

Fig. D,6a. Comparison of the theoretical curve for log $(\mu^*/\sqrt{\tau})$ with experimental data. The experimental data are reduced according to the formula $\mu^* = \mu r_0^2/\sqrt{m\epsilon}$ using the values of ϵ and r_0 given in Table D,6a. The curve He_{th} is calculated by de Boer, *J. Physica 10*, 348 (1943). (1) Trautz, M., and Zimmerman, H. *Ann. Physik 22*, 189 (1935). (2) van Itterbeek, A., and Claes, A. *Physica 5*, 938 (1938). (3) van Itterbeek, A., and Keesom, W. H. *Physica 5*, 257 (1938). (4) Trautz, M., and Heberling, R. *Ann. Physik 20*, 118 (1934).

COMPARISON OF SIMPLE VISCOSITY FORMULAS WITH FORMULA BASED ON THE LENNARD-JONES POTENTIAL. In Art. 4 it was shown that for molecules which repel one another according to an inverse power law, the coefficient of viscosity assumes the simple form

$$\mu = k'T^s \tag{6-6}$$

where the constants k' and s are determined by fitting the experimental data. Similarly, for the Sutherland potential, it was shown that the viscosity is given by

$$\mu = \frac{k_C T^{\frac{1}{2}}}{1 + \dfrac{C}{T}} \tag{6-7}$$

---

[10] The problem of quantum effects in transport properties has recently been studied further by J. de Boer and R. B. Bird [*9e*].

with two adjustable constants, k_C and C, which are obtained by fitting the observed values.

It should be stressed that for molecules whose behavior can be represented by a Lennard-Jones potential neither Eq. 6-6 nor Eq. 6-7 can hold over any large temperature range. This fact is clearly brought out in Table D,6d and in Fig. D,6b, where values of C/T, $C/(\epsilon/k)$, and s are

Table D,6d. Temperature dependence of Sutherland's constant
and the temperature exponent s. From [26] by permission.

$$\mu = k_C T^{\frac{1}{2}}/[1 + (C/T)]$$
$$\mu = k' T^s$$

kT/ϵ	C/T	$C/(\epsilon/k)$	s
0.30	0.5538	0.1661	0.8564
0.50	0.8786	0.4393	0.9677
0.75	1.083	0.8123	1.0200
1.00	1.012	1.012	1.0030
1.25	0.8660	1.083	0.9641
1.50	0.7443	1.116	0.9267
2.00	0.5466	1.093	0.8534
2.50	0.4331	1.083	0.8022
3	0.3669	1.101	0.7684
4	0.2829	1.132	0.7205
5	0.2453	1.227	0.6970
10	0.1857	1.857	0.6566
50	0.1697	8.485	0.6451
100	0.1681	16.81	0.6439
400	0.1680	67.20	0.6438

given as functions of the reduced temperature kT/ϵ. The wide variation of the "constants" with temperature certainly indicates that these simple formulas should not be used for more than interpolation purposes over small ranges in temperature—particularly if the force constants for the Lennard-Jones potential are known for the gas under consideration.

Fig. D,6b also points out that for C/T greater than 1.1 and for s greater than 1.01 it is impossible to choose an ϵ/k which can be used as a parameter in the Lennard-Jones potential. There are a number of such gases whose Sutherland constants or temperature indices lie without the acceptable region; these gases exhibit abnormal viscosities and will be discussed in detail.

ANOMALOUS TEMPERATURE DEPENDENCE OF VISCOSITY. The molecular interaction for some substances deviates so much from the Lennard-Jones potential that there is no possible choice of ϵ/k or r_0 which will allow the viscosity-temperature curves to be fitted with Eq. 6-2. These molecules have strong dipole moments, are very unsymmetrical, or are metallic in nature. Sutherland constants and temperature indices for these gases are given in Table D,6e. These values may be used for interpolations and estimations of the viscosity for such gases. We shall now discuss these anomalous gases in several groups.

Polar molecules: H_2O, NH_3, HBr, HCN, HI, $HgCl_2$. The energy of interaction of polar molecules is quite different from that of nonpolar molecules in that the potential function should contain a term in $1/r^3$ which has an angular dependent coefficient (Stockmayer's potential). Hence, it is not at all surprising that these molecules are anomalous.

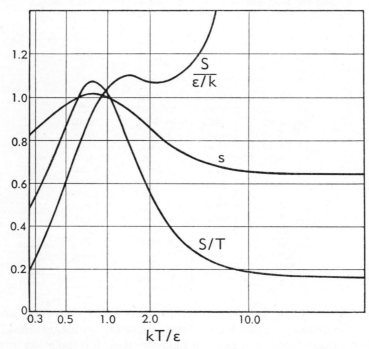

Fig. D,6b.   Temperature dependence of Sutherland's constant C, and the temperature exponent s. From [*26*] by permission.

Cigar-shaped molecules: n-heptane. The transport properties and, in particular, viscosity are not very sensitive to the shape of the molecules. However, if the ratio of the length to the diameter becomes too great, all of the physical properties are affected. Thus the temperature dependence of the viscosity of n-heptane is greater than would be expected for spherical molecules.

Metal vapors and valence unsaturated molecules: Hg, Cd, Zn. The valence unsaturated molecules behave quite differently from those compounds in which the total resultant electron spin is zero. For large separation, where there is essentially no overlap of the electronic wave functions for the two molecules, there is the usual inverse seventh power van der Waals' force of attraction. As the molecules come together the

Table D,6e. Viscosity of anomalous gas. From [*26*] by permission.

$$\mu \times 10^7 = k'T^s$$
$$\mu \times 10^7 = k_C T^{\frac{1}{2}}/[1 + (C/T)]$$

Gas	Temperature range (°K)	k'	s	k_C	C	(C/T) Sutherland constant divided by temperature in middle of range	Reference for viscosity data
H_2O	300–400	2.039	1.079	140.2	459.4	1.313	a
	500–600	1.227	1.164	235.8	1051.	1.911	
	600–700	1.598	1.123	244.4	1108.	1.705	
NH_3	300–400	1.203	1.181	202.7	740.7	2.116	a
	500–600	2.576	1.053	189.4	684.3	1.244	
	600–700	5.207	0.9427	164.7	518.7	0.7980	
HI	300–400	6.889	0.9837	221.9	312.9	0.8940	b
	400–500	10.42	0.9152	229.4	334.4	0.7431	
HBr	300–400	5.004	1.040	245.3	376.2	1.075	a
HCN	300–400	0.7443	1.215	166.3	836.2	2.389	a
	500–600	1.131	1.144	185.4	999.1	1.817	
$HgCl_2$	500–600	1.521	1.180	351.6	1191.	2.165	a
	600–700	4.841	1.000	248.1	656.5	1.010	
	750–850	3.406	1.057	314.1	982.8	1.229	
Zn	850–920	1.384	1.237	757.1	2374.	2.682	b
	920–950	18.68	0.8554	338.9	557.0	0.5957	
Cd	750–850	5.390	1.048	475.5	1011.	1.264	b
	850–900	9.836	0.9592	406.0	734.2	0.8391	
Hg	500–600	7.488	1.039	486.1	640.1	1.164	b
	700–800	8.793	1.018	552.0	776.4	1.035	
	800–900	8.827	1.018	595.7	892.6	1.050	
n-C_7H_{16}	350–450	2.163	0.9789	72.73	363.2	0.9080	b
	450–550	0.6715	1.172	133.1	1022.	2.044	
F_2	50–150	3.237	1.170	244.7	246.9	2.469	c
	200–300	13.52	0.8793	170.7	139.3	0.5572	

Table References.

a. Braune, H., and Linke, R. *Z. physik. Chem. A148*, 195 (1930).
b. Landolt-Börnstein. *Physikalisch-Chemische Tabellen.*
c. Kanda, E. *Bull. Chem. Soc. Japan 12*, 463 (1937).

nature of the potential curve at small separations may assume various forms, depending upon whether the "collision complex" formed by the two molecules is in one of the repulsive or one of the attractive states. These types of interaction are the result of the Pauli principle, which places certain restrictions upon the symmetry properties of the electronic and spin wave functions. From quantum mechanics one can calculate a priori the probability that the collision complex will be in a particular attractive or repulsive state.

By way of elaboration, we may consider the simplest case of two colliding hydrogen atoms. For large separations, the electrons on the two atoms are still quantum mechanically distinguishable, and hence the two atoms attract each other with an interaction potential proportional to $1/r^6$. As the two atoms come closer, the symmetry requirements of the total wave function allow the formation of either a $^1\Sigma$ or a $^3\Sigma$ state. The singlet (attractive) state corresponds to the usual homopolar binding and has force constants $r_0 = 0.5$ A and $\epsilon/k = 51,000°K$. One collision out of every four will follow this potential curve. The triplet state corresponds to the first excited state of the hydrogen molecule (a state in which the atoms repel one another except at large separations) and has force constants [12] $r_0 = 3.5$ A and $\epsilon/k = 3.8°K$. Three out of every four collisions follow this potential.

The metallic vapors Hg, Cd, and Zn, are not valence-saturated and it is to be expected that their collisions should be anomalous in the same sense as the hydrogen atoms. These metal-vapor atoms are initially in the $^1S_0$ state, but their valence electrons are easily promoted.

The interaction potential between mercury atoms has been determined [13] from a study of the experimental Menke distribution function for liquid mercury. It was found that the repulsive energy of mercury atoms is described by an inverse ninth power function better than by an inverse twelfth power function. This use of a smaller power might correspond to the notion that collisions between mercury atoms are a statistical mixture of two sorts—those with large ϵ/k and small r_0 (corresponding to the ground state of Hg_2) and those with small ϵ/k and large r_0 (corresponding to an excited state of Hg_2). If we try to fit the potential function based on the Menke distribution with an inverse twelfth power Lennard-Jones potential, we obtain force constants $\epsilon/k = 1522$ and $r_0 = 2.5$ A. If we insert these force constants into Eq. 6-2, the calculated values for the viscosity of mercury do not agree very well with the experimental measurements (see Table D,6f). It would be interesting to find out whether this discrepancy is due to the two types of collisions or just to the natural softness of these particular atoms.

The preceding discussion should show the molecules for which Eq. 6-2 does not apply. For the simple gases, Eq. 6-2 provides a sound method for interpolating and extrapolating experimental data. In regions of high

Table D,6f. Viscosity of mercury. From [26] by permission.

T (°K)	$\mu \times 10^7$ (calc.)	$\mu \times 10^7$ (exptl.)*
491	4945	4709
603	7466	5831
769	5943	7610
883	8551	8802

* Landolt-Börnstein. *Physikalische-Chemische Tabellen.*

temperature where there are virtually no data, this relationship should be particularly useful. The force constants in Table D,6a obtained from the viscosity should not be used to calculate the equilibrium properties of unsymmetrical, polar, or metallic molecules. The experimental values of the second virial coefficient of organic vapors are considerably larger than values calculated from these parameters. In the hydrocarbons the error varies from a few per cent for ethane to about 20 per cent for *n*-hexane and 60 per cent for cyclohexane [14]. The disagreement is due either to the inadequacy of the Lennard-Jones potential for the molecules or to the fact that inelastic collisions are more probable for complex molecules.

D,7. The Viscosity of Mixtures. The force constants between pairs of unlike molecules, $(r_0)_{ij}$ and ϵ_{ij}/k, appear in the formulas for the viscosity of mixtures of gases. When no experimental data are available, these force constants may be estimated from the simple combining laws:

$$(r_0)_{ij} = \tfrac{1}{2}[(r_0)_i + (r_0)_j] \qquad (7\text{-}1)$$

$$\frac{\epsilon_{ij}}{k} = \left[\left(\frac{\epsilon_i}{k}\right)\left(\frac{\epsilon_j}{k}\right)\right]^{\frac{1}{2}} \qquad (7\text{-}2)$$

Whenever possible they should be calculated directly from experimental diffusion data as discussed in Art. 8.

Formulas for the viscosity of mixtures. The first approximation to the coefficient of viscosity for a ν component gas mixture in terms of the Y functions is

$$[\mu_{1,2\ldots,\nu}]_1 \times 10^7 = \frac{\begin{vmatrix} J_{11} & J_{12} & J_{13} & \cdots & J_{1f} & 1 \\ J_{12} & J_{22} & J_{23} & \cdots & J_{2f} & 1 \\ J_{13} & J_{23} & J_{33} & \cdots & J_{3f} & 1 \\ \cdot & \cdot & \cdot & \cdots & \cdot & \cdot \\ \cdot & \cdot & \cdot & \cdots & \cdot & \cdot \\ \cdot & \cdot & \cdot & \cdots & \cdot & \cdot \\ J_{1f} & J_{2f} & J_{3f} & \cdots & J_{ff} & 1 \\ 1 & 1 & 1 & \cdots & 1 & 0 \end{vmatrix}}{|J_{ij}|} \qquad (7\text{-}3)$$

Table D,7a. Viscosity of binary mixtures. From [26] by permission.

T (°K)		Viscosity H_2-CO_2					Viscosity H_2-O_2					
	%H_2	0.0	19.93	41.29	78.50	100.0	0.0	18.35	39.45	60.30	78.08	100.0
300	EX*	1493	1501	1506	1370	891	2057	2019	1925	1784	1494	889
	CG*	1493	1507	1508	1372	889	2064	2021	1934	1774	1524	889
	CD*	1493	1509	1512	1379	889	2064	2024	1939	1782	1531	889
400	EX	1944	1945	1933	1713	1081	2568	2507	2381	2192	1858	1087
	CG	1920	1926	1913	1698	1065	2567	2506	2388	2178	1857	1065
	CD	1920	1928	1918	1703	1065	2567	2509	2394	2186	1865	1065
500	EX	2353	2358	2321	2026	1256	3017	2950	2790	2556	2158	1259
	CG	2301	2302	2275	1990	1228	3015	2940	2795	2541	2158	1228
	CD	2301	2303	2280	1998	1228	3015	2943	2802	2551	2168	1228
550	EX	5556?	2542	2506	2173	1341	3220	3147	2978	2733	2288	1381
	CG	2479	2478	2445	2130	1308	3224	3140	2986	2714	2302	1308
	CD	2479	2479	2450	2137	1308	3224	3146	2993	2721	2313	1308

Table D,7a (continued)

T (°K)		Viscosity CO₂-N₂O					Viscosity O₂-CO				
	%CO₂ 0.0	40.24	60.33	80.97	100.0	%O₂ 0.0	23.37	42.01	77.33	100.0	
300 EX	1488	1494	1495	1490	1493	1776	1841	1900	1998	2057	
CG	1489	1497	1498	1496	1493	1779	1880	1946	2034	2064	
CD	1489	1523	1524	1513	1493	1779	1884	1897	1998	2064	
400 EX	1493?	1950	1950	1941	1944	2183	2268	2343	2482	2568	
CG	1936	1938	1934	1928	1920	2210	2328	2407	2521	2567	
CD	1936	1965	1961	1946	1920	2210	2292	2358	2485	2567	
500 EX	2355	2365	2365	2358	2353	2548	2650	2741	2908	3017	
CG	2338	2332	2325	2314	2301	2593	2725	2817	2954	3015	
CD	2338	2361	2354	2332	2301	2593	2690	2768	2918	3015	
550 EX	2555	2562	2564	2551	2556						
CG	2525	2517	2508	2495	2479						
CD	2525	2546	2537	2513	2479						

* EX = experimental data; CG = calculated using a geometric mean ϵ/k; CD = calculated using ϵ/k calculated from a single diffusion measurement.

where $|J_{ij}|$ is the νth order determinant of the J_{ij}, the latter being

$$J_{ij} = A_{ij} - B_{ij}, \qquad i \neq j \tag{7-4}$$

$$J_{ii} = A_{ii} - B_{ii} - \sum_{k=1}^{\nu} \left(\frac{X_k}{X_i}\right) \left[A_{ik} + B_{ik}\left(\frac{\mathfrak{M}_k}{\mathfrak{M}_i}\right)\right] \tag{7-5}$$

The A_{ij} and B_{ij} are

$$A_{ij} \times 10^7 = \frac{16}{3}\left[\frac{2\pi m_i m_j}{kT(m_i + m_j)^3}\right]^{\frac{1}{2}} (r_0)_{ij}^2 Y(1, 1; \tau_{ij}) \tag{7-6}$$

$$B_{ij} \times 10^7 = \frac{16}{5}\left[\frac{2\pi m_i m_j}{kT(m_i + m_j)^3}\right]^{\frac{1}{2}} (r_0)_{ij}^2 Y(2, 2; \tau_{ij}) \tag{7-7}$$

For computational purposes we rewrite A_{ij} and B_{ij} as follows:

$$A_{ij} = 0.0088315 \left[\frac{\mathfrak{M}_i \mathfrak{M}_j}{(\mathfrak{M}_i + \mathfrak{M}_j)^3}\right]^{\frac{1}{2}} T^{-\frac{1}{2}}(r_0)_{ij}^2 Y(1, 1; \tau_{ij}) \tag{7-8}$$

$$B_{ij} = 0.0052988 \left[\frac{\mathfrak{M}_i \mathfrak{M}_j}{(\mathfrak{M}_i + \mathfrak{M}_j)^3}\right]^{\frac{1}{2}} T^{-\frac{1}{2}}(r_0)_{ij}^2 Y(2, 2; \tau_{ij}) \tag{7-9}$$

in which:

$(r_0)_{ij}$ = collision diameter in angstroms between unlike molecules.

(ϵ_{ij}/k) = depth of potential well in °K.

X_i, $\mathfrak{M}_i$ = mole fraction and molecular weight of ith component.

$\tau_{ij} = kT/\epsilon_{ij}$ = reduced temperature.

$Y(l, n; \tau_{ij})$ = functions given in Table D,5a.

For computing the viscosity of mixtures containing more than three components, the following hint may be helpful:[11] After calculating the matrix elements J_{ij}, "triangularize" the determinant in the numerator so that the terms lying to the left of the diagonal row going from upper left to lower right are zero. The value of this determinant is the product of the $\nu + 1$ diagonal elements. However, the value of the determinant in the denominator is just equal to the product of the first ν diagonal elements of the determinant in the numerator. Hence the value of viscosity is equal to the lower right-hand element of the triangularized determinant of the numerator.

Comparison of calculated and experimental results. The experimental and calculated viscosities of several simple binary mixtures are compared in Table D,7a. The force constants between like molecules which were used in the calculations are those determined from the viscosity of pure gases; the force constants between unlike molecules are those from diffusion measurements or from Eq. 7-1 and 7-2. The agreement is

---

[11] Further information about the computation of determinants may be obtained by consulting R. A. Frazer, W. J. Duncan, and A. R. Collar [*14a*, p. 106].

excellent in view of the fact that no parameters are specifically adjusted to fit the data.

The same calculations for a three-component mixture of noble gases are shown in Table D,7b. The $(r_0)_i$ and ϵ_i/k used are from viscosity measurements, and the $(r_0)_{ij}$ and ϵ_{ij}/k are from Eq. 7-1 and 7-2. The discrepancy between computed and experimental values is about one per cent, which is certainly satisfactory.

Table D,7b. Viscosity of ternary mixture of Ne-A-He. From [26] by permission.

T (°K)	Volume per cent			$\mu_{1,2,3} \times 10^7$ g/cm sec	
	Ne	A	He	Calc.	Exptl. [14b]
193	55.76	26.70	17.54	2718	2740
	31.93	32.13	35.94	2562	2569
	21.66	58.51	19.83	2429	2411
	21.89	23.82	54.29	2500	2504
373	55.76	26.70	17.54	3205	3237
	31.93	32.13	35.94	3025	3044
	21.66	58.51	19.83	2895	2886
	21.89	23.82	54.29	2938	2957
473	55.76	26.70	17.54	3752	3790
	31.93	32.13	35.94	3551	3574
	21.66	58.51	19.83	3425	3415
	21.89	23.82	54.29	3449	3470

Eq. 7-3, 7-4, 7-5, 7-8, and 7-9 may be used to calculate the viscosity of such industrially important mixtures as flue and fuel gases. A comparison of the calculated and experimental values is given in Table D,7c. The agreement in more than half of the examples is excellent. In some of the other mixtures, there are small discrepancies which may be due to errors in the gas analysis. The calculated values for these multicomponent gas systems are accurate to within approximately one per cent.

Modification of calculations to include gases contaminated with polar components. The viscosity of mixtures which contain small amounts of one polar component, such as water or ammonia, can be approximated by a modification of the above method. The diagonal element J_{ii} is calculated for the nonpolar component in the usual manner with the viscosity force constants from Eq. 7-5, 7-8, and 7-9. For the polar component, which is designated by the subscript p, the B_{pp} may be approximated from viscosity data by the relation,

$$B_{pp} \cong \frac{1}{[2(\mu_p)_{exptl}]} \tag{7-10}$$

Table D,7c. Viscosity of multicomponent mixtures of industrial gases. From [26] by permission.

Composition (volume %)							Temp. °K	$\mu \times 10^7$ Exptl.	$\mu \times 10^7$ Calc.	Ref.
CO_2	O_2	CO	H_2	CH_4	N_2	Heavier hydrocarbons				
8.6	2.3				89.1		293	1756	1761	a
13.3	3.9				82.8		293	1749	1765	a
6.2	10.7				83.1		293	1793	1789	a
10.4		28.5	1.6		59.5		293	1738	1798	a
10.80	2.00		2.20		85.00		300.5	1827	1792	b
							524.5	2715	2661	
							973	4117	4008	
							1279	4856	4753	
6.70	0.10	7.80	2.20		83.20		307.5	1842	1835	b
							519	2655	2653	
							975	4048	4019	
							1285	4808	4783	
6.40	3.00	0.30	0.70		89.60		314	1904	1856	b
							518	2706	2644	
							974.5	4113	4017	
							1287	4895	4777	
6.0	0.10	25.70	11.50		56.70		302	1823	1829	b
							526	2686	2696	
							976	4041	4042	
							1283	4777	4821	
10.6		29.8	3.9	0.3	55.4		293	1743	1794	a
8.9		30.7	3.3	0.4	56.7		293	1747	1797	a
8.7		32.8	1.5	0.2	56.8		293	1749	1802	a
3.70	0.30	27.10	9.50	1.60	57.80		300.5	1815	1816	b

Table D,7c (continued)

Composition (volume %)							Temp. °K	$\mu \times 10^7$ Exptl.	$\mu \times 10^7$ Calc.	Ref.
CO$_2$	O$_2$	CO	H$_2$	CH$_4$	N$_2$	Heavier hydrocarbons				
							565.5	2819	2823	
							981	4045	4041	
							1282	4792	4803	a
1.7	0.9	6.0	57.5	24.0	7.8	2.1	293	1262	1254	a
2.1	0.9	5.7	53.0	24.3	11.7	2.3	293	1304	1290	a
2.0	1.4	4.6	54.9	23.5	11.6	2.0	293	1310	1398	a
3.3	0.6	3.8	51.3	29.6	10.0	1.4	293	1332	1269	a
2.2	0.6	4.1	53.1	29.5	9.2	1.3	293	1306	1254	a
2.2	1.0	4.0	52.3	29.9	9.4	1.2	293	1307	1261	a
2.5	0.8	14.9	53.0	18.1	9.1	1.6	293	1355	1373	a
4.8	0.3	26.4	17.2	2.6	48.2	0.5	293	1714	1743	a
3.5	0.3	27.3	14.4	3.7	50.0	0.8	293	1712	1732	a
3.1	0.5	28.6	17.7	4.2	45.0	0.9	293	1715	1719	a

Table References.

a. eHrning, F., and Zipperer, L. *Gas- u. Wasserfach 79*, 49–54, 69–73 (1936).
b. Schmid, C. *Gas- u. Wasserfach 85*, 92 (1942).

and the A_{pp} may be approximated by[12]

$$A_{pp} \cong 0.91 B_{pp} \tag{7-11}$$

The nondiagonal elements J_{ij} for the nonpolar-nonpolar interactions are calculated either by use of the force constants between unlike molecules obtained from Eq. 7-1 and 7-2 or from diffusion measurements. To get the J_{pi} for polar-nonpolar interactions, use is made of the fact that the energy of interaction between a polar molecule and a nonpolar molecule is only weakly dependent on the orientations and to a good approximation is of the same general form as the energy between two nonpolar molecules. The force constants are given approximately by [15c]

$$(r_0)_{pi} = \left[\frac{(r_0)_p + (r_0)_i}{2} \right] \left[1 + \frac{\sqrt{2}}{2} \frac{\alpha_i t_1}{(r_0)_i^3} \sqrt{\frac{\epsilon_p/k}{\epsilon_i/k}} \right]^{-\frac{1}{6}} \tag{7-12}$$

$$\frac{\epsilon_{pi}}{k} = \sqrt{\left(\frac{\epsilon_p}{k} \right) \left(\frac{\epsilon_i}{k} \right)} \left[1 + \frac{\sqrt{2}}{2} \frac{\alpha_i t_1}{(r_0)_i^3} \sqrt{\frac{\epsilon_p/k}{\epsilon_i/k}} \right]^2 \tag{7-13}$$

where

$(r_0)_p, \dfrac{\epsilon_p}{k}$ = force constants in the Stockmayer potential[13] calculated from second virial data.

α_i = polarizability of ith nonpolar component.

$t_1 = \dfrac{1}{\sqrt{8}} \left[\dfrac{p^2}{\epsilon_p (r_0)_p^3} \right]$ = dimensionless parameter appearing in the Stockmayer potential (see footnote 13).

p = dipole moment of the polar constituent.

Thus, having calculated the J_{ii}, J_{ij}, J_{ip}, and J_{pp}, one may use the formula in Eq. 7-3 to evaluate the viscosity of a gaseous mixture containing one polar contaminant.

In this way the viscosity of moist air was calculated; the results are shown in Table D,7d. Air was assumed to be a pure gas with the force constants given in Table D,6a. It is interesting to note that these calculations suggest that between 100 and 500°K the viscosity decreases with increasing moisture content, while above 800°K the reverse is true. There is as yet no experimental data to substantiate this.

Thus at the present time it is possible to do a good job of calculating

---

[12] The constant 0.91 is based on the fact that B_{pp} and A_{pp} bear almost the same relation to each other as does $Y(2, 2)$ to $Y(1, 1)$ and that $Y(2, 2)/Y(1, 1)$ is approximately constant.

[13] The Stockmayer potential, which includes the interaction of two ideal dipoles, is

$$E(r, \theta_1, \theta_2, \phi) =$$
$$4\epsilon_p \left\{ \left[\frac{(r_0)_p}{r} \right]^{12} - \left[\frac{(r_0)_p}{r} \right]^6 - \frac{t_1}{\sqrt{2}} \left[\frac{(r_0)_p}{r} \right]^3 (2 \cos \theta_1 \cos \theta_2 - \sin \theta_1 \sin \theta_2 \cos \phi) \right\}$$

Rowlinson has given a table of parameters which may be used with this equation [15a].

the viscosity of nonpolar gases and their mixtures and a fair job of estimating the viscosity of mixtures containing one polar component. The rigorous calculation of the transport properties of polar gases cannot be accomplished until the theory has been worked out for polar gases.

Table D,7d. Viscosity of moist air, μ $(10^{-7}$ g/cm sec). From [15] by permission.

Temperature °K	Per cent moisture			
	0.0	0.5	1.0	5.0
100	702	701	700	688
150	1038	1035	1033	1016
200	1337	1335	1333	1315
273.16	1724	1722	1720	1704
300	1851	1849	1847	1832
400	2290	2289	2288	2278
500	2678	2678	2677	2671
600	3034	3034	3035	3033
800	3680	3680	3681	3687
1000	4207	4200	4203	4274
1200	4761	4765	4768	4786
1400	5251	5253	5257	5280
1600	5735	5739	5744	5770
2000	6680	6685	6690	6720
3000	8685	8689	8691	8730
5000	12070	12090	12100	12160

D,8. Diffusion and Self-Diffusion. At the present time it is not possible to make the fullest use of the rigorous kinetic theory since good experimental measurements of diffusion as a function of temperature do not exist. As these measurements become available, valuable information will be obtained about the forces between unlike molecules, in a manner analogous to that used in obtaining the forces between like molecules from viscosity data.

THE COEFFICIENT OF DIFFUSION IN BINARY MIXTURES. The first approximation to the coefficient of binary diffusion is

$$[\mathfrak{D}_{ij}]_1 = \frac{\frac{3}{16}N[2kT/\pi m_{ij}]^{\frac{1}{2}}}{n(r_0)_{ij}^2 Y(1,\,1;\,\tau_{ij})} \tag{8-1}$$

in which n is the total number density. This may be rewritten in a form more suitable for calculating purposes:

$$[\mathfrak{D}_{ij}]_1 = \frac{0.00185832T^{\frac{3}{2}}}{p\mathfrak{M}_{ij}^{\frac{1}{2}}(r_0)_{ij}^2 Y(1,\,1;\,\tau_{ij})} \tag{8-2}$$

in which

$[\mathfrak{D}_{ij}]_1$ = first approximation to coefficient of diffusion in cm² sec⁻¹.

p = pressure in atmospheres.

$(1/\mathfrak{M}_{ij}) = (1/\mathfrak{M}_i) + (1/\mathfrak{M}_j)$.

$(r_0)_{ij}, \epsilon_{ij}/k$ = collision diameter (in angstroms) and potential well depth in °K for interactions between unlike molecules.

$\tau_{ij} = kT/\epsilon_{ij}$.

$Y(1, 1; \tau_{ij})$ = reduced collision integral, Table D,5a.

The expression for the next higher approximation $[\mathfrak{D}_{ij}]_2$ has also been worked out and is

$$[\mathfrak{D}_{ij}]_2 = \frac{[\mathfrak{D}_{ij}]_1}{(1 - \Delta_{ij})} \qquad (8\text{-}3)$$

where

$$\Delta_{ij} = \frac{5[C(\tau_{ij}) - 1]^2[P_{ij}^{(i)}X_i^2 + P_{ij}^{(j)}X_j^2 + P_{ij}X_iX_j]}{[Q_{ij}^{(i)}X_i^2 + Q_{ij}^{(j)}X_j^2 + Q_{ij}X_iX_j]} \qquad (8\text{-}4)$$

$$P_{ij}^{(i)} = \frac{2}{5}\,\mathfrak{M}_i^2\left[\frac{2(\mathfrak{M}_i + \mathfrak{M}_j)}{\mathfrak{M}_j}\right]^{\frac{1}{2}}\frac{(r_0)_i^2}{(r_0)_{ij}^2}\frac{Y(2, 2; \tau_i)}{Y(1, 1; \tau_{ij})} \qquad (8\text{-}5)$$

$$Q_{ij}^{(i)} = \frac{2}{5}\left[\frac{2(\mathfrak{M}_i + \mathfrak{M}_j)}{\mathfrak{M}_j}\right]^{\frac{1}{2}}\left[\frac{(r_0)_i}{(r_0)_{ij}}\right]^2\left[\frac{Y(2, 2; \tau_i)}{Y(1, 1; \tau_{ij})}\right]$$

$$\times \{6\mathfrak{M}_j^2 + [5 - 4B(\tau_{ij})]\mathfrak{M}_i^2 + 8\mathfrak{M}_i\mathfrak{M}_jA(\tau_{ij})\} \qquad (8\text{-}6)$$

$$P_{ij} = 3(\mathfrak{M}_i - \mathfrak{M}_j)^2 + 4\mathfrak{M}_i\mathfrak{M}_jA(\tau_{ij}) \qquad (8\text{-}7)$$

$$Q_{ij} = 3(\mathfrak{M}_i - \mathfrak{M}_j)^2(5 - 4B(\tau_{ij})) + 4\mathfrak{M}_i\mathfrak{M}_jA(\tau_{ij})(11 - 4B(\tau_{ij}))$$

$$+ \frac{16}{25}\frac{(\mathfrak{M}_i + \mathfrak{M}_j)^3}{(\mathfrak{M}_i\mathfrak{M}_j)^{\frac{1}{2}}}\left[\frac{(r_0)_i(r_0)_j}{(r_0)_{ij}^2}\right]^2\left[\frac{Y(2, 2; \tau_i)Y(2, 2; \tau_j)}{Y^2(1, 1; \tau_{ij})}\right] \qquad (8\text{-}8)$$

and $P_{ij}^{(j)}$ and $Q_{ij}^{(j)}$ may be obtained from $P_{ij}^{(i)}$ and $Q_{ij}^{(i)}$ by exchanging i and j in the formulas. Also, A, B, C are functions of τ_{ij} which are tabulated in Table D,5b.

Thus we see that $[\mathfrak{D}_{ij}]_1$ gives the primary dependence of the diffusion coefficient on the pressure, collision diameter, and the $T^{\frac{3}{2}}$ temperature dependence modified by the appropriate Y function. The concentration dependence of the diffusion coefficient appears in $[\mathfrak{D}_{ij}]_2$. The quantity Δ_{ij} is usually less than 0.03; hence this concentration dependence is very slight. That such variation with concentration actually exists is unquestionably true, but there are no experimental data sufficiently good to prove or disprove the exact form of Δ_{ij}.

To the first approximation the coefficient of diffusion depends upon the forces between unlike molecules only; and in the next approximation it depends but slightly upon the forces between similar molecules. Consequently experimental measurements of the temperature dependence of the diffusion coefficient can provide an excellent method for obtaining the force constants, $(r_0)_{ij}$ and ϵ_{ij}/k, between unlike molecules. However, at the present time the necessary data for calculating $(r_0)_{ij}$ and ϵ_{ij}/k are not available.

There are a few measurements of $\mathfrak{D}_{ij}$ at only one temperature. From these measurements we can get some information about the forces between unlike molecules.[14] If it is assumed that $(r_0)_{ij} = \frac{1}{2}[(r_0)_i + (r_0)_j]$, then Eq. 8-2 can be used to get ϵ_{ij}/k from the single measurement of $\mathfrak{D}_{ij}$.

Values of the diffusion coefficients which have been calculated using Eq. 8-2, assuming that the force constants can be approximated by Eq. 7-1 and 7-2, are compared with experimental values in Table D,8a. The force constants between like molecules used in finding the mean force constants are those obtained from viscosity measurements given in Table D,6a. In view of the assumptions made, the agreement is reasonably good and seems to justify the use of Eq. 7-1 and 7-2 for estimating $(r_0)_{ij}$ and ϵ_{ij}/k when diffusion data are unavailable. These empirical combining laws should be discarded as soon as the temperature dependence of $\mathfrak{D}_{ij}$ has been determined experimentally.

DIFFUSION COEFFICIENTS IN MULTICOMPONENT SYSTEMS. The generalized diffusion coefficients, D_{ij}, for use in systems containing more than two components, were defined in Eq. 2-2. These coefficients were defined in such a way that for binary systems, $D_{ij} = \mathfrak{D}_{ij}$. For the general ν component system, the relationship between the diffusion coefficients is considerably more complicated. The first approximation to D_{12} may be expressed in terms of the first approximation to the various binary diffusion coefficients in the gas:

$$[D_{12}]_1 = -\frac{\rho n_1}{\mathfrak{M}_2} \frac{\begin{vmatrix} 0 & A_{23} & A_{24} & \cdot\,\cdot \\ A_{32} & 0 & A_{34} & \cdot\,\cdot \\ A_{42} & A_{43} & 0 & \cdot\,\cdot \\ \cdot\,\cdot\,\cdot & \cdot\,\cdot\,\cdot & \cdot\,\cdot\,\cdot & \cdot\,\cdot \end{vmatrix} + \begin{vmatrix} A_{12} & A_{13} & A_{14} & \cdot\,\cdot \\ A_{32} & 0 & A_{34} & \cdot\,\cdot \\ A_{42} & A_{43} & 0 & \cdot\,\cdot \\ \cdot\,\cdot\,\cdot & \cdot\,\cdot\,\cdot & \cdot\,\cdot\,\cdot & \cdot\,\cdot \end{vmatrix}}{\begin{vmatrix} 0 & A_{12} & A_{13} & A_{14} & \cdot\,\cdot \\ A_{21} & 0 & A_{23} & A_{24} & \cdot\,\cdot \\ A_{31} & A_{32} & 0 & A_{34} & \cdot\,\cdot \\ A_{41} & A_{42} & A_{43} & 0 & \cdot\,\cdot \\ \cdot & \cdot & \cdot & \cdot & \cdot\,\cdot \\ \cdot & \cdot & \cdot & \cdot & \cdot\,\cdot \end{vmatrix}} \tag{8-9}$$

in which the elements A_{ij} are

$$A_{ij} = \frac{n_i n_j}{[\mathfrak{D}_{ij}]_1} + n_j \left(\frac{\mathfrak{M}_j}{\mathfrak{M}_i}\right) \sum_{k \neq i}^{\nu} \frac{n_k}{[\mathfrak{D}_{ik}]_1} \tag{8-10}$$

[14] One might ask why we do not compute both $(r_0)_{ij}$ and ϵ_{ij}/k from binary viscosity data. In principle, there is no reason why this cannot be done—however, the data must be extremely good. Also, it must be remembered that the forces between like molecules enter rather strongly into the binary viscosity formula—even in the first approximation. Hence the coefficient of diffusion certainly provides the best way to evaluate the force constant for pairs of dissimilar molecules.

Table D,8a. Comparison of calculated and observed diffusion coefficients.

Gas pair	Arith. mean $(r_0)_{12}$ Viscosity of pure components	Geom. mean ϵ_{12}/k Viscosity of pure components	Temp. °K	$\mathfrak{D}_{12}$ Calc. cm² sec⁻¹	$\mathfrak{D}_{12}$ Exptl. cm² sec⁻¹	Ref.
H₂-A	3.193	64.3	293.2	0.770	0.77	c
A-N₂	3.550	106	293.2	0.188	0.20	c
A-O₂	3.426	118	293.2	0.188	0.20	c
A-CO₂	3.707	153	293.2	0.136	0.14	c
O₂-N₂	3.557	102	273.2	0.175	0.181	a
			293.2	0.199	0.22	c
He-A	3.059	21.3	273.2	0.653	0.641	a
H₂-O₂	3.201	61.4	273.2	0.689	0.697	a
O₂-CO	3.512	112	273.2	0.175	0.185	a
CO₂-N₂O	3.938	204	273.2	0.092	0.096	a
H₂-CO	3.279	60.6	273.2	0.661	0.651	a
H₂-CO₂	3.482	79.5	273.2	0.544	0.550	a
			288.2	0.597	0.619	b
			293.2	0.616	0.60	c
			298.2	0.634	0.646	d
H₂-N₂O	3.424	85.6	273.2	0.552	0.535	a
O₂-CO₂	3.715	147	273.2	0.128	0.139	a
			293.2	0.146	0.16	c
H₂-N₂	3.325	55.2	273.2	0.656	0.674	a
			288.2	0.718	0.743	b
			293.2	0.739	0.76	c
H₂-CH₄	3.425	67.4	273.2	0.607	0.625	a
			298.2	0.705	0.726	d
H₂-C₂H₄	3.600	82.6	298.2	0.595	0.602	d
CO₂-CH₄	3.939	161	273.2	0.138	0.153	a
CO-N₂	3.636	100	273.2	0.174	0.192	a
CO-CO₂	3.793	145	273.2	0.128	0.137	a
CO₂-N₂	3.839	132	273.2	0.130	0.144	a
			288.2	0.143	0.158	b
			293.2	0.147	0.16	c
			298.2	0.152	0.165	d
H₂-SF₆*	3.922	89.1	298.2	0.473	0.420	d
H₂-C₂H₆	3.693	87.5	298.2	0.556	0.537	d
N₂-C₂H₆	4.050	145	298.2	0.144	0.148	d
N₂-C₂H₄	3.957	137	298.2	0.156	0.163	d
N₂-nC₄H₁₀	4.339	194	298.2	0.0986	0.0960	d
N₂-iso C₄H₁₀	4.511	169	298.2	0.0970	0.0908	d
H₂-cis-butene-2†	4.111	113	298.2	0.413	0.378	d
N₂-cis-butene-2†	4.467	188	298.2	0.0947	0.095	d

* Force constants of pure component estimated from critical data.

† Force constants of pure component estimated from boiling point and second virial coefficient.

Table References.

a. Chapman, S., and Cowling, T. G. *Mathematical Theory of Non-Uniform Gases.* Cambridge Univ. Press, 1939.
b. Boardman, L. E., and Wild, N. E. *Proc. Roy. Soc. London A162*, 511 (1937).
c. Waldman, L. *Naturwissenschaften 32*, 223 (1944).
d. Boyd, C. A., Stein, N., Steingrimsson, V., and Rumpel, W. F. *J. Chem. Phys. 19*, 548 (1951).

n_i is the number of moles per cm^3 of the ith component. Similar expressions may be obtained for the other D_{ij} by permuting the indices or by suitable modifications of the above formulas. There are no data with which to test the validity of these relationships.

THE COEFFICIENT OF SELF-DIFFUSION. If in Eq. 8-2 we set i equal to j, there results the formula for the first approximation to the self-diffusion coefficient for the component i:

$$[\mathfrak{D}_{ii}]_1 = \frac{0.002628T^{\frac{3}{2}}}{p\mathfrak{M}_i^{\frac{1}{2}}(r_0)_i^2 Y(1,\,1;\,\tau_i)} = 3\rho A(\tau_i)[\mu_i]_1 \sim 1.3\rho[\mu_i]_1 \quad (8\text{-}11)$$

The next approximation is

$$[\mathfrak{D}_{ii}]_2 = \frac{[\mathfrak{D}_{ii}]_1}{1-\Delta_{ii}} \quad (8\text{-}12)$$

where

$$\Delta_{ii} = \frac{5(C(\tau_i)-1)^2}{11-4B(\tau_i)+8A(\tau_i)} \quad (8\text{-}13)$$

in which the various quantities have been defined.

In Eq. 8-11 we see that $[\mathfrak{D}_{ii}]_1$ bears a simple relation to $[\mu_i]_1$; indeed, aside from the factor $3A$ (which is slowly varying in τ_i) this is the same relation as is obtained by simple kinetic theory arguments.

Of course a coefficient of self-diffusion and the concept of mutual diffusion of molecules which are physically identical is meaningless. However, it is possible to measure quantities experimentally which are very nearly $\mathfrak{D}_{ii}$.

Interdiffusion of isotopes. If one isotopic form of a gas is allowed to diffuse into another isotopic form of the gas, the progress of the diffusion can be followed by standard isotopic methods. Since the number of neutrons in the atomic nuclei has essentially no effect on molecular interaction, $(r_0)_{ij} = (r_0)_i = (r_0)_j$; $\epsilon_{ij} = \epsilon_i = \epsilon_j$; and if the molecules are sufficiently large, $\mathfrak{M}_{ij} \cong \frac{1}{2}\mathfrak{M}_i$ or $\frac{1}{2}\mathfrak{M}_j$. Hence, Eq. 8-1 can be used to describe this case. With the increasing availability of isotopes, this should prove an interesting method for getting information about intermolecular forces.

Interdiffusion or ortho and para forms. If the ortho form of a molecule is allowed to diffuse into the para form, the progress of diffusion can be followed (by the electric resistance of a hot wire). For this case the interaction between ortho and para, ortho and ortho, and para and para forms can be considered as being described by the same sets of force constants, although the interaction does of course depend to a very slight extent upon the rotational states of the molecule. Also, since $\mathfrak{M}_{ij} = \frac{1}{2}\mathfrak{M}_i = \frac{1}{2}\mathfrak{M}_j$, Eq. 8-11 is also applicable here.

In Table D,8b are shown some experimental self-diffusion constants along with values calculated from Eq. 8-11 using the force constants in

Table D,8b. The coefficient of self-diffusion. From [*26*] by permission.

Gas	T (°K)	$\mathfrak{D}_{11}$		Reference for experimental values
		Calculated cm²/sec	Experimental (corrected to 1 atm) cm²/sec	
Hydrogen	273	1.243	1.285 ± 0.002	a
	85	0.167	0.172 ± 0.008	a
	20.4	0.01043	0.00816 ± 0.0002	a
Krypton	293	0.093	0.093 ± 0.0045	b
Xenon	293	0.055	0.044 ± 0.002	b
Neon	293	0.491	0.473 ± 0.002	c
Argon	326.7	0.213	0.212 ± 0.002	d
	295.2	0.178	0.180 ± 0.001	d
	273.2	0.154	0.158 ± 0.002	d
	194.7	0.0820	0.0833 ± 0.0009	d
	90.2	0.0178	0.028 ± 0.0010	d
Nitrogen	293	0.198	0.200 ± 0.008	e
Methane	292	0.214	0.213 ± 0.007	f
Hydrogen chloride	295	0.127	0.1246	g

Table References.

a. Harteck, P., and Schmidt, H. W.   *Z. physik. Chem.* B*21*, 447 (1933).
b. Groth, W., and Harteck, P.   *Z. Elektrochem. 47*, 167 (1941).
c. Groth, W., and Sussner, E.   *Z. physik. Chem. 193*, 296 (1944).
d. Hutchinson, F.   *J. Chem. Phys. 17*, 1081 (1949).
e. Winn, E. B.   *Phys. Rev. 74*, 698 (1948).
f. Winn, E. B., and Ney, E. P.   *Phys. Rev. 72*, 77 (1947).
g. Braune, H., and Zehle, F.   *Z. physik. Chem.* B*49*, 247 (1941).

Table D,6a, which were obtained from viscosity. The agreement between calculated and experimental results is exceptionally good and demonstrates how measurements of two different properties lead to consistent information about intermolecular forces.

D,9.   Thermal Diffusion.   The contribution of a gradient in the temperature to the diffusion velocity was given by Eq. 2-4. The thermal diffusion ratio k_T was defined by Eq. 2-8 and 2-9. The first approximation $[k_T]_1$ is

$$[k_T]_1 = \frac{5X_i X_j (C(\tau_{ij}) - 1)(S_{ij}^{(j)} X_i - S_{ij}^{(i)} X_j)}{Q_{ij}^{(i)} X_i^2 + Q_{ij}^{(j)} X_j^2 + Q_{ij} X_i X_j} \qquad (9\text{-}1)$$

where

$$S_{ij}^{(i)} = \frac{2}{5}\,\mathfrak{M}_i \left[\frac{2(\mathfrak{M}_i + \mathfrak{M}_j)^3}{\mathfrak{M}_j}\right]^{\frac{1}{2}} \left[\frac{(r_0)_i}{(r_0)_{ij}}\right]^2 \left[\frac{Y(2,\,2;\,\tau_i)}{Y(1,\,1;\,\tau_{ij})}\right]$$

$$- 3\mathfrak{M}_j(\mathfrak{M}_j - \mathfrak{M}_i) - 4\mathfrak{M}_i \mathfrak{M}_j A(\tau_{ij}) \qquad (9\text{-}2)$$

The $Q_{ij}^{(i)}$ and Q_{ij} are defined in Eq. 8-6 and 8-8. The symbols which appear in these equations are defined in Art. 8. It is thus seen that the thermal diffusion ratio does not depend in a simple way on any one of the variables or parameters and may be either positive or negative. The second approximation $[k_T]_2$ has not been calculated for the Lennard-Jones potential. On the basis of calculations made for simpler potentials, the error in $[k_T]_1$ may be as much as ten per cent.

Comparison of calculated and experimental results. One reason why there are more recorded measurements of thermal diffusion than of ordinary diffusion is that the former property may be measured by equilibrium methods. The value of k_T is generally found by analyzing the equilibrium composition in two connected vessels, each of which is maintained at different temperatures. In the absence of external forces and gradients in the pressure, Eq. 2-8 gives for the steady state condition

$$\nabla \left(\frac{n_1}{n} \right) = -k_T \nabla \ln T \tag{9-3}$$

Most experiments are arranged so that this simplifies to a one-dimensional equation, which can be integrated at once to give

$$\Delta \left(\frac{n_1}{n} \right) = \left(\frac{n_1}{n} \right)_{T'} - \left(\frac{n_1}{n} \right)_T = - \int_T^{T'} \frac{k_T dT}{T} \tag{9-4}$$

Since k_T for the Lennard-Jones potential is a complicated function of the temperature, it is impossible to integrate Eq. 9-4 analytically. The mean value theorem of the integral calculus can be used to give

$$k_T(T_r) = \frac{\Delta \left(\dfrac{n_1}{n} \right)}{\ln \left(\dfrac{T}{T'} \right)} \tag{9-5}$$

where T_r is some mean value of the temperature, lying between T and T'. The following relation has been suggested [16] for T_r:

$$T_r = \frac{TT'}{T' - T} \ln \left(\frac{T'}{T} \right) \tag{9-6}$$

The experimental k_T values may be compared with a k_T calculated from Eq. 9-1 for temperature T_r. Such a comparison has been made for a number of gases and is shown in Table D,9a. Eq. 7-1 and 7-2 have been used to find the force constants between dissimilar molecules.

Perhaps a better way to compare the experimental and calculated values is to integrate Eq. 9-4 numerically using Eq. 9-1 for k_T. The $\Delta(n_1/n)$ for several binary mixtures containing hydrogen are given in

Table D,9a.   Thermal diffusion ratios [*16a*].

Gas	% of lighter constituent	$k_T \times 10^2$		T_r (°K)	Ref.
		Obs.	Calc.		
He-Ne	53.8	7.65	8.15	205	a
	53.8	7.82	8.28	330	a
	53.8	7.83	8.39	365	a
	20	5.31	4.53	330	b
	30	7.24	6.21	330	b
	40	8.64	7.45	330	b
	50	9.70	8.15	330	b
	60	10.04	8.26	330	b
He-A	51.2	9.10	9.44	179	a
	51.2	9.20	9.57	205	a
	51.2	9.56	9.61	365	a
	10	2.50	2.59	330	b
	20	4.76	4.94	330	b
	30	6.60	6.98	330	b
	40	8.10	8.93	300	b
	50	9.31	9.79	330	b
Ne-A	51.2	3.50	3.47	179	a
	51.2	3.80	3.85	205	a
	51.2	4.15	4.25	261	a
	51.2	4.77	4.90	406	a
	20	2.33	2.57	324	b
	30	3.39	3.53	324	b
	40	4.07	4.24	324	b
	50	4.57	4.63	324	b
	60	4.67	4.68	324	b
H_2-He	22.2	2.39	1.98	46	c
	81	2.03	2.38	118	d
	81	1.79	2.31	358	d
	50	4.81	3.74	330	e
	60	4.42	3.56	330	e
	70	3.50	3.08	330	e
	80	2.84	2.31	330	e
	90	1.32	1.29	330	e
H_2-A	47	5.14	5.89	167	f
	55.6	5.73	6.25	167	f
	47	6.35	7.71	258	f
	55.6	7.12	8.17	258	f
N_2-He	34.5	7.42	7.12	145	g
	53.1	9.42	9.23	145	g
	34.5	8.31	7.65	261	g
	53.1	10.7*	9.92	261	g

Table D,9a (continued)

Gas	% of lighter constituent	$k_T \times 10^2$		T_r (°K)	Ref.
		Obs.	Calc.		
N₂-A	46	1.01	0.624	157	f
	62.5	0.842	0.596	157	f
	70	0.83	0.536	157	f
	46	1.82	1.32	252	f
	62.5	1.70	1.28	252	f
	70	1.53	1.16	252	f
H₂-N₂	29.4	3.95	3.97	143	f
	42.0	5.21	5.01	143	f
	77.5	4.84	4.44	143	f
	29.4	5.48	5.90	264	f
	42.0	7.49	7.37	264	f
	77.5	6.63	6.36	264	f
H₂-CO₂	53	6.89	8.39	300	h
	53	8.99	9.60	370	h
H₂-CO	24	3.76	3.21	142	f
	53	5.83	5.08	142	f
	24	4.45	4.81	246	f
	53	7.38	7.66	246	f

* By extrapolation.

Table References.

a. Grew, K. E.   *Proc. Roy. Soc. London A189*, 402 (1947).
b. Atkins, B. E., Bastick, R. E., and Ibbs, T. L   *Proc. Roy. Soc. London A172*, 142 (1939).
c. van Itterbeek, A., van Paemel, O., and van Lierde, J.   *Physica 13*, 231 (1947).
d. Murphey, B. F.   *Phys. Rev. 72*, 834 (1947).
e. Heath, H. R., Ibbs, T. L., and Wild, N. E.   *Proc. Roy. Soc. London A178*, 380 (1941).
f. Ibbs, T. L., Grew, K. E., and Hirst, A. A.   *Proc. Phys. Soc. London 41*, 456 (1929).
g. Ibbs, T. L., and Grew, K. E.   *Proc. Phys. Soc. London 43*, 142 (1931).
h. Bastick, R. E., Heath, H. R., and Ibbs, T. L.   *Proc. Roy. Soc. London A173*, 543 (1939).

Table D,9b along with the values of $\Delta(n_1/n)$ calculated in this way. The agreement is reasonably good.

Experimental data are frequently reported as the ratio R_T of the observed thermal diffusion ratio to the corresponding value calculated for rigid spheres

$$[R_T]_{\text{exptl}} = \frac{[k_T]_{\text{exptl}}}{[k_T]_{\text{rig. sph.}}} \tag{9-7}$$

$(k_T)_{\text{rig. sph.}}$ may be calculated from Eq. 9-1 by using the rigid sphere quantities:

$$A = \tfrac{2}{5}, \qquad B = \tfrac{3}{5}, \qquad C = \tfrac{6}{5}, \qquad Y(1, 1) = 1, \qquad Y(2, 2) = 1 \quad (9\text{-}8)$$

and appropriate values of $(r_0)_i$ and $(r_0)_{12}$. Caution must be exercised in comparing experimental and calculated values of R_T in that the basis of reduction, i.e. $(k_T)_{\text{rig. sph.}}$, must be the same in both cases—that is, the same $(r_0)_1$, $(r_0)_2$, and $(r_0)_{12}$ must be used to reduce both the calculated

Table D,9b. Thermal diffusion in gas mixtures. $\Delta\gamma$ = change in per cent H_2. From [26] by permission.

Gas mixture	Average volume % H_2	T_1 (°K)	T_2 (°K)	$\Delta\gamma$ Experimental [16b]	$\Delta\gamma$ Calculated
H_2-Ne	35.6	290.4	90.2	6.9	7.1
	50.9	290.4	90.2	8.2	8.2
	66.7	290.4	90.2	7.7	7.9
H_2-CO	39.7	293.3	90.2	5.6	5.9
	51.7	293.3	90.2	6.6	6.7
	73.7	293.3	90.2	5.7	6.4
H_2-He	32.3	291.7	90.2	3.4	3.8
	50.5	291.7	90.2	4.6	4.2
	65.4	291.7	90.2	3.7	3.7
H_2-N_2	40.9	292.1	64.4	7.6	8.1
	50.8	292.1	64.6	8.4	9.0
	78.0	292.1	64.4	6.3	8.1
H_2-O_2	33.8	293.6	90.2	4.0	5.7
	48.2	293.6	90.2	5.5	7.1
	73.7	293.6	90.2	5.3	6.9

and experimental values of k_T. The ratio R_T is useful for making comparisons since it depends but slightly on the concentration. In Table D,9c, some theoretical and observed values of R_T are compared. ϵ_{ij}/k from single diffusion measurements were used for those gas pairs for which data were available; otherwise Eq. 7-1 and 7-2 were used.

Thermal diffusion of isotopes. The thermal diffusion constant for isotopic mixtures may be calculated from Eq. 9-1 using the $S_{ij}^{(i)}$, $Q_{ij}^{(i)}$, and Q_{ij} obtained from Eq. 9-2, 8-6, and 8-8 by setting $\epsilon_i = \epsilon_j = \epsilon_{ij}$, and $(r_0)_i = (r_0)_j = (r_0)_{ij}$; thus, for isotopes,

$$S_{ij}^{(i)} = \mathfrak{M}_i \left\{ \left[\frac{2(\mathfrak{M}_i + \mathfrak{M}_j)^3}{\mathfrak{M}_j} \right]^{\frac{1}{2}} - 4\mathfrak{M}_j \right\} A(\tau_i) - 3\mathfrak{M}_j(\mathfrak{M}_j - \mathfrak{M}_i) \quad (9\text{-}9)$$

TableD,9c.   Thermal diffusion of gases [*16c*].

Gas mixture	Temp. (°K)	R_T Calc.	R_T Exptl.	Ref.
He–Ne, 53.8% He	585.2	0.68	0.64	a
	233.2	0.67	0.64	a
	117.2	0.65	0.58	a
He–A, 51.2% He	585.2	0.67	0.66	a
	233.2	0.65	0.63	a
	117.2	0.58	0.55	a
He–Kr, 55.0% He	585.2	0.67	0.67	
	233.2	0.63	0.67	
	117.2	0.50	0.55	
He–Xe, 53.6% He	585.2	0.71	0.66	a
	233.2	0.66	0.66	a
Ne–A, 51.2% Ne	585.2	0.61	0.57	a
	233.2	0.48	0.48	a
	117.2	0.25	0.28	a
Ne–Kr, 53.0% Ne	585.2	0.61	0.64	
	233.2	0.43	0.47	
	117.2	0.16	0.30	
Ne–Xe, 54.2% Ne	585.2	0.61	0.66	a
	233.2	0.41	0.46	a
A–Kr, 53.5% A	585.2	0.50	0.61	
	232.2	0.18	0.18	
A–Xe, 56.4% A	585.2	0.48	0.45	a
	233.2	0.14	0.15	a
H_2–He, 53.6% H_2	284	0.62	0.60[b]	
H_2–D_2, 50% H_2	333	0.63	0.52,[c] 0.61[d]	

Table References.

a. Grew, K. E.   *Proc. Roy. Soc. London A189,* 402 (1947).
b. Elliot, G. A., and Masson, I.   *Proc. Roy. Soc. London A108,* 378 (1925).
  vanItterbeek, A., van Paemel, O., and van Lierde, J.   *Physica 13,* 231 (1947).
  Grew, K. E.   *Proc. Phys. Soc. London A62,* 655 (1949).
c. Waldmann, L.   *Z. Physik 124,* 2 (1947).
d. Heath, H. R., Ibbs, T. L., and Wild, N. E.   *Proc. Roy. Soc. London A178,* 380 (1941).
  Grew, K. E.   *Proc. Roy. Soc. London A178,* 390 (1941).

Table D,9d. Thermal diffusion of isotopic molecules [*16a*].

Gas	% of lighter constituent	R_T		T_r (°K)	Ref.
		Obs.	Calc.		
H_2-D_2	50	0.583	0.587	327	a
	~80.4	0.502	0.587	313	b
	~80.4	0.445	0.463	118	b
^{20}Ne-^{22}Ne	90	0.382	0.485	129	c
	90	0.550	0.592	238	c
	90	0.713	0.620	432	c
	90	0.816	0.627	712	c
^{36}A-^{40}A	0.307	0.0673	0.030	129	c
	0.307	0.151	0.075	154	c
	0.307	0.312	0.363	300	c
	0.307	0.466	0.530	555	c
	0.307	0.534	0.581	720	c
^{12}CH$_4$-^{13}CH$_4$	98.9	0.297	. . . . .	450	d
	98.9	. . . . . .	0.445	430	. .
	98.9	0.274	. . . . .	405	d
^{32}O$_2$-^{34}O$_2$	97.5	0.367	0.375	284	e
	97.5	0.475	0.475	386	e
	97.5	0.538	0.504	443	e

Gas	% of lighter constituent	$k_T \times 10^2$		T_r (°K)	Ref.
		Obs.	Calc.		
H_2-D_2	10	1.45	1.48	327	a
	20	2.65	2.66	327	a
	30	3.56	3.54	327	a
	40	4.16	4.12	327	a
	50	4.32	4.34	327	a
	60	4.16	4.22	327	a
	70	3.62	3.76	327	a
	80	2.81	2.91	327	a
	90	1.66	1.67	327	a

Table References.

a. Heath, H. R., Ibbs, T. L., and Wild, N. E.   *Proc. Roy. Soc. London A178,* 380 (1941).
b. Murphey, B. F.   *Phys. Rev. 72,* 834 (1947).
c. Stier, L. G.   *Phys. Rev. 62,* 548 (1942).
d. Nier, A. O.   *Phys. Rev. 56,* 1009 (1939).
e. Whalley, E., and Winter, E. R. S.   *Trans. Faraday Soc. 45,* 1091 (1949).

$$Q_{ij}^{(i)} = A(\tau_i) \left[\frac{2(\mathfrak{M}_i + \mathfrak{M}_j)}{\mathfrak{M}_j} \right]^{\frac{1}{2}} \{ 6\mathfrak{M}_j^2 + [5 - 4B(\tau_i)]\mathfrak{M}_i^2 + 8\mathfrak{M}_i\mathfrak{M}_j A(\tau_i) \}$$

$$(9\text{-}10)$$

$$Q_{ij} = 4A^2(\tau_i) \frac{(\mathfrak{M}_i + \mathfrak{M}_j)^3}{(\mathfrak{M}_i\mathfrak{M}_j)^{\frac{1}{2}}} + 3(\mathfrak{M}_i - \mathfrak{M}_j)^2[5 - 4B(\tau_i)]$$

$$+ 4A(\tau_i)\mathfrak{M}_i\mathfrak{M}_j[11 - 4B(\tau_i)] \quad (9\text{-}11)$$

and we see that $[k_T]_1$ depends only upon (ϵ_1/k) and not upon the collision diameters.

Calculated and experimental values of k_T for isotopic mixtures are compared in Table D,9d. The agreement here is considerably better than for the gas mixtures previously discussed, probably because there is less uncertainty about the nature of the molecular interaction between pairs of like molecules.

Thermal diffusion in multicomponent systems. The α_i defined in Eq. 2-4 may be calculated from the following formulas:

$$\alpha_i = -(n_i\mathfrak{M}_iRT) \frac{\begin{vmatrix} \alpha_{11}^{(1)} & \alpha_{12}^{(1)} & & \alpha_{1s}^{(1)} & \alpha_{11}^{(2)} & \alpha_{12}^{(2)} & \cdots & \alpha_{1s}^{(2)} & 0 \\ \alpha_{21}^{(1)} & \alpha_{22}^{(1)} & \cdots & \alpha_{2s}^{(1)} & \alpha_{21}^{(2)} & \alpha_{22}^{(2)} & \cdots & \alpha_{2s}^{(2)} & 0 \\ \cdot & & & \cdot & \cdot & \cdot & & \cdot & \cdot \\ \cdot & & & \cdot & \cdot & \cdot & & \cdot & \cdot \\ \cdot & & & \cdot & \cdot & \cdot & & \cdot & \cdot \\ \cdot & & \cdot & \cdot & \cdot & & \cdot & \cdot \\ \alpha_{s1}^{(1)} & \alpha_{s2}^{(1)} & \cdots & \alpha_{ss}^{(1)} & \alpha_{s1}^{(2)} & \alpha_{s2}^{(2)} & \cdots & \alpha_{ss}^{(2)} & 0 \\ \beta_{11}^{(1)} & \beta_{12}^{(1)} & \cdots & \beta_{1s}^{(1)} & \beta_{11}^{(2)} & \beta_{12}^{(2)} & \cdots & \beta_{1s}^{(2)} & 1 \\ \beta_{21}^{(1)} & \beta_{22}^{(1)} & \cdots & \beta_{2s}^{(1)} & \beta_{21}^{(2)} & \beta_{22}^{(2)} & \cdots & \beta_{2s}^{(2)} & 1 \\ \cdot & & & \cdot & \cdot & \cdot & & \cdot & \cdot \\ \cdot & & & \cdot & \cdot & \cdot & & \cdot & \cdot \\ \cdot & & \cdot & \cdot & \cdot & & \cdot & \cdot \\ \beta_{s1}^{(1)} & \beta_{s2}^{(1)} & \cdots & \beta_{ss}^{(1)} & \beta_{s1}^{(2)} & \beta_{s2}^{(2)} & \cdots & \beta_{ss}^{(2)} & 1 \\ \delta_{i1} & \delta_{i2} & \cdots & \delta_{is} & 0 & 0 & \cdots & 0 & 0 \end{vmatrix}}{\begin{vmatrix} \alpha_{11}^{(1)} & \alpha_{12}^{(1)} & \cdots & \alpha_{1s}^{(1)} & \alpha_{11}^{(2)} & \alpha_{12}^{(2)} & \cdots & \alpha_{1s}^{(2)} \\ \alpha_{21}^{(1)} & \alpha_{22}^{(1)} & \cdots & \alpha_{2s}^{(1)} & \alpha_{21}^{(2)} & \alpha_{22}^{(2)} & \cdots & \alpha_{2s}^{(2)} \\ \cdot & & & \cdot & \cdot & \cdot & & \cdot \\ \cdot & & & \cdot & \cdot & \cdot & & \cdot \\ \cdot & & \cdot & \cdot & \cdot & & \cdot \\ \alpha_{s1}^{(1)} & \alpha_{s2}^{(1)} & \cdots & \alpha_{ss}^{(1)} & \alpha_{s1}^{(2)} & \alpha_{s2}^{(2)} & \cdots & \alpha_{ss}^{(2)} \\ \beta_{11}^{(1)} & \beta_{12}^{(1)} & \cdots & \beta_{1s}^{(1)} & \beta_{11}^{(2)} & \beta_{12}^{(2)} & \cdots & \beta_{1s}^{(2)} \\ \beta_{21}^{(1)} & \beta_{22}^{(1)} & \cdots & \beta_{2s}^{(1)} & \beta_{21}^{(2)} & \beta_{22}^{(2)} & \cdots & \beta_{2s}^{(2)} \\ \cdot & & & \cdot & \cdot & \cdot & & \cdot \\ \cdot & & & \cdot & \cdot & \cdot & & \cdot \\ \cdot & & \cdot & \cdot & \cdot & & \cdot \\ \beta_{s1}^{(1)} & \beta_{s2}^{(1)} & \cdots & \beta_{ss}^{(1)} & \beta_{s1}^{(2)} & \beta_{s2}^{(2)} & \cdots & \beta_{ss}^{(2)} \end{vmatrix}} \quad (9\text{-}12)$$

where

$$\alpha_{ij}^{(1)} = \frac{1}{2}\sqrt{2\pi RT}\sum_{k\neq i} r_{ik}^2 n_k \mathfrak{M}_j \left[\frac{\mathfrak{M}_k}{\mathfrak{M}_i(\mathfrak{M}_i + \mathfrak{M}_k)}\right]^{\frac{1}{2}} Y(1, 1; \tau_{ik})$$

$$\times \left[\frac{\mathfrak{M}_i}{\mathfrak{M}_j}(\delta_{ij} - \delta_{jk}) - \frac{n_j}{n_i}\right] \quad (9\text{-}13)$$

$$\alpha_{ij}^{(2)} = -\frac{1}{2}\sqrt{2\pi RT}\frac{\mathfrak{M}_i^{\frac{3}{2}}}{\mathfrak{M}_j}\sum_k r_{ik}^2 n_k \frac{\mathfrak{M}_k^{\frac{3}{2}}}{(\mathfrak{M}_i + \mathfrak{M}_k)^{\frac{3}{2}}}$$

$$\times \left[3Y(1, 2; \tau_{ik}) - \frac{5}{2}Y(1, 1; \tau_{ik})\right](\delta_{ij} - \delta_{kj}) \quad (9\text{-}14)$$

$$\beta_{ij}^{(1)} = \frac{16}{15}\sqrt{2\pi RT}\,\mathfrak{M}_i^{\frac{1}{2}}\sum_k \frac{n_k \mathfrak{M}_k^{\frac{3}{2}}}{(\mathfrak{M}_i + \mathfrak{M}_k)^{\frac{3}{2}}}r_{ik}^2$$

$$\times \left[3Y(1, 2; \tau_{ik}) - \frac{5}{2}Y(1, 1; \tau_{ik})\right](\delta_{ij} - \delta_{kj}) \quad (9\text{-}15)$$

$$\beta_{ij}^{(2)} = -\frac{32}{15}\sqrt{2\pi RT}\frac{\mathfrak{M}_i^{\frac{3}{2}}}{\mathfrak{M}_j}\sum_k \frac{n_k \mathfrak{M}_k^{\frac{1}{2}}}{(\mathfrak{M}_i + \mathfrak{M}_k)^{\frac{5}{2}}}r_{ik}^2$$

$$\times \left[\begin{array}{l} \frac{5}{8}(6\mathfrak{M}_j^2 + 5\mathfrak{M}_k^2)Y(1, 1; \tau_{ik})(\delta_{ij} - \delta_{kj}) \\[2mm] -\left[\frac{15}{2}\mathfrak{M}_k^2 Y(1, 2; \tau_{ik}) - 6\mathfrak{M}_k^2 Y(1, 3; \tau_{ik})\right](\delta_{ij} - \delta_{kj}) \\[2mm] + 2\mathfrak{M}_j\mathfrak{M}_k Y(2, 2; \tau_{ik})(\delta_{ij} + \delta_{kj}) \end{array}\right] \quad (9\text{-}16)$$

Since no data on the thermal diffusion properties of mixtures of three or more components are available, this expression has not been checked by comparison with experiment. However, sample calculations made with this formula to examine the effect of the addition of a third component to a binary system do not predict that any particularly surprising results could be obtained from such experiments.

D,10. The Coefficient of Thermal Conductivity. Up to this point the excellent agreement between the experimental results and calculated values is indeed very satisfying. For viscosity, diffusion, and thermal diffusion, the rigorous theory and the Y functions calculated for the Lennard-Jones potential enable one to make accurate interpolations and reasonable extrapolations of the experimental data. It has been found that the theory is consistent within itself, in that force constants obtained from the measurement of one transport property may be used satisfactorily in the computation of other transport properties. Thus a great deal of success has been achieved in the application of the theory to the case of real molecules, the theory being generally applicable to the simpler polyatomic molecules as well as for the monatomic gases for which it was intended. For thermal conductivity we find that the theory is satisfactory for monatomic gases, but that for polyatomic gases very poor agreement between experimental and calculated results can be expected. This occurs because the interaction between the translational and rotational motions has a perceptible effect on the coefficient of viscosity. The Eucken correction, discussed in Art. 11, can be used to bring the calculated values into somewhat better agreement with the available data.

Thermal conductivity of pure gases. For a pure component, the third approximation to the coefficient of thermal conductivity is

$$[\lambda_i]_3 = \frac{25}{32} \sqrt{\frac{m_i k T}{\pi}} \frac{c_{v_i} \mathfrak{IC}(\tau_i)}{(r_0)_i^2 Y(2, 2; \tau_i)} = \frac{5}{2} \frac{[\mu_i]_3 C_{v_i}}{\mathfrak{M}_i} \left[\frac{\mathfrak{IC}(\tau_i)}{\mathfrak{I}(\tau_i)} \right] \tag{10-1}$$

in which

$\mathfrak{M}_1; m_i =$ molecular weight; mass of ith kind of molecule

$(r_0)_1 =$ collision diameter in cm

$\mathfrak{IC}, \mathfrak{I} =$ function of τ given in Table D,5c $[\mathfrak{IC}/\mathfrak{I} \sim 1]$

$Y(2, 2; \tau_i) =$ function of τ given in Table D,5a

$c_{v_i}; C_{v_i} =$ specific heat per gram; per mole

$[\mu_i]_3 =$ third approximation to viscosity as given in Eq. 6-1 and 6-2

This formula is valid for monatomic gases only, for which there is only translational energy. Eq. 10-1 shows how the coefficient of viscosity is related to the heat conductivity in nearly the same way as is found in the simple kinetic theory.

For polyatomic molecules, Eq. 10-1 may be modified by the inclusion of the Eucken assumption, which takes into account approximately the transfer of energy between translation and the internal degrees of freedom. The modified formula for the thermal conductivity discussed in Art. 11 is then

$$[\lambda_i]_3 = \frac{[\mu_i]_3}{\mathfrak{M}_i} \left[C_v + \frac{9}{4} R \right] \left[\frac{\mathfrak{IC}(\tau_i)}{\mathfrak{I}(\tau_i)} \right] \tag{10-2}$$

where R is the gas constant. For monatomic gases, this formula simplifies to that given in Eq. 10-1.

Theoretical and observed values of $\mathfrak{IC}/\mathfrak{I}$ are compared, in Table D,10, the calculations being based on Eq. 10-2. For the noble gases the agreement may be considered quite satisfactory; and for the various polyatomic molecules, the discrepancies are simply the result of the lack of rigor in the Eucken assumption. However, at present the latter affords the best available method for estimating λ.

The coefficient of conductivity of a mixture containing only molecules with no internal degrees of freedom is

$$[\lambda]_1 = \lambda' - \frac{R}{2n} \sum_{i,j}{}' \frac{n_i n_j}{\mathfrak{D}_{ij}} \left(\frac{\alpha_i}{n_i \mathfrak{M}_i} - \frac{\alpha_j}{n_j \mathfrak{M}_j} \right)^2 \qquad (10\text{-}3)$$

where

$$\lambda' = \frac{5}{2} R^2 T \frac{\begin{vmatrix} \alpha_{11}^{(1)} & \alpha_{12}^{(1)} & \cdots & \alpha_{1s}^{(1)} & \alpha_{11}^{(2)} & \alpha_{12}^{(2)} & \cdots & \alpha_{1s}^{(2)} & 0 \\ \alpha_{21}^{(1)} & \alpha_{22}^{(1)} & \cdots & \alpha_{2s}^{(1)} & \alpha_{21}^{(2)} & \alpha_{22}^{(2)} & \cdots & \alpha_{2s}^{(2)} & 0 \\ \vdots & & & & & & & & \\ \alpha_{s1}^{(1)} & \alpha_{s2}^{(1)} & \cdots & \alpha_{ss}^{(1)} & \alpha_{s1}^{(2)} & \alpha_{s2}^{(2)} & \cdots & \alpha_{ss}^{(2)} & 0 \\ \beta_{11}^{(1)} & \beta_{12}^{(1)} & \cdots & \beta_{1s}^{(1)} & \beta_{11}^{(2)} & \beta_{12}^{(2)} & \cdots & \beta_{1s}^{(2)} & 1 \\ \beta_{21}^{(1)} & \beta_{22}^{(1)} & \cdots & \beta_{2s}^{(1)} & \beta_{21}^{(2)} & \beta_{22}^{(2)} & \cdots & \beta_{2s}^{(2)} & 1 \\ \vdots & & & & & & & & \\ \beta_{s1}^{(1)} & \beta_{s2}^{(1)} & \cdots & \beta_{ss}^{(1)} & \beta_{s1}^{(2)} & \beta_{s2}^{(2)} & \cdots & \beta_{ss}^{(2)} & 1 \\ 0 & 0 & \cdots & 0 & n_1 & n_2 & \cdots & n_s & 0 \end{vmatrix}}{\begin{vmatrix} \alpha_{11}^{(1)} & \alpha_{12}^{(1)} & \cdots & \alpha_{1s}^{(1)} & \alpha_{11}^{(2)} & \alpha_{12}^{(2)} & \cdots & \alpha_{1s}^{(2)} \\ \alpha_{21}^{(1)} & \alpha_{22}^{(1)} & \cdots & \alpha_{2s}^{(1)} & \alpha_{21}^{(2)} & \alpha_{22}^{(2)} & \cdots & \alpha_{2s}^{(2)} \\ \vdots & & & & & & & \\ \alpha_{s1}^{(1)} & \alpha_{s2}^{(1)} & \cdots & \alpha_{ss}^{(1)} & \alpha_{s1}^{(2)} & \alpha_{s2}^{(2)} & \cdots & \alpha_{ss}^{(2)} \\ \beta_{11}^{(1)} & \beta_{12}^{(1)} & \cdots & \beta_{1s}^{(1)} & \beta_{11}^{(2)} & \beta_{12}^{(2)} & \cdots & \beta_{1s}^{(2)} \\ \beta_{21}^{(1)} & \beta_{22}^{(1)} & \cdots & \beta_{2s}^{(1)} & \beta_{21}^{(2)} & \beta_{22}^{(2)} & \cdots & \beta_{2s}^{(2)} \\ \vdots & & & & & & & \\ \beta_{s1}^{(1)} & \beta_{s2}^{(1)} & \cdots & \beta_{ss}^{(1)} & \beta_{s1}^{(2)} & \beta_{s2}^{(2)} & \cdots & \beta_{ss}^{(2)} \end{vmatrix}} \qquad (10\text{-}4)$$

The α_i are given by Eq. 9-12 and the $\alpha_{ij}^{(1)}$, $\alpha_{ij}^{(2)}$, $\beta_{ij}^{(1)}$, and $\beta_{ij}^{(2)}$ by Eq. 9-13, 9-14, 9-15, and 9-16. In the case of the gases containing molecules with internal degrees of freedom, a correction similar to the Eucken approximation is necessary. Such an approximation could be obtained by an analysis generalizing the treatment of Art. 11. However, the accuracy of the result does not warrant the complexity of the approximation. In general, little can be said at present about the details of the composition dependence of the conductivity of mixtures of polyatomic molecules.

Table D,10. The ratio $\mathfrak{K}/\mathfrak{g}$. From [26] by permission.

Gas		100°K	200°K	273.2°K	300°K
He	Experimental[a]	0.9933	0.9897		0.9733
	Calculated	1.0042	1.0043		1.0045
CH₄	Experimental[a]	0.9676	1.0258		1.0675
	Calculated	1.0000	1.0002		1.0009
NO	Experimental[a]		0.9504		0.9974
	Calculated		1.0004		1.0013
CO₂	Experimental[a]		0.8788		0.9479
	Calculated		1.0001		1.0003
O₂	Experimental[a]	0.9529	1.0042		1.0320
	Calculated	1.0000	1.0005		1.0015
Air	Experimental[b]	0.9499	1.0022		1.0107
	Calculated	1.0001	1.0008		1.0019
A	Experimental[c]			1.012	
	Calculated			1.0000	
Ne	Experimental[c]			0.988	
	Calculated			1.0037	
Kr	Experimental[c]			1.016	
	Calculated			1.0002	
Xe	Experimental[c]			1.028	
	Calculated			1.0001	

Table References.

a. Johnston, H. L., and Grilly, E. R.   J. Chem. Phys. 14, 233 (1946).
b. Taylor, W. J., and Johnston, H. L.   J. Chem. Phys. 14, 219 (1946).
c. Chapman, S., and Cowling, T. G.   The Mathematical Theory of Non-Uniform Gases, p. 241. Cambridge Univ. Press, 1939.

D,11. The Effects of Chemical Reactions and the Internal Degrees of Freedom.   The discussion of kinetic theory presented thus far in this section has been limited to mixtures of simple molecules. It was assumed that the molecules were spherical and had no internal degrees of freedom. The discussion of the general cases is considerably more complicated. Nevertheless, it is possible to obtain some results without too much difficulty. In the present article the effect of inelastic collisions due to the internal degrees of freedom on the transport properties and the Eucken correction to the coefficient of thermal conductivity are discussed.

The derivation of the equations of continuity and motion depends upon the concepts of conservation of mass and momentum. Since mass and momentum are conserved in the inelastic collisions, these equations remain valid. However, in the development of the equation of energy balance, one must introduce the fact that it is the total energy of the molecule and not simply the kinetic energy which is conserved. This modification leads to an equation identical in form with Eq. 1-9, but in which the quantity u now includes the energy in the internal degrees of freedom. Thus, in all cases, u is the thermodynamic internal energy[15] per gram of the mixture,

$$u = \frac{1}{\rho} \sum_i n_i \mathfrak{M}_i u_i \tag{11-1}$$

The equation of energy balance, Eq. 1-10, remains

$$\rho \left[\frac{\partial u}{\partial t} + (\mathbf{v}_0 \cdot \nabla u) \right] = -(\nabla \cdot \mathbf{q}) - (\mathbf{p} : \nabla \mathbf{v}_0) + \sum_i n_i (\mathbf{X}_i \cdot \mathbf{V}_i) \tag{11-2}$$

Making use of the equation of continuity, the energy balance equation in terms of the temperature is

$$\rho c_v \left[\frac{\partial T}{\partial t} + (\mathbf{v}_0 \cdot \nabla T) \right] = - \sum_i \mathfrak{M}_i K_i u_i + \sum_i u_i (\nabla \cdot (n_i \mathfrak{M}_i \mathbf{V}_i))$$

$$- (\nabla \cdot \mathbf{q}) - (\mathbf{p} : \nabla \mathbf{v}_0) + \sum_i n_i (\mathbf{X}_i \cdot \mathbf{V}_i) \tag{11-3}$$

where c_v is the average specific heat per gram at constant volume,

$$c_v = \frac{1}{\rho} \sum_i n_i \mathfrak{M}_i (c_v)_i \tag{11-4}$$

and

$$(c_v)_i = \left(\frac{\partial u_i}{\partial T} \right)_v \tag{11-5}$$

The possibility of chemical reactions does not affect the transport coefficients directly. The occurrence of collisions in which chemical reactions occur perturbs the distribution function if the system is not in equilibrium. This perturbation possibly leads to slightly different transport coefficients. However, this effect is small and unimportant in most cases [*17,18,19*].

The presence of the internal degrees of freedom does not affect the formal mathematical treatment of the coefficients of diffusion or viscosity.

---

[15] u does not include the kinetic energy associated with the macroscopic flow or the potential energy associated with the external forces.

However, since $\mathfrak{M}_i u_i$ replaces the simple translational kinetic energy terms in the derivation of the energy balance equation, the expression for $\mathbf{q}$ is now

$$\mathbf{q} = \sum_j n_j \mathfrak{M}_j \overline{u_j \mathbf{V}_j} \qquad (11\text{-}6)$$

That is, $\mathbf{q}$ represents the total energy flux. u_j can be written as the sum of two terms: the usual translational term $\frac{1}{2}V_j^2$ and a term representing the energy in the internal degrees of freedom.

To a good approximation, the energy in the internal degrees of freedom is independent of the velocity, and this contribution to $\mathbf{q}$ simply appears in the second term of Eq. 2-21, where now the enthalpy H_i includes this energy in internal degrees of freedom as well as the purely translational contributions. Thus

$$\mathbf{q} = -\lambda \nabla T + \sum_i n_i H_i \mathbf{V}_i - \frac{RT}{n} \sum_{[i,k]} \frac{n_k \alpha_i}{\mathfrak{M}_i \mathfrak{D}_{ik}} (\mathbf{V}_k - \mathbf{V}_i) \qquad (11\text{-}7)$$

where H_i is the enthalpy per mole of component i:

$$H_i = \mathfrak{M}_i u_i + RT \qquad (11\text{-}8)$$

However, the presence of the internal degrees of freedom has an additional effect due to the time lag in the transfer of energy from the translational to the internal degrees of freedom.

Because of the possibility of inelastic collisions, the coefficient of thermal conductivity is sensitive to the nature of the internal degrees of freedom of the molecules. The exact expression for the coefficient of thermal conductivity depends upon the transition probabilities for the transfer of energy among the various degrees of freedom of the molecule, particularly in the probability of transfer from the translational to the internal degrees of freedom.

Eucken [20] made an approximation which applies in the limit that the rate of transfer is fast, i.e. that the rate of transfer is sufficiently fast that the distribution of molecules among the various states is the equilibrium distribution corresponding to the local temperature. Let us consider only a pure gas. Then according to Eq. 10-1 the coefficient of thermal conductivity is

$$\lambda = 2.5 \frac{\mu C_v}{\mathfrak{M}} \frac{\mathfrak{K}}{\mathfrak{J}} \qquad (11\text{-}9)$$

in which C_v is the specific heat per mole.

This expression applies only to a gas made up of molecules without internal degrees of freedom. The molecules of the gas can exist in various internal quantum states.[16] Let us consider the molecules in a

[16] The concept of a quantum state is introduced here, not for any particular accuracy, but rather for convenience of discussion.

particular quantum state as being molecules of a particular chemical species. With this interpretation, the gas can be considered as a reacting mixture of a large number of chemical components. Furthermore, each species can now be considered as devoid of internal degrees of freedom. The inelastic collisions are interpreted as chemical reactions. Furthermore the masses of all the molecules are alike, and to a good approximation all the intermolecular potentials are alike.

The coefficient of thermal diffusion of a mixture of molecules of the same mass with the same law of force between any pair is zero. Hence, from Eq. 11-7 the energy flux for such a mixture is

$$\mathbf{q} = -\lambda'\nabla T + \sum_i n_i(\tfrac{5}{2}RT + E_i')\mathbf{V}_i \tag{11-10}$$

where E_i' is the energy in the internal degrees of freedom per mole in a quantum state i, and λ' is the coefficient of thermal conductivity of the system considered as such a mixture (as distinct from the usual coefficient of thermal conductivity λ). That is, from Eq. 11-9

$$\lambda' = \frac{15}{4}\frac{R\mu\mathcal{K}}{\mathfrak{M}\mathcal{J}} \tag{11-11}$$

where C_v, the specific heat per mole, has been set equal to $3R/2$.

The diffusion velocity given by Eq. 2-2 is, in the case of this simple mixture,

$$n_i\mathbf{V}_i = -n\mathfrak{D}\nabla\left(\frac{n_i}{n}\right) \tag{11-12}$$

where $\mathfrak{D}$ is the coefficient of self-diffusion. In general, n_i/n may depend in a rather complicated manner upon all of the gradients. However, the Eucken approximation may be obtained by assuming that the distribution is the equilibrium distribution characteristic of the local temperature. Hence to this approximation

$$\nabla\left(\frac{n_i}{n}\right) = \left[\frac{d}{dT}\left(\frac{n_i}{n}\right)\right]\nabla T \tag{11-13}$$

and from Eq. 11-10, 11-11, and 11-12 and from the fact that (with all $\mathfrak{M}_i$ equal) $\sum_i n_i\mathbf{V}_i = 0$,

$$\mathbf{q} = -\left[\frac{15}{4}\frac{R\mu\mathcal{K}}{\mathfrak{M}\mathcal{J}} + n\mathfrak{D}\sum_i E_i'\frac{d}{dT}\left(\frac{n_i}{n}\right)\right]\nabla T \tag{11-14}$$

The average energy in the internal degrees of freedom is

$$\overline{E}' = \sum_i E_i'\frac{n_i}{n} \tag{11-15}$$

Hence the internal contribution to the specific heat is

$$C'_v = C_v - \frac{3}{2}R = \sum_i E'_i \frac{d}{dT}\left(\frac{n_i}{n}\right) \tag{11-16}$$

Thus from Eq. 11-12

$$\mathbf{q} = -\left[\frac{15}{4}\frac{R\mu\mathcal{K}}{\mathfrak{M}\mathcal{J}} + n\mathfrak{D}\left(C_v - \frac{3}{2}R\right)\right]\nabla T \tag{11-17}$$

and the coefficient of thermal conductivity is

$$\lambda = \left[\frac{\rho\mathfrak{D}}{\mu}C_v + \left(\frac{15}{4}\frac{\mathcal{K}}{\mathcal{J}} - \frac{3\rho\mathfrak{D}}{2\mu}\right)R\right]\frac{\mu}{\mathfrak{M}} \tag{11-18}$$

The expression is often written in terms of the ratio of specific heats

$$\gamma = \frac{C_p}{C_v} = 1 + \frac{R}{C_v} \tag{11-19}$$

$$\lambda = \frac{1}{4}\left\{\left[15\frac{\mathcal{K}}{\mathcal{J}} - 6\rho\frac{\mathfrak{D}}{\mu}\right]\gamma - \left[15\frac{\mathcal{K}}{\mathcal{J}} - 10\frac{\rho\mathfrak{D}}{\mu}\right]\right\}\frac{C_v\mu}{\mathfrak{M}} \tag{11-20}$$

The quantity $\mathcal{K}/\mathcal{J}$ is always very close to unity and in general the quantity $\rho\mathfrak{D}/\mu$ (a function of temperature) is of the order of unity. With this simplification, Eq. 11-20 reduces to the usual Eucken approximation

$$\lambda = \frac{1}{4}(9\gamma - 5)\frac{C_v\mu}{\mathfrak{M}} \tag{11-21}$$

However, if the molecules interact as rigid spheres, the exact evaluation of $\mathcal{K}/\mathcal{J}$ and $\rho\mathfrak{D}/\mu$ gives

$$\lambda = \frac{1}{4}(7.908\gamma - 3.092)\frac{C_v\mu}{\mathfrak{M}} \tag{11-22}$$

Because of the difficulty of transferring energy from translation to the internal degrees of freedom, Eq. 11-20, 11-21, and 11-22 do not fit the experimental data accurately at moderate (room) temperatures. However, at sufficiently high temperatures Eq. 11-20 should apply.

The formal treatment of the kinetic theory of gases can be extended to polyatomic molecules or to molecules with internal quantum states [21]. It is assumed that the translational motion can be considered classically. However, for convenience the internal degrees of freedom are treated quantum mechanically. In this case one introduces a distribution function, $f_i(\mathbf{r}, \mathbf{v}, t)$, for each internal quantum state i. The single index i refers to the entire set of quantum numbers necessary to specify the internal state of the molecule. Each distribution function then satisfies its own Boltzmann equation. The collision integrals are written in terms of a set of differential cross sections $\Omega_{ij}^{kl}(g, \theta, \phi)$. The cross section $\Omega_{ij}^{kl}(g, \theta, \phi)$ refers to a collision between molecules in states i and j which results in molecules in states k and l. The magnitude of the asymptotic relative velocity is g. The direction of the initial relative velocity is taken as the axis of a polar coordinate system. Then $\Omega_{ij}^{kl}(g, \theta, \phi)$ is the cross section for scattering at the angle θ, ϕ. Now one can make use of the usual arguments to develop the more general Boltzmann equation. The more general Boltzmann equation can be solved in a manner analogous to that used in the treatment of the simpler case. The formal results are given by Wang Chang and Uhlenbeck [21]. However, the results are of no practical value until theoretical estimates of the differential cross sections are available.

The cross sections have not yet been estimated for any realistic molecular models. However, by using special methods, several rather unrealistic molecular models have been considered, and numerical values of the transport coefficients have been obtained. These models are discussed below.

In the formal treatment an additional equation of change appears which expresses the conservation of angular momentum. Also, an additional transport coefficient appears. This coefficient is related to the relaxation time and measures the ease with which the internal motion comes into equilibrium with the translational motion. The Stokes relation between the coefficient of bulk viscosity and the coefficient of shear viscosity is no longer satisfied. The deviation from the Stokes relation depends upon the relaxation time.

Rigid ovaloids. Ishida [22] has studied the kinetic theory of molecules which are rigid and nonspherical, but which have no internal degrees of freedom other than the rotation. He developed a classical generalization of the Boltzmann equation which applies in this case. The Boltzmann equation leads to the ordinary equations of change and to an additional equation expressing the conservation of angular momentum. In the case of spherical molecules this additional equation is not interesting since all of the angular momentum is present in the form of the macroscopic motion of the gas (or at least there is no mechanism for an interchange of the macroscopic angular momentum with that associated with the rotation of the molecules). However, in the case of nonspherical molecules the possibility of interchange of the angular momenta introduces some interesting consequences. It is at this point that the additional transport property related to the relaxation time appears. Ishida suggests the possibility of a new type of wave system. However, this model has not been considered to a sufficient extent to lead to any numerical results for the transport coefficients.

Rough spheres. One of the simplest idealized models for which numerical values have been obtained is the perfectly rough, elastic sphere suggested by Bryan [23]. The methods of Chapman and Enskog, discussed in the first paragraph of this section, were extended to this model by Pidduck [24,1]. The concept of the perfectly rough sphere implies that the molecules do not slip with respect to one another when they collide. Because of this roughness, the molecules may exchange angular momentum with one another and with the translational motion on collision. That is, the forces are not strictly central forces. However, the theory is simplified by the fact that no additional coordinates are needed to describe the orientation of the molecules. In this case the distribution function $f(\mathbf{r}, \mathbf{v}, \boldsymbol{\omega}, t)$ depends on the space and linear velocity coordinates and on the angular velocity $\boldsymbol{\omega}$ of the molecule.

The Boltzmann equation and its solutions can be obtained in much the same manner as in the usual case. The results can be expressed in terms of the dimensionless radius of gyration,

$$\kappa = \frac{4I}{m\sigma^2} \tag{11-23}$$

where I is the moment of inertia, and m is the mass of a molecule. The value of κ ranges from zero in the limit if all the mass is concentrated at the center of the sphere to $\frac{2}{3}$ if all of the mass is on the surface of the sphere. For a sphere of uniform density, $\kappa = \frac{2}{5}$. The first approximation to the coefficient of diffusion of a mixture of such gases turns out to be

$$\mathfrak{D}_{12} = \frac{3N}{8n\sigma_{12}^2} \left(\frac{kT}{2\pi m_{12}}\right)^{\frac{1}{2}} \left[\frac{m_1\kappa_1 + m_2\kappa_2 + (m_1 + m_2)\kappa_1\kappa_2}{m_1\kappa_1 + m_2\kappa_2 + 2(m_1 + m_2)\kappa_1\kappa_2}\right] \tag{11-24}$$

where m_{12} is the reduced mass of molecules of species "1" and "2," defined in Eq. 3-3. This value is related to the smooth sphere value by

$$(\mathfrak{D}_{12})_{\text{rough sphere}} = f_d(\mathfrak{D}_{12})_{\text{smooth sphere}} \tag{11-25}$$

where

$$f_d = \left[\frac{m_1\kappa_1 + m_2\kappa_2 + (m_1 + m_2)\kappa_1\kappa_2}{m_1\kappa_1 + m_2\kappa_2 + 2(m_1 + m_2)\kappa_1\kappa_2}\right] \tag{11-26}$$

is the ratio of the two values. If either κ_1 or κ_2 is zero, f_d becomes unity. For other values of κ_1 and κ_2, f_d is less than unity. In the case of self-diffusion, where $m_1 = m_2$, f_d reduces to

$$f_d = \frac{1 + \kappa}{1 + 2\kappa} \tag{11-27}$$

This quantity, which ranges from unity when κ is zero to 0.714 when κ is $\frac{2}{3}$, is plotted in Fig. D,11a.

The first approximation to the coefficient of viscosity of a pure gas

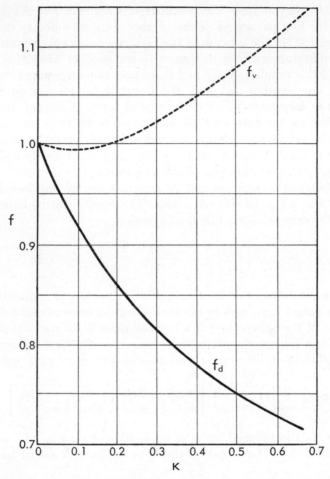

Fig. D,11a. The ratio of the value for rough spheres to the value for smooth spheres of the coefficient of diffusion f_d, and the coefficient of viscosity f_v.

made up of these idealized molecules is given by

$$\mu = \frac{15}{8\sigma^2} \left(\frac{mkT}{\pi}\right)^{\frac{1}{2}} \frac{(1+\kappa)^2}{6+13\kappa} \tag{11-28}$$

Thus, for the viscosity, the ratio of the rough sphere to the smooth sphere value is

$$f_v = \frac{6(1+\kappa)^2}{6+13\kappa} \tag{11-29}$$

This expression is clearly unity when κ is zero. For other values of κ, it ranges from 0.994 to 1.136. The value of f_v is also plotted in Fig. D,11a.

The first approximation to the coefficient of thermal conductivity is

$$\lambda = \frac{9}{16\sigma^2}\left(\frac{k^3 T}{\pi m}\right)^{\frac{1}{2}} \frac{(1+\kappa)^2(37+151\kappa+50\kappa^2)}{12+75\kappa+101\kappa^2+102\kappa^3} \tag{11-30}$$

In terms of the coefficient of viscosity given by Eq. 11-30 this result may be written

$$\lambda = \frac{3k(6+13\kappa)(37+151\kappa+50\kappa^2)}{10m(12+75\kappa+101\kappa^2+102\kappa^3)}\mu \tag{11-31}$$

In this form the result may be compared with the smooth sphere result (with $C_v = \frac{3}{2}R$)

$$\lambda = \frac{15}{4}\frac{R\mu}{\mathfrak{M}} \tag{11-32}$$

For $\kappa = 0$, Eq. 11-31 gives a factor of 5.55 as compared to 3.75 for smooth spheres. The discrepancy is due to the possibility of the interchange of rotational energy with translational energy in the rough sphere model.

One may compare Eq. 11-31 with the result obtained by the Eucken approximation of rapid transfer of energy. Using $\mathfrak{K}/\mathfrak{J} = 1$ (since the present results are limited to the first approximations) and the value of $\rho\mathfrak{D}/\mu$ for rough spheres, as given by Eq. 11-24 and 11-28, the Eucken equation, Eq. 11-20 becomes

$$\lambda = \frac{3k\mu(37+101\kappa+50\kappa^2)}{20m(1+3\kappa+2\kappa^2)} \tag{11-33}$$

The ratio of the rough sphere value to this value given by the Eucken approximation is plotted in Fig. D,11b. It is seen that the ratio is unity for $\kappa = 0$, since in this case it is easy to transfer energy and since equilibrium is established immediately. For other values of κ, the deviation from unity gives a measure of the effect of the relaxation time on the thermal conductivity.

Loaded spheres. The relaxation time or the time required for attainment of equilibrium has not been calculated for a gas made up of rough sphere molecules. However, Jeans [25] has made the corresponding calculations for a gas made up of molecules which are loaded spheres. The model of a loaded sphere consists of a spherical molecule of diameter σ in which the center of gravity lies a short distance r from the geometrical center. It is assumed that $r \ll \sigma$ and that the mass distribution has an axis of symmetry. The moment of inertia about an axis through the center of mass perpendicular to the symmetry axis is I and m is the mass of the molecule. Jeans used an earlier treatment of kinetic theory due to Maxwell, and hence his results are not directly comparable to those just discussed. Nevertheless some of his results are of interest.

Loaded sphere molecules wobble in their motion and transfer rotational energy on collisions. Hence one can inquire as to the equilibrium distribution of energy and the time required for the equilibrium to be established. First it is to be noticed that the rotation of the molecules about their symmetry axes cannot be affected by a collision. Hence there is no mechanism for the attainment of equilibrium insofar as this type of rotation is concerned. However, the rotational energy about the

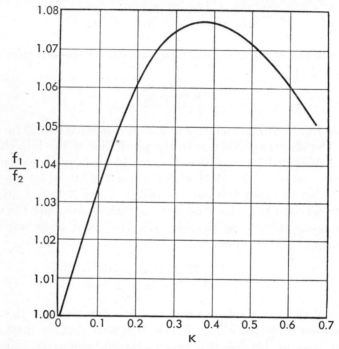

Fig. D,11b. Ratio of thermal conductivity of rough spheres to that predicted by the Eucken approximation for rough spheres.

other two axes does interchange with the translational energy and equilibrium is established. This situation is similar, but not identical, to the case of the two-dimensional rotation of a diatomic molecule.

Let E_t be the mean translational energy per molecule and E_r be the mean rotational energy per molecule, excluding the energy of the rotation about the symmetry axis. Jeans showed that in a uniform gas,

$$\frac{d}{dt} \ln \left| E_r - \frac{2}{3} E_t \right| = -\frac{5}{2} \frac{n}{N} \beta (E_t)^{\frac{1}{2}} \tag{11-34}$$

where n is the molar density and β is a constant depending only on the structure of the molecules

$$\beta = \frac{16r^2\sigma^2}{3I} \left(\frac{2\pi m}{3} \right)^{\frac{1}{2}} \tag{11-35}$$

⟨ 416 ⟩

Eq. 11-34 shows that $|E_r - \frac{2}{3}E_t|$ decreases monotonically to zero. This is consistent with the known equilibrium values of $E_t = \frac{3}{2}kT$ and with the mean rotational energy of a two-dimensional rotator, $E_r = kT$. However, Eq. 11-34 shows that the system approaches equilibrium, i.e. that the equilibrium is stable. Further, if the system is slightly perturbed from equilibrium, the value of $|E_r - \frac{2}{3}E_t|$ decreases exponentially with time, dropping to $1/e$ of its value in a time

$$\tau = \frac{3N}{5\beta n (E_t)^{\frac{1}{2}}} \tag{11-36}$$

The quantity τ is known as the relaxation time. Making use of Eq. 11-35,

$$\tau = \frac{9IN}{80r^2\sigma^2 n} \left(\frac{1}{\pi kTm} \right)^{\frac{1}{2}} \tag{11-37}$$

From elementary kinetic theory, it can be shown that the mean time between collisions of rigid sphere molecules is

$$\tau_c - \frac{N}{4n\sigma^2} \left(\frac{m}{\pi kT} \right)^{\frac{1}{2}} \tag{11-38}$$

This number under standard conditions is of the order of 10^{-10} seconds. The relaxation time is thus

$$\tau = \frac{9}{20} \left(\frac{I}{mr^2} \right) \tau_c \tag{11-39}$$

It is seen that if the moment of inertia is small, energy is transferred very readily and the relaxation time is short. But if the moment of inertia is large, it takes many collisions to transfer the energy and the time required to reach equilibrium is long. The larger the asymmetry r, the easier it is to transfer energy and the smaller is the relaxation time. However, it should be mentioned that this model is of doubtful value since in most cases the transfer of energy probably occurs due to the lack of sphericity of the potential rather than to an asymmetry of the mass distribution.

Jeans also considered the propagation of sound through a gas made up of loaded sphere molecules. He showed that for frequencies ν small compared to $1/\tau$ the velocity of propagation is that characteristic of a perfect gas with a ratio of specific heats $\gamma = \frac{7}{5}$. This is the true ratio of specific heats for loaded spheres. Hence at the low frequencies the rotational motion follows the changes due to the passage of the wave. However, at high frequencies $\nu \gg 1/\tau$, the velocity is that characteristic of a gas with $\gamma = \frac{5}{3}$. This value of γ corresponds to a gas with only translational energy. Hence at frequencies large compared to the reciprocal of the relaxation time, the rotational motion does not follow the change.

If the frequency is of the order of $\nu = 1/\tau$, there is resonance absorption of the sound. Similar calculations could be made for the case of rough spheres.

D,12. Cited References.

1. Chapman, S., and Cowling, T. G. *The Mathematical Theory of Non-Uniform Gases.* Cambridge Univ. Press, 1939. (Notes added in 1951, Cambridge, 1952.)
2. Curtiss, C. F., and Hirschfelder, J. O. *J. Chem. Phys. 17*, 550 (1949).
3. Irving, J. H., and Kirkwood, J. G. *J. Chem. Phys. 18*, 817 (1950).
4. Kirkwood, J. G. *J. Chem. Phys. 15*, 72 (1947).
5. Grad, H. *Commun. on Pure and Appl. Math. 2*, 331 (1949).
6. Kennard, E. H. *Kinetic Theory of Gases.* McGraw-Hill, 1938.
7. Holleran, E. M., and Hulburt, H. M. *J. Chem. Phys. 19*, 232 (1951).
8. Hirschfelder, J. O., McClure, F. T., and Weeks, I. F. *J. Chem. Phys. 10*, 201 (1942).
9a. Kihara, T., and Kotani, M. *Proc. Phys. Math. Soc. Japan 24*, 76 (1942).
9b. deBoer, J., and van Kranendonk, J. *Physica 14*, 442, 451 (1948).
9c. Rowlinson, J. S. *J. Chem. Phys. 17*, 101 (1949).
9d. Hirschfelder, J. O., Bird, R. B., and Spotz, E. L. *J. Chem. Phys. 16*, 968 (1948).
9e. de Boer, J., and Bird, R. B. *Physica 20*, 185 (1954).
10. Lennard-Jones, J. E., and Devonshire, A. F. *Proc. Roy. Soc. London A163*, 53 (1937).
11. Wentorf, R. H., Buehler, R. J., Hirschfelder, J. O., and Curtiss, C. F. *J. Chem. Phys. 18*, 1484 (1950).
12. Hirschfelder, J. O. *Rough Quantum Mechanical Calculation.* Unpublished.
13. Hildebrand, J. H., Wakeham, H. R. R., and Boyd, R. N. *J. Chem. Phys. 7*, 1094 (1939).
14. Rowlinson, J. S. *Dissertation.* Oxford Univ., 1950.
14a. Frazer, R. A., Duncan, W. J., and Collar, A. R. *Elementary Matrices.* Cambridge Univ. Press, 1950.
14b. Trautz, M., and Kipphan, K. F. *Ann. Physik 2*, 746 (1929).
15. Hirschfelder, J. O., Bird, R. B., and Spotz, E. L. *Trans. Am. Soc. Mech. Engrs. 71*, 921 (1949).
15a. Rowlinson, J. S. *Trans. Faraday Soc. 45*, 974 (1949).
15b. Hirschfelder, J. O., Curtiss, C. F., and Bird, R. B. *The Molecular Theory of Gases and Liquids.* Wiley, 1954.
16. Brown, H. *Phys. Rev. 58*, 661 (1940).
16a. Winter, E. R. S. *Trans. Faraday Soc. 46 (2)*, 81 (1950).
16b. van Itterbeek, A., van Paemel, O., and van Lierde, J. *Physica 13*, 231 (1947).
16c. Grew, K. E. *J. Chem. Phys. 18*, 150 (1950).
17. Prigogine, I., and Xhrouet, E. *Physica 15*, 913 (1949).
18. Prigogine, I., and Mahieu, M. *Physica 16*, 51 (1950).
19. Curtiss, C. F. *Ph.D. Dissertation.* Univ. of Wisconsin, 1948. (Published as *Univ. of Wisconsin Nav. Research Lab. Rept. CM-476.*)
20. Eucken, A. *Physik. Z. 14*, 324 (1913).
21. Wang Chang, C. S., and Uhlenbeck, G. E. On the transport phenomena in rarefied gases. *Applied Physics Lab., Johns Hopkins Univ. CM-443*, Feb. 1948.
22. Ishida, Y. *Phys. Rev. 10*, 305 (1917).
23. Bryan, G. H. *Brit. Assoc. Advance. Sci. Rept.*, 83 (1894).
24. Pidduck, F. B. *Proc. Roy. Soc. London A101*, 101 (1922).
25. Jeans, J. H. *Dynamical Theory of Gases*, 1st ed. Cambridge Univ. Press, 1904.
26. Hirschfelder, J. O., Bird, R. B., and Spotz, E. L. *Chem. Revs. 44*, 205ff. (1949).

SECTION E

CRITICAL PHENOMENA

O. K. RICE

E,1. General Considerations and Experimental Background.
When the vapor of a pure substance is compressed isothermally at a
sufficiently low temperature, the pressure will increase until condensation
begins to occur. The vapor will then transform into liquid at constant
pressure, and only when all the vapor has disappeared will the pressure
again increase. On the other hand, if the temperature is high enough the
phenomenon of condensation does not occur; though the substance be
eventually so highly compressed that it resembles a liquid rather than a
gas, the pressure increases gradually through the entire range. The
highest temperature at which condensation occurs is known as the
critical temperature.

According to this description, the isotherms would be expected to
resemble the curves shown in Fig. E,1a. The curve which passes through
the ends of the horizontal parts of the isotherms is called the coexistence
curve, since it is the loci of the molal volumes of liquid and vapor which
are in equilibrium. Thus liquid with the molal volume indicated by
point A is in equilibrium with vapor with the molal volume indicated
by point B, at the temperature for which the isotherm passing through
these points is drawn. This equilibrium occurs at the pressure indicated
by the diagram.

In Fig. E,1a the coexistence curve is shown as a roughly parabolic
curve with a rounded top. It has a definite maximum through which the
isotherm for the critical temperature passes. This maximum also corresponds to a definite pressure and molal volume, known as the critical
pressure and critical volume respectively. The critical volume may, of
course, also be expressed in such units as cm^3 per gram as well as cm^3
per mole.

Both theoretical and experimental evidence exist which indicate that
the idea of a definite critical point, with unambiguous critical temperature, pressure, and volume is probably only an approximation; actually
there appears to be a critical *region*. At least two suggestions have been
made concerning the behavior of the isotherms in this region. Isotherms
of the type shown in Fig. E,1b were inferred from a study of physical
clustering of molecules in the vapor by Rice [1]; isotherms such as shown

in Fig. E,1c were inferred by Mayer and Harrison [*2,3*]. In Fig. E,1b there is a last isotherm, at a temperature which we shall call T_{cr}, which has a finite horizontal portion. Above T_{cr} an isotherm has a more or less flat section, but with nonzero slope. In Fig. E,1c there is a series of isotherms lying between temperatures which we call T_{cr} and T'_{cr}. These isotherms have horizontal sections (delimited by the broken extension of the coexistence curve) but show no discontinuities in slope at the ends of the horizontal portions. In all cases it is supposed that no meniscus can be observed above T_{cr}, and the temperature of the disappearance of the meniscus will generally be assumed to be identical with T_{cr} if equilibrium is established. According to Mayer and Harrison, however, T'_{cr} is the true critical temperature.

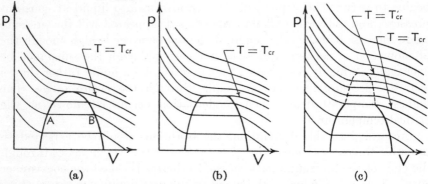

Fig. E,1.   Isotherms in immediate neighborhood of critical temperature; (a) classical theory, (b) theory of Rice, (c) theory of Mayer and Harrison.

Critical temperatures, pressures, and volumes have been determined for many substances and are listed in such standard tables as the Landolt-Börnstein Physikalische-Chemische Tabellen and the International Critical Tables. An extensive list is given in a recent review [*4*], together with a discussion of experimental methods. These constants may be found either by observation and study of the isotherms or by observation of the meniscus (usually in this case only the temperature and volume are readily observed). For the latter method a typical procedure is to place a known amount of liquid in a tube of known volume (hence giving known molal volume), to free the whole system of air, and to observe the behavior as it is heated. According to Fig. E,1a, if the tube were filled so that the molal volume lay to the right of the maximum of the coexistence curve, as is the case with point A in Fig. E,1d, then on heating the tube, the meniscus would gradually approach the bottom of the tube, and at the temperature of point B the tube would be filled with gas. If, on the other hand, we started to the left of the maximum (point A') we should expect the meniscus to rise on heating, and finally (point B')

the tube would be filled with liquid. Only at a molal volume exactly corresponding to the maximum of the curve would the meniscus disappear within the tube. Actually the molal volume which will cause the meniscus to disappear within the tube does not seem to be very precisely defined. Though other explanations have been offered, this fact is sometimes cited as evidence in favor of one of the alternatives represented by Fig. E,1b and E,1c. In any event, it is clear that this method will not give a very good determination of the critical volume.

The critical parameters are frequently found by extrapolating the portions of the coexistence curve below T_{cr} to the point where they meet, rounding them off roughly as in Fig. E,1a. If Fig. E,1b or E,1c is correct, this might give a slightly erroneous value of T_{cr}, but the error will not be serious. Since temperatures and pressures will generally be measured

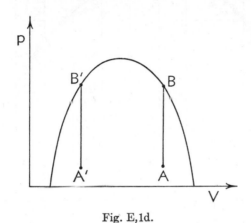

Fig. E,1d.

simultaneously, values of both at the critical point will be found. With this method the critical volume, or more directly the critical density, is found by using the empirical law of Cailletet and Mathias. This law states that the mean of the densities of liquid and vapor is a linear function of the temperature. This line is then extrapolated to give the critical density at the critical temperature.

The applicability of this procedure may be seen from Fig. E,1e, wherein are presented experimental data on a number of substances, as collected by Guggenheim [5]. This figure, by itself, would not be directly useful in finding the critical density ρ_{cr} or the critical temperature of any particular substance, since, actually, reduced densities ρ/ρ_{cr} are plotted against reduced temperatures T/T_{cr}. But it will show well enough how both ρ_{cr} and T_{cr} could be found by plotting ρ against T. The use of reduced densities and temperatures causes the points for the substances considered to lie almost on the same curve, as expected from the law of corresponding states (Sec. C). The curve was drawn according to the equations,

$$\frac{\rho}{\rho_{cr}} = 1 + \frac{3}{4}\left(1 - \frac{T}{T_{cr}}\right) + \frac{7}{4}\left(1 - \frac{T}{T_{cr}}\right)^{\frac{1}{3}} \tag{1-1}$$

$$\frac{\rho}{\rho_{cr}} = 1 + \frac{3}{4}\left(1 - \frac{T}{T_{cr}}\right) - \frac{7}{4}\left(1 - \frac{T}{T_{cr}}\right)^{\frac{1}{3}} \tag{1-2}$$

Eq. 1-1 is for the liquid side and Eq. 1-2 for the vapor side. By subtraction it is seen that the law of Cailletet and Mathias is fulfilled. However, it is also seen that the coexistence curve, though not like Fig. E,1b and E,1c, is still not of the rough parabolic type which might be expected

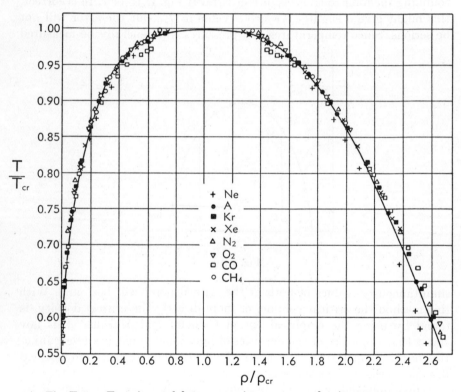

Fig. E,1e.   Experimental data on coexistence curve, density-temperature diagram. After Guggenheim [5, Fig. 2].

from Fig. E,1a. (It is true that Fig. E,1e is a ρ vs. T diagram, but since $(\partial p/\partial T)_V$ and $(\partial \rho/\partial V)_T$ are always finite, a parabolically rounded top on one of the curves would imply a similar shape for the other.) If the curves were really parabolic, the exponent of the last term of Eq. 1-1 and 1-2 would be $\frac{1}{2}$ instead of $\frac{1}{3}$. Also, it is of interest that Eq. 1-1 and 1-2 do not represent parts of a single analytic function. Actually, it is apparent that very little can be discovered about the top of the coexistence curve from Fig. E,1e, except, perhaps, that it is not of the strictly parabolic type. For many purposes, the kind of approximation implied in Fig. E,1a will nevertheless be quite useful.

With this background we may consider in somewhat more detail some of the complex observational material on critical phenomena. When a bomb or tube contains liquid and vapor in amounts such that the over-all molal volume is near the critical volume, an intense opalescence appears as the critical temperature is approached; this opalescence is bluish if observed by scattered light, brownish if observed by transmitted light. The nature of this opalescence and some of the more quantitative measurements are considered in Art. 9. In addition to this opalescence, there appears in the immediate neighborhood of T_{cr} a sort of fog, which gives the impression that the two phases are being dispersed in each other. The exact appearance of the substance under investigation as it approaches the critical temperature depends upon whether the tube containing it has been shaken and, to some extent, upon other details of its past history, the rate of heating, and the way it is handled. Though different observers thus differ on the details, we may perhaps illustrate the kind of behavior observed by quoting from a paper by Mason, Naldrett, and Maass [6] in which they studied the behavior of ethane in a bomb filled to the critical density.

Unshaken bomb. "On heating from 30°C the meniscus remained in the middle of the bomb. Up to 32.20°C the meniscus was sharp and flat, and no opalescence was noticeable except at the meniscus, which appeared brownish by transmitted light and looked like a thin white disc by reflected light. Above 32.20°C the meniscus became less sharp, gradually broadening into a band of dense brown opalescence. The region of opalescence gradually expanded in both directions, and at 32.27°C it could be detected throughout the bomb, while the maximum intensity where the meniscus had been, had greatly diminished. This continued until the temperature was 32.4°C at which point no discontinuity could be detected by transmitted light, but by reflected light a region of greater opalescence could be seen in the middle of the bomb. On heating to 32.5°C, the opalescence disappeared and no heterogeneity could be detected either by reflected or transmitted light.

"On cooling, the opalescence gradually appeared uniformly distributed in the bomb, and [apparently] . . . at greater intensity than at the same temperature on heating. At 32.235°C the contents of the bomb was intensely white by reflected light and reddish brown by transmitted light; on cooling to 32.232°C a dense opalescent band appeared in the middle of the bomb. At 32.231°C the opalescence suddenly seemed to coalesce to form the so-called 'wet-fog' [previously] described by Young [7]. This settled out rapidly to form a sharp meniscus in the middle of the bomb. The opalescence decreased at this point, although it could still be observed, now uniformly distributed. . . . [It] could no longer be seen at 32.0°C."

Shaken bomb. "At 31°C, when the shaking was stopped, the liquid phase settled out immediately. There was no appreciable opalescence. Above 32.1°C there was a gradual increase in the opalescence, and the time required for the phases to separate . . . increased. . . . The opalescence was [apparently] evenly distributed. . . . At 32.19°C the liquid had ceased settling after about 10 sec. At 32.230°C about one minute was required. At 32.231°C the contents of the bomb was intensely brown and turbid and immediately after shaking was stopped, wet clouds could be seen in turbulent motion. About two minutes was required for the phase to separate to form a sharp meniscus. At 32.232°C the turbidity vanished, leaving a completely homogeneous, clear, light brown system, which remained unchanged for several hours at this temperature. The difference between the contents . . . at this temperature and 0.001°C lower was similar to that between a finely dispersed sol and one that has been partially coagulated. With further heating the brown color gradually faded. With cooling down the same effects occurred at precisely the same temperatures as on heating."

It will be observed that the meniscus reappears on cooling in an unshaken bomb at the same temperature at which it disappears or reappears in a shaken bomb. This would seem to be the best value of T_{cr}. The fact that the meniscus disappears at a higher temperature in an unshaken bomb is probably due to lack of equilibrium in this case. It will also be noted that the opalescence and fog tend to be more uniformly distributed in a shaken bomb, as might well be expected.

That the critical phenomena can be seen over a range of molal volumes or densities of the liquid has already been noted above. This was observed by many early workers (see, e.g. Schröer [8] for discussion and references and some experimental work). In their study of ethane Mason, Naldrett, and Maass [6] found that, with shaking, the meniscus appears or reappears within the limits of the tube over a density range of 0.205 to 0.207 g/cm³, or perhaps a slightly larger range. The temperature of appearance or disappearance seemed to be constant (even though the meniscus went out through the top or the bottom) over a somewhat larger range, viz. from about 0.19 to 0.225 g/cm³. The latter range of densities is about that over which the meniscus disappeared within the confines of the bomb when the tube was not shaken. In the case of ethylene, Naldrett and Maass [9] found that the meniscus appeared in the confines of the bomb, with shaking, between densities of 0.210 and 0.215 g/cm³. In this case, the "flat top" of the coexistence curve extended from about 0.205 to 0.225 g/cm³.

More recently, Atack and Schneider [10] have examined the coexistence curve of sulfur hexafluoride with an exceedingly careful temperature control. They apparently found that the meniscus reappeared within the bomb at densities ranging at least from 0.72 to 0.79 g/cm³. However, not all temperatures of reappearance were the same, the coexistence curve showing a rounded top. The total range of temperature over the range of densities noted was only a little over 0.01°. It is difficult to see how it is possible to have the meniscus disappear within the confines of the bomb over a range of temperatures. It is possible that this peculiar result was caused by minute residual traces of impurities.

Actually, there seems to be little doubt that, at least in appearance, the coexistence curve has a flat horizontal top over a small range of densities. Gouy [11] attempted to explain this result as an effect of gravity. The change in pressure with the height h in a column of liquid is given by

$$\frac{dp}{dh} = g\rho \qquad (1\text{-}3)$$

where g is the acceleration due to gravity. The change in density with height then is given by

$$\frac{d\rho}{dh} = \frac{d\rho}{dp}\frac{dp}{dh} = \frac{d\rho}{dp} g\rho \qquad (1\text{-}4)$$

and the relative change in density by

$$\frac{1}{\rho}\frac{d\rho}{dh} = g\rho\beta \qquad (1\text{-}5)$$

where β, the compressibility, is defined as $\rho^{-1}d\rho/dp$. Since β is very great near the critical point, the pressure of the substance in the tube could lead to differences in density along its height of sufficient magnitude so that, for a tube whose average density departs somewhat from the critical density, there would be in it a point at which the density was equal to the critical density.[1] Then the meniscus should appear at this point in the tube at the critical temperature. The range of average densities over which this can happen should be greater, the greater the height of the tube. Very recently, Weinberger and Schneider [12] have investigated the coexistence curve of xenon in a bomb 19 cm long and have compared it to that of a bomb 1.2 cm long (obtained by placing the first bomb on its side). They found that the flat top of the coexistence curve was much longer in the 19-cm bomb than in the 1.2-cm bomb

[1] For example, the compressibility of carbon dioxide just above the critical temperature is almost constant over a density range of 5 to 10 per cent near the critical density. Even 0.1° above the critical temperature, β is about 10 atm⁻¹, while the pressure difference from bottom to top in a 10-cm tube would be around 0.005 atm. Thus there would be a range of densities of about 5 per cent for a tube with the density near the critical density, even 0.1° above the critical temperature.

and that the difference was approximately what was to be expected by application of Eq. 1-3. They also investigated [*13*] the density along the length of a long bomb by mixing a small amount of radioactive xenon with the normal xenon and using this as a tracer. It was found that at temperatures slightly above the critical temperature, density differences developed as expected, equilibrium being attained in something like an hour. From these experiments they concluded that the flat top on the coexistence curve of xenon could be explained by means of gravity, though, of course, no proof could be given that a small flat top of a range of about 1 per cent of the total density would not persist in a tube of zero height.

It is to be noted that while xenon, with its high critical density, is an excellent substance to use to bring out a gravitational effect, it is, for this very reason, a poor substance to use for an investigation of inherent properties which would persist even if there were no gravity. The tubes used by Mason, Naldrett, and Maass [*6*] in their study of ethane were presumably about 8 cm long, but the gravitational effect in them would not be appreciably greater than that in a tube of xenon 1.2 cm long, and it may well be that the density differences were completely eliminated by shaking, as all the observations were made very soon after shaking had ceased. On the other hand, the observations of Weinberger and Schneider [*12*] were apparently made after settling had occurred and sedimentation equilibrium had been reached. The fact that the bombs containing ethane, which had been vigorously shaken, showed uniform opalescence throughout their length, and the fact that a fine mist, presumably indicative of the presence of two finely dispersed phases, is also uniformly distributed when the temperature is very close to the critical temperature, may be taken as evidence that the flat part of the coexistence curve in the case of ethane is real; the same arguments will also apply to ethylene. Nevertheless, it is probably best to reserve final judgment on this matter at the present time.

Note added in proof: Since the main portion of this section was written, some work has appeared which is relevant to the problem under discussion. S. G. Whiteway and S. G. Mason [*121*] have studied the coexistence curves of ethane, ethylene, and xenon in tubes of different height, with and without stirring; H. W. Habgood and W. G. Schneider [*122*] have made studies of the isotherms of xenon and have made thermodynamic deductions therefrom; and H. L. Lorentzen [*123*] has studied the coexistence curve and the isotherms of carbon dioxide by use of an optical method after allowing settling in the gravitational field, with extraordinarily accurate temperature control. These authors all believe that the coexistence curves have a rounded top; however, in the opinion of the present writer, the matter is still not settled. The range of critical densities, for which the meniscus disappeared within the tube with shaking in the case of ethane [*6*], would, according to Guggenheim's curve (Fig. E,1e), correspond to a temperature range of less than 0.001°. It will, therefore, require exceedingly delicate measurements to decide whether the coexistence curve is flatter on the top than Guggenheim's curve; Lorentzen's work gives some hope that this may shortly be accomplished.

We may now turn to a consideration of the isotherms in the critical region. Isotherms have been measured for many substances in the general neighborhood of the critical point, but in few cases have they been measured accurately enough at temperatures close enough together to make them of much value in deciding among Fig. E,1a, E,1b, and E,1c. Ethylene is a substance for which isotherms have been carefully measured in the same laboratory so as to be consistent with the coexistence curve determined by observation of the meniscus. Dacey, McIntosh, and Maass [14,15] believed that they had found horizontal portions in the isotherm above T_{cr} as predicted by Mayer and Harrison (Fig. E,1c); in

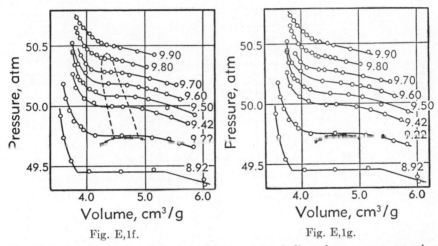

Fig. E,1f.   Fig. E,1g.

Fig. E,1f. Isotherms for ethylene, at temperatures indicated on curves, assuming horizontal portions above T_{cr}, as enclosed by the broken curve. The crosses are from data of Naldrett and Maass [9], obtained by finding the temperature of disappearance of the meniscus for a fixed specific volume. They have been placed on the pressure-volume diagram by interpolation to give the top of the coexistence curve. After Rice [1, Fig. 1].

Fig. E,1g. Isotherms for ethylene assuming no horizontal portions above T_{cr}. Data as in Fig. E,1f. After Rice [1, Fig. 2].

fact, in their diagrams, they showed a sudden change of slope at the end of the horizontal portions of the isotherms above T_{cr}, which would *not* be in accord with the predictions. The data, however, do not necessarily demand a sudden change in slope, nor, for that matter, even a horizontal portion. These data are replotted in Fig. E,1f and E,1g. In the former we have drawn in a set of isotherms showing a horizontal portion but no abrupt changes in slope. In Fig. E,1g there are no horizontal portions. Either one of these sets of curves agrees with the data within experimental error, so it appears that no definite conclusions can be drawn from these data. Some isolated series of data [14, Table III and 15, Table II] might be thought to indicate a horizontal portion of certain isotherms above T_{cr}, but these do not agree too well with the collected data for all the isotherms.

Michels, Blaisse, and Michels [*16*] have made some very accurate measurements on carbon dioxide. In this case, one gains the impression

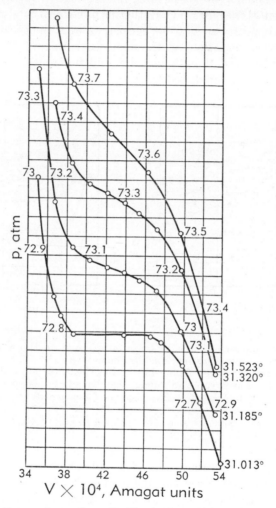

Fig. E,1h. Isotherms for carbon dioxide, in immediate neighborhood of critical temperature (about 31.03°C)—temperatures shown beside curves. Each curve has a different pressure scale, as indicated in the diagram. After Michels, Blaisse, and Michels [*16*, Fig. 4].

that there is a last isotherm with a finite horizontal portion, and that at slightly higher temperatures the isotherm has at all times a negative slope (Fig. E,1h). Mayer and Streeter [*17*] suggested that traces of impurity possibly prevented the isotherms above T_{cr} from having a horizontal portion, but it is difficult to see why impurities should be more effective just above than just below T_{cr}. Unfortunately, Michels, Blaisse, and Michels were not able to observe the meniscus. The coexistence curve that they themselves suggest on the basis of the equation-of-state data does not have a flat top, but is somewhat flattened, as might be expected from Fig. E,1e. The work on carbon dioxide has recently been very carefully repeated by Wentorf and Boyd [18], along with visual observation of the meniscus. Their results agree on the whole very closely with those of Michels, Blaisse, and Michels. They believe, however, that there may be a region, extending approximately 0.02° above T_{cr}, in which the isotherms have a horizontal portion, as in Fig. E,1c. It is scarcely possible to decide from their data whether such an effect is real.

The isotherms of isobutane [19] give an impression similar to those of carbon dioxide, though perhaps less definite. Many other hydrocarbons have been studied by Beattie and his coworkers and reported in recent volumes of the *Journal of the American Chemical Society* and of the *Journal of Chemical Physics*, but no definite conclusion as to the nature of the critical isotherm can be drawn.

The isotherms of sulfur hexafluoride near the critical temperature have been studied by MacCormack and Schneider [20] and by Wentorf and Boyd [18]. In the case of this substance with rather heavy molecules, gravity may have an appreciable effect.[2] MacCormack and Schneider developed a satisfactory method of correcting for the effect of gravity below the critical temperature, but the method they used above the critical temperature was not satisfactory. The correction, however, is not very important once the temperature is a few tenths of a degree above T_{cr}. For temperatures near T_{cr}, Wentorf and Boyd made a rough correction to the results of MacCormack and Schneider by assuming that it was the same as the correction just below T_{cr}. After this latter correction is made, it is found that the minimum values of $|(\partial p/\partial V)_T|$ (i.e. the values at the point of inflection of the isotherm) are approximately proportional to $T - T_{cr}$, which is the result usually observed (e.g. in the case of carbon dioxide). Wentorf and Boyd also made a correction to their own results for the effect of gravity, but since their vessel was not very tall, the correction in this case was unimportant. They studied a series of isotherms within 0.1° above T_{cr}, and when they plotted the minimum value of $|(\partial p/\partial V)_T|$ against $T - T_{cr}$, they found it extrapolated to zero at $T - T_{cr} = 0.04°$; for $T - T_{cr} = 0.04°$ they estimated that $(\partial p/\partial V)_T$ was zero. On this basis they believed it to be probable that in this range of temperatures above the temperature T_{cr} at which the meniscus was observed to disappear, the isotherms have a horizontal portion. It is to be noted, however, that the slope of their curve for $(\partial p/\partial V)_T$ against

---

[2] In the case of the experiments on carbon dioxide, it seems probable that the effect of gravity is not greater than the experimental error.

$T - T_{cr}$ was much steeper than the corrected curve of MacCormack and Schneider and that the latter did not miss the points of Wentorf and Boyd by an amount which was very much outside the presumed limits of error. It seems likely, therefore, that their conclusions should be taken with some reserve.

Very recently Palmer [21] has attempted to measure density gradients in a fluid near the critical temperature by an optical method depending on the refractive index, and by integration to get the density at any height. Use of Eq. 1-3 and 1-4 should then enable him to determine isotherms. These isotherms have been presented by him in several figures.

There is no doubt that great experimental difficulties exist in this field, and there have been many earlier observations on the tendency of density differences to persist in an unshaken bomb, which have been variously interpreted. In some cases, quite appreciable density differences remained at temperatures sufficiently above T_{cr}, so that it appears quite improbable that gravity can be the entire explanation of the phenomenon. This has been cited by Mayer and his collaborators as evidence in favor of isotherms of the type in Fig. E,1c, since as long as there is a horizontal portion it should be possible for layers of different densities to exist in equilibrium with each other, and above T_{cr}, according to their theory, *any* density on the horizontal part is a possible equilibrium state. The question which arises is whether the observed density differences actually do represent equilibrium conditions. It is the belief of the present writer that they probably do not, but the question cannot be said to be fully resolved at present. In any event, a brief résumé of the observations will be of interest.

The early observations have been summarized by Hein [22]. In this work, a series of small floats of differing density were placed in the tube with the substance being studied. The positions of these floats under various conditions would then give an idea of the gradation of density in the system. A float of just the right density would remain in the position occupied by the meniscus after the latter had disappeared, and the temperature could be raised an appreciable amount above T_{cr} before the density in the tube equalized. Hein found, contrary to the experience of most other investigators, that the density differences reasserted themselves on cooling before the meniscus appeared. He found that if the contents of the tube were not stirred the meniscus would disappear without fog formation and reappear with very little fog formation. If the contents were stirred over a portion of the length of the tube by a magnetically controlled stirrer, this part became cloudy and of uniform density; after heating to well above the critical temperature and then cooling, the fog reappeared in this same part. The existence of "memory" is certainly an indication of lack of equilibrium. The presence of impurities might also have played a role in the observations.

More recently, Maass and his coworkers have made an extensive series of measurements on densities near the critical point. They used a small float attached to a quartz spiral, which acted as a sensitive spring balance and which, in some cases, could be moved to various positions in the tube. Fig. E,1i and E,1j, taken from the paper of Tapp, Steacie, and Maass [23] on methyl ether, illustrate the type of result obtained. Fig. E,1i shows that the density on cooling does not follow the curves obtained on heating (the direction of change is indicated by arrows in the figure). Fig. E,1j shows the distribution of density along the tube at various temperatures; it is not stated whether the temperatures were approached from above or below, but it was probably from below. The meniscus disappeared at 126.9°C. Strangely enough, it was stated that

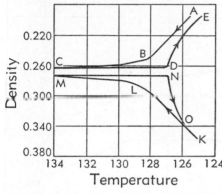

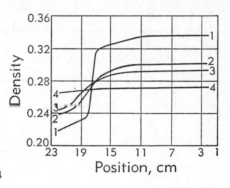

Fig. E, 1i. Density of methyl ether as a function of temperature, near the critical temperature (126.9°C). Curves *ABC* and *EDC* for densities above the position of the meniscus; curves *ONM* and *KLM*, below the position of the meniscus. After Tapp, Steacie, and Maass [23, Fig. 3].

Fig. E,1j. Distribution of density of methyl ether as a function of distance along the tube in the critical region. Curve 1, 125.5°C; curve 2, 126.7°C; curve 3, 127.1°C; curve 4, 135.1°C. After Tapp, Steacie, and Maass [23, Fig. 4].

these density differences did not persist above the critical temperature when the meniscus faded out exactly in the center of the tube without rising or falling noticeably. It will be observed that the density was never equalized throughout the tube in the instance illustrated in Fig. E,1i, although apparently the equivalent of such equalization, as far as experimental conditions would allow, did take place in the experiments of Maass and Geddes [24] on ethylene. The latter also made an interesting observation on the density changes on cooling. It was found that a small change in the density of the order of one-half per cent did occur in the range of temperatures about 0.1°C above that at which the sudden changes characteristic of the separation of phases took place. It was also found that the densities on heating and cooling were different even below the temperature where the meniscus appeared. These were thought to be equilibrium values, but undoubtedly were not, as the system was not stirred.

McIntosh and Maass [*25*] found that the density of the "liquid" and "vapor" phases above the critical point depended on the average density of the material contained in the tube. The density of vapor at a high average density actually exceeded the liquid density at low average density. Mayer and Harrison of course expected that, in the range in which the isotherm (Fig. E,1c) is horizontal, various densities would be in equilibrium with one another. The densities studied by McIntosh and Maass, however, extended well beyond the range over which the isotherm involved appeared even possibly to be horizontal.

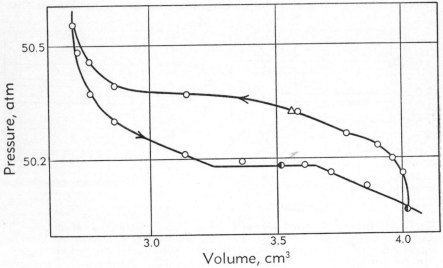

Fig. E,1k.   Hysteresis in pressure of ethylene at 9.60°C.
After Dacey, McIntosh, and Maass [*14*, Fig. 2].

It is to be remarked that in the experiments of Tapp, Steacie, and Maass the contents of the tubes were mechanically stirred, so it appears that some kinds of mixing are not sufficient to equalize the density; it was believed in general that the density differences would not disappear with time. Later, however, Naldrett and Maass [*9*] found that the contents of a tube apparently became uniform on long standing only a small fraction of a degree above the critical temperature, even though conditions were maintained extremely quiet and constant.

During the course of their experiments, Maass and his coworkers made many observations on procedures which cause equalization or reestablishment of the density differences and on the rate at which equilibrium was established.[3] We can give only a few illustrations here.

---

[3] For a review article with references see Maass [*26*]. See also Clark [*27*]; McIntosh, Dacey, and Maass [*28*].

For example, Dacey, McIntosh, and Maass [14] measured the pressure of ethylene at constant temperature after compression and after expansion with the results indicated in Fig. E,1k. The pressures obtained on expansion appear to be equilibrium values. A pressure on the compression curve would fall to that on the expansion curve in 30 to 40 minutes. Incidentally, it was found that the "equilibrium" pressure of a system in which density differences persisted above T_{cr} (insofar as this can be said to be an equilibrium state) was the same as the pressure of the same system in which the density differences had been eliminated by heating to a higher temperature and cooling back to the original temperature.

Maass and Geddes ([24] measured the time required to reach steady values of the density after small changes in temperature. The time required was greater if the temperature was lowered than if it was raised (in spite of the fact that equilibrium with respect to the appearance or disappearance of the meniscus appears to be more readily established on lowering the temperature). The time is also longer the nearer the system is to the center of the critical region.

Among more recent measurements in which some note was taken of the time required to attain equilibrium, we may refer again to Weinberger and Schneider [13] and to the extensive discussion of Palmer [21].

There is as yet no theory which is really adequate to explain the complex series of phenomena, including time lags and hysteresis effects, which have been only sketchily outlined above. Maass, however, pointed out that on compression or lowering of the temperature the system must go to a state of greater organization, so that it might be expected that more time would be required when the equilibrium is approached from this direction than when expansion or raising of the temperature occurs.

E,2. Van der Waals Theory of the Critical Point. An equation of state which is valid for both vapor and liquid states of a system will be capable of explaining condensation phenomena, and a determination of the critical point will come out of it. Some refinements will be necessary if we are to get isotherms of the type shown in Fig. E,1b, E,1c, or even E,1e; but for many purposes these are not needed, and in this article and in the following one we do not consider them. Though the van der Waals equation is at best a rough approximation and, especially, does not reproduce the properties of the liquid with any great fidelity, the way in which it gives the condensation and critical phenomena is illustrative. This well-known deduction will therefore be presented here briefly.

The van der Waals equation, for one mole of substance, may be written in the form

$$p = \frac{RT}{V - b} - \frac{a}{V^2} \tag{2-1}$$

where p is the pressure, T the absolute temperature, V the molal volume, and a and b are the van der Waals constants. This equation gives rise to isotherms of the form shown in Fig. E,2a.

The isotherms for the lower range of temperatures show a region of positive slope. A condition in which pressure increases with increasing volume cannot be a state of stable equilibrium. Instead, the system will separate into two phases. The pressure and the molal volumes of the

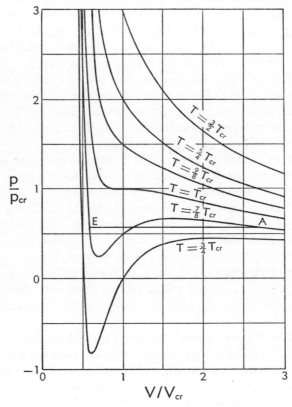

Fig. E,2a. Isotherms according to the van der Waals equation. Note that the scale is very different from, and the range of variable covered much greater than that in Fig. E,1a, E,1b, and E,1c.

phases which are in equilibrium are shown for one of the isotherms in Fig. E,2a and can be found as indicated in Fig. E,2b, where the two shaded areas are equal. In both figures, the points A and E represent the phases which are in equilibrium with each other. In Fig. E,2b, p is shown as the abscissa instead of as the ordinate, in order to facilitate the explanation of the fact that the two areas are equal. The difference ΔF in Gibbs free energy between the points A and E must be zero. But ΔF is also equal to $\int V dp$ taken along the path $ABCDE$. This integral has a positive contribution equal to the area under AB, a negative contribution equal to the area under BCD, and a positive contribution represented by the area under DE. This may be readily seen to give a net area equal to the difference between the shaded areas, which must accordingly be zero.

Separation into phases takes place only at temperatures where part of the isotherm has a positive slope. The critical temperature therefore separates the two regions where a positive $(\partial p/\partial V)_T$ occurs and where

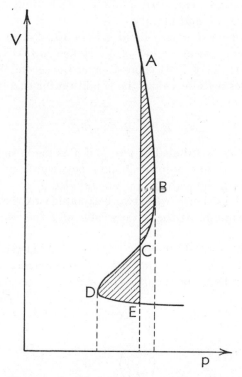

Fig. E,2b.   The van der Waals isotherm, to illustrate condensation.

no positive $(\partial p/\partial V)_T$ is found. The critical isotherm is labeled T_{cr} in Fig. E,2a.

The shape of the curves in Fig. E,2a may be understood by differentiating Eq. 2-1. We obtain

$$\left(\frac{\partial p}{\partial V}\right)_T = -\frac{RT}{(V-b)^2} + \frac{2a}{V^3} \tag{2-2}$$

The maxima and minima exhibited by curves for which T is sufficiently small are the roots of the equation obtained by setting $(\partial p/\partial V)_T = 0$ and clearing of fractions:

$$V^3RT - 2a(V-b)^2 = 0 \tag{2-3}$$

$(\partial p/\partial V)_T$ is also zero when V is infinite, but this zero is lost in the process of clearing of fractions. All other zeros remain unchanged. It can be seen that Eq. 2-3 has no real roots for $V < 0$, since the sign of V^3 is then negative and $(V - b)^2$ is positive. It has one root for $0 < V < b$, since V^3 starts at zero for $V = 0$ and increases as V increases, while $(V - b)^2$ is zero at $V = b$ and increases as V decreases. This root is of no interest physically, since b is a lower limit for V. We see, however, that the other two roots, if they are real, correspond to the minimum and maximum of p and lie between b and infinity.

The first term on the right-hand side of Eq. 2-2 predominates near $V = b$ and for very great values of V. Hence $(\partial p/\partial V)_T$ is negative at both ends of the range of V. It is possible for the second term to predominate at some intermediate value, the condition for this being

$$\frac{a}{RT} > \frac{V^3}{2(V - b)^2}$$

Obviously, this can be fulfilled at any V if T is made small enough; but, since $V^3/2(V - b)^2$ has a lower bound between $V = b$ and $V = \infty$, T can be made large enough so it is not fulfilled at any V. We thus pass from the type of isotherm with two extremums to the type without a minimum or maximum. At the critical value of T the two roots of Eq. 2-3 coincide.

There must be a point where $(\partial^2 p/\partial V^2)_T = 0$ between the two points where $(\partial p/\partial V)_T = 0$. When the latter two coincide, then $(\partial^2 p/\partial V^2)_T$ must vanish at the same point. The simultaneous fulfillment of the conditions

$$\left(\frac{\partial p}{\partial V}\right)_T = 0$$
$$\left(\frac{\partial^2 p}{\partial V^2}\right)_T = 0 \qquad (2\text{-}4)$$

may therefore be taken as the condition for the critical point.

The conditions, Eq. 2-4, can be used to obtain expressions for the critical temperature (T_{cr}), pressure (p_{cr}), and volume (V_{cr}) in terms of the van der Waals constants. The first of Eq. 2-4 gives

$$\frac{RT_{cr}}{(V_{cr} - b)^2} = \frac{2a}{V_{cr}^3} \qquad (2\text{-}5)$$

and the second condition can be readily seen to give

$$\frac{RT_{cr}}{(V_{cr} - b)^3} = \frac{3a}{V_{cr}^4} \qquad (2\text{-}6)$$

Dividing one of these by the other we find

$$V_{cr} = 3b \tag{2-7}$$

Substituting Eq. 2-7 into 2-5 we obtain

$$T_{cr} = \frac{8a}{27Rb} \tag{2-8}$$

and using Eq. 2-7 and 2-8 with Eq. 2-1

$$p_{cr} = \frac{a}{27b^2} \tag{2-9}$$

Combining Eq. 2-7, 2-8, and 2-9 gives

$$\frac{RT_{cr}}{p_{cr}V_{cr}} = \frac{8}{3} = 2.67 \tag{2-10}$$

in which a and b do not appear.

In practice a and b as tabulated are generally determined from T_{cr} and p_{cr} by solving Eq. 2-8 and 2-9. It is then found that the experimental values of V_{cr} lie between $3b$ and $2b$, but are somewhat closer to the latter value. Eq. 2-10 is an equation which can be tested directly experimentally, and the observed values of $RT_{cr}/p_{cr}V_{cr}$ are generally somewhat greater than 2.67, lying between 3.2 and 3.9 for most substances.

The conditions, Eq. 2-4, it should be noted, do not necessarily depend upon any particular equation of state. They necessarily hold if the coexistence curve is of the type shown in Fig. E,1a, and if the isotherms at and above the critical temperature are continuous and have continuous slopes. The isotherm which touches the top of the coexistence curve cannot cut it or touch it anywhere else. Therefore, it must be tangent at that point and have zero slope there. Since the slope must be negative everywhere else, it must have a maximum at the critical point; hence the second derivative must also be zero there. This does not prove that the critical point is the only finite point where the conditions, Eq. 2-4, hold, but this is generally assumed to be the case.

We have discussed the van der Waals equation in some detail because it is the prototype of a particular kind of theory of the critical point, in which it is assumed that the same equation can be used to represent the equation of state of the gas and of the liquid. Other equations have been developed which give a much better representation of the isotherms in both the dilute gas and the neighborhood of the critical point. Among these we may mention the Beattie-Bridgeman equation [29] which contains five empirically determined constants. We may also note that Rocard [30, p. 45] has pointed out that it is possible to get a coexistence curve with a much flatter top than that given by the van der Waals equation on the basis of a theory of the same general type simply by using a more complicated equation of state, which he has interpreted physically.

E,3. Correlation of the Critical Temperature, Pressure, and Volume with Other Properties. A better description of the critical phenomena and a better correlation with the properties of the dilute gases could naturally be obtained with a better equation of state than that of van der Waals. Rowlinson [31] has pointed out that the use of the Beattie-Bridgeman equation is almost equivalent to the use of the virial expansion

$$\frac{PV}{RT} = 1 + \frac{B}{V} + \frac{C}{V^2} + \cdots \tag{3-1}$$

carried out only to the term in V^{-2} and with a particular evaluation of B and C as functions of temperature. By application of Eq. 2-4 to Eq. 3-1, broken off at the term in V^{-2}, the following relations result:

$$V_{cr} = -B_{cr} \tag{3-2}$$

$$3C_{cr} = B_{cr}^2 \tag{3-3}$$

$$\frac{RT_{cr}}{p_{cr}V_{cr}} = 3 \tag{3-4}$$

B_{cr} and C_{cr} are the values at the critical temperature, and, if B and C are known as functions of temperature, Eq. 3-3 can be used to find T_{cr}.

Rather than use the semiempirical evaluations of B and C made by Beattie and Bridgeman, Rowlinson followed another procedure. It is well known that the second virial coefficient B can be calculated from the intermolecular potential energy curve. Lennard-Jones [see 32, Chap. X] has expressed the intermolecular potential energy for nonpolar gas molecules as a function of the intermolecular distance r by an expression of the form $\alpha r^{-12} - \beta r^{-6}$. The second virial coefficient can then be calculated in terms of the constants α and β. In practice the process is reversed, and values of α and β are found empirically which give a good fit for B over a range of temperatures. One can then use the intermolecular potential to calculate C. This can be accomplished by use of a formula of similar nature to that used in calculating B, but more complicated.

Proceeding in this way, Rowlinson has used Eq. 3-2, 3-3, and 3-4 to obtain values of the critical constants. For neon, argon, and nitrogen, calculated values of T_{cr} averaged about 13 per cent too high, and of V_{cr} about 12 per cent too low. The experimental average for RT_{cr}/pV_{cr} was 3.41. Thus a fair correlation was achieved.

For polar gases a term was added to the intermolecular potential to take care of dipole interactions, and again the correlation was on the whole fairly successful. The relationship which is established is essentially one between the properties of the dilute gas and the critical point. The Lennard-Jones potential energy can also correlate at least roughly the properties of the substance in the solid and liquid states, so it is at least a rough approximation to the true potential energy curve. It will, how- ever, not be without interest to attempt to get a more direct correlation between the critical constants and the properties of the solid and liquid.

A number of calculations of the critical parameters have been made, which are based either on the "cell theory" of liquids, or on the "hole theory" of liquids. The cell theory is discussed in Sec. F, but for the present purposes we may take a less sophisticated point of view. We may say briefly that in a cell theory each molecule is supposed to be in a cell formed by its neighbors; in order to study the motion of a given molecule it is assumed that all the neighbors are fixed in their equilibrium positions, or else an average of their various possible positions is taken. The molecule under study is then assumed to move in the resultant potential energy field, which is generally calculated with the aid of the potential energy curves of Lennard-Jones [*32*, Chap. X]. On this basis, the average energy of the molecule and its contribution to the entropy of the system can be estimated; it has been customary to add more or less arbitrarily an amount R per mole to allow for the extra entropy arising from the fact that none of the molecules are actually fixed in position. One can thus calculate isotherms and hence obtain the critical constants. Such calculations have been carried out by Lennard-Jones and Devonshire [*33*] for the rare gases. The critical temperatures are well reproduced, but the calculated values of the critical volumes and of the ratio $RT_{cr}/p_{cr}V_{cr}$ are far off.

It is to be noted that, in the simplest type of cell theory, thermal ex- pansion takes place through an increase in the size of the cell, or, what amounts to the same thing, the interatomic distance. Thus Lennard-Jones and Devonshire assumed that the coordination number remained fixed at (or near) twelve, independently of temperature and volume. This assumption is, of course, somewhat unrealistic, and attempts have been made to modify it, some of which are mentioned at the end of this article.

We shall, however, give a detailed account only of a rather simplified *hole* theory, based principally upon the work of Ono [*34*]. In a hole theory, expansion of the system is assumed to take place by the formation of holes, with a consequent change in coordination number. In the simplest form of the theory, the holes are assumed to be of molecular size, but some account can be taken of their effect on the motion of the neighboring molecules. The essence of the theory is that we assume that the molecules are arranged in a lattice, but that some of the lattice points are vacant. We shall confine ourselves to the case of a rare gas like argon, in which the molecules consist of simple atoms. In this case orientation of the molecules has no effect, and the energy of the lattice depends entirely on the relative number of vacancies occurring in it.

Let L be the total number of lattice points, N the number of atoms, V the total volume, and V_0 the volume which the system would have if there were no vacancies. Then

$$L = N \frac{V}{V_0} \tag{3-5}$$

We shall define the potential energy E_p of the system as the energy the system would have if all atoms were at rest on lattice points. We let $E_{p,0}$ be the value of E_p when $V = V_0$, that is, when there is one atom per lattice point. The total number of contacts between adjacent lattice sites is equal to $LC_N/2$ where C_N is the coordination number peculiar to the lattice. For any given contact, the chance that either end is a lattice site upon which an atom is situated is N/L, assuming completely random arrangement of the atoms. The chance that both ends contain an atom is N^2/L^2, and the total number of contacts between *atoms* is thus $(LC_N/2)N^2/L^2 = (NC_N/2)N/L = N(C_N/2)V_0/V$. It is thus seen that the effective coordination number, which is twice the number of contacts per atom, or $C_N V_0/V$, is inversely proportional to V and that the energy E_p will also be inversely proportional[4] to V, and we may write

$$E_p = E_{p,0} \frac{V_0}{V} \tag{3-6}$$

The assumption that the atoms are randomly arranged on the lattice points neglects the fact that there will be some sorting arising from the attractive forces between the atoms. Thus any arrangement which has a greater number of close contacts will have a lower energy and consequently a greater probability of occurrence than an arrangement with fewer close contacts. An attempt has been made by Ono to take this into account, but we shall neglect it, as the results which are thus obtained are sufficiently accurate for our purposes. The use of a lattice, of course, restricts the motion of the atoms more than they are actually restricted in nature and does not adequately allow for the fact that the holes do not have to be of molecular size. The fundamental idea that the expansion up to the critical point is connected primarily with a decrease in coordination number rather than an increase in interatomic distance seems, however, to be qualitatively borne out from X-ray studies of the molecular distribution in liquid argon [*35*].

In addition to E_p, which depends only on V, there will be a contribution to the total potential energy U of the system due to displacements of the individual atoms from their positions of equilibrium, or more specifically, in the lattice theory, from their particular lattice points.

---

[4] This is based on the assumption that E_p is proportional to the number of contacts between atoms. This is certainly true if only nearest neighbor interactions are considered, but, since the number of next nearest neighbors should decrease in the same way as the number of nearest neighbors with increasing number of holes, it should be true in general.

This contribution we shall call U_0, and we shall write

$$U = E_p + U_0 \tag{3-7}$$

The kinetic energy is still not included in this equation.

With the above background we may now attempt to set up a partition function for the system under consideration. Since we are interested in obtaining an equation of state, it will only be necessary to consider the volume dependent factor of the partition function, which may be written as a configuration integral since quantum effects can certainly be neglected in any liquid at its critical point (with the possible exception of helium). The configuration integral is given by[5]

$$Q_\tau = (N!)^{-1} \iint \cdots \int e^{-U/kT} d\tau_1 d\tau_2 \cdots d\tau_N \tag{3-8}$$

where the $d\tau$ are the volume elements of the individual atoms ($d\tau_i = dx_i dy_i dz_i$). Then

$$p = kT \left(\frac{\partial \ln Q_\tau}{\partial V} \right)_T \tag{3-9}$$

Making use of Eq. 3-7 we may write

$$Q_\tau = e^{-E_p/kT} Q_0 \tag{3-10}$$

where

$$Q_0 = (N!)^{-1} \iint \cdots \int e^{-U_0/kT} d\tau_1 d\tau_2 \cdots d\tau_N \tag{3-11}$$

We may now make use of one of the ideas of the cell theory. According to the cell theory, Q_0 may be considered to be composed of a product of contributions of individual molecules. The contribution of each molecule may be said to be its free volume. The integral has, of course, the dimensions of volume to the Nth power, and since it is divided by $N!$ the exchanges of the indistinguishable atoms are canceled out, as they should be. Let us suppose that when there are no vacancies next to an individual atom its free volume is ω and that when there are only vacancies on the neighboring lattice points its free volume is τ. Let us further suppose that when the average number of neighbor atoms is $C_N V_0/V$ (the effective coordination number, which can run from zero to twelve for argon, where the solid has a cubic close-packed structure), the mean atomic free volume is the geometrical mean $\omega^{V_0/V} \tau^{1-V_0/V}$. Thus we may take $(\omega^{V_0/V} \tau^{1-V_0/V})^N$ as a preliminary value of Q_0. However, there are $L!/N!(L-N)!$ distinguishable ways in which N indistinguishable atoms can be placed on L lattice points. We may, therefore, write

$$Q_0 = L![(L-N)!]^{-1}[N!]^{-1}\omega^{NV_0/V}\tau^{N-NV_0/V} \tag{3-12}$$

[5] Cf. Eq. 7-3, below. For the present purposes we find it convenient to include the factor $(N!)^{-1}$ in the configuration integral, for reasons which will appear in the derivation of Eq. 3-12.

As we have remarked in discussing Eq. 3-6 not all of these distinguishable ways of arranging N atoms on L lattice points are equally probable, and for this reason Eq. 3-12 can be only an approximation, which is, however, sufficient for our present purposes. As noted above, a more exact method of calculation was used by Ono [*34*].

The quantity τ may be evaluated by considering the case in which $L \gg N$, and hence $V \gg V_0$. In these circumstances, Eq. 3-12 reduces to

$$Q_0 = L^N(N!)^{-1}\tau^N \qquad (3\text{-}13)$$

since $L! \cong (L - N)!L^N$ if $L \gg N$. This expression for Q_0 may be compared with the limiting value obtained from Eq. 3-11 for $L \gg N$. We can in this case set $U_0 = 0$, so that Eq. 3-11 becomes

$$Q_0 = (N!)^{-1}V^N \qquad (3\text{-}14)$$

Comparing Eq. 3-13 and 3-14 and taking note of Eq. 3-5, we see that

$$\tau = \frac{V}{L} = \frac{V_0}{N} \qquad (3\text{-}15)$$

Combining Eq. 3-10, 3-12, and 3-6, and using the Stirling approximation for the factorials, we find

$$kT \ln Q_\tau = NkT \ln \tau - \frac{E_{p,0}V_0}{V} + LkT \ln L$$

$$- (L - N)kT \ln (L - N) - NkT \ln N + \frac{NkTV_0}{V} \ln \frac{\omega}{\tau} \qquad (3\text{-}16)$$

From Eq. 3-9, 3-5, and 3-16 and the fact that $Nk = R$ if N is taken equal to Avogadro's number, we now get, on the assumption that ω/τ is independent of V,

$$p = \frac{RT}{V_0} \ln \frac{V}{V - V_0} + \frac{E_{p,0}V_0}{V^2} - \frac{RTV_0}{V^2} \ln \frac{\omega}{\tau} \qquad (3\text{-}17)$$

From Eq. 2-4 we obtain

$$V_{cr} = 2V_0 \qquad (3\text{-}18)$$

$$RT_{cr} = -\frac{E_{p,0}}{2 + \ln (\tau/\omega)} \qquad (3\text{-}19)$$

$$\frac{RT_{cr}}{p_{cr}V_{cr}} = 2.59 \qquad (3\text{-}20)$$

Eq. 3-18 is the same as obtained by Ono, while Eq. 3-19 differs very little from his. For the ratio $RT_{cr}/p_{cr}V_{cr}$, Sato and Ono [*36*] calculate 2.92. In evaluating V_0 it would seem most reasonable to take the value for the solid, say at its normal melting point, where all the atoms are in regular array and where there are no holes. Then the experimental value of V_{cr} is very close to $3V_0$. Ono, however, has used the volume of the liquid near the melting point to evaluate V_0. Ono used the heat of vaporization to evaluate $E_{p,0}$ and evaluated τ/ω in a somewhat empirical way, while Sato and Ono used the Lennard-Jones intermolecular potential. An empirical approach should be sufficiently satisfactory, and to evaluate $E_{p,0}$ and τ/ω we consider the equilibrium between the solid at its melting point, and the vapor, which may be taken to have a molal volume V_v at this point.

For the change in Helmholtz free energy, ΔA, on vaporization of a mole (N atoms) we may write $\Delta A = -kT \ln (Q_{r,v}/Q_{r,s})$ where the subscripts v and s refer to vapor and solid, respectively. For the vapor, E_p and U_0 are zero, and from Eq. 3-11 we will have $Q_{0,v} = V_v^N/N!$. For the solid, $E_p = E_{p,0}$, and since each atom has a free volume ω and since there are no holes, we will get instead of Eq. 3-12 the relation $Q_{0,s} = \omega^N$. Thus, using Eq. 3-15 and the Stirling approximation, we get

$$\Delta A = -RT \ln (V_v/V_0) - RT \ln (\tau/\omega) - E_{p,0} - RT$$

Since for vapor and solid in equilibrium $\Delta F \cong \Delta A + RT$ is zero, we have

$$RT \ln (\tau/\omega) = -E_{p,0} - RT \ln (V_v/V_0) \tag{3-21}$$

and substituting this in Eq. 3-19

$$RT_{cr} = -\frac{E_{p,0}}{2 - E_{p,0}/RT - \ln (V_v/V_0)} \tag{3-22}$$

We shall apply this equation to the case of argon. The quantities in Eq. 3-22 are to be evaluated at the normal melting point, 83.8°K. $-E_{p,0}$ is about 1974 cal per mole [37], and, from the International Critical Tables, $V_v \cong 10,180$ cm³ per mole while $V_0 = 24.50$ cm³ per mole [38]. This gives $T_{cr} = 127°K$, as compared with the experimental value of 151°K. Ono [34] obtained 155° and Sato and Ono [36] obtained 135°. It will be seen that this fairly simple theory gives reasonably good values for the critical parameters.

Other work, involving a correction of the cell theory in the direction of the hole theory has been done by Janssens and Prigogine [39], who obtained fairly good values of T_{cr} and V_{cr} but did not calculate $RT_{cr}/p_{cr}V_{cr}$. Peek and Hill [40] used a cell theory modified by holes, allowing the liquid to choose its own number of holes by minimizing the free energy. They obtained reasonable values of T_{cr} and V_{cr}, but $RT_{cr}/p_{cr}V_{cr}$ is much too small.

Finally we must mention a recent calculation by Kirkwood, Lewinson, and Alder [41] which is based on use of the radial distribution function (see F,4). It has long been known that the equation of state could be derived from the radial distribution function, provided the intermolecular potential is known for spherically symmetrical molecules. Kirkwood,

Born and Green, and Yvon have devised approximate methods for calculating the radial distribution function, as described in F,4. Numerical calculations have been carried out by Kirkwood, Lewinson, and Alder, who have then evaluated the critical parameters by use of Eq. 2-4. They obtain the following results for the best approximation:

$$p_{cr} \frac{r^{*3}}{\epsilon} = 0.199$$

$$\frac{V_{cr}}{Nr^{*3}} = 2.585$$

$$\frac{T_{cr}k}{\epsilon} = 1.433$$

$$\frac{RT_{cr}}{pV_{cr}} = 2.79$$

Here r^* and ϵ are the same parameters used in Eq. 3-65 of Sec. F, and N is Avogadro's number. Using the value of $\epsilon = 1.653 \times 10^{-14}$ erg and $r^* = 3.405 \times 10^{-8}$ cm (r^* is called a by Kirkwood, Lewinson, and Alder) given by them for argon, one obtains $T_{cr} = 172°K$ and $V_{cr} = 61.5$ cm³/mole as compared to experimental values of $T_{cr} = 151°K$ and $V_{cr} = 75$ cm³/mole. Thus the results are in reasonable agreement with experiment. The values of ϵ and r^* given are not quite consistent with the approximations made, and if they were corrected in the manner suggested in Appendix III of Kirkwood, Lewinson, and Alder, the agreement would be somewhat worsened. It must be borne in mind, however, that the equation of state is extremely sensitive to the radial distribution function, so the results are to be considered satisfactory. (See also [124].)

E,4. General Thermodynamics of the Critical Point. In a case of the classical type of critical point (Fig. E,1a) the conditions of Eq. 2-4 are generally taken as determining the critical point. We have the thermodynamic identity

$$\left(\frac{\partial p}{\partial V}\right)_T = -\left(\frac{\partial p}{\partial T}\right)_V \left(\frac{\partial T}{\partial V}\right)_p \tag{4-1}$$

We do not expect $(\partial p/\partial T)_V$ to vanish or to become infinite since

$$\left(\frac{\partial p}{\partial T}\right)_V = \left(\frac{\partial S}{\partial V}\right)_T \tag{4-2}$$

and the entropy S will always be expected to increase at a finite rate with an isothermal increase of volume. This conclusion is confirmed by the experimental isotherms. Hence

$$\left(\frac{\partial T}{\partial V}\right)_p = 0 \tag{4-3}$$

which means that the coefficient of expansion α will be infinite. The coefficient of compressibility β is also infinite because $(\partial p/\partial V)_T = 0$.

Since the following relation holds between the specific heats at constant pressure and volume,

$$C_p = C_v + T\left(\frac{\partial p}{\partial T}\right)_V \left(\frac{\partial V}{\partial T}\right)_p \tag{4-4}$$

it is seen that C_p will be infinite at the critical point. There is no reason to expect C_v to have other than a finite value. Its behavior in the neighborhood of the critical point may be examined with the aid of the thermodynamic equation $T(\partial^2 p/\partial T^2)_V = (\partial C_v/\partial V)_T$, since any anomalous behavior in the neighborhood of the critical point will be reflected in $(\partial C_v/\partial V)_T$. The van der Waals equation gives $(\partial^2 p/\partial T^2)_V = 0$, unless a and b should be taken as functions of the temperature. Even in this case, however, there is no indication that any anomaly should appear in $(\partial C_v/\partial V)_T$ near the critical point. Actually, it has been observed that C_v becomes quite large in the critical region [42; 43; 44, p. 87]. These effects are probably related to clustering of the molecules, a phenomenon which will be discussed in Art. 6 and 7. In this region, C_v depends somewhat on the thermal history of the system, and as with other properties there are marked lags in the establishment of equilibrium.

If either Fig. E,1b or Fig. E,1c applies, the coefficient of expansion, the coefficient of compressibility, and C_p will be infinite all along the horizontal part of the coexistence curve, where $(\partial p/\partial V)_T = 0$. However, in this case it is not necessary that the isotherm which coincides with the horizontal part of the coexistence curve should join it at either end with $(\partial^2 p/\partial V^2)_T = 0$. It is more likely that this derivative will be nonzero in this case. These relationships may be better understood by discussion of the thermodynamic equation for the coexistence curve.

It will be convenient to consider the coexistence curve in a diagram in which T instead of p is plotted as ordinate. Since $(\partial p/\partial T)_V$ is at all points finite and nonzero, the general appearance of the coexistence curve, whether of the type of Fig. E,1a or that of Fig. E,1b or E,1c, will remain unaltered.

If we use the total differentiation sign to indicate differentiation along the coexistence curve, we may write

$$\frac{dV}{dT} = \left(\frac{\partial V}{\partial T}\right)_p + \left(\frac{\partial V}{\partial p}\right)_T \frac{dp}{dT}$$

$$= -\left(\frac{\partial V}{\partial p}\right)_T \left[\left(\frac{\partial S}{\partial V}\right)_T - \frac{\Delta S}{\Delta V}\right] \tag{4-5}$$

by Eq. 4-1 and 4-2 and the Clapeyron equation (ΔS and ΔV are, respectively, the molal entropy and molal volume change on evaporation). This may be written more conveniently in the form

$$\frac{dT}{dV} = \left(\frac{\partial p}{\partial V}\right)_T \left[\frac{\Delta S}{\Delta V} - \left(\frac{\partial S}{\partial V}\right)_T\right]^{-1} \tag{4-6}$$

Eq. 4-6 may be applied to either the liquid side or the vapor side of the coexistence curve. We shall consider first the classical type of coexistence curve, and shall use subscripts v, l, and cr to denote the values of quantities on the vapor side of the coexistence curve, on the liquid side of the coexistence curve, and at the critical point, respectively. In the classical case, we may expand the various quantities in a Taylor series about the critical point. We shall illustrate the use of Eq. 4-6 by applying it to the vapor side of the coexistence curve. We have

$$\left(\frac{\partial p}{\partial V}\right)_{T,v} = \left(\frac{\partial p}{\partial V}\right)_{T,cr} + \left(\frac{\partial^2 p}{\partial V^2}\right)_{T,cr} (V_v - V_{cr}) + \cdots \tag{4-7}$$

and

$$\left(\frac{\partial S}{\partial V}\right)_{T,v} = \left(\frac{\partial S}{\partial V}\right)_{T,cr} + \left(\frac{\partial^2 S}{\partial V^2}\right)_{T,cr} (V_v - V_{cr}) + \cdots \tag{4-8}$$

These expressions are correct up to terms in $V_v - V_{cr}$; we have left off a term $(\partial^2 p/\partial V\partial T)_{cr}(dT/dV)_{cr}(V_v - V_{cr})$ in Eq. 4-7 and a similar term in Eq. 4-8 because $(dT/dV)_{cr} = 0$.

For $\Delta S/\Delta V$ we write

$$\frac{\Delta S}{\Delta V} = \frac{S_v - S_l}{V_v - V_l} \tag{4-9}$$

and proceed to evaluate S_v and S_l, again omitting terms involving $(dT/dV)_{cr}$ in the first degree term, and writing a total derivative as a factor in the second degree term

$$S_v = S_{cr} + \left(\frac{\partial S}{\partial V}\right)_{T,cr} (V_v - V_{cr}) + \frac{1}{2}\left(\frac{d^2 S}{dV^2}\right)_{cr} (V_v - V_{cr})^2 + \cdots \tag{4-10}$$

$$S_l = S_{cr} + \left(\frac{\partial S}{\partial V}\right)_{T,cr} (V_l - V_{cr}) + \frac{1}{2}\left(\frac{d^2 S}{dV^2}\right)_{cr} (V_l - V_{cr})^2 + \cdots \tag{4-11}$$

If we have a classical coexistence curve, or even one as symmetrical as that determined by Eq. 1-1 and 1-2, we can take $V_v - V_{cr} = V_{cr} - V_l$ near the maximum, so that $(V_v - V_{cr})^2 = (V_l - V_{cr})^2$, except for terms of the order of $(V_v - V_{cr})^3$ or $(V_l - V_{cr})^3$; also $(d^2 S/dV^2)_{cr}$ will be the same for liquid and vapor sides. Therefore, from Eq. 4-10, 4-11, and 4-9, we see that $\Delta S/\Delta V$ becomes equal to $(\partial S/\partial V)_T$ at the critical point, as might of course be expected, and that

$$\frac{\Delta S}{\Delta V} - \left(\frac{\partial S}{\partial V}\right)_{T,v} = -\left(\frac{\partial^2 S}{\partial V^2}\right)_{T,cr}(V_v - V_{cr}) + \cdots \tag{4-12}$$

so that Eq. 4-6 becomes

$$\frac{dT}{dV} = -\frac{(\partial p/\partial V)_{T,cr} + (\partial^2 p/\partial V^2)_{T,cr}(V_v - V_{cr}) + \cdots}{(\partial^2 S/\partial V^2)_{T,cr}(V_v - V_{cr})} \tag{4-13}$$

It is seen from Eq. 4-13 that the conditions, Eq. 2-4, must hold if $(dT/dV)_{cr}$ is to be equal to zero, as was indicated by a qualitative argument in Art. 2.

Since the numerator of Eq. 4-13 thus vanishes, it will clearly be of interest to carry the expansion of $(\partial p/\partial V)_{T,v}$ (Eq. 4-7) one stage further. The coefficient of $(V_v - V_{cr})^2$ will be, aside from vanishing terms, $\frac{1}{2}(\partial^3 p/\partial V^3)_{T,cr} + \frac{1}{2}(\partial^2 p/\partial V\partial T)_{cr}(d^2T/dV^2)_{cr}$. Remembering that $dT/dV = (d^2T/dV^2)_{cr}(V_v - V_{cr}) + \cdots$ and that $(\partial^2 S/\partial V^2)_T = \partial^2 p/\partial V\partial T$, we get in place of Eq. 4-13

$$\left(\frac{d^2T}{dV^2}\right)_{cr}(V_v - V_{cr}) + \cdots$$

$$= -\frac{(\partial^3 p/\partial V^3)_{T,cr} + (\partial^2 p/\partial V\partial T)_{cr}(d^2T/dV^2)_{cr}}{2(\partial^2 p/\partial V\partial T)_{cr}}(V_v - V_{cr}) + \cdots \tag{4-14}$$

Equating the coefficients of $V_v - V_{cr}$ and solving for $(d^2T/dV^2)_{cr}$, the curvature of the coexistence curve at the maximum, gives[6]

$$\left(\frac{d^2T}{dV^2}\right)_{cr} = -\frac{(\partial^3 p/\partial V^3)_{T,cr}}{3(\partial^2 p/\partial T\partial V)_{cr}} \tag{4-15}$$

However, if the coexistence curve is correctly given by Eq. 1-1 and 1-2, even $(d^2T/dV^2)_{cr}$ will be zero, and only terms in $(V_v - V_{cr})^2$ or higher will be left in Eq. 4-14. Thus $(\partial^3 p/\partial V^3)_T$ will, in this case, have to vanish at the critical point as well as the lower derivatives. Strictly speaking, since the two sides of the coexistence curve are not analytic continuations of each other, according to Eq. 1-1 and 1-2, this result has been derived only for the vapor side; but it will also hold for the liquid side.

By iteration of the process it can be shown that if $(d^nT/dV^n)_{cr}$ and all lower derivatives are zero, then $(\partial p^{n+1}/\partial V^{n+1})_{T,cr}$ and all lower derivatives will be zero, and conversely.

If, however, $(\partial^4 p/\partial V^4)_{T,cr}$ is the first derivative which is not zero, then when we expand p for the critical isotherm in a Taylor series on either side of the critical point, we obtain

$$p = p_{cr} + \frac{1}{4!}\left(\frac{\partial^4 p}{\partial V^4}\right)_{T,cr}(V - V_{cr})^4 + \cdots$$

[6] For another derivation of this equation see Fowler and Guggenheim [45, pp. 316–317].

We know, however, that $p - p_{cr}$ changes sign at the critical point, so if $(\partial^4 p/\partial V^4)_{T,cr}$ is not zero, it also changes sign and hence must have a discontinuity at the critical point. This means that we will have a different expansion on each side of V_{cr} and that the isotherms in the neighborhood of the critical point will not be single analytic functions of V. In general, of course, our conclusions depend upon the assumed validity of the Taylor expansion in either direction.

We will now investigate the situation when the isotherms are of the type indicated by Fig. E,1b, or E,1c. In these cases we do not have a definite critical volume, at least not at the temperature at which the meniscus disappears. We shall use the subscripts cv and cl to designate the values of quantities on the vapor and liquid branches of the coexistence curve, respectively, where these branches reach the horizontal portion of the coexistence curve.

For Fig. E,1b, or E,1c, Eq. 4-6 holds as before. We shall designate the quantity $\Delta S/\Delta V - (\partial S/\partial V)_T$, considered as a function of T and V, as Γ and shall not attempt in this case a consideration of its behavior. ($\Delta S/\Delta V$ is a function of T only, but $(\partial S/\partial V)_T$ depends on T and V.) We can write in place of Eq. 4-13 for the value of dT/dV along the vapor part of the coexistence curve

$$\frac{dT}{dV} =$$

$$\frac{\left(\frac{\partial p}{\partial V}\right)_{T,cv} + \left[\left(\frac{\partial^2 p}{\partial V^2}\right)_{T,cv} + \left(\frac{\partial^2 p}{\partial V \partial T}\right)_{cv}\left(\frac{dT}{dV}\right)_{cv}\right](V_v - V_{cv}) + \cdots}{\Gamma_{cv} + \left[\left(\frac{\partial \Gamma}{\partial V}\right)_{T,cv} + \left(\frac{\partial^2 \Gamma}{\partial V \partial T}\right)_{cv}\left(\frac{dT}{dV}\right)_{cv}\right](V_v - V_{cv}) + \cdots} \quad (4\text{-}16)$$

with a similar equation for the liquid side. We do not know offhand whether or not dT/dV for the vapor and liquid branches is zero at the critical temperature, for there could conceivably be a discontinuity in slope at the ends of the horizontal portion of the isotherm.

If Fig. E,1b is correct, neither Γ_{cv} nor Γ_{cl} will be zero. For in this case we cannot set $(\Delta S/\Delta V)_{cr}$ equal either to $(\partial S/\partial V)_{T,cv}$ or to $(\partial S/\partial V)_{T,cl}$. It is seen that $(\partial p/\partial T)_V = (\partial S/\partial V)_T$ varies along the horizontal part of the coexistence curve, and by the principle of continuity $(\Delta S/\Delta V)_{cr}$ will be equal to the average value, which is intermediate to $(\partial S/\partial V)_{T,cv}$ and $(\partial S/\partial V)_{T,cl}$. Thus in this case it is sufficient for $(\partial p/\partial V)_{T,cv}$ and $(\partial p/\partial V)_{T,cl}$ to be zero in order for $(dT/dV)_{cv}$ and $(dT/dV)_{cl}$ to vanish. This insures that the critical isotherm comes into the horizontal portion with continuous slope, without demanding that the second derivatives $(\partial^2 p/\partial V^2)_{T,cv}$ and $(\partial^2 p/\partial V^2)_{T,cl}$ vanish. If they do not vanish, the isotherm will have a discontinuity in curvature. In any event, it is quite obvious that if Fig. E,1b is correct some higher derivative must be discontinuous at the ends of the horizontal portion, as a straight line cannot be an analytic continuation of a curve.

In the case of Fig. E,1c, since there is a series of isotherms above T_{cr} with horizontal portions, $(\partial p/\partial T)_V$ and therefore $(\partial S/\partial V)_T$ must be constant across the top of the horizontal portion. As noted in the preceding paragraph, the average value of $(\partial S/\partial V)_T$ must be equal to $\Delta S/\Delta V$ at the top of a coexistence curve with a finite horizontal portion. With $(\partial S/\partial V)_T$ constant we can write $\Delta S/\Delta V = (\partial S/\partial V)_{T,cv} = (\partial S/\partial V)_{T,cl}$, so that Γ_{cv} and Γ_{cl} are zero. Thus we see from Eq. 4-16 that in this case it *is* necessary for $(\partial^2 p/\partial V^2)_{T,cv}$ to be zero if $(dT/dV)_{cv}$ is to be zero; a similar statement holds for the liquid side. If $(\partial^2 p/\partial V^2)_{T,cv}$ and $(\partial^2 p/\partial V^2)_{T,cl}$ are not zero, the coexistence curve will reach T_{cr} with nonzero slope.

E,5. The Surface Tension near the Critical Point. In the classical theory the critical point was the point at which liquid and vapor phases became identical. Under such conditions the surface tension would naturally vanish. In the cases depicted by Fig. E,1b and E,1c, the situation is not quite so clear. It is assumed, however, that the disappearance of the meniscus is associated with the vanishing of the surface tension In fact, as we shall see, the surface tension probably has a causal relation to the critical phenomena. It will therefore repay us to examine the situation with some care [see *1*, pp. 318ff.].

Of course, surface tension is actually a work or free energy term. We may consider a two-phase, one-component system held at constant volume and define the surface tension σ by the equation

$$dE = TdS + \sigma d\alpha \tag{5-1}$$

where the first term on the right-hand side is the heat absorbed and the second term is the work done on the system when the surface area is increased by $d\alpha$. Thus

$$\sigma = e_\sigma - Ts_\sigma \tag{5-2}$$

where e_σ, the surface energy per unit area, is defined as $(\partial E/\partial\alpha)_{T,V}$ and s_σ, the surface entropy per unit area, as $(\partial S/\partial\alpha)_{T,V}$. Eq. 5-1 is of course valid even if T changes, but specializing it for T constant leads to Eq. 5-2, which is a perfectly general expression for σ. Now from Eq. 5-1 we have $(\partial E/\partial T)_{\alpha,V} = T(\partial S/\partial T)_{\alpha,V}$ so that $(\partial e_\sigma/\partial T)_{\alpha,V} = T(\partial s_\sigma/\partial T)_{\alpha,V}$. If we assume that these quantities are independent of the extent of the surface, $de_\sigma/dT = Tds_\sigma/dT$; then differentiation of Eq. 5-2 leads immediately to

$$d\sigma/dT = -s_\sigma \tag{5-3}$$

Thus all the quantities in Eq. 5-2 may be found by measuring σ as a function of T.

Both e_σ and s_σ are found to be positive for practically all liquids. The surface is a region of high energy because a molecule in the surface comes under the influence of fewer neighbors; it is a region of greater entropy because of the greater freedom of motion of the molecules there. If the liquid and vapor actually became identical at the critical point, then both e_σ and s_σ would vanish. However, it is not necessary for this to happen. If the situation is as depicted in Fig. E,1b or Fig. E,1c, the surface tension can vanish without e_σ and s_σ separately becoming zero.

It is an experimental fact that with most liquids σ varies a good deal more rapidly with temperature than either e_σ or s_σ. The question arises as to whether this behavior persists to the critical temperature. Some of the commonly used formulas indicate that σ varies almost linearly with T, but that the curve bends over and that $d\sigma/dT$ becomes equal to zero at the critical temperature T_{cr}. Thus the formula of van der Waals (see [46])

$$\sigma = \sigma_0(1 - T/T_{cr})^n \tag{5-4}$$

where n is approximately 1.20 and σ_0 is also a constant, would give σ this behavior. Probably the most careful measurements of surface tension in the immediate neighborhood of the critical temperature are those of Winkler and Maass [46] on methyl ether and propylene. Although their results fit Eq. 5-4 very closely, these authors believe that the surface tension vs. temperature curve approaches the critical temperature (presumably the temperature at which the meniscus disappears) with finite slope. The curve of Eq. 5-4 bends over to give zero slope in a region so close to the critical point that it is clear it will be extremely difficult to decide this matter experimentally.

Whether or not the liquid and vapor become identical at the critical point, they do become more nearly alike, and so e_σ and $s_\sigma = -d\sigma/dT$ should become smaller as the critical temperature is approached. However, there is another reason which may make the measured value of σ lower than the true value near the critical point, and so make the σ vs. T curve come in with apparently smaller slope, $-d\sigma/dT$, than it really should have. This is the fact that the liquid must contain numerous small bubbles near the critical point. This means that an increase in the extent of the boundary between the two phases is greater than the actual increase in the true surface. This can be visualized by considering what happens when one slices a piece of Swiss cheese. If a cut through the liquid intersects some bubbles, an increase in true surface area will only result from the part which does not go through the bubbles, and will result in a low apparent surface free energy.

It seems, therefore, quite reasonable to suppose that the vanishing of the surface tension at the critical temperature occurs because the second term on the right of Eq. 5-2 (on account of the factor T) overtakes the first term, rather than because each of these terms vanishes. This implies that above the critical temperature the surface tension would become negative, a situation which may be of considerable theoretical importance. Of course, a negative surface tension can never be measured, because it is not possible to find the surface. The surface of a liquid which has negative surface tension will tend to increase spontaneously, so there will be extensive wrinkling and folding and projection of "pseudopodia." In fact, this process will begin when the surface tension is still slightly positive, for it will contribute to the entropy of the surface, and the point of balance between total entropy and total energy might occur when the surface is slightly wrinkled. At the temperature at which the surface tension vanishes, the surface will have reached a convoluted condition of a certain average curvature. However, at this stage there is no force to prevent the surface from either increasing or decreasing. The surface may increase, for example, without change in free energy, entraining part of the vapor phase, and forming a foam or spongy mass until the spongy mass either fills the entire vessel, or the portions of liquidlike material have become so thin that resistance to further pulling out of the liquid film sets in, a matter which will be discussed in Art. 6. If an attempt were made to increase the volume of the spongy mass beyond this point, it would break into submicroscopic drops which would be distributed throughout the volume approximately uniformly. The temperature at which σ became zero thus would be the highest temperature at which there could be any visible segregation of material into a denser and a less dense portion, which accords with our idea that the critical temperature is the temperature for which the surface tension vanishes.

E,6. Association Theory of Condensation and Critical Phenomena. A more detailed understanding of the equilibrium phenomena which occur in the critical region requires the development of a more rational theory of condensation and of its application to that region. This is the object of this article and the next. This article is based upon a study of the formation of clusters of molecules in the vapor phase [1,47,48]. At equilibrium there will be, in addition to single molecules, pairs of molecules (held together by van der Waals forces or hydrogen bonding), triplets, and so forth. Generally, the higher clusters occur in very small numbers, but under certain conditions very large clusters become stable. This corresponds to condensation, and we shall investigate the conditions under which this occurs.

In one mole of gas in volume V we shall suppose that there are n_1 single molecules, n_2 pairs, . . . , n_s clusters of s molecules each, . . . , all in equilibrium with one another. Then

$$\sum_s sn_s = N \tag{6-1}$$

where N is Avogadro's number. We let the concentrations $(n_1/V, n_2/V, \ldots, n_s/V, \ldots)$ be designated as $c_1, c_2, \ldots, c_s \ldots$, respectively, and the respective chemical potentials by $\mu_1, \mu_2, \ldots, \mu_s \ldots$. The latter refer to single clusters rather than moles of clusters, that is $\mu_s = (\partial F/\partial n_s)_{T,p,n_1 n_2, \ldots n_{s-1}, n_{s+1}} \ldots$. If the gas is sufficiently dilute so that the ideal gas laws hold

$$\mu_s = s\phi_s + kT \ln c_s \tag{6-2}$$

where $s\phi_s$ is the value of μ_s when $c_s = 1$.

The process of forming a cluster of s molecules from s single molecules may be considered to be equivalent to the condensation of $s - 1$ molecules on the first one. When s is very large we can write approximately $s\phi_s - s\phi_1 = \beta(s - 1)$, with β a constant of proportionality, and, in the limit, then

$$\phi_\infty - \phi_1 = \beta \tag{6-3}$$

We thus see that β is the free energy of condensation, per molecule, of single molecules at unit concentration uniting to form a very large drop. With a finite cluster we must correct for surface effects, which would be expected to add a term of the form $\gamma s^{\frac{2}{3}}$. The constant γ is proportional to the surface tension, and the number of molecules at the surface of a cluster will, in general, be proportional to $s^{\frac{2}{3}}$. However, a further correction term, which we shall designate as ϵ_s will be needed, for the surface energy will not be proportional to $s^{\frac{2}{3}}$ for small drops. In the building up of a large cluster, the deviations which come in before the proportionality with $s^{\frac{2}{3}}$ is reached will have a residual effect. In addition, we may also expect a contribution to the free energy of the form $-mkT \ln s$, where m is a positive number of the order of unity, in order to take care of the entropy resulting from fluctuations in energy, volume, etc., of the clusters. We write then

$$s\phi_s = s\phi_1 + \beta(s - 1) + \gamma s^{\frac{2}{3}} + \epsilon_s - mkT \ln s \tag{6-4}$$

ϵ_s will be expected to reach a constant value, ϵ_∞, as $s \to \infty$. For $s = 1$, since ϕ_s is then equal to ϕ_1, we see that

$$\epsilon_1 = -\gamma \tag{6-5}$$

At equilibrium the chemical potentials *per molecule*, $\alpha'_s = \mu_s/s$, of all sizes of clusters must be equal. With Eq. 6-2 and 6-4 this gives

$$c_s = e^{(\beta - \alpha s - \gamma s^{\frac{2}{3}} - \epsilon_s + mkT \ln s)/kT} \tag{6-6}$$

where

$$\alpha = \phi_1 + \beta - \alpha'_s = \phi_\infty - \alpha'_s \tag{6-7}$$

In particular, remembering Eq. 6-5

$$c_1 = e^{(\beta - \alpha)/kT} \tag{6-8}$$

α may be determined by use of Eq. 6-1, or it may be considered to be determined by Eq. 6-8, all the other c_s then being evaluable in terms of c_1.

Since, at equilibrium, α'_s can be reinterpreted as the chemical potential per molecule of the actual vapor, containing clusters of all sizes, and since ϕ_∞ is by definition the chemical potential of very large clusters (which amounts to the chemical potential of the liquid), Eq. 6-7 offers a ready interpretation of α. If $\alpha > 0$, then vapor is stable as compared to liquid; if $\alpha < 0$, liquid is stable; $\alpha = 0$ *marks the point of condensation.*

A useful relation may be derived from Eq. 6-7 by differentiating with respect to the pressure p and noting that such a derivative of a free energy is the corresponding volume. This gives

$$(\partial\alpha/\partial p)_T = v_1 - v \qquad (6\text{-}9)$$

where v_1 and v are the volumes per molecule of liquid and vapor respectively.

It is interesting to consider Eq. 6-6 as α decreases and passes through zero (α decreases with increasing p, as indicated by Eq. 6-8 or Eq. 6-9). Decrease of α favors the larger clusters. However, even when $\alpha = 0$, the term $\gamma s^{\frac{2}{3}}$ causes the concentration of clusters to decrease with s. When α has become ever so slightly negative, the large clusters suddenly predominate: condensation occurs suddenly. If γ itself is zero, however, then the concentration of large clusters builds up gradually, and there is no sudden transition as α goes through zero. Since the vanishing of γ has been associated with the critical point, this behavior will profoundly affect the nature of the critical phenomena.

The situation may perhaps be better understood by fixing attention on a particular "reaction," involving clusters with large numbers of molecules, say,

$$2 \text{ clusters of size } s \rightleftarrows 1 \text{ cluster of size } 2s$$

If γ is positive, such a coalescence of two clusters will occur with a lowering of the surface area and consequently with a lowering of the surface free energy. This tends to favor the coalescence. The coalescence is opposed, however, by the loss of entropy, since the freedom of motion of a pair of clusters is much less when they are combined than when they are separate. At a certain definite concentration the driving force toward coalescence will overcome the entropy effect. This is the point of condensation with $\alpha = 0$. When $\gamma = 0$, however, the driving force toward coalescence will not be present, and coalescence will not tend to occur until the free motion of the large clusters is entirely squeezed out at infinite concentration.

However, it will not be necessary to compress the system to zero physical volume before the coalescence occurs. *The concentration c_s should be measured in free volume, not in total volume.* Coalescence occurs when large clusters no longer have any room to move without hitting other large clusters. Hereafter it will be understood that the c_s are to be taken as concentrations in free volume. The effective free volume may differ for clusters of different size, but we shall assume that it approaches a limiting value v_t per cluster for large values of s.

The nature of the phenomena at the critical point will depend strongly upon whether or not the volumes v_1 and v become equal when $v_t = 0$ at the critical temperature. If they do, then liquid and vapor become identical and we expect the classical theory of the critical point to be a good approximation. However, there are reasons to believe that v_1 and v will not coincide when $v_t = 0$ at the critical temperature. When $\gamma = 0$, two clusters which coalesce will suffer no force tending to cause them to reduce their surfaces. The large clusters, therefore, will not be expected to be in their most compact possible form when $v_t = 0$. An infinitesimal force will tend to compress the large coalesced mass with reduction of the total surface, there being no resistance to this process because, with zero surface tension, change in surface area will take place without change in free energy. It is presumed that this change in surface can occur without change in the average curvature or other properties of the surface, which could in themselves change the free energy of the surface; the possibility of such effects is discussed below. Over a range of volumes there will be no change in pressure with volume. This will continue from the point where the clusters first coalesce into one spongy mass with the gaslike or small density portion the external "phase"[7] until a state is reached in which the gaslike portion of the mass has been squeezed out to the point where it is ready to separate into individual bubbles. According to this picture the critical isotherm will have a horizontal portion, as shown in Fig. E,1b and E,1c. Above the critical temperature, such a horizontal portion will not occur, for here the surface tension will be negative, and it will require a force to decrease the volume of the spongy mass which is formed by coalescence of the large clusters. Thus this picture favors Fig. E,1b over Fig. E,1c.

Over the range of volumes for which the isotherm is horizontal when $\gamma = 0$, we can consider that the volume of the spongy mass is equal to the total volume. At larger volumes the spongy mass breaks up into clusters, and at the same time the pressure decreases. The large clusters, therefore, must now be in equilibrium at a lower pressure than that which holds for the horizontal part of the isotherm. At the same time, of course, the large clusters do not fill the entire space. Let us define a molecular volume v' which is the volume (per molecule) which the large

---

[7] Even when the large clusters have coalesced into one continuous mass there will be regions containing single molecules or small clusters which extend throughout the mass, as will be clear from the description of the coalescence process. These portions will have a smaller than average density, and may be called "gaslike."

clusters would occupy if without other change (e.g. in the numbers of large clusters of different sizes, or the density of a given cluster) they were pressed together until the free volume vanished. We may say then that over the range of the horizontal isotherm, $v' = v$, but that for greater volumes $v' < v$. At the large volume end of the horizontal portion ($\alpha = 0$) let us set $v' = v = v_{cv}$. If $v > v_{cv}$ we will also have $v' > v_{cv}$; in fact, v' will be nearly equal to v, for the large clusters will still tend to almost fill the volume, though they do not completely fill it for $v > v_{cv}$. We may suppose that the pressure at which the large clusters come into equilibrium depends on v' for $v > v_{cv}$. Since the pressure is independent of v' for $v' < v_{cv}$ and since we do not expect a sudden break in $\partial p/\partial v'$ at v_{cv}, it is natural to suppose that $p - p_{cr}$ (where p_{cr} is the pressure over the horizontal part of the critical isotherm) is proportional to $(v' - v_{cv})^2$. We shall show that such proportionality also results in $p - p_{cr}$ being proportional to $(v - v_{cv})^2$ in the immediate neighborhood of $v = v_{cv}$. This makes $(\partial p/\partial v)_T$ continuous but $(\partial^2 p/\partial v^2)_T$ discontinuous at $v = v_{cv}$. This behavior is characteristic of a third order transition.

The physical reason for the change in properties of the large clusters at v_{cv} may perhaps be found in increasing thinness of the denser liquidlike portions of the spongy mass as the volume is increased and the portions of small density become larger and more numerous. A change in the average curvature of the surface might also be required by geometrical considerations. These factors could be conceived to result in a resistance to further increase in v'. It might be supposed that as soon as the surface tension vanishes there will be a tendency, or at least a possibility, for the formerly nearly spherical droplets to spread out in such forms as to have the greatest possible surface, such as in sheets or filaments. The question as to whether a filament, for example, will be more stable than a flat surface of bulk liquid is a complicated one, however. The molecules in a filament have considerably more freedom of motion than those on a surface, but they also have fewer neighbors. It is, therefore, difficult to say whether the entropy term (see Eq. 5-2) should be expected to overtake the energy term at a higher or a lower temperature than for a flat surface. If a filament became stable at a temperature lower than that at which the surface tension of a flat surface vanishes, we might expect the system to tend suddenly to go over to filaments, causing what would appear to be a sudden drop to a state of zero surface tension. This certainly does not seem to be the case, nor does there seem to be any reason to suppose that filaments will become stable at just the same temperature as that at which the surface tension vanishes. The same argument will hold for sheets. There must then ultimately be some resistance to further thinning of the denser portions of the system. That this will happen just at the particular volume v_{cv} is perhaps questionable; it might be expected to be a gradually developing effect. If this is the case, the coexistence curve should actually be of the classical type, for then there would be only one volume at which the surface tension was exactly equal to zero. But if it is approximately correct to suppose the effect sets in just at $v = v_{cv}$, then the coexistence curve and the accompanying isotherms will follow Fig. E,1b approximately, though extremely careful experiments might show them to be actually of the classical type but with the coexistence curve considerably flattened at the top. We shall proceed with the discussion on the assumption that Fig. E,1b is at least approximately correct.

In order to show that $p - p_{cr} \sim (v' - v_{cv})^2$ at $T = T_{cr}$ implies $p - p_{cr} \sim (v - v_{cv})^2$ let us consider the variation of α with v when $\gamma = 0$, using Eq. 6-9. We first find a relation between α (when α is small) and the quantity $C = N/v_f$, which we may designate as the total net concentration of individual molecules in the free volume. If α is small and $\gamma = 0$, most of the material of the system is contained in the large clusters and

$$C \cong \sum_s sc_s \tag{6-10}$$

Using Eq. 6-6 we then obtain as an approximation when α/kT is small (in this case the sum in Eq. 6-10 can be replaced by an integral)

$$C = \Gamma(m + 2)e^{(\beta-\epsilon_\infty)/kT}(kT/\alpha)^{m+2} \tag{6-11}$$

With α small and hence the density of clusters large, the free volume v_f should be proportional to the cube of the length through which a cluster is free to move in any direction. The free length will in turn be proportional to $v^{\frac{1}{3}} - v'^{\frac{1}{3}}$.

If $v^{\frac{1}{3}} - v'^{\frac{1}{3}}$ is small compared to $v^{\frac{1}{3}}$ we may write $v^{\frac{1}{3}} - v'^{\frac{1}{3}} = (v - v')/3v^{\frac{2}{3}}$, and hence

$$v_f = \frac{a(v - v')^3}{v^2} \tag{6-12}$$

where a is a proportionality constant, of the order of magnitude of unity. Hence

$$C = \frac{Nv^2}{a(v - v')^3} \tag{6-13}$$

From Eq. 6-11 and 6-13 it thus appears that $\alpha \to 0$, when $v \to v'$, as $(v - v')^{3/(m+2)}$. From Eq. 6-9, then, we see that $p - p_{cr}$ will go to zero as $(v - v')^{3/(m+2)}$. If it also goes to zero as $(v' - v_{cv})^2$, as indicated above, it can now be shown to go to zero as $(v - v_{cv})^2$. For

$$v - v_{cv} = v - v' + v' - v_{cv} = b(v' - v_{cv})^{(2m+4)/3} + v' - v_{cv}$$

where b is a constant of proportionality. The term $(v' - v_{cv})^{(2m+4)/3}$ evidently becomes negligible when v' is very close to v_{cv}, and the conclusion follows. On the basis of the assumption that $p - p_{cr}$ is proportional to $(v' - v_{cv})^2$ in the immediate neighborhood of v_{cv}, then, we find the behavior of the critical isotherm discussed in Art. 4 for the case of an isotherm having a finite horizontal portion, $(\partial p/\partial v)_T$ being zero, but $(\partial^2 p/\partial v^2)_T$ being finite. It will be seen that in order for the pressure to behave in the manner noted, v' must be determined by the fact that $v - v'$ is proportional to $(v - v_{cv})^{(2m+4)/3}$. One point of interest is that if v_1 approaches v_{cv}, the behavior of $p - p_{cv}$ does not approach the behavior of a system with a classical coexistence curve. If v_1 should actually be equal to v_{cv}, an entirely different behavior of $p - p_{cv}$ with $v' - v_{cv}$ would be indicated.

A similar theory to that considered in this article can be developed for the process of evaporation, in which bubbles filled with vapor in the liquid phase have an analogy to the droplets in the vapor phase (see [1, Art. 6]). The details are somewhat less clear, however, and this theory is not taken up here.

E,7. Statistical Theory of Condensation and Critical Phenomena.
The equation of state of a gas may be written in a modified virial form as follows:

$$ p = \frac{kT}{v}\left(1 - \sum_{k=1}^{\infty} \frac{B_k}{v^k}\right) \tag{7-1} $$

where v is the volume per molecule and where the B_k are functions of temperature. A sufficiently precise knowledge of the B_k would make possible an understanding of the condensation and critical phenomena. A certain amount of information concerning these coefficients may be obtained by the use of the methods of statistical mechanics; this information leads to further inferences, which form the bases of the theory of Mayer and Harrison [2,3].

Classical statistical mechanics is adequate for the discussion of practically any substance in the neighborhood of the critical point, and we may write the partition function in the form[8] [49, Chap. XVI]

$$ Q = \frac{1}{N!}\left(\frac{2\pi mkT}{h^2}\right)^{\frac{3N}{2}} Q_\tau \tag{7-2} $$

where N is the number of molecules, m is their mass, h is Planck's constant, k is Boltzmann's constant, T is the absolute temperature, and where Q_τ is the configuration integral.

$$ Q_\tau = \iint \cdots \int e^{-U/kT} d\tau_1 d\tau_2 \cdots d\tau_N \tag{7-3} $$

[8] This is essentially Eq. 24-3 of Sec. B, with the integration with respect to the $\mathbf{p}^N$ carried out.

U is the potential energy of the whole system and $d\tau_i$ is the volume element of the ith molecule. Each of the $d\tau_i$ is integrated over the available volume V. For simplicity, and since this gives the essential elements of the problem, we shall assume that the molecules are spherically symmetric and that the potential energy is a function only of the distance between centers of gravity of pairs of molecules. We may then assume that $d\tau_i = dx_i dy_i dz_i$, where dx_i, dy_i, and dz_i are the coordinates of the center of gravity of the ith molecule, and that U is given by the sum of the potential energies (U_{ij} for the pair i and j) of all pairs of molecules. U_{ij} is a function of the distance r_{ij} between the ith and jth molecules. Formally, we set

$$U = \sum_{i>j}^{N} \sum_{j=1}^{N} U_{ij} \tag{7-4}$$

The sum is taken for $i > j$ in order to avoid including a particular U_{ij} twice, since U_{ji} is identical with U_{ij}. From Eq. 7-4

$$e^{-U/kT} = \prod_{\text{all pairs}} e^{-U_{ij}/kT} = \prod_{i>j}^{N} \prod_{j=1}^{N} e^{-U_{ij}/kT}$$

The U_{ij} have the usual form for an intermolecular potential energy. They may be taken as zero if r_{ij} is greater than a few angstroms; they are negative for smaller values of r_{ij} where the intermolecular forces are attractive, and positive for still smaller r_{ij} where the forces become repulsive.

In order to evaluate Q_r we set

$$e^{-U_{ij}/kT} = 1 + f_{ij} \tag{7-5}$$

It will be seen from this definition that f_{ij} is zero in the region where U_{ij} is zero, positive where U_{ij} is negative, and negative (though never less then -1) where U_{ij} is positive. We now see that we can set

$$Q_r = \iint \cdots \int \prod_{\text{all pairs}} (1 + f_{ij}) d\tau_1 d\tau_2 \cdots d\tau_N$$

$$= \iint \cdots \int \left(1 + \sum_{i>j}^{N}\sum_{j=1}^{N} f_{ij} + \sum_{i'>j'}^{N}\sum_{j'\geq j}^{N}\sum_{i>j}^{N}\sum_{j=1}^{N} f_{i'j'}f_{ij} + \cdots\right)$$

$$d\tau_1 d\tau_2 \ldots d\tau_N \tag{7-6}$$

The first integral (integrand $= 1$) of Eq. 7-6 will obviously be equal to V^N.

In an integral of the type $\iint \ldots \int f_{ij} d\tau_1 d\tau_2 \ldots d\tau_i d\tau_j \ldots d\tau_N$ integration over each of the volume elements except $d\tau_i$ and $d\tau_j$ yields a factor V, so that the integral reduces to $V^{N-2}\iint f_{ij} d\tau_i d\tau_j$. If now we hold x_j, y_j, and z_j fixed and integrate over $d\tau_i$, we see that we will have a contribution to the integrand only if x_i, y_i, and z_i are close to x_j, y_j, and z_j.

The result of this integration will be independent of x_j, y_j, and z_j, provided the corresponding volume element is not too close to the edge of the volume V. If V is large enough this edge effect can be neglected. We may write

$$\int f_{ij}d\tau_i = \int_0^\infty f(r_{ij})4\pi r_{ij}^2 dr_{ij} = \beta_1$$

thus defining β_1. In rewriting this integral we have noted that f_{ij} is a function of r_{ij} and written it $f(r_{ij})$, and we have recast the volume element into the form $4\pi r_{ij}^2 dr_{ij}$. Final integration over $d\tau_j$ yields another factor V, so that the complete integral over all the $d\tau$ becomes, finally, $V^{N-1}\beta_1$. Because of the edge effects, the value of β_1 will actually depend very slightly on V. This dependence will not be noticeable unless V becomes of the same order of magnitude as the actual extension in space of the two molecules. For integrals in which the interactions of only two or a few molecules are involved, this will never be of importance.[9] Since there are $N(N-1)/2 \cong N^2/2$ possible pairs of systems, the second term in Eq. 7-6 will be equal to $N^2 V^{N-1}\beta_1/2$.

We now consider integrals of the form

$$\iiiint f_{i'j'}f_{ij}d\tau_{i'}d\tau_{j'}d\tau_i d\tau_j$$

where i', j', i, and j are all different. It is clear that the integral will be $\beta_1^2 V^2$. The other volume elements will contribute a factor V^{N-4}, so the value of the entire integral will be $V^{N-2}\beta_1^2$. If $j' = j$, however, we must consider $\iiint f_{i'j}f_{ij}d\tau_{i'}d\tau_i d\tau_j$. By first holding x_j, y_j, z_j fixed and integrating successively with respect to $d\tau_{i'}$ and $d\tau_i$, then finally integrating with respect to $d\tau_j$, we see that this integral is equal to $V\beta_1^2$, and again the complete integral will be $V^{N-2}\beta_1^2$. We cannot have $i' = i$ when $j' = j$.

In a similar manner most of the terms in the next sum, containing three f_{ij} terms, will yield on integration $V^{N-3}\beta_1^3$. However there will be some combinations like $f_{32}f_{31}f_{21}$ which on integrating will give

$$V^{N-3} \iiint f_{32}f_{31}f_{21}d\tau_1 d\tau_2 d\tau_3 = 2V^{N-2}\beta_2$$

The final integration, as usual, yields another factor V, and β_2 is defined by the equation. It will be seen that the integrations with respect to $d\tau_1$ and $d\tau_2$ cannot be made independently of each other, since the suffixes

---

[9] In integrals which arise from very high terms in the series of Eq. 7-6, in which the interaction of nearly all the molecules in the system is involved, the volume dependence of the integrals analogous to β_1 will become of importance when the volume V is comparable with the extension in space of the group of interacting molecules (i.e. the group of molecules all of which are close enough together so that any molecule in the group exerts an appreciable force on at least a few of the other molecules in the group, and so that any molecule is bridged to any other molecule in the group by interactions through intermediate molecules). For the time being we neglect this possible volume dependence.

1 and 2 occur in more than one of the f, and so $2\beta_2$ is not equal to β_1^2. It is also clear, however, that combinations of this sort will occur only rarely, and if we ignore them in this and the succeeding terms, the coefficient of each succeeding power of β_1 will be the corresponding binomial coefficient of the power $N^2/2$. To this approximation, then, we may write

$$Q_\tau = (Nv)^N \left(1 + \frac{\beta_1}{Nv}\right)^{N^2/2}$$

where v is the molecular volume. Since $(1 + \beta_1/Nv)^N$ is equal to $e^{\beta_1/v}$, if N is very large, this may be written, to a good approximation,

$$Q_\tau = Q_{\tau,0} = (Nv)^N e^{N\beta_1/2v} \tag{7-7}$$

The pressure is given by the thermodynamic equation

$$p = -\left(\frac{\partial A}{\partial V}\right)_T = -N^{-1}\left(\frac{\partial A}{\partial v}\right)_T$$

where A is the Helmholtz free energy, and $A = -kT \ln Q$ (see [50, p. 235] and A,12). Hence

$$p = \frac{1}{N}\frac{\partial}{\partial v}(kT \ln Q) \tag{7-8}$$

Using Eq. 7-7 and 7-2,

$$p = \frac{kT}{v}\left(1 - \frac{\beta_1}{2v}\right) \tag{7-9}$$

In a more exact expression it will be necessary to include terms in β_2, β_3, etc. The definition of these so-called irreducible integrals may be inferred from the definitions of the first three, which we write down (or rewrite):

$$\beta_1 = \frac{1}{V}\iint f_{12}d\tau_1 d\tau_2 \tag{7-10}$$

$$\beta_2 = \frac{1}{2!V}\iiint f_{32}f_{31}f_{21}d\tau_1 d\tau_2 d\tau_3 \tag{7-11}$$

$$\beta_3 = \frac{1}{3!V}\iiiint (3f_{43}f_{32}f_{21}f_{41} + 6f_{43}f_{32}f_{21}f_{41}f_{31}$$
$$+ f_{43}f_{32}f_{21}f_{41}f_{31}f_{42})d\tau_1 d\tau_2 d\tau_3 d\tau_4 \tag{7-12}$$

In the definition of β_3, the factors 3 and 6 are the number of ways in which the numbers can be cross connected by, respectively, four and five tie lines. The possible methods of cross connections are illustrated in Fig. E,7a. The three possible integrands, $f_{43}f_{32}f_{21}f_{41}$, $f_{41}f_{42}f_{32}f_{31}$, and $f_{31}f_{21}f_{42}f_{43}$ will, for example, all yield the same integral. Hence it is necessary to write down only one if the factor 3 is included.

In general, β_k includes terms arising from all possible connections of k numbers, in which no one of the numbers is connected to only one of the other numbers. Thus the term $f_{41}f_{43}f_{31}f_{32}$ is not included in β_3 because the integration with respect to $d\tau_2$, which involves only one of the f terms, can be handled before the others and yields β_1. In fact, $\int\int\int\int f_{41}f_{43}f_{31}f_{32}d\tau_1 d\tau_2 d\tau_3 d\tau_4 = 2V\beta_2\beta_1$.

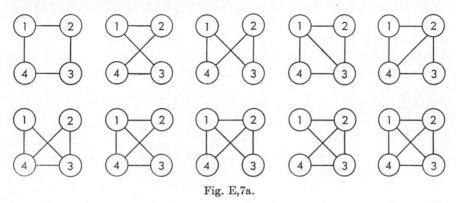

Fig. E,7a.

In terms of the β_k we may write a general expression for Q_τ:

$$Q_\tau = N!e^N v^N e^{N\sum_{k\geq 1}\beta_k v^{-k}/(k+1)}$$

$$\cong N^N v^N e^{N\sum_{k\geq 1}\beta_k v^{-k}/(k+1)}$$

(7-13)

It is of course seen at once that this reduces to Eq. 7-7 if the sum is cut off at $k = 1$. We shall not attempt a rigorous proof of this expression,[10] but will instead give a justification based on examination of a few terms. A factor β_2 will first appear as arising from some of the terms in the sum involving three f_{ij} terms (the first one not written down) in Eq. 7-6. The number of terms which will yield $2!\beta_2 V^{N-2}$ instead of $\beta_1^3 V^{N-3}$ will be given by the number of possible ways of choosing three suffixes, namely $N(N-1)(N-2)/3! \cong N^3/3!$. The factor $3!$ appears in the denominator because the same terms will result from any permutation of the three suffixes. This is quite negligible compared to the total number of terms in the sum involving three f_{ij} terms, so the loss of terms equal to $\beta_1^3 V^{N-3}$ may be neglected. The $N^3/3!$ terms equal to $2!\beta_2 V^{N-2}$ may not be neglected, however. β_2 is of the order of β_1^2, and $2!\beta_2 V^{N-2}$ is therefore larger than $\beta_1^3 V^{N-3}$ by a factor of the order of $V/\beta_1 = Nv/\beta_1$, which is large. The total contribution of these terms to the sum in Eq. 7-6 is $(N^3/3!)2!\beta_2 V^{N-2} = N^N N \beta_2 v^{N-2}/3$. Every combination of three f_{ij} may be

[10] Such a proof is given by a much more complicated route by Mayer and Mayer [*50*, Chap. XIII].

⟨ 461 ⟩

found in every one of the subsequent terms in Eq. 7-6. In the sum involving products of four f_{ij} terms, such a combination is multiplied by every f_{ij} not included in the combination itself; the number of f_{ij} in the combination is negligible compared to the total number. Again, in the sum involving products of five f_{ij} terms, every combination which yields $2!\beta_2 V^{N-2}$ is multiplied by every pair of f_{ij}, except a negligible number, so on integration of the entire sum, each $2!\beta_2 V^{N-2}$ will be multiplied by $(1 + \beta_1/Nv)^{N^2/2} = e^{N\beta_1/2v}$; that is $2!\beta_2 V^{-2}$ will be multiplied by $Q_{\tau,0}$ of Eq. 7-7. Thus the factor $N^N N\beta_2 v^{N-2}/3$ will be multiplied by $e^{N\beta_1/2v}$, or the factor $N\beta_2 v^{-2}/3$ will be multiplied by $Q_{\tau,0}$. Let us now see how this factor occurs in Eq. 7-13. The right-hand side of Eq. 7-13 may be written

$$Q_{\tau,0} e^{N \sum\limits_{k\geq2} \beta_k v^{-k}/(k+1)} = Q_{\tau,0}\left[1 + N\sum_{k\geq2}\frac{\beta_k v^{-k}}{k+1}\right.$$

$$\left. + \frac{N^2}{2!}\left(\sum_{k\geq2}\frac{\beta_1 v^{-k}}{k+1}\right)^2 + \frac{N^3}{3!}\left(\sum_{k\geq2}\frac{\beta_k v^{-k}}{k+1}\right)^3 + \cdots\right] \quad (7\text{-}14)$$

We see that $N\beta_2 v^{-2}/3$ is one of the terms in

$$N\sum_{k\geq2}\frac{\beta_k v^{-k}}{k+1}$$

As a further example let us consider a combination of f_{ij} which will yield $(2!)^2 3!\beta_2^2\beta_3 V^{N-7}$ on integration. Taking out the factor V^N leaves $(2!)^2 3!\beta_2^2\beta_3 V^{-7}$. Each such term will be multiplied by $Q_{\tau,0}$ just as each of the terms $2!\beta_2 V^{-2}$ was multiplied by $Q_{\tau,0}$. There are approximately $\frac{1}{2}(N^3/3!)^2(N^4/4!)$ ways of getting this combination of terms. There should therefore be a term equal to

$$(2!)^2 3!\beta_2^2\beta_3 V^{-7}\tfrac{1}{2}(N^3/3!)^2(N^4/4!) = N^3\beta_2^2\beta_3 v^{-7}/2(3^2 \times 4)$$

in the bracket on the right-hand side of Eq. 7-14. It is readily enough seen that there are $3!/2$ terms occurring in $[\sum\beta_k v^{-k}/(k+1)]^3$ which are equal to $\beta_2^2\beta_3 v^{-7}/(3^2 \times 4)$, and these being multiplied by the factor $N^3/3!$ give the desired value. In a similar way each term in Eq. 7-14 can be verified.

It will be observed that the approximations which are involved in identifying the terms of Eq. 7-14 with those of Eq. 7-6 become poorer the farther along in the series one goes. This would seem to be a difficulty inherent in discussing a system containing a finite number of molecules. In any event, by making N large enough one can insure that the identification will be true with good approximation for an arbitrary number of terms.

From Eq. 7-13 we can now obtain a general expression for the pressure

$$p = \frac{kT}{v}\left(1 - \sum_{k \geq 1} \frac{k\beta_k v^{-k}}{k + 1}\right) \qquad (7\text{-}15)$$

which in effect evaluates the constants of Eq. 7-1. For $(\partial p/\partial v)_T$ we get the expression

$$v\left(\frac{\partial p}{\partial v}\right)_T = -\frac{kT}{v}\left(1 - \sum_{k \geq 1} k\beta_k v^{-k}\right) \qquad (7\text{-}16)$$

The properties of the β_k have been discussed by Mayer and Mayer [50, Chap. XIV]. At very low temperatures, the f_{ij} may become very large in the range of r_{ij} in which they are positive. The principal contribution to the integral β_k will be from regions of the integration space in which all the f_{ij} involved are large and positive. Thus at sufficiently low temperatures all the β_k are positive. At higher temperatures, the regions where f_{ij} is positive become relatively less important, since for most of the region where it is negative f_{ij} remains approximately equal to -1. Any β_k gets smaller, and presumably at sufficiently high temperatures may become negative. This at any rate, is true of β_1, β_2, and β_3, for which actual calculations may be made; it is not possible to be absolutely certain that these are typical, and it is, indeed, of some importance that β_1 does not become negative until a much higher temperature has been reached than for the others. Since the successive β_k involve more and more factors, the number of factors increasing approximately proportionally with k, one may infer that

$$\beta_k = f(k, T)\beta_0^k \qquad (7\text{-}17)$$

where, for high k values, $f(k, T)$ is a more slowly varying function of k than is β_0^k at any given T. This expression certainly holds at low temperatures, and may be used, at any rate on a provisional basis, in discussing the behavior of the β_k.

For high k and low T, the greatest contribution to β_k will come from those regions of the r_{ij} in which as many as possible of the k molecules involved in the integral have simultaneously values of r_{ij} such that the corresponding f_{ij} are a maximum. The large contributions, therefore, will come from arrangements in which the molecules are in a roughly close-packed arrangement. The molecules on the edge of the group (in number proportional to $k^{\frac{1}{3}}$) will not contribute their full factors. An important factor in $f(k, T)$ will, therefore, be of the form $\exp(-\gamma k^{\frac{1}{3}})$ (that is a factor raised to the $k^{\frac{1}{3}}$ power), γ being something like a surface tension. $\exp(-\gamma k^{\frac{1}{3}})$ will be less than 1 (hence γ will be positive) in order to correct for the lesser contribution of the edge molecules. γ will decrease with temperature, since with rising temperature all the pair interactions will contribute less; there will therefore be less difference between the edge molecules and the other molecules.

For low temperatures, any β_k is large and positive, so we infer from Eq. 7-17 that when $v \leqq \beta_0$, the sum in Eq. 7-16 will diverge. Since β_0 decreases with increasing temperature, the value of v at which divergence occurs also decreases with increasing T. Since $f(\mathbf{k}, T)$, on account of the factor $\exp(-\gamma \mathbf{k}^{\frac{1}{3}})$, increases with temperature, the value of the sum $\sum_{k \geqq 1} \mathbf{k} \beta_k v^{-k}$ should increase at any v/β_0 with temperature. The effect of the special behavior of β_1 will be to accentuate this increase with temperature. Thus at low temperatures the divergence will occur when this sum is less than 1. This divergence corresponds to condensation. From a finite value of $-(\partial p/\partial v)_T$, the value of this quantity suddenly becomes equal to zero. Of course, with the sum in Eq. 7-16 diverging, one might actually expect $-(\partial p/\partial v)_T$ to become negative, but such a state would not be thermodynamically stable. Actually, with a finite value of N, the sum must be a finite sum, though with extremely many terms. Thus between the point where the sum starts to rise sharply and the point where it becomes equal to 1 there is a finite though extremely small range of v. Any attempt to go beyond the point where the sum equals 1 is arrested by the appearance of the condensed phase, which keeps the molecular volume v essentially constant in the vapor phase; more precisely, with changing value of N for the vapor phase, it keeps v at just that value which makes the sum equal to 1; the situation is similar to (and it is merely a different description of) that described in Art. 6. We may note that Eq. 7-16 holds only for the vapor phase. Because of the eventual dependence of β_k with large $\mathbf{k}$ on the volume (see footnote 9) it cannot hold for the liquid.

As the temperature increases we might expect eventually to reach a point (see Fig. E,7b) where the divergence of $\sum_{k \geqq 1} \mathbf{k} \beta_k v^{-k}$ occurs when it is just equal to 1. Then $(\partial p/\partial v)_T$ would approach zero without any break and we would no longer have the ordinary type of condensation, with separation of a distinct phase. This would correspond to the temperature T_{cr} of Fig. E,1c. As the temperature increased further, the negative values of the higher β_k would eventually result in a decrease of $\sum_{k \geqq 1} \mathbf{k} \beta_k v^{-k}$ before the value of 1 was reached, as is illustrated in Fig. E,7b. At the last temperature at which the sum reached the value 1, we would have both $(\partial p/\partial v)_T$ and $(\partial^2 p/\partial v^2)_T$ equal to zero (the latter because, as is obvious from Fig. E,7b, $\partial(\sum_{k \geqq 1} \mathbf{k} \beta_k v^{-k})/\partial v$ is equal to zero). These two derivatives are simultaneously zero in the classical critical point, and so the temperature at which this occurred was called the true critical point by Mayer. Since the ordinary type of condensation does not occur above T_{cr}, we expect this to be the last temperature for which the meniscus is visible. Between T_{cr} and T'_{cr}, the isotherms are expected to have the form shown by Fig. E,1c. Actually, the horizontal portions of these isotherms are merely inferred; Fig. E,7b with Eq. 7-16 would indicate that each of these isotherms would have at least one point with $(\partial p/\partial v)_T = 0$, and since $(\partial^2 p/\partial v^2)$ is not equal to zero in the vapor phase except at T'_{cr}, and since the true isotherm can never show a positive slope, the isotherms to the left of the coexistence curve in this case cannot be analytic continuations of the portions to the right.

It is clear that the foregoing description of the critical phenomena is not in accord with the description of Art. 6, and, despite the recent work of Wentorf and Boyd [18], there appears to be increasing evidence that it is probably not, at least in all details, in accord with the experimental

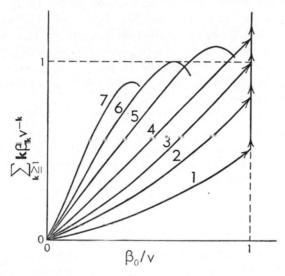

Fig. E,7b. Curves 1, 2, 3, 4, 5, 6, and 7 are for successively higher temperatures. Curve 3 corresponds to T_{cr}, curve 6 to T'_{cr}. No curves should cross until some β_k with large k become negative.

evidence, though it is suggestive of the experimental data. There is no clear-cut agreement among various investigators as to how these apparent conflicts can be reconciled.

It would, of course, be possible for the temperatures T_{cr} and T'_{cr} to coincide. In view of the different conditions determining T_{cr} and T'_{cr} this would demand a set of stringent relationships between the various β_k. In itself this seems unlikely. However, recently Zimm [51] has argued that when $(\partial p/\partial v)_T$ is zero, not only is $(\partial^2 p/\partial v^2)_T$ zero, but so are all higher derivatives. Thus not only would T_{cr} and T'_{cr} coincide, but the critical point would be an essential singularity. Zimm's argument, however, is by no means rigorous.

Rice [1] has suggested that the formalism of Mayer and Harrison breaks down in the critical region because the β_k with large k become volume dependent.[11] The density of the system in the critical region is becoming sufficiently great so that one might expect that, for **k** of the order of N, configurations in which the **k** molecules involved filled the entire volume V would contribute appreciably to the integrals. The $\beta_{\mathbf{k}}$ would then become volume dependent, as noted in footnote 9. The result of this could be to make the large terms in the series important at larger values of v than they would otherwise be. In a sense one might say that these large terms could cause premature divergence of the series, but this would not be an accurate description, since the series is actually not an infinite series (because of the finite value of N) and since just which terms become important depends on the value of N. In any event, under these circumstances, Eq. 7-15 and 7-16 would become invalid. One could make no prediction concerning $(\partial p/\partial v)_T$ after the "divergence" occurred. Since a new expression for p as a function of v would be necessary, there would be an analytic discontinuity; that is, the isotherms for smaller values of v would not be analytic continuations of those at larger values of v.

On the basis of a different type of derivation [52], Mayer [53] has refuted the argument of the preceding paragraph. Unfortunately, space does not permit a detailed discussion of this theory, but an outline of the results may be given. By application of the grand canonical ensemble to a system of fixed volume, it is possible to show that

$$\frac{p}{kT} = \sum_{n \geq 1} b_n z^n \tag{7-18}$$

where z is the activity normalized to equal the density expressed in number of molecules per unit volume at infinite dilution. The b_n are coefficients which can be evaluated as integrals over the coordinates of n molecules in the volume V, and they are functions of V. The volume V is, however, considered to be constant; the density is changed by changing the number of molecules in the fixed volume, and z is, of course, a function of the density. The b_n do not depend upon the density. For finite n, they approach a definite value $b_n^{(0)}$ when V (considered as a parameter) is allowed to approach infinity. It is now possible to define a set of $\beta_{\mathbf{k}}$ in terms of the $b_n^{(0)}$ such that Eq. 7-15 and 7-16 hold. Actually these $\beta_{\mathbf{k}}$ must be equal to the $\beta_{\mathbf{k}}$ of Eq. 7-15 and 7-16, where the latter are not volume dependent, but they are defined in terms of a different set of integrals which do not depend on the density.

However, the limiting process involved in the above procedure may

---

[11] In the original derivation (see Mayer and Mayer, [50]), the $\beta_{\mathbf{k}}$ were so *defined* as to be independent of volume. Other integrals, the so-called cluster integrals, which were related to the $\beta_{\mathbf{k}}$, could become volume dependent, and under these circumstances the relation between them and the $\beta_{\mathbf{k}}$ broke down. The present method of handling the situation is equivalent.

be criticized [54]. We may question whether it is sufficient that $b_n \to b_n^{(0)}$ for *finite* n when $V \to \infty$. The difficulty may perhaps be best seen by considering a large but finite V. One may expect that there will be a special dependence on V of those b_n for which n is greater than, let us say, n_0, where n_0 is so great that n_0 molecules cannot normally be squeezed into a space of a smaller order of magnitude than V. Thus these b_n cannot be said to have reached $b_n^{(0)}$ for this value of V. But just these b_n may be expected to have a considerable influence on the pressure when the density of the system becomes of the order of n_0/V, provided condensation has not already occurred. However, z^n for large n depends very strongly on z and, hence (if we are not in a region of condensation), very strongly on the density. If the higher terms in the series all have the same sign, and if they also become the important terms, a strong dependence of the pressure on the density, which is not observed empirically, probably cannot be avoided. But it is quite possible that the higher terms in the series have alternate positive and negative signs when T is of the order of T_{cr}, and the general description of the system by means of Eq. 7-18 breaks down because the value of z has passed the radius of convergence of the series, even though the function can be continued analytically beyond it [50, p. 466]. If this does happen, conclusions based on the series expansion will not be valid. This view seems to be in accord with recent results of Yang and Lee [55].

It is not proposed here to attempt to settle the questions raised concerning the validity of the theoretical treatments of the critical region given here and in Art. 6. Both treatments are suggestive—neither is rigorous; it may perhaps be hoped that along one or the other of these lines, or perhaps by a combination of them, a definitive theory will eventually emerge.

E,8. Critical Fluctuations. In Art. 6 there was developed a theory of critical phenomena from which it can be inferred that there are variations of density from point to point in the system. These variations undoubtedly occur over a range of distances of the order of a few angstroms or a few tens of angstroms. Superimposed upon these we can have fluctuations which, because of the high compressibility in the critical region, may extend over much greater distances. Fluctuations in density occur, of course, in all substances and under all conditions; they only become noticeable in the critical region, where considerable changes in density can occur without appreciable change in the free energy.

These fluctuations may be studied by means of a simple though not very rigorous theory first developed by Smoluchowski [56] and Einstein [57].[12] We fix our attention upon a certain portion of the substance under consideration, containing n molecules and occupying a volume v

[12] For a more rigorous theory see Tolman [58, pp. 629ff.].

if it has the average density of the system. We wish to calculate the probability of a fluctuation which causes the n molecules to occupy a volume $v + \delta v$, assuming the entire system to remain at constant volume. The volume of the rest of the system, then, will change by $-\delta v$. (The volume, represented in this article and the next by the symbol v, is not to be confused with the molecular volume of the preceding articles.)

The condition for equilibrium at constant volume is that the total Helmholtz free energy A of the system containing, let us say, N molecules and occupying a volume V shall be a minimum. The probability of any fluctuation is equal to $e^{-\delta A/kT}$ where δA is the change in A occurring on account of the fluctuation. We write $A = A' + A''$, where A' is the part of A associated with the n molecules which we have picked out, and where A'' is associated with the other $N - n$ molecules. Then

$$\delta A = \delta A' + \delta A''$$

$$= \left(\frac{\partial A'}{\partial v}\right)_T \delta v - \left(\frac{\partial A''}{\partial (V - v)}\right)_T \delta v$$

$$+ \frac{1}{2}\left(\frac{\partial^2 A'}{\partial v^2}\right)_T (\delta v)^2 + \frac{1}{2}\left(\frac{\partial^2 A''}{\partial (V - v)^2}\right)_T (-\delta v)^2 + \cdots \quad (8\text{-}1)$$

where the partial derivatives are to be evaluated at the condition of equilibrium. Since $(\partial A'/\partial v)_T = -p'$ and $[\partial A''/\partial (V - v)]_T = -p''$ where p' and p'' are the respective pressures, and since these are equal at equilibrium, the first terms drop out, and Eq. 8-1 reduces to

$$\delta A = -\frac{1}{2}\left[\left(\frac{\partial p'}{\partial v}\right)_T + \left(\frac{\partial p''}{\partial (V - v)}\right)_T\right](\delta v)^2 + \cdots \quad (8\text{-}2)$$

$(\partial p'/\partial v)_T$ may be written $-(\beta v)^{-1}$ and $[\partial p''/\partial (V - v)]_T$ may be written $-[\beta(V - v)]^{-1}$, where β is the compressibility. If we assume that V is much larger than v and that the fluctuations δv are themselves small, Eq. 8-2 may then be written approximately as

$$\delta A = (2\beta v)^{-1}(\delta v)^2 \quad (8\text{-}3)$$

and the probability w of the fluctuation becomes

$$w = e^{-(2\beta vkT)^{-1}(\delta v)^2} \quad (8\text{-}4)$$

The average value of the square of the fluctuations, $\overline{(\delta v)^2}$, can now be readily derived on the basis of the assumptions that $\overline{(\delta v)^2}$ is small compared to v^2 and that the number of quantum levels between volumes v and $v + dv$, and hence the intrinsic probability of this range of volumes, is proportional to dv over the range of volumes likely to occur. Under these conditions (noting that $dv = d(\delta v)$), and simultaneously expressing the fluctuations in terms of density (if $\overline{(\delta v)^2} \ll v^2$, then $\overline{(\delta v)^2}/v^2 = \overline{(\delta \rho)^2}/\rho^2$),

$$\frac{\overline{(\delta v)^2}}{v^2} = \frac{\overline{(\delta \rho)^2}}{\rho^2} = \frac{1}{v^2} \frac{\int_{-\infty}^{\infty} (\delta v)^2 w d(\delta v)}{\int_{-\infty}^{\infty} w d(\delta v)} \tag{8-5}$$

$$= \frac{\beta k T}{v}$$

using Eq. 8-4 and evaluating the known integral. It is to be noted that the relative mean square of the fluctuation is inversely proportional to the selected observed volume v.

In the immediate neighborhood of the critical point, β becomes very large, and, according to Eq. 8-5 (which actually would not hold under the circumstances since $\delta \rho$ is assumed small compared to ρ), the fluctuation would become practically indefinitely large. But before the fluctuation became extremely great, the material in the volume v would be outside the density range for which β is very large. To take care of this it is necessary to consider the higher terms in Eq. 8-2. Very close to the critical point $\partial^3 A / \partial v^3 = -\partial^2 p / \partial v^2$ is very small as well as $\partial p / \partial v$. We assume then that all terms with powers of δv less than the fourth drop out. Leaving out the terms in p'', which as before will be negligible, we can then write approximately, instead of Eq. 8-3

$$\delta A = (24\beta_3 v^3)^{-1}(\delta v)^4 \tag{8-6}$$

where we have set $v^3(\partial^3 p / \partial v^3)_T = \beta_3^{-1}$. The coefficient β_3 is dimensionally independent of v and is therefore an intensive property of the system. $\overline{(\delta v)^2}/v^2 = \overline{(\delta \rho)^2}/\rho^2$ may now be evaluated from the quotient of integrals in Eq. 8-5 using

$$w = e^{-(24\beta_3 v^3 k T)^{-1}(\delta v)^4}$$

We obtain

$$\frac{\overline{(\delta \rho)^2}}{\rho^2} = \frac{\Gamma(\frac{3}{4})}{\Gamma(\frac{1}{4})} \frac{(24\beta_3 v^3 k T)^{\frac{1}{2}}}{v^2} = \frac{1.65(\beta_3 k T)^{\frac{1}{2}}}{v^{\frac{1}{2}}} \tag{8-7}$$

which contrasts with Eq. 8-5 in that it depends on $v^{-\frac{1}{2}}$ instead of v^{-1}. Even if β^{-1} is not zero, Eq. 8-6 gives a greater δA and hence a smaller fluctuation than Eq. 8-3 when v is chosen small enough. Whenever this is true for average δv, Eq. 8-6 and 8-7 are better than Eq. 8-3 and 8-5; when v is great enough so that Eq. 8-3 gives a much greater δA than Eq. 8-6, this means that the higher terms in Eq. 8-1 may be neglected and Eq. 8-3 and 8-5 are to be used.

We must note, however, that if the critical point is not of the classical type there is a region in which all derivatives of p are negligibly small. The fluctuations will not cause an appreciable increase in free energy until they are great enough to carry the fluctuating portion of the system to a condition outside of the critical region. The effect would be somewhat similar to what would arise if one had to go to still higher terms in Eq. 8-2, and the influence of the chosen v would be further lessened. Indeed, from Fig. E,1e it is to be inferred that one certainly should go to a higher term.

Unless the system is in a state in which β^{-1} is exactly zero, we can ultimately find a volume large enough so that Eq. 8-5 holds. Thus the fluctuations in a large volume are as great as ever, but fluctuations in a small volume are suppressed. This means that the fluctuations are more uniform over a large volume. This fact may be expressed by saying that correlations of the fluctuations in different parts of the system become more important near the critical point. The fluctuations have been considered from this point of view by Ornstein and Zernike [*59; 60; 61*, pp. 80ff.; see also *62*]. They begin by discussing a very small volume, designated for convenience as dv, which is smaller than the size of a single molecule. This volume will be considered to be occupied if there is a molecule with its center of gravity in it; there is, therefore, either one or no molecule in it, the respective probabilities being ρdv and $1 - \rho dv$, with $\delta\rho$ in these two cases being $(1/dv) - \rho$ and $-\rho$ respectively. $\overline{(\delta\rho)^2}$, then, is equal to $[(1/dv) - \rho]^2\rho dv + \rho^2(1 - \rho dv)$, where ρ is the molecular or number density.

$$\overline{(\delta\rho)^2} \cong \frac{\rho}{dv} \tag{8-8}$$

since dv is small. The result is seen to be quite independent of the properties of the system, other than its density. The fact that the fluctuation in a larger volume has a different value can arise only because of the interatomic forces, which cause fluctuations in one portion of the system to be correlated with fluctuations in another. This follows because Eq. 8-8 may be shown to hold for a perfect gas for any dv, provided only it is small compared to the total volume of the system (this may be verified for sufficiently large dv by inserting the appropriate value of β in Eq. 8-5).

In general, the average value of $\delta\rho$ for any one of the volumes dv is zero, but if the fluctuations are assumed to be given, at some particular instant, for all the volumes except one of them (which may be taken as being located at the origin of coordinates) then the value of $\overline{\delta\rho}$ for the latter (designated as $\overline{\delta\rho(0)}$) will not be zero, on account of the correlations. Ornstein and Zernike made the assumption[13] that $\overline{\delta\rho(0)}$ depends linearly on the fluctuation $\delta\rho(x)$ which occurs at the point x, y, z (being, of course,

---

[13] We shall use functional indications like (x) and (0) as abbreviations for the more complete indications (x, y, z) and $(0, 0, 0)$, which give the values of all three coordinates. The functional indication $(x_1 - x)$ used below likewise stands for $(x_1 - x, y_1 - y, z_1 - z)$. The quantities f and g are functions of the distances indicated (i.e. $f(x)$ is a function of the distance of x, y, z to the origin, and $f(x_1 - x)$ is a function of the distance between x, y, z and x_1, y_1, z_1) rather than of the separate coordinates.

also a function of the distance of the point x, y, z to the origin). In view of the fact that $\delta\rho$ can take only two widely varying values, neither of them small, this assumption may seem somewhat questionable. However, if it be made, we can add the contributions of all the small volumes, obtaining

$$\overline{\delta\rho(0)} = \int_{-\infty}^{\infty} \int_{-\infty}^{\infty} \int_{-\infty}^{\infty\prime} f(x)\,\delta\rho(x)\,dv \qquad (8\text{-}9)$$

($dv = dxdydz$) where $f(x)dv$ is the proportionality factor, it being understood that the integrand is not continuous. The prime indicates that the element at the origin is not to be included in the integral.

On the other hand we may wish to consider the correlation of two of our little volumes, say those at x, y, z and at x_1, y_1, z_1. If the fluctuation at x_1, y_1, z_1 has a certain value, that at x, y, z may be expected to have a certain average value, which we suppose to be given by

$$\overline{\delta\rho(x)} = g(x_1 - x)\,\delta\rho(x_1)\,dv_1 \qquad (8\text{-}10)$$

where $g(x_1 - x)dv_1$ is now the proportionality factor. It might be supposed that $g(x_1 - x)dv_1$ should be identical with $f(x_1 - x)dv_1$, and $f(x_1 - x)dv_1$ will indeed give the direct effect of the fluctuation at x_1, y_1, z_1 on that at x, y, z. However the fluctuation at x_1, y_1, z_1 has its influence on all points, and the latter in turn influence the fluctuations at x, y, z. All these secondary effects are taken care of in Eq. 8-10. Suppose we had a fixed fluctuation at x_1, y_1, z_1 and varying fluctuations influenced by the fluctuation at x_1, y_1, z_1 at all other points. Then for the effect at the origin we could write from Eq. 8-9

$$\overline{\delta\rho(0)} = f(x_1)\,\delta\rho(x_1)\,dv_1 + \int_{-\infty}^{\infty} \int_{-\infty}^{\infty} \int_{-\infty}^{\infty\prime\prime} f(x)\,\overline{\delta\rho(x)}\,dxdydz \qquad (8\text{-}11)$$

where the double prime indicates that the elements of volume at x_1, y_1, z_1 and at the origin are not to be included in the integral. The direct effect of the fluctuation at x_1, y_1, z_1 is taken care of by the first term of Eq. 8-11, while the indirect effect is handled by the integral; so we use Eq. 8-10 to get $\overline{\delta\rho(x)}$. Also from Eq. 8-10, taking the special case that x, y, z is the origin, we have $\overline{\delta\rho(0)} = g(x_1)\,\delta\rho(x_1)\,dv_1$; hence

$$g(x_1)\,\delta\rho(x_1)\,dv_1 = f(x_1)\,\delta\rho(x_1)\,dv_1$$
$$+ \int_{-\infty}^{\infty} \int_{-\infty}^{\infty} \int_{-\infty}^{\infty\prime\prime} f(x)g(x_1 - x)\,\delta\rho(x_1)\,dv_1dxdydz \qquad (8\text{-}12)$$

Incidentally we may now remark that the fact that the first term on the right-hand side of Eq. 8-11 is proportional to $\delta\rho(x_1)dv_1$ means that $\overline{\delta\rho(0)}$ and $\overline{\delta\rho(x)}$ will be proportional to this quantity, so that the form of Eq. 8-10 is not arbitrary, but follows from the other assumptions. If we now divide by $\delta\rho(x_1)dv_1$ and change the variables of integration to $\xi, \eta, \zeta = x - x_1, y - y_1, z - z_1$, Eq. 8-12 becomes, since $g(\xi) \equiv g(-\xi)$,

$$g(x_1) = f(x_1) + \int_{-\infty}^{\infty} \int_{-\infty}^{\infty} \int_{-\infty}^{\infty''} f(x_1 + \xi)g(\xi)d\xi d\eta d\zeta \qquad (8\text{-}13)$$

We now multiply by $dx_1dy_1dz_1$ and integrate again. We set

$$F = \int_{-\infty}^{\infty} \int_{-\infty}^{\infty} \int_{-\infty}^{\infty'} f(x_1)dx_1dy_1dz_1$$

$$= \int_{-\infty}^{\infty} \int_{-\infty}^{\infty} \int_{-\infty}^{\infty'} f(x_1 + \xi)dx_1dy_1dz_1 \qquad (8\text{-}14)$$

(where the primes indicate that the element at the origin is to be left out of the first integral and the element at $x_1 + \xi, y_1 + \eta, z_1 + \zeta = 0$ is to be omitted in the second) and

$$G = \int_{-\infty}^{\infty} \int_{-\infty}^{\infty} \int_{-\infty}^{\infty'} g(x_1)dx_1dy_1dz_1 = \int_{-\infty}^{\infty} \int_{-\infty}^{\infty} \int_{-\infty}^{\infty'} g(\xi)d\xi d\eta d\zeta \qquad (8\text{-}15)$$

(where the primes indicate that the element at the origin is to be omitted). We then find from Eq. 8-13, $G = F + FG$, or

$$1 + G = (1 - F)^{-1} \qquad (8\text{-}16)$$

We are now in a position to consider the relation between Eq. 8-5 and 8-8. The fluctuation of the *number* of molecules in a volume $dv = dxdydz$ is given by $\delta\rho(x)dxdydz$. Therefore, for a large volume v we may write[14]

$$(\delta\rho)^2 = v^{-2}\left(\iiint_v \delta\rho(x)dxdydz\right)^2$$

$$= v^{-2}\left(\iiint_v \delta\rho(x)dxdydz\right)\left(\iiint_v \delta\rho(x_1)dx_1dy_1dz_1\right)$$

$$= v^{-2}\iiint\iiint_{v^2} \delta\rho(x)\delta\rho(x_1)dxdydzdx_1dy_1dz_1 \qquad (8\text{-}17)$$

x_1, y_1, z_1 being only formally different from x, y, z. We can average over the fluctuations and consider separately that part of the integral which is contributed by those volume elements for which $x_1, y_1, z_1 = x, y, z$. The latter contribute an amount $v^{-2}[\overline{(\delta\rho(x))^2}dv]v$ which, by Eq. 8-8, equals ρv^{-1}. For the rest of the integral we note that $\overline{\delta\rho(x)\delta\rho(x_1)}$ will be a function of the distance between x, y, z and x_1, y_1, z_1. If v is large compared to the volume over which $\overline{\delta\rho(x)\delta\rho(x_1)}$ is appreciable, we can hold x, y, z constant and integrate with respect to $x - x_1, y - y_1, z - z_1$ ($= \xi, \eta, \zeta$) first, extending this integration to infinity. Integration with

[14] The symbol beneath the integral signs indicates the range of integration.

respect to x, y, z then yields a factor v. Thus we will have

$$\overline{(\delta\rho)^2} = \rho v^{-1} + v^{-1} \int_{-\infty}^{\infty} \int_{-\infty}^{\infty} \int_{-\infty}^{\infty'} \overline{\delta\rho(x)\delta\rho(x_1)} d\xi d\eta d\zeta$$

Rewriting Eq. 8-10 as $\overline{\delta\rho(x)} = g(\xi)\delta\rho(x_1)dv_1$, multiplying by $\delta\rho(x_1)$, and averaging again we see that $\overline{\delta\rho(x)\delta\rho(x_1)} = g(\xi)\overline{(\delta\rho(x_1))^2}dv_1$ which by Eq. 8-8 equals $g(\xi)\rho$. Applying this to the integral just written down, and using Eq. 8-15 and 8-16 we obtain

$$\overline{(\delta\rho)^2} = \rho v^{-1}(1 + G) = \rho v^{-1}(1 - F)^{-1} \tag{8-18}$$

Unless β is very close to zero or the total volume of the system is very small, we can find a volume v large enough so that Eq. 8-5 is valid, and $\overline{(\delta\rho)^2}$ of Eq. 8-5 becomes identical with $\overline{(\delta\rho)^2}$ of Eq. 8-18. Thus F and G can be evaluated. It is seen that in the immediate neighborhood of the critical point, F approaches 1 and G becomes very large. From this we would infer that near the critical point $g(\xi)$ would have appreciable values over a large range of values of ξ, η, ζ. We have just seen that $g(\xi)dv_1 = \overline{\delta\rho(x)\delta\rho(x_1)}/\overline{(\delta\rho(x_1))^2}$ so that $g(\xi)$ gives a measure of the actual correlation of the fluctuations, and we already expect this correlation to be large near the critical point.

A more convincing demonstration of the range of $g(\xi)$ can be obtained by actually finding an expression for $g(\xi)$ for large values of ξ, η, ζ [61, pp. 80ff.; 63; 64]. Since $f(x)$ represents the direct effect of the fluctuation at the origin on that at x, y, z, it is closely related to the intermolecular forces and should have a similar range. Let us turn to Eq. 8-13 and consider a position x_1, y_1, z_1 which is beyond the effective range of $f(x_1)$. Then the first term on the right-hand side, $f(x_1)$, can be neglected. The contributions to the integral will all come from a narrow region in which ξ, η, ζ are nearly equal to $-x_1$, $-y_1$, $-z_1$. Since $g(-\xi)$ will be equal to $g(\xi)$ we can replace $f(x_1 + \xi)$ by $f(-x_1 + \xi)$, in which case the contributions to the integral come from the neighborhood of x_1, y_1, z_1. We may replace $g(\xi)$ by its Taylor expansion in three variables about x_1, y_1, z_1. Since $f(-x_1 + \xi)$ is symmetrical about x_1, y_1, z_1, all the terms from first derivatives of $g(\xi)$ drop out in the integration, as do all terms arising from cross terms like $\partial^2 g(x_1)/\partial x_1 \partial y_1$, since this derivative will be multiplied by $(\xi - x_1)(\eta - y_1)$. (Our notation is designed to indicate that the derivative $\partial^2 g(\xi)/\partial \xi \partial \eta$ is to be evaluated at x_1, y_1, z_1.) Therefore, if we carry the expansion to second derivatives only we see that Eq. 8-13 becomes

$$g(x_1) = Fg(x_1) + \tfrac{1}{2}F'\nabla^2 g(x_1) \tag{8-19}$$

where $\nabla^2 g(x_1) = \partial^2 g(x_1)/\partial x_1^2 + \partial^2 g(x_1)/\partial y_1^2 + \partial^2 g(x_1)/\partial z_1^2$ and

$$F' = \int_{-\infty}^{\infty} \int_{-\infty}^{\infty} \int_{-\infty}^{\infty} x^2 f(x) dx dy dz$$

The solution of Eq. 8-19 with spherical symmetry has the form

$$g(x_1) = \frac{A}{r} e^{-r/\kappa} \tag{8-20}$$

where $\kappa^2 = \frac{1}{2}F'/(1 - F)$ and $r = \sqrt{x_1^2 + y_1^2 + z_1^2}$, and where A is a constant. It is seen that κ determines the range of $g(x_1)$ and that this becomes very large when the critical point is approached, since F approaches 1.

E,9. Light Scattering in the Critical Region. The fluctuations in density which we have discussed in Art. 8 may be studied by means of light scattering, which results, in the neighborhood of the critical point, in the well-known phenomenon of critical opalescence. This phenomenon is discussed qualitatively in Art. 1. If we can choose the volumes v large enough so that Eq. 8-5 holds, but still small compared to the cube of the wavelength of the light, the opalescence may be discussed approximately by assuming that light is scattered independently from the separate volumes. It will appear that the result is independent of the size chosen for v. The scattering arises from the change in the optical dielectric constant D (equal to the square of the index of refraction) caused by the fluctuations in density.

As the light passes over the dielectric, its electric vector at any point oscillates, and we can represent the magnitude of the electric field as a function of the time t by an expression of the form $E \sin (2\pi\nu t)$, where E is the amplitude of the field strength and ν is the frequency. This oscillating electric field produces an electric moment in the dielectric, which is equal at any instant to $(E/4\pi)(D - 1) \sin (2\pi\nu t)$ per unit volume. If there were no fluctuations in density, the oscillations of neighboring volume elements would be of the same amplitude and in phase (the volumes being small compared to the wavelength of the light). This gives rise to the propagation of the light with the velocity characteristic of the medium. The scattering is superimposed upon this simple propagation, and may be said to be the result of light emitted by oscillating dipoles whose magnitudes are the difference between those characteristic of the medium as it actually exists at the instant in question, and those characteristic of a medium whose density has the average value and the average dielectric constant, which we shall call D_0. Thus the effective scattering dipole for a volume v of instantaneous dielectric constant D is $(E/4\pi)(D - D_0)v \sin (2\pi\nu t) = M \sin (2\pi\nu t)$, the equation defining M. Insofar as the fluctuations of one of the small volumes v are independent of those of neighboring volumes, the scattering from each volume may be considered to be independent of that of its neighbors, and the intensity of scattering found by simple addition.

The time average of the energy which such a dipole radiates per unit area per second at a distance r and at an angle ϕ made by the direction of the beam of scattered light with the direction of displacement of positive and negative charge, is known from electromagnetic theory. It is given by

$$i = \frac{2\pi^3 M^2 \nu^4 D_0^{\frac{1}{2}}}{c^3 r^2} \sin^2 \phi \qquad (9\text{-}1)$$

where c is the velocity of light in vacuum.[15]

The incident light, with electric vector $E \sin (2\pi\nu t)$, has a rate of flow of energy per cm² per sec of $(c/8\pi)E^2 D_0^{\frac{1}{2}}$. Dividing by this, inserting the value of M in Eq. 9-1, and setting $c/\nu = \lambda$, we have

$$\frac{i}{I} = \frac{\pi^2 (D - D_0)^2 v^2 \sin^2 \phi}{r^2 \lambda^4} \qquad (9\text{-}2)$$

Experimentally we are more interested in the angle θ between the direction of propagation of the incident beam and the direction of propagation of the scattered beam than we are in ϕ. If the incident light is unpolarized, the electric vector, and thus the direction of the dipole, can be in any direction perpendicular to the direction of propagation of the incident beam. In Fig. E,9a we let IO be the direction of the incident beam, OS the direction of the scattered beam, and OD the direction of the electric vector of the incident beam. In the spherical triangle SCD,

---

[15] Eq. 9-1 is the same, except for the factor $D_0^{\frac{1}{2}}$, as one of the unnumbered equations on page 293 of Slater and Frank's *Introduction to Theoretical Physics* (McGraw-Hill, 1933) (their θ is our ϕ and their $\omega = 2\pi\nu$). Slater and Frank's equation was derived for a vacuum. The electric field produced by an oscillation at a great distance r, is proportional to $M\nu^2/c^2$. This would be divided by D_0 in a dielectric medium; however, c would be replaced by the velocity in the medium, $c/D_0^{\frac{1}{2}}$, thus leaving the field strength unchanged. The rate of flow of energy (Poynting's vector), however, depends on $D_0^{\frac{1}{2}}$ (see Slater and Frank, page 254), which accounts for this factor in Eq. 9-1. D_0 is equal to the square of the index of refraction, and its value varies slightly with the wavelength of light. The magnetic permeability may, for light waves, always be taken as 1.

The factor $D_0^{\frac{1}{2}}$ in Eq. 9-1 reflects the effect of oscillations in the dielectric forced by the oscillations of the oscillator of moment amplitude M. One might therefore suppose that the use of Eq. 9-1 is justified as long as the volume v in which M is located is small compared to λ^3, where λ is the wavelength. However, the dielectric constant itself is calculated by an equation such as Eq. 9-4, below, which itself already includes the mutual interaction of the polarization of the various parts of the medium, and in this calculation a uniform electric field is assumed. There is, therefore, a certain lack of consistency in our treatment, as was pointed out by Rocard [65]. Furthermore, if v becomes comparable to λ^3, then, since the mutual interaction of the molecules is already taken into account and should not be counted twice, it appears from a consideration of the way in which Eq. 9-1 is derived, that it would be preferable for the $D_0^{\frac{1}{2}}$ not to appear. Since D_0 is not far from unity for a liquid near its critical point, this factor is probably not too important for this case; in the similar treatment for a binary liquid system near its critical solution temperature, it may be of more importance.

the side SC is $\pi/2 - \theta$, the side SD is ϕ, and the side CD is designated as ϕ', while the dihedral angle SCD opposite side SD is $\pi/2$. Thus by a well-known formula of spherical trigonometry $\cos \phi = \cos \phi' \sin \theta$. With θ fixed, ϕ' can take any value with equal probability, depending upon the accidental direction of the electric vector, if the incident light is unpolarized. Thus the average value

$$\overline{\sin^2 \phi} = 1 - \overline{\cos^2 \phi} = 1 - \overline{\cos^2 \phi'} \sin^2 \theta = 1 - \tfrac{1}{2} \sin^2 \theta = \tfrac{1}{2}(1 + \cos^2 \theta)$$

In order to give the average intensity of light per unit area scattered at angle θ by a volume v, we will replace $\sin^2 \phi$ in Eq. 9-2 by $\tfrac{1}{2}(1 + \cos^2 \theta)$, and $(D - D_0)^2$ by its average $\overline{(D - D_0)^2}$. The scattering per unit volume

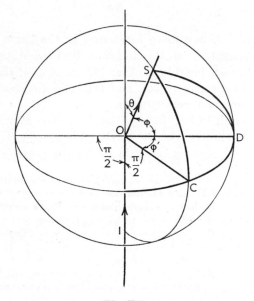

Fig. E,9a.

will be given by multiplying this result by $1/v$, since there are $1/v$ of the volumes v in unit volume. We thus obtain (using the subscript 0 to denote scattering by unit volume)

$$\frac{i_0}{I} = \frac{\pi^2 \overline{(D - D_0)^2} v (1 + \cos^2 \theta)}{2r^2 \lambda^4} \tag{9-3}$$

$\overline{(D - D_0)^2}$ can be found from the average fluctuation in density if the relation between D and ρ is known. D and ρ are generally assumed to be related by the Clausius-Mossotti equation. However, an equation recently derived by Onsager,

$$(D - 1)(2D + 1)/9D = K\rho \tag{9-4}$$

where K is a constant for a given liquid, apparently fits the experimental data better [66, p. 352]. This gives

$$\rho \frac{dD}{d\rho} = (D - 1) \frac{2D^2 + D}{2D^2 + 1} \cong D_0 - 1 \tag{9-5}$$

the last relation following because $D_0 - 1$ is usually small near the critical point, and $D - D_0$ is very small. Therefore, approximately

$$\overline{(D - D_0)^2} = (D_0 - 1)^2 \overline{(\delta\rho)^2}/\rho^2 \tag{9-6}$$

which with Eq. 8-5 gives, when substituted into Eq. 9-3, the Einstein-Smoluchowski relationship[16] [56,57]

$$\frac{i_0}{I} = \frac{\pi^2 (D_0 - 1)^2 \beta k T (1 + \cos^2 \theta)}{2r^2\lambda^4} \tag{9-7}$$

The total intensity of scattered light i_t is obtained by multiplying by the element of area of a sphere of radius r, namely $r^2 \sin \theta d\theta d\phi$, and integrating over all directions in space. This gives

$$\frac{i_t}{I} = \frac{8\pi^3 (D_0 - 1)^2 \beta k T}{3\lambda^4} \tag{9-8}$$

Eq. 9-7 will be valid as long as it is possible to choose a v (for which Eq. 8-5 will hold) that is small compared with λ^3. If we have to consider correlated fluctuations over a volume comparable with λ^3, we get coherent scattering of light over distances comparable with a wavelength, which results in destructive interference. Let us consider the scattering of a parallel beam of light in the direction θ from the neighborhood of a point O (Fig. E,9b and E,9c). We take the z' axis in the direction of the incident light and the $x'z'$ plane as the plane of the incident and scattered beams. From the two special cases shown in Fig. E,9b and E,9c it is clear that light scattered from a point x', y', z' will be out of phase with light scattered from O by[17] $(2\pi z'/\lambda)(1 - \cos \theta) + (2\pi x'/\lambda) \sin \theta$, where λ is the wavelength.[18] If θ is zero, therefore, there will be no destructive interference, and Eq. 9-7 should hold very close to the critical point. It will be limited by one's inability, right at the critical point, to find a volume v, contained in the system, large enough to make Eq. 8-5 hold,

---

[16] In the literature Eq. 9-7 and 9-8 are usually found with the additional factor $(D + 2)^2/9$, coming from use of the Clausius-Mossotti equation.

[17] The expression $(2\pi z'/\lambda)(1 - \cos \theta) + (2\pi x'/\lambda) \sin \theta$ may be replaced by use of trigonometric identities by $(4\pi/\lambda)[z' \sin (\theta/2) + x' \cos (\theta/2)] \sin (\theta/2) = (4\pi x/\lambda) \sin (\theta/2)$, where x (defined by the equation) is equal to the distance of the point x', z', y' from a line drawn through the origin at an angle $\theta/2$ to the z' axis, as is indicated in Fig. E,9d $x = PR + OQ$.

[18] In the light of footnote 15 it seemed best to treat this as wavelength in vacuum. The neglect of the effect of the dielectric on the interference phenomena will not be serious, in any event, for a one-component system at its critical point.

and by radiation damping, which will prevent i_0/I from becoming too large. For angles appreciably greater than zero, we may attempt to use Eq. 8-7. If we apply Eq. 8-7 to Eq. 9-3, using Eq. 9-6, the scattering is not independent of v, but will increase with v as $v^{\frac{1}{2}}$. However, if we choose too large a v there will be destructive interference, as we have just seen. The light wave, in other words, will choose a value of v for us which will

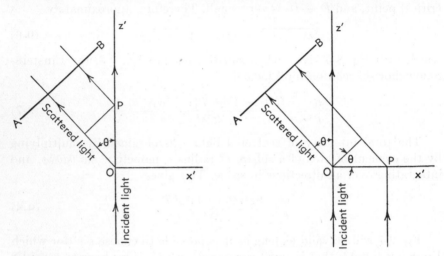

Fig. E,9b. The point x', y', z' is designated as P.

Fig. E,9c. The point x', y', z' is designated as P.

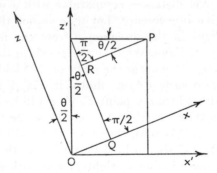

Fig. E,9d. The point $x,'$ y', z' is designated as P.

be smaller than and at least roughly proportional to λ^3. The scattering then becomes proportional to $\lambda^{-\frac{1}{2}}$ instead of λ^{-4}. However the dependence on $\lambda^{-\frac{1}{2}}$ cannot be an exact law, both because of the limitations on Eq. 8-7, which we have already discussed, and because the dependence on wavelength will be related to the exact way in which the correlation of the fluctuations falls off with distance. It is clear, however, that the dependence of the scattering on wavelength will become less marked near the critical point.

⟨ 478 ⟩

Ornstein and Zernike [59,60,61,64][19] have derived an equation, based on their theory of the correlation of fluctuations, which gives a λ^{-2} dependence near the critical point. Though it suffers from the weakness of the assumed linear character of the correlation of the fluctuations which results in Eq. 8-9, it appears to be the best theoretical treatment presently available, and we shall proceed with a brief presentation.

Returning to Fig. E,9b and E,9c, let us suppose that the light scattered from O reaches the wave front AB at a time t. Then from Eq. 9-3, and using Eq. 9-6, its electric vector (which is proportional to the square root of the intensity) on the front AB due to light scattered from O may be set proportional to $(D_0 - 1)(\delta\rho(O)/\rho)\lambda^{-2} \cos(\omega t)$, where $\delta\rho(O)$ is the fluctuation at the origin and ω is 2π times the frequency of the light. To discuss the scattering from other points in the neighborhood of O we shall transfer to the axes x and z shown in Fig. E,9d (y will be the same as y'). Then from footnote 17, it is seen that the phase at AB of light scattered from a point x, y, z will be greater by αx where the quantity $\alpha = -(4\pi/\lambda) \sin(\theta/2)$. Its electric vector will be proportional to $(D_0 - 1)(\delta\rho(x)/\rho)\lambda^{-2} \cos(\omega t + \alpha x)$ where $\delta\rho(x)$ is the fluctuation in density at point x, y, z, the type of notation introduced in footnote 13 being used (except for sin and cos). The intensity at the wave front of the light scattered by a large volume v will (leaving out the constant factor $(D_0 - 1)^2/\rho^2$) be proportional to

$$\lambda^{-4} \left[\iiint_v \delta\rho(x) \cos(\omega t + \alpha x) dx dy dz \right]^2 \tag{9-9}$$

The integral may be reduced in the same way as the integral of Eq. 8-17. We average over the fluctuations and write the expression (9-9) in the form

$$\lambda^{-4} \iiiiii_{v^2} \overline{\delta\rho(x)\delta\rho(x_1)} \cos(\omega t + \alpha x) \cos(\omega t + \alpha x_1) dx dy dz dx_1 dy_1 dz_1$$

Now, as for the integral of Eq. 8-17, we introduce the variables ξ, η, $\zeta = x - x_1$, $y - y_1$, $z - z_1$ in place of x_1, y_1, z_1. We separate the part contributed by those regions of the integration space for which $\xi = \eta = \zeta = 0$, using Eq. 8-8. For the rest of the integral we recall that $\overline{\delta\rho(x)\delta\rho(x_1)} = g(\xi)\rho$. We thus obtain

$$\lambda^{-4}\rho \iiint_v \cos^2(\omega t + \alpha x) dx dy dz +$$

$$\lambda^{-4}\rho \iiiiii_{v^2}' g(\xi) \cos(\omega t + \alpha x) \cos(\omega t + \alpha x - \alpha\xi) d\xi d\eta d\zeta dx dy dz \tag{9-10}$$

[19] Rosenfeld [61], except for a difference resulting from his way of handling the difficulty mentioned in footnotes 15 and 18 and a term of negligible magnitude, comes out with a result that is exactly equivalent, though in very different form (see his footnote p. 88, and his Eq. 59).

We are interested in the average intensity at the wave front AB, and we shall now average over t. The first integral then reduces to $v/2$. To average the second integral we note that $\cos(\omega t + \alpha x - \alpha\xi) = \cos(\omega t + \alpha x)\cos(\alpha\xi) + \sin(\omega t + \alpha x)\sin(\alpha\xi)$. The average of $\cos^2(\omega t + \alpha x)$ with respect to t is $\frac{1}{2}$ and that of $\cos(\omega t + \alpha x)\sin(\omega t + \alpha x)$ is zero. Thus expression (9-10) reduces to

$$\frac{\lambda^{-4}\rho v}{2} + \frac{\lambda^{-4}\rho}{2} \underset{v^2}{\int\int\int\int\int\int}{}' g(\xi)\cos(\alpha\xi)d\xi d\eta d\zeta dx dy dz$$

$$= \frac{\lambda^{-4}\rho v}{2}\left(1 + \int_{-\infty}^{\infty}\int_{-\infty}^{\infty}\int_{-\infty}^{\infty}{}' g(\xi)\cos(\alpha\xi)d\xi d\eta d\zeta\right)$$

$$= \frac{\lambda^{-4}\rho v}{2}(1 + G_c) \tag{9-11}$$

where G_c is defined by the equation.[20] As before, it is legitimate to extend the second integration to infinity if v is very large. A relation similar to Eq. 8-16

$$1 + G_c = (1 - F_c)^{-1} \tag{9-12}$$

with

$$F_c = \int_{-\infty}^{\infty}\int_{-\infty}^{\infty}\int_{-\infty}^{\infty}{}' f(x)\cos(\alpha x)dx dy dz \tag{9-13}$$

can be obtained by multiplying Eq. 8-13 by $\cos(\alpha x_1)dx_1 dy_1 dz_1$ and integrating.[21] Since $f(x)$ is a function which approaches zero at distances from the origin much greater than molecular dimensions, we may expand the cosine in Eq. 9-13, using only the first two terms in the series. Then comparing with Eq. 8-14 we see that

$$F - F_c = \frac{1}{2}\alpha^2 F' = \frac{8\pi^2 F'}{\lambda^2}\sin^2\left(\frac{\theta}{2}\right) \tag{9-14}$$

where

$$F' = \int_{-\infty}^{\infty}\int_{-\infty}^{\infty}\int_{-\infty}^{\infty}{}' x^2 f(x)dx dy dz \tag{9-15}$$

The derivation of Eq. 9-7 is essentially equivalent to using a very large wavelength in the above calculation of an expression (Eq. 9-11)

[20] Substituting for ξ, η, ζ the polar coordinates r, θ', ϕ', with the polar axis along the ξ axis, integration with respect to θ' and ϕ' can be performed and G_c put into the form

$$\int_0^{\infty}{}' \{[g(r)\sin(\alpha r)]/\alpha r\}4\pi r^2 dr$$

which, substituted into Eq. 9-11, gives the usual form of scattering equation in terms of the "distribution function" $g(r) \equiv g(\xi)$.

[21] To handle the double integration we set $\cos(\alpha x_1) = \cos[\alpha(x_1 + \xi) - \alpha\xi] = \cos[\alpha(x_1 + \xi)]\cos(\alpha\xi) + \sin[\alpha(x_1 + \xi)]\sin(\alpha\xi)$ and note that the sine terms will contribute nothing to the integrals since the sine is an odd function and g and f are even functions.

proportional to the intensity at the wave front AB. As the wavelength becomes very large, $F - F_c$ approaches zero and G_c approaches G. To correct Eq. 9-7, we should therefore multiply by $(1 + G_c)/(1 + G) = (1 - F)/(1 - F_c) = [1 + (F - F_c)/(1 - F)]^{-1}$, where $1 - F$ can be evaluated from Eq. 8-5 and 8-18 and $F - F_c$ from Eq. 9-14. The final result is

$$\frac{i_0}{I} = \frac{\pi^2(D_0 - 1)^2 kT(1 + \cos^2 \theta)}{2\beta^{-1}r^2\lambda^4 + 16\pi^2 r^2\lambda^2 F'\rho kT \sin^2 (\theta/2)} \tag{9-16}$$

Since $f(x)$ is of importance only for distances of the order of molecular dimensions, F' will be very small, and the last term in the denominator will usually be negligible. However, when β is very large it predominates, and then i_0/I becomes proportional to λ^{-2} instead of to λ^{-4}. In making this statement we neglect the variation of D_0 with λ.

It is possible to use the deviation of the scattering from the Einstein-Smoluchowski formula (Eq. 9-7 or Eq. 9-8) to make an estimate of the spatial dimensions of the fluctuations, that is, to say how many molecules on the average cooperate in producing these fluctuations at any temperature in the neighborhood of the critical temperature. For a system of fixed volume in the critical region just above the critical temperature, $\partial p/\partial v$ will be roughly proportional to $T - T_{cr}$; hence β will be proportional to $(T - T_{cr})^{-1}$. Eq. 9-7 or Eq. 9-8, then, predicts that the scattering for any given wavelength will give a straight line if plotted against $(T - T_{cr})^{-1}$. Deviations from this straight line begin to occur when the fluctuations begin to occur over a distance comparable with the wavelength of light. This is somewhat obscure if one merely looks at Eq. 9-16; it is best considered in connection with the integral G_c, which begins to deviate from G when the function g, which measures the correlations of the fluctuations, deviates appreciably from zero for distances comparable with a wavelength, and $(1 + G_c)/(1 + G)$ is a measure of the deviation of the scattering from the straight line mentioned above. $(1 + G_c)/(1 + G)$ is a function of λ for fixed temperature, and if sufficiently accurate measurements could be made for a sufficiently great range of λ so as to determine this function, it should theoretically be possible to solve the integral equation for g and so to arrive at determination of the correlation of fluctuations.

Eq. 9-16 has been criticized by Rocard [67], because when an integration is performed over the angles, an infinite result is obtained. Rocard [65] has himself proposed an alternative theory, but this theory is, in the opinion of the writer, open to grave objections. We have already indicated in the qualitative discussion that the last term in the denominator of Eq. 9-16 should become zero for very small angles θ, so that the equation reverts to Eq. 9-7, and we have noted that the validity of the latter is limited by the finite volume of the containing vessel [68]. It would appear, however, that the scattering from any unit volume of fluid should not become infinite even if the total volume is infinite. As already noted, infinite scattering will certainly be prevented by radiation damping, which will, if important, cause a breakdown in the validity of the equations. Actually the apparent infinite scattering at the critical point is caused by such a small range of θ that the effect is not important. At the critical point, Eq. 9-16 may be written for fixed λ

$$\frac{i_0}{I} = \frac{n(1 + \cos^2 \theta)}{r^2(1 - \cos \theta)}$$

where n is a constant. With $r = 1$ cm and $\theta = \pi/2$ so that $\cos \theta = 0$, it is found experimentally that i_0/I is of the order of 10^{-3} for carbon dioxide (see below), so n is of the order of 10^{-3}. If we multiply i_0/I by $r^2 \sin \theta d\theta d\phi$ (where ϕ is now the other polar angle) and integrate with respect to ϕ between $\phi = 0$ and $\phi = 2\pi$ and with respect to θ between $\theta = \theta_1$ and $\theta = \pi$, we obtain very approximately, if θ_1 is very small,

$$\frac{i_t}{I} = 4\pi n(\ln 2 - 1) - 4\pi n \ln (1 - \cos \theta_1)$$

It can be seen that with $n = 10^{-3}$ the contribution of the last term becomes alarmingly large only if θ_1 is so small that $\ln (1 - \cos \theta_1)$ is of the order of -100. This will make θ_1 very small indeed. In some cases, however, n may be larger than 10^{-3}.

There is only a limited amount of experimental material which can be compared with Eq. 9-16. Bhattacharyya [69] has measured the scattering at right angles ($\theta = \pi/2$) from carbon dioxide at its critical density in the neighborhood of the critical point. Apparently complete equilibrium conditions were not obtained since the opalescence was slightly different for rising and falling temperatures. From data given, and from his curves, values of i_0/I at $r = 1$ cm at the critical point and at 1° above the critical point are about 10.34×10^{-4} and 5.1×10^{-4}, respectively, for $\lambda = 5400$ A. The refractive index $\sqrt{D_0}$ for the critical density (0.460 g/cm³) and for this wavelength is about 1.1066 [70]. Using the data at the critical temperature where $\beta = \infty$, we find from Eq. 9-16 that F' is equal to about 33×10^{-14} cm², or $\sqrt{F'} = 5.8 \times 10^{-7}$ cm. It is seen from Eq. 9-15 that $\sqrt{F'}$ is a rough measure of the radius of action of the molecular forces, and the value obtained is unexpectedly large. However, if this value is used, together with $\beta = 1.0$ atm⁻¹ [16], in Eq. 9-16 to calculate the value of i/I_0 at $r = 1$ for 1° above the critical temperature, we obtain $i/I_0 = 5.6 \times 10^{-4}$, so that Bhattacharyya's results are consistent in this respect. He also measured the variation with wavelength and found the λ^{-2} law to be obeyed very close to the critical point. However, at somewhat less than 1° away from the critical point he found that it obeyed the λ^{-4} law. Actually, with the value of F' found, the second term in the denominator of Eq. 9-16 is still somewhat larger than the first term for $\theta = \pi/2$ at a temperature 1° above the critical temperature, so that one should actually expect a dependence on the wavelength intermediate between a λ^{-2} and a λ^{-4} law.

Andant [71] has measured the extinction coefficients of ethyl ether and methyl acetate due to the scattering near the critical point. In both cases the variation with wavelength changes from a λ^{-4} to a λ^{-2} law as the critical point is approached. This change, in the case of the ether, begins at $T - T_{cr}$ equal to about 0.15° and is apparently complete at about $T - T_{cr} = 0.07°$. The deviation of the extinction coefficient for decreasing temperature[22] from that which would be expected from Eq. 9-8 begins at about $T - T_{cr} = 0.15$, so this is consistent enough; but the scattering from ether at right angles follows Eq. 9-16 only fairly well as one gets close to the critical point. The above statements are based on relative values. Andant made a determination of the absolute value of the scattering at 1.2° above the critical point and compared it with the Einstein-Smoluchowski equation (Eq. 9-7; see footnote 16). He found good agreement. However, he used a value of β of 1.12×10^{-7} dynes^{-1} cm^2, or about 10^{-1} atm^{-1}, which is unreasonably small, and does not seem easily reconcilable with the quoted data of Ramsay and Young [72]. The validity of his agreement may, then, perhaps be questioned, although it is true that the fact that the transition from Eq. 9-7 to Eq. 9-16 occurs so close to the critical temperature would indicate either a much smaller value of β than is found for carbon dioxide or a smaller value of F'. Eq. 9-7 seems to have been reasonably well tested by a number of writers [66, p. 352].

Cataldi and Drickamer [73] and Babb and Drickamer [74] have measured the scattering of light from ethane and ethylene. In these cases the scattering was reported to be very intense, so that multiple scattering became a problem. Therefore, Blosser and Drickamer [75] measured the extinction coefficient of ethane. At a density of 0.2005 g cm^{-3} and 33.076°C, the extinction became great. This must be close to the critical point of the sample used, though this is not reported, and the accepted critical temperature is nearly a degree lower [6]. The value of the refractive index is probably about 1.1 in this case, and the data are apparently in accord with the Einstein-Smoluchowski equation, if β under the conditions mentioned is around 50 to 100 atm^{-1}. However, the correlation of fluctuations must be small in this case, as is indicated by the fact that only small deviations from the λ^{-4} law are found (except for one case rather far removed from the critical point which is probably spurious).

Mason and Maass [76] have recently measured the opalescence of ethylene. They found the results to be reproducible as long as they were

[22] Opalescence for increasing temperatures was different, but was not measured in great detail.

above the critical temperature and no condensation occurred. At the critical density the opalescence was inversely proportional to $T - T_{cr}$ very close to the critical temperature, indicating a very small value of F'; however, they apparently had no difficulty with secondary scattering. Once condensation occurred, there were appreciable time lags in obtaining the equilibrium value of the opalescence even when the temperature was again brought past T_{cr}. Just below T_{cr} more than three hours were needed to establish equilibrium. The effect of impurities was also studied. Two as different as air and oleic acid were found to have essentially no effect if opalescences were compared at the same values of $T - T_{cr}$. Murray and Mason [77] have used opalescence measurements near T_{cr} as a means of measuring density gradients in the tube.

It is of interest to note that there is no observable critical opalescence in hydrogen [78]. This is to be expected because T_{cr} is so small and because D_0 is very close to 1.

The opalescence of binary liquid systems near the critical mixing point arises from fluctuations in concentration rather than in density, but these fluctuations can be calculated on exactly the same principles as the fluctuations in density in one-component systems; the opalescence has much the same character. It is, therefore, apropos to mention that Rousset [79] has made a study of a number of binary liquid mixtures. He found that in some cases there were no deviations from the λ^{-4} law even at the critical point. In these cases there was no asymmetry in the light scattered forward and backward. In some others, deviations from the λ^{-4} law occurred, and there was asymmetry in the scattering. In no case, however, did the variation with wavelength become as low as λ^{-2}, and the asymmetry at the critical point was not as great as contemplated by the Ornstein and Zernike law, Eq. 9-16.

Furth [80, p. 59] has recently reported on some measurements of binary liquid mixtures, and also finds that they can be classified into two classes, one of which (class II—for example, water-isobutyric acid) shows strong asymmetry, weak opalescence, approximate λ^{-2} dependence near the critical point, and a temperature variation similar to that which would be expected from Eq. 9-16. Class I liquid pairs (for example, aniline-cyclohexane) show strong opalescence, less asymmetry (but still some, and an angular dependence not at all like that expected from Eq. 9-7), approximate λ^{-4} dependence even near the critical point, and opalescence varying inversely as $T - T_{cr}$. This situation definitely seems anomalous. A Fourier inversion was applied to the scattering results to obtain actual expressions for $g(r)$. The class II liquid pairs show a monotonic decrease in $g(r)$ while class I pairs show a minimum, with negative correlations at large r. Very close to the critical point the range of correlation in each case extends to about 1,000 A. (See also [125,126].)

Zimm [81], working with a perfluoromethylcyclohexane-carbon

tetrachloride mixture, observed a strong asymmetry in scattering by mixtures less than 0.2° above the critical mixing temperature and extrapolated to zero angle in order to be able to use the analogue of Eq. 9-7 to calculate the rate of change of activity of a component with its concentration (the analogue of β^{-1}).

Earlier references to work on scattering by binary liquid systems can be found in the papers by Rousset [79] and Zimm [81].

We will conclude these remarks on the experimental results concerned with scattering of visible light with a brief mention of the phenomenon of depolarization. It will be clear that if the scattering is observed at an angle of 90° from the incident beam and in the horizontal plane, then no scattered light should be observed if the electric vector of the incident beam is horizontal. If the electric vector is vertical, the scattered light should also be vertically polarized. Actually in the latter case a small amount of depolarization takes place, and in the former a small amount of light is observed which is a mixture of horizontally and vertically polarized light. Mie [82] has shown that, on account of quadripole and magnetic dipole effects, such depolarization effects would be expected from isotropic groups of molecules if the size of the group is of the order of magnitude of the wavelength of the light used. Krishnan [83] has performed some experiments in some binary liquid systems, in particular, phenol and water, and has concluded that such large groups or clusters, having a composition different from the average composition, can exist as far as 25° or so from the critical mixing temperature. His conclusions have, however, been criticized [84,85] (but see [83,86]). In any event, it seems probable that this experiment is quite sensitive (actually the conclusions depend on the relative horizontal and vertical polarization in the weak scattering with horizontal electric vector), and there might be only exceedingly small numbers of such large clusters as far as 25° from the critical point. Depolarization near the critical point has also been discussed by Rocard [67], Rousset [79], and Oster [66, pp. 344ff.].

The scattering of X rays is a phenomenon very closely related to the scattering of visible light, and a treatment which is in principle very similar to that given above may be used in its discussion. The scattering at small angles is related to long-range correlations of densities while scattering at larger angles is related to the arrangement of atoms in the immediate neighborhood of a given atom and is often used to determine the atomic or molecular distribution in a liquid [87]. The relation between small-angle scattering and large-distance correlations, and vice versa, holds also for visible light, as is indeed evident from the qualitative discussion following Eq. 9-8.

Vineyard [88] has made an analysis of the small-angle scattering and has applied to it earlier experimental data on argon. He has found that the results can be explained by supposing that there are droplets or clusters in the system (or bubbles of vapor if the system is liquid). But these clusters in the gas or vapor cannot contain more than ten to twenty molecules, even rather close to the critical point (which it must be stated is not too closely approached in the experimental results), though the small-angle scattering is greater near the critical region. Wild [89] has measured small-angle scattering for nitrogen and has applied Vinegard's calculation to this case. He has found a tendency for the size of the regions of inhomogeneity to increase in the neighborhood of the critical point, but even so they do not grow large enough to contain more than twenty or thirty molecules. These sizes may seem small for the immediate neighborhood of the critical point, but as noted at the beginning of Art. 8 there are probably short-range variations in density, which may be what are picked up by the X rays.

E,10. Two-Component Systems. Many of the properties of the critical region of pure substances are paralleled in two-component systems. We may begin our discussion with a consideration of the solubility curve of a binary liquid system, such as is illustrated schematically in Fig. E,10a. The coordinates which are used in this case are temperature and composition, say mole fraction of component B. The solubility curve is a coexistence curve. A "tie line," such as ab in Fig. E,10a, drawn parallel to the composition axis, connects two liquid phases which have compositions indicated by the points a and b at the end of the line, and which can coexist in equilibrium with each other. Above the maximum of the coexistence curve only a single homogeneous phase can exist. The temperature of this maximum is called the consolute temperature or the critical solution temperature, and it is a true critical point.

We may at this point make note of the familiar fact that the coexistence curves of binary liquid systems show considerably more variety than those for the liquid-vapor equilibrium of one-component systems. It is possible, for example, to have lower critical points, *below* which the system is homogeneous; systems are known for which there is both an upper and a lower critical point, so that only for a certain range of temperatures can two phases exist in equilibrium.

The chemical potential μ_A, or activity a_A, of component A will have the same value at point a of Fig. E,10a as at point b. A similar statement can be made about μ_B or a_B. Using C with appropriate subscript to denote the concentration of a particular component where there is a single phase, or the average concentration where there are two phases in equilibrium with each other, we see that along the line ab we may write $(\partial\mu_A/\partial C_A)_T = (\partial a_A/\partial C_A)_T = (\partial\mu_B/\partial C_B)_T = (\partial a_B/\partial C_B)_T = 0$. Elsewhere along the isotherm, these derivatives are always positive. In comparing this case with the liquid-vapor equilibrium of a one-component system, the variable p may be replaced by a, and the variable V may be replaced by the reciprocal of the concentration; in actual practice, however, we frequently use μ instead of a and almost always use C rather than its reciprocal. Bearing these correspondences in mind, the theoretical treatments of Art. 4, 5, 6 [90], 7 [91], (see also [92]), 8, and 9 [57] can be repeated, with appropriate changes, for the binary liquid systems.

It can be shown thermodynamically [90,93] that at an upper critical temperature we must have $(\partial \overline{S}_A/\partial C_A)_{T,p} < 0$ and $(\partial \overline{S}_B/\partial C_B)_{T,p} < 0$, where $\overline{S}_A$ and $\overline{S}_B$ are the respective partial molal entropies. These differential coefficients must be positive for a lower critical temperature.[23] The evaluation of the critical solution temperature in terms of the properties of the liquids involved has been discussed by Hildebrand [94]. Some statistical mechanical calculations and various thermodynamic observations have also been made [95; 96; 45, pp. 356ff.; 97, p. 95; 98; 99; 100; 101].

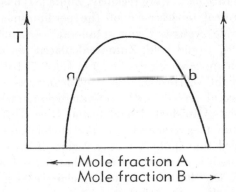

Fig. E,10a.   Solubility curve of a binary liquid system, showing a tie line, *ab*.

The questions raised in connection with Fig. E,1a, E,1b, and E,1c occur again in the case of binary liquid systems, and the matter is certainly not unequivocally settled by the available experimental evidence. Examination of the coexistence curves given in the Landolt-Börnstein tables and elsewhere gives the impression that many of them are extremely flat at the critical temperature. This has been noted by various investigators; for example, Woodburn, Smith, and Tetewsky [102] found in the course of an investigation of critical solution temperatures of organic binary mixtures that the temperature at which the liquid became homogeneous appeared to be independent of concentration over a range of concentrations. Some examples of binary liquid mixtures in which a careful study of the coexistence curve indicates the strong probability of a flat horizontal portion at the top of the coexistence curve are the

---

[23] These criteria for upper and lower critical temperatures will also hold for the two-phase two-component systems in which one phase is liquid and the other vapor (which are considered below), provided a constant pressure diagram is used.

following: phenol-water [103]; acetic anhydride-cyclohexane [104]; aniline-cyclohexane [105,106,107,108]; acetone-carbon disulfide [109]; methyl acetate-carbon disulfide [110]. In the last two cases the flat portion appears to extend over a particularly great range of concentrations. On the other hand, careful studies of acetic anhydride-carbon disulfide [104] and of perfluoromethyl cyclohexane-carbon tetrachloride [81] appear to indicate rounded coexistence curves. One difficulty in working with the binary liquid mixtures and in drawing conclusions from the results arises from the extremely great influence on the critical temperature of small amounts of impurities [107, p. 78].

Very little work has been done with a view to determining whether there is a critical region, where the mixture is homogeneous, for which the chemical potential is independent of concentration, as was anticipated by McMillan and Mayer. Most of this has seemed inconclusive, and has been reviewed by Rice [90]. More recently, Zimm [81] has reported experiments on the critical opalescence of the perfluoromethylcyclohexane-carbon tetrachloride system. Using small-angle scattering so that the analogue of Eq. 9-7 would hold, Zimm calculated $(\partial\mu/\partial C)_T$ (in analogy to $(\partial p/\partial v)_T$, which appears disguised as β in Eq. 9-7) from a quantitative measure of the light scattering. His conclusion was that this system behaved as a classical system, with no finite region in which $(\partial\mu/\partial C)_T$ for the two components vanished. Rowden and Rice [105,107] have made differential pressure measurements on the cyclohexane-aniline system, and have concluded that if there is any region of constant μ above the critical temperature it cannot extend more than 0.2 to 0.3 degrees beyond that temperature. On the other hand, Sinclair [111] has very recently repeated earlier work on the triethylamine-water system and has found that the composition of the vapor phase is independent of concentration of the liquid phase for a considerable range of liquid compositions up to 1.5°C below the (lower) critical temperature. It would thus appear that in this system there is a considerable range of constant μ in the homogeneous region. (See, however, [127].)

For any binary liquid system in which the critical phenomena are of the classical type, the criteria for a critical point are

$$\left(\frac{\partial\mu_A}{\partial C_A}\right)_T = \left(\frac{\partial\mu_B}{\partial C_B}\right)_T = 0$$

$$\left(\frac{\partial^2\mu_A}{\partial C_A^2}\right)_T = \left(\frac{\partial^2\mu_B}{\partial C_B^2}\right)_T = 0$$

(10-1)

fully analogous to Eq. 2-4. If the critical point is not of the classical type, appropriate modifications may be made, but Eq. 10-1 can still be used for approximate considerations.

The liquid-vapor equilibrium in two-component systems has also been extensively studied [see e.g. *112*, Chap. III, IV; *113*; *114*; *115*; *116*; *117*; *118*; *119*]. In principle these will not differ from the binary liquid systems; the fact that when two phases are present one of them is a vapor does not materially alter the situation. However, because the pres-

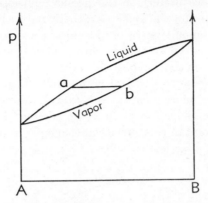

Fig. E,10b. Constant temperature diagram: liquid-vapor equilibrium in two-component system, showing a tie line, *ab*, which connects liquid and vapor compositions that are in equilibrium with each other. Abscissas in Fig. E,10b to E,10k as in Fig E,10a.

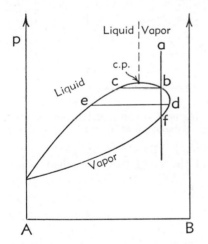

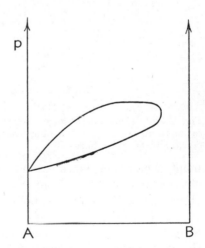

Fig. E,10c. Constant temperature diagram, showing critical point c.p. Liquid and vapor regions may be said to extend around to the dotted line, which does *not*, however, represent a phase transition.

Fig. E,10d. Constant temperature diagram, as in Fig. E,10c, but showing a range of critical concentrations.

sure is an important variable for a vapor phase (and also because a relatively large range of pressure has been commonly used), a greater variety is introduced into the observations. Fig. E,10a is essentially a constant pressure diagram; actually measurements may be made either at atmospheric pressure or at the vapor pressure of the mixture, but the range of pressures encountered is sufficiently small so as not to affect appreciably the properties of the liquid phase.

In studying the liquid-vapor equilibrium, constant pressure diagrams may be used, but we prefer for the present purposes to use constant temperature diagrams for the most part, the variables being concentration and pressure. A common type of liquid-vapor coexistence curve is shown in Fig. E,10b. This curve, of course, shows no critical point. However, if the temperature be raised beyond the critical point of one of the pure substances (in this case the critical point of B will probably be reached first, since it is the more volatile substance) the curve will appear as shown in Fig. E,10c. Since the tie lines are horizontal, Eq. 10-1 will hold for the maximum point of this curve (labeled c.p.), and it will be a critical

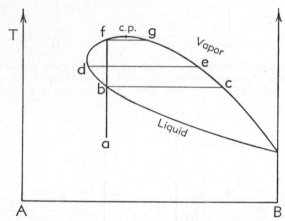

Fig. E,10e.   Constant pressure diagram, showing critical point. Retrograde condensation occurs just before reaching f on raising temperature of mixture from point a. bc, de, and fg are tie lines.

point. The vapor curve extends around the bend to the critical point. There may be a flat horizontal portion at the top of the coexistence curve (Fig. E,10d) if the critical point is not of the classical type. Apparently such a flat portion has not been observed for organic mixtures, but Schröer [8, pp. 100, 101] claims to have observed something related to this (but perhaps not quite consistent with it) for aqueous salt solutions.

An interesting phenomenon occurs if, starting with a vapor of the composition indicated by the point a (Fig. E,10c), the pressure is lowered. Upon reaching b, liquid of the composition c will condense out. This condensation caused by *lowering* the pressure is called retrograde condensation [116, pp. 823ff.]. (Retrograde condensation of another kind can occur on *raising the temperature*, as indicated in Fig. E,10e, which is for a constant pressure above the critical pressure of component A, which is assumed to have the lower critical pressure.)

⟨ 490 ⟩

Continuing decrease of the pressure in Fig. E,10c will result in tie lines like *de* and eventual disappearance of the liquid phase at *f*.

If the point *a* had been directly above the critical point, lowering of the pressure would have resulted in a separation of the phases at the critical point with a meniscus appearing near the center of the tube. The two phases have the same density at the critical point, if the critical point is of the classical type. With further lowering of the pressure, there would continue to be two phases, and eventually the liquid would all evaporate. With *a* to the left of c.p., lowering the pressure would result in only the normal type of vaporization phenomenon.

A constant temperature diagram just at the critical temperature for *B* would look like Fig. E,10f or E,10g, assuming only one liquid phase to be present. The slope of the liquid curve would presumably be zero at

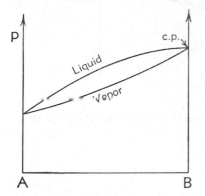

Fig. E,10f. Constant temperature diagram, at critical temperature of *B*.

Fig. E,10g. Constant temperature diagram at critical temperature of *B*, showing range of critical concentrations.

the right-hand side of the diagram, because as the temperature was lowered from the temperature of Fig. E,10c the critical point, for which the slope is always zero, would approach the right-hand side of the diagram. There might be a finite horizontal portion to the liquid curve, as shown in Fig. E,10g.

If all the critical temperatures for all intermediate mixtures lie below that for component *A*, the area enclosed by the coexistence curve will become smaller and smaller, and it will disappear at the critical temperature of *A*. If the critical temperature of *A* is less than that of some of the mixtures (a situation rarely, if ever, occurring in practice), the vapor curve will approach zero slope for 100 per cent *A* at the critical temperature of *A*, and above this temperature there will be a range of temperatures where there will be two critical points, as shown in Fig. E,10h.

If some intermediate mixture has a lower critical temperature than either of the components, the situation at this lowest critical temperature will be as indicated in Fig. E,10i, with the slope of the coexistence curve vanishing at the critical point (the slope of the vapor curve vanishing to the right and that of the liquid curve vanishing to the left in Fig. E,10i). Above this temperature the coexistence curve will separate into two parts, with each having a critical point as shown in Fig. E,10j.

It is to be noted that the assumption of continuity of slope, which has been made in the above three paragraphs, can apply to the liquid curve

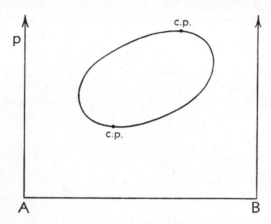

Fig. E,10h.   Constant temperature diagram showing two critical points.

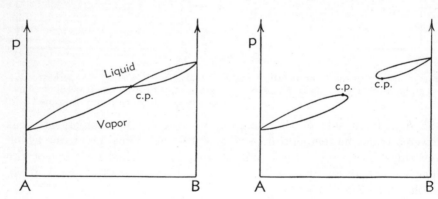

Fig. E,10i.   Constant temperature dia-   Fig. E,10j.   Constant temperature diagram at lowest critical temperature.   gram showing two critical points.

only, or to the vapor curve only, as the case may be, but not to both simultaneously. It is not inconceivable, as a matter of fact, that it might apply to neither. Then the curve to the left of *B* in Fig. E,10f would not be horizontal, and the curvature of the curve to the left of c.p. in Fig. E,10c would approach infinity as the condition corresponding to Fig. E,10f was approached. Though this must happen to the *right* of c.p. in Fig. E,10c, it seems unlikely, from what we know of critical phenomena in general, that it will also occur to the left. It must be stated, however,

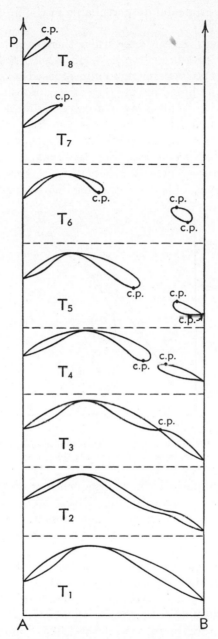

Fig. E,10k. Series of constant temperature diagrams, illustrating possible effects of increasing temperature. T increases $T_1 \rightarrow T_8$.

that the actual experimental data available in the literature throw little light on this matter.

Interesting situations can arise when there is a maximum or minimum in the vapor pressure curve [113, pp. 329ff.; 114]. Evaporation or condensation at a maximum or minimum proceeds exactly as for a pure liquid, the vapor and liquid having the same composition and no change in pressure occurring. The process involves a marked change in the volume of the system and is quite different from what happens at a critical point where a meniscus appears or disappears with an infinitesimal change in volume. Nevertheless, Eq. 10-1 hold for the homogeneous phase just above a maximum or just below a minimum. This gives rise to an interesting relation between the maximum or minimum point and

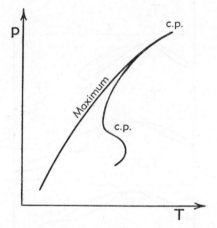

Fig. E,10l.   Maxima and critical points of Fig. E,10k
on pressure-temperature diagram.

the critical point. Suppose we have a sequence of events with increasing temperature such as is shown in Fig. E,10k. Here we have sketched a series of coexistence curves on a common pressure-composition diagram, the higher the curve on the diagram the higher the temperature. (Each curve has a separate pressure scale—plotted on the same pressure scale they would overlap badly, and the diagram would be very confusing.) If we plot the pressure of the maximum and of the critical point as a function of the temperature, we will get a diagram like Fig. E,10l. The remarkable feature of this diagram is that where any two lines come together they are tangent to one another. This follows because all the lines are determined by the conditions set by Eq. 10-1, and may be seen as follows. We have along any one of these lines

$$d \left(\frac{\partial \mu_A}{\partial C_A} \right)_{T,p} = \frac{\partial^2 \mu_A}{\partial p \partial C_A} \, dp + \frac{\partial^2 \mu_A}{\partial T \partial C_A} \, dT = 0$$

since $(\partial^2\mu_A/\partial C_A^2)_{p,T} = 0$. Since $(\partial\mu_A/\partial p)_{T,C_A} = \overline{V}_A$, the partial molal volume, and $(\partial\mu_A/\partial T)_{p,C_A} = -\overline{S}_A$, the partial molal entropy, we see that the equation of the lines in Fig. E,10l is

$$\frac{dp}{dT} = \frac{(\partial\overline{S}_A/\partial C_A)_{p,T}}{(\partial\overline{V}_A/\partial C_A)_{p,T}} \tag{10-2}$$

which is quite analogous to the Clapeyron equation. (A similar equation holds with subscript B substituted for subscript A.) Since the quantities on the right-hand side will be functions of p, T, and C_A only, it is clear that dp/dT must be the same for any of the lines in Fig. E,10l at a point where they coincide, inasmuch as they will not coincide in this diagram (except by a rare coincidence) unless C_A as well as p and T are the same for the two lines.

It will be noted that the temperatures at which two critical points coincide (i.e. T_3 and between T_6 and T_7) on Fig. E,10k correspond to points on the critical curve in Fig. E,10l where dp/dT is infinite. By Eq. 10-2, then, we must have $(\partial\overline{V}_A/\partial C_A)_{p,T} = 0$ and $(\partial\overline{V}_B/\partial C_B)_{p,T} = 0$. In a manner very similar to that by which the criteria for upper and lower critical points were obtained for constant pressure diagrams on binary liquid systems [90] it may be shown that $(\partial\overline{V}_A/\partial C_A)_{p,T}$ and $(\partial\overline{V}_A/\partial C_B)_{p,T}$ must be positive for an upper critical point (critical point at a maximum pressure) in a diagram like Fig. E,10k and negative for a lower critical point. If an upper and lower critical point coincide, therefore, as they do at T_3 and between T_6 and T_7 of Fig. E,10k, these differential coefficients become zero. If dp/dT should become zero on a diagram like Fig. E,10l, as it sometimes does experimentally, then $(\partial\overline{S}_A/\partial C_A)_{p,T}$ and $(\partial\overline{S}_B/\partial C_B)_{p,T}$ must be zero, and the fusion of the two critical points will be observable on a set of constant pressure diagrams instead of on a set of constant temperature diagrams such as shown in Fig. E,10k.

Pressure-temperature diagrams of the type shown in Fig. E,10l are very commonly used to present the results of extended studies of liquid-vapor equilibrium in two-component systems. Such a diagram can be thought of as a projection on the T,p plane of a three-dimensional diagram, the concentration, say C_B, being plotted on the third axis perpendicular to and above the paper. A simple diagram of this type is shown in Fig. E,10m. Here, AA' is the vapor pressure curve for A, and BB' is the vapor pressure curve for B, while $A'C'D'B'$ is the critical curve. Constant temperature curves may be thought of as sections of the three-dimensional diagram on a plane parallel to the p and C_B axes. The coexistence curves such as are seen in Fig. E,10b, E,10c, and E,10h will extend from AA' up to BB' (which is in a plane above the paper), from AA' to $A'C'D'B'$, and from one part of $A'C'D'B'$ to another part, respectively. The family of coexistence curves, such as Fig. E,10b, Fig. E,10c, and Fig. E,10h will generate a surface, of which the lower part is the boundary of the liquid phase, and of which the upper part is the boundary of the vapor phase. These two sheets run smoothly into each other at the critical curve. A plane of constant composition cuts these sheets in curves like $CC'C''$ and $DD'D''$, which are tangent to the critical curve at the critical points C' and D'. The curves CC' and DD' are bubble-point curves of the liquid, and the curves $C''C'$ and $D''D'$ are dew-point curves for the vapor for the particular composition considered. AA' is simultaneously the dew-point and bubble-point curve for A, while BB' is simultaneously the dew-point and bubble-point curve for B.

From diagrams of this type, it is possible to plot pressure-volume isotherms if measurements of the density are available. Isotherms of this

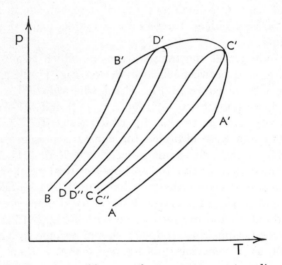

Fig. E,10m.   A possible type of pressure-temperature diagram.

type have been discussed in some detail by Caubet [*113*, pp. 296–303, 346–348] and have been mentioned by Boyd [*117*]. Since they are of less importance for the understanding of the phenomena than the diagrams we have considered, we do not take them up here. But it should be emphasized that Eq. 2-4 do not hold for the critical points of binary mixtures, though some attempts have been made to use them.

Numerous binary systems have been studied. Systems of the type shown in Fig. E,10m are common, except that the critical curve is practically always contained between temperatures corresponding to A' and B' instead of extending beyond as shown in Fig. E,10m. Fig. E,10l is also a common type, except that the critical curve does not, in general, bend back to the left at the lower pressure end. In other words, referring to Fig. E,10k, the small "island" to the right generally disappears just at the critical temperature of pure B. Our illustrations have been chosen to show theoretical possibilities rather than actual experimental observations. References to the original experimental results may be found in the Landolt-Börnstein Tables, the International Critical Tables, and in a review article by Katz and Kurata [116]. Aqueous salt solutions have been studied by Schröer [8] and by Secoy [120].

In closing we may note that there has been little application to binary systems of the idea that a critical point is a point where the surface tension vanishes. Rice [90,48] and Atack and Rice [108] have applied the idea to a study of the effect of a small amount of a third component on binary liquid systems, using the Gibbs adsorption equation to study the effect of the third component on the interfacial tension, and have shown that this approach is capable of throwing light on the observed phenomena.

E,11.   Cited References and Bibliography

Cited References

1. Rice, O. K.   *J. Chem. Phys. 15*, 314; errata, 615 (1947).
2. Mayer, J. E., and Harrison, S. F.   *J. Chem. Phys. 6*, 87 (1938).
3. Harrison, S. F., and Mayer, J. E.   *J. Chem. Phys. 6*, 101 (1938).
4. Kobe, K. A., and Lynn, R. E, Jr.   *Chem. Revs. 52*, 117 (1953).
5. Guggenheim, E. A.   *J. Chem. Phys. 13*, 253 (1945).
6. Mason, S. G., Naldrett, S. N., and Maass, O.   *Can. J. Research B18*, 103 (1940).
7. Young, F. B.   *Phil. Mag. 20*, 793 (1910).
8. Schröer, E.   *Z. physik. Chem. 129*, 79 (1927).
9. Naldrett, S. N., and Maass, O.   *Can. J. Research B18*, 118 (1940).
10. Atack, D., and Schneider, W. G.   *J. Phys. & Colloid Chem. 55*, 532 (1951).
11. Gouy, A.   *Compt. rend. 115*, 720 (1892); *116*, 1289 (1893).
12. Weinberger, M. A., and Schneider, W. G.   *Can. J. Chem. 30*, 422 (1952).
13. Weinberger, M. A., and Schneider, W. G.   *Can. J. Chem. 30*, 847 (1952).
14. Dacey, J., McIntosh, R., and Maass, O.   *Can. J. Research B17*, 206 (1939).
15. McIntosh, R., Dacey, J., and Maass, O.   *Can. J. Research B17*, 241 (1939).
16. Michels, A., Blaisse, B., and Michels, C.   *Proc. Roy. Soc. London A160*, 358 (1937).
17. Mayer, J. E., and Streeter, S. F.   *J. Chem. Phys. 7*, 1019 (1939).
18. Wentorf, R. H., Jr., and Boyd, C. A.   *Univ. Wisconsin, Nav. Research Lab. Rept. CM-724*, 1952.
19. Beattie, J. A., Edwards, D. G., and Marple, S., Jr., *J. Chem. Phys. 17*, 576 (1949).
20. MacCormack, K. E., and Schneider, W. G.   *Can. J. Chem. 29*, 699 (1951).
21. Palmer, H. B.   *Univ. Wisconsin, Nav. Research Lab. Rept. CM-740*, 1952; *J. Chem. Phys. 22*, 625 (1954).
22. Hein, P.   *Z. physik. Chem. 86*, 385 (1914).
23. Tapp, J. S., Steacie, E. W. R., and Maass, O.   *Can. J. Research 9*, 217 (1933).
24. Maass, O., and Geddes, A. L.   *Trans. Roy. Soc. London A236*, 303 (1937).
25. McIntosh, R. L., and Maass, O.   *Can. J. Research B16*, 289 (1938).
26. Maass, O.   *Chem. Revs. 23*, 17 (1938).
27. Clark, A. L.   *Chem. Revs. 23*, 1 (1938).
28. McIntosh, R. L., Dacey, J. R., and Maass, O.   *Can. J. Research B17*, 231 (1939).
29. Beattie, J. A., and Bridgeman, O. C.   *Proc. Am. Acad. Arts Sci. 63*, 229 (1929); *J. Am. Chem. Soc. 50*, 3133, 3151 (1928).
30. Rocard, Y.   *Changements de Phases*. Société de Chimie Physique, Paris, 1952.
31. Rowlinson, J. S.   *J. Chem. Phys. 19*, 831 (1951).
32. Fowler, R. H.   *Statistical Mechanics*, 2nd ed. Macmillan, 1936.

33. Lennard-Jones, J. E., and Devonshire, A. F.   *Proc. Roy. Soc. London A163*, 53 (1937).
34. Ono, S.   *Mem. Fac. Eng. Kyushu Imp. Univ. 10*, 195 (1947).
35. Eisenstein, A., and Gingrich, N. S.   *Phys. Rev. 62*, 261 (1942).
36. Sato, T., and Ono, S.   *J. Phys. Soc. Japan 4*, 103 (1948).
37. Rice, O. K.   *J. Chem. Phys. 12*, 289 (1944).
38. Baly, E. C. C., and Donnan, F. G.   *J. Chem. Soc. 81*, 907 (1902).
39. Janssens, P., and Prigogine, I.   *Physica 16*, 895 (1950).
40. Peek, H. M., and Hill, T. L.   *J. Chem. Phys. 18*, 1252 (1950).
41. Kirkwood, J. G., Lewinson, V. A., and Alder, B. J.   *J. Chem. Phys. 20*, 929 (1952).
42. Pall, D. B., Broughton, J. W., and Maass, O.   *Can. J. Research B16*, 230 (1938).
43. Pall, D. B., and Maass, O.   *Can. J. Research B16*, 449 (1938).
44. Michels, A., and Strijland, J.   *Changements de Phases*. Société de Chimie Physique, Paris, 1952; *Physica 18*, 613 (1952).
45. Fowler, R. H., and Guggenheim, E. A.   *Statistical Thermodynamics*. Macmillan, 1939.
46. Winkler, C. A., and Maass, O.   *Can. J. Research 9*, 65 (1933).
47. Frenkel, J.   *J. Chem. Phys. 7*, 200, 538 (1939).
48. Rice, O. K.   *J. Phys. Chem. 54*, 1293 (1950).
49. Rushbrooke, G. S.   *Statistical Mechanics*. Oxford Univ. Press, 1949.
50. Mayer, J. E., and Mayer, M. G.   *Statistical Mechanics*. Wiley, 1940.
51. Zimm, B. H.   *J. Chem. Phys. 19*, 1019 (1951).
52. Mayer, J. E.   *J. Chem. Phys. 10*, 629 (1942).
53. Mayer, J. E.   *J. Chem. Phys. 19*, 1024 (1951).
54. Katsura, S., and Fujita, H.   *J. Chem. Phys. 19*, 795 (1951); *Progr. Theoret. Phys. Japan 6*, 498 (1951).
55. Yang, C. N., and Lee, T. D.   *Phys. Rev. 87*, 404 (1952).
56. Smoluchowski, M.   *Ann. Physik 25*, 205 (1908); *Phil. Mag. 23*, 165 (1912).
57. Einstein, A.   *Ann. Physik 33*, 1275 (1910).
58. Tolman, R. C.   *The Principles of Statistical Mechanics*. Oxford Univ. Press, 1938.
59. Ornstein, L. S., and Zernike, F.   *Proc. Roy. Acad. Sci. Amsterdam 17*, 793 (1914).
60. Ornstein, L. S., and Zernike, F.   *Physik. Z. 27*, 761 (1926).
61. Rosenfeld, L.   *Theory of Electrons*. Interscience, 1951.
62. Klein, M. J., and Tisza, L.   *Phys. Rev. 76*, 1861 (1949).
63. Zernike, F.   *Proc. Roy. Acad. Sci. Amsterdam 18*, 1520 (1916).
64. Ornstein, L. S., and Zernike, F.   *Physik. Z. 19*, 134 (1918).
65. Rocard, Y.   *J. phys. radium 4*, 165 (1933).
66. Oster, G.   *Chem. Revs. 43*, 319 (1948).
67. Rocard, Y.   Chap. XIV and Chap. XV in Cabannès, J. *La diffusion moléculaire de la lumière*. Les Presses Universitaires de France, Paris, 1929.
68. Placzek, G.   *Physik. Z. 31*, 1052 (1930).
69. Bhattacharyya, D. K.   *Proc. Indian Assoc. Cultivation Sci. 8*, 277 (1923).
70. Phillips, P.   *Proc. Roy. Soc. London A97*, 225 (1920).
71. Andant, A.   *Ann. physique 1*, 346 (1924).
72. Ramsay, W., and Young, S.   *Phil. Trans. Roy. Soc. London A178*, 57 (1887).
73. Cataldi, H., and Drickamer, H. G.   *J. Chem. Phys. 18*, 650 (1950).
74. Babb, A. L., and Drickamer, H. G.   *J. Chem. Phys. 18*, 655 (1950).
75. Blosser, L. G., and Drickamer, H. G.   *J. Chem. Phys. 19*, 1244 (1951).
76. Mason, S. G., and Maass, O.   *Can. J. Research B26*, 592 (1948).
77. Murray, F. E., and Mason, S. G.   *Can. J. Chem. 30*, 550 (1952).
78. White, D., Friedman, A. S., and Johnston, H. L.   *J. Am. Chem. Soc. 72*, 3565 (1950).
79. Rousset, A.   *Ann. physique 5*, 63 (1936).
80. Furth, R.   *Changements de Phases*. Société de Chimie Physique, Paris, 1952.
81. Zimm, B. H.   *J. Phys. Chem. 54*, 1306 (1950).
 2. Mie, G.   *Ann. Physik 25*, 377 (1908).

83. Krishnan, R. S.   *Proc. Indian Acad. Sci. A2*, 221 (1935).
84. Mookerjee, B. K.   *Indian J. Phys. 12*, 15 (1938).
85. Parthasarathy, S.   *Phil. Mag. 29*, 148 (1940).
86. Krishnan, R. S.   *Phil. Mag. 29*, 515 (1940).
87. Gingrich, N. S.   *Revs. Mod. Phys. 15*, 90 (1943).
88. Vineyard, G. H.   *Phys. Rev. 74*, 1076 (1948).
89. Wild, R. L.   *J. Chem. Phys. 18*, 1627 (1950).
90. Rice, O. K.   *Chem. Revs. 44*, 69 (1949).
91. McMillan, W. G., Jr., and Mayer, J. E.   *J. Chem. Phys. 13*, 276 (1945).
92. Frenkel, J.   *Acta Physicochim. U.R.S.S. 8*, 261 (1938).
93. Prigogine, I., and Defay, R.   *Thermodynamique Chimique.* Desoer, Liège, 1950.
94. Hildebrand, J. H., and Scott, R. L.   *The Solubility of Non-Electrolytes*, 3rd ed. Reinhold, 1950.
95. Kirkwood, J. G.   *J. Phys. Chem. 43*, 97 (1939).
96. Parlin, R. B., and Eyring, H.   *Chem. Revs. 44*, 47 (1949).
97. Prigogine, I.   *Changements de Phases.* Société de Chimie Physique, Paris, 1952.
98. Barker, J. A., and Fock, W.   *Discussions Faraday Soc. 15*, 188 (1953).
99. Timmermans, J., and Lewin, J.   *Discussions Faraday Soc. 15*, 195 (1953).
100. Andon, R. J. L., Cox, J. D., and Herington, E. F. G.   *Discussions Faraday Soc. 15*, 168 (1953).
101. Copp, J. L., and Everett, D. H.   *Discussions Faraday Soc. 15*, 174 (1953).
102. Woodburn, H. M., Smith, K., and Tetewsky, H.   *Ind. Eng. Chem. 36*, 588 (1944).
103. Hill, A. E., and Malisoff, W. M.   *J. Am. Chem. Soc. 48*, 918 (1926).
104. Jones, D. C., and Betts, H. F.   *J. Chem. Soc. London*, 1177 (1928).
105. Rowden, R. W., and Rice, O. K.   *J. Chem. Phys. 19*, 1423 (1951).
106. Zimm, B. H.   *J. Chem. Phys. 20*, 538 (1952).
107. Rowden, R. W., and Rice, O. K.   *Changements de Phases.* Société de Chimie Physique, Paris, 1952.
108. Atack, D., and Rice, O. K.   *Discussions Faraday Soc. 15*, 210 (1953); *J. Chem. Phys. 22*, 382 (1954).
109. Clusius, K., and Ringer, W.   *Z. physik. Chem. A187*, 186 (1940).
110. Clusius, K., and Ulmke, H.   *Z. physik. Chem. A189*, 331 (1941).
111. Sinclair, R.   *Thesis*, Univ. Chicago, 1952.
112. Duhem, P.   *Traité Élémentaire de Mécanique Chimique*, Vol. IV. Librairie Scientifique, A. Hermann, Paris, 1899.
113. Caubet, F.   *Z. physik. Chem. 40*, 257 (1902).
114. Caubet, F.   *Z. physik. Chem. 49*, 101 (1904).
115. Kuenen, J. P.   *Z. physik. Chem. 24*, 667 (1897).
116. Katz, D. L., and Kurata, F.   *Ind. Eng. Chem. 32*, 817 (1940).
117. Boyd, C. A.   *J. Phys. & Colloid Chem. 54*, 1347 (1950).
118. Cook, D., and Longuet-Higgins, H. C.   *Proc. Roy. Soc. London A209*, 28 (1951).
119. Haselden, G. G., Newitt, D. M., and Shah, S. M.   *Proc. Roy. Soc. London A209*, 1 (1951).
120. Secoy, C. H.   *J. Phys. & Colloid Chem. 54*, 1337 (1950).
121. Whiteway, S. G., and Mason, S. G.   *Can. J. Chem. 31*, 569 (1953).
122. Habgood, H. W., and Schneider, W. G.   *Can. J. Chem. 32*, 98, 164 (1954).
123. Lorentzen, H. L.   *Acta Chem. Scand. 7*, 1335 (1953).
124. Zwanzig, R. W., Kirkwood, J. G., Stripp, K. F., and Oppenheim, I.   *J. Chem. Phys. 21*, 1268 (1953).
125. Quantie, C.   *Proc. Roy. Soc. London A224*, 90 (1954).
126. Fürth, R., and Williams, C. L.   *Proc. Roy. Soc. London A224*, 104 (1954).
127. Kohler, F.   *Monatsh. Chem. 82*, 913 (1951).

Bibliography

Atack, D., and Schneider, W. G.   Solubility measurements in the critical temperature region. *J. Phys. & Colloid Chem. 54*, 1323 (1950).

Chynoweth, A. G., and Schneider, W. G.   Ultrasonic propagation in binary liquid systems near their critical solution temperatures. *J. Chem. Phys. 19*, 1566 (1951).

Curtiss, C. F., Boyd, C. A., and Palmer, H. B.   Thermodynamics [and acoustics] of the critical point. *J. Chem. Phys. 19*, 801 (1951).

Gamburg, D. Yu.   Volume behavior of dilute gaseous solutions near the critical point of the pure solvent. *Doklady Akad. Nauk S.S.S.R. 79*, 459 (1951).

Goldstein, L.   On the theory of coherent scattering processes in liquids. *Phys. Rev. 84*, 466 (1951).

Holder, C. H., and Maass, O.   The hydrogen chloride-propylene reaction in the region of the critical temperature. *Can. J. Research B16*, 453 (1938).

Holder, C. H., and Maass, O. Solubility measurements in the region of the critical temperature. *Can. J. Research B18*, 293 (1940).

Mason, S. G., and Maass, O.   Measurement of viscosity in the critical region. Ethylene. *Can. J. Research B18*, 128 (1940).

Mondain-Monval, P., and Quiquerez, J.   Binary and ternary systems. III. Rise in viscosity and opalescence in the critical region. *Bull. Soc. Chim. 12*, 380 (1945).

Naldrett, S. N., and Maass, O.   The viscosity of carbon dioxide in the critical region. *Can. J. Research B18*, 322 (1940).

Nozdrev, V. F.   Velocity of supersonic waves in organic liquids in the critical region. *Doklady Akad. Nauk S.S.S.R. 63*, 251 (1948).

Olds, R. H., Reamer, H. H., Sage, B. H., and Lacey, W. N.   Phase equilibrium in hydrocarbon systems. *Ind. Eng. Chem. 41*, 475 (1949).

Price, P. J.   Second-order transitions and critical points. *J. Chem. Phys. 19*, 1281 (1951).

Schneider, W. G.   Sound velocity and sound absorption in the critical temperature region. *Can. J. Chem. 29*, 243 (1951).

Semenshenko, V. K.   Chemocritical phenomena. *Doklady Akad. Nauk S.S.S.R. 74*, 335 (1950).

Semenchenko, V. K.   Second-order phase transitions and critical phenomena. *J. Phys. Chem. U.S.S.R. 21*, 1461 (1947); *25*, 121 (1951).

Semenchenko, V. K., and Skripov, V. P.   Specific heat of liquid binary mixtures in the critical region. *J. Phys. Chem. U.S.S.R. 25*, 362 (1951).

Tisza, L.   On the general theory of phase transitions. Chap. 1 of *Phase Transformations in Solids*. Edited by Smoluchowski, R., Mayer, J. E., and Weyl, W. A. Wiley, 1951.

Tisza, L.   The theory of critical points. *J. Phys. & Colloid Chem. 54*, 1317 (1950).

Zimm, B. H.   Molecular theory of the scattering of light in fluids. *J. Chem. Phys. 13*, 141 (1945).

SECTION F

PROPERTIES OF LIQUIDS AND LIQUID SOLUTIONS

JOHN M. RICHARDSON

STUART R. BRINKLEY, JR.

F,1. Introduction. Before undertaking a discussion of the liquid state, it is desirable to attempt a definition of this state of matter. It is traditional to consider three states of matter: gas, liquid, and solid. From a molecular point of view, one can characterize a gas by the fact that the molecules only occasionally interact and that the energy of such a system involves only negligible contributions from the interaction energy. It is the most disordered state of matter. In a liquid the molecules are in constant interaction with one another, a given molecule being in more or less intimate association with a rather vaguely defined shell of nearest neighbors. However, the thermal motion is sufficiently violent to prohibit the intermolecular attractions from binding the molecules into a rigid, ordered system. The degree of order in a liquid is rather hard to describe in clear cut qualitative terms. However, it can be said that a liquid is sufficiently ordered to manifest rather small fluctuations in the number of molecules neighboring a given molecule, but otherwise the system is quite disordered, there being no discernible pattern in the arrangement. In a solid the thermal motion is sufficiently weak for the system to closely approach configurations of minimum potential energy. As far as we know, these configurations always correspond to a periodic structure. Thus a solid occurs in a crystalline form with a high degree of order extending over long distances. As an exception to this statement one immediately seizes upon the case of noncrystalline solids such as glass. It seems to be generally true that such substances are not in true thermodynamic equilibrium. They have become frozen in a metastable range of configurations from which the configurations of minimum potential energy are not readily accessible. These substances must be regarded as supercooled liquids.

From the standpoint of a theoretician working in statistical mechanics, a liquid could be most fruitfully defined as a nonperiodic state of matter whose density is too large to allow a rapid convergence of the virial expansion, i.e., too large to allow an imperfect gas description.

It is not possible to delimit the range of the liquid state by means of phase transitions. It is always possible to differentiate liquids from solids this way since it is not possible to go from the liquid to the solid state without suffering a phase transition. However, it is possible to go continuously from the liquid to the gaseous state by increasing the pressure and temperature above the critical point.

It is interesting to attempt a mechanical definition of the liquid state. First of all, a liquid is a fluid—a generic term for all substances which flow under arbitrarily small shear stress. But gases are also fluids. However, the situation can be saved by the additional requirement that a liquid must be able to withstand negative pressures. Facetiously, one might say that a liquid is a substance which can splash.

In the discussion of the liquid state, the authors have quite drastically limited the scope. First of all, it was felt desirable to avoid topics discussed elsewhere in the volumes. Many topics have been neglected arbitrarily. To name a few: electrolytes, associated liquids, dielectric phenomena, quantum effects, and high polymer solutions. The considerations have been limited very largely to equilibrium considerations which can be treated using as a model a classical system composed of spherical molecules interacting with central forces.

We have emphasized almost completely the theoretical approach to the subject. Space limitations have precluded exhaustive empirical correlations of liquid properties. Furthermore, these have been adequately presented in several excellent treatises. In the discussion of theories of the equilibrium properties, the authors have considered only the more recent and important developments and in so doing have tried to bring into prominence the methodological aspects.

F,2. Statistical Mechanical Description of Liquids.

Notation. In the discussion of the statistical mechanics theories of the liquid state we will use notation rather frequently used in the field. However, we will find it convenient to use two distinct types of notation: one for general developments on a relatively abstract level, and the other for more explicit expressions which can be immediately used for computational purposes. In order to avoid confusion later, it seems desirable at this point to describe the notation in considerable detail.

We first describe the more explicit notation. Position is to be described by a vector $\mathbf{r} = (x, y, z)$ referred to an arbitrary origin. A differential volume element enclosing $\mathbf{r}$ will be denoted by $d\mathbf{r}$. (The symbol $d\mathbf{r}$ is not to be confused with $d\mathbf{r}$ which denotes a differential vector.) Suitable subscripts and superscripts will be used to designate positions of particular entities or dummy variables of integration. For instance, $\mathbf{r}_1$ may be used to denote the position of the molecule labeled by 1. The symbol $\mathbf{r}_{12}$ denotes $\mathbf{r}_2 - \mathbf{r}_1$, the vector distance from 1 to 2. The symbol r denotes the absolute value of $\mathbf{r}$ and correspondingly r_{12} denotes the scalar distance between 1 and 2. Sometimes $\mathbf{R}$ is used to denote an arbitrary reference position. The symbol ∇ denotes the gradient, a vector operator equal to

$$\left(\frac{\partial}{\partial x}, \frac{\partial}{\partial y}, \frac{\partial}{\partial z}\right)$$

For general developments, a more abstract and abbreviated notation is convenient. If a function g depends on the positions of molecules s and s', we will denote this by writing $g(s, s')$ even though it may depend only upon the scalar distance between s and s'. In this case the function would be written $g(r_{ss'})$ in the more explicit notation, or simply $g(r)$ if the molecule labels are irrelevant. If molecule 1 is not equivalent to molecules 2 and 3, then $g(1, 2)$ is a function differing from $g(2, 3)$, that is, the functional dependences upon their arguments may be different. Similar considerations apply to functions of one or of three or more molecular positions.

We use the symbol $d(s)$ to denote a differential volume element in the configuration space of molecule s. Thus the expression $\int d\mathbf{r}_{s'} g(\mathbf{r}_s, \mathbf{r}_{s'})$ in the explicit notation becomes $\int d(s') g(s, s')$ in the abbreviated notation. The symbol $d\{N\}$ denotes a volume element in the configuration space of N molecules, labeled $1, \ldots, N$, and is equal to $d(1) \ldots d(N)$. If one desires, the molecule label can be interpreted to represent more than the translational coordinates.

Model. Our discussion of statistical mechanics theories of the liquid state is limited to the classical treatment of systems composed of spherical molecules interacting with central forces. This means that the theoretical results can be applied in an approximate way to real systems satisfying the following requirements. The internal motion (rotation, vibration, etc.) may be separated in such a way that one may define a potential energy involving only the positions of the molecular centers. In this way the internal motions will enter only in a separate factor of the partition function and can thereby be eliminated from explicit consideration. The assumption of central forces means that there can be no saturation effects in the molecular interactions. That is, the interaction energy between a given pair of molecules is negligibly affected by the presence of a third molecule. This does not imply, however, that the given pair is unaffected by the third. It simply means that a superposition of pair interactions is a good approximation to the total interaction energy of the three molecules. This requirement essentially limits our considerations to "nonassociated" liquids in which there is no tendency toward the formation of well-defined compounds. Thus our model of a liquid can be defined by writing the total potential energy in the form

$$U_N = \sum_{\substack{s,s'=1 \\ s>s'}}^{N} \phi(s, s') \tag{2-1}$$

If all of the molecules are identical, the ϕ functions will all be of the same form. Most of our considerations will be limited to one-component systems.

We wish to limit our considerations, still further, to uncharged molecules possessing negligible dipole moments. Thus we are to be concerned only with nonpolar nonelectrolytes. These requirements mean that as the intermolecular distance increases to large values, the interaction potential must decrease faster than the inverse cube of the distance.

In the present state of development of the theory of liquids it is customary to use empirical interaction potentials. These may be calibrated by consideration of the second and higher order virial coefficients pertaining to an imperfect gas, transport properties of gases, etc. A frequently used form is the Lennard-Jones potential

$$\phi(r) = -ar^{-6} + br^{-m} \tag{2-2}$$

where a and b are adjustable constants and where the exponent m is conventionally assigned values ranging from about 8 to 12, depending on the types of molecules interacting. The first term represents a van der Waals attraction and the second term, a rather fictitious type of repulsion chosen for mathematical convenience. Another commonly used potential is

$$\phi(r) = -ar^{-6} + ce^{-r/r_0} \tag{2-3}$$

in which a, c, and r_0 are adjustable constants. The repulsive term here conforms somewhat more closely to the results of quantum theory than does the repulsive term of the Lennard-Jones potential.

A few remarks are in order concerning the use of classical theory. Classical theory neglects the effects due to the wave nature of particles (in this case, the wave nature of the molecule as a whole) and those due to the symmetry restrictions associated with Bose-Einstein or Fermi-Dirac statistics. The only liquid in which symmetry restrictions play a really decisive role is liquid helium below 2.2°K. In other liquids the neglect of the wave nature is sometimes quantitatively important but does not seem to have very drastic qualitative consequences.

The quantum treatment of liquids can be phrased in such a way that it mathematically resembles the classical theory. We can define an effective classical potential U_{eff} by the relation [1,2]

$$e^{-\beta U_{\text{eff}}} = V^N (Z_N^0)^{-1} \sum_{\nu} |\Psi_\nu|^2 e^{-\beta E_\nu} \tag{2-4}$$

where $\beta = 1/kT$ and where Ψ_ν and E_ν are the wave function and energy of the νth stationary state of a system of N molecules in the volume V. Z_N is the quantum mechanics partition function defined by

$$Z_N = \sum_\nu e^{-\beta E_\nu}$$

Now the validity of the classical viewpoint reduces to the question of how strongly temperature-dependent U_{eff} is. The validity of the exclusive use of pair interactions depends upon the possibility of devising some suitable method for approximately representing U_{eff} as a sum of such interactions.

  Distribution functions and thermodynamic quantities. Theoretical studies of the equilibrium state involve the calculation of thermodynamic properties and of certain extrathermodynamic properties such as the local order in the vicinity of a given molecule. All of the thermodynamic properties can be calculated if we know, for instance, the Helmholtz free energy $A_N(\beta)$ for the system of N molecules. For a condensed system the excess Helmholtz free energy $\bar{A}_N(\beta)$, that is, the amount beyond the perfect gas value, is given by

$$\bar{A}_N(\beta) = \beta^{-1} \ln \left[V^{-N} Z_N(\beta) \right] \tag{2-5}$$

where $Z_N(\beta)$ is the Gibbs phase integral defined by [3]

$$Z_N(\beta) = \int \cdots \int d(1) \cdots d(N) e^{-\beta U_N} \tag{2-6}$$

in which the integrations extend over all positions of the molecules within a container of volume V.

  Sometimes it is more convenient to work with the grand canonical ensemble. In this case we have for a one-component system

$$e^{\beta p V} = \sum_N \frac{e^{\beta \mu^* N} Z_N(\beta)}{N!} = \sum_N \frac{1}{N!} \int d\{N\} e^{\beta(\mu^* N - U_N)} \tag{2-7}$$

where p is the pressure and μ^* is the chemical potential defined in terms of the absolute chemical potential by the relation

$$\mu^* = \mu + \beta^{-1} \ln \left(\frac{2\pi m}{\beta h^2} \right)^{\frac{3}{2}} \tag{2-8}$$

in which m is the molecular mass and h is Planck's constant. For more detailed discussion of statistical mechanics formulas, a standard treatise on statistical mechanics may be consulted, e.g. that of Mayer and Mayer [3].

  In liquids it is of interest to consider the singlet, pair, and triplet (first, second, and third order) distribution functions (d.f.) in configuration space. The singlet d.f. $\rho(s)$ is defined by the statement that $\rho^{(1)}(s)d(s)$

is the probability that molecule s be found in the volume element $d(s)$. This d.f. is of not great interest since in a uniform liquid

$$\rho^{(1)}(s) = V^{-1} \tag{2-9}$$

The pair d.f. is in similar fashion defined by the statement that $\rho^{(2)}(s, s')d(s)d(s')$ is the joint probability that molecule s be found in $d(s)$ and s' be found in $d(s')$. Similarly, $\rho^{(3)}(s, s', s'')d(s)d(s')d(s'')$ is the joint probability that molecule s be found in $d(s)$, s' in $d(s')$, and s'' in $d(s'')$.

The radial d.f. is defined by

$$\rho^{(1)}(s)\rho^{(1)}(s')g(s, s') = V^{-2}g(s, s') = \rho^{(2)}(s, s') \tag{2-10}$$

In a system in equilibrium it is given by

$$V^{-2}g(s, s') = \left[\frac{1}{Z_N(\beta)}\right] \int \cdots \int d(1) \cdots d(s - 1)d(s + 1)$$
$$\cdots d(s' - 1)d(s' + 1) \cdots d(N)e^{-\beta U_N} \tag{2-11}$$

The radial d.f. is of direct experimental interest since it is possible to determine it by means of X-ray scattering [4,5].

In a liquid, $g(1, 2)$ would depend only upon the scalar distance r between molecules 1 and 2 so that we could write $g(1, 2) = g(r)$. The function $g(r)$ has the microscopic significance that it gives the ratio of the number density at a given point averaged with a given molecule fixed at a distance r away to the number density averaged without this constraint. Thus $g(r)$ measures the local order in the vicinity of a given molecule. For complete randomness or disorder, g would have the value unity everywhere. For a highly ordered structure such as a crystal, g would possess a series of sharp maxima corresponding to the shell of nearest neighbors, next nearest neighbors, etc., and would rapidly approach zero for distances less than a molecular diameter. In the case of a typical liquid, the above characteristics are repeated except in a blurred fashion such that perhaps two maxima would be clearly discernible, and for distances over several molecular diameters the deviation from unity would be negligible. The average number of other molecules contained within the distance of the first minimum beyond the first maximum may be interpreted as the coordination number.

The radial d.f. is related to the pressure p and internal energy E by the formulas

$$pC = \frac{1}{\beta} - \frac{2\pi}{3} C \int_0^\infty r^2 dr g(r) r \phi'(r) \tag{2-12}$$

and

$$\frac{E}{N} = \frac{3}{2\beta} - 2\pi C \int_0^\infty r^2 dr g(r) \phi(r), \tag{2-13}$$

where $C = N/V$ is the number density. However, it is not possible to calculate exactly certain other thermodynamic functions, the entropy for instance, knowing $g(r)$ for only one state of the system. One must know g for a sequence of states connecting the state of interest with a reference state. However, it is shown later in Art. 4 that it is possible to calculate approximately the Helmholtz free energy (and hence the entropy) knowing $g(r)$ only for the state in question.

F,3. Cell Theories of Liquids. The cell theories of liquid structure were originally based upon a physical model emphasizing the quasi-crystal properties of a liquid. The models are based upon the fact that, especially near the melting point, a molecule in a liquid does not have very much freedom of motion. It can be assumed, at least for short periods of time, that any given molecule is restricted by the neighboring molecules to motion in a cell composed of the molecules of the first coordination shell. Eyring and Hirschfelder [6] and Lennard-Jones and Devonshire [7] have employed the cell model in the formulation of theories of the liquid state that are quite successful in interpreting the properties of simple nonpolar liquids. Kirkwood [8] has recently shown how the cell model is related, by means of well-defined approximations, to the classical statistical mechanics of the canonical ensemble. This paper utilizes a procedure that may be called the statistical mechanical cell method. In the latter part of this article, we employ an analogous procedure in the grand canonical ensemble to develop a refined cell theory of liquid mixtures, and it is shown that the Lennard-Jones and Devonshire theory is a special form of this more general theory. Before proceeding with this development, we wish first to comment briefly on the free volume theory of liquids.

Free volume theory. The basic concepts of the free volume theory can be approached by analogy with the theory of imperfect gases. Consider a gas composed of N rigid spherical molecules of diameter d enclosed in a container of volume V. An approximation to the configurational partition function can be obtained by expanding the partition function per molecule in powers of $1/V$ and discarding quadratic and higher terms. The result [9] may be written

$$\frac{Z_N(T)}{N!} = \frac{V^N}{N!}\left(1 - \frac{Nb}{V}\right)^N \tag{3-1}$$

where $b = (4\pi/6)d^3$ is four times the volume of a spherical molecule. Using the Sterling approximation we may write Eq. 3-1 in the form,

$$\frac{Z_N}{N!} = e^N(v - b)^N \tag{3-2}$$

where $v = V/N$. We may regard $v - b$ as the free volume denoted by v_f.

For the case of higher densities one can retain the free volume concept defined by

$$\frac{Z_N}{N!} = (ev_f)^N \tag{3-3}$$

if one regards it as a function of v for the case of rigid spheres. If the inside of the container is at a uniform potential U_0 we obtain

$$\left(\frac{Z_N}{N!}\right)^{1/N} = ev_f e^{-U_0/kT} \tag{3-4}$$

If U_0 be taken to be some sort of average of the potential energy of a real liquid divided by the number of molecules, the possibility of a closer correspondence between our crude model and actual systems is achieved. These considerations lead us to the refined definition of v_f for the general case of N identical molecules:

$$\frac{Z_N}{N!} = (ev_f)^N e^{-\langle U \rangle_{av}/kT} \tag{3-5}$$

where $\langle U \rangle_{av}$ is the average potential energy of the system. A further refinement is the replacement of e by σ, which has a minimum value of unity but approaches e at low densities. We remark that $R \ln \sigma$ is the so-called communal entropy [6]. In free volume and cell theories, σ has customarily been assigned the value e, resulting in a contribution of R per mole to the entropy and RT per mole to the free energy. It has been mistakenly assumed that the quantity is required in order to include in the partition function, calculated on the basis that each molecule is constrained to a cell, the effects of interchangeability of molecules between cells for the liquid state. It has been suggested [10] that the communal entropy appears discontinuously at the melting point, where it contributes an amount R per mole to the liquid. This view has been criticized by Rice [11], who holds that σ is a function of liquid density. Kirkwood [8] has clarified the point in showing that σ corrects for the effect of multiple occupancy of cells and vacant cells in a cell theory in which only single occupancy is explicitly considered. The value e corresponds to equal probability for all possible modes of single and multiple occupancy (e.g. as for the perfect gas) and vacancies of the cells; the value 1 corresponds to the possibility of single occupancy only.

The usefulness of the above form of the partition function depends on the circumstance that there are many rough intuitive methods for estimating v_f. The cell method, which can be generalized to any desired degree of rigor, can, of course, be used for the calculation of v_f, but the free volume concept does not play an essential role in such theories.

Eyring and Hirschfelder [6] have estimated the free volume and average potential energy from elementary considerations and have formulated a theory that is surprisingly good in view of the approximations involved. The free volume is calculated approximately by considering a linear lattice with the lattice constant taken to be $v^{\frac{1}{3}}$, where v is the molecular volume of the liquid. If one molecule is permitted to move in the lattice direction between the two adjacent molecules which are fixed in their lattice positions, the moving molecule can travel a maximum distance of $2(v^{\frac{1}{3}} - d)$. The molecule, if situated in a cubic lattice, would have similar freedom of motion in the two perpendicular directions, and the free volume is taken to be given approximately by

$$v_f = 8(v^{\frac{1}{3}} - d)^3$$

$$= 8\left[\left(\frac{V}{N}\right)^{\frac{1}{3}} - 0.7816\left(\frac{b}{N}\right)^{\frac{1}{3}}\right]^3 \qquad (3\text{-}6)$$

where V is the molar volume, b is the van der Waals constant, and 0.7816 is a constant appropriate for a simple cubic lattice. (For a body-centered cubic lattice, the constant is 0.7163 and for a face-centered cubic lattice, it is 0.6962.) The potential energy is taken to be approximately equal to the negative of the energy of vaporization per molecule. Hildebrand [12] has shown that the energy of vaporization per mole can be expressed by a function of the type $a(T)/V^n$, where the exponent n is approximately unity. Therefore, it is assumed that

$$\langle U \rangle_{\text{av}} = -\frac{a(T)}{v} \qquad (3\text{-}7)$$

The function $a(T)$ can be identified with the van der Waals attraction term. If σ is assumed to be constant, Eq. 3-5, 3-6, and 3-7 are sufficient to determine the thermodynamic state of the liquid. The equation of state turns out to be

$$\left[p + \frac{a(T)}{V^2}\right](V - 0.7816b^{\frac{1}{3}}V^{\frac{2}{3}}) = RT \qquad (3\text{-}8)$$

This equation has the form of the van der Waals equation, except that the excluded volume, instead of being a constant, varies as the two-thirds power of the volume. This theory gives fairly good agreement with experiment with respect to the coefficients of compressibility and thermal expansion for a variety of liquids. It can be shown [12] to imply the Hildebrand rule that the vapor concentration p_v/RT is a universal function $\Delta_v H/RT$, where $\Delta_v H$ is the heat of vaporization, and Trouton's rule can be obtained in the form $\Delta_v H/RT_b = 10.4$, where T_b is the normal boiling point. The numerical value of Trouton's constant thus obtained is in excellent agreement with experiment.

Cell method in the grand canonical ensemble. By formulating the cell method in the grand canonical ensemble, the authors [13] have found it possible to put the cell theory on a simple and logically coherent basis. This formulation also provides a convenient starting point for generalizations of the cell method to give results of any desired degree of accuracy. In the one-component case this theory can be regarded as a refinement of the Lennard-Jones and Devonshire [7] theory to which it reduces with the use of a simple approximation. For this reason we treat the Lennard-Jones and Devonshire theory—which has historical priority—as a logical sequel later in this article.

We start the analysis by considering the configurational summation operation in the grand canonical ensemble,

$$\mathcal{S}(\ ) = \prod_{\alpha=1}^{r} \sum_{N_\alpha=0}^{\infty} \frac{1}{N_\alpha!} \int_V d\{N_\alpha\}(\ ) \tag{3-9}$$

where N_α is the number of molecules of species α ($\alpha = 1, \cdots, r$), and

$$\int_V d\{N_\alpha\} = \int \cdots_V \int d(1) \cdots d(N_\alpha)$$

is the operation of integration in the configuration space of N_α molecules of species α confined to a volume V. In the case of no molecules of species α the integration written in Eq. 3-9 is to be replaced by unity. The operator $\mathcal{S}$ has the significant property that it may be factored into a product of summation operators, each factor referring to a cell denoted by v_i.

$$\mathcal{S} = \prod_i \mathcal{S}_i \tag{3-10}$$

$$\sum_i v_i = V \tag{3-11}$$

where

$$\mathcal{S}_i(\ ) = \prod_{\alpha=1}^{r} \sum_{n_{\alpha,i}=0}^{\infty} \frac{1}{n_{\alpha,i}!} \int_{v_i} d\{n_{\alpha,i}\}(\ ) \tag{3-12}$$

The operator $\mathcal{S}_i$ has the same meaning as $\mathcal{S}$ except that it sums over the numbers and configurations of molecules contained in the cell v_i instead of in the total volume V.

Now it can be shown that the pressure p is equal to the maximum value of a certain functional $\hat{p}$ given by

$$-\beta\hat{p}V = \mathcal{S}P(\ln P - \beta \sum_\alpha \mu_\alpha^* N_\alpha + \beta U) \tag{3-13}$$

where $1/\beta = kT$ (the Boltzmann constant times the absolute temperature), P is a distribution function (over numbers and configurations) subject to the restriction $\mathcal{S}P = 1$, μ_α^* is the chemical potential[1] of species α, and U is the potential energy. The absolute chemical potential is given by

$$\mu_\alpha = \mu_\alpha^* - \beta^{-1} \ln \left(\frac{2\pi m_\alpha}{\beta h^2} \right)^{\frac{3}{2}} \tag{3-13a}$$

where m_α is the mass of a molecule of species α. The functional $\hat{p}$ is to be maximized with respect to the functional form of P. It can be readily shown that the P maximizing $\hat{p}$ is the grand canonical distribution function.

Now we construct the cells so that they are all equivalent. For instance, we could choose them to be the unit cells of a face-centered cubic lattice. Furthermore we let the distribution function take the approximate factored form

$$P = \prod_i \rho(i) \tag{3-14}$$

in which all of the functions $\rho(i)$ have the same dependence upon the states of the cell i to which each corresponds and where $\mathcal{S}_i\rho(i) = 1$. Let us make the further approximation that $\rho(i)$ vanishes if more than one molecule is contained in cell i. Now let $\rho(i)$ take the more explicit form

$$\rho(i) = \left\{ \begin{matrix} \rho_0 \\ \rho_\alpha(\mathbf{r}) \end{matrix} \right\} \tag{3-15}$$

where ρ_0 = probability of vacancy in cell i, and $\rho_\alpha(\mathbf{r})d\mathbf{r}$ = probability that one molecule of species α is located in the volume element $d\mathbf{r}$ lying at a vector distance $\mathbf{r}$ from the cell center *and* that no other molecules are contained in the cell.

With the above approximations, and with the help of Eq. 3-10 we obtain the result

$$-\beta\hat{p}v = \rho_0 \ln \rho_0 + \sum_{\alpha=1}^{r} \int_v d\mathbf{r}\rho_\alpha(\mathbf{r})[\ln \rho_\alpha(\mathbf{r}) - \beta\mu_\alpha^*]$$

$$+ \tfrac{1}{2}\beta \sum_{\alpha,\alpha'=1}^{r} \int_v d\mathbf{r} \int_v d\mathbf{r}'\rho_\alpha(\mathbf{r})\rho_{\alpha'}(\mathbf{r}')W_{\alpha\alpha'}(\mathbf{r} - \mathbf{r}') \tag{3-16}$$

where

$$W_{\alpha\alpha'}(\mathbf{r} - \mathbf{r}') = \sum_{\mathbf{R}} \phi_{\alpha\alpha'}(|\mathbf{r} - \mathbf{r}' - \mathbf{R}|) \tag{3-17}$$

In Eq. 3-16, $\int_v d\mathbf{r}$ denotes the integration over the cell volume v. In Eq. 3-17, $\phi_{\alpha\alpha'}(|\mathbf{r} - \mathbf{r}' - \mathbf{R}|)$ is the interaction energy between a molecule of species α at a position $\mathbf{r}$ in a cell and another molecule of species α' at a

[1] The chemical potential μ_α^* is defined here so that at zero density it approaches $kT \ln C_\alpha$ where C_α is the number of molecules of species α per unit volume.

position $\mathbf{r}'$ in another cell whose center is located at a vector distance $\mathbf{R}$ from the center of the first cell. The summation over $\mathbf{R}$ in Eq. 3-17 should exclude $\mathbf{R} = 0$. The normalization condition $\mathcal{S}_i\rho(i) = 1$ takes the explicit form

$$\rho_0 + \sum_{\alpha=1}^{r} \int_v d\mathbf{r}\rho_\alpha(\mathbf{r}) = 1 \tag{3-18}$$

Keeping the cell shape fixed, the functional form of the approximate distribution function $\Pi_i\rho(i)$ is determined completely by the cell volume v, the number ρ_0, and the functions $\rho_\alpha(\mathbf{r})$, $\alpha = 1, \cdots, r$, within the restriction imposed by Eq. 3-18. The dependence of $\tilde{p}$ on v is only through the distribution function even though the form of Eq. 3-16 disguises this fact. Thus $\tilde{p}$ should be maximized with respect to v, ρ_0, and $\rho_\alpha(\mathbf{r})$ subject to the normalization condition Eq. 3-18. This operation yields finally the following subsidiary conditions

$$\ln \rho_\alpha(\mathbf{r}) = \ln \rho_0 + \beta(\mu_\alpha^* - w_\alpha(\mathbf{r}))$$

$$w_\alpha(\mathbf{r}) = \sum_{\alpha'=1}^{r} \int_v d\mathbf{r}'\rho_{\alpha'}(\mathbf{r}')W_{\alpha\alpha'}(\mathbf{r} - \mathbf{r}') \tag{3-19}$$

$$\beta p v = 1 - \rho_0 - \tfrac{1}{6}\beta \sum_{\alpha,\alpha'=1}^{r} \int_v d\mathbf{r} \int_v d\mathbf{r}'\rho_\alpha(\mathbf{r})\rho_{\alpha'}(r')\tilde{W}_{\alpha\alpha'}(\mathbf{r} - \mathbf{r}')$$

$$\tilde{W}_{\alpha\alpha'}(\mathbf{r} - \mathbf{r}') = \sum_{\mathbf{R}} |\mathbf{r} - \mathbf{r}' - \mathbf{R}|\phi'_{\alpha\alpha'}(|\mathbf{r} - \mathbf{r}' - \mathbf{R}|) \tag{3-20}$$

Eq. 3-19 arises from the variation of $\tilde{p}$ with respect to the distribution functions. It is an integral equation for the determination of $\rho_\alpha(\mathbf{r})$ and must be supplemented by the normalization condition, Eq. 3-18. In the one-component case it is identical to a result obtained by Mayer and Careri [*14*] by somewhat different methods and analogous to the integral equation Kirkwood [*8*] obtained under the constraint of single occupancy. Eq. 3-20 arises from the variation of $\tilde{p}$ with respect to the cell volume v and may be seen under close scrutiny to conform to the kinetic theory definition of pressure. To obtain, in principle at least, the solution of the problem we must solve Eq. 3-18, 3-19, and 3-20 along with Eq. 3-16 (with p replacing $\tilde{p}$) for ρ_0, $\rho_\alpha(\mathbf{r})$, v, and p. This unfortunately cannot be done exactly. It is necessary to resort to approximations (e.g. those used by Kirkwood [*8*]). One achieves greater logical coherence and the obvious preservation of thermodynamic consistency if one introduces the approximations into the expression for the functional $\tilde{p}$ before taking the variations.

In Eq. 3-16 let

$$\rho_\alpha(\mathbf{r}) = \rho_\alpha\delta(\mathbf{r}) + \psi_\alpha(\mathbf{r}) \tag{3-21}$$

where $\rho_\alpha = \int_v d\mathbf{r}\rho_\alpha(\mathbf{r})$ is the occupation probability of species α and $\delta(\mathbf{r})$ is the Dirac delta function. Also let

$$\rho_\alpha(\mathbf{r}) = \rho_\alpha\varphi_\alpha(\mathbf{r}) \tag{3-22}$$

where $\varphi_\alpha(\mathbf{r})$ is the distribution function for a cell occupied by species α. The normalization condition, (3-18) is equivalent to

$$\rho_0 + \sum_\alpha \rho_\alpha = 1 \tag{3-23}$$

$$\int_v dv\varphi_\alpha(\mathbf{r}) = 1 \tag{3-24}$$

Substituting Eq. 3-21 and 3-22 into Eq. 3-16 and neglecting terms quadratic in $\psi_\alpha(\mathbf{r})$, we obtain

$$-\beta\hat{p}v = \rho_0 \ln \rho_0 + \tfrac{1}{2}\beta \sum_{\alpha,\alpha'} \rho_\alpha\rho_{\alpha'} W_{\alpha\alpha'}(0)$$

$$+ \sum_\alpha \rho_\alpha \int_v d\mathbf{r}\varphi_\alpha(\mathbf{r})\{\ln \rho_\alpha\varphi_\alpha(\mathbf{r})$$

$$- \beta\mu_\alpha^* + \beta \sum_{\alpha'} \rho_{\alpha'}[W_{\alpha\alpha'}(\mathbf{r}) - W'_{\alpha\alpha}(0)]\} \tag{3-25}$$

The effect of neglecting terms quadratic in the $\psi_\alpha(\mathbf{r})$ is to divide the term resulting from the interaction energy into two terms, one containing the interaction energy when all particles are at the cell centers and the other approximating the additional interaction energy arising from displacements of the particles from their cell centers. We note that the integral of Eq. 3-25 converges whether or not the distribution function vanishes at the cell boundary even if a potential function with excessively steep repulsion energy is employed.

As a final approximation, we assume that $\varphi_\alpha(\mathbf{r})$ is spherically symmetrical, $\varphi_\alpha(\mathbf{r}) = \varphi_\alpha(r)$, and we replace the integration over the cell volume v by integration over a sphere of equivalent volume. Eq. 3-25 can then be written in the form

$$-\beta\hat{p}v = \rho_0 \ln \rho_0 + \tfrac{1}{2}\beta \sum_{\alpha,\alpha'} \rho_\alpha\rho_{\alpha'} W_{\alpha\alpha'}(0)$$

$$+ 4\pi r^{*3} \sum_\alpha \rho_\alpha \int_0^1 \xi^2 d\xi\varphi_\alpha(r^*\xi)[\ln \rho_\alpha\varphi_\alpha(r^*\xi)$$

$$- \beta\mu_\alpha^* + \beta \sum_{\alpha'} \rho_{\alpha'}\langle\Delta W_{\alpha\alpha'}\rangle] \tag{3-26}$$

$v = \tfrac{4}{3}\pi r^{*3}$, $\xi = r/r^*$, where $\langle\Delta W_{\alpha\alpha'}\rangle$ is identical with the spherically smoothed excess interaction energy introduced by Lennard-Jones and

Devonshire [7]

$$\langle \Delta W_{\alpha\alpha'} \rangle = \frac{1}{4\pi} \int_0^{2\pi} d\varpi \int_0^{\pi} \sin\theta d\theta [W_{\alpha\alpha'}(\mathbf{r}) - W_{\alpha\alpha'}(0)] \qquad (3\text{-}27)$$

where θ and ϖ are the polar and azimuthal angles of $\mathbf{r}$. With the assumption of spherical symmetry, Eq. 3-24 becomes

$$4\pi r^{*3} \int_0^1 \xi^2 d\xi \varphi_\alpha(r^*\xi) = 1 \qquad (3\text{-}28)$$

We regard $\hat{p}$ as a functional of the occupation probabilities ρ_0 and ρ_α, the normalized distribution functions $\varphi_\alpha(r)$, and the cell volume v, and we wish to maximize $\hat{p}$ at constant temperature, total volume, and chemical potentials with respect to v, ρ_0, the ρ_α, and the functional form of the $\varphi_\alpha(r)$, subject to the normalization relations, Eq. 3-28, and the identity relation, Eq. 3-23. The solution to this variation problem is readily obtained by the method of Lagrange multipliers. We remark that the functional form of the distribution functions $\varphi_\alpha(r)$ is to be held constant in evaluating the variation of $\hat{p}$ with respect to the cell volume v. After the elimination of the Lagrangian multipliers, the stationary value of $\hat{p}$ is given by

$$\beta p v = -\ln \rho_0 + \frac{1}{2}\beta \sum_{\alpha\alpha'} \rho_\alpha \rho_{\alpha'} W_{\alpha\alpha'}(0) - \sum_\alpha \rho_\alpha \beta \frac{\partial}{\partial\beta} \ln \Gamma_\alpha \qquad (3\text{-}29)$$

and by

$$\beta p v = 1 - \rho_0 - \frac{1}{2}\beta v \frac{\partial}{\partial v} \sum_{\alpha,\alpha'} \rho_\alpha \rho_{\alpha'} W_{\alpha\alpha'}(0) + \sum_\alpha \rho_\alpha v \frac{\partial}{\partial v} \ln \Gamma_\alpha \qquad (3\text{-}30)$$

where

$$\Gamma_\alpha = \int_0^1 \xi^2 d\xi e^{-\beta \sum_{\alpha'} \rho_{\alpha'} \langle \Delta W_{\alpha\alpha'} \rangle} \qquad (3\text{-}31)$$

Eq. 3-29 is the expression for the stationary value of $\hat{p}$, which we interpret to be the pressure as it is defined as the normalization factor in the partition function for the grand canonical ensemble. Eq. 3-30 results from the variation of $\hat{p}$ with respect to the cell volume, and it is equivalent to the virial expression for the pressure. The equality of these two expressions provides a relation for determining the density of vacancies, ρ_0. The distribution functions are given by

$$\varphi_\alpha(r) = \frac{e^{-\beta \sum_{\alpha'} \rho_{\alpha'} \langle \Delta W_{\alpha\alpha'} \rangle}}{4\pi r^{*3} \Gamma_\alpha} \qquad (3\text{-}32)$$

The excess chemical potentials μ_α^* are related to the occupation probabilities by

$$\beta\mu_\alpha^* = \ln \rho_\alpha - \ln \rho_0 - \ln (4\pi r^{*3}\Gamma_\alpha)$$

$$+ \beta \sum_{\alpha'} \rho_{\alpha'} W_{\alpha\alpha'}(0) - \beta \frac{\partial}{\partial\beta} \ln \Gamma_\alpha \quad (3\text{-}33)$$

The quantity pV may be regarded a thermodynamic potential for the set of independent state variables consisting of temperature, volume, and the chemical potentials. It satisfies the fundamental relation,

$$dpV = SdT + pdV + M \sum_\alpha \rho_\alpha d\mu_\alpha \quad (3\text{-}34)$$

where $V = Mv$ and μ_α is the chemical potential per molecule of species α. Since, according to Eq. 3-13a, the difference $\mu_\alpha - \mu_\alpha^*$ is a function of temperature only, we can define an excess entropy S^*, per volume V, by the relation,

$$S^* = S + M \sum_\alpha \frac{\rho_\alpha d(\mu_\alpha - \mu_\alpha^*)}{dT} \quad (3\text{-}35)$$

and rewrite Eq. 3-34 in the form,

$$dpV = S^*dT + pdV + M \sum_\alpha \rho_\alpha d\mu_\alpha^* \quad (3\text{-}36)$$

Therefore, we evaluate the excess entropy by means of the relation,

$$\frac{S^*}{Mk} = -\beta^2 \left(\frac{\partial pv}{\partial\beta}\right)_{V,\mu_\alpha^*} \quad (3\text{-}37)$$

Since the variational function $\hat{p}$ is stationary with respect to v, ρ_0, ρ_α, and φ_α, this relation can be written

$$\frac{S^*}{Mk} = -\beta^2 \left(\frac{\partial \hat{p}v}{\partial\beta}\right)_{v,\mu_\alpha^*,\rho_0\rho_\alpha,\varphi_\alpha} \quad (3\text{-}38)$$

and we obtain

$$\frac{S^*}{Mk} = -\rho_0 \ln \rho_0 - \sum_\alpha \rho_\alpha \ln \rho_\alpha$$

$$+ \sum_\alpha \rho_\alpha \ln (4\pi r^{*2}\Gamma_\alpha) - \sum_\alpha \rho_\alpha\beta \frac{\partial}{\partial\beta} \ln \Gamma_\alpha \quad (3\text{-}39)$$

Our expression for the pressure satisfies Eq. 3-38 completely, since we can employ similar methods to show that

$$\left(\frac{\partial pV}{\partial V}\right)_{T,\mu_\alpha^*} = p \quad \text{and} \quad \frac{1}{M}\left(\frac{\partial pV}{\partial\mu_\alpha}\right)_{v,r} = \rho_\alpha$$

are satisfied. Furthermore, the validity of the second of these relations confirms our identification of ρ_0 and ρ_α and the probability of vacancies and the occupation probability of species α, respectively. It follows that the mole fraction X_α of species α is given by

$$X_\alpha = \frac{\rho_\alpha}{1 - \rho_0} \tag{3-40}$$

Now we may suppose that the cells are formed by a face-centered cubic lattice with lattice constant a. Then $v = \frac{4}{3}\pi r^{*3} = a^3/\sqrt{2}$ and $(r^*/a)^3 = 3\sqrt{2}/8\pi$. We define a function G_α by the relation,

$$G_\alpha = 2(r^*/a)^3 \Gamma_\alpha \tag{3-41}$$

and an effective value β^* of the variable β by

$$\beta^* = \beta(1 - \rho_0) \tag{3-42}$$

It is convenient to define a function Φ by the relation,

$$\Phi_\alpha = \tfrac{1}{2}\beta^* \sum_\alpha X_{\alpha'} W_{\alpha\alpha'}(0) \tag{3-43}$$

We take $M = N/(1 - \rho_0)$, where N is Avogadro's number, so that V becomes the molar volume. With these substitutions, Eq. 3-29 becomes

$$\frac{pV}{RT} = 1 - \sum_\alpha X_\alpha v \left[\frac{\partial \Phi_\alpha}{\partial v} - \frac{\partial \ln G_\alpha}{\partial v}\right] \tag{3-44}$$

Using Eq. 3-13a and 3-33, we obtain an expression for the chemical potential per mole of species α.

$$\mu_\alpha = \mu_\alpha^0(T) + RT \ln \frac{X_\alpha RT}{V - \mu_\alpha^{(i)}} \tag{3-45}$$

where

$$\mu_\alpha^0(T) = -RT \ln \left(\frac{2\pi m_\alpha kT}{h^2}\right)^{\frac{3}{2}} kTJ(T) \tag{3-46}$$

is the chemical potential of species α in its standard state consisting of the ideal gas at unit pressure, and where

$$\frac{\mu_\alpha^{(i)}}{RT} = 2\Phi_\alpha - \ln (2\sqrt{2}\,\pi G_\alpha) - \frac{\beta^* \partial \ln G_\alpha}{\partial \beta^*} - \ln \rho_0 \tag{3-47}$$

The molar entropy is given by

$$S = \sum_\alpha X_\alpha \left[S_\alpha^0(T) - R - R \ln \frac{X_\alpha RT}{V}\right] + S^{(i)} \tag{3-48}$$

where

$$S_\alpha^0(T) = -\frac{d\mu_\alpha^0(T)}{dT} \tag{3-49}$$

is the entropy of species α in its standard state, and where

$$S^{(i)} = - \frac{\rho_0 \ln \rho_0}{1 - \rho_0} + \sum_\alpha X_\alpha \left[\ln \left(2 \sqrt{2\pi}G_\alpha \right) - \beta^* \frac{\partial \ln G_\alpha}{\partial \beta^*} \right] \quad (3\text{-}50)$$

The Helmholtz work content A and the energy content E can be evaluated by means of the standard relations,

$$A = \sum_\alpha X_\alpha \mu_\alpha - pV$$

$$E = A + TS$$

For the work content, we obtain

$$A = \sum_\alpha X_\alpha \left[\mu_\alpha^0(T) + RT \ln \frac{X_\alpha RT}{V} \right] + A^{(i)} \quad (3\text{-}51)$$

where

$$\frac{A_i}{RT} = \frac{\rho_0 \ln \rho_0}{1 - \rho_0} + \sum_\alpha X_\alpha [\Phi_\alpha - \ln \left(2 \sqrt{2}\, \pi G_\alpha \right)] \quad (3\text{-}52)$$

and where we have used Eq. 3-29 to evaluate the quantity pV. For the energy content, we obtain

$$E = \sum_\alpha X_\alpha E_\alpha^0(T) + E^{(i)} \quad (3\text{-}53)$$

where

$$E_\alpha^0(T) = \mu_\alpha^0(T) - RT + S_\alpha^0(T) \quad (3\text{-}54)$$

is the energy content of species α in its standard state, and where

$$\frac{E^{(i)}}{RT} = \sum_\alpha X_\alpha \left[\Phi_\alpha - \beta^* \frac{\partial \ln G_\alpha}{\partial \beta^*} \right] \quad (3\text{-}55)$$

The density of vacancies is determined by the requirement that Eq. 3-29 and 3-30 give identical values of the pressure. Therefore, ρ_0 must satisfy the relation,

$$\frac{-\ln \rho_0}{1 - \rho_0} = 1 - \sum_\alpha X_\alpha \left[\frac{\partial v \Phi_\alpha}{\partial v} + v \frac{\partial \ln G_\alpha}{\partial v} + \beta^* \frac{\partial \ln G_\alpha}{\partial \beta^*} \right] \quad (3\text{-}56)$$

This equation determines ρ_0 as an explicit function of the cell volume v, the effective reciprocal temperature β^*, and mole fractions X_α. Therefore, the right-hand sides of Eq. 3-44, 3-47, 3-50, 3-52, and 3-55 are also explicit functions of these variables. The temperature and volume are also explicit functions of β^* and v,

$$kT = \frac{1 - \rho_0}{\beta^*}$$

$$V = \frac{Nv}{1 - \rho_0}$$

(3-57)

Therefore, the pressure and the thermodynamic properties have been expressed as functions implicit in temperature and volume and explicit in the mole fractions with β^* and v as parameters that can be eliminated by numerical methods.

The intermolecular potential function $U_{\alpha\alpha'}(R)$ can be written formally as

$$U_{\alpha\alpha'}(R) = U(R; \lambda_{\alpha\alpha'}^{(1)}, \lambda_{\alpha\alpha'}^{(2)}, \cdots)$$

(3-58)

where $\lambda_{\alpha\alpha'}^{(1)}$, $\lambda_{\alpha\alpha'}^{(2)}$, . . . are parameters characteristic of the interaction of molecules of species α and α. If effective values of these parameters $\lambda_{\alpha}^{(1)}$, $\lambda_{\alpha}^{(2)}$, . . . are determined by the requirement that

$$U(R; \lambda_{\alpha}^{(1)}, \lambda_{\alpha}^{(2)}, \cdots) = \sum_{\alpha} X_{\alpha'} U_{\alpha\alpha'}(R)$$

(3-59)

then the function G_{α} defined by Eq. 3-31 and 3-41 can be written as

$$G_{\alpha}(\beta^*, v) = g(\beta^*, v; \lambda_{\alpha}^{(1)}, \cdots)$$

(3-60)

The function $g(\beta^*, v; \lambda^{(1)}, \ldots)$ is formally the same as the function introduced by Lennard-Jones and Devonshire [7] and in their papers denoted by g, and it is numerically identical with theirs if we take Eq. 3-58 to be the Lennard-Jones [15] potential function with inverse twelfth power repulsion. Similarly, the function Φ, defined by Eq. 3-43, can be written as

$$\Phi_{\alpha}(\beta^*, v) = \varphi(\beta^*, v; \lambda_{\alpha}^{(1)}, \cdots)$$

(3-61)

Before considering the explicit functional form of the functions g and φ, we wish first to describe the cell theory of Lennard-Jones and Devonshire. It will turn out that their theory can be expressed in terms of these same functions.

Theory of Lennard-Jones and Devonshire. It is possible to obtain the results of Lennard-Jones and Devonshire [7] from our previous results by specializing the variational expression, Eq. 3-26, to the one-component case and by imposing the further requirement that there be no vacancies. To specialize to the one-component case, let us drop the subscript α wherever it occurs, there being now only one species under consideration. The requirement of no vacancies means that $\rho_0 = 0$ and that the probability of single occupancy $\rho = 1$ (ρ was formerly ρ_{α}). Using the normalization condition, Eq. 3-28, and Eq. 3-13a relating μ to μ^*, we can finally rewrite Eq. 3-26 in the form

$$\beta(\mu - \hat{p}v) = \frac{1}{2}\beta W(0) - \ln\left(\frac{2\pi m}{\beta h^2}\right)^{\frac{3}{2}}$$

$$+ 4\pi r^{*3}\int_0^1 \xi^2 d\xi \varphi(r^*\xi)[\ln \varphi(r^*\xi) + \beta\langle\Delta W\rangle] \quad (3\text{-}26a)$$

In this expression $\hat{p}$ can be varied only with respect to $\varphi(r^*\xi)$ and $v(= \frac{4}{3}\pi r^{*3})$. We still retain the constraint of normalization

$$4\pi r^{*3}\int_0^1 \xi^2 d\xi \varphi(r^*\xi) = 1 \quad (3\text{-}28a)$$

The variation of $\hat{p}$ with respect to φ under the constraint (3-28a) gives

$$\varphi(r^*\xi) = (3v\Gamma)^{-1}e^{-\beta\langle\Delta W\rangle} \quad (3\text{-}62)$$

where

$$\Gamma = \int_0^1 \xi^2 d\xi e^{-\beta\langle\Delta W\rangle} \quad (3\text{-}31a)$$

The variation with respect to v simply gives a special case of Eq. 3-30:

$$\beta p v = 1 - \frac{1}{2}\beta v \frac{\partial}{\partial v}W(0) + v\frac{\partial}{\partial v}\ln \Gamma \quad (3\text{-}30a)$$

which is simply the Lennard-Jones and Devonshire equation of state.

Substituting Eq. 3-62 into the expression, Eq. 3-26a, for $\hat{p}$, now a maximum denoted by p, we obtain the following expression for the Helmholtz free energy

$$\beta(\mu - pv) = \beta(A/N)$$

$$= \frac{1}{2}\beta W(0) - \ln v_{\mathrm{f}}\left[\left(\frac{2\pi m}{\beta n^2}\right)^{\frac{3}{2}}\right] \quad (3\text{-}63)$$

where N is the total number of molecules in the system, and where

$$v_{\mathrm{f}} = 3v\Gamma$$

$$= 4\pi\int_0^{r^*} r^2 dr e^{-\beta\langle\Delta W\rangle} \quad (3\text{-}64)$$

For convenience we repeat here the definitions of $W(0)$ and $\langle\Delta W\rangle$ for the case of one component:

$$W(\mathbf{r}) = \sum_{\mathbf{R}} \varpi(|\mathbf{r} - \mathbf{R}|) \quad (3\text{-}17a)$$

$$\langle\Delta W\rangle = \frac{1}{4\pi}\int_0^{2\pi} d\varpi \int_0^\pi \sin\theta d\theta[W(\mathbf{r}) - W(0)] \quad (3\text{-}27a)$$

where θ and ϖ are the polar and azimuthal angles of $\mathbf{r}$.

In order to correct for the neglect of vacancies and multiple occupancies, it is customary to add a term $- \ln \sigma$ on the right-hand side of Eq. 3-63, this term being defined in such a way that the right answer would be obtained if the theory were made as accurate as possible under the restriction of single occupancy. This term in the modified form, $R \ln \sigma$, $(R = $ Avogadro's number $\times k)$ is known as the communal entropy and is discussed earlier in this part.

In terms of the functions g and φ, defined by Eq. 3-60 and 3-61, Eq. 3-30a can be written

$$\beta p v = 1 - v \frac{\partial \varphi}{\partial v} + v \frac{\partial \ln g}{\partial v} \tag{3-44a}$$

where $\varphi = \varphi(\beta, v; \lambda^{(1)}, \cdots)$ and $g = g(\beta, v; \lambda^{(1)}, \cdots)$. Eq. 3-63 can be written

$$\frac{A^{(i)}}{RT} = \varphi - \ln (2 \sqrt{2} \pi g) - 1 \tag{3-52a}$$

for the excess Helmholtz free energy.

Evaluation of the cell theory functions. We conclude our discussion of the cell theory by giving the results obtained when a particular form of the intermolecular potential function is employed. For this purpose, we choose the Lennard-Jones [15] potential function with an inverse twelfth power repulsion, which can be written in the form

$$\phi(r) = 4\epsilon \left[\left(\frac{r^*}{r} \right)^{12} - \left(\frac{r^*}{r} \right)^{6} \right] \tag{3-65}$$

where ϵ is the absolute value of the energy at its minimum and r^* is the separation distance for which $\phi(r) = 0$. For interaction in a multicomponent system, we employ Eq. 3-65 in a more general form, namely,

$$\phi_{\alpha\alpha'} = 4\epsilon_{\alpha\alpha'} \left[\left(\frac{r^*_{\alpha\alpha'}}{r} \right)^{12} - \left(\frac{r^*_{\alpha\alpha'}}{r} \right)^{6} \right] \tag{3-66}$$

and define derived potential function parameters ϵ_α and r^*_α so as to satisfy

$$\epsilon_\alpha (r^*_\alpha)^{12} = \sum_{\alpha'} X_{\alpha'} \epsilon_{\alpha\alpha'} (r^*_{\alpha\alpha'})^{12}$$

$$\epsilon_\alpha (r^*_\alpha)^{6} = \sum_{\alpha'} X_{\alpha'} \epsilon_{\alpha\alpha'} (r^*_{\alpha\alpha'})^{6} \tag{3-67}$$

We now define reduced variables ξ_α and η_α for the multicomponent system by

$$\xi_\alpha = \beta \epsilon_\alpha, \qquad \eta_\alpha = \frac{(r^*_\alpha)^3}{v} \tag{3-68}$$

For the case of one component, consistent with the use of Eq. 3-65, the subscript α can simply be dropped in Eq. 3-68. Now it can be shown that functions employed in the Lennard-Jones and Devonshire theory have a functional dependence given by

$$g(\beta, v; \lambda^{(1)}, \cdots) = g(\xi, \eta)$$
$$\varphi(\beta, v; \lambda^{(1)}, \cdots) = \varphi(\xi, \eta)$$

(3-69)

Also, the functions employed in the general cell theory have a functional dependence given by

$$g(\beta^*, v; \lambda_\alpha^{(1)}, \cdots) = g(\xi_\alpha^*, \eta_\alpha)$$
$$\varphi(\beta^*, v; \lambda_\alpha^{(1)}, \cdots) = \varphi(\xi_\alpha^*, \eta_\alpha)$$

(3-70)

where $\xi_\alpha^* = \beta^* \epsilon_\alpha$.

Wentorf, Buehler, Hirschfelder, and Curtiss [16] have evaluated the function $g(\xi, \eta)$, including in their calculations the contributions to the integral of the first three shells of neighboring molecules. They obtain

$$g(\xi, \eta) = \int_0^{0.30544} \sqrt{\zeta}\, e^{-f(\xi, \eta, \zeta)} d\zeta$$

(3-71)

where

$$f(\xi, \eta, \zeta) = 12\xi[\eta^4 L(\zeta) - 2\eta^2 M(\zeta)]$$

$$L(\zeta) = \lambda(\zeta) + \frac{1}{128}\lambda\left(\frac{\zeta}{2}\right) + \frac{2}{729}\lambda\left(\frac{\zeta}{3}\right)$$

$$M(\zeta) = \mu(\zeta) + \frac{1}{16}\mu\left(\frac{\zeta}{2}\right) + \frac{2}{27}\mu\left(\frac{\zeta}{3}\right)$$

$$\lambda(\zeta) = (1 + 12\zeta + 25.2\zeta^2 + 12\zeta^3 + \zeta^4)(1 - \zeta)^{-10} - 1$$

$$\mu(\zeta) = (1 + \zeta)(1 - \zeta)^{-4} - 1$$

Extensive tables of the function $g(\xi, \eta)$ and of the necessary integrals to permit the calculation of its first derivatives have been published by Wentorf, Buehler, Hirschfelder, and Curtiss [16].

The function $\varphi(\xi, \eta)$ has been evaluated by Lennard-Jones and Ingham [17]. Then results can be expressed in the form,

$$\varphi(\xi, \eta) = 6.0660\xi\eta^4 - 14.4540\xi\eta^2$$

(3-72)

Finally, we wish to mention that Salsburg and Kirkwood [18] have extended the Lennard-Jones and Devonshire theory to multicomponent systems by methods that are an extension of the statistical theory of Kirkwood [8]. This treatment leads to a mixture theory of only approximate validity. Their treatment retains the uncertainty associated with the communal entropy and leads to the result that the ordinary equations of the Lennard-Jones and Devonshire theory can be applied with derived potential energy function parameters ϵ and r^* satisfying

$$\epsilon(r^*)^{12} = \sum_{\alpha,\alpha'} X_\alpha X_{\alpha'} \epsilon_{\alpha\alpha'} (r^*_{\alpha\alpha'})^{12}$$

$$\epsilon(r^*)^6 = \sum_{\alpha,\alpha'} X_\alpha X_{\alpha'} \epsilon_{\alpha\alpha'} (r^*_{\alpha\alpha'})^6$$

(3-73)

It is difficult to estimate the numerical effects of employing this mixture rule in the place of the exact one as developed by the method of the grand canonical ensemble.

F,4. Theories of the Radial Distribution Function.

Introduction. There is an interesting class of theories characterized by the fact that the radial distribution function (defined in Art. 2) appears explicitly as the dependent variable. The cell method discussed in Art. 3 can give a reasonable approximation to the radial d.f., but in this case the result is not the dependent variable of the theory—it is a by-product foreign to the main line of development.

Some workers call the theories of the class considered here the integral equation method. This is much too general a description since practically all cooperative theories involving a continuum of states yield integral equations at some point in their development. Sometimes the name "kinetic theory method" is used because of the possibility of deriving some of the theories from Liouville's equation describing the collective motion of a dense swarm of representative points in phase space. In this case, Liouville's equation is integrated over the coordinates and momenta of all of the molecules except the two of interest whose relative configurations are statistically described by the radial d.f. In the resultant equation, one introduces the Maxwell-Boltzmann distribution of momenta and then requires the distribution of configurations to be stationary. Then one obtains an integro-differential equation connecting the pair d.f. $\rho^{(2)}(1, 2)$ (assumed now to be a function only of the scalar distance between molecules 1 and 2) with the average forces arising from the other molecules which involves the use of the triplet d.f. $\rho^{(3)}(1, 2, 3)$ with the position of molecule 3 playing the role of a variable of integration. The d.f. $\rho^{(3)}$ can be expressed in terms of $\rho^{(2)}$ and $\rho^{(1)}$ (assumed to be constant) by means of an approximation to be discussed later (see Eq. 4-14). One now has an integro-differential equation involving only $\rho^{(2)}$ (or $g^{(2)}$, using relation $\rho^{(2)}(1, 2) = \rho^{(1)}(1)\rho^{(1)}(2)g(1, 2)$) with $\rho^{(1)}$ appearing as a constant parameter. This is an interesting approach but involves irrelevant and redundant features, the nonequilibrium features initially brought in by the use of Liouville's equation later being discarded. The same result can be obtained with greater logical economy entirely within the framework of equilibrium statistical mechanics. For this reason the appellation "kinetic theory method" seems quite unsatisfactory. We prefer to define the class of theories presently under consideration by the fact that the radial d.f. appears explicitly as the dependent variable or can be made to do so by a simple transformation.

In the following paragraphs we consider three distinct theories of the radial d.f. The first is that of Kirkwood [19], and the second, Born and Green [20,21]. Although Born and Green used the kinetic theory method, described above, in the derivation of their basic integral equation, these two theories can be based upon a general theorem relating the derivative of $\ln \rho^{(2)}$ with respect to some parameter to the average force (defined with respect to this parameter) acting upon molecules 1 and 2. It is characteristic of these theories that the average force theorem above yields directly an integro-differential equation for $\rho^{(2)}$, after $\rho^{(3)}$ is approximated by

$$\rho^{(3)}(1, 2, 3) \cong (\rho^{(1)})^{-3}\rho^{(2)}(1, 2)\rho^{(2)}(2, 3)\rho^{(2)}(3, 1) \qquad (4\text{-}1)$$

in which $\rho^{(1)}$ is regarded as constant. This is the so-called "superposition approximation" first introduced by Kirkwood [19] and independently by Yvon [22]. The word "superposition" arises from the fact that Kirkwood was thinking in terms of the logarithms of the d.f., proportional to the correspondingly defined local free energies. To continue, we have now obtained an integro-differential equation. The next step taken by all of the above authors is the integration of this equation to obtain an integral equation. Because of a certain inherent lack of symmetry in these integral equations it is impossible to derive them from variational principles.

The third theory considered here was devised recently by one of the present authors [23]. This theory has a logical structure completely unlike that of the first two theories. Here we start by deriving an approximate expression for the configurational Helmholtz free energy as a functional of the radial distribution function g. Finding the minimum value of this free energy with respect to variations of g yields an integral equation similar but not identical to those of Kirkwood and of Born and Green. The derivation of the free energy expression employs an approximation very similar to the superposition approximation but slightly less stringent in that proportionality instead of equality is assumed in Eq. 4-1—as a matter of fact, the success of the theory rests heavily upon this slight deviation from the usual statement of the approximation.

A discussion of theories of the radial d.f. is hardly complete without mention of the elegant work of Mayer [24]. This work is derived from the earlier work of McMillan and Mayer [25] and of Mayer [26] in which d.f.'s in a system described by a given set of concentrations are related to the d.f.'s in the system with another set of concentrations. The relations are essentially a linear transformation of the set of all orders of d.f.'s in one case to yield the set in the other case. In particular, the set of d.f.'s for a condensed system can be given as a linear transformation of the set for a perfect gas and vice versa. This latter set is of course known and can be easily written down. In the 1947 paper, Mayer takes these results and simplifies them by the introduction of certain G functions proportional to the d.f.'s, the proportionality factors depending only upon the thermodynamic state of the system to which the d.f. refer. He then introduces a parameter y which, for example, could be the temperature, the strength of a perturbation potential, Kirkwood's coupling parameter λ, etc. He finally defines a set of ψ functions which are certain convenient linear combinations of the set of $\partial \ln G/\partial y$. From the original equations connecting the set of G corresponding to one set of concentrations with the set, now denoted by G^*, corresponding to other concentrations, Mayer derives a set of integral equations in which ψ^* are transformed by certain kernels K (dependent only upon G) into ψ. The integral equation derived by Kirkwood can be obtained as a special case by introducing certain approximations into the general equations of Mayer.

Unfortunately, the limitations of space preclude from this article a really adequate description of Mayer's work because of the mathematical complexities inherent in an exact development of a high degree of generality. Readers wishing to familiarize themselves further with this work are urged to consult the original papers quoted above [*24,25,26*].

Theory of Kirkwood. In 1935, Kirkwood [*19*] was the first to make a successful attack on the problem of computing the radial d.f. on a statistical mechanics basis and of relating it to thermodynamic properties. About the same time, Yvon [*22*] independently developed a theory equivalent to that of Born and Green. For convenience in exposition we present a version of Kirkwood's theory that is considerably less general than that given in his original paper [*19*]. His theory is based upon a somewhat artificial device: namely, the introduction of a coupling parameter λ into the potential energy of N identical molecules as indicated in the following expression:

$$U_N(\lambda) = \lambda \sum_{s=2}^{N} \phi(1, s) + \sum_{\substack{s,s'=2 \\ s>s'}}^{N} \phi(s, s') \tag{4-2}$$

Thus when $\lambda = 1$ we have the correct expression for the potential energy of all of the N molecules, and when $\lambda = 0$, the potential energy of $N - 1$ molecules with molecule 1 missing. With this device, molecule 1 can be continuously and reversibly decoupled from the system.

We first proceed to construct the approximate statistical mechanics formulas for the fictitious system in which molecule 1 is coupled to an intermediate degree ($0 < \lambda < 1$). The first order or singlet d.f. of molecule s is for this case defined by

$$\rho^{(1)}(s,\,\lambda) = \left[\frac{1}{Z_N(\beta,\,\lambda)}\right] \int \cdots \int d(1) \cdots$$

$$d(s-1)d(s+1) \cdots d(N)e^{-\beta U_N(\lambda)} \quad (4\text{-}3)$$

where $\beta = 1/kT$ and where the integrations extend over all positions within a container of volume V. The Gibbs phase integral for this case is $Z_N(\beta,\,\lambda)$ and is given by

$$Z_N(\beta,\,\lambda) = \int \cdots \int d(1) \cdots d(N)e^{-\beta U_N(\lambda)} \quad (4\text{-}4)$$

In a liquid the singlet d.f. is independent of position (except close to the wall of the container), and consequently it has the value $1/V$ determined by the normalization condition $\int d(s)\rho^{(1)}(s,\,\lambda) = 1$. The pair and radial d.f. are given by

$$\rho^{(2)}(s,\,s',\,\lambda) \equiv V^{-2}g(s,\,s',\,\lambda) = \left[\frac{1}{Z_N(\beta,\,\lambda)}\right] \int \cdots \int d(1) \cdots$$

$$d(s-1)d(s+1) \cdots d(s'-1)d(s'+1) \cdots d(N)e^{-\beta U_N(\lambda)} \quad (4\text{-}5)$$

The triplet and higher order d.f. are given by obvious extensions of the above formula. When λ is equal to unity the d.f. revert to those for the real system, namely $\rho^{(1)}(s)$, $\rho^{(2)}(s,\,s')$, etc., defined in Art. 2. With λ vanishing, one can readily derive the relation $g^{(2)}(1,\,s,\,0) = 1$ neglecting terms of the order of N^{-1}.

In treating the thermodynamic properties of the liquid, we will direct our attention to the excess Helmholtz free energy $\bar{A}_N(\beta)$ defined as the excess of Helmholtz free energy for the actual system over the perfect gas value (that is, the value that would exist for the actual system if we could imagine the intermolecular forces vanishing). It is evident that

$$\bar{A}_N(\beta) = -\beta^{-1}\ln\left[\frac{Z_N(\beta)}{V^N}\right] \quad (4\text{-}6)$$

and similarly that

$$\bar{A}_N(\beta,\,\lambda) = -\beta^{-1}\ln\left[\frac{Z_N(\beta,\,\lambda)}{V^N}\right] \quad (4\text{-}7)$$

for the partially decoupled system. One can derive the relations

$$\bar{A}_N(\beta,\,1) = \bar{A}_N(\beta)$$
$$\bar{A}_N(\beta,\,0) = \bar{A}_{N-1}(\beta) \quad (4\text{-}8)$$

When N is large the excess chemical potential *per molecule*, from which all other excess thermodynamic quantities may be derived, can be expressed in the form

$$\bar{\mu}_N(\beta) = \bar{A}_N(\beta) - \bar{A}_{N-1}(\beta) \quad (4\text{-}9)$$

Using Eq. 4-8 we may write

$$\bar{\mu}_N(\beta) = \bar{A}_N(\beta, 1) - \bar{A}_N(\beta, 0)$$

$$= \int_0^1 d\lambda \, \frac{\partial \bar{A}_N(\beta, \lambda)}{\partial \lambda} \tag{4-10}$$

Using the original definition of $\bar{A}_N(\beta, \lambda)$, we obtain

$$\frac{\partial \bar{A}_N(\beta, \lambda)}{\partial \lambda} = \left\langle \frac{\partial U_N'(\lambda)}{\partial \lambda} \right\rangle_{\mathrm{av}} = (N-1)\langle \phi(1, 2) \rangle_{\mathrm{av}}$$

$$= C \int d(2) g(1, 2, \lambda) \phi(1, 2) + O(N^{-1}) \tag{4-11}$$

where $C = N/V$ is the number density of molecules. We finally obtain

$$\bar{\mu}_N(\beta) = C \int_0^1 d\lambda \int d(2) g(1, 2, \lambda) \phi(1, 2) \tag{4-12}$$

from which may be derived the connection between all thermodynamic quantities and the sequence of radial d.f. for all degrees of coupling between molecule 1 and the remainder of the system. Thus, if we can find some means for calculating $g(1, 2, \lambda)$, our problem is solved.

The original definition of $g(1, 2, \lambda)$, Eq. 4-5, is unsuitable for computational purposes since it would involve $3N$ integrations over the translational coordinates of the N molecules. We seek, instead, an approximate equation involving a relatively small number of operations.

To this end we first state the average force theorem using λ as the parameter. In this theorem $-\beta^{-1} \ln g(1, 2, \lambda)$ plays the role of the local free energy of molecules 1 and 2 with molecule 1 partially coupled to a degree measured by λ. Differentiation of this quantity with respect to λ gives the desired result

$$-\frac{1}{\beta} \frac{\partial \ln g(1, 2, \lambda)}{\partial \lambda} = \phi(1, 2)$$

$$+ N \int d(3) \left[\frac{\rho^{(3)}(1, 2, 3, \lambda)}{\rho^{(2)}(1, 2, \lambda)} - \frac{\rho^{(2)}(1, 3, \lambda)}{\rho^{(1)}(1, \lambda)} \right] \phi(1, 3) \tag{4-13}$$

where terms of the order of N^{-1} have been neglected. Using the so-called superposition approximation expressed by Eq. 4-1, we write

$$\rho^{(3)}(1, 2, 3, \lambda) \cong V^{-3} g(1, 2, \lambda) g(2, 3, \lambda) g(3, 1, \lambda) \tag{4-14}$$

Since the degree of coupling of molecule 1 has negligible ($O(N^{-1})$) influence on the distribution of molecules 2 and 3, we have $g(2, 3, \lambda) = g(2, 3)$, which is of the same functional form as $g(1, 2, 1)$. We have already shown that

$$\rho^{(2)}(1, 2, \lambda) = V^{-2} g(1, 2, \lambda)$$

and that

$$\rho^{(1)}(1, \lambda) = V^{-1}$$

Introducing these expressions into the average force theorem (4-13) we obtain the following nonlinear integro-differential equation

$$-\frac{1}{\beta}\frac{\partial \ln g(1, 2, \lambda)}{\partial \lambda} = \phi(1, 2)$$

$$+ C \int d(3)[g(2, 3) - 1]g(1, 2, \lambda)\phi(1, 3) \quad (4\text{-}15)$$

where $C = N/V$ is the number density defined previously. This equation is to be solved for $g(1, 2, \lambda)$ with the boundary condition $g(1, 2, 0) = 1$.

For computational purposes, it is desirable to express the quantities in the last equation in more conventional mathematical form. Let the scalar distance between molecules 1 and 2 be denoted by R, between 2 and 3 by r, and between 1 and 3 by r'. Make the following notational replacements: $g(1, 2, \lambda) \to g(R, \lambda)$, $g(1, 3, \lambda) \to g(r', \lambda)$ which of course is of the same functional form as $g(R, \lambda)$, and $g(2, 3) \to g(r)(= g(r, 1))$. After integrating Eq 4-15 with respect to λ from 0 to λ, we obtain the following result in a form first derived by Kirkwood and Boggs [27]:

$$\ln g(R, \lambda) = -\beta\lambda\phi(R)$$

$$+ \pi C R^{-1} \int_0^\infty r dr[K(R - r, \lambda) - K(R + r, \lambda)][g(r) - 1] \quad (4\text{-}16)$$

$$K(t, \lambda) = -2\beta \int_0^\lambda d\lambda' \int_{|t|}^\infty r' dr' g(r', \lambda')\phi(r')$$

This is a nonlinear integral equation of a peculiarly intractable type. An exact analytic solution is manifestly impossible at the present state of development of mathematics, no matter what the choice of ϕ may be. Kirkwood and Boggs [28] obtained an approximate solution to Eq. 4-16 for the case of hard spheres (with no interaction for separations larger than that of closest approach) by linearizing the equation with respect to the deviations of the g from unity in the range $r > a$, where a is the sphere diameter. For a density given by $v/v_0 = 1.45$ (where $v = C^{-1}$ is the actual molecular volume, and where v_0 is the molecular volume for closest packing), g started at a maximum value of about 2.1 at $r = a$ decreasing to a first minimum value of about 0.7 at $r = 1.7a$ followed by a series of maxima and minima of decreasing amplitude finally approaching the value $g = 1$ for large r. More recently, Kirkwood, Maun, and Alder [29] have given a numerical solution of Eq. 4-16 for the same case (hard spheres). They obtained for the same density $(v/v_0 = 1.45)$ a solution very close to the approximate analytical solution of Kirkwood and Boggs except for r slightly larger than a where the numerical solution was appreciably larger—in fact, at $r = a$, $g \cong 2.7$ instead of 2.1. These workers find very interestingly that for densities larger than a certain critical density given by $v/v_0 = 1.24$ no integrable solution exists. It is surmised that this corresponds to the limit of stability of the liquid phase of hard spheres, and that at higher densities (up to that of closest packing) a crystalline phase must exist. Using Eq. 4-12, thermodynamic functions were computed for various densities. In particular, equation of state data $\beta pv - 1 = f(v/v_0)$ were obtained which were compared with the free volume expression $\beta pv - 1 = [(v/v_0)^{\frac{1}{3}} - 1]^{-1}$ obtained by Eyring and Hirschfelder [6]. The free volume result for $\beta pv - 1$ was in the order of 0.5–1.0 larger than the Kirkwood-Maun-Alder numerical results in the range $1 < v/v_0 < 5.5$. It is not surprising that the force volume theory gives excessively high values of the pressures, since this theory, in effect, puts excessive constraints on the motion of the molecules.

Kirkwood, Lewinson, and Alder [30] have given numerical solutions to Eq. 4-16 for the case of a modified Lennard-Jones interaction potential. Explicitly the new potential is given by

$$\phi(1, 2) \equiv \phi(R) = \epsilon\gamma(x), \qquad x = R/a \qquad (4\text{-}17a)$$

where

$$\gamma(x) = \infty, \qquad 0 \leq x < 1; \qquad \gamma(x) = 4(x^{-12} - x^{-6}), \qquad x \geq 1 \qquad (4\text{-}17b)$$

Thus ϕ is the interaction potential for a pair of hard spheres of diameter a which attract according to the well-known Lennard-Jones potential when they are not in contact. The solutions for the radial d.f., g, in this case are quite similar to those obtained for the hard spheres without supplementary interaction except that $g(a)$, corresponding to near contact, is less than the maximum value of g, whereas in the previous case $g(a)$ was the maximum. Also, as is to be expected, the g are now temperature dependent, the high temperature limit being identical to the previous case. The system composed of hard spheres without supplementary interaction exhibited no liquid-gas transition. The addition of an attractive potential in the present case introduces such a transition along with the allied critical phenomena.

Theory of Born and Green. The procedure followed by Born and Green [20,21] is rather closely related to that of Kirkwood as far as the calculation of the radial d.f. itself is concerned. In the present case we start with a different version of the average force theorem. Instead of using a "force" defined in terms of an artificial coupling parameter λ (in which case the "force" is $\partial U/\partial \lambda$) we use the actual mechanical force acting upon molecule 1 with the associated parameter now being the position of this molecule. We consider here the d.f. for the actual system without the artificial device of partial coupling. The first order or singlet d.f. is

$$\rho^{(1)}(s) = \left[\frac{1}{Z_N(\beta)}\right]\int \cdots \int d(1) \cdots$$

$$d(s-1)d(s+1) \cdots d(N)e^{-\beta U_N} \quad (4\text{-}18)$$

$$= V^{-1}$$

where U_N is the total potential energy and Z_N the Gibbs phase integral, both discussed in Art. 3. The pair and radial d.f. are given by

$$\rho^{(1)}(s, s') = V^{-2}g(s, s') = \left[\frac{1}{Z_N(\beta)}\right]\int \cdots \int d(1) \cdots$$

$$d(s-1)d(s+1) \cdots d(s'-1)d(s'+1) \cdots d(N)e^{-\beta U_N} \quad (4\text{-}19)$$

Taking the gradient of $-\beta^{-1}\ln g(1, 2)$ with respect to the position of molecule 1 gives the average force theorem:

$$-\beta^{-1}\nabla_1 \ln g(1, 2) = \nabla_1\phi(1, 2)$$

$$+ (N-2)\int d(3)\frac{\rho^{(3)}(1, 2, 3)}{\rho^{(2)}(1, 2)}\nabla_1\phi(1, 3) \quad (4\text{-}20)$$

Introducing the superposition approximation, Eq. 4-1, and neglecting terms of the order N^{-1} we obtain

$$-\beta^{-1}\nabla_1 \ln g(1, 2) = \nabla_1\phi(1, 2) + C\int d(3)g(1, 3)g(2, 3)\nabla_1\phi(1, 3) \quad (4\text{-}21)$$

Introducing more conventional notations, namely, $g(1, 2) \to g(R)$, $g(1, 3) \to G(r')$, $g(2, 3) \to g(r)$, $\phi(1, 2) \to \phi(R)$, etc., and integrating the resultant expression with respect to R, we finally obtain, after certain tedious manipulations, the result

$$\ln g(R) = -\beta\phi(R)$$

$$+ \pi C R^{-1}\int_0^\infty rdr[K(R-r) - K(R+r)][g(r) - 1] \quad (4\text{-}22)$$

$$K(t) = \beta\int_{|t|}^\infty dr'(r'^2 - t^2)g(r')\phi'(r')$$

in which the prime on the ϕ denotes differentiation with respect to its argument. This equation is presented in a form obtained by Kirkwood [29] and is to be compared with Eq. 4-16 of his theory. It is to be noted that the Born and Green result is in some ways simpler than that of Kirkwood in that the complications arising from the presence of the coupling parameter λ are avoided. However, this simplicity is bought at a price: Born and Green do not have at their disposal such a convenient relation as Eq. 4-12 for the computation of thermodynamic functions. In fact, Kirkwood introduces the coupling parameter λ into his treatment of the Born and Green theory presumably so that Eq. 4-12 can be used.

Born and Green give an approximate analytic solution to Eq. 4-22 by the following procedure. Let

$$g(r) = e^{-\beta\phi(r)+f(r)} \tag{4-23}$$

and neglect powers of $f(r)$ higher than the first. Eq. 4-22 then reduces to

$$-rf(r) = C \int_0^\infty ds \int_{-s}^s dt(s^2 - t^2)(t + r)[f(t + r) + u(t + r)$$

$$+ f(t + r)u(t + r)]u'(s)[1 + f(s)] \tag{4-24}$$

where

$$u(r) = e^{-\beta\phi(r)} - 1 \tag{4-25}$$

To obtain an easily soluble equation, it is necessary to replace $f(r)$ by an average value $\langle f(r) \rangle = \epsilon - 1$ wherever it occurs multiplied by $u'(r)$ or $u(r)$. This rather drastic approximation reduces the final results to a semiquantitative status. We get finally

$$rf(r) = 2\pi C \int_0^\infty sds \int_{-s}^s dt(t + r)[f(t + r) + \epsilon u(t + r)]\epsilon u(s) \tag{4-26}$$

This equation can be readily solved by means of Fourier transformations. Extending the definitions of $f(r)$ and $u(r)$ to negative values of their arguments by the relations $f(-r) = f(r)$ and $u(-r) = u(r)$, we can write the Fourier transforms

$$isg(s) = \int_{-\infty}^\infty rdrf(r)e^{2(\pi irs)} \tag{4-27}$$

and

$$isv(s) = \int_{-\infty}^\infty rdru(r)e^{2(2\pi irs)} \tag{4-28}$$

Taking the Fourier transform of Eq. 4-26 we get

$$sg(s) = Cs[g(s) + \epsilon v(s)]\epsilon v(s) \tag{4-29}$$

Solving for $g(s)$ and making the inverse transformation, we get the desired solution

$$irf(r) = \int_{-\infty}^{+\infty} sdse^{(2\pi irs)} \frac{C\epsilon v(s)}{1 - C\epsilon v(s)} \tag{4-30}$$

For sufficiently small densities, that is C small, $C\epsilon v(s)$ never exceeds unity so that Eq. 4-30 can be expanded in powers of C. This case evidently corresponds to the gaseous phase. As C increases, $C\epsilon v(s)$ attains the value unity somewhere and a singularity appears in the integrand, at $s = \pm s_0$, say. The solution is then indeterminate by an arbitrary multiple of $\sin(2\pi irs_0)$, the arbitrariness being removable by the requirement that $\int r^2 dr[g(r) - 1]$ be finite. This case, according to Born and Green, corresponds to the liquid state. Using the original definition of ϵ, we find it to be given by

$$2\pi(\epsilon - 1)v(0) = \int_{-\infty}^{+\infty} s\,ds\, \frac{C\epsilon v(s)}{1 - C\epsilon v(s)} \tag{4-31}$$

McLellan [31] has devised an approximate analytic method for solving Eq. 4-22 by assuming

$$g(r) = e^{-\beta\phi(r)} \qquad\qquad r > 3r_0/2$$

$$= e^{-\beta\phi(r)} \left(1 + \sum_{m=1}^{\infty} c_m r^m\right) \qquad r < 3r_0/2 \tag{4-32}$$

where r_0 is the value of r for which $\phi(r)$ is a minimum. The coefficients c_m were determined by an appropriate iterative procedure. The results are in good agreement with the experimental curves for $g(r)$ determined by X-ray diffraction.

Kirkwood and coworkers [29,30] have solved Eq. 4-22 by numerical methods for two cases: (1) hard spheres and (2) hard spheres attracting according to a Lennard-Jones potential. In their work, they have introduced the coupling parameter λ so that Eq. 4-22 is modified by the substitution $K(t) \to K(t, \lambda)$, where the new kernel is defined by

$$K(t, \lambda) = \beta\lambda \int_{|t|}^{\infty} dr'(r'^2 - t^2)g(r', \lambda)\phi'(r') \tag{4-33}$$

The results are in quite close quantitative agreement with those obtained from the Kirkwood theory.

Variational method. One of the present authors [23] has recently developed a variational method for the calculation of the radial d.f. and of the pertinent thermodynamic functions. We start by considering the excess Helmholtz free energy $\bar{A}_N(\beta)$ defined by Eq. 4-6 and repeated here for convenience:

$$\bar{A}_N(\beta) = -\beta^{-1} \ln \left[\frac{Z_N(\beta)}{VN}\right] \tag{4-34}$$

where $Z_N(\beta)$ is the Gibbs phase integral. This equation can be rewritten in the form

$$e^{-\beta\bar{A}_N\beta} = V^{-N} \int \cdots \int d(1) \cdots d(N)e^{-\beta U_N} \tag{4-35}$$

where the integrations extend over all configurations within the volume V and where

$$U_N = \sum_{\substack{s,s'=1 \\ s>s'}}^{N} \phi(s, s') \tag{4-36}$$

is the potential energy of the system of N molecules.

Let us consider the variational function

$$\beta\hat{\bar{A}}_N = V^{-N} \int \cdots \int d(1) \cdots d(N) P_N (\ln P_N + \beta U_N) \quad (4\text{-}37)$$

in which $P_N = P_N(1, \cdots, N)$ is an arbitrary distribution function to be varied under the constraints of constant β and of normalization defined by

$$V^{-N} \int \cdots \int d(1) \cdots d(N) P = 1 \quad (4\text{-}38)$$

It can be readily proven using Eq. 4-35 that the minimum value of $\hat{\bar{A}}$ is the excess Helmholtz free energy (defined only for equilibrium), $\bar{A}_N$ given by Eq. 4-35 or 4-34.

Let us express P_N in the form

$$P_N = \prod_{\substack{s,s'=1 \\ s>s'}}^{N} g(s, s') \prod_{\substack{s,s',s''=1 \\ s>s'>s''}}^{N} g^{(3)}(s, s', s'') \cdots \quad (4\text{-}39)$$

in which the g of a given order are of the same functional form and are invariant to permutation of their arguments (i.e. $g(s, s') = g(s', s)$). Let us require that

$$P_1(1) = 1 \quad (4\text{-}40a)$$

which is trivial, and that

$$P_2(1, 2) = g(1, 2) \quad (4\text{-}40b)$$

$$P_3(1, 2, 3) = g(1, 2)g(2, 3)g(3, 1)g^{(3)}(1, 2, 3) \quad (4\text{-}40c)$$

etc., where $P_n(1, \ldots, n)$, $n < N$, is an nth order d.f., the same system (not the highest order d.f. for a system of n molecules) defined by

$$P_n(1, \cdots, n) = V^{-N+n} \int \cdots \int d(n+1) \cdots d(N) P_N(1, \cdots, N) \quad (4\text{-}41)$$

The relation (4-40b) thus requires $g(1, 2)$ to be the radial d.f. Later, we will have occasion to explicitly use the following relations derivable from the relations immediately above:

$$V^{-1} \int d(2)g(1, 2) = 1 \quad (4\text{-}42a)$$

and

$$V^{-3} \iiint d(1)d(2)d(3)g(1, 2)g(2, 3)g(3, 1)g^{(3)}(1, 2, 3) = 1 \quad (4\text{-}42b)$$

Inserting Eq. 4-39 into 4-37, using the constraints on the g expressed by Eq. 4-40a, 4-40b, 4-40c, . . . , and 4-41, and remembering the definition of U_N (Eq. 4-36), we finally obtain

$$\beta\hat{\bar{A}}_N = \tfrac{1}{2}C^2 \iint d(1)d(2)g(1, 2)[\ln g(1, 2) + \beta\phi(1, 2)]$$

$$+ \tfrac{1}{6}C^3 \iiint d(1)d(2)d(3)g(1, 2)g(2, 3)g(3, 1)g^{(3)}(1, 2, 3) \ln g^{(3)}(1, 2, 3)$$

$$+ \cdots \quad (4\text{-}43)$$

where C is the number density N/V. Terms of the order of unity and smaller have been neglected in Eq. 4-43 since $\beta \hat{\bar{A}}_N$ is of the order of N. This is an otherwise exact result in which correlations of order n and higher do not appear in the first $n - 2$ terms.

Now let us make the approximation of setting fourth and higher order g's equal to unity. The additional approximation of setting the third order g equal to unity would be equivalent to the superposition approximation expressed by Eq. 4-1. However we will make a slightly different approximation, namely,

$$g^{(3)}(1, 2, 3) = 1 - \gamma = \text{const} \tag{4-44}$$

where γ is to be determined by the third order normalization condition, Eq. 4-42b. After some manipulations involving the use of Eq. 4-42a we find

$$\gamma = V^{-3} \iiint d(1)d(2)d(3)[g(1, 2) - 1][g(2, 3) - 1][g(3, 1) - 1] \tag{4-44}$$

neglecting terms of the order of γ^2. It is evident that γ is a very small quantity of the order of V^{-2}.

Introducing these approximations into Eq. 4-43 we obtain

$$\beta \hat{\bar{A}}_N = \tfrac{1}{2}C^2 \iint d(1)d(2)g(1, 2)[\ln g(1, 2) + \beta\phi(1, 2)]$$

$$- \tfrac{1}{6}C^3 \iiint d(1)d(2)d(3)[g(1, 2) - 1][g(2, 3) - 1][g(3, 1) - 1] \tag{4-45}$$

in which we have used the approximation $\ln (1 - \gamma) \cong -\gamma$. If we require $g(1, 2)$ to depend only upon the relative coordinates of molecules 1 and 2, Eq. 4-45 can be recast in the form

$$\frac{\beta \hat{\bar{A}}_N}{N} = \frac{1}{2} C \int d(2)g(1, 2)[\ln g(1, 2) + \beta\phi(1, 2)]$$

$$- \frac{1}{6} C^2 \iint d(2)d(3)[g(1, 2) - 1][g(2, 3) - 1][g(3, 1) - 1] \tag{4-46}$$

where molecule 1 is held fixed at an arbitrary position in the midst of the system. Eq. 4-46 is too minimized with respect to the functional form of g under the constraint (4-42a).

However, when one enters into the details of this process one finds that there are certain unpleasant features associated with the finiteness of the volume V. Therefore, it is desirable to go to the limit infinite volume keeping $C = N/V$ fixed. In view of the fact that in a system of finite volume g differs from unity at large separations by an increment of the order of V^{-1}, one must proceed with caution. If this increment occurs linearly in the integrand of an integral extending over the volume V, it will contribute a term of the order of unity to the result. If we allow the volume to become infinite first and then extend the range of integration over the volume (now infinite), the increment will contribute nothing since it vanished when we initially let the volume become infinite. If we reverse the order of these processes, the increment will contribute a finite amount. Thus there is a paradox here which must be removed before we can obtain a meaningful expression for infinite volume. It can be removed by modifying Eq. 4-46 so that the increment occurs in each integrand to higher powers than the number of integrations over V. This can be accomplished by the subtraction of

$$\tfrac{1}{2}C \int d(2)[g(1, 2) - 1] = 0$$

from Eq. 4-46. We can now take the limit $V \to \infty$ with impunity giving

$$\beta\hat{a} = \tfrac{1}{2}C \int d(2)\{g(1, 2)[\ln g(1, 2) - 1 + \beta\phi] + 1\}$$
$$- \tfrac{1}{6}C^2 \iint d(1)d(2)[g(1, 2) - 1][g(2, 3) - 1][g(3, 1) - 1] \quad (4\text{-}47)$$

where

$$\hat{a} = \lim_{V \to \infty} \frac{\bar{A}_N}{N}$$

The constraint (4-42a) can now be dropped and must be replaced by the condition

$$\lim_{r_{12} \to \infty} g(1, 2) = 1 \qquad (4\text{-}48)$$

The proof of this lies beyond the scope of this section. The quantity $\hat{a}$ when minimized with respect to g under the new constraint (4-48) is equal to $\bar{a}$, an approximation to the excess Helmholtz free energy per molecule, and the resultant g is an approximation to the radial d.f.

It may be of interest to note that if we set $g = e^{-\beta\phi}$ in $\hat{a}$ we get the imperfect gas expression for $\bar{a}$ correct up to the third virial coefficient. If we minimized $\hat{a}$ for the imperfect gas case we would get a better answer. Whether or not it would be exact up to the fourth virial coefficient must remain an open question at the present time.

At an arbitrary density we could use Eq. 4-47 directly inserting for g a trial function with a finite number of parameters which we could adjust to give the best form of g and the best value of $\hat{a}$. Alternatively, we can solve the variational problem analytically, in which case we obtain the following integral equation for g:

$$\ln g(1, 2) = -\beta\phi(1, 2) - C \int d(3)[g(1, 3) - 1][g(2, 3) - 1] \quad (4\text{-}49)$$

We could then solve this equation by suitable approximate methods.

Eq. 4-49 in the above form does not exhibit any obvious connections with the integral equation of Kirkwood or of Born and Green. The similarity with the Born and Green integro-differential equation (4-21) can be brought out if we take the gradient of Eq. 4-49 with respect to the position of molecule 1 giving

$$-\beta^{-1}\nabla_1 \ln g(1, 2) = \nabla_1\phi(1, 2) + C \int d(3)g(1, 3)g(2, 3)\nabla_1 w(1, 3) \quad (4\text{-}50)$$

where
$$w(1, 3) = -\beta^{-1} \ln g(1, 3) \quad (4\text{-}51)$$

is the potential of average force acting on molecules 1 and 3. In deriving Eq. 4-50 we have used the fact that $\int d(3)g(1, 3)$ is independent of the position of molecule 1. Eq. 4-50 differs from Eq. 4-21 of Born and Green only in the presence of $w(1, 3)$ in the integrand instead of $\phi(1, 3)$. Thus in Eq. 4-50 we compute an approximate average of the *average* force that the surrounding molecules exert on 1 and 2, whereas Born and Green compute an approximate average of the *actual* force.

Unfortunately, the variational method has not been carried sufficiently far to make available detailed analytic or numerical results. However, certain remarks of methodological interest may be in order. First of all, the present method enjoys all of the practical advantages inherent in variational procedures. Secondly, it is much simpler and is more symmetrical. Thirdly, it allows the direct computation of thermodynamic functions in an obviously self-consistent manner.

F,5. Transport Processes.

Hydrodynamic description. In discussing transport processes in liquids, we will confine ourselves to multicomponent (or one-component) systems in which no chemical reactions occur and in which no external or long range forces operate. Further limitations are implied by the requirement that an adequate set of observables be provided by the following densities:

1. Concentrations C_α, $\alpha = 1, \cdots, n$, of the relevant chemical species expressed in moles per unit volume. (Elsewhere in this section, e.g. Art. 3 and 4, concentrations have been expressed in number of molecules per unit volume.)

2. Momentum density (or mass current) $\mathbf{m} = \rho\mathbf{q}$, where ρ is the mass density and $\mathbf{q}$ is the particle velocity. Here we must regard ρ and $\mathbf{m}$ as primary quantities and $\mathbf{q}$ as a derived quantity defined in terms of them.

3. Total energy density $\rho(e + \frac{1}{2}q^2)$, where e is the specific internal energy as measured by an observer moving with the fluid, and where $\frac{1}{2}q^2(q = |\mathbf{q}|)$ is the specific kinetic energy of bulk motion as measured by a fixed observer. Again, $\rho(e + \frac{1}{2}q^2)$ must be regarded as a primary quantity and e as a derived quantity defined in terms of it and previously defined primary quantities.

Returning to the limitations implied by the requirements that these densities constitute an adequate set of observables, we must first say what we mean by the term "adequate." This term is intended to mean that the rate of change of the distribution of densities at a given time can be expressed to a good approximation as a function of the distributions at the same time. This requirement of adequacy limits our considerations to not excessively high frequency phenomena in the case of ordinary liquids of low molecular weight, and to very low frequency phenomena in the case of peculiar liquids of high molecular weight that exhibit visco-elastic effects and other complicated relaxation phenomena under ordinary experimental conditions.

Our study of transport processes is concerned with the macroscopic description and molecular basis of the irreversible parts of the rates of change of the above-mentioned density distributions within the limitations already prescribed. First, we will give the hydrodynamic equations, macroscopically describing the rates of change, in order to define certain derived quantities such as stress, diffusion currents, and heat current. The irreversible relations between these and the primary density distributions define the so-called transport coefficients exemplified by shear and bulk viscosity, diffusion constants, etc. The thermodynamics of irreversible processes, discussed in Sec. J of this volume, is concerned with the correct macroscopic formulation of the transport coefficients.

We now summarize the equations of hydrodynamics. For a more detailed discussion of these equations in this form see II,F. For the concentrations C_α and the molecular weights $\mathfrak{M}_\alpha$, we have

$$\frac{\partial C_\alpha}{\partial t} + \nabla \cdot (\mathbf{q}C_\alpha + \mathbf{J}_\alpha) = 0, \quad \alpha = 1, \cdots, n \tag{5-1}$$

where $\mathbf{J}$ is the current of species α referred to axes moving with the velocity $\mathbf{q}$ (mobile axes). These equations express the conservation of each species individually. Evidently, the mass density ρ is related to the concentrations C_α by the formula

$$\rho = \sum_{\alpha=1}^{n} \mathfrak{M}_\alpha C_\alpha \tag{5-2}$$

In a similar fashion, the mass current (or momentum density) $\mathbf{m}$ is related to the currents of the individual species in the following way:

$$\mathbf{m} = \sum_{\alpha=1}^{n} \mathfrak{M}_\alpha (\mathbf{q}C_\alpha + \mathbf{J}_\alpha)$$

$$= \rho\mathbf{q} + \sum_{\alpha=1}^{n} \mathfrak{M}_\alpha \mathbf{J}_\alpha \tag{5-3}$$

so that

$$\sum_{\alpha=1}^{n} \mathfrak{M}_\alpha \mathbf{J}_\alpha = 0 \tag{5-4}$$

Multiplying Eq. 5-1 by $\mathfrak{M}_\alpha$, summing over α, and using Eq. 5-2, 5-3, and 5-4, we obtain the usual equation of continuity

$$\frac{\partial \rho}{\partial t} + \nabla \cdot (\rho \mathbf{q}) = 0 \tag{5-5}$$

expressing the conservation of mass.

The momentum density $\mathbf{m} = \rho \mathbf{q}$ satisfies the equation

$$\frac{\partial}{\partial t} \rho \mathbf{q} + \nabla \cdot (\rho \mathbf{q} \mathbf{q}) = \nabla \cdot \sigma \tag{5-6}$$

where σ is the stress tensor. The hydrostatic pressure p is defined in terms of the stress σ according to the formula

$$p = -\tfrac{1}{3} \sum_{a=1}^{3} \sigma_{aa} \equiv -\tfrac{1}{3} \text{ trace } \sigma \tag{5 7}$$

where a labels the Cartesian coordinates x, y, z. The shear stress is defined by

$$\tau = \sigma + \mathbf{1} p \tag{5-8}$$

The total energy density $\rho(e + \tfrac{1}{2} q^2)$ satisfies the equation

$$\frac{\partial}{\partial t}\left[\rho\left(e + \frac{1}{2} q^2\right)\right] + \nabla \cdot \left[\rho \mathbf{q}\left(e + \frac{1}{2} q^2\right)\right] = -\nabla \cdot \mathbf{J}_Q + \nabla \cdot \sigma \cdot \mathbf{q} \tag{5-9}$$

where $\mathbf{J}_Q$ is the heat current. The term $\nabla \cdot \sigma \cdot \mathbf{q}$ expresses the rate of performance of work against the stress.

Eq. 5-1, 5-6, and 5-9 introduce the new quantities $\mathbf{J}_\alpha$, σ, and $\mathbf{J}_Q$ whose dependence upon the densities C_α, $\rho \mathbf{q}$, and $\rho(e + \tfrac{1}{2} q^2)$ is determined by the particular properties of the material under consideration. These dependences can be empirically determined; however, the thermodynamics of irreversible processes provides general guidance in the proper formulation of these relationships.

The first step is to define entropy for a system not in equilibrium. Let us assume that this can be done, and further let us assume that we can define at a given point in space a specific entropy s which is dependent only upon the primary densities (C_α, $\rho \mathbf{q}$, and $\rho(e + \tfrac{1}{2} q^2)$) at the same point. This pointwise dependence is of course an approximation and is valid only when the variation of macroscopic properties is not excessively large over intermolecular distances. At a point we assume the thermodynamic formula

$$Td(\rho s) = d(\rho e) - \sum_{\alpha=1}^{n} \mu_\alpha dC_\alpha \tag{5-10}$$

to hold. This equation defines the temperature T and the chemical potentials μ_α at a point in a nonequilibrium system. It is to be noted that the velocity $\mathbf{q}$ does not appear here, it being assumed that bulk motion has no effect on the entropy. We can define a thermodynamic pressure p' by the relation

$$p' = \rho(Ts - e) + \sum_{\alpha=1}^{n} \mu_\alpha C_\alpha \tag{5-11}$$

The hydrostatic pressure p and the thermodynamic pressure p' are identical if the system is in equilibrium; otherwise, they are not.

The equation of entropy transport will contain a source term which contains all of the irreversible effects in the dependence of the primary densities upon the quantities $\mathbf{J}_\alpha$, σ, and $\mathbf{J}_Q$. The structure of the entropy source term forms the basis for deductions of the thermodynamics of irreversible processes. Introducing the mobile derivative

$$\frac{d}{dt} = \frac{\partial}{\partial t} + \mathbf{q} \cdot \nabla \tag{5-12}$$

and using Eq. 5-1, 5-6, and 5-9 we arrive at the entropy transport equation

$$\rho \frac{ds}{dt} = -\nabla \cdot \left[T^{-1} \left(\mathbf{J}_Q - \sum_{\alpha=1}^{n} \mu_\alpha \mathbf{J}_\alpha \right) \right]$$

$$+ T^{-1} \left(\sum_\alpha \mathbf{J}_\alpha \cdot \mathbf{X}_\alpha + \boldsymbol{\pi} : \dot{\boldsymbol{\varepsilon}} + \mathbf{J}_Q \cdot \mathbf{X}_Q \right) \tag{5-13}$$

where

$$\boldsymbol{\pi} = \sigma + \mathbf{1}p' \tag{5-14}$$

and where

$$\mathbf{X}_\alpha = -T\nabla(\mu_\alpha T^{-1}) \tag{5-15a}$$

$$\dot{\boldsymbol{\varepsilon}} = \text{sym} \ (\nabla \mathbf{q}) \tag{5-15b}$$

$$\mathbf{X}_Q = -T^{-1}\nabla T \tag{5-15c}$$

The term $\boldsymbol{\pi} : \dot{\boldsymbol{\varepsilon}}$ can be expressed in the more extended form

$$\boldsymbol{\pi} : \dot{\boldsymbol{\varepsilon}} = \sum_{a=1}^{3} \sum_{b=1}^{3} \pi_{ab} \dot{\varepsilon}_{ba} \tag{5-16}$$

and the expression in Eq. 5-15b is intended to mean

$$\dot{\epsilon}_{ab} = \frac{1}{2}\left(\frac{\partial q_a}{\partial x_b} + \frac{\partial q_b}{\partial x_a}\right) \tag{5-17}$$

where the indices a, b label the Cartesian coordinates. The quantities $\mathbf{J}_\alpha$, π, and $\mathbf{J}_Q$ we call the generalized fluxes, using the term "flux" in a rather loose generalized sense. Correspondingly, the quantities $\mathbf{X}_\alpha$, $\dot{\epsilon}$, and $\mathbf{X}_Q$ are called forces. We will call π the nonequilibrium stress. $\dot{\epsilon}$ is the well-known rate-of-strain tensor. The second line of Eq. 5-13, composed of a sum of fluxes multiplied by forces divided by T, is the entropy source density and gives the local rate of entropy increase (as measured by a mobile observer moving with the velocity $\mathbf{q}$) arising from irreversible processes. The divergence term in Eq. 5-13 gives the local rate of entropy change (again, as measured by a mobile observer) arising from entropy transported from elsewhere. It is obvious that the divergence term does not contribute to the rate of change of the total entropy of the system (assumed to be closed), whereas the source density does.

It is permissible to interchange the roles of π and $\dot{\epsilon}$ in the entropy source density and to call $\dot{\epsilon}$ a flux and π a force. This would be semantically more reasonable in view of the physical interpretations of $\dot{\epsilon}$ and π. However, since we will eventually express the fluxes in terms of the forces, we will prefer to keep π a flux and $\dot{\epsilon}$ a force because the definitions of shear and bulk viscosities emerge more naturally this way.

If p and p' were identical, the nonequilibrium stress π would equal the shear stress τ, in which case there would be no room for bulk viscosity effects. Thus the distinction between p and p' is quite important; it is often overlooked.

If the fluxes and forces are not too large, it follows from general considerations that the currents can be expressed as linear combinations of the forces with the coefficients depending only upon the state of the medium at the point in question. Taking into account the tensorial properties of an isotropic medium (liquid or gas; in general, fluid), we may write

$$\mathbf{J}_\alpha = \sum_{\alpha'=1}^{n} L_{\alpha\alpha'}\mathbf{X}_{\alpha'} + L_{\alpha Q}\mathbf{X}_Q, \quad \alpha = 1, \cdots, n$$

$$\tag{5-18a}$$

$$\mathbf{J}_Q = \sum_{\alpha'=1}^{n} L_{Q\alpha'}\mathbf{X}_{\alpha'} + L_{QQ}\mathbf{X}_Q$$

$$\pi = (\eta_D - \tfrac{2}{3}\eta)\mathbf{1}\dot{\epsilon} + 2\eta\dot{\epsilon} \tag{5-18b}$$

where

$$\dot{\epsilon} = \sum_{a=1}^{3} \dot{\epsilon}_{aa} \equiv \text{trace } \dot{\epsilon} = \nabla \cdot \mathbf{q} \tag{5-19}$$

is the rate of dilatation. The coefficients in Eq. 5-18a and 5-18b are called kinetic coefficients. The coefficients $L_{\alpha\alpha'}$, α, $\alpha' = 1, \cdots, n$, are closely related to the diffusion constants; the coefficient L is closely related to the thermal conductivity; $L_{\alpha Q}$ to the thermal diffusion constant; and $L_{Q\alpha'}$ is associated with the reciprocal effect. The precise connection between these coefficients and the usual empirically defined quantities will be considered later. The coefficients η and η_0 are the shear and bulk (sometimes called dilatational) viscosities, respectively.

It is to be noted that there is no coupling between $\mathbf{J}_\alpha$ and $\mathbf{J}_Q$ on the one hand and $\dot{\epsilon}$ on the other, and, reciprocally, none between π and $\mathbf{X}_\alpha$ and $\mathbf{X}_Q$. This is not a result of the thermodynamics of irreversible processes but of the tensorial requirements associated with isotropic media. In media such as crystals lacking centers of symmetry, such a coupling may occur. Also, if the forces are sufficiently large, quadratic terms would have to be included in Eq. 5-18a and 5-18b, in which case a nonlinear coupling would occur, even in isotropic media. For instance, the expression for π might include a term proportional to $\mathbf{1X}_Q \cdot \mathbf{X}_Q$. However, we will not consider nonlinear effects here.

In Eq. 5-18b the effects of bulk and shear viscosity can be separated. Taking the trace of Eq. 5-18b and dividing by 3 we obtain

$$-(p - p') = \eta_D \dot{\epsilon} \tag{5-20}$$

Multiplying this last result by $\mathbf{1}$ and subtracting it from Eq. 5-18b we obtain

$$\tau = 2\eta(\dot{\epsilon} - \tfrac{1}{3}\mathbf{1}\dot{\epsilon}) \tag{5-21}$$

There are certain further restrictions on the kinetic coefficients which must be considered. The first set of restrictions arises from Eq. 5-4. If this relation is to be preserved independently of the values of the forces then we must have

$$\sum_{\alpha=1}^{n} \mathfrak{M}_\alpha L_{\alpha\alpha'} = 0 \tag{5-22a}$$

and

$$\sum_{\alpha=1}^{n} \mathfrak{M}_\alpha L_{\alpha Q} = 0 \tag{5-22b}$$

A nontrivial result of the thermodynamics of irreversible processes is that

$$\sum_{\alpha'=1}^{n} L_{\alpha\alpha'}\mathfrak{M}_{\alpha'} = 0 \tag{5-22c}$$

and that

$$\sum_{\alpha=1}^{n} L_{Q\alpha}\mathfrak{M}_\alpha = 0 \tag{5-22d}$$

All of these relations express the fact that there can be no dissipation associated with the bulk motion of the fluid. A more compelling way of stating this might be that the mere fact that the observer moves past a container filled with a multicomponent mixture cannot in itself introduce dissipation.

Further restrictions are the famous reciprocal relations of Onsager [*32*]. In terms of the kinetic coefficients concerning us here, these relations take the form

$$L_{\alpha\alpha'} = L_{\alpha'\alpha}, \quad \alpha, \alpha' = 1, \cdots, n$$
$$L_{\alpha Q} = L_{Q\alpha}$$

(5-23)

Since there are no cross effects between the shear and bulk viscosities, the Onsager relations do not pertain to them.

A last set of restrictions arises from the second law of thermodynamics requiring the entropy source density to be non-negative. The substitution of the relations (5-18a) and (5-18b) into the entropy source density in Eq. 5-13 gives a quadratic form in the forces. This quadratic form must then be positive indefinite. More explicitly, the shear viscosity η and the bulk viscosity η_D must both be non-negative, and the matrix of L coefficients must be positive indefinite.

There are $(n + 1)^2$ L coefficients; however, because of the restrictions stated above, only $\frac{1}{2}n(n + 1)$ of them are independent.

To complete our discussion we must establish the connection between the kinetic coefficients and the traditional quantities such as the diffusion constants, thermal conductivity, etc. The shear and bulk viscosities need no further discussion since they are most commonly defined as they appear here. In the case of the L coefficients the situation is entirely different. From this point on, we will limit the discussion to the case of two components and will follow closely the treatment of de Groot [*33*]. We first must decide on a set of state variables. The thermodynamic state of a two-component system is described by 3 variables. We choose the temperature T, the thermodynamic pressure p', and one of the specific concentrations $c_\alpha = C_\alpha/\rho$, $(\alpha = 1, 2)$, c_1, say. The specific concentrations are connected by an identical relation, namely

$$\sum_{\alpha=1}^{2} \mathfrak{M}_\alpha c_\alpha = 1$$

so that two of them convey no more information than one. Following de Groot we introduce the quantity

$$Q_1^* = \frac{L_{1Q}}{\mathfrak{M}_1 L_{11}}$$

(5-24)

called the "heat of transfer." Expressing the forces $\mathbf{X}_Q$ and $\mathbf{X}_\alpha$ in terms of our new set of thermodynamic state variables (partial derivatives must be interpreted accordingly), we find

$$\mathfrak{M}_1 \mathbf{J}_1 = - \mathfrak{M}_2 \mathbf{J}_2$$

$$= \mathfrak{M}_1^2 L_{11} \left[(v_2 - v_1)\nabla p' - \mathfrak{M}_2^{-1} c_2^{-1} \frac{\partial \mu_1}{\partial c_1} \nabla c_1 \right.$$

$$\left. - (Q_1^* - h_1 + h_2)T^{-1}\nabla T \right] \quad (5\text{-}25)$$

where v_α and h_α are the partial specific volume and enthalpy, respectively, of component α. Defining the diffusion constant according to Fick's law

$$\mathbf{J}_1 = -D_{11}\nabla c_1 \quad (5\text{-}26)$$

assuming other gradients to vanish, we find

$$D_{11} = \mathfrak{M}_1^2 L_{11} \mathfrak{M}_2^{-1} c_2^{-1} \frac{\partial \mu_1}{\partial c_1} \quad (5\text{-}27)$$

Similarly, the thermal diffusion constant can be defined by considering the coefficient of ∇T.

Unfortunately, limitations of space preclude an exhaustive survey of the relations between the L coefficients and the variously defined transport coefficients. Readers wishing to pursue these matters further are urged to consult de Groot's treatise [*33*].

Molecular theories. A rational approach to the formulation of a rigorous molecular theory of transport processes involves just defining the pertinent macroscopic densities (namely C_α, $\rho\mathbf{q}$, and $\rho(e + \frac{1}{2}q^2)$) in terms of the average values of certain functions of the coordinates and momenta of the component molecules. Using the microscopic equations of motion one then obtains the quantities $\mathbf{J}_\alpha$, σ, and $\mathbf{J}_Q$ as average values of certain other functions of coordinates and momenta. To relate the derived quantities to the primary densities (or to other well-defined state variables) one must consider a particular statistical distribution. We will not enter here into the problem of constructing an appropriate distribution beyond stating that at the time of interest it must have already attained a quasi-stationary state with respect to processes not directly described by the primary macroscopic densities.

To discuss this program adequately would require space far in excess of that available here. Consequently we direct the reader to the literature [*34*] where he will find isolated transport phenomena discussed in an approximate manner with a frequent emphasis upon the underlying physical picture.

F,6. Surface Tension of Liquids. In the previous parts of this section, the properties of liquids and liquid solutions have been considered in the bulk under the assumption that the molecular environment is isotropic. We now consider briefly the properties of the interference between a liquid phase and some other phase, with a view to interpreting the properties of the interface in terms of the properties of the bulk phases.

The thermodynamic treatment of the interface between two phases was developed by Gibbs [35]. This treatment is based upon the introduction of a mathematical surface of separation of constant density between the two phases and the assumption that the two phases remain homogeneous up to the surface of separation. Each extensive property of the system is then regarded as the sum of three terms: The contribution of each bulk phase and a residual part that is assigned to the surface of separation. The various properties assigned to this surface depend upon its position, and the surface can be arbitrarily located so as to make the surface contribution to any one of the extensive properties zero.

On the microscopic scale, the region of transition between two phases is a zone of finite thickness within which the structure of the fluid undergoes continuous modification. From a statistical point of view, the variation of density of the fluid through the surface zone is of primary importance. For theoretical purposes, it is convenient to define the interface as a surface of constant density such that if the phases remained homogeneous up to the surface, the number of molecules on either side of the surface of separation would be the same as in the actual system. However, a better definition, called the surface of tension, can be based upon thermodynamic arguments [36] that will now be presented.

We suppose the surface of separation between liquid phase α and the saturated vapor phase β to be a surface of constant density but to be otherwise unspecified. The total volume V is thus divided into a part V_α occupied by the liquid and a part $V_\beta = V - V_\alpha$ occupied by the vapor. If C_α and C_β are the number density in the liquid and vapor proper, respectively, and E_α and E_β are the corresponding internal energies per mole, and if the phases are supposed to be homogeneous up to the surface, the total energy of the two phases is

$$\left(C_\alpha V_\alpha \frac{E_\alpha}{N} + C_\beta V_\beta \frac{E_\beta}{N} \right)$$

The difference between the actual total energy E and this quantity is the total surface energy E_s,

$$E_s = E - \left(C_\alpha V_\alpha \frac{E_\alpha}{N} + C_\beta V_\beta \frac{E_\beta}{N} \right) \tag{6-1}$$

If C and E denote the actual number density and internal energy per mole, we may write

$$E_s \neq \Sigma = \frac{1}{N} \int_{-a}^{0} (CE_1 - C_\alpha E_\alpha)dz + \frac{1}{N} \int_{0}^{b} (CE_1 - C_\beta E_\beta)dz \tag{6-2}$$

where Σ is the total area of the interface and $b - a$ is the thickness of the surface zone. As the limits of integration, a and b can be replaced by any larger values. The coordinate z is in the direction normal to the surface from phase α to phase β. In writing Eq. 6-2, advantage is taken of the fact that the principle contributions to the integrals come from a region close to the surface and that the surface may be considered to be planar in a region of microscopic dimensions. We remark that the latter assumption will not be valid in the consideration of very small droplets for which the surface of tension will have a radius of curvature of microscopic dimension.

The difference $CE_1 - C_\alpha E_\alpha$ can be expressed as

$$- \int_{-a}^{0} \frac{\partial}{\partial z} (CE_1) dz$$

Substituting in Eq. 6-2 and integrating once by parts, one obtains

$$\frac{E_s}{\Sigma} = - \frac{1}{N} \int_{-a}^{b} z \frac{\partial}{\partial z} (CE_1) dz \qquad (6\text{-}3)$$

The surface entropy S_s and superficial Helmholtz free energy A_s are similarly defined and expressed by the analogous formulas,

$$\frac{S_s}{\Sigma} = - \frac{1}{N} \int_{-a}^{b} z \frac{\partial}{\partial z} (CS_1) dz \qquad (6\text{-}4)$$

$$\frac{A_s}{\Sigma} = - \frac{1}{N} \int_{-a}^{b} z \frac{\partial}{\partial z} (CA_1) dz \qquad (6\text{-}5)$$

where S and A are the entropy and Helmholtz free energy, respectively, per mole. The surface energy, surface entropy, and superficial Helmholtz free energy are related by the thermodynamic relation

$$E_s = A_s + TS_s \qquad (6\text{-}6)$$

The surface tension γ is analogous to the pressure, and

$$dA_s = \gamma d\Sigma - S_s dT$$
$$dE_s = T dS_s + \gamma d\Sigma \qquad (6\text{-}7)$$

It follows from the second of Eq. 6-7 that the surface tension is the superficial Helmholtz free energy per unit surface,

$$A_s = \gamma \Sigma \qquad (6\text{-}8)$$

Eq. 6-6, 6-7, and 6-8 lead at once to the Kelvin equation,

$$E_s = - \Sigma T^2 \frac{d}{dT} \left(\frac{\gamma}{T} \right) \qquad (6\text{-}9)$$

Since the internal energy per molecule is not the same in the bulk liquid and vapor phases, it is clear that the choice of the surface of separation is not arbitrary. If the surface is displaced a distance z_0 in the z direction, the value of the surface energy will be changed by the amount $\Sigma z_0 (C_\beta E_\beta - C_\alpha E_\alpha)/N$. Since the surface energy and the surface tension are connected by Eq. 6-9, it is necessary, if the surface energy is to be unique, that the surface of tension be defined so as to assure the consistency of Eq. 6-3 and 6-9.

A cell theory of surface tension has been developed by Lennard-Jones and Corner [*37,38*], and a theory based upon the methods of the radial distribution function has been formulated by Kirkwood and Buff [*39,40,41*]. The former theory, which is based upon a rather explicit physical model, will be briefly reviewed before discussing the more satisfactory theory based upon the radial distribution method.

The cell theory of surface tension. The cell theory of surface tension has not at present achieved the generality of the cell theory of bulk liquid phases as presented in Art. 3. Lennard-Jones and Corner [*37,38*] have extended the theory of Lennard-Jones and Devonshire to include a surface phase and have been able to calculate the Helmholtz free energy associated with unit area of surface. The development is based upon a number of assumptions. The vapor pressure of the vapor phase is neglected. The surface tension depends upon which plane of the cell lattice forms the surface. It is expected that the surface is formed by the lattice plane leading to minimum surface tension. Except for the surface layer, the lattice points are assumed to be unaffected by the presence of the surface. The lattice points of the surface layer are displaced toward the interior of the liquid so as to minimize the potential energy (correctly the Helmholtz free energy) of the complete system. Finally, it is assumed that the free volumes of the molecules in the interior of the liquid are unaffected by the presence of the surface and that the free volume of a molecule in the surface layer can be calculated by consideration of the potential field of the neighboring molecules which are held fixed in their lattice sites.

If the contribution of communal entropy is included in Eq. 3-63, the Lennard-Jones and Devonshire expression for the Helmholtz free energy of a mole of liquid in the interior can be written

$$\beta \left(\frac{A}{N} \right) = \frac{1}{2} \beta W(0) - \ln \left[\Sigma v_f \left(\frac{2\pi m}{k^2 \beta} \right)^{\frac{3}{2}} \right] \qquad (6\text{-}10)$$

For a mole of liquid bounded by a surface, the potential energy function can be written $W_s(0, z)$ depending upon the distance z by which the surface layer is displaced toward the interior. If z_0 is the displacement for which $W_s(0, z)$ is a minimum, the Helmholtz free energy A' of a mole of liquid bounded by a surface is written

$$\beta \left(\frac{A'}{N} \right) = \frac{1}{2} \beta W_s(0, z) - \ln \left[\Sigma' \left(\frac{2\pi m}{k^2 \beta} \right)^{\frac{3}{2}} \right]$$

$$- \left(\frac{1 - N_s}{N} \right) \ln v_f - \frac{N_s}{N} \ln v_{f,s} \quad (6\text{-}11)$$

where N_s is the number of molecules in the surface layer and $v_{f,s}$ is the free volume of a surface molecule. Accordingly, the surface tension is given by

$$\gamma \Sigma = \frac{1}{2} \left[W_s(0, z) - W(0) \right] + N_s kT \ln \left(\frac{v_f}{v_{f,s}} \right) \quad (6\text{-}12)$$

if the communal entropy of the mole of liquid in the interior is equal to the communal entropy of a mole of liquid bounded by a surface $\Sigma = \Sigma'$. Corner [38] has used this expression to calculate the surface tension of a liquid made up of spherical nonpolar molecules arranged in a face-centered cubic lattice and obeying the Lennard-Jones intermolecular potential function. Detailed calculations showed that the surface corresponds to the (111) lattice plane. The quantity $W_s(0, z) - W(0)$ was obtained by detailed calculations of the contributions of all lattice points making a significant contribution. The free volume of a molecule in the surface layer was obtained by a modification of the procedure employed in the interior of the liquid. In this case, the hexagonal packing of the surface layer permits the approximation of replacing the potential function by one having cylindrical symmetry. For liquid argon at 90°K the calculated value of the surface tension is 23.1 dynes/cm compared to an experimental value of 11.9 dynes/cm.

Surface tension from the radial distribution function. Kirkwood and Buff [39,40,41] have employed the theory of the radial distribution function to formulate a theory of the surface tension. Their development admits of solution to various degrees of approximation. A somewhat less general but more straightforward derivation has been given by Green [42], whose presentation is followed in this discussion.

Kirkwood and Buff obtain the surface tension directly by calculating the total stress across a surface normal to the surface of separation. We again consider a liquid phase α and vapor phase β in contact, with a surface zone of thickness $b - a$. If the component of the stress per unit area in a direction normal to this normal surface is σ_{11}, the surface tension is obtained by subtracting the pressure $p_\alpha = p_\beta$ in the uniform fluid from the stress component and by integrating over a strip of unit length and of sufficient width to extend through the surface zone. This procedure is in agreement with the experimental measurement of the surface tension, and it yields the formula

$$\gamma = \int_{-a}^{0} (\sigma_{11} - p_\alpha)dz + \int_{0}^{b} (\sigma_{11} - p_\beta)dz \qquad (6\text{-}13)$$

Transforming this expression in the same way as Eq. 6-2, we obtain

$$\gamma = \int_{-a}^{b} z \frac{\partial \sigma_{11}}{\partial z} dz \qquad (6\text{-}14)$$

where we have made use of the fact that the pressures of the uniform liquid and vapor are equal. The final expression for the surface tension, Eq. 6-14, is independent of the location of the surface of separation. We have already seen that this is not true of the surface energy.

In Art. 5, it has been shown that

$$\sigma_{11} = C\beta^{-1} - \tfrac{1}{2}C^2 \int dr g(\mathbf{r}, z)\phi'(r)r^{-1}r_1^2 \qquad (6\text{-}15)$$

where r_1 is the component of the vector $\mathbf{r}$ in a direction normal to the normal surface. In Art. 2 the internal energy per molecule has been expressed in the form

$$\frac{E}{N} \equiv \frac{3}{2}\beta^{-1} + \frac{1}{2}C \int dr g(\mathbf{r}, z)\phi(r) \qquad (6\text{-}16)$$

In Eq. 6-15 and 6-16 our notation emphasizes that the radial distribution function in the surface zone will depend upon the distance z of the point from the surface, the angle between the vector $\mathbf{r}$ and the z direction, as wel as upon the distance r. Green [42, p. 70] has shown that the first and second order distribution functions are connected by a relation that is analogous to the relation between second and third order distribution functions that we have discussed in an earlier part (Art. 4). This can be written

$$\frac{\partial C}{\partial z} = \beta C \int dr g\phi'(r)r^{-1}r_3 \qquad (6\text{-}17)$$

where r_3 is the z component of $\mathbf{r}$. We now introduce the approximation

$$g(\mathbf{r}, z) = C_\alpha g_\alpha(r) \quad \text{when (1) and (2) are both in liquid}$$

$$= 0 \quad \text{when (1) or (2) is in the vapor} \qquad (6\text{-}18)$$

where $g_\alpha(r)$ is the ordinary radial distribution function for the homogeneous liquid. This approximation is only valid if the density of the vapor is negligible compared to that of the liquid. Then Eq. 6-17 gives

$$\frac{\partial C}{\partial z} = 2\pi\beta C_\alpha^2 \int_{0}^{\infty} \int_{-(r,z)}^{r} g_\alpha(r)\phi'(r)r^{-1}r_3 \cdot r\, dr_3 dr \qquad (6\text{-}19)$$

where (r, z) denotes the smaller of the two quantities r or z. This gives

$$\frac{\partial C}{\partial z} = \pi\beta C_\alpha^2 \int_{z}^{\infty} g(r)\phi'(r)(r^2 - z^2)dr \qquad (6\text{-}20)$$

From Eq. 6-15, we obtain

$$\frac{\partial \sigma_{11}}{\partial z} = \beta^{-1} \frac{\partial C}{\partial z} - \frac{1}{2} \pi C_\alpha^2 \int_z^\infty g(r)\phi'(r)(r^2 - z^2)dr$$

$$= \tfrac{1}{2}\pi C_\alpha^2 \int_z^\infty g(r)\phi'(r)(r^2 - z^2)dr \qquad (6\text{-}21)$$

The surface tension is obtained with the aid of Eq. 6-14

$$\gamma = \tfrac{1}{2}\pi C_\alpha^2 \int_0^\infty z \int_z^\infty g(r)\phi'(r)(r^2 - z^2)drdz$$

or

$$\gamma = \tfrac{1}{8}\pi C_\alpha^2 \int_0^\infty g(r)\phi'(r)r^4 dr \qquad (6\text{-}22)$$

Eq. 6-22 has been previously obtained by Fowler [*43*] by a treatment employing the same approximation to the radial distribution function as that employed here. Fowler's treatment, based on a more explicit model than that of Kirkwood and Buff, does not lead to the more general theory of the latter authors.

The surface energy can be evaluated similarly to the surface tension. Employing Eq. 6-16, one obtains

$$\frac{\partial}{\partial z}\left(\frac{CE}{N}\right) = \frac{3}{2}\beta^{-1}\frac{\partial C}{\partial z} + \pi C_\alpha^2 \int_z^\infty g(r)\phi(r)rdr \qquad (6\text{-}23)$$

As an approximation to the thermodynamically defined surface of tension, Kirkwood and Buff employ a surface of separation satisfying

$$\int_{-a}^b z \frac{\partial C}{\partial z} dz = 0 \qquad (6\text{-}24)$$

This definition leaves the total number of molecules unchanged when it is assumed that the phases remain homogeneous up to the surface. With this definition, Eq. 6-23 reduces to

$$\frac{E_s}{N\sigma} = -\frac{1}{2}\pi C_\alpha^2 \int_0^\infty g(r)\phi(r)r^3 dr \qquad (6\text{-}25)$$

Kirkwood and Buff have made a direct comparison of Eq. 6-22 and 6-25 with experiment for liquid argon at 90°K. They employed an experimentally determined radial distribution function and obtained $\gamma = 14.9$ dynes/cm and $E/N\sigma = 27.2$ dynes/cm. The experimental values are $\gamma = 11.9$ dynes/cm and $E/N\sigma = 35$ dynes/cm. This agreement is very satisfactory in view of the approximations that have been employed.

Without giving their derivation in detail, we will now summarize the general expressions of Kirkwood and Buff. The surface tension is given by

$$\gamma = -\beta^{-1}\Gamma_0^{(1)} + \tfrac{1}{2}\int d\mathbf{r}\Gamma_0^{(2)}(\mathbf{r})\phi'(r)r^{-1}r_1^2 \qquad (6\text{-}26)$$

where $\Gamma_0^{(1)}$ and $\Gamma_0^{(2)}$ are the superficial number density and superficial pair density, respectively, defined as special cases of the functions,

$$\Gamma_j^{(1)} = \int_{-\infty}^0 z_1^j(C - C_\alpha)dz_1 + \int_0^\infty z_1^j(C - C_\beta)dz_1 \qquad (6\text{-}27)$$

$$\Gamma_j^{(2)} = \int_{-\infty}^0 j[C(z_1)C(z_2)g(z_1,\mathbf{r}) - C_\alpha^2 g_\alpha(r)]dz_1$$

$$+ \int_0^\infty z_1^j[C(z_1)C(z_2)g(z_1,\mathbf{r}) - C_\beta^2 g_\beta(r)]dz_1 \qquad (6\text{-}28)$$

The functions defined by Eq. 6-27 and 6-28 are the z_1 moments of the superficial number density and of the superficial pair density. The generalization of Eq. 6-26 to a multicomponent system is

$$\gamma = \beta^{-1}\sum_i (\Gamma_0^{(1)})_i + \tfrac{1}{2}\sum_{i>j}\int d\mathbf{r}[\Gamma_0^{(2)}(\mathbf{r})]_{ij}\phi'(r)r^{-1}r_1^2 \qquad (6\text{-}29)$$

where $(\Gamma_0^{(1)})_i$ and $(\Gamma_0^{(2)})_{ij}$ are, respectively, the superficial number density of species i and the superficial pair density of species i and j, defined by expressions that are obvious generalizations of Eq. 6-27 and 6-28. The Born-Green approximate integro-differential equation, discussed in Art. 3, is applied in the present application in the form of relations between the z_1 moments of the superficial number density and superficial pair density in the form,

$$\Gamma_\nu^{(1)} = -\frac{\beta}{\nu + 1}\int d\mathbf{r}\Gamma_{\nu+1}^{(2)}\phi'(r)r^{-1}r_3 \qquad (6\text{-}30)$$

The distance z_0 between an equimolecular surface of separation and the surface of tension is given by

$$z_0 = -\frac{1}{2\gamma}\int d\mathbf{r}(r_3^2\Gamma_1^{(2)} + r_3\Gamma_2^{(2)})\phi'(r)r^{-1} \qquad (6\text{-}31)$$

When the approximation (6-18) previously employed for $g(\mathbf{r}, z)$ is inserted in Eq. 6-26 to 6-30, the result already obtained as Eq. 6-22 and 6-25 is obtained. Near the critical point, where the density of the vapor can no longer be considered negligible compared to that of the liquid, we would assume

$Cg(\mathbf{r}, z) = C_\alpha^2 g_\alpha(r)$ when both (1) and (2) are in the liquid

$\phantom{Cg(\mathbf{r}, z)} = C_\beta^2 g_\beta(r)$ when both (1) and (2) are in the vapor

$\phantom{Cg(\mathbf{r}, z)} = C_\alpha C_\beta g_{\alpha\beta}(r)$ when (1) is in the vapor and (2) is in the

$\phantom{Cg(\mathbf{r}, z) =}$ liquid or when (1) is in the liquid and (2) is in the vapor   (6-32)

Here g_α and g_β are the ordinary radial distribution functions characteristic of bulk liquid and vapor, respectively, and $g_{\alpha\beta}$ is a correlation function between molecules in liquid and vapor whose form cannot be further specified by the present state of the theory. When these assumptions are employed with Eq. 6-26 to 6-30, one obtains

$$\gamma = \frac{\pi}{8} \int_0^\infty r^4 \phi'(r)[C_\alpha^2 g_\alpha - 2C_\alpha C_\beta g_{\alpha\beta} + C_\beta^2 g_\beta]dr \qquad (6\text{-}33)$$

$$\frac{E_s}{N\sigma} = -\frac{\pi}{2} \int_0^\infty r^3 \phi(r)[C_\alpha^2 g_\alpha - 2C_\alpha C_\beta g_{\alpha\beta} + C_\beta^2 g_\beta]dr \qquad (6\text{-}34)$$

These expressions have been previously obtained by Fowler [43] by means of a calculation applicable only to this model. They form the basis for Fowler's theory of the parachor.

The parachor. Macleod [44] proposed an empirical equation for the surface tension in the form

$$\gamma \sim (\rho_\alpha - \rho_\beta)^4 \qquad (6\text{-}35)$$

where ρ_α and ρ_β are the bulk densities of liquid and vapor, respectively. Sugden [45] has defined the parachor P by

$$P = \frac{\gamma^{\frac{1}{4}}}{C_\alpha - C_\beta} \qquad (6\text{-}36)$$

and it has been shown that the parachor is a sum of constants characteristic of individual atoms or structures of the molecule.

Eq. 6-34 can be written in the approximate form

$$\frac{E_s}{N\sigma} = K_1(C_\alpha - C_\beta)^2$$

$$K_1 = -\frac{\pi}{2} \int_0^\infty r^3 \phi(r)g(r) \qquad (6\text{-}37)$$

in the neighborhood of the critical point where we may assume $g_\alpha = g_\beta = g_{\alpha\beta} = g$. If, in the neighborhood of the critical point, the temperature is expanded in powers of $(C_\alpha - C_\beta)^2$, one has

$$T = T_{cr} - K_2(C_\alpha - C_\beta)^2 + \cdots \qquad (6\text{-}38)$$

which is simply a statement of the fact that the pressure-specific volume curve has a horizontal tangent at the critical point. Substituting Eq. 6-37 and 6-38 into Eq. 6-9 and integrating, we obtain

$$\gamma \sim \frac{K_1 T}{K_2}\left(\frac{T_{cr}}{T} - 1 - \ln\frac{T_{cr}}{T}\right) \sim \frac{K_1}{K_2}\frac{(T_{cr} - T)^2}{2T}$$

$$\sim K_1 K_2 T_{cr}^{-1}(C_\alpha - C_\beta)^4 \qquad (6\text{-}39)$$

in the neighborhood of the critical point, which furnishes some interpretation of Macleod's rule. It should be noted that this rule actually holds over a far wider range of temperature than can be justified by the approximations in the above derivation.

The surface tension and vapor pressure of droplets. The molecular theory of Kirkwood and Buff can be used to estimate the effect of radius of curvature on the surface tension of droplets. The excess of pressure within the droplet over that of the vapor is then given by the well-known Kelvin equation

$$p_\alpha - p_\beta = \frac{2\gamma(R)}{R} \tag{6-40}$$

where $\gamma(R)$ is the surface tension of a droplet of radius R.

In applying the molecular theory to the estimation of $\gamma(R)$, it is assumed that the distance z_0 between the equimolecular surface of separation and the surface of tension is independent of the radius of curvature. However, the effect of curvature must be considered in evaluating the superficial number density of the surface of tension. If the surface of tension has a radius of curvature R, the superficial number density is given by

$$\Gamma_0^{(1)} = \int_{-R}^{0} (C - C_\alpha)\left(1 + \frac{z}{R}\right)^2 dz + \int_0^\infty (C - C_\beta)\left(1 + \frac{z}{R}\right)^2 dz \tag{6-41}$$

Now, the surface of tension is a distance z_0 below the surface for which $\Gamma_0^{(1)}$ vanishes, and the superficial number density on this surface is

$$\Gamma_0^{(1)}(z_0) = \Gamma^* = z_0(C_\alpha - C_\beta)\left[1 + \frac{z_0}{R} + \frac{1}{3}\left(\frac{z_0}{R}\right)^2\right] \tag{6-42}$$

Gibbs has shown that the surface tension and chemical potential are connected by

$$d\gamma = -\Gamma^* d\mu \tag{6-43}$$

For isothermal changes, subject to equilibrium between the phases,

$$d\mu = \frac{1}{C_\alpha} dp_\alpha = \frac{1}{C_\beta} dp_\beta \tag{6-44}$$

Differentiating the Kelvin equation and employing Eq. 6-42, 6-43, and 6-44 we obtain the Tolman equation,

$$\frac{d \ln \gamma}{d \ln R} = \frac{\frac{2z_0}{R}\left[1 + \frac{z_0}{R} + \frac{1}{3}\left(\frac{z_0}{R}\right)^2\right]}{1 + \frac{2z_0}{R}\left[1 + \frac{z_0}{R} + \frac{1}{3}\left(\frac{z_0}{R}\right)^2\right]} \tag{6-45}$$

which can be integrated from $R = \infty$ (plane surface) to a radius of curvature R with the result

$$\ln \frac{\gamma(R)}{\gamma(\infty)} = \int_{\infty}^{R} \frac{\dfrac{2z_0}{R^2}\left[1 + \dfrac{z_0}{R} + \dfrac{1}{3}\left(\dfrac{z_0}{R}\right)^2\right]}{1 + \dfrac{2z_0}{R}\left[1 + \dfrac{z_0}{R} + \dfrac{1}{3}\left(\dfrac{z_0}{R}\right)^2\right]}\, dr \qquad (6\text{-}46)$$

It is probable that the assumption that z_0 is independent of R is no longer valid for drops so small that z_0 is of the order of R.

F,7. Cited References and Bibliography.

Cited References

1. Wigner, E. *Phys. Rev. 40*, 749 (1932).
2. Mayer, J. E., and Band, W. *J. Chem. Phys. 15*, 141 (1947).
3. Mayer, J. E., and Mayer, M. G. *Statistical Mechanics.* Wiley, 1940.
4. Zernike, F., and Prins, J. A. *Z. Physik 41*, 184 (1927).
5. Debye, P., and Menke, H. *Physik. Z. 31*, 797 (1930).
6. Eyring, H., and Hirschfelder, J. O. *J. Phys. Chem. 41*, 249 (1937).
7. Lennard-Jones, J. E., and Devonshire, A. F. *Proc. Roy. Soc. London A163*, 53 (1937); *A165*, 1 (1938).
8. Kirkwood, J. G. *J. Chem. Phys. 18*, 380 (1950).
9. Fowler, R. H., and Guggenheim, E. A. *Statistical Thermodynamics*, 3rd ed. Cambridge Univ. Press, 1952.
10. Hirschfelder, J. O., Stevenson, D., and Eyring, H. *J. Chem. Phys. 5*, 896 (1937).
11. Rice, O. K. *J. Chem. Phys. 6*, 476 (1938).
12. Hildebrand, J. L., and Scott, R. L. *The Solubility of Nonelectrolytes*, 3rd ed. Reinhold, 1950.
13. Richardson, J. M., and Brinkley, S. R., Jr. To be published.
14. Mayer, J. E., and Careri, G. *J. Chem. Phys. 20*, 1001 (1952).
15. Lennard-Jones, J. E. *Proc. Roy. Soc. London A106*, 463 (1924).
16. Wentorf, R. H., Buehler, R. J., Hirschfelder, J. O., and Curtiss, C. F. *J. Chem. Phys. 18*, 1484 (1950).
17. Lennard-Jones, J. E., and Ingham, A. E. *Proc. Roy. Soc. London A107*, 636 (1925).
18. Salsburg, D. W., and Kirkwood, J. G. *J. Chem. Phys. 20*, 1538 (1952).
19. Kirkwood, J. G. *J. Chem. Phys. 3*, 300 (1935).
20. Born, M., and Green, H. S. *Proc. Roy. Soc. London A188*, 10 (1946).
21. Green, H. S. *Proc. Roy. Soc. London A189*, 103 (1947).
22. Yvon, J. *Actualities Scientifiques et Industrielles.* Hermann et Cie, Paris, 1935.
23. Richardson, J. M. To be published.
24. Mayer, J. E. *J. Chem. Phys. 15*, 187 (1947).
25. McMillan, J. M., Jr., and Mayer, J. E. *J. Chem. Phys. 13*, 276 (1945).
26. Mayer, J. E. *J. Chem. Phys. 10*, 629 (1942).
27. Kirkwood, J. G., and Boggs, E. M. *J. Chem. Phys. 10*, 394 (1942).
28. Kirkwood, J. G., and Boggs, E. M. *J. Chem. Phys. 9*, 514 (1941).
29. Kirkwood, J. G., Maun, E. K., and Alder, B. J. *J. Chem. Phys. 18*, 1040 (1950).
30. Kirkwood, J. G., Lewinson, V. A., and Alder, B. J. *J. Chem. Phys. 20*, 929 (1952).
31. McLellan, A. G. *Proc. Roy. Soc. London A210*, 509 (1952).
32. Onsager, L. *Phys. Rev. 37*, 405 (1931).
33. de Groot, S. R. *Thermodynamics of Irreversible Processes.* Interscience, 1951.
34. See, for instance: Green, H. S. *Molecular Theory of Fluids.* Interscience, 1952; Glasstone, Laidler, and Eyring. *Theory of Rate Processes.* McGraw-Hill, 1941; Montroll, E. W., and Green, M. S. Statistical Mechanics of Transports and Nonequilibrium Processes. To appear in the 1954 volume of *Annual Reviews of Physical Chemistry*.

35. Gibbs, J. W.   *Collected Works*, Vol. I. Longmans, Green & Co., 1928.
36. Tolman, R. C.   *J. Chem. Phys. 16*, 758 (1948); *17*, 118, 333 (1949).
37. Lennard-Jones, J. E., and Corner, J.   *Trans. Faraday Soc. 36*, 1156 (1940).
38. Corner, J.   *Trans. Faraday Soc. 44*, 1036 (1948).
39. Kirkwood, J. G., and Buff, F. P.   *J. Chem. Phys. 17*, 338 (1949).
40. Buff, F. P., and Kirkwood, J. G.   *J. Chem. Phys. 18*, 991 (1950).
41. Buff, F. P.   *J. Chem. Phys. 19*, 1591 (1951).
42. Green, H. S.   *Molecular Theory of Fluids*. Interscience, 1952.
43. Fowler, R. H.   *Proc. Roy. Soc. London A159*, 229 (1937).
44. Macleod, D. B.   *Trans. Faraday Soc. 19*, 38 (1923).
45. Sugden, S.   *The Parachor and Valency*. Routledge, London, 1930.

Bibliography

Adams, N. K.   *The Physics and Chemistry of Surfaces*, 3rd ed. Oxford Univ. Press, 1942.
Born, M., and Green, H. S.   *A General Kinetic Theory of Liquids*. Cambridge, 1949.
de Groot, E. R.   *Thermodynamics of Irreversible Processes*. Interscience, 1951.
Fowler, R. H., and Guggenheim, E. A.   *Statistical Thermodynamics*, 3rd ed. Cambridge Univ. Press, 1952.
Frenkel, J.   *The Kinetic Theory of Liquids*. Oxford, 1946.
Green, H. S.   *Molecular Theory of Fluids*. Interscience, 1952.
Guggenheim, E. A.   *Modern Thermodynamics by the Methods of Willard Gibbs*. Methuen, 1933.
Guggenheim, E. A.   *Thermodynamics: An Advanced Treatment for Chemists and Physicists*. North-Holland Publishing Co., 1949.
Harned, H. S., and Owen, B. B.   *Physical Chemistry of Electrolytic Solutions*, 2nd ed. Reinhold, 1950.
Hildebrand, J. H., and Scott, R. L.   *The Solubility of Nonelectrolytes*, 3rd ed. Reinhold, 1950.
Prigogine, I.   *Etude thermodynamique des processes irréversibles*. Dunod, Paris; Weaver, Liège, 1947.

SECTION G

PROPERTIES OF SOLIDS AND SOLID SOLUTIONS

P. P. EWALD

CHAPTER 1. THE SOLID STATE IN GENERAL

G,1. Definition of Solids. For the purposes of the engineer the solid state of matter may be defined as that in which matter can rest in equilibrium under a constant shearing stress. Neither fluids nor gases have this property.

G,2. Homogeneous Solids. The physical properties of solids are linked with the notion of a homogeneous solid. By this is understood that the same laws, including the values of the physical constants, hold in every element of volume of the body. If this concept is carried to its mathematical extreme by allowing the "element of volume" to decrease indefinitely, we obtain the mathematically simple, but physically unrealistic, concept of a homogeneous continuum. Actually, since solids are built of atoms, the decrease in the dimensions of the volume considered has to be halted at least before reaching a stage where the inclusion or omission of a single atom from the volume makes a marked difference. A volume which is large compared to the atomic distances and yet small compared to the distances over which there is a perceptible change of the conditions impressed on the body, such as stresses, fields, etc., is often called a physical element of volume in distinction to its mathematical counterpart. In physical and engineering applications this physical element must often be taken larger than that demanded solely by the atomistic structure. This is the case either when the material has a coarser structure which may be visible under the microscope or even on a larger scale. A metal, with its microcrystalline structure, and a brick wall are examples of solid bodies for which "engineering properties" like elastic modulus or heat conductivity can be usefully defined throughout the body by considering as "physical elements of volume" volumes containing many microcrystals or many bricks. Timber affords another material of this kind which, besides, gives an example of an anisotropic substance, i.e. one in which there are physical properties which show directional properties (e.g. strength with and across the grain). It lies in our decision whether or not we wish to consider a body as homogeneous; but by making a decision we limit the means of investigation to those appropriate to the point of view taken and, in particular, to the possibility of defining the proper physical element of volume. The elastic properties of an ordinary, microcrystalline metal bar can only be obtained by applying a stress which is very nearly constant over a large number of microcrystals and cannot be obtained by pressing down the diamond point of a hardness tester. The latter method, on the other hand, may be used to explore the properties of the individual crystallites of the metal. Where—as in this particular case of hardness testing—the "technical" methods yield results which do not readily lend themselves to being incorporated in quantitative relations, the ultimate reason for this unsatisfactory result may well lie in the indefiniteness of the point of view taken regarding the scale of the element of volume.

G,3. Stages of the Theory of Solids. It is the aim of a theory of the solid state to explain the properties of solid bodies in bulk by the properties of those homogeneous constituents into which the bodies can be successively decomposed by more minute investigation; this will ultimately lead down to solids which are homogeneous except on the atomic scale. Thus the technical characteristics of a spun wire cable are reduced to those of its individual wires, the latter to those of its crystallites, and these to the physical properties of the kinds of crystals occurring in the wire. In speaking of a further explanation of these physical properties, we usually mean the last step in which we try to go right down to the properties of the constituent atoms as they are known from the wave mechanical theory of atoms and from the experimental methods adapted to this stage.

G,4. Crystals and Amorphous Bodies. As a result of the investigations by means of X-ray and electron diffraction (confirmed also by neutron diffraction) we know that solid bodies which are homogeneous on the atomic scale are of two distinct kinds: crystals and amorphous bodies. There is very little transition between these kinds, and therefore a body will approach very closely to one or the other of the ideal types which can be described thus:

Crystals. Their characteristic is the internal, three-dimensional periodicity of the arrangement of atoms. The space occupied by the crystal is divided into equal parallelopipeds, called *cells*, each containing similar atoms in the same arrangement which form the *basis* of the cell. The entire crystal is thus like a van leaving the factory door tightly packed with the same type of boxes, each containing the same array of objects. Thermodynamically, a crystal has a well-defined area of existence in a p, T diagram; on crossing the borderline of this area the crystal will melt (transition to liquid) or transform to a clearly distinct type of crystal (polymorphic transition) or sublimate (transition to gas) or, finally, decompose chemically. Such transitions are accompanied by sudden changes in the physical properties and, in general, by a definite amount of heat of transition. These transitions are also, in general, reversible, although there may be exceptions to this which are attributed to delays or suspended action.

Amorphous bodies. In amorphous bodies, there is no long range regularity of atomic arrangement, except in the statistical sense that the density is the same everywhere. There may be a short range order. Thus the same small group of atoms may occur regularly (e.g. the SiO_4 group in a glass), but the orientation of the group, and its further surroundings, will vary irregularly. Only a statistical description of the assembly can be given by indicating, for each kind of atom, the number of its own and of different kinds of atoms which are to be found on the average at increasing distances from it. Such distribution curves are deduced from the diffuse diffraction halos which are obtained by passing X rays through an amorphous body. These halos are quite distinct from the sharp diffraction spots produced by a typical crystal. On the other hand, the halos from amorphous solid bodies are sharper and contain more detail than those obtained from liquids. This shows that in liquids the order is still further reduced to relations between neighboring atoms. Thermodynamically, amorphous bodies have no well-defined domain of existence in a p, T diagram. There are no sharp transitions, not even for melting; instead, there are continuous changes over a range of p, T values. In the case of glass this is called the region of softening. No sudden latent heat of fusion occurs. Amorphous bodies are therefore sometimes looked upon as being undercooled liquids, and as long as they yield—even if very slowly—to an applied shearing stress, this seems an acceptable point of view. It does, however, not explain the enormous increase of viscosity which takes place on the cooling of a glass melt as compared to the undercooling of water. The investigation of the amorphous state of high polymers has cast some light on this difference, which has to do with the tendency of the small groups of atoms present in the melt to link up to form chains and an irregular network of chains in the hardening undercooled melt.

G,5. Solid Solutions: Mixed Crystals. The strict periodicity of the typical crystal breaks down for many reasons:

It cannot hold at the surface.

It cannot hold because of the heat motion of the atoms which gives them irregular displacements. Even at $T = 0$ there remains what is known as the zero-point motion; this is explained by the general principle of quantum theory formulated by Heisenberg, according to which a particle (here an atom) cannot be assigned simultaneously sharp values of position and of velocity—which would be necessary for defining a strictly periodic structure.

The fact that atoms occur as isotopes with different weights (and different spins) but with the same bonding properties gives rise to a lack of true periodicity which makes itself strongly felt in neutron diffraction, though not so much in the more usual physical properties.

Furthermore, it is quite likely that the process of crystal growth is conducive to misplacement of atoms: atoms may be prevented from attaining their correct positions at the right moment, and later the access to that position may be blocked by other atoms.

Few substances are chemically pure; the impure atoms will find a place by either squeezing themselves in between the regular atoms and giving rise to a local deformation, or by replacing one or more of the regular atoms and again destroying the periodicity.

All these disturbances are localized and need not affect the long range regularity of the crystal.

There are, however, the so-called solid solutions, in which the percentage of "impurity" may be so high that it is not possible to decide which of the brands of atoms is to be regarded as regular or which as the impurity. Cases of this kind occur, for example, as "mixed crystal" of KCl and KBr, or as "solid solutions" of Ag and Cu. Many of the technically important alloys are solid solutions and derive their valuable engineering properties from the internal stresses created by the nonperiodicity. Examples are steel (Fe and C), copper-tungsten (hard copper), copper-gold (mint gold).

In the case of eutectics, simultaneous crystallization of two distinct phases takes place; these are so closely interspersed that fairly high magnification may be required to detect them under the microscope. Although the eutectic thus appears homogeneous even on a small scale, it is not so on an atomistic scale.

G,6. Structure and Texture. The meaning of the *structure* of a solid body has been explained above; it is really the structure of an idealized single crystal of perfect internal periodicity. This is amplified in the next article. It also includes such deviations from periodicity as are characteristic for the homogeneous material on an atomistic scale, e.g. temperature motion, or alien atoms in the case of a solid solution; in many instances it also includes aperiodicity introduced by finite size, e.g. the grains in a metal.

The term *texture* is used when referring to the arrangement of the microcrystals or crystallites in a solid body which may yet be homogeneous on the next scale, the macroscopic, or engineering scale. The term originated with the study of fibrous material, such as asbestos, or textile fibers. Here periodic, crystalline elements are arranged in a partial order, for instance so that one of the directions of periodicity is more or less parallel to the axis of the fiber, while there is a random distribution of the crystallites in other respects. The term texture was then applied

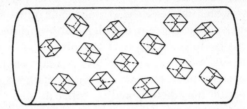

Fig. G,6a.   Texture of drawn aluminum wire. (After [1].)

to metals in which a partial orientation of the crystallites is produced by cold working. As an example, Fig. G,6a shows the texture of drawn aluminum wire [1]: the little cubes are not meant to indicate the actually quite irregular shape of the crystallites, but their edges show the distribution of equivalent directions.

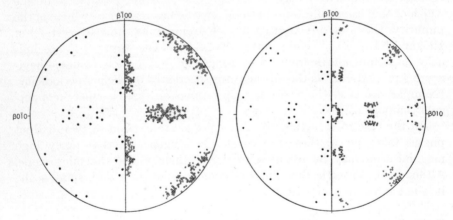

Fig. G,6b.   Texture of α-brass crystallizing in matrix of β-brass (after [2]). The diagrams show the distribution of the normals to the (111) and (200) planes observed by X rays (right halves of the diagrams), and deduced from an assumed mechanism of transformation (left halves). The β-brass matrix was textured by rolling before the transformation took place.

The description of a texture has to use statistical concepts, since one has to indicate the frequency of occurrence of any particular orientation of the crystallites in the entire body. This is usually given in the form of *pole figures* which can be derived directly from a series of X-ray diffraction patterns. They show the orientation of several crystallographic directions with regard to the specimen on a large sphere surrounding the specimen by marking where this direction produced from any of the crystallites intersects the sphere.

Typical results, as found for recrystallized β brass by Straumanis and Weerts [2], are shown in the right-hand halves of Fig. G,6b for the directions of the cube body diagonals and cube edges, respectively. The sphere has been projected on its equatorial plane by stereographic projection, i.e. by connecting each point of the upper hemisphere to the pole of the lower hemisphere and marking the intersection of this connecting line with the equatorial plane. This projection of the surface in three dimensions gives a one-to-one relation to the plane which can be easily drawn; the angles between lines on the sphere are the same as those between their projections.

CHAPTER 2. CRYSTALS AND THEIR GEOMETRY

G,7. Definition of the Ideal Crystal. The concept of the ideal crystal is obtained by stressing the periodicity of the internal arrangements of a homogeneous solid on the atomic scale. The advantage of this concept is that it is amenable to simple mathematical use, and thereby renders well many features observed in real crystals.

Periodicity in three dimensions is linked with the existence of a parallelotop of repetition, called the cell (often, and unnecessarily, the unit cell), three concurrent edges of which are the vectors a_1, a_2, a_3 (short a_i) which are called the axes or translations. The contents of the cell form the basis of the crystal. The basis may be regarded as consisting of discrete atoms which may, in turn, be considered extended or condensed to point atoms; or the basis can be thought of as given by a density function $\rho(x)$ without any reference to atomistic structure, where the "density" ρ is any property such as true mass, or charge, or scattering power, or electric moment per unit volume.

It is obvious that the same periodic structure can be referred to an infinity of different axes, cells, and bases. For instance, if any useful set of axes be doubled in length, the cell volume and the basis will be eight times what it was before, and the basis itself will have a special configuration, namely, the parallel repetition of the 8 previous bases; but the new axial system serves equally well as the old one to describe the distribution of matter. It is one of the main mathematical requirements that all physical properties connected with the ideal crystal must be invariant against such changes of axes.

The axes are in general any three noncoplanar vectors and require 6 axial parameters for their determination, namely, their three lengths and the three angles between them: in the usual older crystallographic notation they would be a, b, c, α, β, γ. In vector notation they follow from a_1^2, a_2^2, a_3^2, $(a_2 a_3)$, $(a_3 a_1)$, $(a_1 a_2)$, i.e. from the coefficients expressing the length of the vector of position $\mathbf{x} = x_1\mathbf{a}_1 + x_2\mathbf{a}_2 + x_3\mathbf{a}_3$ by means of the ternary quadratic form

$$\mathbf{x}^2 = \mathbf{a}_1^2 x_1^2 + \mathbf{a}_2^2 x_2^2 + \mathbf{a}_3^2 x_3^2 + 2(\mathbf{a}_2\mathbf{a}_3)x_2x_3 + 2(\mathbf{a}_3\mathbf{a}_1)x_3x_1 + 2(\mathbf{a}_1\mathbf{a}_2)x_1x_2$$

In cases of symmetry, the axes can be chosen so as to conform to the symmetry; this reduces the number of axial parameters which have to be stated. Thus for cubic crystals only one parameter, the length of edge of the cubic cell, remains to be given, the axial angles being 90°; for hexagonal crystals only two, namely, the axial lengths along the hexagonal axis and at right angles to it, must be given individually.

G,8. Geometry of the Simple Lattice. If we consider equal cells stacked along all three directions, the corners form a simple lattice or a translation lattice. The positions of those corners, referred to one corner as origin, are given by the lattice vectors

$$\mathbf{x}_l = l_1\mathbf{a}_1 + l_2\mathbf{a}_2 + l_3\mathbf{a}_3, \quad \text{or shorter } \mathbf{x}_l = l_i\mathbf{a}_i$$

where the coordinate numbers l_i are (positive or negative) integers. By choosing any three corners not in one line, a plane is defined, and this contains an infinite number of further corners in a periodic two-dimensional array based on a cell in the shape of a parallelogram. Such a plane is called a net plane of the lattice, and it is one of a set of parallel net planes of the same kind following upon one another at an interval d, the identity period of the planes, which, given the axes, is determined by the orientation of the set of planes. Net planes are said to have a rational position within the lattice because they pass through three points $\mathbf{x}_l$ $\mathbf{x}_{l'}$, $\mathbf{x}_{l''}$ with integer coordinate numbers (l_i), (l_i'), (l_i''), respectively. The external faces observed on a crystal are always rational planes when referred to a suitable system of axes; indeed it was from this observation that the concept of the periodic internal structure of crystals was formed by a reversal of the line of thought given above. Because of the limited accuracy of observation, the term "rational position" must be interpreted in physics usage as implying small integers (l_i), (l_i'), (l_i''), whereas mathematically speaking no such restriction exists. Observations on the optical goniometer or by the usual X-ray methods yield direct statements about the planes of a crystal. On the goniometer the crystal is set with an edge between two of its planes parallel to the axis of rotation of the crystal. On rotating, any plane that is parallel to this edge will get into a position where it reflects the signal into the telescope. These planes are said to form a zone with the common direction as zone axis. In rotating the crystal from one reflecting position to the next, the angles between the normals to the external faces of the zone are measured. Any two faces determine a zone axis, and, conversely, any two zone axes determine a single face containing them. It is from the measurements of zone angles that the axial system is found in which all the faces occupy low rational positions.

G,9. The Reciprocal Lattice: Physical and Fourier Space. The direction of the normal to a net plane can be conveniently obtained as that of the vector product of two vectors lying in the net plane. Such vectors are, for example, $\mathbf{x} - \mathbf{x}''$ and $\mathbf{x}' - \mathbf{x}''$, where $\mathbf{x}$, $\mathbf{x}'$, $\mathbf{x}''$ are the points which were used above to define the plane. In the set of parallel net planes there is one passing through the origin, and we may therefore set $\mathbf{x}'' = 0$. This makes the vector product

$$[\mathbf{x}\mathbf{x}'] = [l_1\mathbf{a}_1 + l_2\mathbf{a}_2 + l_3\mathbf{a}_3, \; l_1'\mathbf{a}_1 + l_2'\mathbf{a}_2 + l_3'\mathbf{a}_3]$$
$$= [\mathbf{a}_2\mathbf{a}_3](l_2 l_3' - l_3 l_2') + [\mathbf{a}_3\mathbf{a}_1](l_3 l_1' - l_1 l_3') + [\mathbf{a}_1\mathbf{a}_2](l_1 l_2' - l_2 l_1')$$
$$= v_a(\mathbf{b}_1 h_1 + \mathbf{b}_2 h_2 + \mathbf{b}_3 h_3)$$

where the h_i are three integers compounded from the integers l_i and l_i', while

$$\mathbf{b}_1 = \frac{[\mathbf{a}_2\mathbf{a}_3]}{v_a}, \qquad \mathbf{b}_2 = \frac{[\mathbf{a}_3\mathbf{a}_1]}{v_a}, \qquad \mathbf{b}_3 = \frac{[\mathbf{a}_1\mathbf{a}_2]}{v_a}$$

are the vectors first introduced by Gibbs as reciprocal to the vectors $\mathbf{a}_i$, and $v_a = (\mathbf{a}_1[\mathbf{a}_2\mathbf{a}_3])$ is the volume sustained by the vectors $\mathbf{a}_i$, i.c. the volume of the cell.

Thus if the reciprocal vectors $\mathbf{b}_i$ be taken to construct a lattice, the lattice vectors

$$\mathbf{h} = h_1\mathbf{b}_1 + h_2\mathbf{b}_2 + h_3\mathbf{b}_3 \quad (h_i \text{ integer})$$

all represent directions of normals to net planes in the crystal lattice.

In taking out the common factor n of h_1, h_2, h_3,

$$\mathbf{h} = n\mathbf{h}^* = n(h_1^*\mathbf{b}_1 + h_2^*\mathbf{b}_2 + h_3^*\mathbf{b}_3)$$

where $\mathbf{h}^*$ is the vector to the lattice point nearest the origin on the lattice row. In other words, the length of $\mathbf{h}^*$ is the identity period for the row determined by the ratios $h_1^*:h_2^*:h_3^*$. This identity period can be shown to be reciprocal to that of the corresponding net planes of the crystal lattice which was called d above:

$$|\mathbf{h}^*|d = 1$$

The three smallest integers h_i^* giving the direction of the normal in terms of the b_i axes are called the *Miller indices* of a plane. Their interpretation in terms of the crystal axes $\mathbf{a}_i$ is that the three intercepts which the plane (not passing through the origin) cuts off on the $\mathbf{a}_i$ axes are inversely proportional to the three integers. These Miller indices are often called h, k, l instead of h_i. Thus the axial planes themselves are

(100), (010), and (001). The octahedral and rhombododecahedral planes in a cubic crystal are (111) and (110) respectively, these symbols to be written down with all permutations and ± signs of the components. Planes of different orientations, which, however, are equivalent by the symmetry of the crystal, are called a form, and the symbol $\{h, k, l\}$ is used to designate them.

Between the crystal lattice (axes $\mathbf{a}_i$) and its reciprocal (axes $\mathbf{b}_i$) there exists a relation of duality of which the correspondence between lattice rows in one and net planes in the other lattice is but a first example. The full relation is contained in the statement that one lattice is the Fourier transform of the other. Putting it in more physical terms, the crystal is given a localized description in physical or crystal space (axes $\mathbf{a}_i$), for instance, by indicating the positions of point atoms or the density $\rho(\mathbf{x})$ from point to point. In Fourier space (axes $\mathbf{b}_i$) the same crystal is resolved into all-pervading plane waves, each one of which bears no reference to any particular point of crystal space. This is the same relation as between coordinate space and momentum space in wave mechanics. The mathematical formalism of Fourier transformation helps to sift the mathematical technique from the physical ideas.

G,10. Symmetry. Symmetry of a homogeneous body can be defined as the equivalence of directions within the body. Directions related by symmetry must be undistinguishable from one another by all physical tests. A direction is indicated by a unit vector $\mathbf{s}$; this includes the distinction of a positive sense along the direction.

A symmetry element is an operation which transforms a set of directions into an equivalent set. Thus any rotation of an isotropic body like glass produces no difference in its physical reactions, and any direction $\mathbf{s}$ within the body will be equivalent to any other direction $\mathbf{s}'$. In a crystal only certain symmetry elements occur, namely, inversions, 2-, 3-, 4-, and 6-fold rotations, and reflections. The inversion changes any direction $\mathbf{s}$ into $-\mathbf{s}$; that a direction and its opposite are not equivalent in all crystals is shown by piezoelectric crystals like quartz and tourmaline of which a suitably cut plate shows a positive charge on one side and a negative charge on the other when compressed normal to the plate. The rotations declare as equivalent a set of 2, 3, 4, or 6 directions which are all equally inclined to a certain direction, the axis of rotation, and which have equal angles between neighboring directions. Thus the four body-diagonals of a cube are equivalent by virtue of the fourfold axis of rotation directed normal to a cube face. A reflection, finally, makes equivalent any two directions of which the unit vectors $\mathbf{s}$ and $\mathbf{s}'$ have the same resolved parts in a fixed plane, the plane of reflection or mirror plane.

Whereas the symmetry elements are really operations or, mathematically, linear transformations which bring any vector $\mathbf{s}$ into equivalent positions, they can conveniently be represented by the invariant element contained in their definition, namely, the inversion by the origin or center of inversion, the rotations by their axes of rotation, and the reflection by the mirror plane.

The inversion i, the twofold rotation 2, and the reflection m are not independent, since $2i = m$; i.e. rotating by 180° about an axis and then inverting about a point of this axis produces the reflection on a mirror plane m which intersects the axis normally at the center of inversion. Thus only two of these three elements are needed; but it is often convenient to use all three.

G,11. Crystal Classes and Systems.   Other symmetry elements than those mentioned, for instance 5- or 8-fold rotations, are not compatible with the three-dimensional periodicity of crystal structure on purely geometrical grounds. Again, on similar grounds, the symmetry elements can only be combined in a limited way. Thus the line of intersection of two mirror planes m and m' is automatically an axis of rotation. If the order of this axis is not to exceed 6, the highest possible in a crystal, the angle included by m and m' cannot be less than $\pi/6 = 30°$. In fact, no angles between m and m' other than 30° and 45° and their multiples can occur, because otherwise the number of intersecting mirror planes, obtained by repeated reflections on one another, would be infinite; this corresponds to an axis of rotation of infinite order, i.e. cylindrical symmetry, which cannot occur in a crystal.

It has been shown early in the development of crystallography that there are only 32 different ways of combining the crystallographic symmetry elements provided they all pass through one point—which is left unchanged in all symmetry operations. These 32 combinations are called the crystal classes, or the point groups; the latter name indicates the characteristic of these composite symmetries as being representations of the much wider mathematical concept of "group." The first aim of the older, descriptive or morphological, study of crystals was to find the class to which each kind of crystal belongs; this was achieved by observing the positions of the faces by means of the goniometer and by adding as much physical information as became available, e.g. from pyro- or piezoelectric and from optical behavior and by methods of etching the faces. Representatives of all 32 classes are known, though in rather unequal numbers.

The crystal classes can be classified in seven crystal systems by collecting those which have some features in common and which, therefore, are best referred to a similar system of axes. Thus all crystals which have four 3-fold axes of rotation belong to the cubic system. Their axes of reference are the concurrent edges of a cube, and these directions may be either 4- or 2-fold axes of rotation, whereas the directions of the cube diagonals are in all cubic classes 3-fold axes. Crystals with only one 4-axis are *tetragonal*, those with three orthogonal 2-axes are *orthorhombic*, those with a single 6-axis *hexagonal*, those with a single 3-axis *trigonal* or *rhombohedral*, those with a single 2-axis or a mirror plane *monoclinic* and, lastly, those with no symmetry or only a center of inversion *triclinic*.

G,12. Space Groups: Crystal Structure. To consider the interior of a crystal amounts to repelling its boundaries on all sides to an indefinite infinity. In this case there exists a further covering operation which is closely related to the symmetry elements we have been considering. This is a translation, i.e. a parallel displacement of the entire body. Such a displacement would be hard to detect experimentally, even for a finite body, if it were on an atomic scale; for the unlimited body it will be a true covering operation if each atom is shifted to a position held by a similar atom before the translation. The three translations of the simple lattice, introduced in Art. 7 are an example.

The addition of translations adds to the list of crystallographic symmetry elements:

Translations as such, in particular by integer values of the cell edges a_1, a_2, a_3;

Glide reflections, i.e. reflections on a plane m followed by a translation along a direction lying in m;

Screws, i.e. rotations about an axis followed by a displacement of the body in the direction of the axis of rotation.

Again these operations are not entirely independent. Take, for example, a cubic crystal which has an internal periodicity (identity period) a along the cube edge. If the same direction is that of a fourfold screw axis, then the translation accompanying a rotation by 90° can only be $\pm a/4$ or $\pm a/2$, as otherwise the periodicity would be destroyed. If this crystal also had a mirror plane at right angles to the screw axis, then the translation could only be $a/2$, because a reflection turns a right-hand screw into a left-hand one. The translation $+a/4$ differs from $-a/4$ ($= +3a/4$), whereas the translation $+a/2$ is the same as $-a/2$.

In the Schoenflies-Fedorov theory of space groups all geometrically consistent spatial arrangements of symmetry elements are constructed. As soon as two symmetry elements are assumed which do not go through the same point, repeated application of the symmetry operation creates sets of parallel, like, equidistant symmetry elements. A space group then is represented by a kind of spatial scaffolding of interpenetrating or intersecting sets of parallel axes, screw axes, mirror-, and glide mirror planes. There are 230 such arrangements.

A second way of visualizing a space group is by letting the symmetry operations act on an individual particle, say a single atom, which is introduced at some point into the scaffolding. This is like introducing a bead between the mirrors of a kaleidoscope: the atom will be reproduced throughout the entire space by the symmetry operation. We thus arrive at a lattice with certain translations a_i and a certain basis of symmetrically and physically equivalent atoms. Calling x, y, z the coordinates of the atom introduced at an arbitrary point, a list of the coordinates of the equivalent positions, or a drawing of these positions in the cell, gives a second representation of the space group.

In an actual crystal there will, in general, be several atoms in the cell which are not symmetrically and/or physically equivalent, for instance different atoms of a molecule. The entire array of atoms can then be regarded as an interpenetration of arrangements of the simpler type in which all atoms are equivalent, or, alternatively, as the repetition of a group of different atoms by the space group symmetry elements. This group of atoms may be a molecule or part of a molecule, or, as in many metals, it may be a single atom; it is sometimes spoken of as the asymmetric unit, because no symmetry requirements are placed upon it.

G,13. The Determination of Crystal Structure by Means of X Rays. The general scheme of periodic arrangement of matter inside a crystal was developed independently by Schoenflies and Fedorov early in the 1890's. It was not until 1912 that this purely formal scheme could be filled with specific detail. The discovery of the diffraction of X rays by von Laue, Friedrich, and Knipping in 1912 and its brilliant reinterpretation and development in the hands of W. H. and W. L. Bragg [3] and by their schools has led to an exact knowledge of the atomic arrangement in an ever-increasing number of crystals of ever-growing chemical and structural complexity. The methods of structure determination were developed on such simple substances as copper, iron, diamond, rock salt, zincblende ZnS, calcite $CaCO_3$; later, complex salts like $K_2(PtCl_4)$, $K_2(PtCl_6)$, and, in the years before and after 1930, the great group of silicates were discussed and the chemical views about such substances confirmed or modified. The first studies of organic structures go back to W. H. Bragg's study of naphthalene; nowadays not much hesitation is felt in tackling organic crystals the molecules of which contain many tens of atoms, while the study of even more complicated substances, like proteins, though not yet successful, begins to look promising. The number of solid substances of which the structure is known is probably somewhere near 5,000; this is still a small fraction of the about 200,000 substances chemically distinguished, but the quantitative detail revealed by the X-ray methods surpasses by far the more topological information inferred from purely chemical experimentation.

This is not the place to deal with the methods of crystal structure determination. It will suffice to point out that there are, in general, three steps. The first is the determination of the axes a_i which sustain the cell.

This information is obtained from the purely geometrical diffraction data, namely the angles under which diffracted (or, in Bragg's terminology, "reflected") rays occur. This step is comparable to the determination of the axial system of a crystal by goniometric measurement of the external faces; with X rays, reflections are also obtained from the much more numerous internal net planes, and this lends added precision to the determination of the cell shape. Besides, an absolute scale of length is used by employing monochromatic X rays, with the result that the axial lengths and the volume of the cell become known. Assuming the chemical composition and the density as given, the number of molecules forming the basis of the cell is found from the geometrical diffraction data.

The next step is based on the observation that in many cases not the full array of diffracted rays is observed which would be expected from a simple lattice constructed on the translations a_i. Some spots are seen to be missing on the photographs according to easily established laws. These so-called absences lead in many cases to the determination of the space group according to which the crystal is built. In suitable cases, this entails a restriction on the shape of the molecule by demanding that it have a certain symmetry. This alone may decide between different stereochemical formulations of the molecule.

The third step is the determination of the coordinates of the atoms forming the basis. The higher the symmetry of the space group, the greater is the reduction in the number of coordinates which have to be determined independently. The particular configuration of the basis is without influence on the directions, in which diffracted rays appear, and on the absences; but it influences the intensities observed. (Absences might, of course, be considered as particular cases of vanishing intensity, but in contrast to other zero intensities they must occur for any basis conforming to the space group.) It is thus finally a discussion of the observed intensities which leads to the knowledge of the distribution of the atoms or, more generally, of the scattering power for X rays.

The results can be given in either of two ways: by locating within the cell only the centers of the atoms (these correspond to the maxima of scattering power), or by giving the entire, continuous distribution of scattering power. The first scheme corresponds more closely to a discontinuous picture of the crystal as built up from discrete atoms; the second gives a continuous picture which is more suggestive of the wave mechanical concept of a crystal. If details of bond formation between the atoms are to be studied, the second picture is of course necessary. The scattering power in each element of volume is proportional to the number of electrons in this element, and thus the electron density $\rho(x)$ is obtained by this study. In order to visualize this three-dimensional function, projections or sections of $\rho(x)$ are shown by their contour lines. Fig. G,13 [4] gives as an example the projection of one quarter of the cell of strychnine hydrogen bromide $C_{21}H_{22}N_2O_2 \cdot HBr \cdot 2H_2O$ on the y, z plane. The orthogonal cell of this orthorhombic structure has edges $a = 7.64$, $b = 7.70$, $c = 33.20$ A and contains four molecules. The figure, together with similar projections along the y and z axes, shows the complicated spatial configuration of the molecule. $\rho(\mathbf{x})$ is shown by the contour lines.

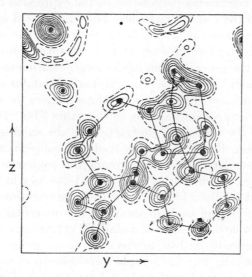

Fig. G,13.   Projection of structure of strychnine hydrogen bromide. (From [4].)

Zero density is given by the dotted contours; small negative density values beyond the zero contours are to be understood as caused by the finite resolving power of the experimental methods, and are not entered in the diagram. There are 25 atoms of nearly equal scattering power, C, N, O. For the heavy Br (left upper corner), only every fifth contour line is shown.

CHAPTER 3. FORMAL CRYSTAL STATICS

G,14.   Historical Survey.   The development of crystal dynamics is closely tied up with the beginnings of the theory of elasticity about 1820. The pioneers in this field, in particular Cauchy and Poisson, made full use of the concept of molecular structure of solid matter and of central forces acting from one molecule to the others. On this basis they obtained the differential equations between the two tensor quantities of stress and strain. Each of these quantities has six independent components, and the most general linear relations between them contain $6^2 = 36$ coefficients. This number is cut down because the scheme of coefficients must be symmetric across its main diagonal for reasons of energy; otherwise, a suitable cyclic change in the stress components would be accompanied by a finite amount of work and the internal energy of the body would not be determined solely by the actual stress (or strain) components. The remaining scheme of 21 elastic coefficients expresses the generalized Hooke's law. Actually, the derivation from the molecular picture led to only 15 independent coefficients or, in other words, to six relations between the 21 coefficients permissible in the expression of Hooke's law. These are called the Cauchy relations. The existence of symmetry, as in crystals, implies further relations, or restrictions on the number of independent coefficients; for the case of full rotatory symmetry, as in an isotropic body, the general formalism of linear relation requires only two independent elastic constants, e.g. Young's modulus and the shear modulus. The addition of Cauchy's relations reduces the number to one; this can also be expressed as leading to the value $\frac{1}{4}$ for "Poisson's ratio," i.e. the ratio of the transverse contraction to the axial lengthening of a rod under tension. Experiment disproved this consequence of Cauchy's theory, and discredited for ninety years the approach based on the molecular picture. It was not until 1914 that the flaw in Cauchy's argument was found by Born [5]; it lay in the simplification which Cauchy and all his followers had made in assuming the molecular or force centers to form a simple lattice instead of an actual crystal structure or at least one of the composite lattices foreseen in space group theory. Born's discovery opened the way for a rapid development of crystal dynamics along the lines of classical mechanics. A later impetus came to the theory of the solid state with the advent of wave mechanics in 1926; this theory led to understanding the interatomic and intermolecular forces which are usually called chemical forces.

G,15. Crystal Statics.

ELASTIC CONSTANTS. The principal assumption of Born's theory is that the crystal is a mechanical system in a position of stable equilibrium. The atoms are at points

$$\mathbf{x}_l^k = l_i \mathbf{a}_i + \mathbf{x}^k$$

where $l_i \mathbf{a}_i$ stands for the sum $l_1 \mathbf{a}_1 + l_2 \mathbf{a}_2 + l_3 \mathbf{a}_3$, a lattice vector, and $\mathbf{x}^k$ is the basis vector which denotes the displacement of the kth kind of atoms from the origin corner of the lth cell. The distance between any two atoms is

$$\mathbf{x}_l^k - \mathbf{x}_{l'}^{k'} = (l_i - l_i')\mathbf{a}_i + \mathbf{x}^k - \mathbf{x}^{k'}$$

and we denote its absolute value by

$$|\mathbf{x}_l^k - \mathbf{x}_{l'}^{k'}| = r_{l-l'}^{kk'}$$

It is now assumed that any two atoms act on each other with a central force derivable from a potential

$$V_{l-l'}^{kk'} = V(r_{l-l'}^{kk'})$$

The energy per cell of the (unbounded) crystal is the same for all cells and can be obtained by summing the contributions from all atoms to the atoms of the "first" cell $l' = 0$:

$$U = \tfrac{1}{2} \sum_{l,k,k'} V_l^{kk'}$$

For convergence it must be assumed that V diminishes rapidly enough with increasing l. In the case of electrostatic potentials ($\sim 1/r$), the neutrality of the crystal as a whole is essential.

For equilibrium, U is a minimum. This implies that the gradient of U with respect to the virtual displacement of any atom from the equilibrium position is zero, or, in other words, that the total force exerted on any atom by all others vanishes.

We now wish to find the stress-strain relation, i.e. we want to express the elastic constants in terms of the potentials $V_l^{kk'}$. To that end we have first to define a homogeneous stress and a homogeneous strain in terms of the atomic model.

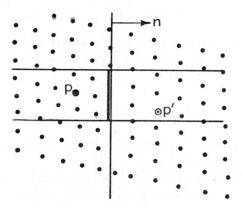

Fig. G,15.   Definition of stress.

Stress. Imagine the crystal to be divided in a left and a right part by a plane of normal direction **n**, which, for simplicity, we assume to be a net plane of the lattice, so that it is periodic with a certain parallelogram of area A as a unit of repetition. Consider the force transmitted through this plane from all atoms P which lie in the left half of the crystal to all atoms P' to the right of the plane which lie within a cylinder erected normally on A. If $\mathbf{f}_{PP'}$ is the force between any two of these atoms, the total force transmitted per unit area is

$$\mathbf{S}(\mathbf{n}) = \frac{1}{A} \sum_{P'} \sum_{P} \mathbf{f}_{PP'}$$

The force will vary with **n**, the direction of the normal to the dividing plane, but it is independent of the precise position of the plane. If, by shifting the plane parallel to itself to the left, a former atom P becomes a P', this will not change the flux of force through the surface, because in equilibrium the total force flux which the atom "emits" to the right (in its position P) is equal to the force flux it "absorbs" from the left (in position P'). It can be shown that **S** is a linear vector function of **n**. Now if the left half of the crystal were removed, the force **S** would have to be applied per unit area of the dividing surface in order to keep the right half in its position. Thus **S** is the stress, by the method usually adopted to define it.

Strain. A homogeneous strain is one produced by a general deformation of the shape of the cell or of the axes $\mathbf{a}_i$ sustaining the cell. This cell deformation leads to a change of shape of the crystal on the macroscopic scale; there may also exist a deformation of the basis, but it would not be directly observable macroscopically (it could in principle be observed by accurate X-ray measurements). The displacement of an atom in a homogeneous strain is thus

$$\delta \mathbf{x}_l^k = l_i \delta \mathbf{a}_i + \delta \mathbf{x}^k$$

of which $\delta \mathbf{x}^k$ is an internal or hidden displacement. Writing **u** for the displacements, and x (or y or z) for a coordinate in a Cartesian system, the last equation can be written

$$u_{lx}^k = \sum_y u_{xy} y_l + u_x^k \tag{15-1}$$

where the sum has to be extended over the three components of the lattice vector (symbolized by y_l), and where the u_{xy} are the six components of the symmetric strain tensor which are left over from the nine possible quantities u_{xy} if we disregard displacements which are expressible as rigid rotations. The hidden displacements u_x^k are themselves functions of the macroscopic strain; they vanish in the natural, i.e. strain-free, state of the crystal and are the same in each cell, provided the strain is homogeneous.

In order to obtain the stress-strain relation we have to find what change in the force flux through an arbitrarily oriented unit area (normal **n**) is produced by an arbitrary strain. The change of distance between two atoms has components

$$\delta(\mathbf{x}_l^k - \mathbf{x}_{l'}^{k'})_x = \sum_y u_{xy}(y_l - y_{l'}) + (u_x^k - u_x^{k'}) \tag{15-2}$$

and the change in the x component of the force acting from one atom to the other is given by the second derivatives of the potential $V_{l-l'}^{kk'}$, multiplied by the corresponding components of the displacements. Thus the z component of the force exerted on $\binom{k'}{l'}$ by $\binom{k}{l}$ will change through the x component of the displacements by an amount

$$-\left(\frac{\partial^2 V^{kk'}(r)}{\partial x \partial z}\right)_{r=r^{kk'}_{l-l'}} \left[\sum_y u_{xy}(y_l - y_{l'}) + (u_x^k - u_x^{k'})\right] \quad (15\text{-}3)$$

and the total change of the z component of this force is obtained by summing over the x, y, z components of the displacements. In order to find the total force acting on atom $\binom{k}{l}$ after displacement from the natural state (in which it is nil), one has to sum expressions such as the last one over all atoms $\substack{k \\ l} \neq \substack{k' \\ l'}$. This would be possible provided the potentials $V^{kk'}(r)$ between any two types of atoms were known. Otherwise, the sums over all lattice points remain unknown in magnitude; but certain symmetry properties are easily recognized as following from the symmetry of the second derivatives. Adopting Born's symbolism, we denote these lattice sums by brackets containing the quantities on which they depend. Let $\mathbf{F}^k$ be the force acting on an atom of kind k in the deformed state, and F_x^k one of its components. Further, let S_{xy} be the stress component, i.e. the y component of the force flux through unit surface normal to x. Then the following expressions arise:

$$F_x^k = \sum_{k',y}\begin{bmatrix} kk' \\ xy \end{bmatrix} u_y^{k'} - \sum_{y,z}\begin{bmatrix} k \\ x,\,yz \end{bmatrix} u_{yz} \quad (15\text{-}4)$$

$$S_{xy} = -\sum_{y,z}\begin{bmatrix} k \\ x,\,yz \end{bmatrix} u_z^k - \sum_{x',y'}[xyx'y']u_{x'y'} \quad (15\text{-}5)$$

In particular, the coefficients in the first line show the contributions to the x component of the force on any atom k coming from the hidden displacements of the basis and from the cell deformation, respectively. In the second line, the coefficients denote the influence which these two types of deformation exert in producing a stress component. It will be noted that the same coefficient occurs in both lines; this is a form of reciprocity theorem.

In the above expressions, the variables are the six deformation components and the $3(r-1)$ basis displacements which remain after attaching the (arbitrary) origin to one of the r basis atoms. It remains now to be shown that the latter $3(r-1)$ variables are determined by the former six and can be eliminated. This follows from the principle of detailed equilibrium which states that all F_x^k must vanish. This condition gives $3r$ linear relations between the $3r+3$ variables, so that the basis displacements are uniquely determined by the strain components. Introducing this linear dependence into the expression of S_{xy}, this becomes

$$S_{xy} = - \sum_{x'y'} \{[xyx'y'] + [xy; x'y']\}u_{x'y'}$$

$$= \sum_{x'y'} c_{xy \atop x'y'} u_{x'y'}$$

$$(15\text{-}6)$$

This is the generalized Hooke's law which expresses the components of the stress tensor as linear functions of those of the strain tensor; the coefficients are the elastic coefficients.

Since the three component indices x, y, z can be distributed in $3^4 = 81$ different ways over the four index positions on c, there seem to be 81 coefficients. However, the symmetry $S_{xy} = S_{yx}$ and $u_{x'y'} = u_{y'x'}$ of the two tensors reduces this number to 36. Furthermore, both brackets are invariant against transposing the index groups xy and $x'y'$; this brings the number of coefficients to 21, the number required by the "multi-constant theory." No further reduction is possible in the general case of a composite lattice because the symmetry properties of the second square bracket are exhausted. This bracket, as we will remember, summarized the contribution of the basis deformation to the stress. It is zero in structures where no basis deformation occurs in a homogeneous strain; this is the case in those crystals where every atom lies at a center of symmetry, so that whatever the homogeneous deformation may be (which is itself centrosymmetric) the forces on each atom cancel by symmetry. Examples of such structures are the Bravais lattices, in particular the body-centered cubic lattices of Li, Na, K, Mo, W, α-Fe, etc. and the face-centered cubic lattices of Cu, Ag, Au, Al, Pb, γ-Fe, Ni, Pt, etc. The centrosymmetry about each atom holds for all the many NaCl-type and CsCl-type substances and also for the Perovskite-type crystals, such as barium titanate $BaTiO_3$. However, it does *not* hold for the hexagonal close packing in which Be, Mg, Zn, Ti, and other metals crystallize, nor for the vast majority of structures, including the diamond type ones.

In case the second brackets in the sum for S_{xy} are zero, the higher symmetry of the first bracket expression reduces further the number of independent elastic coefficients. This bracket turns out to be invariant against any changes of position of its four indices, so that only the following forms occur:

$xxxx$ 3   times
$xxxy$ 3.2 times
$xxyy$ 3   times
$xxyz$ 3   times

The number of coefficients is then 15, as obtained by Cauchy.

The six equations

$$[xyxz] = [xxyz] \quad \text{and} \quad [xyxy] = [xxyy]$$

which hold for the first but not for the second brackets in Eq. 15-6 are called Cauchy's relations.

Although the four-subscript nomenclature is useful for discussing the symmetry properties of the elastic constants, it is too cumbersome for ordinary use.

Following Voigt [6], one replaces the index pairs according to the scheme

$$
\begin{array}{cccccc}
xx & yy & zz & yz & zx & xy \\
1 & 2 & 3 & 4 & 5 & 6
\end{array}
\tag{15-7}
$$

and e.g. $c_{xx \atop zy}$ by c_{14}. The same replacement is made in renaming the stress and strain components as $S_1 \ldots S_6$ and $u_1 \ldots u_6$. Calling **C** the matrix with elements c_{ik} (i, $k = 1 \cdots 6$, $c_{ik} = c_{ki}$) the stress strain relation is

$$\mathbf{S} = \mathbf{Cu} \tag{15-8}$$

The Cauchy relations in this notation are

$$
\begin{array}{ll}
c_{12} = c_{66} & c_{14} = c_{56} \\
c_{13} = c_{55} & c_{25} = c_{46} \\
c_{23} = c_{44} & c_{36} = c_{45}
\end{array}
\tag{15-9}
$$

In the case of cubic crystals, since x, y, and z are equivalent, the relations reduce to two, e.g.

$$c_{12} = c_{23} = c_{44} \quad \text{and} \quad c_{36} = c_{45} \tag{15-10}$$

COMPARISON OF ELASTIC THEORY TO EXPERIMENT.

Measurement of elastic constants on single crystals. A first check of the theory consists in testing the validity of the Cauchy relations in cases where they should hold according to Born's theory. Unfortunately such measurements have been made only on few of the many suitable substances; the list below, though not complete, is representative. It will be seen that the relation $c_{23} = c_{44}$ is fairly well fulfilled for NaCl and KCl, far better than for the crystals listed in the second half of Table G,15 where the relation should not hold. Quimby and his school (e.g. Rose) have shown that to a certain extent the exact fulfillment of the relation is fortuitous, certainly in the case of NaCl and KCl, because of the different temperature dependence of the two coefficients. None of the metals fulfills the relations, even though their atoms are centered on a simple Bravais lattice. This can be held as a clear indication that metals do not conform to the main assumption of Born's theory, namely that

Table G,15. Elastic constants of cubic crystals.* The constants are given in units of 10^{11} dynes/cm².

Substance	c_{11}	c_{12}	c_{44}	Remarks
NaCl	4.94	1.37	1.28	Cubic ionic crystals. Each atom a center of symmetry. Cauchy relation $c_{12} = c_{44}$ *should* hold in this block.
NaBr	3.30	1.31	1.33	Bridgeman. *Proc. Am. Acad.*
KCl {	3.70	0.81	0.79	*Arts Sci. 64,* 19 (1929).
	3.88	0.64	0.65	Försterling. *Z. Physik 2,* 172
KBr	3.33	0.58	0.62	(1920).
KI	2.67	0.43	0.42	
CaF₂	16.4	4.48	3.38	Composite crystals. Atoms not on centers. $c_{12} = c_{44}$ *need not* hold in this block.
NaClO₃	6.50	−2.10	1.20	
FeS₂	36.1	−4.74	10.55	
Cu	17.0	12.3	7.52	Cubic metals. All atoms on centers. $c_{12} = c_{44}$ *should* hold in this block.
Ag	12.0	8.97	4.36	
Al	10.8₂	6.2₂	2.8₄	
Fe	23.7	14.1	11.6	

	c_{11}	$3c_{12}$	c_{44}	c_{13}	c_{33}	
Mg	5.94	6.09	1.14	2.03	5.94	Hexagonal metals. Atoms not on centers. Cauchy relations $c_{11} = 3c_{12}$ and $c_{13} = c_{44}$ *need not* hold in this block.
Zn	16.3	7.65	3.79	5.08	6.23	
Cd	12.1	14.43	1.85	4.42	5.13	

* Condensed from Schmid and Boas, *Kristallplastizität,* p. 21. Springer, 1935.

The reader should be warned of the confusion of nomenclature: Schmid-Boas, Barrett, and engineers throughout call elastic moduli (Young's, shear) the coefficients c when expressing stress in terms of strain; the dimension of coefficient is force/area. Seitz, Mott, and most physicists, following Voigt's nomenclature, call the above the elastic constants and the coefficients in the inverse relation moduli. To the physicist, then, Young's modulus should be Young's constant.

the crystal behaves as a system having a position of static, stable equilibrium. According to wave mechanics, all atomic systems are essentially dynamical in nature, and in the case of the metals, where part of the electrons are free to move within the whole crystal, this aspect is dominant, while it is not so important for NaCl-type crystals consisting of ions with closed shells.

The different nature of metals is also shown by the fact that for a single crystal of a pure metal the range of applicability of a linear law is restricted to the lowest stresses and strains, so as to make it doubtful whether any such law exists for a perfect metal crystal. If a metal single crystal is subjected to a stress, it will usually slip; this plastic deformation does not go back on taking away the stress. The purer the metal, the lower generally lies the stress at which slip sets in in a definite crystallographic direction and with a definite slip plane. Significant figures are critical stresses of the order of 100 g/mm² for metals with impurity content of 0.1 per cent, going down with increasing purity to 7 g/mm² for mercury crystals with impurity content of the order of 10^{-6} per cent. Here again the difference appears between the forces which stabilize NaCl and those which act in a metal.

ELASTIC PROPERTIES OF POLYCRYSTALLINE MATERIAL. The knowledge of the elastic behavior of a single crystal is the foundation from which to deduce the elastic properties of a polycrystalline material, such as a metal. This might be attempted by simply averaging the stress-strain relation of the single crystal over all orientations of the crystal grains in the polycrystalline material. This could easily be done for a random angular distribution over all orientations, or, in the case of a textured material, by weighting each orientation with the probability of its occurrence.

In fact, however, the problem is much more complicated on account of the boundary conditions at each grain boundary. Across each boundary, the stress must be the same and the displacements (or at least their components normal to the boundary) must be the same. We are given only a macroscopic value of stress and strain, an integral value over a great number of grains, and the microscopic stress and strain distribution has to be obtained from the integral value under due consideration of the grain orientation. St. Venant's principle helps to formulate the mathematical treatment by assuming that the details of stress and strain distribution in one layer soon cease to influence the distribution in another layer some distance away by anything but the average values. Theories of this type have been given by Bruggemann [7]; see also Boas' book [8, Chap. 4].

G,16. Piezoelectricity. The property that some crystals develop charges on their faces on being compressed was discovered by Haüy in 1782 and used for the construction of an electroscope. Perfected by Curie, this instrument was used extensively in the early days of radioactivity. Nowadays the main field of application of piezoelectric crystals like quartz, tourmaline, and Rochelle salt is in radio valves and as frequency standards.

From the crystallographic point of view, piezoelectricity is a direct manifestation of the deformation of the basis, i.e. of the displacements u^k in Eq. 15-4 and 15-5 which remain hidden in the stress-strain relation. Provided a direction s in a crystal is polar, i.e. that none of the symmetry operations turns **s** into −**s**, then the centroids of the positive and the negative electric charges contained in each cell need not coincide and their distance may have a resolved part along **s**, say d, measured from the centroid of the negative to that of the positive charge. If the value of the charges be $\pm q$, then $P_s = qd$ is the electric moment of the cell, resolved along **s**. With $N = 1/v_a$ cells per unit volume (v_a is the volume of each cell), the electric moment per unit volume in direction **s** is $P_s = Nqd$. This moment itself is not observable, but its "divergence" (in the vector-analytic sense) is, since div **P** $= -\rho$, where ρ is a charge density. In the interior of a homogeneous crystal **P** is the same everywhere and div **P** $= 0$, but at a crystal face there is a surface divergence, div **P** $= (\mathbf{P}_n)_{\text{ext}} - (\mathbf{P}_n)_{\text{int}} = -(\mathbf{P}_n)_{\text{int}}$, where ext and int denote the external and the internal values of the normal component $\mathbf{P}_n$ of **P**. Thus on a face at right angles to the direction **s** one would expect to find a charge per unit area of amount $-Nqd$, and on the opposite face $+Nqd$. If a suitable crystal were broken in vacuo this charge might be verified. However, if the crystal lies in air, the charges in its faces will soon attract ions and be compensated. This must be regarded as the normal state of, say, a column-shaped crystal of tourmaline.

Let us now compress this column along its axis. Then both the general cell deformation and the internal deformation of the basis will change the distance d of the charge centroids in each cell and thus also change the charges appearing at the end faces. This additional charge is observable; since all deformations are proportional to the stress, it is proportional to the weight used for loading the crystal.

The reverse effect, used in radio-frequency standards, is even more instructive. Here a piezoelectric crystal plate is acted upon by the electric field of a condenser. We may imagine this field primarily to exert opposite forces on the positive and negative charges within each cell, thus deforming the basis. As a consequence of this, and in order to restore the internal equilibrium at each atom, the cell has to deform, and thus a deformation of the entire crystal plate on a macroscopic scale follows. This deformation becomes particularly large if, in an alternating electric field, resonance occurs between the field frequency and the frequency of some mode of elastic proper vibration of the plate. The latter frequency can be calculated from the ordinary elastic equations using the elastic constants of the crystal and the dimensions of the plate.

CHAPTER 4. CRYSTAL DYNAMICS

G,17. Historical Survey. The assumption of a regular atomic arrangement in crystals was reactivated shortly before the discovery of X-ray diffraction by crystals. Papers by Einstein [9], Madelung [10], and above all by Born and von Kármán [11] on the specific heat of crystals restored the confidence in the correctness of the assumption of internal regularity; these authors explained the newly observed relations between specific heat, infrared Restrahl wavelength, and elastic constants; they applied the Planck quantization of energy and the energy distribution function to the proper vibrations of the crystal. All this was elaborated and systematized by M. Born in his *Dynamik der Kristallgitter* (Teubner, 1915) and was later extended and brought up to date with the progress of quantum mechanics in the second edition of this book which appeared in 1923 as an article in *Enzyklopaedie d. Mathem. Wiss.*, Bd. V, and separately under the title: *Atomtheorie des festen Zustandes* [5].

The optical consequences of assuming a periodic, anisotropic arrangement of atoms or "resonators," which by themselves show no preference for any direction, had been discussed by Ewald [*12*] in 1912, with the result that such structural anisotropy would lead to the known laws of propagation of light in crystals. In particular, he derived the correct Fresnel "normal surface" which embodies these laws. No quantitative comparison of calculated and observed double refractions could be made at the time, because no crystal structures were as yet known. But some years later a quantitative comparison became possible not only for double refraction but also for rotatory power, calculated and observed, and was successfully carried through by a number of authors (Born and coworkers, Bragg, Hylleraas, and others).

At this stage of crystal dynamics the theory was essentially a classical theory, namely that of a mechanical system oscillating about a position of stable equilibrium. The "elastic spectrum," i.e. the set of proper frequencies of the structure had to be found by the methods well known to any reader of Rayleigh's *Theory of Sound;* quantum mechanics entered in a twofold manner, but only as an addition to the classical theory: first in distributing the total energy (thermal energy) among the proper vibrations, and again in attempting to explain the forces acting between the atoms (or ions) from a knowledge of their quantum laws of constitution and of interaction. The first application proved successful in the theory of specific heat, namely the transfer of the method of energy distribution, which had been developed by Planck for the black body radiation, to the elastic radiation representing the thermal energy of the solid body. But the second application did not give too good an account of the interatomic forces, even though the observable properties demanded only a rather simplified statement of these (central forces). The following articles describe the range and limitations of this early stage of the theory.

With the advent of Schrödinger's wave mechanics in 1926, the methods of atomic quantum theory began to influence crystal dynamics in a much more profound way than previously. A survey of this development is given in Art. 22.

G,18. The Elastic Spectrum of a Crystal.

A general consequence of periodicity. In order to bring out the features characteristic of a crystal, we assume it to have a perfectly periodic structure filling all space. The equivalence of all cells in space and time is compatible with plane waves traveling through the structure in any direction. Such a wave will produce a changing state of distortion in an arbitrarily chosen first cell; this we assume simply periodic in time in order to extend periodicity also to this variable. In a neighboring cell the same state of distortion must occur (otherwise the cells could be distinguished), but not necessarily at the same instant, i.e. with the same phase, as in the first cell. In the directions x, y, or z of the three cell edges a_1, a_2, a_3, neighboring cells may have different time lags φ_1, φ_2, φ_3 of their periodic deformations as against those of the first cell; to ensure equivalence of all cells, these same phase differences must repeat from cell to cell along the directions x, y, z, and they must compound linearly to a phase difference φ_l if one goes l_1 steps along x, l_2 along y, or l_3 along z: $\varphi_l = l_1\varphi_1 + l_2\varphi_2 + l_3\varphi_3$. If $D_0e^{-2\pi i \nu t}$ represents the displacement of the atoms in the first cell ($l = 0, 0, 0$), then the displacement in the lth cell ($l = l_1, l_2, l_3$) will be

$$D_l = D_0 e^{-2\pi i(\nu t - l_1\varphi_1 - l_2\varphi_2 - l_3\varphi_3)}$$

Since the l_i are essentially the coordinate vector $x_l = l_i a_i$, taken from an arbitrarily chosen origin in crystal space, the exponential represents a plane wave with wave vector $\mathbf{k} = \varphi_i \mathbf{b}_i$, where $\mathbf{b}_i$ are the axes reciprocal to the a_i (see Art. 9).

The assumption of a state in a first (or "zero") cell and its phase-modulated repetition in the other cells is characteristic of the lattice periodicity. It occurs, therefore, not only in the classical part of crystal dynamics, but also in the wave mechanics formalism. In either case the state D_0, the frequency ν and the wave vector $\mathbf{k}$ are not independent; they are linked, in the first case by the laws of motion, in the second by the Schrödinger equation. We will discuss this relation in the first case.

Proper vibrations of a finite system. To begin with, consider an isolated cell and the atoms contained in it, the basis. Let their number be Z, so that $f = 3Z$ coordinates are required to fix their positions in space. f is the number of degrees of freedom of the basis. By being cut out of the crystal, the basis will be deformed unless we apply external forces to the individual atoms so as to replace the forces, originating in other cells, which were severed by the cutting out process. As these forces serve only to maintain the equilibrium position of the system, we assume them to be constant in time; we call them the suspending forces of the basis. Assuming them applied, we find the atoms of the cut-out cell in the same configuration as in the crystal, and this, according to Born's fundamental hypothesis, is a position of stable equilibrium.

Now we know from general dynamics that a system of f degrees of freedom has exactly f proper modes of vibration about a position of stable equilibrium. In each of these modes every coordinate has a simple harmonic dependence on time, with common frequency ν, and all coordinates pass simultaneously through the equilibrium value. Thus no phase differences other than 0 and π occur between the displacements u of the atoms, and the phase π can be taken care of by the sign of the amplitude A if the displacements are taken from the equilibrium position. Thus in the jth proper mode of vibration the displacement along any one of the f coordinates x_s will be

$$u_s^j = A_s^j \cos 2\pi(\nu^j t - \gamma^j)$$

the phase γ^j does not depend on the coordinate index s, but it will vary from one proper mode to another. For each proper mode j the amplitudes A_s stand in definite ratios, and their absolute values can be fixed by some arbitrary common factor, a process known as normalization. We may represent the f amplitudes of one such mode by a vector $\mathbf{A}^j$ in an f-dimensional Cartesian space in which the reduced displacements $u_s\sqrt{m_s}$ are being plotted. The normalization may be taken to give unit length to this vector. This vector goes under the name of *eigenvector*; it describes in f-dimensional space the shape of the oscillation in the jth proper mode, or, in the optical analogy, its polarization.

It is a characteristic of the proper vibrations belonging to different modes that their eigenvectors are orthogonal (in f-dimensional space). Together with the normalization this gives the relation

$$\mathbf{A}^j \cdot \mathbf{A}^{j'} = \delta_{jj'} = \begin{cases} 0 & \text{for } j \neq j' \text{ (orthogonality)} \\ 1 & \text{for } j = j' \text{ (normalization)} \end{cases}$$

The scalar product $\mathbf{A}^j \cdot \mathbf{A}^{j'}$ signifies that the products of corresponding displacement components along all of the f coordinates have to be summed. This orthogonality of the eigenvectors makes the proper modes independent of one another; speaking in physical terms, it assures that any two vibrations j and j' are uncoupled and that there is no transfer of energy from one mode to another.

The orthogonality of the $\mathbf{A}^{j'}$ further permits them to be used as the axes of a second Cartesian (f-dimensional) coordinate system in place of the original one. In this system the displacement amplitudes of one proper mode are represented by a point on one of the axes, its distance α^j from the origin expressing the absolute amplitude of this proper mode. Clearly an arbitrarily given displacement, e.g. the initial displacement of the system, may be represented by a point (or vector from the origin) in the first f-dimensional Cartesian system by plotting the given data; but it can also be resolved along the second system, i.e. expressed as a superposition of eigenvectors $\mathbf{A}^j$, each taken with a uniquely determined general amplitude α^j. The α^j are called the normal coordinates of the system. Each proper mode of vibration takes place with a frequency ν^j, which follows from the equations of motion. In general, the ν^j will all be different; the whole set of f proper frequencies is called the spectrum of the system. In the course of the vibration, restoring forces between the atoms will be produced by their displacements, and they determine the acceleration of each atom. The resulting frequency, and the amplitude of each particle, are such that these internal forces of the system are just consumed by the inertia terms of the motion.

It may happen that one or more frequencies ν^j coincide; this can occur fortuitously, or, in the case of a symmetrical system, systematically. If p frequencies coincide, this frequency and the modes connected with it are called p-fold degenerate. In this case the choice of proper modes is not uniquely determined, since a linear combination of one set of proper modes may lead to a different set which also fulfills the orthogonality

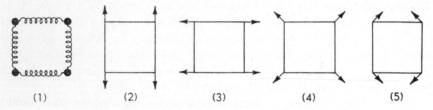

(1)   (2)   (3)   (4)   (5)

Fig. G,18. Proper modes of vibration of a square configuration of four masses coupled by equal springs.

requirement. As an example consider four equal masses at the corners of a square which are held by equal springs along the sides of the square (Fig. G,18). Fig. G,18(2) and (3) show two types of displacements corresponding to a twofold degenerate frequency; (4) and (5) show the superpositions (2) + (3) and (2) − (3) which form a second orthogonal set of displacements equivalent to the first one. As soon as the symmetry of the system is disturbed, the equivalence of the sets ceases; but by making a proper choice the proper vibrations of the not strictly symmetrical system will develop continuously from those of the symmetrical system. In the above example, let the vertical sides become slightly shorter than the horizontal ones, so that the square deforms to a rectangle. Vibrations (2) and (3) will persist as proper vibrations, but with slightly different proper frequencies. If, on the other hand, by a change of angles the square deforms to a rhomb, vibrations (4) and (5) will persist nearly unchanged in shape and with a slight splitting up of their frequencies. Thus whenever the conditions that led to degeneracy are slightly changed by a "perturbation," the nature of this perturbation determines the appropriate set of proper vibrations of the degenerate system from which the vibrations of the less symmetrical system develop; this particular set is called the "zero order approximation." Simultaneously there will be a slight splitting up of the degenerate frequency, but no major shift of frequency. This small frequency difference can be determined from the zero order approximation, i.e. without knowing the corresponding change of the vibrational pattern which is produced by the perturbing forces (i.e. the first order approximation). This is one of the main ideas in the classical and in the wave mechanical study of the behavior of molecules and crystals.

Proper vibrations of a crystal. In order to understand the proper vibrations of a periodic crystal we have to combine the results of the two preceding subarticles. To clarify the ideas, suppose we are dealing with a crystal such as calcite ($CaCO_3$) in which firmly bound groups of atoms form a radical CO_3, while there are also single atoms located between such groups and shared equally by them. For simplicity assume that there is only one set of atoms $CaCO_3$ in the cell—actually the smallest cell with which calcite can be properly described contains two units $CaCO_3$. If this basis is cut out, and the suspending forces are introduced, there exist 15 proper vibrations. Six of these are of frequency zero, and therefore degenerate. These are translations along, and rotations about, mutually orthogonal x, y, and z directions, whereby the basis remains undeformed. These motions may be regarded as improper proper vibrations in which no restoring forces are being evoked and whose frequency is therefore zero. (The "suspending forces" were assumed constant and therefore not of the restoring type; besides, they give rise to neither resultants nor moments.) Further, six proper modes are internal modes of the CO_3 radical which contain no displacement of the centroid or rotation, i.e. angular momentum, of this group. If the internal binding forces of this group are strong, these six proper frequencies will be high. They will not all be different because of the degeneracy produced by the trigonal symmetry of this group (this leads to two twofold degeneracies). Finally, the last three proper frequencies, on account of the orthogonality to the first six, must leave the center of the whole group at rest and produce no resultant moment. This is achieved by combining the external or improper vibrations of the CO_3 radical with those of the Ca atom (which, taken by itself, has only improper, no internal vibrations). Thus a translation of the CO_3 group in the direction of Ca is combined with a translation of Ca in the opposite direction in such ratio that the centroid remains fixed, and a rotation of Ca and the centroid about either of two directions normal to their line of connection is combined with a rotation of the CO_3 group about a parallel axis through its centroid, so that the angular momentum is nil. These last three proper vibrations have smaller frequencies than the previous six, because the binding strength between Ca and the radical is likely to be smaller than the internal coupling in CO_3 and because the masses to be set in motion are larger.

It will be understood that this construction of the proper vibrations of the group $CaCO_3$ from the proper and improper vibrations of its parts gives only an approximation. No account is taken of the fact that, e.g. in the last modes discussed above, the CO_3 group does not strictly rotate as a rigid body on account of its coupling to the Ca atom. The discussion gives, however, a useful approximation to the actual motion, and it can be extended, as follows, to the case of the whole crystal.

Assume now that the basis we have been considering is reinserted in the lattice of the crystal. Then the "suspending forces" have to be replaced by those exerted by the atoms in the neighboring cells. These forces are the same for the equilibrium condition, but if we impose similar displacements on the neighbor cells as on the zero cell, extra forces arise from the mutual displacements. The crystal as a whole has again 6 improper vibrations, namely, three translations and three rotations as a rigid body. These may be considered as the repetition of the first six improper vibrations of the zero cell from cell to cell without any phase difference. Since the relative displacements all remain zero, the frequencies remain strictly zero. According to the principle enounced in the discussion of a general consequence of periodicity, the translations of the zero cell could also be repeated with a phase shift from cell to cell. Consider this phase shift $2\pi\varphi$ first to be small. Then there is a small relative displacement from cell to cell, but no internal displacement within the cells. The small extra cell-to-cell force has to displace the whole basis and, the smaller φ, the less the frequency of this vibration is removed from zero. This motion represents an elastic wave in the crystal, of wavelength extending over $1/\varphi$ cells. In the unbounded crystal any wavelength is possible; in a finite crystal only those φ-values are permissible for which the wavelength fits the boundary conditions imposed at the surface. In either case, as φ increases, so does the cell-to-cell force and the frequency. There is a natural limit to $2\pi\varphi$, namely, π ($\varphi = \frac{1}{2}$). In this case neighboring cells have opposite translations, and the (longitudinal or transverse) wave has a wavelength extending over two cells. The corresponding frequencies ν_{max}, which can differ for the longitudinal and the two transverse waves, are the natural limits of this branch of the entire spectrum which extends there from $\nu = 0$ continuously (in the case of the unbounded crystal) or discontinuously (for the crystal with boundary conditions). This branch of the spectrum is called the acoustic spectrum. Increasing φ beyond $\frac{1}{2}$ yields no new frequencies, since the effect is to substitute a positive progressive wave by a negative progressive one; however, to obtain a complete set of proper modes, both types of waves (or their combination to standing waves of the cosine and the sine type) have to be considered.

Again it will be apparent that as φ increases, the growing cell-to-cell forces produce a departure from the pure translational displacement of each basis. The latter presents a good approximation only insofar as the internal coupling of the basis is strong compared to the cell-to-cell coupling. This may be assumed to be the case throughout the spectrum in crystals which contain definite molecules or radicals.

The result so far can be stated as follows: Owing to the periodic repetition of the basis and to the cell-to-cell coupling the six degenerate, improper modes of vibration of the single basis are spread out to a continuous (or, for the bounded crystal, discontinuous) spectrum of finite length $0 \ldots \nu_{max \text{ (long. or transv.)}}$ corresponding to elastic waves of wavelength from ∞ to 2 times the cell edges. Each wave corresponds to a wave vector $\mathbf{k} = \varphi_i \mathbf{b}_i$ as stated previously. This can be represented in reciprocal (or Fourier) space. All vectors within the limits $-\frac{1}{2} < \varphi_i < \frac{1}{2}$ are permitted, and it can be shown that they fill this space with uniform density. The number of oscillation states of the crystal with wave vectors within an element of volume dv_b of Fourier space is thus proportional to dv_b. These states will fall into a frequency range $\nu \cdots \nu + d\nu$, but in order to find all states within this range an integration over all suitable wave vectors of different directions has to be performed. This requires knowledge of the formula of dispersion, namely, the relation between $\mathbf{k}$ and ν. In the simple case of assuming frequency-independent elastic constants, such as Young's modulus or the shear modulus in the usual theory of elasticity, ν is proportional to $|\mathbf{k}|$ and the number of states between ν and $\nu + d\nu$ is proportional to the volume of a spherical shell of inner and outer radii $|k|$ and $|k + dk|$, i.e. proportional to $4\pi\nu^2 d\nu$ up to the point where the cutoff of frequencies begins because of the limitations on the variation of $\mathbf{k}$. This is important in the theory of specific heats (Art. 20).

A similar phase-modulated repetition can be applied to any one of the proper modes of vibration of the zero cell, say one of frequency ν^j. Again the "suspending forces" which were assumed constant for the determination of ν^j will now be modified by the relative displacements of the atoms in neighboring cells, depending on the type of deformation (the eigenvector) of each cell and on the phase differences φ_i between the states of the cells. Thus every ν^j is split up into a band of frequencies. If the internal coupling is strong compared to the cell-to-cell coupling, this band will be short; it may extend on either side of ν^j. As the cell-to-cell coupling comes into prominence, so will the band extend and the actual displacements be modified. In the case of all carbonates, for example, some recurring frequencies, or better short frequency bands, can be found in the infrared frequency range ($\nu = 10^{12}$ to 10^{13} sec^{-1}) and attributed to the modes of the CO_3 group, modified by the attachment of this group to the other atoms in the crystal. These narrow high frequency bands of the elastic spectrum are often called the optical branches because of their importance for the refractive index in the infrared. There will, of course, be a number of them, either separated or overlapping on the frequency scale.

G,19. Theory of Residual Rays (Reststrahlen). The results obtained for the dynamic spectrum find an immediate application in explaining the very high refractive and absorptive index of many crystals for selected wavelengths in the infrared. This arises as a resonance phenomenon upon excitation of a proper state of vibration by the alternating field of the incident optical wave. The wavelength of infrared light waves is of the order of 5μ, i.e. ten thousand times larger than the lattice constant of rock salt. The variation of the electric field from cell to cell thus introduces only a very small phase difference for the states of vibration of the cells, and an equal phase difference can be found for vibrations within the various frequency bands extending from the proper and improper frequencies of the atoms or groups which compose the crystal. Consider, for example, the CO_3 (carbonate) group in $CaCO_3$ (calcium carbonate). This doubly negative group has a positively charged C at the center and negatively charged O's at the corners of a regular triangle. If this group were brought between the plates of a condenser, with its plane parallel to the plates, it would be deformed, C being attracted by the negative, O_3 by the positive plate, so that the group would acquire an electric moment parallel and proportional to the field. If the field of the condenser is an alternating one of slowly increasing frequency, then a sharp increase of the alternating electric moment of the CO_3 group will take place when the impressed frequency approaches the proper frequency of the particular mode of vibration just considered. As in all resonance cases, a reversal of phase occurs on passing through the exact proper frequency; this implies a reversal of the sign of the electric moment. Now the refractive index of a body is caused by the alternating electric moments which the constituent particles of the body acquire under the effect of the optical field. Therefore, the resonance of the CO_3 group produces a large positive contribution to the refractive index on the low frequency side, and a large negative contribution on the high frequency side of the proper frequency. The refractive index behaves as in the left half of Fig. G,19a for a single resonance frequency. The dotted curve is the theoretical curve neglecting dissipative losses; the solid curve takes these into account and agrees well with the observed type of curve. The right half of the figure shows the refractive index when there are two active frequencies.

Only those proper vibrations of the crystal lattice will respond to the excitation by the optical field in which a variable electrical moment is being formed. This is not always the case, even if the atoms are charged. Consider, for example, the mode of the CO_3 group in which the central C remains fixed, and the O atoms oscillate radially. The symmetry of the system at any instant excludes a linear electric moment. This mode can therefore not be excited by the optical field, even if the electric vector lies in the plane of the group; nor would the group emit like a dipole and contribute to the refractive index even if this mode were excited for some other reason.

It is instructive to consider a crystal such as rock salt in which no larger groups than single atoms—or better ions—can be distinguished.

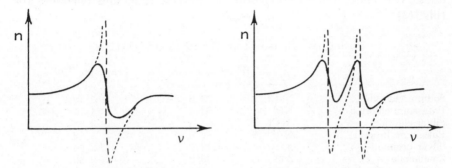

Fig. G,19a.   Refractive index for (left) one, (right) two proper frequencies. The dotted curve corresponds to no damping.

Let Fig. G,19b represent a row of Na^+Cl^- placed between the plates of a condenser. If a steady voltage is applied, the deformation of the type shown by the arrows takes place; it will, however, be very small. This deformation is of the same type as the fastest mode of this chain of atoms, viz. the one in which the greatest restoring forces are being evoked by having opposite displacements of neighboring particles. The

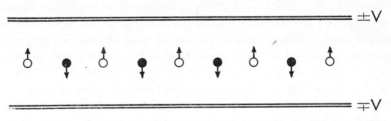

Fig. G,19b.   Displacements of Na^+Cl^- ions giving rise to the Reststrahl frequency in NaCl ($\lambda = 52\mu$, $\nu = 6 \times 10^{13}$ sec^{-1}).

frequency of this mode forms the end of the continuous frequency band extending from zero frequency. Therefore, if the electric field varies with this frequency, the amplitude of the displacements will become large by resonance. In consequence of this, a strong reaction of the solid body to the incident electrical field takes place, i.e. the refractive index has a sharp and high maximum, so that the body shows metallic reflection for this frequency. This effect is used experimentally for isolating monochromatic infrared light out of a continuous infrared spectrum ("Reststrahl" method, Rubens and Wood).

The interpretation of Reststrahl frequencies gives valuable information about the dynamic spectrum of the crystal, and about the forces stabilizing the structure of the crystal, or of certain groups within it. Table G,19 lists some of the main frequencies. Their investigation with higher resolving power shows that in fact these frequencies split into groups of lines. The more refined application of crystal dynamics accounts for this [14].

Table G,19. Reststrahl wavelengths and frequencies.

		Wavelength, microns	Frequency, 10^{12} sec^{-1}
Sodium chloride	NaCl	52.0	5.76
Potassium chloride	KCl	63.4	4.74
Silver chloride	AgCl	81.5	3.68
Potassium bromide	KBr	82.6	3.62
Silver bromide	AgBr	112.7	2.66
Zincblende	ZnS	30.9	9.80
Fluorite	CaF_2	31.6	9.50
Calcite	$CaCO_3$	93.0 / 116.1	3.22 / 2.58

G,20. Theory of Specific Heat. A superposition of its proper modes of vibration, each with unspecified amplitude A and phase γ is the most general motion a dynamical system can perform. As a consequence of their orthogonality, the energy of the system is the sum of the energies of the proper modes. Each proper mode of vibration may thus be considered equivalent to an independent oscillator of frequency ν, even if this "oscillator" is not localized but is spread over the whole extent of the crystal. The general thermal motion consists of the superposition of all proper modes with arbitrary (or better random) phases and certain average amplitudes. On these, classical statistical mechanics makes the statement that each mode carries the same energy, namely kT for each mode ($\frac{1}{2}kT$ for kinetic, $\frac{1}{2}kT$ for potential energy). Since the number of modes—for an infinite as well as for a finite crystal—is independent of T, this equipartition of energy makes the specific heat c, i.e. the increase of internal energy per increase of temperature, a constant (independent of T). While this is approximately true at high temperatures, it contradicts the measurement which shows that c, in accordance with Nernst's theorem, decreases and becomes practically zero at very low temperatures.

According to quantum statistics, the energy of an oscillator of frequency ν, as given by Planck's expression, is

$$\frac{h\nu}{e^{h\nu/kT} - 1}, \quad \text{or} \quad kT\frac{y}{e^y - 1}, \quad y = \frac{h\nu}{kT}$$

For small y (large T) this expression equals the classical value kT which is independent of frequency, and leads back to equipartition if $kT \gg h\nu_{max}$. However, as y grows with decreasing temperature, only the fraction ye^{-y} of the equipartition energy, i.e. the energy $h\nu e^{-h\nu/kT}$ will fall on the mode of frequency ν.

In order to express the internal energy u of the crystal the number $N(\nu)d\nu$ of proper modes within a frequency interval $d\nu$ must be known. This depends on the structure of the crystal, and on the interatomic forces, and a full answer can only be given in the simplest case of alkali halides on a wave mechanics foundation (Kellermann [13], Blackman [14], Löwdin [15]). On the simplifying assumption that the elastic constants are independent of frequency, $N(\nu)$ is proportional to ν^2 in the lowest (acoustic) branch of the dynamic spectrum, except for irregularities at the beginning and end of this branch (see Art. 18). If, then, this branch constitutes the entire spectrum, as in the case of the alkali halides having atoms of approximately equal weight, the inner energy is equal to

$$\frac{4\pi v_a}{c^3} \int_0^{\nu_{max}} \frac{h\nu^3 d\nu}{e^{h\nu/kT} - 1}$$

Debye introduced the characteristic temperature θ and the function D:

$$\theta = \frac{h\nu_{max}}{kT}, \qquad D(x) - \frac{3}{x^3}\int_0^x \frac{y^3 dy}{e^y - 1}, \qquad x = \frac{\theta}{T}$$

With these, the energy per cell of the crystal is

$$U = \frac{4\pi}{3}\frac{v_a}{c^3} \nu_{max}^3 \cdot kTD\left(\frac{\theta}{T}\right)$$

Now ν_{max}/c is the length of the longest wave vector **k** associated with a proper state of vibration in any direction. The wave vectors fill uniformly the first cell of the reciprocal lattice in Fourier space, and the length ν_{max}/c is thus a function of direction. In order to obtain a single value we substitute a sphere of volume equal to that of this cell, i.e. in a cubic crystal we make $\frac{4}{3}\pi \mathbf{k}_{max}^3 = 1/v_a$. This reduces the first factors to 1. We further take into account that each wave vector occurs for three independent waves: one longitudinal and two transverse vibrations. This produces a factor 3. Finally, by taking the energy per mole instead of per cell containing one molecule, the Boltzmann constant k has to be replaced by the gas constant R. Thus:

Energy per mole: $\qquad U = 3RTD\left(\frac{\theta}{T}\right)$

Specific heat per mole: $C_v = \dfrac{dU}{dT}$

Now for small x $(T \gg \theta)$, $D(x) = 1 + \frac{3}{8}x + \cdots$. For low temperatures, $x \to \infty$, $\lim x^3 D(x) = \pi^4/5$. Thus

	$T \gg \theta$	$T \ll \theta$
U	$3RT$	$\dfrac{3\pi^4}{5} RT \left(\dfrac{T}{\theta}\right)^3$
C_v	$3R$	$\dfrac{12\pi^4}{5} R \left(\dfrac{T}{\theta}\right)^3$

The result that the specific heat per mole of any solid is $3R$, i.e. about 6 cal/degree, is *Dulong and Petit's rule*. It appears here as the limiting case for high temperatures. For low temperatures, on the other hand, the consequence of Nernst's theorem comes true, that is, that the specific heat vanishes for $T \to 0$ in an order higher than the first. The T^3 law for C_p, or T^4 law for U has found experimental confirmation in cases where internal transformations (e.g. from a disordered to an ordered state) could be excluded.

We have so far only discussed the thermal energy contained in the—always present—acoustic branch of the dynamic spectrum. The other branches extend often little beyond the proper frequencies of the free radical groups. Here the cell-to-cell coupling can be neglected in a first approximation. Planck's formula determines the energy assigned to each of these distinct frequencies. Their contribution to the internal energy and specific heat is, therefore,

$$u' = \sum_j \frac{h\nu^j}{e^{h\nu^j/kT} - 1} = \begin{cases} \sum_j kT & \text{for high} \\ \sum_j h\nu^j e^{-h\nu^j/kT} & \text{for low} \end{cases} \text{temperature}$$

$$C' = \begin{cases} k \cdot (\text{number of frequencies } j) & \text{for high} \\ \sum_j \frac{(h\nu^j)^2}{k} \frac{1}{T^2} e^{-h\nu^j/kT} & \text{for low} \end{cases} \text{temperature}$$

Formulas of the mixed type, involving the characteristic temperature θ, a lattice property, and the proper frequencies of isolated groups of atoms, were proposed on empirical grounds before their relation had been clarified in the general theory.

G,21. Direct Evidence of the Lattice Vibrations by X-Ray Diffraction. The most direct evidence of the lattice vibrations is contained in the temperature effects on the diffraction of X rays, which were first given a theoretical treatment by Debye (1913). A perfectly periodic arrangement of atoms would give infinitely sharp directions of diffraction. In this case the lines or spots of a monochromatic X-ray diffraction photograph would have widths reflecting only the geometrical properties of the slit or pinhole system by which the direction of the incident ray is confined. The temperature motion in the crystal perturbs its periodicity, and, in principle, diffracted intensity is spread throughout in all directions. Imagine the temperature motion to set in gradually. Then the intensity in the "theoretical" directions will diminish, and the part taken away will appear as a background scattering. This reduces the intensity observed in the line or spot, firstly because of the lower peak intensity, and secondly because the peak is measured from the general background level. The reduction will be stronger in high order diffraction than in low orders. For the order is represented by three integers (h, k, l) which indicate, respectively, the number of wavelengths of path difference with which neighboring atoms in the three axial directions of the crystal lattice contribute to the emission in the direction in which the diffracted ray is observed. If now an atom is displaced by a certain fraction of its distance to a neighbor, a larger phase shift is produced for a high order than for a low order diffraction. As a consequence, the intensity distribution in the diffraction pattern falls off exponentially with increasing angle of diffraction (Debye's temperature factor, later corrected by Waller). The exponent is a function of T/θ, where θ is the same characteristic temperature as in the theory of specific heat. θ can be determined by observing intensities diffracted at different temperatures.

In the more refined forms of the theory the irregular motion of each atom cannot be regarded as unconnected to those of the other atoms. The relation is given by the resolution of the motions into the proper vibrations of the whole system (Brillouin [16], Laval [17]). Consider the displacements under a single proper mode; in neighboring cells the displacements are the same except for a phase difference φ. At any instant the strict periodicity of the crystal is only disturbed by this "modulation" of the positions of the atoms. As a consequence of this particularly simple deformation, the direction of diffraction is shifted from the "theoretical" direction by an amount which is proportional to φ, i.e. small for the long-wave, elastic, proper vibrations, and larger for the short, high frequency ones. The distribution of the diffracted intensity in the directions differing from the "theoretical" ones can thus be considered an image of the proper modes existing in the crystal. From measurements of this distribution, the elastic constants have been derived (Wooster [18,19]). Jahn and later Born [20] have developed the theory of this temperature background scattering, and Lonsdale [63] has extended its experimental study. Much observation and interpretation, however, remains to be done. Recent advances are due to Warren (1951).

X-ray measurements of the temperature effect (James-Waller-Hartree [*21*]) settled one problem of general importance at an early date while it was still controversial, namely, the question of zero-point energy. According to Planck's theory of radiation, an oscillator of frequency ν can only emit or absorb energy in quanta $h\nu$. Its state can only change by this amount of energy, but the absolute energy level of its nth state might be $nh\nu$ or $nh\nu$ + const. The constant would have the significance of its energy at temperature zero, when the oscillator must be in its lowest state, $n = 0$. There were strong indications that the oscillator always retained an energy $\frac{1}{2}h\nu$, but there was no straightforward experimental evidence on this. This zero-point energy, applied to the proper modes of vibration, causes a perturbation of the strict periodicity of the crystal, and a background scattering, which persists at $T = 0$, and it reduces the absolute intensity of diffraction into the "theoretical" directions by a further factor. As soon as methods had been worked out by W. L. Bragg [*3*] and his coworkers for putting the measured intensities on an absolute scale, the comparison between observed and calculated intensities at various temperatures confirmed unambiguously the existence of the zero-point motion.

These measurements also gave information on the average displacement of the atoms in the course of their irregular motion. At room temperature these are of the order of 8 to 10 per cent of the atomic distances in the alkali halides; they are somewhat larger for the lighter than for the heavier atoms and depend on the direction in nonisometric crystals, e.g. in hexagonal magnesium. The presence of zero-point energy was not understandable in the system of classical mechanics. It is, however, a direct consequence of one of the basic principles of wave mechanics, Heisenberg's uncertainty principle. According to this, it is not possible to determine accurately the simultaneous values of pairs of "canonical" variables in the sense of the Hamiltonian formulation of dynamics; such pairs are coordinate and momentum components q_x and p_x, angles and the corresponding angular momentum components φ and γ, energy and time E and t, etc. Heisenberg's principle introduces the quantum constant h as a measure of the uncertainty Δq and Δp which is inherent in the determination of canonical pairs; it states that, whatever measuring devices be used,

$$\Delta p \Delta q \cong h \quad \text{(i.e. of the order of } h\text{)}$$

is the best determination obtainable because of the inevitable interaction between the system to be measured and the measuring device (which itself is at the best an atomic system or a light wave). In fact this indeterminacy is a direct consequence of the wave-particle duality.

Classically, the lowest energy state of an oscillator is one of rest at the origin; this implies that both the coordinate $q = 0$ and the momentum

$p = 0$, and both are sharply defined. According to the above relation, p can only be fixed within a range Δp, and q within a corresponding range $\Delta q \cong h/\Delta p$. Thus even at temperature $T = 0$ neither the momentum nor the location of the oscillator are sharply determined. Extending this idea to a row of atoms in a crystal lattice, this row cannot have the perfect periodicity which is necessary for avoiding all background scattering between the Bragg reflections.

We shall repeatedly encounter Heisenberg's principle at other stages of crystal dynamics.

CHAPTER 5. WAVE MECHANICS
AND CRYSTAL DYNAMICS

G,22. Survey. The formulation of the wave mechanics method of handling atomic problems (Schrödinger, 1926) opened the way to an understanding of forces between atoms on a previously unknown scale. In particular, the nature of the covalent bond was discovered by Heitler and London (1927) and new light was shed on the van der Waals forces between molecules [20]. These discoveries were evidently of great importance for the understanding of the atomic forces acting in a crystal; in particular the first included the elucidation of the two characteristic properties of covalent bonds, viz. the saturation, and the directedness. Neither of these properties was contained in Born's original assumption of central forces between the constituent particles of a crystal, where undirected forces from each particle acted on any other particle, irrespective of the presence of the surrounding particles. In the newly developing subject of chemical physics the general principles of wave mechanics were applied to the study of individual molecules, their states and statistics, their spectra, and their reactions to external forces. Also discussed were the bridges or bonds formed between adjacent molecules in the solid state by hydrogen and hydroxyl bonds. All this led to a deeper understanding of the atomic architecture in crystals, especially in those containing easily discernible molecules or radical ions. The precision methods of determining the charge distributions in crystals from X-ray data by means of Fourier synthesis (e.g. Robertson, 1936) served to guide and check the theoretical calculations.

The atomic forces in metals remained obscure until Sommerfeld's application of Fermi statistics to the free electrons opened the path (Sommerfeld, Bloch, 1927). This work, soon expanded by Brillouin (1930), Mott (1930), Slater [23,24], and Seitz (1933), achieved remarkable successes in explaining not only physical properties of some metals, but the complex phenomena of alloying in binary and ternary metal systems (cf. Raynor) [25,26,27,28].

The whole tendency of this development is distinct from that of Born's dynamics, because the introduction of the highly individualized atomic forces determined by wave mechanics gets the theory closer to the most fundamental problem of crystal dynamics, namely, that of finding the reason why a particular substance crystallizes as it does, and what values of temperature, pressure, and composition determine the limits of existence of a particular structure. At the same time it becomes clear that an answer to this question cannot be given in a general way; it requires, on the theoretical side, an amount of detailed quantitative work, much the same as the establishing of, say, each ternary phase diagram requires a prolonged and meticulous experimental study.

The emphasis on the molecular forces and interactions in most parts of the wave mechanical treatment reduces the importance of the periodic aspect of the crystal, which dominated Born's original theory. This change of emphasis facilitates the discussion of the many phenomena in crystals with incomplete periodicity. A number of properties of physical interest and of great technical importance are encountered in disturbed crystals. To mention some of these: the hardness, strength, and corrosion of metals can be decisively affected by alloying; phosphorescence and photoconductivity of inorganic and organic crystals depend on the presence of traces of alien atoms which are imbedded in the crystal; the development of the faces of a growing crystal is influenced by traces of other substances in the solution. The explanation of such properties is based on an intimate knowledge of the energy states at the impurity centers as well as on the general state of the crystal as a whole. Much of the modern work on the solid state consists of the application of wave mechanics along these lines. Any adequate account of this theoretical development would become too voluminous and detailed, so reference to the bibliography must replace it. All that is attempted in the next article is to give some general introductory remarks on the wave mechanics method, illustrated by some examples. According to what has been stated above, molecular rather than crystal states are discussed.

G,23. The Method of Wave Mechanics.

One-electron problems. Consider a single electron of mass m, charge e, velocity v, momentum $p = mv$, kinetic energy $T = \frac{1}{2}(mv^2) = p^2/2m$, which moves in a conservative field of force $\mathbf{F} = -\operatorname{grad} V$, where V is the potential energy of the electron. In classical mechanics its motion is derived from the Hamiltonian equations; these are obtained from the "Hamiltonian function," i.e. the expression of the total energy E of the particle (= sum of kinetic and potential energies) in terms of the coordinates and the momentum of the particle. Using the position vector $\mathbf{x}$ and momentum vector $\mathbf{p}$, we obtain the statement of conservation of energy:

$$H(\mathbf{p}, \mathbf{x}) = \frac{\mathbf{p}^2}{2m} + V(\mathbf{x}) = E$$

It is this equation which is transformed into Schrödinger's wave equation, an operator equation, by replacing $\mathbf{p}$ by the gradient operator $(\hbar/i)\nabla$, or, in coordinates, by replacing p_x, p_y, p_z, respectively, by

$$\frac{\hbar}{i}\left(\frac{\partial}{\partial x}, \frac{\partial}{\partial y}, \frac{\partial}{\partial z}\right)$$

This gives

$$H\left(\frac{\hbar}{i}\nabla, x\right) = -\frac{\hbar^2}{2m}\nabla^2 \cdot + V(x)\cdot = E\cdot$$

The · indicates that an undetermined quantity has to be inserted in this operator, Schrödinger's function ψ. By the replacement of $\mathbf{p}$, this operator involves only the coordinates, i.e. $\mathbf{x}$; thus ψ will be a function of $\mathbf{x}$ alone. Dividing by the coefficient of ∇^2 we obtain

$$\nabla^2\psi + \frac{2m}{\hbar^2}[E - V(\mathbf{x})]\psi = 0 \quad \text{(Schrödinger equation)}$$

This partial differential equation of the wave equation type determines ψ together with either boundary conditions (in the case of a domain with boundaries) or conditions of regularity (for infinite space). The boundary/regularity conditions cannot be fulfilled except for certain values of E; thus they fix the possible energy values of the electron. These may form a discrete set of values E_n, or a continuous set. The equation itself, and these consequences, are analogous to the differential equation for the vibrations of a string (one dimension) or a membrane (two dimensions), provided that we assume the density or tension to vary so as to render the dependence of the bracket on $\mathbf{x}$. It is also the same equation as that of a light wave traveling in a medium of refractive index proportional to $\sqrt{E - V(\mathbf{x})}$.

The quantity ψ is not itself observable—as little as the amplitude of the light wave would be. However, its squared magnitude is observable; it is interpreted as the electron density $\rho(\mathbf{x})$, i.e. $\rho(\mathbf{x})dv_x$ is the probability of finding the electron in an element of volume dv_x surrounding the position $\mathbf{x}$. If ψ is complex and ψ^* is its conjugate complex, then

$$\rho(\mathbf{x}) = |\psi(\mathbf{x})|^2 = \psi(\mathbf{x})\psi^*(\mathbf{x})$$

The energy E is associated with a frequency $\pm\nu$ according to the equation $h\nu = E$. The full expression of the wave character of the electron is then

$$u(x, t) = \psi(x)e^{\pm 2\pi i(E/h)t}$$

This function fulfills the time-dependent Schrödinger equation

$$\frac{\hbar^2}{2m}\nabla^2 u - V(x)u = \frac{\hbar}{i}\frac{\partial u}{\partial t}$$

Field-free electron. Assume the electron to move in field-free space. The solution of

$$\nabla^2\psi + \frac{2m}{\hbar^2}E\psi = 0$$

which satisfies the regularity condition is

$$\psi(\mathbf{x}) = Ae^{2\pi i(\mathbf{kx})}, \quad \text{with } \mathbf{k}^2 = \frac{2m}{\hbar^2}E$$

Completing this expression with the time factor $e^{-2\pi i(E/\hbar)t}$ as prescribed in the general theory of wave mechanics, we see that this represents a wave progressing in the direction of the wave vector $\mathbf{k}$. The amplitude A has to be adapted so that the probability of finding the electron at any point is correctly expressed; A^2 measures the density of the electron stream in a beam of cathode rays. The relation between E and $\mathbf{k}$ is important: E proportional to $\mathbf{k}^2$. Substituting the classical value $E = p^2/2m$ (since $V = 0$), we see that $\mathbf{k} = \mathbf{p}/h$: wave vector and classical momentum are the same, except for the conversion factor h. This correspondence between the particle description and the wave description of an electron was given by de Broglie (1925) and led to Schrödinger's theory.

Central force. If the electron undergoes a central force of attraction, as in the case of the hydrogen atom, there will be a greater probability of finding it close to the center than at large distances r. Thus ψ will be large for small values of r and fall off (exponentially) as $r \to \infty$. The spread of the ψ function may be explained in more physical terms: If the electron, ceding to the attraction, were initially to remain close to the nucleus, its position would be highly restricted. Heisenberg's principle of uncertainty then prevents the momentum from having a well-restricted value, so that, in terms of Bohr orbits, there must exist elliptical orbits of all orientations besides circular ones, and these eventually carry the electron far away from the nucleus. It is even to be found at points which are forbidden by considerations of energy on pure Newtonian mechanics; ψ extends to infinity and is not limited by the "sphere of zero velocity" which confines a planetary motion of given energy.

For the application to crystal dynamics, we are less interested in the strict solution for the hydrogen atom; we illustrate the effect of a central force in the next example.

Three-dimensional square well potential. Let the potential acting on the electron be a "square well," defined by

$$V(r) = \left.\begin{array}{c} -V_0 \\ 0 \end{array}\right\} \text{ for } r \left\{ \begin{array}{ll} \leqq a & \text{"inner region"} \\ > a & \text{"outer region"} \end{array}\right. \tag{23-1}$$

We are interested in finding solutions depending on r only. By introducing $y(r) = r\psi(r)$, the Schrödinger equation is

$$\frac{d^2y}{dr^2} + \frac{2m}{\hbar^2}[E + V(r)]y = 0 \tag{23-2}$$

The boundary conditions are:

$r = 0$	ψ regular,	$\therefore y = 0$
$r \rightarrow \infty$	$\psi \rightarrow 0$, exponentially	$\therefore y \rightarrow 0$
$r = a$	ψ and $d\psi/dr$ continuous,	$\therefore y$ and dy/dr continuous

For the inner region, $r < a$, put $\frac{2m}{\hbar^2}(E + V_0) = \alpha^2$, and

for the outer region, $r > a$, put $\frac{2m}{\hbar^2}E = \beta^2 = -b^2$

Then solutions satisfying the conditions at $r = 0$ and $r = \infty$ must be of the form

$$r < a: \quad y = A \sin \alpha r \tag{23-3}$$

$$r > a: \quad y = Be^{-br} \tag{23-3a}$$

From the conditions at $r = a$ we get

$$A \sin \alpha a = Be^{-ba}$$

$$\alpha A \cos \alpha a = -bBe^{-ba}$$

This requires

$$\alpha a \cot \alpha a = -ab \tag{23-4}$$

a transcendental equation which determines the relation between the possible energy states E_n in terms of the depth and width of the potential

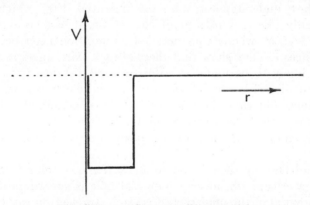

Fig. G,23a. "Square well" potential.

well. A graphical discussion of this relation is to be found in Schiff [*29*, cf. also *38*]. Looking at the solution we see that the exponential vanishing of y (and ψ) for large r requires the energies E_n to be negative. Since $E = 0$ corresponds to an electron at rest at infinity (or at least outside the well), a state of attachment of the electron to the well will be reached only by lowering the energy below 0. If this lowering does not bring E below the bottom of the well, α^2 is positive, α real, and the state in the interior of the well is

$$\psi(r) = A\alpha \frac{\sin \alpha r}{r} \tag{23-5}$$

This state corresponds to a central plateau with surrounding ripples, like the diffraction image surrounding the shadow of a small sphere. The larger α the narrower are the ripples and the smaller is the (negative) binding energy E_n, all of which corresponds to a high momentum and kinetic energy of the electron in the well; only a discrete sequence of such states is, however, allowed, because α must satisfy the condition of Eq. 23-4.

The interpretation of this solution is then that the electron oscillates to and fro in the well, that it is being reflected from the walls of the well in most cases and therefore interferes with its own representative wave, so as to produce the ripples, and that it sometimes penetrates into the potential wall surrounding it. Even when it roams about in the outside region, the existence of the well makes it unlikely to find the electron at a great distance, as shown by the exponential decay of Eq. 23-3a. Thus the square well is the simplest model of an electron trap, a concept which plays an important part in the theory of semiconductors, phosphors, etc.

Theorem of Mott and Gurney. Mott and Gurney [*30*, p. 82] have proved a theorem on the state of an electron in the presence of a "potential hole." By this they understand a spherical potential $V(r)$ which behaves asymptotically like that of a point charge, i.e. it can be finally represented by $-e^2/\kappa r$, whereas no detailed assumption need be made for small distances r. They show that there always exist states in which the electron is likely to be found at a fairly large distance from the hole, without it tending either to diffuse away to infinite distance or to coalesce with the hole, and that these states have a small binding energy. In fact, the states they describe are similar to those of the electron of a hydrogen atom in a very high state of excitation (large Bohr orbit, small energy).

Mott and Gurney then go on to show that a similar state will be possible in a crystal whenever a potential hole is superimposed on the periodic potential of the undisturbed crystal. An electron can be circling this hole at a large distance of, say, five to ten times the atomic distance in the crystal, and in this state its energy lies by about 0.1 electron volt below that which it would have without the presence of the hole. This gives a good picture of "shallow electron traps," the existence of which is needed for explaining conduction phenomena in semiconductors. The potential hole itself may for instance be caused by an interstitial positive ion, such as excess Zn^+ in ZnS. (Mott and Sneddon [*31*, p. 225].)

Electron in a periodic field. Consider a simple type of periodic field by assuming square potential wells to be arranged in a periodic pattern. From the earlier discussion we saw that an electron would not be confined to the interior of a single well; it would diffuse out and eventually reach other wells where it would be found with equal probability as in the first well. The equivalence of all the wells is borne out by the mathematical form of the solution which is constructed on the same principles that were discussed in Art. 18 for constructing the mechanical lattice vibrations. Let $\psi_{n,0}(\mathbf{x})$ be one of the possible states of the electron in the presence of a well at $\mathbf{X}_0 = 0,0,0$, i.e. the nth solution satisfying the equations of Art. 23. Then the same solution will also hold centered at the well at $\mathbf{X}_l = l_1\mathbf{a}_1 + l_2\mathbf{a}_2 + l_3\mathbf{a}_3$, but it might be given a phase difference without destroying the equivalence of the wells. Thus a solution of the Schrödinger equation which expresses this equivalence is obtained as

$$\psi_{n,k}(\mathbf{x}) = \sum_l e^{2\pi i(\mathbf{kX}_l)}\psi_n(\mathbf{x} - \mathbf{X}_l)$$

This may either be interpreted as a phase-modulated superposition of the electron state ψ_n for a single well, or as a plane wave $e^{2\pi i(\mathbf{kx})}$ of wave vector $\mathbf{k}$, amplitude-modulated with the function $\sum_l e^{-2\pi i(\mathbf{k},\mathbf{x}-\mathbf{X}_l)}\psi_n(\mathbf{x} - \mathbf{X}_l)$ which repeats from cell to cell.

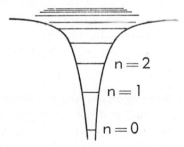

Fig. G,23b.   Potential of single central attractive force and sequence of sharp levels.

For reasons analogous to those discussed in the case of the vibrational spectrum of a crystal (Art. 18) the energy level E_n which belongs to $\psi_n(x)$ will be displaced on account of the phase difference. The wave vector $\mathbf{k}$ can vary throughout the first cell of the lattice reciprocal to that of the crystal, and surfaces of equal energy shift can be constructed in this cell. If we are interested only in the energy values, each value E_n will widen out into an energy band of varying density of states.

This discussion is largely independent of the particular assumption of a square well potential. Any potential of an attractive central force leads to solutions for a single electron, whereby the electron is very nearly confined to the interior of the well for its lowest energy states, with very little diffusion out, and where higher energy states exist with increased spread away from the center. If we think of the atomic nuclei of, say, a copper crystal already in place and now add the first electron, this will sink into one of the wells near a nucleus, and practically stay there, because of the weak diffusion from the deep level of one of the nuclei to that of one of the other nuclei. The same will be true for the further electrons until the atomic cores have one charge each. In a single atom the last electron would assume a ground state, or one of a series

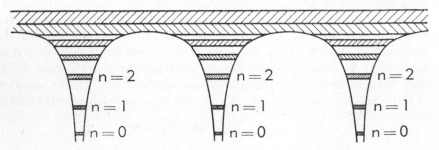

Fig. G,23c. Widening of energy levels in a crystal.

of excited states. Generally the lowest excited state has an energy which is higher than the ground state by the order of 1 electron volt, whereas the energy differences between excited states are less. In the crystal these levels are widened to bands; even if the ground band remains distinct, the excited states will merge into a continuous energy band. Fig. G,23c indicates this band structure. The existence of energy bands for the states of an electron in a solid is one of the foundations upon which the modern theory of solids rests.

G,24. The Many-Electron Problem. If there are n electrons, as in an atom, molecule, or in one mole of a crystal, $3n$ coordinates and $3n$ momenta (or n vectors $\mathbf{x}$ and n vectors $\mathbf{p}$) are needed for the representation of the system in classical mechanics. The system is represented by a single point moving in $6n$-dimensional space. This space is called "phase space," and it consists of the $3n$-dimensional "configuration space" for $\mathbf{x}$ and "momentum space" for $\mathbf{p}$. A relation between the $\mathbf{x}$ and $\mathbf{p}$ representing the "energy surface" on which the representative point of the conservative system is constrained to move is given by the Hamiltonian $H(\ldots \mathbf{x} \ldots \mathbf{p} \ldots) = E$.

Part of this high-dimensional representation reappears in the multielectron problem of wave mechanics when the components p_k are replaced by $(\hbar/i)(\partial/\partial x_k)$ in converting the Hamiltonian into an operator. This eliminates the momentum, and the resulting Schrödinger equation is again a partial differential equation of the second order in the coordinates x_k. The ψ function is thus a function in configuration space only; it is determined by the Schrödinger equation, by requirements of regularity in unlimited space or otherwise by boundary conditions, and finally by a peculiar symmetry which forms the expression of Pauli's principle. These various requirements can be met only for certain values of E, the energy, which appears in the Schrödinger equation as an unknown parameter. These "eigenvalues" E_n are then the possible energies of the system; they form a discrete or a continuous spectrum.

The squared absolute value of ψ, $|\psi(x_1, y_1, z_1; x_2, y_2, z_2; \ldots; x_n, y_n, z_n)|^2$ is taken, as previously, to signify the density, or probability, of the system, with electron 1 being at x_1, y_1, z_1, electron 2 at x_2, y_2, z_2, and so on. This function in $3n$-dimensional configuration space is not observable. We have to project it into 3-dimensional physical space to get observable results. We could, for example, ask for the density distribution ρ_1 of electron 1 (assuming we knew which electron we mean by this). This density at point x_1, y_1, z_1 is obtained by allowing all other electrons to roam through their spaces, provided electron 1 is at its proper place. Thus it is

$$\rho_1(x_1, y_1, z_1)$$

$$= \frac{1}{N} \int |\psi(x_1, y_1, z_1; x_2, y_2, z_2; \ldots; x_n, y_n, z_n)|^2 dx_2 dy_2 \cdots dy_n dz_n$$

N is a "normalizing factor" which expresses that electron 1 must be found somewhere, i.e. that

$$\int \rho_1(x_1, y_1, z_1) dx_1 dy_1 dz_1 = \frac{1}{N} \int |\psi(x_1 \cdots z_n)|^2 dx_1 \cdots dz_n = 1$$

In a similar way we might have projected $|\psi|^2$ into the x_2, y_2, z_2 subspace in order to find $\rho_2(x_2, y_2, z_2)$, the density distribution of electron 2.

The ψ function alone is not sufficient as a description of a multi-electron system because it ignores the electron spin. It is well known that Planck's constant h has the dimension of an angular momentum. The theory of atomic spectra showed the necessity of attributing to each electron a "spin" of value $\pm\frac{1}{2}(h/2\pi)$, i.e. $\pm\frac{1}{2}\hbar$. In Dirac's extension of Schrödinger's theory, the spin is properly incorporated in quantum mechanics; for our purposes, however, it suffices to characterize the spin of each electron by a value σ which is either $+\frac{1}{2}\hbar$ or $-\frac{1}{2}\hbar$, and to amplify the ψ function by the introduction of these spin arguments. Thus the complete description of the state is now

$$\Psi = \psi(x_1, y_1, z_1; \cdots; x_n, y_n, z_n) S(\sigma_1, \sigma_2, \cdots, \sigma_n)$$

According to Dirac's theory there exist forces and energy terms due to the spin-spin interaction of two electrons, and to the interaction between the spin and the angular "orbital" momentum of the same or other electrons (and also of the nucleus). These direct effects of spin on energy however, are, mostly less important than the indirect effect in which the spin only acts as a selector or governor in admitting only one half of the states following from the Schrödinger equation alone. This selection of the actual states is expressed by *Pauli's principle* which postulates: The actual states of atomic systems are antisymmetric in all electrons. This means that if any two electrons are interchanged in their roles Ψ changes to $-\Psi$.

The most important consequence of Pauli's principle is this: Assume ψ to depend in the same manner on the coordinates of two electrons, say the first and second. Then interchanging these produces no difference in ψ. Therefore the interchange must convert S into $-S$. If the two spins σ_1 and σ_2 were alike, i.e. have the same value, the exchange could not produce the change of sign. Therefore, two electrons which are in the same configuration (have the same orbit) must have opposite spins. It also follows that not more than two electrons can share the same configuration. For if electrons 1, 2, and 3 enter in the same way in ψ, then all three spins σ_1, σ_2, and σ_3 would have to be opposed to one another, which is impossible. For this reason Pauli's principle is called the exclusion principle; it explains the architecture of the periodic system and the saturation property of the covalent bond.

Except for the 2-electron problem presented by the helium atom (or lithium ion), no strict solutions for many-electron systems have been found. We shall see in the next articles how approximations have been constructed in much more complicated cases. Applying the strict wave mechanics procedure to a crystal would imply finding a solution of the Schrödinger equation in a space of very high (infinitely high) dimension. The ψ function would have to be bounded for all coordinate values, and this condition would determine the eigenvalues $E \ldots _n \ldots$ which depend on a correspondingly high number of quantum numbers n. Spin would have to be considered and antisymmetric states selected. Any observable particulars, such as charge densities, currents, and electric moments, would be obtainable by projection into physical space. Impossible as this treatment is, it shows that the full interchange of electrons and the effect of their electric interaction would be contained in the solution— features which have to be inserted a posteriori in the approximate solutions to be discussed presently.

G,25. The Hartree Approximation by the "Self-Consistent Field" Method.

Hartree's original method of finding the electron distribution in an atom starts out by assuming known the distribution of all electrons except one. Let there be n electrons, and let i be one of which the distribution is to be determined. Then the interaction of the kth electron with the ith is assumed to be given by a potential $V_{ik}(x_i)$, and $V_i(x_i) = \sum_k V_{ik}(x_i)$ is the potential field in which electron i moves, apart from the potential of the nucleus. The three-dimensional Schrödinger equation for electron i is solved assuming a plausible value V_i^0 of V_i, and the same is done for the other electrons. There results a set of densities $\bar{\rho}_i$, $\bar{\rho}_k$, . . . for the electrons, and these will in general not build up the assumed potentials V_{ik}^0 (or, alternately, $\bar{\rho}_k$ will differ from the value of $-\nabla_k^2 V_{ik}^0 = \rho_k^0$). This difference indicates how the V_{ik}^0 have to be modified, and after repeated readjustment the final stage will be a self-consistent field, that is, one in which the Schrödinger equation for each electron produces the correct density distribution of that electron, namely, the one which is assumed in establishing the distribution of the other electrons.

It is obvious that it is easier to solve (by computational methods) these successive three-dimensional Schrödinger equations, than it is to tackle the polydimensional problem. On the other hand, the replacement of the true interaction potential $+e^2/r_{ik}$ of two electrons at distance r_{ik} by the potential V_{ik} (which results from the average distribution of electron k and depends only on x_i) is an approximation which is bound to destroy some significant features, notably the strong repulsive effect of the two electrons when they approach each other closely. Again the method neglects the spin effects and may well lead to an infringement of the Pauli principle.

The second of these criticisms is met by Fock's modification of the Hartree method. Here, advantage is taken of the identity of all electrons in order to construct a ψ function of the whole system which is antisymmetric in any two electrons. As in Hartree's method, the averaged potentials V_{ik}^0 are used. In consequence of this simplification, the Schrödinger equation is separable, i.e. the solution appears as a product of functions each of which refers to one electron only:

$$\psi(x_1, x_2, \cdots, x_n) = \psi_1(x_1)\psi_2(x_2) \cdots \psi_n(x_n)$$

If ψ_1 corresponds, for example, to an electron in the K shell, ψ_2 to an electron farther out, in the L shell, etc., this solution would localize each electron in a particular orbit. Actually the electrons cannot be identified, and a product function like $\psi_1(x_2)\psi_2(x_1) \cdots \psi_n(x_n)$ would be equally justified. With all possible products, an antisymmetric solution can be constructed in the expression often known as the Slater determinant:

$$\psi(x_1, x_2, \cdots, x_n) = \begin{vmatrix} \psi_1(x_1) & \psi_1(x_2) & \cdots & \psi_1(x_n) \\ \psi_2(x_1) & \psi_2(x_2) & \cdots & \psi_2(x_n) \\ \cdots & \cdots & \cdots & \cdots \\ \psi_n(x_1) & \psi_n(x_n) & \cdots & \psi_n(x_n) \end{vmatrix}$$

This may be interpreted as expressing the full interchangeability of all electrons. It is antisymmetric because by interchange of any two electrons, i.e. any two columns of the determinant, the function reverses sign. If each function ψ_i (the pure orbital function of an electron) is replaced by a function φ_i which includes also the spin of the electron, a determinant of the same form in φ is the starting point of the Fock method of treating the many-electron problem. For the details the reader is referred to Mott and Sneddon [*31*, Chap. 5 and 6]. Again successive approximations, beginning with suitably assumed potentials V_{ik}^0 or V_i^0, result in achieving consistency between the potentials and the final electron distributions.

These methods were first applied to single atoms and their results checked on the energy values of the atomic states and on the electron distribution as obtained by X-ray diffraction methods ("atomic factor" in X-ray diffraction). They have later found wide application in determining the atomic states in crystals (Wigner and Seitz, Slater, and others).

For crystals the method must be modified to take account of the neighboring atoms, i.e. to construct a periodic solution. This is done in the following way: Imagine each atom, for example in a copper crystal, to be enclosed in a soap bubble, and blow these bubbles out until they flatten against one another. Each atom is then allotted a certain space, which was introduced by Schoenflies as its "fundamental domain." In a simple Bravais lattice all space is divided up into congruent fundamental domains, each containing one atom; in a composite lattice there are different types of fundamental domains. The Hartree or Fock method is now applied to each domain with the boundary condition—which is general for wave mechanics—that ψ and grad ψ be continuous at the boundary. Actually this condition cannot be satisfied strictly over the whole polyhedral surface of the fundamental domain; it is, however, approximated by fulfilling it at a number of points on the surface. Considerations of symmetry are of course applied to the construction of the solution. An alternative method, which is best justified in cases where the atoms are in positions of high symmetry, consists in substituting for the fundamental domain a sphere of equal volume and prescribing the boundary conditions on its surface.

Once the self-consistent ψ function has been found, the energy of the state can be determined by the evaluation of an integral.

G,26. The Heitler-London Atomic Function Method.

If we imagine two atoms at a and at b to be so widely separated that there is practically no interaction, each would be in its ground state which we will presume to be expressed by $\psi_a(x_1)$ and $\psi_b(x_2)$, respectively, insofar as two valence electrons 1 and 2 are concerned. Considering the two uncoupled atoms as forming, nevertheless, one system, the state of this system regarding the two electrons is given by the product

$$\psi(x_1, x_2) = \psi_a(x_1)\psi_b(x_2)$$

As the atoms come nearer to each other, interaction potentials will come into play. These will eventually modify the functions ψ_a and ψ_b; but even before this change becomes important there will occur an overlapping of the functions ψ_a and ψ_b at places where they already have detectable magnitude. This means that there will occur an exchange of electrons, because electron 1 which was originally confined to close distances from nucleus a can now diffuse through to nucleus b, and vice versa. In other words, each electron belongs to the whole system, not to a specific nucleus. One can also look at the situation in this way: The above function ψ which localizes electron 1 at a and 2 at b leads to the

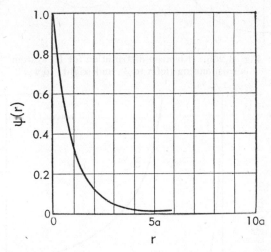

Fig. G,26a. Function $(\pi a^3)^{-\frac{1}{2}}e^{-r/a}$ for H atom ground state.
$a = \hbar^2/me^2 = 0.531 \times 10^{-8}$ cm.

same energy as a second state in which 2 is at a and 1 is at b. This degeneracy requires the symmetric and the antisymmetric functions ψ_+ and ψ_- to be formed, where

$$\psi_\pm(x_1, x_2) = \psi_a(1)\psi_b(2) \pm \psi_a(2)\psi_b(1)$$

The energies E_+ and E_- which belong to these states will differ if the interaction potential is taken into account—in the same manner in which the energy contained in the spring coupling of a symmetrical double pendulum leads to a split of the frequency. If the ψ_a and ψ_b are complemented by spin functions, so as also to comprehend the spin states of the two electrons, the Pauli principle requires that only the antisymmetrical one of the functions be retained. For equal spin of the two electrons (symmetry in electron spins), this requires the antisymmetrical orbital function ψ_- to be chosen, and for opposite spin the function ψ_+ is indicated.

The simplest illustration is afforded by the London-Heitler treatment of the H_2 molecule. Fig. G,26a shows the ψ function for the spherically symmetric ground state of a H atom, the square of which gives the electronic density at any point a distance r from the nucleus. Fig. G,26b

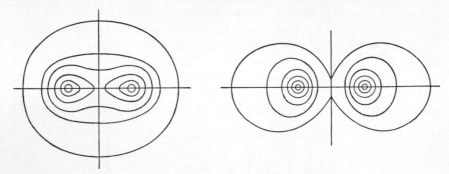

Fig. G,26b.   Electron distribution for H_2 system corresponding (left) to ψ_+ and (right) to ψ_-.

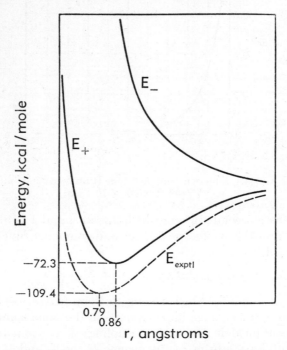

Fig. G,26c.   Energy vs. distance for H_2 system.

(left) gives the contour lines of the axially symmetric density following from ψ_+ in a H_2 molecule, taking the nuclear distance to have the actual value. Fig. G,26b (right) shows the same for the ψ_- state. Lastly, Fig. G,26c shows the energy values corresponding to ψ_+ and ψ_- as the nuclei are brought together from infinite distance $r = \infty$. It is seen that only the curve for E_+ leads to a minimum value of the energy, which determines the equilibrium distance. Two hydrogen atoms with parallel electron spin can only form ψ_-, E_-, and repel each other at all distances when colliding. This is seen from Fig. G,26c because the E_- curve shows no minimum. It can also be deduced from the charge distribution in Fig. G,26b (right) which shows that the charge is driven outward (the median plane between the nuclei is a nodal plane); thus it pulls the nuclei apart.

Although the Heitler-London method can be extended to some other cases where the atomic functions ψ are sufficiently well known (He, alkali atoms), it cannot be called generally applicable. Its main importance lies in its simple explanation of the typical covalent bond.

G,27. The Molecular Orbital Method. In this method an entire molecule is considered, and states of a valence electron are sought which have a symmetry appropriate to that of the molecule, e.g. axial symmetry for a molecule AB, plane symmetry without or with a threefold axis for molecules ABC and AAA, respectively, and so on. These "molecular orbitals" are analogous to the various electronic states of a single atom, and they are presumed filled by the valence electrons in the order of their energy values. The electronic interactions are taken account of, as in the case of Hartree's method, by suitable potentials which correspond to the density distributions of electrons rather than to the actual distances between them. Symmetry of the molecule reduces the number of states which together form a group corresponding to a shell K or subshells L_I, L_{II}, L_{III} in the atomic case. The energy difference between such groups is far smaller than that between atomic shells; this accounts for the relatively small binding energies of molecules, and for the possibility of easy transition of a molecule from one valence state to another.

For the widely separated atoms the energy values and the quantum numbers of the corresponding states are known from spectroscopic data and theory. As the atoms approach and interact, the degenerate ones among the energy levels split up (as in the Zeeman or Stark effects) and the sublevels move up or down. An indication of the directions of these changes can be obtained by considering, as a limiting case, a coincidence of the atomic cores so that the system of external or valence electrons can be compared to that of a single atom.

G,28. The Valence Orbital Method. This method takes as the starting point a two-electron function representing the chemical bond between two atoms. The two electrons have opposite spin and therefore form the equivalent of a closed group in the previous method. Taking for example the diamond structure, four bonds would start out from every carbon core (consisting of the nucleus and the two K electrons). If the bonds are not to interfere, they must be constructed from atomic states which are orthogonal to one another and have, together, the symmetry appropriate to the atomic position in the crystal. Pauling has shown how this can be achieved for carbon by a "hybrid" state, i.e. a state obtained by combining one electron in a $2s$ state with three electrons in $2p$ states of different orientations. Considering two nearest atoms, a valence orbital can be constructed by combining the atomic orbitals much in the same way as in the Heitler-London treatment of the hydrogen molecule. Thus a saturated bond is obtained which is directed in the sense that its axis includes the tetrahedral angle with the other bonds issuing from the same atom.

The valence orbital method is the wave mechanics interpretation of the system introduced by Lewis for rendering the bonding properties in the structural formulas of molecules. It has found wide application in the calculation of molecular states and their energies.

G,29. Summary of Methods, Resonance, and Bond Order. Depending on the nature of the chemical bond in each particular case, different starting points will give the quickest approach to the determination of the quantum configuration by one of the methods described in the previous articles. Since the multidimensional strict treatment is not feasible, the Hartree-Fock idea of a self-consistent solution fulfilling the symmetry requirement of the Pauli principle is used to find an approximate solution. The methods differ in the construction of this answer.

Much work has been spent in relating these methods to the established chemical approach. The bonds in chemical formulas are shown by dashes or by double dots in numbers representing single or multiple bonds. These symbols were interpreted by Lewis as indicating paired electrons. The wave mechanical theory led to a full justification of this view. There are, however, many cases, especially in organic chemistry, where several structural formulas appear equally suitable, e.g. in the distribution of double bonds in benzene and its derivatives. Here the wave mechanical idea of resonance between states having the same or very nearly the same energy sets in. It makes a distinction between the competing structural formulas impossible, because each of these (so-called Kékulé) configurations contributes to the actual structure. This may be interpreted by stating, for example, that a particular bond which appears to be a single bond in one, and a double bond in others of the structural formulas will have single bond character for part of the period in which the resonance between the "pure" states occurs, and double bond character for the rest of the time. Thus a bond can be given a certain "order," indicating what proportion of the pure characters it contains.

Much of Pauling's work is based on this consequence of the idea of resonance. A relation between bond order and bond length can be established from empirical data and gives a check on the bond orders in cases where they have not been calculated. Alternately, the bond-order/bond-length curve allows prediction of atomic distances; in some aromatic crystals this reaches an accuracy of 0.01 angstrom, nearly that of the best X-ray determinations (Coulson).

The resonance concept also applies to the mixing of states where a transfer of charge takes place, so that the bond has partly ionic character.

CHAPTER 6. THE ENERGY BAND STRUCTURE OF SOLIDS

G,30. Survey: Conductors, Semiconductors, and Insulators. According to Art. 23, energy levels which are sharp for an isolated atom will be split up into energy bands by the interaction of this atom with others in a crystal. This is discussed under a more physical aspect in Art. 31. The splitting is very small for the deep levels, that is those of large binding energy, which are filled by the electrons of the atomic core, but the high levels, which correspond to electronic states at the surface of the atoms, are influenced strongly by the interaction with neighboring atoms. As a result we have to consider energy bands of varying widths from which to pick the states of the chemically (and crystal-dynamically) active outer electrons. The highest of these energy bands overlap, or conflue, and form a continuous band of varying density of states, while the lower bands may remain separated by gaps which increase as the widths of the bands decrease and as the difference between the average energy values of successive bands increases. Fig. G,23c indicates this condition.

If we consider the atoms of the crystal brought together from infinite separation to their actual distances, the total number of states remains unchanged. To reach the ground state of the system the levels will have to be filled with electrons successively according to the energy values, as far as the Pauli principle permits to place them, i.e. not more than two electrons (of different spin) in each orbital state. Thus the "inner" electrons fill the practically unperturbed states within the atomic core. For the outer electrons (valence electrons) different situations may arise which determine whether the crystal will be a metal (a conductor), a nonmetal (insulator), or a semiconductor.

Nonmetal. Let there be altogether n valence electrons per mole to be placed, and assume that the lowest open energy levels form an energy band, the "valence band," which is separated by a gap from the next higher band, the "conduction band." If the electrons occupy all the possible states contributing to the valence band, then the substance has no electrical conductivity. This follows from the following facts:

1. The states making up the valence band are obtained from single-atom states by a modulation as discussed in Art. 31. To each modulation with wave vector $\mathbf{k}$ there exists the modulation with vector $-\mathbf{k}$; these may be combined to form standing rather than progressive waves. No charge is transported by this pair of waves. In order to carry current, at least some of the electrons have to be raised to a state outside of the valence band.

2. The transition from the valence to the conduction band requires a finite input of energy because of the gap existing between the bands. The energy difference between the highest level of the valence band and the lowest level of the conduction band can be regarded as an activation energy which must be supplied before conduction can take place. The characteristic feature of Ohm's law is proportionality of current and field, down to the smallest currents and lowest temperatures. This is irreconcilable with an activation energy.

3. The magnitude of the energy gap in insulators is usually of the order of one or a few electron volts. The thermal energy kT for $T = 300°K$ is equivalent to approximately $\frac{1}{40}$ electron volt. The thermal energy is thus quite insufficient to lift an electron across the gap. This can occur with significant probability only if the gap is of the order of, say, $\frac{1}{20}$ electron volt. The typical insulator can be compared to an atom of the inert gas type in which all possible electronic states of given principal quantum number are occupied by electrons. The large energy gap between the ground state and the first excited state of such atoms is shown by their large excitation (and correspondingly large ionization) potential.

Metal. If the valence band is only partly filled, or if it overlaps with the higher bands, the substance has metallic conductivity. Under the action of a field an electron can be accelerated, i.e. it finds a continuous series of higher energy states which are not occupied; there is no need for an electron wave of wave vector $\mathbf{k}$ to be balanced by one of vector $-\mathbf{k}$. Such transitions of state are possible even for the smallest applied fields; the activation energy is zero and Ohm's law holds.

This interpretation of the metallic state suggests an analogy to the state of an atom or a molecule which is "unsaturated" in the sense that its electrons do not form a complete shell or subgroup. These atoms or molecules are chemically active, whereas closed shells lead to stable and inert systems. The chemical activity of metals is shown especially at their surfaces by their strong affinity to oxygen, their easy corrosion, and their strong adsorption of vapors. In fact it requires highest vacuum and elaborate precautions to prepare a truly clean metal surface.

In the periodic system the metallic elements are to be found in the first halves of the short periods and later everywhere, except for the elements preceding the inert gases. The nonmetallic character is thus the exception; it occurs where an electron shell or subshell is completed (inert gas) or nearly completed. In the heavier atoms the energy differences between successive shells becomes smaller. There the elements preceding the heavy inert gases form semimetals or, with the more usual name, semiconductors, such as As and Se before krypton, Sb and Te before xenon, and Bi and Po before radon. For a fuller discussion the details of the quantum states of increasing principal quantum number have to be taken into account (Pauling).

Semiconductors. These are defined as substances having an electronic conductivity which tends to zero with decreasing temperature, in contrast to the electronic conductivity of a metal which increases with decreasing temperature.

This behavior is explained by assuming an unusually small energy gap, of the order of the thermal energy, $\frac{1}{40}$ electron volt, between the filled and the unfilled bands. At $T = 0$ all electrons are in the lowest band, the valence band, which they fill; with increasing temperature they are lifted into higher states in ever increasing numbers, thus gradually populating the conduction band. Semiconductors in which this happens, such as Si and Ge, are called intrinsic semiconductors, in contrast to those where intermediate energy steps are necessary to break down the gap into steps which can be overcome by thermal energy. Such steps are provided by certain alien atoms, impurities, which are imbedded in the crystal lattice and which destroy its regularity.

Conductivity arises from two sources: firstly the electrons which have entered the conduction band are free to move preferentially in the direction of the applied field, and secondly the creation of unfilled states in the valence band permits a reorientation of the velocities of the electrons in this band, because it destroys the rigid balancing of positive and negative velocities in the field direction, which holds as long as the valence band is completely filled (insulator). In an intrinsic semiconductor the number of unoccupied states in the valence band equals the number of occupied states in the conduction band, and one could expect equal contributions to the conductivity from both bands. Actually the redirection of the electronic velocities in the nearly filled valence band encounters greater resistance than their proper orientation in the sparsely filled conduction band. The conduction by the negative electrons in the latter band outweighs the conduction by the "positive holes," i.e. the missing electrons of the valence band in the best studied intrinsic semiconductors.

Impurity semiconductors, however, show both effects. In one type, the n (negative charge) semiconductors, the impurity atoms act as donors, i.e. they provide excess electrons. An example is a pentavalent phosphorus atom inserted in the diamond-type lattice formed by the tetravalent germanium atoms. It can be shown that the extra electron produces an energy level which is just below the lower edge of the conduction band; the corresponding state is a hydrogen-like state of the electron surrounding—at great distance—the P^+ ion which has the four valence electrons required for the lattice bonds to the germanium neighbors. This is the kind of state discussed by Mott and Gurney [30]. From this state the electron can be promoted easily by thermal energy to one in the conduction band. An impurity content of the order of one atom in a thousand provides electrons in sufficient numbers to account for the conductivity.

The second type of impurity conductors are the p (positive hole) semiconductors. Again consider the germanium lattice and replace a tetravalent Ge by a trivalent Al. Then to complete the chemical bonding an electron has to be removed from the general lattice, i.e. from an upper level of the valence band, and will be used up in a localized bond Al—Ge. This makes Al a negative ion. The vacancy created in the valence band leads to the possibility of rearranging the states of the other valence electrons which are repelled by the Al^-. The effect is the same as if a positive charge were forming a hydrogenlike wave function centered on the Al^-. The corresponding energy state lies slightly above the upper edge of the valence band. Thus the Al acting as an acceptor for an electron gives rise to an energy state to which electrons from the valence band can be lifted by thermal energy, thus producing "positive hole" conductivity.

Differentiation between n and p semiconductors is possible by means of the Hall effect. For a more detailed discussion of this as well as of the rectifying effects of semiconductors, the reader is referred to Slater's excellent account [32]. A crysal containing side-by-side n- and p-semiconducting regions is known as a transistor and has remarkable current amplifying properties, equalling those of electronic tubes.

G,31. The Energy Bands. The formation of gaps in the energy spectrum is, as shown in the last paragraphs, fundamental for the theory of solids. It can be understood by considering a highly simplified model of the state of an electron in a crystal. Let the action of the crystal on the electron be represented by a periodic potential $V(x)$ of small fluctuation. In any direction x the period is equal to the distance d between equivalent lattice planes normal to x. The Schrödinger equation (see p. 593) is then the same as that for a light wave moving in a medium of periodically varying refractive index. A single light wave will travel through such a laminated medium ordinarily without being strongly affected by the inhomogeneity. The wave front, for simplicity assumed parallel to the lamination, will at places be advanced and at others retarded compared to the position it would have reached in a homogeneous medium of the same average optical density, and the wavelets which are being reflected back at each inhomogeneity cannot build up to any strong optical field. This condition changes when the wavelength of the main wave is equal to twice the identity period d. For then the wavelets which are being reflected at, say, the planes of maximum refractive index will come together with equal phases, the $\lambda/2$ path difference being that of the main wave between successive planes, and further $\lambda/2$ arising from the traveling back of the reflected wave over the same distance. The main wave can therefore not travel by itself; instead, it is coupled to a wave of the opposite wave vector. The condition for this to happen, $\lambda = 2d$, can be expressed as $kd = \frac{1}{2}$ by means of the wave vector $\mathbf{k}$ of length $k = 1/\lambda$. If the wave front is inclined at an angle $90 - \theta$ to the lamination, the corresponding condition is Bragg's condition $n\lambda = 2d \sin \theta$ or $kd \sin \theta = n/2$. The integer n, the order of the reflection, measures how many full wavelengths of path difference lie between successive reflected wavelets. The result is, that whenever the Bragg condition is fulfilled, or very nearly fulfilled, a single plane progressive wave does not constitute a possible optical field, and that a wave pair is the simplest field. If the two waves have exactly opposite direction, they can be combined to form standing waves of the $\cos 2\pi kx$ and the $\sin 2\pi kx$ type; if the waves are inclined ($\theta \neq \pi/2$), factors may be split off which produce standing waves in the direction normal to the lamination.

Applying this to the motion of the electrons in a periodic potential of small amplitude, the wave vector energy relation (Art. 23) of the field-free electron, $k^2 = (2m/h^2)E$, will hold nearly unchanged as long as a single progressive wave exists. When, however, the wave vector very nearly satisfies the Bragg condition, the two types of standing waves occur. Where one of these standing waves, say the cosine wave, gives nodes (i.e. zero values of ψ), the other type has antinodes (maximum values). This means that the electron densities represented by the two waves are shifted by $d/2$ against each other. Thus if in one state the electrons are preferentially found at the lowest potential values, they are found at the highest potential in the other state. This is true for all electrons, provided the Bragg condition is strictly fulfilled; as k deviates from the required value, the statement holds for a diminishing fraction of all electrons.

As a consequence of this difference of electrostatic energy between the two states, the wave vector energy relation of Art. 23 must be replaced by that of Fig. G,31a which shows the characteristic gaps in the allowed energy values. The width of the gaps depends on the amplitude of fluctuation of the potential $V(x)$.

These gaps occur whenever the Bragg condition predicts a reflection, or, in the geometrical representation of the theory of X-ray diffraction,

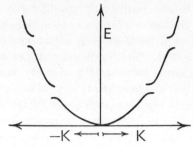

Fig. G,31a. Wave-vector energy relation in a periodic field. The energy gaps occur when the wave vector satisfies the Bragg condition.

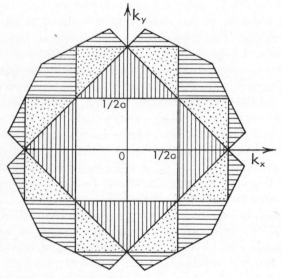

Fig. G,31b. The first four Brillouin zones of a square, two-dimensional lattice of lattice constant a.

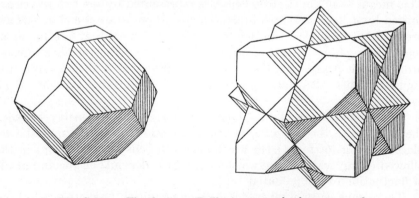

Fig. G,31c. The first two Brillouin zones of a face-centered cubic lattice, according to Hund and Mrowka.

whenever the wave vector of one wave approaches the planes midway between two lattice points of the reciprocal lattice. These planes are called the surfaces of Brillouin zones; the *Brillouin zones* themselves are the parts of reciprocal space which are cut out by surfaces of successive order. In Fig. G,31b these zones are drawn in two dimensions for a square lattice; successive zones are distinguished by shading. The volume of the first zone is obviously that of the cell of the reciprocal lattice, i.e. $1/v_a$, where v_a is the volume of the crystal cell; it can also be shown that the separate parts of the outer Brillouin zones always add up to the same volume. If we remember that the possible **k** vectors for the electronic states fill reciprocal space with constant density, we see that each Brillouin zone accommodates the same number of states as the first, i.e. $2n$ per unit volume of the crystal, if there are n atoms per unit volume. The relation between Fig. G,31a and G,31b is this: Fig. G,31a gives a section through the origin of Fig. G,31b in any direction, but only the first and higher order reflections on one particular set of planes is shown (i.e. gaps at equidistant values of k), whereas Fig. G,31b shows that further zone boundaries would be crossed on such a section and would result in further gaps.

The diagram of the first two Brillouin zones for a face-centered cubic lattice is shown in Fig. G,31c.

G,32. Theory of Metallic Conduction.

The metal in its equilibrium state. The concept that free "conduction" electrons carry the current in metals was first used by Riecke, later by Drude and Lorentz in their theories. They assume that the lattice of positively charged metal atoms is pervaded by an electron gas, the particles of which collide after an average free path λ with the atoms and thereby lose any unidirectional motion which they may have picked up in following the electric field force during their free flight. In these collisions the energy acquired by the electrons is passed on to the lattice, so that its thermal vibrations are increased; this is the origin of Joule's heat and of resistance. The main idea expressed in this model has been taken over into the present theory of conductivity. But it required a long development to overcome the difficulty arising from applying the equipartition theorem of classical statistics to the lattice/electron-gas system. According to this theorem of Hamiltonian mechanics each electron would have on the average, at temperature T, kinetic energy of amount $\frac{3}{2}kT$ (k is Boltzmann's constant), while each lattice vibration would have on the average twice this amount ($\frac{3}{2}kT$ each for kinetic and potential energy). Multiplying by the number of atoms per mole, L, and remembering that $Lk = R$, the universal gas constant, the lattice alone gives the correct specific heat per mole of metal, $3R \cong 6$ cal/degree and mole (Dulong and Petit's law), whereas the addition of the specific heat of the electrons increases this value by 50 per cent and contradicts experiment.

Only after the discovery of electron spin (Uhlenbeck and Goudsmit, 1925) could it be found that Boltzmann statistics may not be applied to particles with spin. In fact, in statistics based on classical dynamics, there is no inherent limitation to the number of particles which may have the same state and, therefore, the same energy; the spread of the energy values is caused only by the irregular interactions of the particles— their collisions—and the probability $p(u)$ of finding a particular particle in a state of energy u is, according to Boltzmann, proportional to $e^{-u/kT}$,

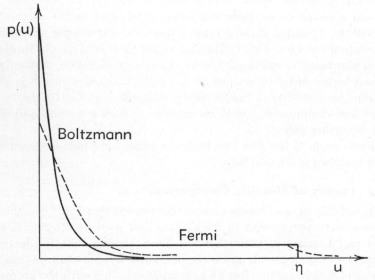

Fig. G,32a. Probability $p(u)$ of finding a particle with energy u shown for a lower and a higher temperature (solid and dashed lines) according to Fermi statistics and to Boltzmann statistics (schematic, not to scale).

irrespective of the presence of other particles of the same energy. The Pauli principle (1925), which excludes more than two electrons in the same orbital state, changes this independence; it leads directly to Fermi statistics (1926). This new form of statistics spreads out the range of energy values occupied by the particles of the system: the tendency of the particles for crowding in the states of lowest energies is opposed by the exclusion principle, with the result that all the energy states from the lowest up to a very high level are each occupied by two electrons of opposite spins and that an irregular occupation, including vacancies, takes place only at the top energy level. (This occupation has been compared to that of a hotel on a sports day when all the cheap rooms are solidly occupied and straggling occurs only for the top price rooms.) The probability of finding a particle of given spin with energy u is, according to Fermi,

$$p(u) = \frac{1}{A e^{u/kT} + 1} = \frac{1}{e^{(u-u_0)/kT} + 1}$$

The normalization constant A, which depends on T, or the equivalent $u_0(T)$, has to be adapted so as to normalize p, e.g. by demanding that $\int p(u)du = 1$. The value of u_0 for $T \to 0$ can then be found to be $\eta = (h^2/2m)(3n/8\pi)^{\frac{2}{3}}$, where n is the number of electrons per unit volume; η is an energy which is characteristic for the distribution. Corresponding curves of the Boltzmann and the Fermi distribution are shown in Fig. G,32a for two different temperatures (solid and dashed lines). The lower the temperature the more sudden will be the transition from occupied to vacant energy levels in the neighborhood of $u = \eta$; for $u = \eta$, $p = \frac{1}{2}$. For $(u - u_0)/kT > 1$, $p(u)$ is approximately $e^{-(u-u_0)/kT}$, i.e. there is finally a Maxwell-Boltzmann tail end to the Fermi curve, with u_0 acting as an activation energy.

Sommerfeld (1928) first applied systematically Fermi statistics to the electron gas [in a metal. One result is immediately apparent: the electrons contribute very little to the specific heat, because only those at the tail end of the distribution can change their state. At ordinary temperatures the change of thermal energy is taken up by the lattice vibrations. Only when, at very low temperatures, this lattice specific heat diminishes as T^3 (cf. Art. 20) could one expect the electronic specific heat to show up in a term proportional to T itself. This has, in fact, been observed (see [61,62]).

The enormous effect of the Fermi distribution in raising the average energy $\bar{u} = \frac{3}{5}u_0$ can be appreciated by converting the limiting energy η into electron volt or into equivalent temperature according to the equipartition law (see Table G,32).

Table G,32.   Limiting energy of Fermi distribution.*

Metal	N$\underline{o}$ of free electrons per atom	η, erg	η, ev	$\eta = k\theta$, °K
Na	1	5.0×10^{-12}	3.14	36,500
Au	1	8.8×10^{-12}	5.54	64,000
Cu	1	11.1×10^{-12}	7.00	81,000
Al	$\begin{cases} 3 \\ 2 \end{cases}$	$\begin{aligned} 18.6 \times 10^{-12} \\ 14.2 \times 10^{-12} \end{aligned}$	$\begin{aligned} 11.6 \\ 8.8 \end{aligned}$	$\begin{aligned} 135,000 \\ 103,000 \end{aligned}$

* Becker, R.   *Theorie der Elektrizität*, Vol. II, Chap. D. Teubner, Leipzig, 1933.

A different means to the same end is to convert the energy η into an electron wave vector whose magnitude $k = 1/\lambda$; $\eta = p^2/2m = (h^2/2m)k^2$. Since η is proportional to $n^{\frac{2}{3}}$, n being the number of atoms per unit volume, it follows that the limiting wavelength is of the order of the atomic distances, or the largest values of k are of the order of the cell edge in the reciprocal lattice provided there is one conduction electron per atom. The significance of this condition lies in its relation to the Brillouin zone structure (see Art. 33).

So far only the field-free state of the metal has been considered. The quantities determining it are the number of electrons per atom, the number of atoms per cm^3 (or the lattice constant), the number of possible states per energy interval, and the energy levels themselves. Using these quantities several important properties can be connected, notably the electron emission at high temperatures (Richardson effect), the potential difference at the surface of contact of two metals (Volta), the thermo-electric electromotive force (Seebeck) and its reverse, the electro-thermal effect (Peltier). A discussion of these effects will be found in Becker (Vol. II), Mott and Jones, or Seitz [*37,60*].

Electric conductivity. A theory of conductivity was given by Sommer-feld by calculating the change of the Fermi distribution by an applied electric field using the older concept of a mean free path of the electrons. There remained to be explained, however, the fact of a mean free path and of its dependence on temperature. After the discovery of the interference phenomena of electrons in crystals (Davisson and Germer, 1927; Thomson, 1927) it became evident that the passage of electrons through metals had much in common with the passage of X rays through metals, provided the electron wavelength was not larger than the atomic distance in the metal. We saw that this is true for the electrons at the top levels of the Fermi distribution. It was then (1930–32) that Bloch, Brillouin, Nordheim [*33*], and Peierls [*34*] gave the theory a firmer foundation by studying the scattering of electron waves on the elastic thermal waves of the lattice of atoms. Houston had pointed out that the electrons would suffer no loss of energy in collisions with a perfectly regular lattice. In fact the propagation of an electron wave of wavelength longer than the atomic distance is comparable to that of a light wave in a transparent crystal: no diffracted rays can be split off, and, as Lorentz showed in 1906 for light, in his *Theory of Electrons* (published in 1909), whatever wavelets are being scattered on the regularly arranged atoms are all again united without loss of intensity to form the one progressive wave front. Lorentz showed that scattering, i.e. deflection of energy into other directions, occurs as soon as the periodicity of the scattering centers is disturbed, either by faults and impurities in the crystal, or by thermal density fluctuations.

While this classic result can be applied to the propagation of slow electrons ($\lambda > a$), the optical analogy to fast electrons ($\lambda < a$) are X rays. For these the scattered wavelets issuing from periodically arranged atoms can collect in several directions, namely those of the diffracted rays, and they cancel out in all other directions. Although now a sheaf of plane waves constitutes the simplest optical field, the flow of energy is still the same everywhere in the crystal. But again, irregularities of the crystal produce irregular scattering without enhancement of the wavelets in definite directions. Therefore a general diffusion of energy in all directions takes place in a disturbed crystal, and the previously sharp interference phenomena are spread out and are connected by a general background which takes energy out of the sheaf of plane waves. In the case of X rays this weakening of the progressive wave field is an extinction rather than an absorption, because the energy still exists, redistributed, in the form of optical energy. Besides extinction there can also occur true absorption, in which optical energy is transformed into excitation of atoms or into electron energy by means of the photoeffect.

There are different stages of the theory of electric conduction according to whether only extinction or also absorption of electron waves is taken account of. In the first case the thermal motion of the lattice is taken as given and provides the irregularities which produce the extinction of the electron waves. The extinction defines a length, say that in which the amplitude of the wave is reduced by a factor e^{-1}, and this may be introduced into the Sommerfeld theory as a mean free path of the electron. Even if this method is successful in accounting for one of the assumed quantities in Sommerfeld's theory, it is not satisfactory because it fails to show the energy transfer from the electron to the lattice, i.e. the source of Joule's heat. The more profound treatment is then to consider the electron gas (under the influence of the applied electric field) and the lattice as a single quantized system. The thermal motion of the lattice is thereby resolved into its proper vibrations and the interaction with the electron can be regarded as a collision between an electron wave and a "phonon," i.e. one of the quantized proper vibrations of the acoustic branch of the dynamical spectrum of the lattice. In this collision, energy which the electron acquired by moving along the electric field lines is transferred from it to the lattice—a process which corresponds to the true absorption of X rays by the excitation of an atom. Besides, the electron waves are thrown out of their directions, i.e. they suffer scattering and extinction, leading to a mean free path. The temperature dependence of the electronic resistivity at high temperatures is linear in a first approximation. This may be restated by saying that the cross section of the atoms for the scattering of electrons is proportional to the square of their mean thermal amplitude. The more refined theory explains the deviations from linearity observed for many metals. At low temperatures, $T \ll \theta$, where θ is the Debye temperature known from the specific heat, the scattering is much reduced, because only the long thermal waves of low momentum survive. The theory leads to a T^5 law for the resistance. In this region, however, scattering by lattice defects becomes predominant.

Thermal conductivity of metals. Wiedemann and Franz found in 1853 that the thermal and the electrical conductivity of metals are proportional to each other and that their quotient is proportional to T and independent of the metal. The Drude-Lorentz theory accounted for this result; in calculating the thermal conductivity the unknown quantities which had to be assumed for the calculation of each of the conductivities cancelled out in the quotient, namely the number of conduction electrons per cm^3 and the mean free path.

The wave mechanical calculation of the thermal conductivity proceeds along the following lines. Suppose the temperature in a metal bar is higher in the left half than in the right. Then the electron waves of those electrons which correspond to the tail end of the Fermi distribution will have shorter wavelengths in the left half than in the right. Electron

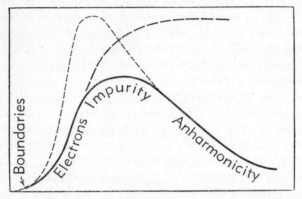

Fig. G,32b. Heat conductivity according to different causes (after A. H. Wilson, *Semiconductors and Metals*, Cambridge Univ. Press, 1939).

waves traveling to the right will transport more energy per electron than those traveling to the left. Since the wavelength is of the order of the atomic distances, both waves will interfere with the thermal waves of the atomic lattice and they will be strongly scattered; alternately, the elastic thermal waves are scattered on the electron waves, so that for all waves a mean free path can be defined. This brings the problem back to the assumptions of the Lorentz-Drude theory, including a determination of the "free paths" for electron and thermal waves. The exact theory shows that this process is the main process at high temperatures, and it gives the Wiedemann-Franz relation with a coefficient c (in the relation $\sigma_{\text{thermal}}/\sigma_{\text{electric}} = cT$) which is $(\pi^2/3)(k^2/e^2)$ instead of $2k^2/e^2$ (according to the classical theory).

At very low temperatures only the long elastic waves of the lattice survive and they cannot scatter the electron waves, except over small angles. Therefore, the thermal conductivity due to electrons becomes large at low temperature; it varies as T^{-2}. Actually, however, this statement leaves out the effect of impurities or other lattice defects including, for the lowest temperatures, the grain boundaries, which impose a mean free path on both electron and lattice waves and cut down thermal conduction.

The lattice conductivity is additional to the electronic conductivity of heat. It suffers changes at high temperatures because at large amplitudes the lattice vibrations are no longer independent, but coupled, i.e. one wave is scattered on the other. Wilson illustrates the effects of these causes at various temperatures in a diagram, Fig. G,32b, in which the thermal conductivity is plotted against temperature and the main causes of thermal resistance are indicated.

G,33. Band Structure of Metals and Alloys. In a way the most fundamental problem of crystal dynamics is that of explaining why a substance crystallizes in a particular type of atomic arrangement. This problem has been attacked with the semidescriptive methods of stereochemistry and of thermochemistry in the case of inorganic and, even more so, of organic crystals. The wide experience gained of crystal structures by means of X-ray diffraction analysis has been summarized repeatedly. On the basis of general principles and of analogies, it is often possible to predict crystal structures from the chemical formula and even incomplete experimental data, and to check their correctness by X rays.

The case of metals is different. The forces between the atoms are very little directed; the valence electrons, with their attachment to a particular atom destroyed, create a general coherence rather than a bond from atom to atom. As a consequence a large number of pure metals crystallize in one of the two equally dense closest packings of equal spheres, those of cubic and of hexagonal symmetry.

Great progress has been made recently in the understanding of alloys. Two metals with very similar structures, like silver and gold, are found to crystallize out uniformly for all compositions of the alloy; they form a "continuous series of solid solution." In the case of less similar metals, solid solution of one in the other only takes place for small concentrations. The temperature-concentration diagram of a binary alloy is usually divided into a number of fields corresponding to homogeneous crystallization in different "phases." Often these fields contain concentrations which center around a simple stoichiometric formula, and one distinguishes intermetallic compounds of definite crystal structure type. But the range of existence of a phase can be quite extended either on one or both sides of the stoichiometric concentration, or in some cases even not actually including the correct concentration. One must therefore admit that the compound itself contains solute atoms in fairly large proportions, and that the whole concept of a compound is not as suitable for metals as in other parts of chemistry. Fig. G,33a (from Barrett [35]) shows a typical phase diagram, that of the system Ag-Cd, and indicates the structures associated with some of the phases.

Hume-Rothery [*36*] and, later, Norbury drew attention to the importance of the electron-to-atom ratio for the determination of the structure of a phase. The number of electrons to be counted for this purpose is equal to the number of the group in the periodic system; it is 1 for Ag, 2 for Cd, 3 for Al, up to the fifth group, and is 0 for the transition metals in group eight (Fe, Co, Ni; Ru, Rh, Pd; Pt, Ir, Os). Thus the

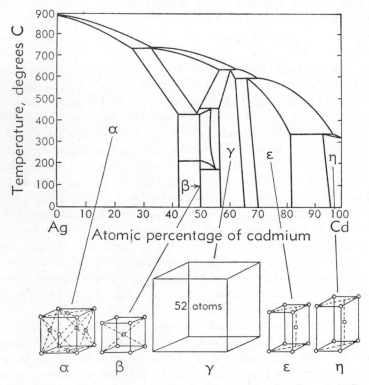

Fig. G,33a. Phase diagram of the Ag-Cd system (after Barrett [*35*]).

β-structure shown above in the diagram, which has two atoms per cell, occurs for AgCd as well as for FeAl at an electron-to-atom ratio of 3:2, and the γ-brass structure (γ in the diagram), which has 52 atoms per cell, occurs for Ag_5Cd_8, Cu_9Al_4, Fe_5Zn_{21} and many others with the ratio 21:13. Evidently in comparing these structures the sites have to be filled differently with atoms of one kind, so as to arrive at the correct composition. This again shows that atoms have a less specific action in a metal than in nonmetals.

The electron-to-atom ratio is a rule rather than a strict law; it introduces a variable which is of significance for the presence of a certain type of structure, but this variable is not the only determining factor.

The wave mechanical theory provides a more fundamental approach which has been carried through successfully to a quantitative determination of the phase boundaries for several binary and ternary alloys. This discussion is based on the concept of Brillouin zones and the departure from the simple wave-vector to energy relation $E \sim k^2$ near the zone boundary (Fig. G,31a). This creation of an energy depression leads to the following situation. Suppose we start out from pure silver and add increasing quantities of cadmium (cf. Fig. G,33a). The first Brillouin zone accommodates states for $2n$ electrons, if n is the number of atoms per cm³, i.e. for the face-centered lattice of Ag, $n = 4/a^3$, where a (cm) is the edge of the cubic cell. Monovalent silver has only one valence electron per atom. The Brillouin zone is thus half filled as indicated by the sphere in Fig. G,33b. If now divalent Cd replaces some Ag atoms, each Cd

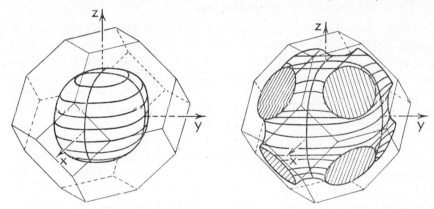

Fig. G,33b. The first Brillouin zone of a face-centered cubic lattice showing the energy surface (left) when half filled with electrons and (right) after addition of further electrons (after Mott and Jones [*37*]).

brings in an additional electron. These electrons fill the next higher energy levels outside of the sphere. If we imagine the filled sphere expanding by this introduction of electrons, it would first touch the zone boundary at the midpoints of the eight hexagons (or (111) planes) which lie at a distance of $\sqrt{3}/2a$ from the origin (the square remnants of the cube faces (100) lie at a distance $1/a$ for the reciprocal of a face-centered cubic lattice). The volume of the energy surface, still assumed spherical, when it first touches the zone boundaries is $(4\pi/3)(\sqrt{3}/2a)^3$, i.e. $\pi \sqrt{3}/2$ times the cell volume a^{-3}. This volume accommodates states for $\pi \sqrt{3}$ electrons, or $\pi \sqrt{3}/4 = 1.36$ electrons per atom. One might thus expect that the cubic face-centered phase could accommodate up to 36 atomic per cent of Cd. Actually, a slightly higher percentage of Cd can be introduced without increasing the energy unduly (which would lead to instability of this arrangement), because of the energy depression at the Brillouin boundaries. The surface of constant energy extends out before reaching the boundary as if attracted by it, so that more electrons of the same energy can be held;[1] (Fig. G,33b). From the phase diagram it is seen that only if the Cd percentage increases beyond 42 per cent will the placing of further electrons in the face-centered cubic lattice require so much energy that a fundamental rearrangement (to the β phase) is energetically preferred.

This one example may suffice to indicate the new understanding which the wave mechanics of metals has opened up in a field where there exists a confusing wealth of experimental results which previously lacked coordination by theory. The reader is referred to Mott and Jones [37], to Raynor's [38] and Hume-Rothery's monographs [36], and to Cottrell's book [39].

G,34. Band Structure of Insulators.

Dielectric breakdown. In a perfect insulator the valence band of energy levels is fully occupied by electrons and there is an energy gap between this band and the unfilled next higher band. Only a very high field strength together with temperature fluctuations or other lattice irregularities can impart to an electron sufficient energy to cross the gap; once this is achieved it is free to be accelerated by the field and to create further "free" electrons by collision with other atoms. In ionic crystals, however, a second, slower process takes place and becomes predominant. In this, a strong electric field liberates ions from their lattice sites and accelerates them. Under the impact of the first ions others will be set free, and, owing to the heat generated by these local currents, the rate of this process of disintegration will increase quickly, leading to breakdown. In crystals, canals are being formed in definite crystallographic directions which may be regarded as those of smallest dielectric strength.

Electric breakdown has been studied extensively, for example by von Hippel [40].

Lattice defects. The great power of the concept of energy bands for solids appears especially in the discussion of a large class of phenomena caused by irregularities in the lattice structure. Defects in the periodicity, such as missing atoms, displaced atoms, and impurity atoms, prevent a rigorous lattice-dynamical treatment for which periodicity would be essential. This latter treatment leads to assigning energy values to the entire crystal; it therefore omits all localization. On the other hand, it may be assumed, or even proven from general mathematical theorems, that if a volume which contains a large number of atoms be cut out in the perfectly periodic crystal, the distribution of energy levels associated

---

[1] The depression of energy (as against the $E \sim k^2$ relation) can also be called an extension of the wave vectors belonging to the same energy; the k vectors reach the boundary without the energy being greater than for smaller k vectors in other directions.

with the finite number of atoms in this volume will be very close to that for the infinite crystal (except that the total number of energy levels is reduced according to the number of atoms). This makes it possible to attach a localization in crystal space to the levels originally defined in momentum or Fourier space, i.e. in the space in which the wave vectors of the modulated electron wave functions are shown. By a similar argument one can conclude that an irregular atom will produce a localized deformation of the energy level structure; its influence on the electronic state falls off rapidly with increasing distance from the defect. Thus it is justifiable to draw an energy level scheme in crystal space and to indicate the deformation of this scheme in the neighborhood of a lattice defect.

There are many types of lattice defects, of which those are bound to occur in a crystal at ordinary temperatures, for which the energy associated with their production is of the order of kT. At $T = 300°K$ this energy is 0.026 ev. For polar crystals the discussion has been centered on the following types:

1. Schottky defects. These are missing atoms, i.e. vacant lattice sites. It is likely that such holes are first formed at the surface of the crystal and diffuse to the interior.

2. Frenkel defects. These consist of both an atom which, having left its regular site, migrates in the crystal as an interstitial atom and of the site that has become vacant; the latter can also move slowly by an exchange of places.

3. F centers. These were first introduced by Pohl for explaining the phenomena in colored alkali halide crystals. For these it is characteristic that an electron is trapped in the neighborhood of an excess charge, so that neutrality is restored. This may happen by the removal of a negative ion from a lattice site and its replacement by an electron, or by the introduction of excess positive ions into interstitial positions and the capture of an excess electron by negative ions nearby.

4. Impurity centers. These are alien atoms of uncertain location in the lattice. Because these atoms have a different scheme of energy levels from that of the regular constituents of the crystal, they may be regarded as presenting new localized energy levels rather than as deforming the general level arrangement of the crystal (see Art. 22). These centers are assumed for explaining phosphorescence and the related phenomenon of photoconductivity.

Much successful work has been devoted to the calculation of the influence of lattice defects on the energy levels and to the subsequent interpretation of experimental data. One of the most impressive phenomena is the formation of "F centers" in alkali halide crystals by exposure to X rays or to alkali vapor. The coloring of the crystal can be sharply limited by diaphragms, and later the colored parts can be displaced by applying electric fields. The fact that the crystal has acquired color signifies that energy differences corresponding to the "*F* absorption band" have been created as the result of either removing negative ions (the probable action of X rays) or of introducing excess metal ions (by diffusion of alkali vapor to interstitial positions).

The problem of interpretation is, in general, a twofold one: to derive a suitable type of defect, and to calculate the change of energy levels. This is neither a straightforward nor an easy problem, especially since the energy differences are small, of the order of a few tenths of an electron volt, and since the influence of temperature on the phenomena is therefore strong. It is necessary to collect a large amount of circumstantial evidence from many fields in order to construct a consistent picture of the behavior of the nonideal solid. Such fields are: the dielectric and conductive properties, the electric breakdown, magnetic susceptibility, thermodynamic behavior, phosphorescence, the sensitivity of the emissivity and the photoconductivity of phosphors to infrared irradiation, and the mechanical properties such as density, slip properties, and strength. All these properties are defect-sensitive and therefore strongly influenced by traces of impurities and by plastic deformation which creates defects. A discussion would be out of place here, since no single simple mechanism has been evolved, and probably none exists. There exist good books summarizing this subject which is equally attractive from the points of view of fundamental and of technical research.

CHAPTER 7. COOPERATIVE PHENOMENA
IN SOLIDS

G,35. Survey. The very fact that crystallization takes place is the best example of what has been termed a cooperative phenomenon. It seems not too hard to understand that a crystal can grow by deposition of fresh molecules on an already formed pattern—regardless of whether these molecules come from the melt, the solution, or the vapor surrounding the crystal. But before this can happen, a considerable number of molecules must have come together without the help of a preestablished pattern or field of chemical forces, so as to form a nucleus which will then grow. Is the formation of nuclei, the nucleation, a matter of chance encounter or of systematic application of a "repeatable step," similar to the formation of a high polymer? Are the nuclei miniature crystals of exactly the same atomic arrangement as the large crystal? Are they 3-, 2-, or 1-dimensional? How do their size and number depend on the temperature, and on the undercooling of the melt, or the supersaturation of the solution or of the vapor? All such questions require an understanding of the fact that only by the cooperative effort of a large number of molecules will conditions arise which make the crystal the thermo-dynamically stable system it generally is.

A second good example of cooperative action is given by ferro-magnetism. We may describe it in terms of the now abandoned theory of Weiss because the salient point would be the same in Heisenberg's wave mechanical theory of ferromagnetism. Above a certain temperature, the Curie temperature (780°C), steel is not ferromagnetic. If we cool steel in a magnetic field through the Curie temperature and then take the field away, we find that the steel has itself become a permanent magnet. It is understandable that in the field the magnetic moments of the iron atoms are preferentially directed along the lines of magnetic force. But why do they remain so orientated when the field ceases to act? Why do they do it in steel and not in nonferromagnetic substances? Weiss's answer was: because the alignment of the many magnetic moments creates an internal magnetic field which stabilizes their orientation. The permanent magnetization is thus a result of this cooperative action. Weiss's mathematical development gave an excellent rendering of the temperature dependence of the magnetization, and further details; it had, however, to be discarded in its fundamental assumption that the internal field arises from magnetic interaction, because the actual atomic mag-netic moments are much too small to produce a sufficiently strong orientation which would withstand the disorienting influence of temper-ature. Heisenberg showed, after the discovery of the spin, that spin, acting as a governing agent in selecting atomic states, accounts for a sufficiently strong stabilization of the magnetic moments.

A third phenomenon of the cooperative type is the disorder-order transition in alloys (see Art. 38).

G,36. Crystal Growth.

Static theories. The ideal thermodynamically stable shape of a fully grown crystal was determined by W. Gibbs. The free energy of a finite crystal consists of two parts, the first proportional to the volume, the second to the surface of the crystal. (Further parts, proportional to the length of the edges and number of corners may be left out of considera-tion.) Given the volume, that shape of the crystal is stable which leads to the lowest surface free energy. Since this free energy per unit area (= surface tension) depends on the orientation of the crystal surface, a minimum total value is obtained when the areas of the symmetrically nonequivalent faces stand in a certain ratio, i.e. for a definite crystal "habit." Thermodynamic equilibrium would be strictly reached in a batch of crystallization only if a single big crystal develops, rather than a crop of small ones, because this reduces the surface part of the free energy while leaving the volume part unchanged.

This purely static theory of crystal form is true to a certain extent. The habit of crystals is found constant under given conditions of crystallization, and in some cases where surface tensions are known from experiment or theory the habit conforms to Gibbs' law. It is also easily observed under the microscope that small crystals in the neighborhood of larger ones suddenly disappear; the disappearance shows the acceleration typical of instability, because the smaller the crystal gets, the greater is the gain of free energy per mass transferred from the small to the large crystal.

Often, however, Gibbs' law has little relation to the conditions valid for crystals, either ready formed or growing, because these differ considerably from the final equilibrium postulated by Gibbs. Modifications of the crystal habit occur by changing the conditions of crystallization, and especially by adding solutes to the solutions (e.g. urea to a sodium chloride solution) even though these alien molecules do not enter the crystal. Growth often stops at a moderate size in spite of the presence of many small crystals.

This kind of remoteness of the thermodynamical argument holds in even more important aspects than that of crystal habit. If a substance occurs in different crystallographic modifications, such as carbon as diamond and graphite, or SiO_2 as quartz, cristobalite, and tridymite, only one of these modifications is thermodynamically stable at ordinary temperature and pressure. All other modifications should thus transform into the stable one, often with considerable gain in free energy. While such transformations occur at temperatures close to the theoretical transformation temperatures (e.g. white tin into gray tin in cold winters), they fail to proceed at lower temperatures although the gain in free energy would be even greater. All the metallographic processes which use quenching profit from this inhibition against arriving at the thermodynamically stable states once the system is well below the equilibrium transition temperature. Where a slow transformation to the stable state occurs in a technical material, it usually is undesirable and leads to failures.

The inhibitions against a change of phase as well as the normal process of crystal growth show the need for a kinetic instead of static approach.

Statistical theory of nucleation. Owing to the density fluctuations which occur in all statistical systems of many particles it will happen that molecules instantaneously are brought together in the same small volume in numbers exceeding the average for this volume. Statistical theory makes the probability of finding such an aggregate proportional to $e^{\Delta S/k}$, where ΔS is the decrease of entropy which occurs through the aggregation. In general, for example in a noncrystallizing solution, the molecules will again disperse. If the instantaneous aggregate is to act as a nucleus for crystallization, conditions must be found to give it stability. These have been formulated by Volmer [*41*] and improved by Becker [*42*] and by Mayer [*43*]. The change of free energy achieved by the aggregation consists both of a volume effect which is the same decrease as for a corresponding volume of the bulk crystal and which can be found from the heat of crystallization, and of an increase determined by the surface of the aggregate and the surface tension in it. Together, this leads to a critical radius of the aggregate (assumed roughly spherical) from which on an aggregate will be stable, i.e. grow. Aggregates of the critical size are regarded as the nuclei. The theory attempts to predict the rate of nucleation as a function of temperature and of supersaturation. It is primarily a theory for the crystallization from the vapor phase; in the case of solutions, the viscosity of the liquid and the concentration gradients near the surface have to be taken into account.

The growing crystal. The growth velocity v of a particular surface of a crystal is defined as the distance this surface is displaced in unit

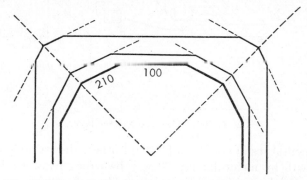

Fig. G,36a.　Velocity of growth and development of faces.

time along the direction of its normal. The final habit of the crystal consists of those surfaces for which v is smallest. If a small crystal at first contains faces of high v, these will be pushed out so fast that their area diminishes and they finally vanish (Fig. G,36a).

It seems natural to assume that the growth velocity is proportional to the supersaturation above the growing face, or, in the melt, to the undercooling. That these factors have a strong influence on v is certain, but recent investigations show that the connection is not simple. This is in part due to the effect the growth velocity itself has on determining these factors. The precipitation of the solute on the face, in fact, produces the concentration gradient, and the heat liberated by the precipitation changes the solubility just above the surface, or it changes the temperature gradient and the viscosity in the case of the melt.

By far the greatest complication, however, results from our scanty knowledge of the mechanism of precipitation. Theoretical and experimental workers concur in showing that it is much easier for an additional layer of material on an existing surface to extend over the whole surface than to deposit the first small part of such a layer. If one assumes that the deposit consists of one monomolecular layer at a time, it is understandable that molecules will be easily fixed at the reentrant step of the layer, where they are held by a greater number of bonds than when they exist singly on the surface. Again, as in nucleation, the difficulty lies in explaining the beginning of the layer, which starts with a two-dimensional nucleus formed of molecules which were previously free to move over the surface like a two-dimensional gas. (The surface mobility of molecules on crystal surfaces was amply demonstrated by Volmer [41].) There is agreement on the fact that the growth velocity is determined by the rate of this nucleation of layers rather than by the time required for covering the substrate surface.

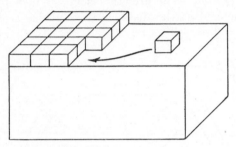

Fig. G,36b.   Growing surface layer.

Experimental results of Bunn [44] and others show that the assumption of growth by molecular layers may be wrong by several orders of magnitude. He showed by motion picture films of growing surfaces that layers are started, usually near the middle of the surface, and that they usually grow from a center outward. These observable layers are several hundred to thousand angstroms thick. They end in steep cliffs which move forward with undiminished thickness as the layer expands. While one layer is still extending, a second one will develop on top of it and its cliff moves forward with the same velocity as the lower cliff. The interpretation of these pictures is still very uncertain. The apparent outward motion of the cliff may result from a stream of material moving inward and piling up to form the cliff. The reason for the latter, however, is unknown. At any rate, the picture seems to differ considerably from the assumptions on which the theoretical attempts of explaining growth were based.

The Bristol school has been engaged for many years in the study and clarification of a particular type of crystal imperfection, the dislocation (cf. Art. 39). Frank propounds the view that some kinds of dislocations are essential for the surface nucleation. The reader is referred to the extensive "Discussion on Crystal Growth" held in Bristol in 1949 and published by the Faraday Society. He will see for himself the complexity of the subject. An impressive confirmation of Frank's prediction of spiral growth steps centered on a dislocation has been given by Dawson and Vand [45], Verma [46], and others.

G,37. Ferromagnetism and Allied Cooperative Phenomena.

Ferromagnetism. Ferromagnetism is a consequence of the interaction between the electronic spin and the magnetic field. This interaction influences the selection of atomic or molecular orbital states from which the state of the crystal is derived and thereby exerts a strong influence on the electrostatic energy of the crystal. For the production of ferromagnetism certain conditions regarding the number of atomic neighbors and energy levels have to come together; this makes it understandable that there are but few ferromagnetic materials and that these contain atoms with not completely filled inner shells. (This is true also for the manganese in the Heusler alloys.) The wave mechanical theory, first stated by Heisenberg, has recently been considerably improved. The reader is referred to Slater [47, Chap. 14].

Ferromagnetic materials were the first for which a "domain theory" was developed. This theory became necessary when measurements of the magnetic anisotropy of single crystal iron had shown that it could not be explained by the simple magnetic dipole interaction which was postulated in Weiss' theory. Honda and his school in Japan did much to develop the domain theory which goes back to the ideas and models of Ewing.

In these models a large number of small, strongly magnetized, compass needles are mounted in a regular array, e.g. a quadratic net along x and y. The needles have a tendency to take up parallel positions so that north and south poles of neighboring needles get closest. The alignment along x or y is, theoretically and experimentally, the stablest position. Generally this alignment can only be obtained by an external force, e.g. a strong magnet. Without it the system remains in a state of local ordering only; the whole model is broken up into several domains, in which the needles are parallel, but with different directions in each. Suppose now that, initially, full alignment along the x axis (saturation) is obtained with the help of a magnet and that the magnet is then moved to another direction in the x, y plane. The compass needles will not follow the direction of the magnet at once. Their internal or cooperative field keeps them bound to very nearly the original alignment parallel to x. Only as the magnet is turned by more than 45°, there suddenly occurs a change in the model, part of the needles turn over into the y direction and form a domain of the now energetically preferred orientation. In part of the model the needles may remain parallel to x (depending on the strength of the external magnetic field). At the boundary between two domains there are strong "demagnetizing fields" and the orientation of the needles is indefinite and intermediate.

The domain theory has been fully justified for actual ferromagnetic materials, especially through the new experimental methods of making domain boundaries visible at the metal surfaces by the deposition of colloidal iron oxides in the strongly inhomogeneous magnetic fields prevailing at the boundaries. It can be demonstrated how, with increasing magnetization, the domain walls wander within a single crystal of iron, and a quantitative explanation of the hysteresis loop can be obtained. The latter is closely connected to the formation of "Néél spikes" acute-angled domains which are bypassed by a moving domain wall and do not partake readily in the reorientation process during magnetization; during demagnetization they reappear.

The recent advances in ferromagnetism are largely due to the group of workers at the Bell Telephone Laboratories: Bozorth, Shockley, and others. Another active group, under Néél, is in Grenoble.

Ferroelectric solids. For ordinary solids the dielectric constant ε does not often exceed values of the order 10 (relative to empty space), but there are some crystals where, in certain temperature ranges, it reaches values of the order of 10,000 and higher. Since substances of this kind are very desirable for technical use, much applied and pure research has been done on them. Seignette (or Rochelle) salt (sodium potassium tartrate) was the first substance of which this property became known, later it was discovered for barium titanate and related compounds, and new ferroelectric substances are being found currently.

The high dielectric constant goes back to a large electric moment per unit volume which is produced by an external field. The Weiss theory seems much more applicable to the case of electric moments cooperating in the formation of a strong internal electric field than to the magnetic case, because the electric interaction of even moderate molecular electric moments produces much stronger forces than do the magnetic interactions. The formal results of Weiss's theory fit the ferroelectric phenomena, which are very similar to the ferromagnetic ones, especially with regard to the existence of a Curie temperature above which the dielectric constant is normal, and to the temperature dependence of ε below this temperature. An important difference is, however, the existence of a lower Curie temperature below which the ferroelectric property is again lost. The temperature range of ferroelectric behavior is between 10 and 50 degrees Centigrade. The lower Curie point shows that the full explanation requires more elements than enter into the Weiss theory.

Barium titanate, $BaTiO_3$, is best understood. Accurate X-ray investigation shows that in the ferroelectric temperature range this otherwise cubic structure is slightly compressed along the z axis so as to become tetragonal. The TiO_3 radical, which normally exists as an octahedral complex (by the sharing of oxygen between adjacent radicals) is deformed by a displacement of the $(4 + 2)$ O ions downward (by slightly different amounts, as indicated in the drawing) and an upward displacement of the central Ti^{4+}. (These displacements are measured relative to the Ba positions.) The result is that a strong electric moment is produced in this group, sufficient to account for the observed dielectric constant.

Again in rotating the direction of the external field there occurs a breaking up of the entire crystal into domains in which any one of the equivalent directions x, y, or z of the cubic structure becomes the tetragonal principal axis.

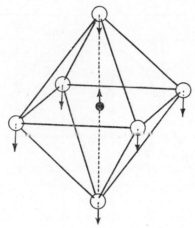

Fig. G,37.   Deformation of TiO_6 radical in barium titanate in the ferroelectric range (after Evans [64]).

Antiferromagnetic solids.   The existence of these bodies was postulated before it was confirmed by neutron diffraction. In these bodies there is an alignment of nuclear magnetic moments but in an alternating sense, so that no magnetic moment per unit volume results. Since the nuclear spin contributes to the nuclear magnetic moment, the nuclear spin has a regular distribution among the atomic nuclei in the lattice. The scattering cross section for neutrons differs considerably for some nuclei of opposite spins, and therefore these nuclei act in the same way as atoms of different weight would act in scattering X rays. Thus neutron diffraction reveals details of the structure of solids which future crystal dynamics will have to take into account. Examples of antiferromagnetism are provided by the oxides of the transition elements, Mn, Co, Ni, Fe, $\cdots$ including the ferrites.

G,38.   Order-Disorder Phenomena.   Many physical properties of solids depend on the previous thermal and mechanical treatment. Cold-working of metals by rolling, drawing, hammering, and thermal treatment like annealing and quenching produces fundamental changes of hardness, brittleness, strength, electrical resistivity, magnetic, and other properties. In nonmetals, especially in mixed crystals, similar changes occur, though generally they are less spectacular and of less technological importance.

Accurate investigation of the intensities of diffracted X rays shows that in many of these cases the difference between the untreated and the treated material lies in a different degree of order of the crystal structure. In a faulty or disordered structure the electrical resistivity is higher because of increased scattering of the electron waves; measurement of the resistivity is thus often a convenient first step in ascertaining the state of order. Fig. G,38 shows the resistivity of copper-gold alloys as a func-

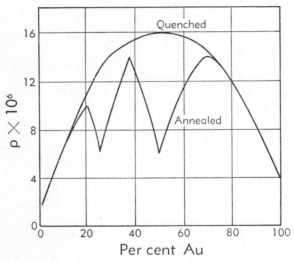

Fig. G,38. Resistivity in the Cu-Au system (after Barrett [*35*]). Upper curve is for quenched material and lower curve is for annealed material.

tion of the composition after quenching and after annealing. By quenching, the disordered arrangement is "frozen in"; the greatest disorder occurs at equal numbers of Cu and Au atoms, and there the resistivity is highest. Annealing gives the atoms a chance to exchange places and thereby to arrive at an ordered arrangement of slightly lower free energy. This can be fully successful only if the number of gold atoms stands in some simple ratio to the total number of atoms, so that one set of equivalent lattice sites can be occupied in all cells.

Two types of order have been defined, long range order (Gorsky, Bragg and Williams [*3*]) and short range order (Bethe, Peierls). For defining long range order (or better disorder), we first consider a fully ordered arrangement. Taking the case of the first minimum of resistivity in Fig. G,38, suppose the fully ordered arrangement is that of Cu_3Au, where the three Cu atoms are occupying the face centers, and Au the corners of the cubic cell. Two deviations from strict periodicity (order) can occur: first by misplacing some of the atoms, i.e. exchanging Au and Cu against each other, while leaving the composition unchanged at 25 atom per cent Au; secondly by departing from this composition, in which case disorder is bound to occur. In the first case we have full order if we find an Au at each corner, and full disorder if the probability of finding it there is the same as at any site, namely x, where x is the atomic concentration of Au. If by some means (e.g. X-ray diffraction) we can determine the actual probability p of finding a corner occupied by an Au atom, then the long-range order parameter **O** is introduced as

$$\mathbf{O} = \frac{p - x}{1 - x}$$

It is zero for $p = x$ and unity for $p = 1$. This expression can also be used for Au contents greater than the ideal one.

The use of **O** lies in its connection with the entropy increase of the alloy due to disordering. This is determined by the probability p and can thus be expressed in terms of **O**. To obtain the change of free energy, the change of internal energy of the crystal owing to disordering may not be neglected. Bragg and Williams make the assumption that the significant part of the internal energy is proportional to **O**. The condition of minimum free energy determines **O** as a function of T by equations very similar to those in Weiss's theory which express the magnetization in terms of T. At low temperatures, order should be perfect; it should cease entirely beyond a "Curie" temperature which is higher the more effectively order modifies the internal energy. The transition from order to disorder on heating the ordered alloy absorbs heat and leads to a sharp peak in the specific heat vs. temperature curve resembling the letter λ. For this reason, transitions of this type are called λ transitions; they require less heat of transformation than phase transitions of the ordinary kind which involve changes of aggregation or of crystal structure.

The short range order **o** was introduced by Bethe for an alloy of composition AB as follows: Let p be the probability that the nearest atom to an A atom is again an A atom. Since by mere random distribution this probability would be $\frac{1}{2}$,

$$\mathbf{o} = 1 - 2p$$

is taken as the short range order parameter. Its dependence on T can be easily expressed in terms of a combination of the assumed interaction energies between neighbors AA, BB, AB. On the other hand the long range order parameter **O** is connected to **o**, since it is the short range order which eventually produces the long range order. For a fuller discussion of the implications of this approach to the theory of specific heat the reader is referred to Mott and Jones [*37*], or S. Siegel's chapter in *Phase Transformations in Solids*.

CHAPTER 8. MECHANICAL PROPERTIES OF CRYSTALS

G,39. Slip.

The phenomena of slip. The testing of solid materials for strength is as old as their use for construction, but the methods devised for this purpose are still aiming at practical utility and simplicity rather than at a more fundamental understanding. Ordinary metals for technical use are fine-grained polycrystalline material, so that the physical properties result as average values over many individual crystals of random orientation. Although this averaging brings some simplification to the results, the presence of a great number of different grains is a handicap to understanding what changes in an individual grain are held responsible for starting a process—like fracture—which finally spreads to all grains.

The strength of a polycrystalline material ultimately depends on the strength of the individual small crystals, the crystallites. Physical investigation of the relevant properties could proceed only after methods had been developed to grow metals systematically in single crystal form. Excepting Andrade's [48] earlier work on Hg, Pb, and Sn single crystals and their slip directions, the large-scale investigation of the plastic properties of metal crystals began in the 1920's, when methods for growing single crystals and for measuring their slip were being simultaneously developed. Long before this the effects of slip had been registered by mineralogists in rocks and by metallographers in metals. This study was more of a geometrical nature. In the case of minerals it proved that under the action of the geological forces slip had taken place in a way characteristic of the crystal, i.e. with certain slip planes and in certain directions within the plane. This was concluded from the traces of slip planes observed on the faces of large crystals, and from optical effects in polycrystalline rock sections or etched metal sections. The new work aimed at finding quantitative laws for the slip taking place under known forces.

Polanyi and Schmid [49] used hexagonal crystals (Zn and Cd) rather than cubic ones so as to avoid the complication arising from the presence of several crystallographically equivalent slip systems. The wire- or pencil-shaped single crystal is hung from a spring the bending of which is calibrated in terms of force, and the lower end of the crystal is drawn down by the turning of a screw. As slip sets in, inclined elliptic bands appear at irregular intervals on the initially uniform wire surface, visible by their different reflecting power for light. These bands are called slip ellipses. Their planes are the slip planes, their major axes coincide nearly but not strictly with the direction of slip in the slip plane.

The geometry of slip can be discussed on the model which Polanyi proposed and which was found correct by all observations (Fig. G,39a)· The drawing on the left shows the undeformed Zn wire, its slip plane (normal to the hexagonal axis) inclined at an angle χ to the axis of the wire. The slip direction in this plane is that of the digonal axis marked by the arrow. In slipping, each block of the model (or section of the crystal) slips in the direction of the arrow. In a pure shear strain the result would be the shape shown in front and side view in Fig. G,39a. There is a lengthening of the crystal, and it flattens out to a band. By measuring the slip ellipses, the angles χ and λ can be found, where λ is the angle between the direction of slip and the wire axis. Thence the amount of slip can be found, i.e. the slip of one slip plane against a second one at unit distance from the first.

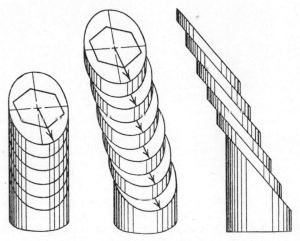

Fig. G,39a.   Polanyi's model of crystal slip.

In Polanyi's extensiometer the ends of the wire remain on the same vertical line. According to the drawing on the right of Fig. G,39b this implies that the slip planes do not retain their original angle χ but tend to become parallel to the wire axis. It also means that the deformation, instead of being a pure shear, contains a period of bending. This is called a flexural slip; it presents an undesirable complication. If pure shear slip is to be produced, the ends of the crystal must be free to move sideways, as indicated in the center part of Fig. G,39b. This type of deformation was first approximately materialized by Bausch in studying the slip of tin and is now being applied preferably.

One of the fundamental results of the early investigations is that of strain hardening. The first slips require much less force along the wire axis than later slips. Part of this hardening is a purely geometrical consequence of the increasing tilt of the slip planes, and this part is called orientation hardening. It would be avoided in the pure shear extensometer. By far the greater part is, however, a true increase of resistance to slip with increasing amount of slip.

If a total force F is applied at the wire ends in the direction of the wire axis (vertically), then the tension T in the wire is F/A, where A is the area of a horizontal cross section. The vertical force per unit area of a slip plane at angle χ to the wire axis is $\sin \chi$ times this value (because the area of the slip plane is $A/\sin \chi$). The resolved part of this vertical stress in the slip direction (at angle λ to the wire axis) is $\tau = T \sin \chi \cos \lambda$, and its component normal to the slip plane is $\nu = T \sin^2 \chi$. τ is the resolved part of the shearing stress in the slip plane along the direction of slip, and ν is the normal stress on the slip plane.

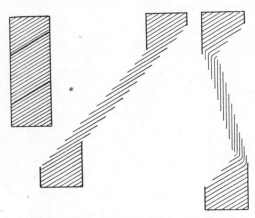

Fig. G,39b.   Pure and flexural slip.

Polanyi and Schmid's laws concerning the setting-in of slip are these:

1. Slip occurs if τ exceeds a critical value τ_{cr}.
2. The normal stress ν is without influence on slip.

The second proposition was proved, inter alia, by performing slip experiments under high hydrostatic pressure, which had no effect.

The value of τ_{cr} is lowest at the beginning of a slip measurement. The above expression for τ shows that, since $\chi < \lambda < 90°$, the most favorable inclination of the slip plane is $\chi = 45°$. As χ becomes smaller in the flexural slip process, this explains orientation hardening. The actual (solid) curve for Zn, Fig. G,39c, indicates a sharp increase of τ_{cr} from 145 gr/mm² when slip began to 1138 gr/mm² after 250 per cent stretch. The dashed curve indicates what part of the total stress is due to orientation hardening.

It will be noticed that the initial critical stress is absolutely very low compared to any technical value given for the elastic limit of a metal in the polycrystalline state. This initial value is lower the less impurities a metal contains. Possibly the finite limiting value is caused by constitutional lattice defects, and slip would occur under even smaller stresses if these could be avoided. The hardening can easily be understood as being the result of disturbances of the regularity of the lattice left over from the previous slip processes. Annealing, often only rest at room temperature, softens the crystal again, a process known as recovery.

The slip phenomenon in zinc is perhaps the simplest, but its elements are generally valid. The law of critical resolved stress holds also for molecular crystals, as Kochendörfer [65] has shown for naphthalene. This is the more remarkable, as the bulky organic molecules in this crystal are held together by forces widely differing from the electronic cohesion forces among metal atoms.

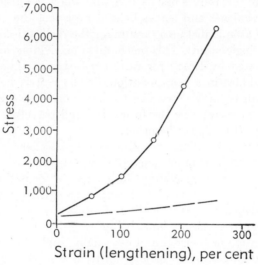

Fig. G,39c.   Total stress hardening (solid curve)
and orientation hardening (dashed curve).

In general there will be several slip systems in a crystal with different slip planes, but sometimes they have common slip directions. Usually the slip directions are those having the greatest line density of atoms. The initial values of τ_{cr} are different for different slip systems of the same crystal, and the rate of hardening differs. Slip along one system hardens the other systems—which seems reasonable on the assumption that any slip leaves over lattice irregularities, and that these affect any further slip. Where there are competitive slip systems the one will become active which has preferred orientation, i.e. the highest resolved shear, and at the same time a sufficiently low τ_{cr}. Double and multiple slip occurs in all cubic metals on account of the presence of equivalent slip systems. The micrographic study of polished and etched metal surfaces reveals the slip systems operating in the crystallites and often allows their geometrical identification.

The slip process: Dislocations. Naive inspection of a completed slip band might lead to the conclusion that the part of the crystal above the slip plane slips bodily along the half below. In this movement, however, the cohesion of the two halves would be nearly destroyed, and a correspondingly large amount of work would have to be put in before slip starts. This model of the slip process is thus not acceptable.

Instead, slip must be the result of motions taking place locally only. For these to occur the crystal can not be a perfect lattice; it must possess vacancies or irregularities, either as an effect of its formation, or as a result of the applied stresses, or for both reasons. These irregularities are called dislocations. If a dislocation wanders through the crystal, the atoms rearrange themselves one by one, and when the dislocation reaches the surface it vanishes and leaves behind a part of the crystal that has slipped by one atomic distance (assuming the dislocation to consist of a vacancy for a single atom). This mechanism of yielding has been beautifully demonstrated by Bragg for rafts consisting of thousands of small uniform air bubbles in a soap solution. If the raft is held by two end plates which can be moved parallel to one another, a shear is set up in the raft and it gives way by the formation and traveling of dislocations from one side of the raft to the other.

The theory of dislocations was discussed by Becker [50], Prandtl [51], and Dehlinger [52] in a more general way, stressing the importance of thermal fluctuations for providing the energy of formation of a dislocation. Actually, Becker's considerations led to a theory of creep rather than of slip. Creep is the slow yielding of a test piece to a constant stress; it is comparable to a viscous flow, being a unidirectional motion caused by the combination of thermal and externally applied stresses.

The more detailed model of a dislocation was developed in 1934 in Germany (Polanyi, Orowan [53,54]) and in England (Taylor [55]). In the last 10 years the Bristol school under Mott, and the United States groups, notably Seitz, Shockley, Zener, have extended this theory in several important aspects. Firstly, the general wave mechanical understanding of the metallic state has led to evaluations of the energy involved in forming a dislocation. Secondly, dislocations were classified into different geometrical types (largely through the work of J. M. and W. G. Burgers [56,57,58] in Holland), and a more realistic picture of dislocations and of the slip steps was developed. Thirdly, the effects of other imperfections of the lattice, like impurity atoms, and degrees of order in solid solutions were studied. Lastly, it was discussed how dislocations are influenced by conditions of growth, and how they in turn influence the mechanism of growth.

All this has led to the conviction that dislocation theory forms a valid starting point for the understanding of the slip process. There remain, however, major problems to be answered: What is the number of dislocations per unit volume; how is it influenced by the mechanical and thermal history of the sample and by its impurity content? Why is dislocation movement contagious, i.e. how do slip planes develop from slip taking place in the slip direction? How is this connected to crystal structure? What determines the rate of stress hardening, and of recovery? For a discussion the reader is referred to W. G. Burgers' book [58] and to the Bristol "Conference on Strength of Solids" (see Mott).

G,40. Strength and Fracture. The process by which a polycrystalline tensile specimen breaks under increasing stress is called fracture, and the limiting stress is the strength of the material. If a material shows slip prior to fracture, this will lead to necking, as in steel. If it breaks without slip, the material is called brittle; otherwise it is ductile.

The process of fracture has been studied on single metal crystals and is found to differ from that of slip. In general, the planes laid bare by fracture are not the slip planes, but other crystallographically well-defined planes; different planes may come into action, depending on the orientation of the wire axis.

Sohncke [59] established for rock salt that fracture takes place when the normal tension on the crystallographic fracture surface (the cube surface in the case of rock salt) exceeds a critical value. This law was found confirmed in metals. It leads to the correct dependence of strength upon the orientation of the fracture plane in the wire. The condition of brittle fracture is that the orientation be such that the critical normal stress on the fracture plane be reached before the critical shear component in the slip direction of any slip plane be reached.

As in the case of slip there is a hardening, i.e. increase of strength by previous deformation, and a recovery by annealing or aging. In distinction to slip which becomes easier at higher temperatures, fracture is hardly affected by temperature.

G,41. Twinning. An important type of deformation is twinning. This can occur as the result of mechanical action, or by recrystallization (see Art. 42). In the first case the result outwardly resembles that of slip. However, there is the important difference that slip, created by repeatable steps, can have any magnitude, while twinning consists of the nonrepeatable change from an initial configuration to a final one which is related to the first by symmetry. The crystal cannot stop halfway between the two positions, nor can it exceed the end position. If the upper surface of a crystal is to move to the left by a certain distance, then in the absence of strain hardening this would be achieved by slip on a single plane and without any internal deformation of the crystal half above the slip plane. By twinning, the same displacement of the upper surface can only be obtained by moving the twinning plane through the crystal and deforming the upper half crystal to the mirror image of its previous self. On account of the change of general shape produced, the grains of polycrystalline metals are usually broken up into fine steps by twinning and these show up, on etching, as striation. The dynamical laws of twinning are complicated, and not very much is known of them.

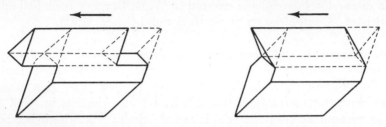

Fig. G,41.   Deformations: Slip (left) and twinning (right).

G,42.   Recrystallization. One of the early methods of preparing metal single crystals (Czochralski) consists in giving a polycrystalline sample an extension of a few per cent and then annealing it carefully at a certain temperature. The grain size which results from this processing depends on the degree of extension and on the temperature; by finding optimum conditions and repeating the process, the sample can be converted into a single grain.

This process is called recrystallization. It may be desirable, as in the case mentioned, or undesirable because it reduces the strength which is higher the finer the grain.

In principle, recrystallization is part of crystal growth, the peculiar circumstance being that growth of one suitably oriented crystal takes place by absorbing the less suitably oriented parts. The influence of the previous strain on the reorientation shows that recrystallization is closely connected to existing dislocations; it is not astonishing that it also is sensitive to impurities. The recrystallization in a position of twinning has been extensively studied by Burgers.

For the subject of recrystallization and the related one of precipitation from solid solutions of metals the reader is referred to W. C. Burgers' handbook volume and to Geisler's chapter in *Phase Transformations in Solids,* both of which contain copious references and surveys of the very extended literature. (See Bibliography for Chap. 6.)

G,43.   Cited References and Bibliography.

Cited References

1. Glocker, R.   *Materialprüfung mit Röntgenstrahlen.* Springer, Berlin, 1936.
2. Straumanis, M., and Weerts, J.   *Z. Physik* 78, 1 (1932).
3. Bragg, W. L., and Williams, E. J.   *Proc. Roy. Soc. London* A145, 699–730 (1934); A151, 540–566 (1935); A152, 231–252 (1935).
4. Robertson, J. H., and Beevers, C. A.   *Acta Cryst.* 4, 270 (1951).

5. Born, M. *Atomtheorie des festen Zustandes*. Teubner, Leipzig, 1923.
6. Voigt, W. *Lehrbuch der Kristallphysik*. Teubner, Leipzig, 1910.
7. Bruggemann, D. A. G. *Elastizitätskonstanten von Kristallaggregaten; Dissertation*, Utrecht, 1930.
8. Boas, W. *An Introduction to the Physics of Metals and Alloys*. Melbourne Univ. Press, 1947.
9. Einstein, A. *Ann. Physik 34*, 170 (1911); *35*, 679 (1911).
10. Madelung, E. *Physik. Z. 11*, 898 (1910).
11. Born, M., and von Kármán, Th. *Physik. Z. 13*, 297 (1912); *14*, 15 (1913).
12. Ewald, P. P. *Dissertation*, Munich, 1912; *Ann. Physik 49*, 1, 117 (1916).
13. Kellermann, E. W. *Proc. Roy. Soc. London A178*, 17 (1941).
14. Blackman, M. *Proc. Roy. Soc. London A148*, 384 (1935); *A159*, 416 (1937).
15. Löwdin, P. O. *A Theoretical Investigation of Some Properties of Ionic Crystals. Dissertation*, Uppsala, 1948.
16. Brillouin, L. *Ann. physique 17*, 88 (1922).
17. Laval, J. Réflexion sélective des rayons-X. *Colloques Internationaux C.N.R.*, 16–20. Bordeaux, 1948.
18. Prince, E., and Wooster, W. A. *Acta Cryst. 4*, 191 (1951).
19. Ramachandran, G. N., and Wooster, W. A. *Nature 164*, 839 (1949).
20. Begbie, G. H., and Born, M. *Proc. Roy. Soc. London A188*, 179 (1947).
21. James, R. W., Waller, I., and Hartree, D. R. *Proc. Roy. Soc. London A118*, 334 (1928).
22. London, F. *Trans. Faraday Soc. 33*, 8 (1937).
23. Slater, J. C. *Phys. Rev. 38*, 1109 (1931).
24. Slater, J. C. *Revs. Mod. Phys. 6*, 209–80 (1934).
25. Raynor, G. V., and Waldron, M. B. *Nature 162*, 566 (1948).
26. Raynor, G. V., and Waldron, M. B. *Phil. Mag. 40*, 198–206 (1949).
27. Raynor, G. V., and Wakeman, D. W. *Phil. Mag. 40*, 404–17 (1949).
28. Raynor, G. V., et al. *Proc. Phys. Soc. London B64*, 177–206 (1951).
29. Schiff, L. I. *Quantum Mechanics*. McGraw-Hill, 1949.
30. Mott, N. F., and Gurney, R. W. *Electronic Processes in Ionic Crystals*, 2nd ed. Oxford Univ. Press, 1948.
31. Mott, N. F., and Sneddon, I. N. *Wave Mechanics and Its Applications*. Oxford Univ. Press, 1948.
32. Slater, J. C. *Quantum Theory of Matter*. McGraw-Hill, 1951.
33. Nordheim, L. W. Kinet. Theorie d. Metallischen Zustands. Müller-Pouillet, *Lehrbuch der Physik*, Vol. 1, 243–876. Braunschweig, 1934.
34. Peierls, R. *Ann. Physik 3*, 1055–1101 (1929).
35. Barrett, C. S. *Structure of Metals*. McGraw-Hill, 1943.
36. Hume-Rothery, W. The structure of metals and alloys. *Inst. Metals London Monograph and Rept. Ser. 1*, 1945.
37. Mott, N. F., and Jones, H. *The Theory and the Properties of Metals and Alloys*. Oxford Univ. Press, 1945.
38. Raynor, G. V. An introduction to the electron theory of metals. *Inst. Metals London Monograph and Rept. Ser. 4*, 1947.
39. Cottrell, A. H. *Theoretical Structural Metallurgy*. Longmans, Green & Co., 1948.
40. Von Hippel, A. *Revs. Mod. Phys. 22*, 221–37 (1950).
41. Volmer, M. *Kinetik der Phasenbildung*. Dresden and Leipzig, 1939.
42. Becker, R., and Döring, W. *Ann. Physik 24*, 719–52 (1935).
43. Mayer, J. J. *Chem. Phys. 5*, 67 (1937).
44. Bunn, C. W. *Chemical Crystallography*. Oxford Univ. Press, 1944.
45. Dawson, I. M., and Vand, V. *Nature 167*, 467 (1951).
46. Verma, Ajit Rau. *Phil. Mag. 42*, 1005 (1951).
47. Slater, J. C. *Quantum Theory of Matter*. McGraw-Hill, 1951.
48. Andrade, E. N. da C. *Phil. Mag. 27*, 869 (1914).
49. Polanyi, M., and Schmid, E. *Z. Physik 16*, 336 (1923).
50. Becker, R. *Z. Physik 26*, 919 (1925).
51. Prandtl, L. *Z. angew. Math. u. Mech. 8*, 85 (1928).
52. Dehlinger, U. *Ann. Physik 2*, 749 (1929).

53. Polanyi, M.   *Z. Physik 89*, 660 (1934).
54. Orowan, E.   *Z. Physik 89*, 605 (1934).
55. Taylor, G. I.   *Proc. Roy. Soc. London A145*, 362 (1934).
56. Burgers, J. M.   *Proc. Amst. Acad. 42*, 239 (1939).
57. Burgers, J. M.   *Proc. Phys. Soc. London 52*, 23 (1940).
58. Burgers, W. G.   Rekristallisation, Verformter Zustand und Erholung. Masing, G., ed. *Handbuch der Metallphysik*, Bd. 3, 2. Akad. Verlagsgesellschaft, Leipzig, 1941.
59. Sohncke, A. L.   *Pogg. Ann. 137*, 177 (1869).
60. Seitz, F.   *The Modern Theory of Solids*. McGraw-Hill, 1940.
61. London, F.   *Superfluids*, Vol. 1. Wiley, 1950.
62. Zemansky, M. W.   *Heat and Thermodynamics*. McGraw-Hill, 1951.
63. Lonsdale, K., and Smith, H.   *Proc. Roy. Soc. London A179*, 8–50 (1941).
64. Evans, H. T.   *Acta Cryst. 4*, 377 (1951).
65. Kochendörfer, A.   *Z. Krist. 97*, 263–299 (1937).

Bibliography

Chapter 1

Eucken, A.   *Lehrbuch der chemischen Physik*, Bd. 2, 2. Akad. Verlagsgesellschaft, Leipzig, 1944.
Joffé, A.   *The Physics of Crystals*. McGraw-Hill, 1928.
Kleber, W.   *Angewandte Gitterphysik*, 2. Aufl. de Gruyter, Berlin, 1949.
Rice, F. O., and Teller, E.   *The Structure of Matter*. Wiley, 1949.
Voigt, W.   *Lehrbuch der Kristallphysik*. Teubner, Leipzig, 1910.
Wooster, W. A.   *Crystal Physics*. Cambridge Univ. Press, 1938.

Chapter 2

Bunn, C. W.   *Chemical Crystallography*. Oxford Univ. Press, 1944.
Ewald, P. P.   *Z. Krist. 56*, 129–156 (1921).

Chapter 3

Bishop, J. F. W.   *Phil. Mag. 42* (1951).
Boas, W.   The interaction between the crystals of an aggregate during plastic deformation. *Intern. Congress Mech. London*, 1948.
Boas, W., Huber, A., and Schmid, E.   *Helv. Phys. Acta 7*, 620–632 (1934); *8*, 674–681 (1935).
Cady, W. G.   *Piezoelectricity*. McGraw-Hill, 1946.
Fürth, R.   *Phil. Mag. 40*, 1227–1233 (1949).
Love, A. E. H.   *The Mathematical Theory of Elasticity*. Cambridge Univ. Press, 1920.
Löwdin, P. O.   *A Theoretical Investigation of Some Properties of Ionic Crystals. Dissertation*, Uppsala, 1948.
Mason, W. P.   *Piezoelectric Crystals and Their Applications to Ultrasonics*. Van Nostrand, 1950.
Michaud, R.   Contribution à l'étude des réactions mutuelles des cristaux dans la déformation des métaux polycristallins. *Publs. sci. et tech. Ministère air, France*, 1950.
Rose, F. C.   *Phys. Rev. 49*, 50 (1936).
Taylor, G. I.   *J. Inst. Metals 62*, 307 (1938).
Voigt, W.   *Lehrbuch der Kristallphysik*. Teubner, Leipzig, 1910.

Chapter 4

Born, M.   *Atomtheorie des festen Zustandes*. Teubner, Leipzig, 1923.
Brillouin, L.   *Wave Propagation in Periodic Structures and Crystal Lattices*. McGraw-Hill, 1946.
Ewald, P. P.   Erforschung des Aufbaus der Materie mit Röntgenstrahlen. *Handbuch der Physik*, Bd. 23, 2. Springer, Berlin, 1933.
James, R. W.   *The Optical Principles of the Diffraction of X-Rays*. Bell, London, 1948.

Kellerman, E. W.   Proc. Roy. Soc. London A178, 17 (1941).
Olmer, P.   Dispersion des ondes élastiques dans l'aluminium. Colloq. intern. centr natl. recherche sci. Bordeaux, 20–25 (1948).
Wood, R. W.   Physical Optics. Macmillan, 1934.
Zachariasen, W. H.   Theory of X-Ray Diffraction in Crystals. Wiley, 1945.

Chapter 5

Born, M.   Atomtheorie des festen Zustandes. Teubner, Leipzig, 1923.
Coulson, C. A.   Valence. Oxford Univ. Press, 1952.
Eyring, H., Walter, J., and Kimball, G. E.   Quantum Chemistry. Wiley, 1944.
Hartree, D. R.   Repts. Progr. in Phys. 11, 113–143 (1946–47).
Herzberg, G.   Molecular Spectra and Molecular Structure. Prentice-Hall, 1939.
London, F.   Trans. Faraday Soc. 33, 8 (1937).
Mott, N. F., and Gurney, R. W.   Electronic Processes in Ionic Crystals, 2nd ed. Oxford Univ. Press, 1948.
Mott, N. F., and Jones, H.   The Theory and the Properties of Metals and Alloys. Oxford Univ. Press, 1945.
Mott, N. F., and Sneddon, I. N.   Wave Mechanics and its Applications. Oxford Univ. Press, 1948.
Rice, O. K.   Electronic Structure and Chemical Binding. McGraw-Hill, 1940.
Rice, F. O., and Teller, E.   The Structure of Matter. Wiley, 1949.
Schiff, L. I.   Quantum Mechanics. McGraw-Hill, 1949.
Seitz, F.   The Modern Theory of Solids. McGraw-Hill, 1940.
Slater, J. C.   Phys. Rev. 38, 1109 (1931).
Syrkin, Y. K., and Dyatkina, M. E.   Structure of Molecules and the Chemical Bond. Interscience, 1950.
van Arkel, A. E.   Molecules and Crystals in Inorganic Chemistry. Butterworth, London, 1949.
Wells, A. F.   Structural Inorganic Chemistry. Oxford Univ. Press, 1951.
Wilson, A. H.   The Theory of Metals. Cambridge Univ. Press, 1936.

Chapter 6

Barrett, C. S.   Structure of Metals. McGraw-Hill, 1943.
Becker, R.   Theorie der Elektrizität. Teubner, Leipzig, 1933.
Bethe, H., and Sommerfeld, A.   Electronentheorie der Metalle. Handbuch der Physik, Bd. 24. Springer, Berlin, 1933.
Boas, W.   An Introduction to the Physics of Metals and Alloys. Melbourne Univ. Press, 1947.
Borelius, G.   Grundlagen des metallische Zustandes. Physikalische Eigenschaften der Metalle. Masing, G., ed. Handbuch der Metallphysik, Bd. 1, 181–520. Akad. Verlagsgesellschaft, Leipzig, 1935.
Brillouin, L.   Wave Propagation in Periodic Structures and Crystal Lattices. McGraw-Hill, 1946.
Chalmers, B., ed.   Progress in Metal Physics, Vol. 1 and 2. Butterworth, Interscience, 1949, 1950.
Cottrell, A. H.   Theoretical Structural Metallurgy. Longmans, Green & Co., London, 1948.
Dehlinger, U.   Chemische Physik der Metalle und Legierungen. Akad. Verlagsgesellschaft, Leipzig, 1939.
Frerichs, R.   Phys. Rev. 76, 1869–1875 (1949).
Fröhlich, H.   Theory of Dielectrics, Dielectric Constant and Dielectric Loss. Clarendon Press, 1949.
Garlick, G. F. J.   Phosphors and phosphorescence. Repts. Progr. in Phys. 12, 34–55 (1948–49).
Halla, F.   Kristallchemie und Kristallphysik metallischer Werkstoffe. Barth, Leipzig, 1951.
Hume-Rothery, W.   The structure of metals and alloys. Inst. Metals London Monograph and Rept. Ser. 1, 1945.

Hume-Rothery, W.   Atomic theory for students of metallurgy. *Inst. Metals London Monograph and Rept. Ser. 3*, 1946.
Hund, F., and Mrowka, B.   *Ber. Sächs. Akad. Wissenschaft B7*, 185–206 (1935).
Jost, W.   *Diffusion und Chemische Reaktionen in festen Stoffen*. Steinkopff, Dresden, 1937.
Justi, E.   *Leitfähigkeit und Leitungsmechanismus fester Stoffe*. Vandenhoeck, Göttingen, 1948.
Leverenz, H. W.   *An Introduction to Luminescence of Solids*. Wiley, 1950.
Meissner, W.   Elektronenleitung. *Handbuch der Experimentalphysik*, Bd. 11, 2. Akad. Verlagsgesellschaft, Leipzig, 1935.
Mott, N. F., and Gurney, R. W.   *Electronic Processes in Ionic Crystals*, 2nd ed. Oxford Univ. Press, 1948.
Mott, N. F., and Jones, H.   *The Theory and the Properties of Metals and Alloys*. Oxford Univ. Press, 1945.
Mott, N. F., and Sneddon, I. N.   *Wave Mechanics and its Applications*. Oxford Univ. Press, 1948.
Pauling, L.   *Proc. Roy. Soc. London A196*, 343 (1949).
Raynor, G. V.   An introduction to the electron theory of metals. *Inst. Metals London Monograph and Rept. Ser. 4*, 1947.
Rice, F. O., and Teller, E.   *The Structure of Matter*. Wiley, 1949.
Seitz, F.   *The Modern Theory of Solids*. McGraw-Hill, 1940.
Seitz, F.   *The Physics of Metals*. McGraw-Hill, 1943.
Seitz, F.   *Revs. Mod. Phys. 18*, 384–408 (1946).
Selwood, P. W.   *Magnetochemistry*. Interscience, 1943.
Slater, J. C.   *Revs. Mod. Phys. 6*, 209–280 (1934).
Smoluchowski, R., et al.   *Phase Transformations in Solids*. Wiley, 1951.
Whitehead, S.   *Dielectric Phenomena*. Benn, London, 1932.
Whitehead, S.   *Dielectric Breakdown of Solids*. Clarendon Press, 1951.
Wilson, A. H.   *The Theory of Metals*. Cambridge Univ. Press, 1936.
Wilson, A. H.   *Semiconductors and Metals*. Cambridge Univ. Press, 1939.
Wright, R. W.   *Proc. Phys. Soc. London A64*, 350 (1951).

Chapter 7

Bethe, H. A.   *Proc. Roy. Soc. London A150*, 552 (1935).
Bozorth, R. M.   *Ferromagnetism*. Van Nostrand, 1951.
Buckley, H. E.   *Crystal Growth*. Wiley, 1951.
Cwilong, B. M.   *Proc. Roy. Soc. London A190*, 137 (1947).
Geisler, A. H.   *Phase Transformations in Solids*, pp. 387–535. Wiley, 1951.
Gorsky, W.   *Z. Physik 50*, 64 (1928).
Kittel, C.   *Revs. Mod. Phys. 21*, 541–583 (1949).
Mayer, J., and Goeppert-Mayer, M.   *Statistical Mechanics*. Wiley, 1940.
Peierls, R.   *Proc. Roy. Soc. London A154*, 207 (1936).
Selwood, P. W.   *Magnetochemistry*. Interscience, 1943.
Stoner, E. C.   *Magnetism and Atomic Structure*. Methuen, London, 1926.
Stoner, E. C.   *Repts. Progr. in Phys. 11*, 43–112 (1946–47).
Turnbull, D.   Kinetics of solidification of Hg-droplet aggregates. *Am. Phys. Soc. Bull., Schenectady Meeting*, June, 1951.
van Hippel, A.   *Revs. Mod. Phys. 22*, 221–237 (1950).
van Vleck, J. H.   *The Theory of Electric and Magnetic Susceptibilities*. Oxford Univ. Press, 1932.
van Vleck, J. H.   *Am. J. Phys. 18*, 495–509 (1950).
van Vleck, J. H.   Discussions on crystal growth. *Discussions Faraday Soc. 5*, 1949.

Chapter 8

Bausch, K.   *Z. Physik 93*, 479 (1935).
Bragg, W. L.   *Trans. North East Coast Inst. Engrs. & Shipbuilders 62*, 25–34 (1945).
Cabrera, N., and Mott, N. F.   *Repts. Progr. in Phys. 12*, 163–184 (1948–49).

Cottrell, A. H.   Theory of dislocations. In Chalmers, B., *Progress in Metal Physics*, Vol. 1. Butterworth, London, 1949.

Dawson, I. M., and Vand, V.   *Nature 167*, 476 (1951).

Elam, C. F.   *The Distortion of Metal Crystals*. Oxford Univ. Press, 1935.

Eshelby, J. D.   *Phil. Mag. 40*, 903–913 (1949).

Eshelby, J. D., Frank, F. C., and Nabarro, F. R. N.   *Phil. Mag. 42*, 351–364 (1951).

Finch, G. I.   *Proc. Phys. Soc. London A63*, 785 (1950).

Foreman, A. J., Jaswon, M. D., and Wood, J. K.   *Proc. Phys. Soc. London A64*, 156–162 (1951).

Frank, F. C.   *Discussions Faraday Soc. 5*, 67 (1949).

Halla, F.   *Kristallchemie und Kristallphysik metallischer Werkstoffe*. Barth, Leipzig, 1951.

Heidenreich, R. D., and Shockley, W.   Report on conference on strength of solids. *Phys. Soc. London*, 57–74 (1948).

Kuhlmann, D.   *Proc. Phys. Soc. London A64*, 140–155 (1951).

Mark, II., Polanyi, M., and Schmid, E.   *Z. Physik 12*, 58 (1922).

Mott, N. F., and Nabarro, F. R. N.   Proceedings Bristol conference on strength of solids. *Inst. Phys. London*, 1948.

Mott, N. F., and Nabarro, F. R. N.   An attempt to estimate the degree of precipitation hardening with a simple model. *Proc. Phys. Soc. London 52*, 86 (1940).

Orowan, E.   *Repts. Progr. in Phys. 12*, 185–232 (1948–49).

Rotherham, L.   Creep of metals. *Inst. Phys. London*, 1951.

Schmid, E.   *Proc. Intern. Congress Appl. Mech.* Delft, 1924.

Schmid, E., and Boas, W.   *Kristallplastizität*. Springer, Berlin, 1935.

Schmid, E., and Boas, W.   Symposium on internal stress in metals. *Inst. Metals London Monograph and Rept. Ser. 5*, 1947

Taylor, G. I., and Elam, C. F.   *Proc. Roy. Soc. London A102*, 643 (1923); *A108*, 28 (1925).

Taylor, G. I., and Quinney, H.   *Proc. Roy. Soc. London A143*, 307 (1934).

Wilman, H.   *Proc. Phys. Soc. London A64*, 329–350 (1951).

SECTION H

RELAXATION PHENOMENA IN GASES

KARL F. HERZFELD

CHAPTER 1. GENERAL CONSIDERATIONS ON RELAXATION

H,1. General Discussion of Resonance and Relaxation Phenomena.

Resonance. We are accustomed to find dispersion and absorption, e.g. in optics, usually in connection with resonance phenomena. These occur typically if there exist an inertial force and a Hooke's law restoring force. When such a system is acted upon by a simple harmonic external force, this force has to be balanced by two components, the restoring force, which is in phase with the deflection, and the inertial force, which is 180 degrees out of phase with the deflection. The sum of the two (the difference of their absolute magnitudes) has to balance the external force. For a given amplitude, the restoring force is independent of the frequency, while the inertial force increases proportionally to the square of the frequency. Accordingly, starting at low frequency, inertia is unimportant, and the system follows the external force quasi-statically. With increasing frequency, the inertial force balances, for a given amplitude, more and more of the restoring force, so that a higher amplitude is needed to balance the external force. At resonance the inertial force balances the Hooke's law force completely, and therefore in this idealized case the amplitude goes to infinity. Beyond the resonance frequency the inertial force determines the motion and, accordingly, the resultant motion is 180 degrees out of phase compared to the external force. With increasing frequency the inertial force becomes more and more important, and since for a given amplitude it increases with ω^2, the amplitude has to decrease, at very high frequencies, proportionally to ω^{-2}.

If there also exists a viscous force proportional to the velocity, with not too large a coefficient, this force produces a component of the displacement 90 degrees out of phase compared to the external force (watt component), and prevents the amplitude from becoming infinite. In general, however, the effects of the viscous force are appreciable only in the region where the inertial and restoring forces nearly compensate each other, i.e. near resonance. One gets, for example, for optical dispersion and absorption the expressions given below and shown in Fig. H,1

$$n^2 - 1 = \frac{A(\nu_0^2 - \nu^2)}{(\nu_0^2 - \nu^2)^2 + \nu^2\nu'^2}, \qquad 2n\alpha = \frac{A\nu'\nu}{(\nu_0^2 - \nu^2)^2 + \nu^2\nu'^2} \qquad (1\text{-}1)$$

Here 2α is the absorption coefficient for intensity per cm, ν_0 the resonance frequency, and ν' the half width of the absorption line, which is proportional to the constant of the viscous resistance, and A porportional to

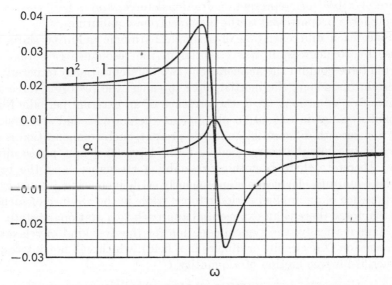

Fig. H,1.   Dispersion and absorption by resonance processes.
Logarithmic frequency scale.

the magnitude of the force. Both formulas (1-1) can be deduced from a unified expression for the "complex refractive index"

$$n^2(1 - i\alpha)^2 - 1 = \frac{A}{\nu_0^2 - \nu^2 + i\nu\nu'} \qquad (1\text{-}2)$$

Similar response curves can be found in series LCR circuits, where L governs the inertial, $1/C$ the restoring, and R the viscous force.

Relaxation phenomena.[1]   The mathematical characteristics here are that either the term representing a Hooke's law restoring force or the inertial term is missing. An example of the first case is given by the

---

[1] The relaxation phenomena take their name from mechanical aftereffects, in which the final strain is established gradually after the application of a sudden stress. If the stress is applied to a test specimen by pulling the holding jaws a certain distance apart, the gradual further extension of the specimen relaxes the stress. The verb relax is to be used as a transitive or passive verb. The gradual extension relaxes the stress; or the stress is being relaxed. The verb is not intransitive or active; i.e. it is wrong to say the stress relaxes.

Debye theory of free dipoles in an alternating electric field, where there is rotational inertia and friction, but no restoring force. An *LR* circuit also belongs here. An example of the second case is given by the discharge of a condenser through a resistance. Mathematically analogous is the rate equation for a monomolecular chemical reaction

$$\frac{1}{k}\frac{dn'}{dt} = -(n' - n_0) \tag{1-3}$$

where $(1/k)(dn'/dt)$ represents a frictional force, and $-(n' - n_0)$ a restoring force proportional to the distance from equilibrium.

Since each differentiation of a simple harmonic quantity shifts the phase by 90 degrees, it was essential in the resonance case that the inertial force contain the acceleration (two differentiations) to permit, at a certain frequency, the inertial force to cancel the restoring force and so give free vibrations or, in the presence of an external periodic force, resonance. Since in relaxation phenomena there are second and first, or first and zeroeth differential quotients present, such compensation is not possible, because the corresponding terms have 90 degree phase difference. Therefore there is nothing resembling resonance, and the value of the amplitude decreases monotonously with increasing frequency in the presence of an applied periodic force, while in the absence of such an external force there is an exponential approach to a stationary state.

Mathematically, the typical equation for the first kind of relaxation phenomenon (*LR* circuit, or dipoles in a field), which will not interest us further, is for free motion of a quantity U

$$\frac{\partial^2 U}{\partial t^2} + \frac{1}{\tau}\frac{\partial U}{\partial t} = 0 \tag{1-4}$$

where τ is a constant, called the relaxation time. The solution is (U_0, U' constants)

$$U = U'e^{-t/\tau} + U_0 \tag{1-5}$$

If an external force $Ae^{i\omega t}$ is applied to the system and written on the right side of Eq. 1-4, the solution is

$$U = \frac{Ae^{i\omega t}}{-\omega^2 + i\omega/\tau} + U'e^{-t/\tau} + U_0 \tag{1-6}$$

It is of interest that the first part of this solution can be directly found from Eq. 1-2 by setting the restoring force equal to zero, i.e. $\nu_0 = 0$, and writing $2\pi\nu' = 1/\tau$.

The typical equation describing a relaxation phenomenon of the second kind for the quantity U is

$$-\frac{\partial U}{\partial t} = \frac{1}{\tau}(U - \overline{U}) \tag{1-7}$$

Here $\overline{U}$ is the equilibrium value of U, so that if $U = \overline{U}$ it does not change any further. The general solution of Eq. 1-7 is

$$U = (U_0 - \overline{U})e^{-t/\tau} + \overline{U} \tag{1-8}$$

where U_0 is the initial value of U. Accordingly, the difference between the momentary value U and the final value $\overline{U}$ decreases by the factor $1/e$ every time the interval τ elapses. Therefore τ is called the relaxation time.

Assume now that the equilibrium value $\overline{U}$ is not constant, but is itself made to change periodically with time.

$$\overline{U} = \overline{\overline{U}} e^{i\omega t} \tag{1-9}$$

$\overline{\overline{U}}$ being the amplitude of the change. In this case, the general solution of Eq. 1-7 is

$$U = \frac{\overline{\overline{U}}}{1 + i\omega\tau} e^{i\omega t} + U'e^{-t/\tau} \tag{1-10}$$

The second term, which dies out exponentially, would take care of initial conditions and presents a "transient." For the following only the first term is of interest and shall now be discussed.

Firstly, notice that $\omega\tau$ occurs in the expression. Therefore, the quantity

$$2\pi \frac{\tau}{\text{period}}$$

is important, *not*

$$\frac{\tau}{\text{period}}$$

Secondly, if $\omega\tau$ is small, one has

$$U = \overline{\overline{U}} e^{i\omega t} = \overline{U} \tag{1-11}$$

The quantity U always has the equilibrium value to which it has time enough to adjust itself (quasi-stationary case).

Thirdly, if $\omega\tau$ increases, the amplitude of U decreases, and a phase difference between U and $\overline{U}$ develops.

One has for the amplitude

$$|U| = \frac{\overline{\overline{U}}}{\sqrt{1 + \omega^2\tau^2}} \tag{1-12}$$

This decreases with increasing ω slowly at first

$$|U| = \overline{U}(1 - \tfrac{1}{2}\omega^2\tau^2) \tag{1-12'}$$

and then goes to zero if $\omega\tau$ is very large compared to unity, in which case U cannot follow $\overline{U}$ at all.

The phase angle is given by

$$\tan^{-1} \omega\tau \tag{1-13}$$

and increases from 0 to $\pi/2$ at very high frequencies.

H,2. Discussion of Energy Exchange Between Internal and External Degrees of Freedom as Relaxation Phenomenon. The relaxation phenomenon which is the most frequent cause of increased absorption in fluids (namely, the only cause in ideal polyatomic gases, and a cause in most liquids) is the slowness of exchange between the external and internal degrees of freedom; the dividing line between "external" and "internal" degrees of freedom does not yet need to be fixed.

The effect of a compression makes itself felt directly in the translational energy of the molecules and is partly transferred to other degrees of freedom only from the translation. If no other than translational energy exists ($\frac{3}{2}RT$ in an ideal gas), the temperature rise and therefore the pressure rise for a given compression is higher than if part of the energy is transferred to other degrees of freedom.

If the energy transfer to other degrees of freedom is characterized by a relaxation time τ, the amount transferred will depend on the rapidity of the change.

Since it is possible that some degrees of freedom (e.g. rotation) get adjusted very rapidly, we will for the moment distinguish external degrees of freedom as those rapidly adjusted, and internal degrees of freedom as those requiring the relaxation time τ. Designate the corresponding specific heats as they are measured when the temperature is raised slowly (as in a calorimetric experiment) as $\tilde{C}$ and C'

$$C = \tilde{C} + C'$$

When the compression and the consequent energy rise in the translational (external) degrees of freedom are so slow that an appreciable change takes a time long compared to τ, the exchange can follow the compression and the full specific heat comes into play. When the rate of compression increases, the transfer to and from the internal degrees of freedom becomes less and less effective and a smaller and smaller part of C' contributes to the total effective specific heat. Finally, if the time required for compression is short compared to τ, the energy transfer to the internal degrees of freedom cannot follow at all, and the effective specific heat is $\tilde{C} = C - C'$. If, after the compression is over, the density remains constant at the final high value, the energy is then transferred by collisions from the external to the internal degrees of freedom, the temperature of the external degrees of freedom (and with it, the pressure) drops and that of the internal degrees of freedom rises, until equilibrium is attained. (See also Art. 15.)

The relaxation equation is written formally:

$$\frac{\partial E'}{\partial t} = -\frac{1}{\tau}[E' - E'(T_{tr})] \tag{2-1}$$

Here E' is the energy of the internal degrees of freedom, $E'(T_{tr})$ the energy which they would have if they were in equilibrium with the external temperature T_{tr}, and τ is the relaxation time. Eq. 2-1 is deduced for certain cases in more detail in Art. 3, starting with the assumption of transfer by collision.

Writing

$$E' = C'T' \tag{2-2}$$

one can rewrite Eq. 2-1 as

$$\frac{\partial T'}{\partial t} = -\frac{1}{\tau}(T' - T_{tr}) \tag{2-3a}$$

If Eq. 2-2 is not generally true, one may at least write for small temperature changes

$$E' - E_0' = C'(T' - T_0) \tag{2-3b}$$

To illustrate the meaning of Eq. 2-3 it will be applied first to a step function, then to periodic changes.

Assume first that the temperature of the external degrees of freedom has been raised by sudden compression from T_0 to T_1. One wishes to find the adjustment of the internal temperature. Then, from conservation of energy

$$\tilde{C}(T_1 - T_0) = C'(T' - T_0) + \tilde{C}(T_{tr} - T_0) \tag{2-4a}$$

or

$$T_{tr} = T_1 - \frac{C'}{\tilde{C}}(T' - T_0) \tag{2-4b}$$

Therefore Eq. 2-3a takes the form

$$\frac{\partial T'}{\partial t} = -\frac{1}{\tau}\frac{\tilde{C} + C'}{\tilde{C}}(T' - T_2) \tag{2-4c}$$

where

$$T_2 = T_0 + \frac{\tilde{C}}{C}(T_1 - T_0)$$

is the final temperature. Then

$$T' - T_0 = (T_2 - T_0)(1 - e^{-t/\tau'}) \tag{2-5a}$$

with[2]

$$\tau' = \frac{C - C'}{C}\tau \tag{2-5b}$$

Next, consider the periodic case, rewriting Eq. 2-3a as

$$\frac{\partial T'}{\partial t} = -\frac{1}{\tau}(T' - T_{tr}) = -\frac{1}{\tau}(T' - T_0) + \frac{1}{\tau}(T_{tr} - T_0) \tag{2-6a}$$

---

[2] If the temperature of the external degrees of freedom were kept at T_1 instead of allowed to go down, one would have τ instead of τ' in the exponent and T_1 instead of T_2.

and

$$T_{tr} - T_0 = T_{max}e^{i\omega t} \tag{2-6b}$$

One gets then, after the transients have died out (see Eq. 1-10)

$$(T' - T_0) = \frac{1}{1 + i\omega\tau}(T_{tr} - T_0) \tag{2-6c}$$

H,3.   Exchange of Internal Energy. The Relaxation Equation.
Assume first that the internal energy has two quantum states only, the
lower i with energy ϵ_i and "weight" g_i, and the upper j with energy ϵ_j
and "weight" g_j. The number of particles in i is n_i and in j, n_j. The
number of particles going per second from i to j is then written

$$k_{ij}n_i \tag{3-1a}$$

In gases k_{ij} is proportional to N, the total number of particles per cm³,
or the number of collisions a particle in state i makes. In liquids, we
do not know how k_{ij} depends on the density.

Similarly, the number of particles returning from j to i is given by

$$k_{ji}n_j \tag{3-1b}$$

and the total change of particles in j is given by

$$-\frac{\partial n_j}{\partial t} = k_{ji}n_j - k_{ij}n_i = \frac{\partial n_i}{\partial t} \tag{3-2}$$

In temperature equilibrium at T_0, the k's have certain values, and the n's
have values n^0. Then

$$k_{ji}^0 n_j^0 - k_{ij}^0 n_i^0 = 0$$

or

$$\frac{n_j^0}{n_i^0} = \frac{k_{ij}^0}{k_{ji}^0} \tag{3-3}$$

But the value of the left side is determined by equilibrium statistical
mechanics, and therefore

$$k_{ij}^0 = k_{ji}^0 \frac{g_j}{g_i} e^{-\frac{\epsilon_j - \epsilon_i}{kT}} \tag{3-4}$$

If $\epsilon_j - \epsilon_i$ is large compared to kT, k_{ij} is much smaller than k_{ji}; physically
this is so because collisions which activate the vibrations have to have
$\epsilon_j - \epsilon_i$ more energy than those which deactivate a molecule, and are
therefore correspondingly rarer. Nonetheless

$$k_{ij}^0 n_i^0 = k_{ji}^0 n_j^0$$

because there are so many more molecules which can be activated than
there are which can be deactivated.

From Eq. 3-3 one has, with $n_i + n_j = n$

$$k_{ij}^0 n = (k_{ij}^0 + k_{ji}^0)n_j^0 \tag{3-5}$$

If the value of n_j is different from the equilibrium value, one can write Eq. 3-2:

$$\frac{\partial n_j}{\partial t} = k_{ij}^0 n - (k_{ij}^0 + k_{ji}^0)n_j = (k_{ij}^0 + k_{ji}^0)(n_j^0 - n_j) \qquad (3\text{-}6)$$

This is a typical relaxation equation, leading to a relaxation time

$$\tau = (k_{ij}^0 + k_{ji}^0)^{-1} = \frac{1}{k_{ji}^0}\left(1 + \frac{g_j}{g_i}\,e^{-\frac{\epsilon_j - \epsilon_i}{kT}}\right)^{-1} \qquad (3\text{-}7)$$

Since usually

$$k_{ij} \ll k_{ji} \longleftrightarrow |\epsilon_j - \epsilon_i| \gg kT \qquad (3\text{-}8)$$

the second term in the parenthesis in Eq. 3-7 is small, and hence τ is approximately equal to the time necessary for deactivation. However, if the temperature is so high that $k_{ij} \cong k_{ji}$, τ is approximately equal to half the time necessary for deactivation. If one has now a small periodic variation of the density and the temperature of the external degrees of freedom, T_{tr}, which determines the reaction rate, one gets instead of Eq. 3-2, by keeping only first orders of the varying terms

$$-\frac{\partial n_j}{\partial t} = k_{ji}^0 n_j - k_{ij}^0 n_i + s\left(\frac{\partial k_{ji}}{\partial s}\,n_i - \frac{\partial k_{ij}}{\partial s}\,n_i\right)$$
$$+ (T_{tr} - T_0)\left(\frac{\partial k_{ji}}{\partial T}\,n_j - \frac{\partial k_{ij}}{\partial T}\,n_i\right) \quad (3\text{-}9)$$

In the second and third terms one can replace the n by their equilibrium values, since these terms have the factors s and $T_{tr} - T_0$, which are assumed small of the first order. Therefore

$$-\frac{\partial n_j}{\partial t} = k_{ji}^0 n_j - k_{ij}^0 n_i + s\left(\frac{\partial k_{ji}}{\partial s}\,n_j^0 - \frac{\partial k_{ij}}{\partial s}\,n_i^0\right)$$
$$+ (T_{tr} - T_0)\left(\frac{\partial k_{ji}}{\partial T}\,n_j^0 - \frac{\partial k_{ij}}{\partial T}\,n_i^0\right) \quad (3\text{-}10)$$

An isothermal change in density should not affect the equilibrium (3-3) in the first order. Therefore, from a logarithmic differentiation of Eq. 3-3

$$\frac{1}{k_{ji}^0}\frac{\partial k_{ji}}{\partial s} = \frac{1}{k_{ij}^0}\frac{\partial k_{ij}}{\partial s} \qquad (3\text{-}11)$$

and therefore

$$\frac{\partial k_{ji}}{\partial s}\,n_j^0 - \frac{\partial k_{ij}}{\partial s}\,n_i^0 = \frac{\partial k_{ji}}{\partial s}\left(n_j^0 - \frac{k_{ij}^0}{k_{ji}^0}\,n_i\right) = 0$$

Furthermore, from Eq. 3-4

$$\frac{\partial k_{ij}}{\partial T} = \frac{\partial}{\partial T}\left(k_{ji}\frac{n_j^0}{n_i^0}\right) = \frac{n_j^0}{n_i^0}\frac{\partial k_{ji}}{\partial T} + k_{ji}\frac{\partial}{\partial T}\frac{n_j^0}{n_i^0}$$

and

$$\frac{\partial k_{ji}}{\partial T} n_j^0 - \frac{\partial k_{ij}}{\partial T} n_i^0 = \frac{\partial k_{ji}}{\partial T} n_j^0 - n_i^0 \frac{n_j^0}{n_i^0} \frac{\partial k_{ji}}{\partial T}$$

$$-k_{ji} n_i^0 \frac{\partial}{\partial T} \frac{n_j^0}{n_i^0} = -k_{ji} \left(\frac{\partial}{\partial T} n_j^0 - \frac{n_j^0}{n_i^0} \frac{\partial}{\partial T} n_i^0 \right)$$

$$= -k_{ji} \left(1 + \frac{n_j^0}{n_i^0} \right) \frac{\partial n_j^0}{\partial T} = -(k_{ji} + k_{ij}) \frac{\partial n_j^0}{\partial T}$$

Next, write the first terms on the right side of Eq. 3-10

$$k_{ji}^0 n_j - k_{ij}^0 n_i = (k_{ji}^0 + k_{ij}^0) n_j - k_{ij}^0 n$$

$$= (k_{ji}^0 + k_{ij}^0) \left(n_j - \frac{k_{ij}^0}{k_{ij}^0 + k_{ji}^0} n \right)$$

$$= (k_{ji}^0 + k_{ij}^0)(n_j - n_j^0)$$

Substitute the value of τ from Eq. 3-7. Then Eq. 3-10 takes the form

$$-\frac{\partial n_j}{\partial t} = \frac{1}{\tau} \left[n_j - n_j^0 - (T_{tr} - T_0) \frac{\partial n_j^0}{\partial T} \right] \tag{3-12}$$

In the calculation T_{tr} has been written for T since it is assumed that the translational energy of the molecules is responsible for the transitions involved and therefore determines the rate.

The internal energy belonging to the degree of freedom considered here is, per mole,

$$E' = \frac{N}{n} (\epsilon_j n_j + \epsilon_i n_i - \epsilon_i n) = \frac{N}{n} (\epsilon_j - \epsilon_i) n_j \tag{3-13}$$

where N is Avogadro's number. Multiplying Eq. 3-12 with $(\epsilon_j - \epsilon_i) N/n$, one has

$$-\frac{\partial E'}{\partial t} = \frac{1}{\tau} [E' - E'(T_0) - (T_{tr} - T_0) C']$$

$$= \frac{1}{\tau} [E' - E'(T_{tr})] \tag{3-14}$$

which is identical with Eq. 2-1. The latter equation is therefore proved for the case where only one excited state is of importance.

We have used the relation

$$E'(T_{tr}) = E'(T_0) + (T_{tr} - T_0) \frac{\partial E'}{\partial T} \tag{3-15}$$

The above development is, with a slight modification by Kneser [3], due to Rutgers [5]. An earlier deduction [2] by Kneser was incorrect.

One other case has been treated by Landau and Teller [4], namely a harmonic oscillator. There is no restriction here that only one excited state is of importance, but it is assumed that the interaction between the internal degrees of freedom and the translational motion is weak. In that case it can be shown (Art. 28) that for most laws of interaction, the quantum number of the oscillator can only change by $+1$ or -1. Furthermore, the rate constant k_{ij} is a product of two factors, the first given by the transition probability of the oscillator, under light action, from state i to state j, the other factor only depending on the translational motion and the energy of the quantum jump. Since for a harmonic oscillator all quantum jumps involve the same energy, the second factor is the same for all deactivating jumps $j \to j - 1$ and is the same for all activating jumps $j \to j + 1$ (but of course, different from that for the deactivating jumps.) The optical transition probability for the oscillator for a transition $j + 1 \to j$ or $j \to j + 1$ is proportional to $j + 1$. Therefore,

$$k_{j+1,j} = (j + 1)k_{10} \tag{3-16a}$$

$$k_{j,j+1} = (j + 1)k_{01} = (j + 1)k_{10}e^{-h\nu/kT} \tag{3-16b}$$

One now writes the set of equations

$$-\frac{\partial n_0}{\partial t} = k_{01}n_0 - k_{10}n_1$$

$$-\frac{\partial n_1}{\partial t} = k_{12}n_1 + k_{10}n_1 - k_{21}n_2 - k_{01}n_0$$

$$-\frac{\partial n_j}{\partial t} = k_{j,j+1}n_j + k_{j,j-1}n_j - k_{j+1,j}n_{j+1} - k_{j-1,j}n_{j-1} \tag{3-17}$$

Multiplying the equation having $-\partial n_j/\partial t$ on the left with j and adding all the equations, one gets

$$-\frac{\partial}{\partial t}\sum_0^\infty jn_j = \sum_0^\infty jk_{j,j+1}n_j + \sum_1^\infty jk_{j,j-1}n_j$$

$$- \sum_0^\infty jk_{j+1,j}n_{j+1} - \sum_1^\infty jk_{j-1,j}n_{j-1} \tag{3-18}$$

Because of the factor j, no term with $j = 0$ occurs and the first and third sum may also be begun with $j = 1$. Now consider, for example, the expression $k_{i,i+1}n_i$, with a given i. This will occur twice: in the first sum, if $i = j$; there it will be $ik_{i,i+1}n_i$; in the fourth sum, with $i = j - 1$; there it will be $-(i + 1)k_{i,i+1}n_i$. Therefore, the first and fourth sum together will give

$$-\sum_0^\infty k_{i,i+1}n_i$$

This starts from zero, since the fourth expression contains $-k_{01}n_0$ which does not occur in the first. Similarly, $k_{i,i-1}n_i$ occurs in $ik_{i,i-1}n_i$ in the second and in $-(i-1)k_{i,i-1}n_i$ in the third sum, and these give together

$$+ \sum_1^\infty k_{i,i-1}n_i$$

Therefore Eq. 3-18 can be rewritten, using j again as index instead of i

$$-\frac{\partial}{\partial t} \sum jn_j = \sum_1^\infty k_{j,j-1}n_j - \sum_0^\infty k_{j,j+1}n_j \tag{3-19}$$

Up to now the calculation is valid for any system; introducing now the assumptions (3-16) one has

$$-\frac{\partial}{\partial t} \sum jn_j = \sum_1^\infty jk_{10}n_j - \sum_0^\infty (j+1)k_{01}n_j$$

$$= k_{10} \sum jn_j - k_{01} \sum jn_j - k_{01} \sum n_j \tag{3-20}$$

Now

$$E' = \sum \epsilon_j n_j = h\nu \sum jn_j \tag{3-21}$$

Therefore, one has, by multiplying Eq. 3-20 with $h\nu$ ·

$$-\frac{\partial}{\partial t} E' = (k_{10} - k_{01})E' - h\nu k_{01}N \tag{3-22}$$

This can be treated as was Eq. 3-6, with

$$\frac{1}{\tau} = k_{10}^0 - k_{10}^0 \tag{3-23}$$

One has

$$-\frac{\partial}{\partial t} E' = (k_{10}^0 - k_{01}^0)[E' - E'(T_0)] + (T_{tr} - T_0)\left[\frac{\partial}{\partial T}(k_{10} - k_{01})\right]E'(T_0)$$

$$- (T_{tr} - T_0)h\nu N \frac{\partial}{\partial T} k_{01} \tag{3-24a}$$

The second term of Eq. 3-24a can be written

$$(T_{tr} - T_0)E'(T_0)\left(\frac{\partial k_{10}}{\partial T} - e^{-h\nu/kT}\frac{\partial k_{10}}{\partial T} - k_{10}\frac{h\nu}{kT^2}e^{-h\nu/kT}\right)$$

$$= (T_{tr} - T_0)h\nu e^{-h\nu/kT}N\frac{\partial k_{10}}{\partial T} - k_{10}(T_{tr} - T_0)\frac{h\nu}{kT^2}e^{-h\nu/kT}E'(T_0) \tag{3-24b}$$

The third term of Eq. 3-24a can be expressed as

$$-(T_{tr} - T_0)h\nu e^{-h\nu/kT}N\frac{\partial k_{10}}{\partial T} - (T_{tr} - T_0)k_{10}\frac{(h\nu)^2}{kT^2}Ne^{-h\nu/kT} \quad (3\text{-}24c)$$

Adding these two expressions, it is seen that the first terms cancel, and one finds

$$-k_{10}(T_{tr} - T_0)\frac{h\nu}{kT^2}e^{-h\nu/kT}[E'(T_0) + h\nu N]$$

$$= -(k_{10} - k_{01})(T_{tr} - T_0)\frac{h\nu}{kT^2}e^{-h\nu/kT}\frac{k_{10}}{k_{10} - k_{01}}Nh\nu\frac{e^{h\nu/kT}}{e^{h\nu/kT} - 1}$$

$$= -\frac{1}{\tau}(T_{tr} - T_0)C' = -\frac{1}{\tau}[E'(T_{tr}) - E'(T_0)] \quad (3\text{-}24d)$$

Inserting in Eq. 3-24a one gets, as in Eq. 3-14

$$-\frac{\partial E'}{\partial T} = \frac{1}{\tau}[E' - E'(T_{tr})] \quad (3\text{-}24e)$$

Therefore, the result is that in the Landau-Teller case the relaxation times of the different quantum states are the same.

Bourgin [1] has investigated the general case in which the relaxation times of different quantum states are not equal. With some approximation he has been able to deal with a ground and two excited states. The problem is quite similar to the case where there are two vibrational degrees of freedom, with two different relaxation times. This is discussed in detail in Art. 8 and 9.

CHAPTER 2. METHODS OF MEASURING RELAXATION TIMES

DISPERSION AND ABSORPTION OF ULTRASONIC WAVES

H,4. Propagation of Plane Ultrasonic Waves. The most frequently used method of investigation of relaxation times in gases is through use of their influence on the propagation of sound waves of high frequency. In any progressive sound wave there are alternating compressions and dilations, accompanied by velocity and temperature changes.

To remove all complications which do not affect the process directly, we consider only the one-dimensional case of a plane wave progressing in the x direction. We assume the amplitude so small that quadratic terms in the equation of motion can be neglected.

Furthermore, we consider only simple harmonic processes where every variable is proportional to $e^{i\omega t}$, the linearity of the equations permitting us to build any wave form according to the superposition principle.

Of the quantities characterizing the gas, some will have zero values for the gas at rest, like the average particle velocity u; others will oscillate in the sound wave around equilibrium values, like the temperature, pressure, and density.

The quantities u, $T - T_0$, $p - p_0$, $\rho - \rho_0$ will, under the restrictions given above, all be proportional to

$$e^{i\omega\left(t-\frac{x}{a}\right)-\alpha x} \tag{4-1}$$

Here a is the (real) phase velocity of the sound wave and α is the absorption coefficient for the amplitude in reciprocal lengths, so that $1/\alpha$ is the distance over which the amplitude decreases by the factor e (for the intensity, the absorption coefficient is 2α).

Defining the compression (relative density increase) s by

$$\rho = \rho_0(1 + s)$$

one has the linearized continuity equation

$$\frac{\partial s}{\partial t} + \frac{\partial u}{\partial x} = 0 \tag{4-2a}$$

or

$$i\omega s - \left(i\frac{\omega}{a} + \alpha\right) u = 0$$

$$s = \frac{1}{a}\left(1 - \frac{i\alpha}{\omega} a\right) u \tag{4-2b}$$

One additional linear relation between s and u is now needed to eliminate one of the two, cancel out the other, and so find a dispersion equation. Such an equation will be the equation of motion, giving density times acceleration equal to the force per unit volume; the latter is given as the (tensor) gradient of the stress tensor.

$$\rho_0 \frac{\partial u}{\partial t} = \frac{\partial \sigma}{\partial x} \tag{4-3a}$$

or

$$i\omega u = \frac{1}{\rho_0} \frac{\partial \sigma}{\partial x} \tag{4-3b}$$

One must now express the stress by the variables s and u, and it is here that relaxation phenomena make their appearance. For gases, there are two kinds, principally distinguished by the way they appear in the equations.

The first kind of relaxation is the adjustment of the translational energy to the most probable distribution under the circumstances; it exists also in monatomic gases and is described by the macroscopic coefficients of viscosity and heat conduction, as they appear in the

Navier-Stokes equations. Very high frequencies may require additional coefficients (see Art. 17).

The second kind of relaxation is due to the slowness of energy exchange between the translational degrees of freedom, which determine the pressure and are directly affected by external work done on the gas, and the internal degrees of freedom—rotational and vibrational—which can exchange energy with the outside world only over the translational degrees of freedom, radiation effects being neglected. This process will appear in the energy equation and will result in an effective specific heat different from the static one.

The two effects are not exactly additive, but are usually treated as such; in the following this is also done.

One writes the stress tensor as a sum of the negative hydrostatic pressure and of a tensor which has the shear stress as nondiagonal term:

$$\sigma = -p_0 - (p - p_0) + \frac{4}{3}\mu\frac{\partial u}{\partial x} \tag{4-4}$$

Using the continuity equation to eliminate $\partial u/\partial x$ (this is possible only in one-dimensional processes) one has

$$\sigma = -p_0 - (p - p_0) - \frac{4}{3}\mu\frac{\partial s}{\partial t}$$

$$= -p_0 - \left(\frac{dp}{ds} + \frac{4}{3}\mu i\omega\right)s \tag{4-5}$$

where, for small amplitudes

$$p - p_0 = \frac{dp}{ds}s$$

has been written. Inserting Eq. 4-5 in Eq. 4-3b and using Eq. 4-2b, one has

$$1 = \frac{1}{a^2}\left(1 - \frac{i\alpha}{\omega}a\right)^2\left(\frac{1}{\rho_0}\frac{dp}{ds} + \frac{4}{3}\frac{\mu i\omega}{\rho_0}\right) \tag{4-6}$$

as the dispersion equation. The next task is the calculation of dp/ds. This will be done separately for the two relaxation effects.

H,5. The Effect of Viscosity and Heat Conduction. Here we neglect internal relaxation. We have the equation of state, which may be written

$$\frac{dp}{p} = \frac{dT}{T} + ds \tag{5-1a}$$

and the enthalpy equation per unit volume[3]

$$\frac{1}{v}C_p\frac{\partial T}{\partial t} = \frac{v\partial p}{v\partial t} + \lambda\frac{\partial^2 T}{\partial x^2} \tag{5-2a}$$

[3] λ is the coefficient of heat conductivity.

Using again the linear approximation and periodic processes

$$T - T_0 = \frac{T_0}{p_0}(p - p_0) - T_0 s \qquad (5\text{-}1\text{b})$$

$$C_p i\omega(T - T_0) = v_0 i\omega(p - p_0) + v_0\lambda \frac{\partial^2 T}{\partial x^2} \qquad (5\text{-}2\text{b})$$

Eliminate $T - T_0$ between Eq. 5-1b and Eq. 5-2b

$$C_v \frac{p - p_0}{p_0} - C_p s = v_0\lambda \frac{1}{i\omega} \frac{\partial^2}{\partial x^2}\left(\frac{p - p_0}{p_0} - s\right) \qquad (5\text{-}3)$$

or

$$\left[C_v - v_0\lambda \frac{i\omega}{a^2}\left(1 - \frac{i\alpha}{\omega}a\right)^2\right]\frac{p - p_0}{p_0} = \left[C_p - v_0\lambda \frac{i\omega}{a^2}\left(1 - \frac{i\alpha}{\omega}a\right)^2\right]s \quad (5\text{-}4)$$

from which

$$\frac{dp}{ds} = \frac{p - p_0}{s}$$

may be found and inserted into Eq. 4-6. If one assumes the effect of viscosity and heat conductivity to be small (i.e. $\alpha a/\omega \ll 1$, see below), one finds

$$a^2 = a_0^2 = \gamma \frac{RT}{\mathfrak{M}} \qquad (5\text{-}5)$$

$$\alpha_{\text{class}} = \frac{2}{3}\frac{\omega^2}{\rho_0 a_0^3}\left[\mu + \frac{3}{4}(\gamma - 1)\frac{\lambda}{c_p}\right] \qquad (5\text{-}6)$$

where c_p is the specific heat per gram, i.e.

$$c_p = \frac{C_p}{\mathfrak{M}} = \gamma \frac{C_v}{\mathfrak{M}}$$

The higher approximations are discussed in Art. 17. The effect of viscosity in Eq. 5-6 was first calculated by Stokes [9]; that of heat conduction by Kirchhoff [7].

For an ideal gas, Eq. 5-6 may be simplified, since for a monatomic gas one has

$$\lambda = 2.5 \frac{C_v}{\mathfrak{M}}\mu$$

For a polyatomic gas, this may be written, according to Eucken [6]

$$\lambda = \frac{1}{4}(9\gamma - 5)\frac{C_v}{\mathfrak{M}}\mu \qquad (5\text{-}7)$$

and therefore Eq. 5-6 is written

$$\frac{\alpha_{\text{class}}}{f^2} = \frac{8}{3}\pi^2 \frac{1}{\rho_0 a_0^3}\mu\left[1 + \frac{3}{16}\frac{\gamma - 1}{\gamma}(9\gamma - 5)\right] \qquad (5\text{-}8\text{a})$$

The factor $\rho_0 a^2$ may be written

$$\frac{\mathfrak{M}}{v_0} \gamma \frac{RT}{\mathfrak{M}} = \gamma p$$

and therefore another way of writing Eq. 5-8 is

$$\frac{\alpha_{\text{class}} a_0}{\omega} = \frac{2}{3} \omega \frac{\mu}{p} \frac{1}{\gamma} \left[1 + \frac{3}{16} \frac{\gamma - 1}{\gamma} (9\gamma - 5) \right] \qquad (5\text{-}8\text{b})$$

From Eq. 5-8b it follows that $\alpha_{\text{class}}/\omega$ is a function of ω/p and T_0 only.

Kohler [8] has introduced the relaxation time for translational energy, τ_{tr}, and the time between collisions, τ_{c}, into this formula.

It is clear that finite viscosity and heat conductivity only exist because the gas cannot immediately adjust its distribution to a thermodynamic equilibrium distribution. Kohler shows that independent of the molecular model

$$\mu = p \tau_{\text{tr}} \qquad (5\text{-}9)$$

τ_{tr} being inversely proportional to the density (or to p at constant T_0). For the rigid sphere model (see Sec. B) of diameter d

$$\mu = 0.499 \frac{8}{\pi} p \; \frac{\text{mean free path}}{\text{mean speed}} - 1.271 p \tau_{\text{c}} \qquad (5\text{-}10)$$

If one defines as average time between collisions

$$\tau_{\text{c}} = \frac{\text{mean free path}}{\text{mean speed}}$$

then

$$\tau_{\text{tr}} = 1.271 \tau_{\text{c}}$$

For other than rigid molecules, "collision" is not easily defined; one then takes Eq. 5-10 as the definition of the collision time. If the viscosity obeys the Sutherland formula, then τ_{c} for a given gas under different conditions varies as

$$\tau_{\text{c}} \sim \frac{\sqrt{T}}{1 + C/T} \frac{1}{p} \qquad (5\text{-}11)$$

With Eq. 5-9, one has then[4]

$$\frac{\alpha_{\text{class}} a_0}{\omega} = \frac{2}{3} \frac{1.271}{\gamma} \left[1 + \frac{3}{16} \frac{\gamma - 1}{\gamma} (9\gamma - 5) \right] \omega \tau_{\text{c}} \qquad (5\text{-}12)$$

H,6. The Effect of Slow Energy Exchange. Call C_V the total (static) specific heat of a gas. The degrees of freedom contributing to it shall be divided into two groups; the external and internal degrees of

[4] The factor in [ ] is: for $\gamma = \frac{5}{3}$, 1.75; for $\gamma = \frac{7}{5}$, 1.407; for $\gamma = \frac{4}{3}$, 1.328; for $\gamma = 1.28$, 1.267.

freedom. The former contains the translational degrees and such others as are in temperature equilibrium with them. Accordingly a temperature T_{tr} will be ascribed to them. The internal degrees of freedom are those for which, under the circumstances considered, relaxation phenomena play a role. The static contribution they make to C_V is called C'; their momentary temperature T'. The following equations for sound propagation are then valid:

The continuity equation (4-2a) or (4-2b).

The linearized equation of motion (without friction). (See Eq. 4-3a and 4-4.)

$$\frac{\partial u}{\partial t} = -\frac{1}{\rho_0}\frac{\partial p}{\partial x} = -\frac{1}{\rho_0}\left(\frac{dp}{ds}\right)\frac{\partial s}{\partial x} \tag{6-1}$$

or (see Eq. 4-6)

$$\rho_0 \frac{ds}{dp} = \frac{1}{a^2}\left(1 - \frac{i\alpha'a}{\omega}\right)^2 \tag{6-2}$$

The main point in which the further development differs from that in Art. 5 is the assumption that the equation of state depends only on the translational temperature T_{tr}. Therefore Eq. 5-1a is replaced by

$$\frac{dp}{p} = \frac{dT_{tr}}{T_{tr}} + ds \tag{6-3a}$$

or

$$\frac{p - p_0}{p_0} = \frac{T_{tr} - T_0}{T_0} + s \tag{6-3b}$$

Furthermore, the enthalpy equation in the absence of heat conduction is, instead of Eq. 5-2a and 5-2b,

$$(C_p - C')(T_{tr} - T_0) + C'(T' - T_0) = v_0(p - p_0) = RT_0\frac{p - p_0}{p_0} \tag{6-4}$$

One has next the relaxation equation, connecting T' and T_{tr},

$$-\frac{\partial T'}{\partial t} = \frac{1}{\tau}(T' - T_{tr}) = \frac{1}{\tau}[T' - T_0 - (T_{tr} - T_0)] \tag{6-5a}$$

or

$$(T' - T_0) = \frac{1}{1 + i\omega\tau}(T_{tr} - T_0) \tag{6-5b}$$

which inserted into Eq. 6-4a gives

$$\left(C_p - C' + \frac{C'}{1 + i\omega\tau}\right)(T_{tr} - T_0) = \frac{RT_0}{p_0}(p - p_0) \tag{6-6}$$

Accordingly one has an effective specific heat

$$(C_p)_{\text{eff}} = C_p + C'\left(\frac{1}{1 + i\omega\tau} - 1\right) = C_p - C'\frac{i\omega\tau}{1 + i\omega\tau} \tag{6-7}$$

One now eliminates $T_{tr} - T_0$ from Eq. 6-3 and gets

$$\frac{p - p_0}{p_0} = \frac{p - p_0}{p_0} R \left(C_p - C' + \frac{C'}{1 + i\omega\tau} \right)^{-1} + s$$

or

$$\rho_0 \frac{s}{p - p_0} = \rho_0 \frac{ds}{dp} = \frac{\mathfrak{M}}{RT_0} \left(1 - \frac{R}{(C_p)_{\text{eff}}} \right) \qquad (6\text{-}8)$$

Write the sound velocity at low frequency as

$$\frac{1}{a_0^2} = \frac{\mathfrak{M}}{RT_0} \frac{C_p - R}{C_p}$$

then one finds for the equation of propagation

$$\frac{C_p}{C_p - R} \left(1 - \frac{R}{(C_p)_{\text{eff}}} \right) = \left(\frac{a_0}{a} - i\alpha' \frac{a_0}{\omega} \right)^2 \qquad (6\text{-}9)$$

One inserts on the left Eq. 6-7 and finds after some algebra

$$1 - \frac{RC'}{C_V C_p} \frac{i\omega\tau}{1 + i\omega \frac{C_p - C'}{C_p} \tau} = 1 - \frac{RC'}{C_V(C_p - C')} \frac{i\omega\tau'}{1 + i\omega\tau'} \qquad (6\text{-}10)$$

with

$$\tau' = \frac{C_p - C'}{C_p} \tau \qquad (6\text{-}11)$$

Squaring out and separating real and imaginary parts one gets

$$\left(\frac{a_0}{a} \right)^2 - \left(\alpha' \frac{a_0}{\omega} \right)^2 = 1 - \frac{RC'}{C_V(C_p - C')} \frac{\omega^2 \tau'^2}{1 + \omega^2 \tau'^2} \qquad (6\text{-}12)$$

$$\alpha' \frac{a_0^2}{a\omega} = \frac{1}{2} \frac{RC'}{C_V(C_p - C')} \frac{\omega\tau'}{1 + \omega^2 \tau'^2} \qquad (6\text{-}13a)$$

or

$$\alpha' = \frac{a}{a_0} \frac{1}{2a_0} \frac{RC'}{C_V(C_p - C')} \frac{\omega^2 \tau'}{1 + \omega^2 \tau'^2} \qquad (6\text{-}13b)$$

Since the energy transfer is possible only in collisions, one can write

$$\tau = Z\tau_c$$

where τ_c is the time between collisions and Z is the average number of collisions to effect an energy transfer. Z is independent of τ_c, i.e. of the pressure (for a possible exception, see Art. 10). Therefore

$$\tau' = \frac{C_p - C'}{C_p} Z\tau_c \qquad (6\text{-}14)$$

Accordingly a_0/a and α/ω (or $2\pi\alpha(a/\omega)$, the absorption per wavelength) are functions only of the product $\omega\tau_c$, i.e. of ω/p, so that one can effect the same change by doubling the frequency or halving the pressure.

H,7. Discussion of the Dispersion and Absorption Equations.
Eq. 6-12 is complicated because it contains α^2 (the same complication
exists for strongly absorbing substances in optics). However, if we wish
to calculate a/a_0 to $\frac{1}{2}$ per cent we could neglect $(\alpha a_0/\omega)^2$ if the absorption
per wavelength is smaller than 0.62. This value, however, cannot be
reached under any imaginable circumstances (see below). It is therefore
customary to neglect this term and write

$$\left(\frac{a_0}{a}\right)^2 = 1 - \frac{RC'}{C_V(C_p - C')} \frac{\omega^2\tau'^2}{1 + \omega^2\tau'^2} \tag{7-1}$$

A curve representing Eq. 7-1 is shown in Fig. H,7 (curve A). The extreme
values of the velocity are given by a

$$a = a_0, \qquad \omega\tau' = 0, \qquad (C_V)_{\text{eff}} = C_V$$

and

$$a^2 = a_0^2 \frac{C_p - C'}{C_V - C'} \frac{C_V}{C_p}$$

at $\omega\tau' = \infty$, with an effective specific heat $C_V - C'$. The inflection point
occurs at $\omega\tau' = 1$, i.e. a frequency

$$f' = \frac{1}{2\pi\tau} \frac{C_p}{C_p - C'} \tag{7-2}$$

The absorption can be represented in different ways:
If one chooses $\alpha'(a/\omega)(a_0/a)^2$, the resulting curve is shown as curve B
in Fig. H,7. It has a maximum at $\omega\tau' = 1$, i.e. at the same point where
the $(a_0/a)^2$, Eq. 7-1, has an inflection point. The height of the maximum
depends only on the specific heats concerned, and is

$$\left[\alpha' \frac{a}{\omega} \left(\frac{a_0}{a}\right)^2\right]_{\text{max}} = \frac{1}{4} \frac{RC'}{C_V(C_p - C')} \tag{7-3}$$

In the extreme case where all the degrees of freedom but the translational
have the same time of relaxation (or all that have not yet been completely shut out) the right side is

$$\frac{1}{4} \frac{C'}{(\frac{3}{2}R + C')\frac{5}{2}} = \frac{1}{10} \frac{C'}{\frac{3}{2}R + C'} \tag{7-4}$$

so that 0.1 is the maximum possible value. If we consider instead α', we
have

$$\alpha'\left(\frac{a_0}{a}\right) = \frac{1}{2a_0} \frac{RC'}{C_V(C_p - C')} \frac{\omega^2\tau'}{1 + \omega^2\tau'^2}$$

$$= \frac{1}{2a_0\tau'} \frac{RC'}{C_V(C_p - C')} \frac{\omega^2\tau'^2}{1 + \omega^2\tau'^2} \tag{7-5}$$

This means that if ω is varied one gets a shape as shown by curve C in

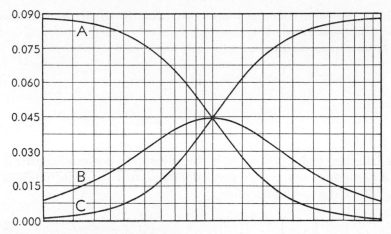

Fig. H,7.   Dispersion and absorption due to relaxation. Curve A: $(a_\infty/a)^2 - 1$ and $2(\alpha a/\omega^2)(a_\infty/a)^2$.   Curve B: $2(\alpha a/\omega)(a_\infty/a)^2$.   Curve C: (shifted) $(a/a_0)^2 - 1$ and $2\alpha\tau' a_\infty^2/a$.   Logarithmic frequency scale.

Fig. H,7. The inflection point is again at $\omega\tau' = 1$; at low frequency, one has

$$\alpha' = \frac{1}{2a_0} \frac{RC''}{C_V(C_p - C')} \omega^2\tau' = \frac{1}{2a_0} \frac{RC''}{C_V C_p} \omega^2\tau$$

$$= \frac{1}{2a_0} \frac{RC'}{C_V C_p} Z\omega^2\tau_c \qquad (7\text{-}6)$$

One sees that the pressure and frequency dependence are the same as for the classical absorption. One can therefore write for low frequency

$$\frac{\alpha'}{\alpha_{\text{class}}} = \frac{3}{4} \frac{\gamma}{1.271} \left[1 + \frac{3}{16} \frac{\gamma - 1}{\gamma} (9\gamma - 5)\right]^{-1} \frac{RC'}{C_V C_p} Z \qquad (7\text{-}7)$$

At high frequencies ($\omega\tau' > 1$), one has

$$\alpha' = \frac{1}{2a} \frac{a^2}{a_0^2} \frac{1}{\tau'} \frac{RC'}{C_V(C_p - C')} = \frac{1}{2a\tau} \frac{RC'}{(C_p - C')(C_V - C')} \qquad (7\text{-}8)$$

i.e. α' is independent of the frequency, but proportional to the pressure (to reach this stage, one has to go to higher frequencies at higher pressures).

One can change Eq. 7-1 into

$$\left(\frac{a}{a_0}\right)^2 = 1 + \frac{RC'}{C_p(C_V - C')} \frac{\omega^2\tau_w^2}{1 + \omega^2\tau_w^2} \qquad (7\text{-}9)$$

where

$$\tau_w = \frac{C_V - C'}{C_V} \tau \qquad (7\text{-}10)$$

This is the form commonly used, particularly by Kneser. It has an inflection point at $\omega\tau_w = 1$.

Similarly one finds

$$\alpha'\frac{a}{\omega} = \frac{1}{2}\frac{RC'}{\sqrt{C_pC_V(C_p - C')(C_V - C')}}\frac{\omega\tau_M}{1 + \omega^2\tau_M^2} \qquad (7\text{-}11a)$$

with

$$\tau_M = \sqrt{\frac{C_p - C'}{C_V - C'}\frac{C_V}{C_p}}\,\tau_w \qquad (7\text{-}11b)$$

The left side, multiplied by 2π is the absorption per wavelength; it has its maximum at $\omega\tau_M = 1$ (a point different from the inflection point of Eq. 7-9), and a maximum value

$$\left(\alpha'\frac{a}{\omega}\right)_{\max} = \frac{1}{4}\frac{RC'}{\sqrt{C_pC_V(C_p - C')(C_V - C')}} \qquad (7\text{-}12)$$

A final convenient form is

$$\alpha'a\left(\frac{a}{a_0}\right)^2 = \frac{1}{2}\frac{RC'}{C_p(C_V - C')}\frac{\omega^2\tau_w}{1 + \omega^2\tau_w^2} \qquad (7\text{-}13)$$

which has the same inflection point as Eq. 7-9.

To sum up the content of the last two articles as far as they supply a means to calculate relaxation times:

If the whole dispersion curve (Eq. 7-1 or 7-9) is known, it gives us both C', the amount of the specific heat involved, and, through the inflection point, the relaxation time. If one has not reached the region where dispersion is measurable, the accuracy of the measurement gives an upper limit for

$$\frac{C_V - C'}{C_V}\frac{RC'}{C_VC_p}\,\omega^2\tau^2$$

If the whole absorption curve is known, it gives us the same amount of information as if the whole dispersion curve were known. However, the knowledge of the position and height of the maximum (either Eq. 7-3, 7-12, or 7-13) gives us both C' and τ.

Finally, if only the low frequency absorption is known, one gets, from $\alpha'/\alpha_{\text{class}}$, the product $C'Z$.

Historically, Watson [14] calculated the rate at which energy would be exchanged between translation and rotation for rough molecules. Jeans [12] suggested that slow energy exchange with vibrational degrees of freedom might affect sound velocity. But at the time there was no chance of discovering this effect with the experimental means available. In 1925, Pierce [13] discovered dispersion and, soon afterward, Abello [10] excess absorption. This led Herzfeld and Rice [11] to introduce the idea of slow energy exchange between vibration and translation and to deduce the expression for absorption and dispersion at low frequencies. Kneser [2,3] and Rutgers [5] then gave the formulas for the whole frequency range. Some of the different expressions shown above are shown here for the first time and will be deduced in detail in a forthcoming book.

H,8. Two Different Degrees of Freedom. Excitation in Parallel. In the preceding discussion we have assumed the existence of a single relaxation time. As has been shown in Art. 3, all transitions making up each vibrational degree of freedom may be assigned such a single relaxation. However, a polyatomic molecule has several vibrational degrees of freedom, and the question arises how these are excited. Two extreme cases can be imagined, which may be called excitation in parallel and excitation in series. In the former, each degree exchanges energy with the translation independently of any other and has its own relaxation time. In the latter, only one particular degree of vibrational freedom exchanges energy with the translation in collision directly, while the energy then seeps out from this particular degree of freedom into the others. Of course, in a complicated molecule, all combinations between these extremes are possible.

In the present article, the case of parallel excitation is discussed. For the sake of simplicity, we limit ourselves to two vibrational degrees of freedom; their static specific heats are called C_1' and C_2', their relaxation times τ_1 and τ_2. A calculation quite similar to the one given in Art. 6 leads then to

$$(C_V)_\text{eff} = C_V - C_1' \frac{i\omega\tau_1}{1 + i\omega\tau_1} - C_2' \frac{i\omega\tau_2}{1 + i\omega\tau_2} \tag{8-1}$$

Again, one has

$$\left(\frac{a_0}{a} - i\alpha' \frac{a_0}{\omega}\right)^2 = \frac{C_p}{C_V}\left[1 - \frac{R}{R + (C_V)_\text{eff}}\right] \tag{8-2}$$

If one again neglects $(\alpha a_0/\omega)^2$, one finds easily, by taking the reciprocal of Eq. 8-2

$$\left(\frac{a}{a_0}\right)^2 \left(1 + 2i\frac{\alpha' a}{\omega}\right) = \frac{C_V}{C_p}\left(C_p - C_1' \frac{i\omega\tau_1}{1 + i\omega\tau_1} - C_2' \frac{i\omega\tau_2}{1 + i\omega\tau_2}\right)$$
$$\left(C_V - C_1' \frac{i\omega\tau_1}{1 + i\omega\tau_1} - C_2' \frac{i\omega\tau_2}{1 + i\omega\tau_2}\right)^{-1} \tag{8-3}$$

Multiplying out, one finds after some calculation

$$\left(\frac{a}{a_0}\right)^2 \left(1 + 2i\frac{\alpha' a}{\omega}\right)$$
$$= 1 + \frac{R}{C_p(C_V - C_1' - C_2')}\left(C_1'' \frac{i\omega\tau_1''}{1 + i\omega\tau_1''} + C_2'' \frac{i\omega\tau_2''}{1 + i\omega\tau_2''}\right) \tag{8-4a}$$

or

$$\left(\frac{a}{a_0}\right)^2 = 1 + \frac{R}{C_p(C_V - C_1' - C_2')}$$
$$\left(C_1'' \frac{\omega^2 \tau_1''^2}{1 + \omega^2 \tau_1''^2} + C_2'' \frac{\omega^2 \tau_2''^2}{1 + \omega^2 \tau_2''^2}\right) \quad \text{(8-4b)}$$

$$\frac{\alpha'}{\omega}\left(\frac{a}{a_0}\right)^2 = \frac{1}{2a}\frac{R}{C_p(C_V - C_1' - C_2')}\left(C_1'' \frac{\omega^2 \tau_1''}{1 + \omega^2 \tau_1''^2} + C_2'' \frac{\omega^2 \tau_2''}{1 + \omega^2 \tau_2''^2}\right) \quad \text{(8-4c)}$$

The connection between the quantities C_1', C_2', τ_1, and τ_2, which appear in the energy exchange, and the quantities τ_1'', τ_2'', which give the inflection points[5] in the dispersion and absorption curve, and C_1'' and C_2'', which are the apparent specific heats involved, is as follows:

$$\tau_1'' = \left(1 - \frac{C_1'}{C_V}\right)\tau_1 + \frac{C_1'C_2'}{C_V^2}\tau_1\tau_2\left[\left(1 - \frac{C_1'}{C_V}\right)\tau_1 - \left(1 - \frac{C_2'}{C_V}\right)\tau_2\right]^{-1} \quad \text{(8-5a)}$$

$$\tau_2'' = \left(1 - \frac{C_2'}{C_V}\right)\tau_2 + \frac{C_1'C_2'}{C_V^2}\tau_1\tau_2\left[\left(1 - \frac{C_2'}{C_V}\right)\tau_2 - \left(1 - \frac{C_1'}{C_V}\right)\tau_1\right]^{-1} \quad \text{(8-5b)}$$

As in the case of coupled oscillators, τ_1'' and τ_2'' are farther apart (due to the second term in Eq. 8-5) than would be

$$\left(1 - \frac{C_1'}{C_V}\right)\tau_1 \quad \text{and} \quad \left(1 - \frac{C_2'}{C_V}\right)\tau_2$$

the inflection points if only one or the other of the two degrees of freedom were present. If τ_1 and τ_2 are very far apart (e.g. have a ratio of 100 or more), one can write ($\tau_1 \gg \tau_2$)

$$\tau_1'' = \left(1 - \frac{C_1'}{C_V}\right)\tau_1 + \frac{C_1'C_2'}{C_V(C_V - C_1')}\tau_2 \quad \text{(8-6a)}$$

$$\tau_2'' = \left(1 - \frac{C_2'}{C_V - C_1'}\right)\tau_2 \quad \text{(8-6b)}$$

Eq. 8-6b means that in the region where dispersion due to degree two is observed, the effects of degree one have completely disappeared and the system acts as if its initial specific heat were $C_V - C_1'$.

After the τ'' values have been found, the apparent specific heats C'' are calculated from

$$C_1'' + C_2'' = C_1' + C_2' \quad \text{(8-7a)}$$

$$C_1''\tau_1'' + C_2''\tau_2'' = \left(1 - \frac{C_1' + C_2'}{C_V}\right)(C_1'\tau_1 + C_2'\tau_2) \quad \text{(8-7b)}$$

It follows from Eq. 8-7 that the absorption at low frequencies is given by

[5] For one degree of freedom, this quantity was called τ_w in Eq. 7-10.

$$\alpha' = \frac{1}{2a_0} \frac{R}{C_p C_V} \omega^2 (C_1' \tau_1 + C_2' \tau_2) \tag{8-8}$$

If there are more than two vibrational degrees of freedom, Eq. 8-4, 8-7, and 8-8 may be generalized immediately, but the equations connecting τ'' and τ (8-5) are of higher algebraic order.

Experimentally, one needs considerable accuracy to be able to distinguish two relaxation times not too far apart. Fig. H,8 shows a number

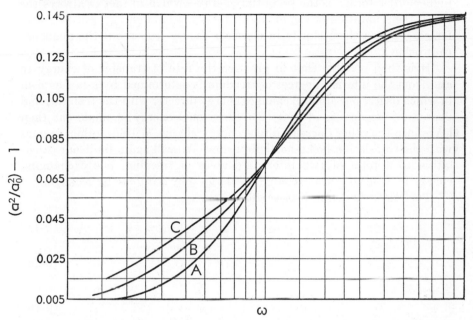

Fig. H,8.   Dispersion in the presence of two relaxation times: $C_1' = C_2' = R$. Curve A: $\tau_2 = \tau_1$. Curve B: $\tau_2 = 2\tau_1$; $\tau_1(B) = 1.343\tau_1(A)$. Curve C: $\tau_2 = 5\tau_1$; $\tau_1(C) = 1.522\tau_1(A)$. Logarithmic frequency scale.

of curves for two fully excited vibrations; $C_V = \frac{9}{2}R$, $C_1' = C_2' = R$. The following curves are shown:

A. $\tau_2 = \tau_1$ $\tau_1'' = \tau_2'' = \tau_w = \frac{7}{9}\tau_1$ $C_1'' = C_2'' = R$

B. $\tau_2 = 2\tau_1$ $\tau_1'' = 0.462\tau_1$ $C_1'' = 1.473R$

   $\tau_2'' = 1.872\tau_1$ $C_2'' = 0.527R$

   τ_1 for this curve is chosen as $1.343\tau_1$ for curve A, so as to give close coincidence.

C. $\tau_2 = 5\tau_1$ $\tau_1'' = 0.522\tau_1$; $\tau_2'' = 3.37\tau_1$ $C_1'' = 1.39R$; $C_2'' = 0.61R$

   The τ_1 of this curve is chosen equal to $1.522\tau_1$ of curve A. Since both τ_1 and τ_2 are proportional to τ_c, and the τ_1'' and τ_2'' are linear homogeneous in τ_1, τ_2, a/a_0 and $\alpha' a/\omega$ are still functions of ω/p only.

H,9. Two Different Degrees of Freedom. Excitation in Series. If the forces in a molecule obey Hooke's law exactly, i.e. if the potential energy is exactly a quadratic function of the deviation from equilibrium, one can, both classically and in quantum theory, introduce "normal coordinates," each describing one mode of motion. These are excited independently of each other, and no energy is transferred between them. However, if the forces deviate slightly from Hooke's law, i.e. if there are higher order terms in the potential energy—which in fact is always the case—the separation of the modes is not strict, and energy will be transferred between them slowly in classical theory (see about the quantum case below).

It is then possible that in practice the rate of transfer of energy to and from the internal degrees of freedom is determined by a mechanism in which degree *one* alone exchanges energy directly with the translational degrees of freedom, and that this vibrational energy of mode *one* then leaks into the other degrees, direct energy change of these other degrees with the translation being negligibly slow. We will again limit our calculation to a total of two internal degrees of freedom, *one* exchanging energy by collision, *two* exchanging energy only with *one* by leakage.

The relaxation equations are then

$$-\frac{\partial T_1}{\partial t} = \frac{1}{\tau_1}(T_1 - T_{tr}) + \frac{1}{\tau_2}(T_1 - T_2) \qquad (9\text{-}1a)$$

$$-\frac{\partial T_2}{\partial t} = \frac{1}{\tau_2}(T_2 - T_1) \qquad (9\text{-}2a)$$

or

$$T_1 - T_0 = \left(1 + i\omega\tau_1 + \frac{\tau_1}{\tau_2}\frac{i\omega\tau_2}{1 + i\omega\tau_2}\right)^{-1}(T_{tr} - T_0) \qquad (9\text{-}1b)$$

$$T_2 - T_0 = \frac{1}{1 + i\omega\tau_2}(T_1 - T_0) \qquad (9\text{-}2b)$$

Therefore, proceeding as in Art. 6, one finds as effective specific heat

$$(C_p)_{eff} = C_p - C_1' - C_2'$$
$$+ \left(C_1' + \frac{C_2'}{1 + i\omega\tau_2}\right)\left(1 + i\omega\tau_1 + \frac{\tau_1}{\tau_2}\frac{i\omega\tau_2}{1 + i\omega\tau_2}\right)^{-1} \qquad (9\text{-}3)$$

One then proceeds as in Art. 8 and finds again, for the sound velocity, Eq. 8-4b, and for the absorption, Eq. 8-4c.

The values for τ_1'' and τ_2'' are given by the different sign in Eq. 9-4 below.

$$\tau'' = \frac{1}{2}\left(1 - \frac{C'}{C_V}\right)\left\{\frac{C'}{C_1'}\tau_1 + \frac{C_V - C_2'}{C_V - C'}\tau_2\right.$$
$$\left. \pm \left[\left(\frac{C'}{C_1'}\tau_1 - \frac{C_V - C_2'}{C_V - C'}\tau_2\right)^2 + 4\frac{C_2'}{C_1'}\tau_1\tau_2\right]^{\frac{1}{2}}\right\} \qquad (9\text{-}4)$$

with the abbreviation

$$C' = C_1' + C_2'$$

One has again Eq. 8-7a, but Eq. 8-7b is replaced by

$$C_1'' \tau_2'' + C_2'' \tau_1'' = C_1' \tau_2 \tag{9-5}$$

Since τ_1 is proportional to the collision time, it is therefore inversely proportional to p, but τ_2—being an internal conversion time—is independent of p, τ_1'', τ_2'' are now in general less dependent on p than would be expressed by p^{-1}, and therefore a/a_0 and $\alpha a_0/\omega$ are no longer functions of ω/p alone.

One sees from Eq. 9-4 that if the internal conversion is very fast ($\tau_2 \ll \tau_1$), one has only one effective relaxation time

$$\tau_1'' = \frac{C_V - C'}{C_V} \frac{C'}{C_1'} \tau_1$$

affecting the total vibrational specific heat $C' = C_1' + C_2'$.

Since Eq. 8-4b, 8-4c, and 8-7a are valid in both mechanisms, the frequency dependence is the same; only the different pressure dependence may be used to distinguish between the two mechanisms, because for excitation in series the same value of ω/p should give a different value for a/a_0 and $\alpha a/\omega$ if p is different.

However, there is a third case possible, where even this difference disappears, and everything is again a function of ω/p. This case was first discussed by Schwartz and Slawsky [18]. It corresponds to excitation in series so that the equations of this article are valid. Here, however, the energy transfer from one vibrational degree of freedom to the other can only occur during a collision, so that τ_2 is also proportional to τ_c, i.e. to p^{-1}. Actually this seems to be normally the only possibility for excitation in series according to quantum theory. Classically of course, direct energy transfer is possible between vibrations of different frequency. But in quantum theory, the difference between $h\nu_1$ and $h\nu_2$ must come from somewhere, and can usually come only from translational energy during a collision. The only exception may be a degeneracy (rational relation between ν_1 and ν_2) or in molecules so large that they have a nearly continuous band of frequency so that the energy difference $h\nu_1 - h\nu_2$ can be made up by one or several quanta from other vibrations.

In view of this discussion, one should expect in general the two modes of excitation (Art. 8 and 9) to be indistinguishable experimentally, since they give the same absorption (and dispersion) formulas as functions of ω and p, and differ only in the way the measured constants C_1'' and C_2'', τ_1'' and τ_2'' are related to C_1', C_2', τ_1, τ_2. Since τ_1 and τ_2 are not known, the only possibility would be to see which set of three equations (8-5a), (8-5b), and (8-7b), or (9-4) (two equations) and (9-5) give consistent values for τ_1, τ_2, provided all four measured constants are measured with sufficient accuracy (which seems not easy to achieve).

Historically, Bourgin [1] and Richards [16] first investigated the behavior of several degrees of freedom, and of gas mixtures (Art. 10). Buschmann and Schäfer [17] first distinguished excitation in parallel and in series, but were of the opinion that they gave different dependence on the frequency. That both assumptions lead to a simple superposition of dispersion terms is first shown here (although the results were first used by Cheng [15]). In a forthcoming book the generalization to many degrees of freedom will be given.

H,10. Gas Mixtures. It was observed at an early date that some substances, admixed even in small quantities, have a very marked effect on the dispersion and absorption of ultrasonic waves in gases. General considerations of such an effect were made by Eucken [19]. The natural assumption is made that only pairs of molecules interact (there might be one exception to that; see Art. 11). This same assumption—that transfer of energy occurs only between pairs of molecules—is also made for liquid solutions, where it is the simplest assumption, but where deviations are not out of the question. One qualitative statement can be made in case one has a large amount of substance A with a small admixture of B: If the exchange of energy between molecules A is very inefficient, while that between molecules A and B is very efficient, then a very small amount of B may appreciably decrease the effective relaxation time of the mixture, decreasing the low frequency absorption. In the opposite case, however, in which the efficiency of energy exchange between molecules A is high and that between A and B low, a very small amount of B will not appreciably affect the effective relaxation time of the mixture, which will be near that of pure A.

An analogy will make that clear. Consider a vessel filled with water, as a picture of the internal energy; the picture of energy exchange will be given by the flow of water out of this vessel. In the first case, where the energy exchange between molecules of A is very inefficient, the picture of energy exchange in pure A is given by many very small pinholes. Adding very little B means then, adding a few, but much larger holes, which may make a very considerable difference in the resultant flow. In the second case the exchange between A, being already efficient, is represented by many holes of appreciable size. Replacing some A molecules by inefficient B, i.e., at worst, plugging up a fraction of the holes, cannot affect the flow in a higher proportion than the (supposedly small) ratio B/A.

Consider first a mixture of two gases A and B. Call the mole fraction of A: $1 - X$; that of B: X. The total pressure is p. Each of these gases shall be treated as a gas with a single relaxation time, when by itself.

Call τ_A the relaxation time of gas A at the pressure p (i.e. at a pressure equal to the total pressure of the mixture); similarly call τ_B the relaxation time of a molecule B in pure B at pressure p. Furthermore, call τ_{AB} the relaxation time of one molecule A in otherwise pure B of pressure p, and τ_{BA} the relaxation time of one molecule B in pure A.

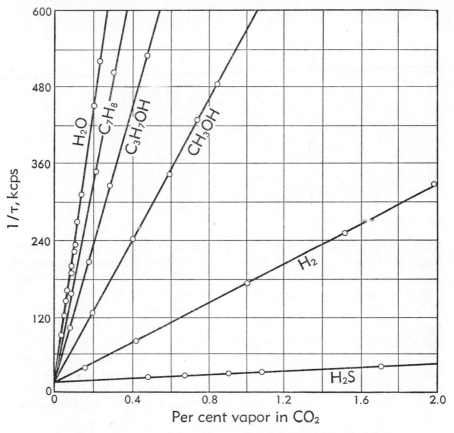

Fig. H,10. Frequency of maximum absorption in CO_2 with different admixtures, according to Fricke and Knudsen ([68] by permission).

The number of deactivations per second of a molecule A in the mixture is (see Fig. H,10)

$$\frac{1}{\tau_1} = \frac{1 - X}{\tau_A} + \frac{X}{\tau_{AB}} \tag{10-1a}$$

since it makes only $(1 - X)$ times as many collisions with other molecules A than it would have made if only A had been present at pressure p, and X times as many with B molecules than if these alone had been present at pressure p. Similarly, the number of active collisions per second of a molecule B is

$$\frac{1}{\tau_2} = \frac{1 - X}{\tau_{BA}} + \frac{X}{\tau_B} \tag{10-1b}$$

One treats now the mixture exactly as one would a single gas with several degrees of internal freedom excited in parallel (see Art. 8).

For this purpose one has

$$C_V = C_{VA}(1 - X) + C_{VB}X \tag{10-2a}$$

$$C_1' = C_A'(1 - X), \qquad C_2' = C_B'X \tag{10-2b}$$

For a_0, one has

$$a_0^2 = \frac{RT}{\mathfrak{M}_A(1 - X) + \mathfrak{M}_B X}\left(1 + \frac{R}{C_V}\right) \tag{10-3}$$

One finds, for example, the low frequency absorption,

$$\frac{\alpha'}{\omega^2} = \frac{R}{2C_p C_V a_0}(C_1'\tau_1 + C_2'\tau_2)$$

$$= \frac{R}{2a_0 C_p C_V}\left[\frac{C_A'(1 - X)}{\dfrac{1 - X}{\tau_A} + \dfrac{X}{\tau_{AB}}} + \frac{C_B'X}{\dfrac{1 - X}{\tau_{BA}} + \dfrac{X}{\tau_B}}\right]$$

H,11. Triple Collisions in Pure Gases and Mixtures. The question may be raised whether triple collisions play an important role in energy transfer. It is not possible, at present, to define sharply "triple collision," and, accordingly, to calculate their number better than to their order of magnitude, although their dependence on concentration may be fixed exactly. One can proceed in the following manner: single out a particular molecule A and follow it on its way. It will make collisions with other molecules B; if no third molecule C is near the molecule with which A collides, one has a double collision; if a third molecule C is sufficiently close to the molecule B with which A collides, one has a triple collision. The difficulty consists in knowing what "close enough" means. Since one is interested in energy transfer, "close enough" obviously means "within the range of interaction forces." It may be said that the third molecule must be within a spherical shell of radius $(r_2 + r_3)$ and thickness r' around the second molecule, i.e. within a spherical shell of approximate volume $4\pi(r_2 + r_3)^2 r'$. If the mole fraction of the third kind of molecule is X_3, and the total pressure is p, there are $X_3 p/kT$ molecules of the third kind in a unit volume. The fraction of molecules of the "second" kind which have a particle of the third kind nearby is given by the ratio of the shell volume $4\pi(r_2 + r_3)^2 r'$ to the total volume multiplied by the total number of molecules of the third kind, or

fraction of molecules B in pairs with C $= 4\pi(r_2 + r_3)^2 r' X_3 p/kT$ (11-1)

If, with rough approximation, one writes

$$r_2 = r_3 = 4r'$$

multiplies numerator and denominator with the Avogadro number N, and uses van der Waals' b per mole where

$$b = \tfrac{2}{3}\pi(2r)^3 N \tag{11-2a}$$

then

fraction of molecules B paired with $C = \dfrac{3}{4} b X_3 \dfrac{p}{RT}$ (11-2b)

A better numerical understanding may be gained, if one introduces the mole volume at 1 atm and 300°K, namely 24,600 cm³, measures b in cm³, and sets $p_0 = 1$ atm. Then

$$\frac{bp}{RT} = \frac{b}{24{,}600}\frac{p}{p_0}\frac{300}{T} \tag{11-2c}$$

One may suggest that the expression for the fraction of pairs given above should be multiplied by $e^{\epsilon/kT}$, where ϵ is the dissociation energy of the pair; however, for most gases except H_2O, and room temperature or above, this factor will be surely less than 2 and may be absorbed in the other uncertainties of the calculation.

The following data for ϵ/k (in degrees K) are taken from Hirschfelder and rounded off.

Gas	He	Ne	A	H_2	N_2	O_2	CO_2	N_2O	CH_4	H_2O
$\dfrac{\epsilon}{k}$	6	36	120	37	96	118	185	190	143	600–900

The value for H_2O is estimated by setting ϵ proportional to the Sutherland constant C.

For water vapor as B, $1/Z_{AAB}$ ought to be multiplied with $e^{\sqrt{\epsilon_A \epsilon_B}/kT}$, $1/Z_{ABB}$ with $e^{\epsilon_B/kT}$.

If, then, one molecule of the second kind out of 100 is a partner in a pair, every hundredth collision of the molecule A with B will be a collision with a pair, and the time between triple collisions will be 100 times that between normal collisions.

In cases of normal A (mole fraction $1 - X$) and small B (mole fraction X) there will be three kinds of triple collisions in which an A partakes: AAA, AAB, and ABB, with the following reciprocal times between collisions:

$$\left(\frac{1}{\tau_c}\right)_A (1 - X)^2 2\sqrt{\frac{3}{4}}\frac{b}{24{,}600}\frac{p}{p_0}\frac{300}{T}$$

$$\left(\frac{1}{\tau_c}\right)_{AB} (1 - X)X2\sqrt{\frac{2m_A + m_B}{2(m_A + m_B)}}\frac{b}{24{,}600}\frac{p}{p_0}\frac{300}{T} \tag{11-3}$$

$$\left(\frac{1}{\tau_c}\right)_{AB} X^2 2\sqrt{\frac{2m_A + m_B}{4m_B}}\frac{b}{24{,}600}\frac{p}{p_0}\frac{300}{T}$$

In the above, the factor 2 is written since the collision may occur with either of the two partners of the pair; the square root corrects for relative velocity, but only varies between 1 and $\frac{1}{2}$. Therefore, we are going to omit it and write b' instead of b to indicate a quantity of the order of van der Waals' b. One has finally

$$\frac{1}{\tau_1} = \left(\frac{1}{\tau_c}\right)_A \left\{ \frac{1-X}{Z_A} + \frac{b'}{12{,}300}\frac{p}{p_0}\frac{300}{T} \right.$$

$$\left[(1-X)^2 \left(\frac{1}{Z_{AAA}} - \frac{3}{2}\frac{1}{Z_A} \right) + (1-X)X \left(\frac{1}{Z_{AAB}} - \frac{1}{Z_{AB}} - \frac{1}{2}\frac{1}{Z_A} \right) \right]$$

$$\left. + \frac{(\tau_c)_A}{(\tau_c)_{AB}} \left[\frac{X}{Z_{AB}} + X^2 \frac{b'}{12{,}300}\frac{p}{p_0}\frac{300}{T}\left(\frac{1}{Z_{ABB}} - \frac{1}{Z_{AB}} \right) \right] \right\} \quad (11\text{-}4\text{a})$$

The negative terms occur because the triple collision had already been counted as several double collisions; e.g. the triple collision AAB had been counted as two collisions AB and one AA. Arranging this according to powers of X, one has

$$\frac{1}{\tau_1} = \left(\frac{1}{\tau_c}\right)_A \left\{ \frac{1}{Z_A} + \frac{b'}{12{,}300}\frac{p}{p_0}\frac{300}{T}\left(\frac{1}{Z_{AAA}} - \frac{3}{2}\frac{1}{Z_A} \right) \right.$$

$$+ X\left[\frac{(\tau_c)_A}{(\tau_c)_{AB}}\frac{1}{Z_{AB}} - \frac{1}{Z_A} - \frac{b'}{12{,}300}\frac{p}{p_0}\frac{300}{T}\left(\frac{2}{Z_{AAA}} - \frac{5}{2}\frac{1}{Z_A} \right) - \frac{1}{Z_{AAB}} + \frac{1}{Z_{AB}} \right]$$

$$+ X^2 \frac{b'}{12{,}300}\frac{p}{p_0}\frac{300}{T}\left[\frac{1}{Z_{AAA}} - \frac{1}{Z_{AAB}} \right.$$

$$\left. \left. + \frac{(\tau_c)_A}{(\tau_c)_{AB}}\frac{1}{Z_{ABB}} - \frac{1}{Z_A} + \frac{1}{Z_{AB}}\left(1 - \frac{(\tau_c)_A}{(\tau_c)_{AB}} \right) \right] \right\} \quad (11\text{-}4\text{b})$$

An expression analogous to (11-4) is valid for $1/\tau_2$. If τ_2 is very short compared to τ_1, one has

$$\tau_1'' = \frac{C_V - C'}{C_V}\tau_1$$

It follows from Eq. 11-4b that for the pure gas A $(X = 0)$

$$\frac{1}{\tau_1} = \left(\frac{1}{\tau_c}\right)_A \left[\frac{1}{Z_A} + \frac{b'}{12{,}300}\frac{p}{p_0}\frac{300}{T}\left(\frac{1}{Z_{AAA}} - \frac{3}{2}\frac{1}{Z_A} \right) \right] \quad (11\text{-}4\text{c})$$

Since $1/\tau_c$ is proportional to p, the second term in Eq. 11-4c is proportional to p^2. If—as we assume—τ_1 in the pure gas has been found as proportional to p, the last term is negligible, i.e. triple collisions in the pure gas have not a sufficiently larger efficiency to overcome their rarity, as compared to double collisions; in other words

$$Z_{AAA} \gg \frac{b'}{12{,}300}\frac{p}{p_0}\frac{300}{T}Z_A \quad (11\text{-}5)$$

or, if $b' \cong 40$ cm³, a change in p by 1 atm should produce in f''/p a change of $\frac{1}{8}(Z_A/Z_{AAA})$ per cent.

For example, in CO_2 with $b/12{,}300 \cong 0.0035$, f''/p will vary at room temperature with pressure as

$$1 + 0.0035 \frac{p}{p_0} \frac{Z_A}{Z_{AAA}}$$

A variation of 10 per cent in f''/p means, for a variation of p from 1 to 3 atm,

$$0.1 = 0.0035 \times 2 \times \frac{Z_A}{Z_{AAA}}$$

or

$$Z_A = 14 Z_{AAA}$$

Buschmann and Schäfer believe they have found such an effect in CO_2 [*17*].

Similarly, for C_6H_6, $b/12{,}300 \cong 0.01$ and the variation of f''/p with pressure is given by

$$1 + 0.01 \frac{p}{p_0} \frac{Z_A}{Z_{AAA}}$$

On the other hand, a careful investigation of the relaxation time of N_2O, pure and in the presence 10 to 50 per cent of He, A, N_2, made by Walker, Rossing and Legvold [*19a*] does not show any signs of triple collision. τp for pure N_2O at 0.25, 0.5, 1 and 2 atm is 0.94; 0.93; 0.93; 0.93×10^{-6} sec atm⁻¹.

It is possible that Buschmann and Schäfer's result is due to insufficient corrections for ideality; for an example of such an effect, see Boudart [*19b*].

Since we are mainly interested in cases where collisions with the impurity are more efficient than those between two A, i.e. $Z_{AB} < Z_A$, an equation like (11-5) with Z_{AB} on the right instead of Z_A would be even stronger, which means that the term with b' in the factor of X may also be neglected.

If B is a gas like H_2O or NH_3, one may therefore write, approximately, assuming $Z_{ABB} \ll Z_{AB} \ll Z_A$; $Z_{ABB} < Z_{AAA}$;

$$\frac{1}{\tau_1} = \frac{1}{(\tau_c)_A} \left\{ \frac{1}{Z_A} + X \frac{(\tau_c)_A}{(\tau_c)_{AB}} \frac{1}{Z_{AB}} \right.$$
$$\left. + X^2 \frac{b'}{12{,}300} \frac{p}{p_0} \frac{300}{T} \left[\frac{(\tau_c)_A}{(\tau_c)_{AB}} \frac{1}{Z_{ABB}} - \frac{1}{Z_{AAB}} \right] \right\} \quad (11\text{-}4d)$$

If a term in X^2 appearing in the relaxation time τ (or in τ_1') is to be interpreted as due to triple collisions, its relative size must be proportional to p, and the ratio of the coefficients is

$$\text{coefficient of } X^2 \text{:coefficient of } X = \frac{b'}{12{,}300} \frac{p}{p_0} \frac{300}{T} \left[\frac{Z_{AB}}{Z_{ABB}} - \frac{(\tau_c)_{AB}}{(\tau_c)_A} \frac{Z_{AB}}{Z_{AAB}} \right]$$

To illustrate this result, H. and L. Knötzel [20] have carefully measured the vibrational relaxation of O_2 as a function of water vapor content. Since C' is very small, one can write $\tau'' = \tau$. Their data can be written:

$$f'' = \frac{1}{2\pi\tau_1} = 40 + 0.195 \times 10^6 X + 0.132 \times 10^9 X^2$$

Since $\tau_c = 1.6 \times 10^{-10}$ sec, $b/12{,}300$ for O_2 is about 0.0028, and for H_2O is about 0.003, one can put as a first approximation $(\tau_c)_A = (\tau_c)_{AB}$; one finds, with O_2 as A, H_2O as B, and neglecting the effect of collisions of two O_2 and one H_2O as compared to those of one O_2 and two H_2O

$$Z_A = 2.5 \times 10^7, \qquad Z_{AB} = 5{,}000, \qquad Z_{ABB} = 0.02e^{\epsilon_B/kT}$$

The last number proves the necessity of introducing the exponential factor for triple collisions since no Z can be smaller than unity. For $\epsilon_B/k = 900°$, the exponential factor is 20, making $Z_{ABB} \cong 0.4$; for $\epsilon_B/k = 1200°$, the exponential factor is 55, making $Z_{ABB} = 1.1$. Both values are acceptable within the experimental accuracy.

A different interpretation is due to M. Boudart who finds the quadratic term absent if D_2O is used instead of H_2O. He believes the effect due to a resonance between the O_2 and an H_2O vibration with subsequent deactivation of the H_2O vibration by collision (private communication).

EXPERIMENTAL METHODS IN ULTRASONICS

H,12. Methods for Low Frequencies. The difficulty of measuring absorption at low frequencies is due to the smallness of the absorption coefficient, which is usually proportional to ω^2 in that region. Velocity measurements cannot be made by using the interferometer (Art. 13), since this presupposes plane waves. However the production of plane waves is only possible if the source (or a concave mirror or plastic lens) has a diameter of many wavelengths, otherwise diffraction from the edges of the source is important. For wavelengths of, for example, more than 1 cm (i.e. air frequencies less than 30 kc) this would require far too large equipment. Two methods have been used.

Reverberation method. The reverberation method for the measurement of weak absorption has been introduced by Kneser and Knudsen [22] and recently used by E. Meyer [23]. Vibrations in a closed vessel are excited at a frequency large compared to the fundamental characteristic frequency of the vessel, and, after shutting down the source, the decay of the vibrations is measured.

The acoustic energy is lost partly through absorption in the gas (an effect proportional to the volume v) partly through loss through the surface (friction at the surface, radiation) an effect proportional to the surface area A.

If I is the total intensity, the total sound energy is $(I/a)v$. One has therefore for the loss of energy

$$-\frac{v}{a}\frac{dI}{dt} = \alpha I v + I \sigma A$$

or

$$-\frac{dI}{dt} = I\left(\alpha a + \sigma a \frac{A}{v}\right) \tag{12-1}$$

If this is integrated to

$$I = I_0 e^{-t/\tau} \tag{12-2a}$$

one has

$$\frac{1}{\tau} = \alpha a + \sigma a \frac{A}{v} \tag{12-2b}$$

By measuring the decay time for two vessels with different ratio of surface to volume, A/v, one can separate the two effects and find the absorption.

To be justified in using a formula like (12-1), one must excite the gas so that the sound is distributed within the vessel as uniformly as possible. This one tries to do by exciting many different modes of vibration, having nearly the same frequency, which means that there must be an appreciable band width in the source. If only one mode were excited, the location of the nodes with respect to the outer hull of the vessel would greatly influence the surface loss, and one could not then repeat in general the same geometrical picture for a vessel of different size, i.e. the ratio of the first and the second terms would not be proportional to A/v. The accomplishment of this uniform distribution of the sound field is the first difficulty of the method.

The second difficulty lies in the necessity of making the surface losses sufficiently small so that the absorption losses form an appreciable—the larger if possible—part of the total losses and therefore need not be calculated as a small difference between two large experimental values

To give an estimate, take $\alpha = 2 \times 10^{-14}f^2$, $f = 10^4$, and $a = 3.5 \times 10^4$ cm/sec. The first term on the right side of Eq. 12-2b is 0.07, which would give, in the absence of surface losses, a reverberation time of 14 seconds.

Modified reverberation method. A modified reverberation method, also used by Knudsen, is based on the measurement of the stationary state. In the stationary state the amount of sound energy radiated into the reverberation chamber is equal to the amount of sound lost. Since this latter is proportional to the sound intensity (see Eq. 12-1), one finds

$$\alpha + \sigma \frac{A}{v} = \frac{1}{Ia} \times \text{(energy produced per second)}$$

This is, therefore, a relative method; one keeps the source constant and measures the ratio of the stationary sound energy in two different gases.

As in the preceding method, one must prevent (with fans and by attaching the sound sources to a moving support) the formation of standing wave patterns.

This method also measures loss only, not velocity.

The modified Kundt tube method for measuring both velocity (dispersion) and absorption. The Kundt tube is a tube with its diameter much smaller than its length. If the Kundt tube were excited by a piston making small oscillatory motions and filling the cross section of the tube uniformly, one would have plane waves in the tube.

Actually one uses as a source either a piston with diameter smaller than that of the tube, or a microphone clamped at the circumference so that its membrane does not have a uniform amplitude across the tube.

In such a case, the direct loss by viscosity and heat conduction within the gas is negligible compared to that due to friction and heat conduction on the walls. Since the wavelength is much larger than the tube diameter, the velocity gradient along the axis is much less steep than at the wall (it seems that this might affect the planarity of the wave). The loss at the wall is given by an apparent absorption coefficient α''

$$\alpha'' = k'' \frac{1}{r} \frac{1}{a_0} \sqrt{\frac{\mu}{2\rho}} \left[1 + (\gamma - 1) \sqrt{\frac{\lambda}{\gamma\mu}} \right] \sqrt{\omega} \qquad (12\text{-}3)$$

The velocity is also changed to

$$a = a_0 \left\{ 1 - k' \frac{1}{r} \sqrt{\frac{\mu}{2\rho}} \left[1 + (\gamma - 1) \sqrt{\frac{\lambda}{\gamma\mu}} \right] \frac{1}{\sqrt{\omega}} \right\} \qquad (12\text{-}4)$$

k' and k'' are constants which should theoretically be unity for a smooth tube, but actually must be determined by standardization. In the case of Eq. 12-4 this is best done by using the value for dry air at 19°C [21]

$$a_0 = 342.94 \text{ m/sec}$$

In the case of Eq. 12-3, k'' is found by standardizing with argon (e.g. $k'' = 1.15$).

With present electrical oscillators, it is best to keep the distances constant and to determine resonance by varying the frequency. Having determined the equivalent length of the tube with air, one then finds the resonance frequency to an accuracy of at least 1:3,000. The half width Δf of the resonance allows the calculation of the loss

$$\Delta f = \frac{1}{2\pi} a\alpha'' \qquad (12\text{-}5)$$

Since it is assumed that in this frequency range the loss through classical absorption within the gas is negligible compared to the loss at the wall, and since the contribution of short relaxation times to the absorption is comparable to or a few times larger than the classical loss, the latter will also be negligible compared to the loss at the wall; they do not therefore appear in the expression. On the other hand, a relaxation time of the order of 10^{-4} seconds will give, at these frequencies, a much larger contribution to the loss, even if C' is small. This will show up if the loss (or Δf, Eq. 12-5), is plotted against $\sqrt{\omega}$, since the loss at the wall, Eq. 12-3, gives then a straight line, while the loss due to relaxation is, at the beginning, proportional to $(\sqrt{\omega})^4$ and will therefore give a deviation from the straight line.

According to an oral communication by E. Meyer, the deviation of the constants k' and k'' from unity is due to the theoretical approximation.

H,13. The Ultrasonic Interferometer. The ultrasonic interferometer was first used by Pierce [*13*] with piezoelectric plates, then magnetostrictive rods as sources. It was then further developed by many others, mostly using piezo quartz.

Hubbard [*25*] used the instrument as a resonator, including it in an electric measuring circuit so that it could be used for both velocity and absorption measurements in the range of 200 kc to several Mc; by using low pressures, its range has been extended to about 200 Mc/atm.

The method of measuring velocity is obvious; one sets the reflector on a standing wave "crevasse," then moves the reflector to the nth crevasse farther on. The distance is $n/2$ wavelengths. There are two methods to find absorption. The half width of the crevasse measures the Q of the resonating system; the loss is partly absorption in the gas, partly reflection loss and mechanical and electrical loss apart from the gas. The measurement has to be made at at least two reflector positions to eliminate the extraneous losses. The other method consists in measuring the decrease in the depth of the crevasse, i.e. the decrease in the reaction of the gas on the crystal, with increasing distance of the reflector. Hubbard's interferometer theory (which is similar to the theory of electrical transmission lines with loss) has to be applied to find absorption; a considerable number of crevasses decreasing in depth must be measured to get the dependence, unmarred by accidental error.

A precaution that is necessary in interferometric work is the avoidance of intensities which are too high. They might produce harmonics and will produce local heating of the gas near the crystal by sound absorption and by direct heating from the quartz. Usually, a.c. voltages of less than 0.1 volt on the quartz crystal are safe. Another precaution is the choice of a good crystal which does not show secondary resonances (crevasses) near the principal one. This was considered highly important in the past; however, Alleman [*24*] has shown that such secondary maxima are often due to improper alignment (see below). Whether that was the principal, but unknown, source of secondary resonances in the past, or whether the crystals presently available commercially are so much better, is not quite certain.

One must now distinguish cases of low or high absorption. Taking the case of low absorption first, it is possible to get very high accuracy in velocity measurements.

From the purely mechanical standpoint, the present limitations are the accuracy of the screw moving the reflector. It is easily possible to get a screw accurate to 0.001 mm (e.g. from Brown and Sharpe Mfg. Co.) and if one measures over a distance of 1 cm, this would give an accuracy of 1 in 10,000. The accurate setting on the minimum of the crevasse requires first that its position be sufficiently steady, which means stability of the oscillator frequency f; this must be very high—better than 2 cycles in 2 Mc—because the crystal resonance is so sharp that a small frequency variation changes the current enough so that one cannot set on the minimum. Secondly, the amplitude of the current must be stable (guarding against fluctuations of the line voltage); otherwise one cannot detect the bottom of the crevasse with certainty. Thirdly and most importantly, the crystal surface and reflector must be parallel; otherwise one gets apparent secondary minima which broaden the crevasse and make the bottom position of the crevasse uncertain (for details, see below).

If all these conditions are fulfilled, one may expect an accuracy of 1 in 3,000 and under particularly favorable circumstances, 1 in 10,000. However, this requires temperature control to 0.05°K.

For low absorption, one best uses the width of the crevasse as a measure, since the depth does not decrease sufficiently over the short distance available. Here, the three requirements mentioned for the velocity measurements are much stricter; the screw, however, need not be good over a long distance, but must permit the measurement of small distances so that the shape of a crevasse—not its absolute position—may be followed. Since it is necessary to determine the shape of the crevasses— actually their half width—and since, under favorable conditions these are very sharp, their positions and shape must be accurately fixed during the time a measurement lasts. For example, for N_2 at 1 atm and 3 Mc, in a particular experiment, one of the first crevasses had a half width of 0.01 mm. This means that with a screw good to 0.001 mm, one can only read the width to 10 per cent, and frequency fluctuations of a few cycles make it impossible to get the half width at all.

At intermediate absorptions, the picture changes; the peaks get much broader and increase in width. The maximum is not so sharp any more, and many fewer peaks can be measured. For example, in nitrogen at 2 Mc and $\frac{1}{5}$ atm the absorption coefficient is about 3 ($\alpha\lambda \cong 0.05$) and about 6 peaks can be read. In this case the velocity measurement is accurate to about $\frac{1}{2}$ per cent, and an improvement in the quality of the screw would not help. At even higher absorptions—if they are achieved by decreasing the pressure—the reaction of the gas on the crystal becomes very small and accordingly the "crevasse" so shallow that there is difficulty in measuring. In the region of the maximum of $\alpha\lambda$, the velocity may be accurate to 2 per cent.

To sum up, the present accuracy of the interferometer seems to be as follows: At low absorption, it is possible to get very high accuracy in the velocity measurement. Further accuracy would require improvement in the screw, in the stability of the oscillator, in temperature control, and—to get significant results—the purity of the gas. The majority of the absorption measurements in this region cannot be trusted; some of the best (Zmuda [*27*]) give an accuracy of 10 per cent.

For moderately high absorption, the velocity measurements are much less accurate (perhaps to $\frac{1}{2}$ per cent), and no simple method for improvement seems in sight. For even higher absorption, the accuracy decreases even further. Most absorption measurements are not very reliable; e.g. those of Swomley [*26*] in H_2 and of Cheng [*15*] in C_6H_6 scatter by at least 50 per cent.

Methods to measure absorption directly for low pressures (high values of f/p) have been developed by Parker, Adams, and Stavseth [*28a*], and Greenspan and Thompson [*28b*]. The former, useful around 20–50 Mc/atm, determines the geometrical factor at atmospheric pressure (negligible absorption). The latter, useful at 100–200 Mc/atm, uses plane waves in an interferometer with negligible standing wave ratio.

Another method uses the "quartz wind." A beam of progressive sound waves, of intensity I, carries a linear momentum I/a. If the energy $\alpha\Delta x \cdot \tau$ is absorbed in a layer of unit cross section and thickness Δx, the momentum $\alpha\Delta x(\tau/a)$ is transferred per second. This is equivalent to a body force which, depending on conditions, produces either a flow or a pressure difference [*28c*].

H,14. The Optical Method. An optical method to measure absorption and velocity has been developed by Grobe [*28*], in which the progressive sound wave is used as a grating. The position of the first diffracted image determines the grating constant (wavelength of sound); the intensity of the first image is proportional to the sound intensity and, therefore, if taken at different distances along the sound wave allows the determination of absorption. In general, optical methods have the disadvantage that they need high sound intensity to give sufficient diffracted light; high sound intensity leads to local heating of the gas and to distortion of the wave form. Petersen [*29*] has used Grobe's method with compressed gases (10 atm, 4 Mc), which not only permits penetration of the lower range but, because of the higher gas density, gives stronger diffracted light (i.e. allows lower sound intensities). The accuracy is, in his absorption measurements, about 15 per cent. Acoustic wind must be prevented by screens.

DIRECT MEASUREMENTS OF RELAXATION TIME

H,15. The Jet Method. Kantrowitz [*31*] has developed a method for the direct measurement of relaxation times in gases. The physical principle is as follows:

Consider a gas emerging as a jet from a high pressure tank through a nozzle. The kinetic energy is acquired from the internal energy of the gas and results in a temperature drop. If the nozzle is long enough, the expansion is sufficiently slow that all degrees of freedom participate, and the static specific heat C_p governs the process. If now the jet is stopped, the deceleration lasting for a time t, the kinetic energy of the jet is changed back to thermal energy. If t is large compared to τ, again all degrees of freedom can follow, the process is again governed by the static value C_p, and the end temperature and pressure are equal to the original (tank) temperature and pressure. If, on the other side, $t \ll \tau$, only the external degrees of freedom are active during the stoppage and compression, the specific heat $C_p - C'$ is effective, and immediately after the gas is stopped the temperature (stagnation temperature) is higher and the pressure (stagnation pressure) is lower than are the corresponding initial quantities. This is then followed during a time interval of order τ by an irreversible process of adjustment between external and internal degrees of freedom, during which process the temperature drops to the initial temperature, the gas expands, and the pressure remains constant.

The time of stoppage of the gas jet t depends on the size of the obstacle (e.g. the diameter d of the Pitot tube), and has the order of magnitude d/u. To give a more detailed calculation, one can distinguish (according to Griffith [*30*]) three regions: I, that of expansion; II, that of stoppage of the jet; III, that of irreversible adjustment.

One has in I,

$$C_p(T_0 - T_\mathrm{I}) = \frac{\mathfrak{M}}{2} u^2 \tag{15-1a}$$

and

$$p_0^{\frac{1-\gamma}{\gamma}} T_0 = p_\mathrm{I}^{\frac{1-\gamma}{\gamma}} T_\mathrm{I} \tag{15-2a}$$

with

$$\gamma = 1 + \frac{R}{C_V} \tag{15-3a}$$

In region II,

$$\frac{\mathfrak{M}}{2} u^2 = (C_p)_\mathrm{eff}(T_\mathrm{II} - T_\mathrm{I}) \tag{15-1b}$$

$$p_\mathrm{I}^{\frac{1-\gamma'}{\gamma'}} T_\mathrm{I} = p_\mathrm{II}^{\frac{1-\gamma'}{\gamma'}} T_\mathrm{II} \tag{15-2b}$$

with

$$\gamma' = 1 + \frac{R}{(C_V)_{\text{eff}}} \tag{15-3b}$$

One has from Eq. 15-1a and 15-1b,

$$C_p T_0 + [(C_p)_{\text{eff}} - C_p] T_I = (C_p)_{\text{eff}} T_{II} \tag{15-4}$$

Eliminating T_I and T_{II} with the help of Eq. 15-2a and 15-2b and introducing the abbreviation

$$g = \frac{C_p}{(C_p)_{\text{eff}}} - 1$$

one gets

$$\ln \frac{p_{II}}{p_0} = \frac{g}{1+g} \ln \frac{p_I}{p_0} + \frac{\gamma}{(\gamma-1)(1+g)} \ln \left[1 + g - g \left(\frac{p_I}{p_0} \right)^{\frac{\gamma-1}{\gamma}} \right] \tag{15-5a}$$

This is always negative for $p_I < p_0$

For small values of g, one has

$$\frac{p_0 - p_{II}}{p_0} = g \left\{ \ln \frac{p_0}{p_I} - \frac{\gamma}{\gamma - 1} \left[1 - \left(\frac{p_I}{p_0} \right)^{\frac{\gamma-1}{\gamma}} \right] \right\} \tag{15-5b}$$

The difference between the tank pressure p_0 and the stagnation pressure at the Pitot tube, p_{II}, is measured and gives g.

Up to now the process has been isentropic. It is followed by adjustment between the degrees of freedom, so that the whole thermal energy is again distributed over C_p, i.e.

$$C_p T_{III} = C_p T_0, \qquad T_{III} = T_0$$

Since this occurs at constant pressure, an entropy change is involved equal to

$$\Delta S = R \ln \frac{p_0}{p_{II}} \quad (\text{see Eq. 15-5a}) \tag{15-6}$$

since the temperature dependent terms in the entropy are equal,

$$C_p \ln T_{III} = C_p \ln T_0$$

The next problem is to connect t and therefore $(C_p)_{\text{eff}}$ with the hydrodynamic flow. Griffith assumed a cylindrical Pitot tube, with an opening equal to 0.620 of the outer diameter d and with a flat ending. Graphical integration of the flow problem showed that the left side of Eq. 15-5a is only a function of the dimensionless quantity (u is the speed of the jet, see Eq. 15-5a)

$$\frac{C_p - C'}{C_p} \tau \frac{u}{d}$$

One gets then the values in the following table.

Table H,15. Pressure difference in stopped jets.

$\dfrac{C_p - C'}{C_p} \tau \dfrac{u}{d}$	0.1	0.33	1	3	10
$\dfrac{p_0 - p_{II}}{p_0}$	0.0828	0.226	0.480	0.723	0.908

In his experiments, Pitot tubes made from glass tubing were used with diameters between 0.007 in. and 0.024 in. The nozzles were one-half inch long with 0.07 or 0.04 in. diameter of the exit, and with flow speeds of about 120 m/sec.

A different direct method was recently [30a] developed by Smiley, Winkler, and Slawsky [32] and by Bleakney and Griffith. In this method a shock travels down a shock tube. Behind it, the gas is adiabatically (but not quite isentropically) compressed and is at higher temperature. The shock itself is only a few mean free paths thick. If the gas has internal degrees of freedom which are slowly adjusted, the energy increase is at the beginning transmitted to the translational and rotational degrees of freedom only, the gas behind the shock being hotter and less dense than it would otherwise be. The energy then flows slowly into the vibrational degrees of freedom; the temperature goes down and the density up. The effect is observed in a Mach-Zehnder interferometer, which reacts to density (see IX,A,3). In a gas without relaxation, the fringes are sharply displaced at the shock front. In a gas with relaxation, like CO_2, the initial displacement is less and the fringes are curved until they reach their final displacement at some distance behind the shock. The values for the relaxation time do not agree too well with other data. For more detail, see VIII,E,6.

Instead of using an interferometer, Greene, Cowan and Hornig [30b] reflect light from the advancing shock and measure the dependence of the intensity on the angle. Assuming a density distribution

$$\rho = \rho_1 + (\rho_2 - \rho_1)(1 + e^{-4x/L})^{-1}$$

the intensity for the angle of incidence β is proportional to

$$(1 + \tan^4 \beta) \left(\frac{1}{2\lambda} \cos \beta \right)^2 \left[\sinh \left(\pi^2 \frac{L}{\lambda} \cos \beta \right) \right]^{-2}$$

and the appearance of L/λ in the argument makes its determination possible.

Direct determination of τ. An entirely new method of directly measuring relaxation times of different vibrational degrees of freedom has been developed by Gorelik, Slobodskaya, and Cottrell [*30c*]. It is applicable if the vibration involved is optically active, i.e. absorbs infrared light. The gas, contained in a vessel, is illuminated with monochromatic light of the proper wavelength. The light intensity is modulated, e.g. sinusoidally. The light absorption excites the individual vibration, which then transfers its energy gradually to the translational degrees of freedom, increasing the temperature and pressure. The pressure variation is picked up by a microphone; the phase difference between the pressure signal and the light modulation permits a calculation of the relaxation time.

CHAPTER 3. RELAXATION OF TRANSLATIONAL MOTION

H,16. Classical Viscosity and Heat Conduction in Monatomic Gases. Monatomic gases should show only the classical absorption, Eq. 5-8a. Effects due to the possible formation of double molecules should exist least in helium and neon; nonetheless, the earlier absorption measurements in these two gases gave values appreciably above the classical.

With an interferometer, van Itterbeek and Thys, and van Itterbeek and Mariens [*36*] found the absorption in He and Ne to be six to four times the classical. However, this absorption was almost independent of pressure; from 1 atm to 0.25 atm it only increased by 10 per cent, and if the classical absorption was subtracted the rest decreased with decrease in pressure.

Therefore, it seems probable that there was some constant loss not connected with absorption present in their case (see also Art. 18). Finally, Greenspan [*34*], using the direct receiver method at high frequency and low pressure (high absorption), found the classical expression confirmed. Van Itterbeek and Verhaegen [*37*] also found excellent agreement.

In argon the classical value was found by Keller [*35*] using the optical method.

H,17. Very High Frequencies. In Art. 5 the effects of viscosity and heat conduction—i.e. of translational relaxation—have been calculated in first approximation.

The exact solution of Eq. 5-4 is easy in the absence of heat conduction and has been given by Lucas [*45*].

The more exact calculation is simplified, according to Greenspan [*34*], by the introduction of an effective Reynolds number Re, defined by

$$Re = a_0 \frac{\rho}{\mu} \frac{a_0}{\omega} = \frac{a_0^2}{\omega} \frac{\rho}{\mu} \qquad (17\text{-}1a)$$

Re decreases with increasing frequency. Using Eq. 5-5 and 5-10, one has

$$Re = \frac{\gamma}{1.271} \frac{1}{\omega \tau_c} \tag{17-1b}$$

Next, one needs the Prandtl number, Pr,

$$Pr = \frac{\lambda}{\mu} \frac{\mathfrak{M}}{C_V} \tag{17-1c}$$

The propagation equation (5-4) can then be written as

$$1 - \left[1 + \frac{4i}{3Re}\left(1 + \frac{3}{4}Pr\right)\right]\left(\frac{a_0}{a} - \frac{i\alpha a_0}{\omega}\right)^2$$
$$+ \frac{Pr}{Re}\left(\frac{i}{\gamma} - \frac{4}{3Re}\right)\left(\frac{a_0}{a} - \frac{i\alpha a_0}{\omega}\right)^4 = 0 \tag{17-2}$$

The solution of Eq. 17-2 is

$$\left(\frac{a_0}{a} - i\frac{\alpha a_0}{\omega}\right)^2 = \frac{3Re}{8Pr\left(1 - \frac{3}{4}i\frac{Re}{\gamma}\right)}$$
$$\times \left\{\left[Re^2 + \frac{8i}{3}Re\left(1 + \frac{3}{4}\frac{\gamma-2}{\gamma}Pr\right) - \left(\frac{4}{3} - Pr\right)\right]^{\frac{1}{2}}\right.$$
$$\left. - Re - \frac{4}{3}i\left(1 + \frac{3}{4}Pr\right)\right\} \tag{17-3}$$

For low values of ω (large Re) this coincides with the result of Art. 5. For small Re (large ω) the fundamental equations of Art. 5 are not exact enough. In the kinetic theory of gases, the expressions for shear stress and heat flow arise from the deviation of the molecular distribution function from its equilibrium value, i.e. the Maxwell distribution function. This deviation is not calculated exactly (see Sec. B), but by a power development in the powers of the mean free path (in sound propagation, the development parameter is actually the ratio of mean free path to sound wavelength). Usually, only the first power of the mean free path is kept; it follows from this that the shear stress (through the viscosity constant) and the heat flow (through the heat conductivity) are proportional to the mean free path.

Now, however, one has to keep additional terms proportional to the square of the ratio of mean free path to wavelength. This introduces three new constants, ϵ_1, ϵ_2, ϵ_3, which depend on the molecular model.

We assume again small amplitudes, neglecting quadratic terms. The stress in a plane wave is then

$$\tau_{xx} = -p + \frac{4}{3}\mu\frac{\partial u}{\partial x} + b_2\frac{1}{\rho}\frac{\partial^2 p}{\partial x^2} - \frac{2}{3}\frac{b_3}{T}\frac{\partial^2 T}{\partial x^2} \tag{17-4a}$$

the heat flow is

$$-\lambda \frac{\partial T}{\partial x} + \frac{2}{3} b_1 \frac{\partial^2 u}{\partial x^2} \tag{17-4b}$$

Here b_1, b_2, b_3 are new constants (Uhlenbeck and Wang Chang [42] write w_2 for b_2, w_3 for b_3/T, $\theta_2 T$ and θ_4 for b_1).

The calculations have been carried further only for monatomic molecules. In this case, according to Wang Chang

$$\lambda = \frac{15}{4} \frac{R}{\mathfrak{M}} \mu \delta \quad \text{or} \quad Pr = \frac{5}{2} \delta \text{ (see Eq. 17-1c)}$$

$$b_1 = \frac{\mu^2}{\rho} (\delta^2 \epsilon_1 + \delta \epsilon_2); \qquad b_2 = \epsilon_3 \frac{\mu^2}{p}; \qquad b_3 = \epsilon_2 \delta \frac{\mu^2}{\rho} \tag{17-5}$$

ϵ_1, ϵ_2, ϵ_3, δ are new constants of order of magnitude 1, which depend on the molecular model (Greenspan [34] writes N'' for $\mu\delta/\rho$).

Wang Chang calculates the constants for three molecular models: I, Maxwell molecules, points with an attractive potential $\cong -1/r^4$; II, Lennard-Jones model, with constants given, for He, by de Boer and Michels [41]; III, hard spheres.

Table H,17.   Constants for three molecular models.

Model	ϵ_1	ϵ_2	ϵ_3	δ
I	$-\frac{45}{8}$	3	2	1.000
II	$-\frac{45}{8} \times 1.008$	3×0.855	2×1.007	1.004
III	$-\frac{45}{8} \times 1.017$	3×0.800	2×1.014	1.009

The dispersion equation, given by Wang Chang [42], may now be written, in analogy with Eq. 17-2

$$1 - \left[1 + \frac{4}{3} \frac{i}{Re} \left(1 + \frac{3}{4} Pr \right) \right] \left(\frac{a_0}{a} - \frac{i\alpha a_0}{\omega} \right)^2$$

$$+ \frac{Pr}{Re} \left[\frac{i}{\gamma} - \frac{4}{3Re} \left(1 - \frac{4}{15} \epsilon_2 + \frac{5}{6} \frac{\epsilon_3}{Pr} - \frac{4}{75} Pr\epsilon_1 \right) \right] \left(\frac{a_0}{a} - \frac{i\alpha a_0}{\omega} \right)^4 = 0 \tag{17-6}$$

The solution is developed into a power series by Wang Chang as follows:

$$\frac{a}{a_0} = 1 + Re^{-2} \left[\frac{2}{3} + \frac{5}{9} \epsilon_3 + \left(\frac{2}{3} - \frac{8}{45} \epsilon_2 \right) Pr - \left(\frac{3}{50} + \frac{8}{229} \epsilon_1 \right) Pr^2 \right]$$

$$\tag{17-7a}$$

For $\alpha a_0/\omega$ one gets deviations from the classical value only for terms of order Re^{-3}. From Eq. 17-7a one finds numerically for helium

$$\frac{a - a_0}{a_0} = 44.4\mu^2\left(\frac{f}{p}\right)^2, \qquad \frac{f}{p}\text{ in Mc/atm}$$

Classically (Navier-Stokes), the numerical factor would be 27.2 instead of 44.4.

Greenspan writes the exact solution for the de Boer-Michels model:

$$\left(\frac{a_0}{a} - i\frac{\alpha a_0}{\omega}\right)^2 = Re\{[Re^2 + 1.662iRe - 8.573]^{\frac{1}{2}} - Re - 3.843i\}$$

$$\times \,(11.671 - 3.012iRe)^{-1} \quad (17\text{-}7\text{b})$$

Experiments have been made by Greenspan for helium, and by Boyer [38] for argon. The sound velocity in helium is measured up to about $Re = 0.15$ ($f \cong 1.5/\tau_0$), the absorption up to $Re \cong 0.7$ ($f \cong 1/3\tau_0$). Boyer has measured the velocity in argon up to $Re \cong 3.8$ ($f = 20/\tau_0$). Greenspan found a dispersion which below $Re = 2$ is even larger than Eq. 17-6 indicates; the absorption, on the other hand, agrees very well with the classical theory in the whole measured range from $Re = 90$ to $Re = 0.7$, while below $Re = 10$ the theory of Burnett, Uhlenbeck, and Wang Chang gives distinctly lower values. However, the gas contained a constant amount of air at 0.0075 mm Hg, and the correction for its presence was made in a straightforward manner, neglecting the effects described in Art. 18.

Boyer's velocity measurements for argon at 0°C and 0.9701 Mc, lead to the following values of the numerical factor, instead of 44.4:

p, cm Hg	3.3	1.5	0.65	0.22
Factor	355	255	100	51.4

which means that—perhaps for experimental reasons—the increase of velocity with frequency comes out too high, particularly if the effect is small.

To sum up, the disagreement between experiment and theory is still such that one cannot form a judgment about the theory.

The expression (17-4) was first proposed by Brillouin [39], Jones [44], and Rocard [47]; Burnett [40] then calculated the coefficients for hard molecules. Further extensions of [41] were made by Herzfeld [43], who first applied the result to ultrasonic waves. This was done later independently by Primakoff [46] and Tsien and Schamberg [48], the former correcting a mistake of Herzfeld's. Finally, Wang Chang and Uhlenbeck [42], further correcting the approximate calculations of their predecessors, found the coefficients for other molecular models. Truesdell [*48a*] has discussed the theory in detail.

H,18. Additional Absorption in Mixtures. There exists an additional absorption in mixtures, just because they are mixtures. The physical ideas involved are simple. If one has a density gradient in a gas, more gas molecules move from high density to low density than in the opposite direction. However, in a mixture the lighter molecules move faster than the heavier ones; therefore the flow of lighter molecules to lower densities is greater relative to their concentration than the flow of the heavier ones. This is the first reason for a periodic unmixing process occurring in the sound wave, which is countered by irreversible diffusion, resulting in a loss. Secondly, the periodic temperature differences in the sound wave also produce unmixing by the process of thermal diffusion. The theory has been treated by Rocard [*51*], Meixner [*50*], and recently by Kohler [*49*] whose result is given below.

In the formula for the classical absorption (5-6) μ is the viscosity of the mixture. It is not possible to use Eq. 5-7, but the experimental value for the heat conductivity must be used in Eq. 5-6 with

$$c_p = [(1 - X)C_{v_A} + XC_{v_B} + R][(1 - X)\mathfrak{M}_A + X\mathfrak{M}_B]^{-1} \quad (18\text{-}1)$$

The resultant contribution from heat conduction may be relatively much larger than calculated from Eq. 5-7, e.g. for 50 per cent helium-argon, although this formula is well applicable for air.

The additional absorption, due to the effects described at the beginning of this article, depends upon pressure and frequency in the same manner as classical absorption, and may therefore be described formally by an additional volume viscosity μ'', which has to be added to μ in Eq. 5-6. It contains the following quantities needing explanation; the γ of the mixture, the coefficient of diffusion D, and the coefficient of thermal diffusion D_T. The γ of the mixture is

$$\gamma = 1 + R[(1 - X)C_{v_A} + XC_{v_B}]^{-1} \quad (18\text{-}2)$$

D and D_T are defined in the general equation of flow in diffusion at uniform pressure, which is proportional to

$$-D \text{ grad } X - D_T \text{ grad } (\ln T)$$

D is inversely proportional to the pressure so that $D\rho$ is pressure independent. D_T/D is pressure independent, $[1/(1 - X)X]D_T/D$ finite at all X.

$$\mu'' = \frac{3}{4}\gamma\rho D \left[\frac{\mathfrak{M}_B - \mathfrak{M}_A}{(1 - X)\mathfrak{M}_A + X\mathfrak{M}_B} + \frac{\gamma - 1}{\gamma} \frac{1}{(1 - X)X} \frac{D_T}{D} \right]^2 \quad (18\text{-}3)$$

According to Kohler, Eq. 18-3 gives a contribution of only 0.3 per cent to α in air. For 50 per cent helium-argon mixtures, it increases the α value by a factor 1.9. Even for 1 per cent argon in helium, the factor is still about 1.3. This great effect of impurities might partly explain the large values of α found by earlier experiments (Art. 16). In the case just discussed, the term in Eq. 18-3 containing the mass difference—which is due to the first effect discussed at the beginning of this article—is considerably more important than that containing thermal diffusion.

CHAPTER 4. RELAXATION OF ROTATIONAL ENERGY IN MOLECULES WITHOUT ELECTRONIC EXCITATION

H,19. Hydrogen and Deuterium. The time between collisions for hydrogen at 23°C is 0.7×10^{-10} sec; at 90°K it is 0.3×10^{-10} sec. The characteristic temperatures are for hydrogen 5958°K, for deuterium 4211°K, and the corresponding vibrational specific heats at 300°K are $0.9 \times 10^{-6}R$ and $1.6 \times 10^{-4}R$. Therefore, vibrational relaxation effects are negligible at room temperature or below.

The effect of a delayed exchange between rotational and translational degrees of freedom was first detected in these gases. Van Itterbeek and his coworkers [36] measured the absorption in the interferometer at 0.6 Mc between 1 and 0.4 atm, and found it 20 times the classical value for H_2, and 10 times the classical for D_2 at room temperature. Although some objection may be raised against these measurements (the pressure dependence does not agree with the theoretical one and the absorption for H_2 is too high), the calculated relaxation times, 2×10^{-8} sec for H_2 and half this value for D_2, at 15°C and 1 atm agree with other values to be discussed. Recently, van Itterbeek and Verhaegen [37] have found exactly $\alpha \sim 1/p$ for 0.5 Mc and have also confirmed the correct absorption for H_2. From their last measurements, one has, for α/α_{class}, n-H_2, 79.5°K, 8.8; n-H_2, 90°K, 12; p-H_2, 79.5°K, 13; p-H_2, 90°K, 18. Since C' for p-H_2 at 90°K is 0.54R, one gets $Z = 360$. This applies in practice to the transition $2 \rightarrow 0$. Zartmann [54] found a ratio of $\alpha/\alpha_{class} = 28$, or $Z = 400$. Huber and Kantrowitz [33] have measured the relaxation time for H_2 directly with the jet method, the results being as follows: At 284–287°K, $\tau = 1.04$–1.15×10^{-8} sec, $Z = 155$–172; at 207°K, $\tau = 1.18 \times 10^{-8}$ sec, $Z = 205$. E. S. and J. L. Stewart [53] were able to measure the dispersion for H_2, using 3.9 and 6.2 Mc crystals and pressures between 1 and 0.5 atm. They found the mid-point of the dispersion curve at 10 Mc/atm, which leads to an average relaxation time of 1.8×10^{-8} sec, or $Z = 260$. E. S. Stewart's absorption data [26] do not disagree with this, but scatter quite a bit. The dispersion curve does not quite fit the shape given by Eq. 7-9.

To investigate this point further, Rhodes [52] measured the velocity in normal and para hydrogen up to 45 Mc/atm. In hydrogen, the rotational energy values over kT are given by $(82.6/T)j(j + 1)$. In para hydrogen, j can take only even values. In the latter case, only states 0 and 2 contribute to the specific heat at 197°K, states 0, 2, and 4 at 298.4°C. Rhodes then calculates the dispersion at 197°K for a two-state system, to which the theory is exactly applicable; at 298.4°K, one has a three-state system. Assuming that the relaxation time for the $2 \to 0$ transition is shorter than for the $4 \to 2$ transition, the latter would be more important for low frequencies, the former for high ones. Accordingly, Rhodes fitted the experimental dispersion curve to one with two relaxation times and got the following data:

Table H,19. Dispersion in H_2 according to Rhodes.

	Normal H_2			Para H_2		
	$? \to 0$			$2 \to 0$		$4 \to 2$
T, °K	288	298	197	298	197	298
Midpoint, Mc/atm	10	7.2	6.6	7.2	6.6	20
$\tau \times 10^8$ sec	1.8	1.72	1.74	1.72	1.74	0.79
Z	260	250	350	250	350	110

The dispersion curve is flatter than what would correspond to a mid-point of 10 Mc/atm; e.g., at 2 Mc/atm the velocity has increased by 0.72 per cent instead of by 0.4 per cent as would follow from Eq. 7-9.

H,20. Rotational Absorption and Dispersion in Other Gases.

Nitrogen. Keller [35] found, with the optical method, the absorption in N_2 to be 1.3 of the classical, which from Eq. 7-7 gives a $Z_{rot} \cong 4.5$. Zmuda [27], using the ultrasonic interferometer, found at intermediate frequencies for this ratio 1.4 ± 0.1, with a $Z_{rot} = 6$. If the vibrational dispersion formula were applicable, this would lead to a frequency at the mid-point of the dispersion curve of about 130 Mc/atm. Zmuda's dispersion measurements did not quite reach the mid-point but seemed to confirm the frequency of 130 Mc/atm; Boyer's data [38] agree fairly well with Zmuda's. In the high frequency range α/α_{class} starts to decrease as it should according to Eq. 6-13a. Parker, Adams, and Stavseth [28a] find $\alpha'/\alpha_{class} = 1.24$ or $Z = 3.6$. Hornig and his coworkers [30b] get $Z = 20$.

Oxygen. Absorption and dispersion at high frequencies have been measured by Thaler [*57*]. He finds the low frequency ratio $\alpha/\alpha_{\text{class}} \cong 3.4$, which leads to $Z_{\text{rot}} = 36$ and a dispersion curve midfrequency of about 50 Mc/atm. The actual measurements show the midvalue at about 53 Mc/atm, but the velocity does not show any flattening out even when the value corresponding to $\gamma = \frac{5}{3}$ (monatomic) is reached. One must therefore assume that the rise due to translational relaxation (see Art. 16) already contributes here and in N_2. For both gases, the shape of the curve seems to differ from the simple expression (7-9). Boyer's data do not agree too well with those of Thaler. According to Parker, Adams, and Stavseth [*28a*], $\alpha'/\alpha_{\text{class}} = 1.19$ or $Z = 3$.

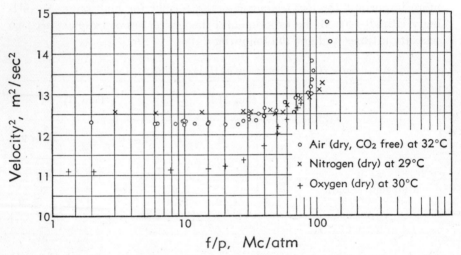

Fig. H,20.   Rotational dispersion in N_2, O_2, and air according
to Zmuda, Thaler, and Ener and Hubbard.

Thaler found indications that 10 per cent water vapor does not affect the efficiency of the exchange between rotational and translational energy.

Air. Air was investigated in the ultrasonic interferometer by Ener, Gabrysh, and Hubbard [*56*]. The mid-point of the dispersion curve lies at 116 Mc/atm, between that of N_2 and O_2. That gives a τ of 2.29×10^{-9} sec, with a time between collisions of 1.45×10^{-10} sec, or a Z of 16. For the low frequency absorption one finds $\alpha/\alpha_{\text{class}} = 2.4$, or $Z = 21$. The former gives $Z = 51$ for N_2-O_2 collisions, the latter gives $Z = 100$. Measurements by Braithwaite [*55*], showing a much earlier rise, could not be confirmed.

Experimental data for the above three gases are plotted in Fig. H,20.

Ammonia. This gas was also measured by Keller [*35*], who found $\alpha/\alpha_{\text{class}} = 1.67$. By applying Eq. 7-7, modified for nonlinear molecules, one gets $Z_{\text{rot}} = 9$.

CHAPTER 5. RELAXATION OF VIBRATIONAL ENERGY IN MOLECULES WITHOUT ELECTRONIC EXCITATION

EXPERIMENTAL RESULTS

H,21. Nitrogen, Oxygen, Air.

Nitrogen. The characteristic temperature of vibration, θ, is 3336°, giving a vibrational specific heat of $0.0019R$ at 300°K, of $0.58R$ at 1273°K. Accordingly, the vibrational effects should not affect velocity or absorption at room temperature, but should be appreciable at 1273°K.

According to Huber and Kantrowitz [33] one finds, with the jet method, the results in Table H,21 together with the time between collisions for 1 atm, calculated from the viscosity measurements of Vasilesco [63]. Their N_2 contained about 0.05 per cent H_2O.

Table H,21. Vibrational relaxation times in N_2.

T,° K	300	550	601	703	1273
$\tau_c \times 10^{10}$ sec	1.4	2.1	2.5	2.6	3.6
$\tau_v \times 10^3$ sec	>0.05*	5.9	2.9, 2.7, 3.4	2.6	0.15*
$Z_v \times 10^{-6}$	>0.4*	28	12, 11, 14	10	0.42*

Shilling and Partington [62] have measured the sound velocity at 3000 cycles and found the effective C_V at room temperature to be $2.47R$ and at 1273°K to be $2.675R$. Henry [59] has first interpreted these data as due to relaxation, giving the numbers marked by asterisks in Table H,21. Measurements by Bender [58], which put the relaxation time near 100°C at about 1.5×10^{-7} sec, disagree widely with the above values.

Oxygen. This gas was one of the first to be investigated; careful measurements by Kneser [60] and Knudsen and his coworkers [61] studied the effect of impurities, particularly H_2O. θ is equal to 2228°, the vibrational specific heat at 300°K is $0.031R$, at 1273°K it is $0.78R$. The time between collisions is 1.6×10^{-10} sec at 300°K for one atmosphere, 4.5 at 1273°K.

The most recent measurements have been made by H. and L. Knötzel [20] with a resonance method and a frequency between 500 and 4500 cycles. Their results are shown in Fig. H,21a and H,21b. They find for the frequency of maximum $\alpha a/\omega$ (which is equal to the inflection point frequency, because of the low value of the specific heat of vibration),

$$f' = 40 + 195(1000X) + 132(1000X)^2 \quad \text{in cycles/sec}$$

X being the mole fraction of added H_2O vapor. As mentioned in Art. 11, the quadratic term is due to triple collisions. For NH_3 instead of H_2O

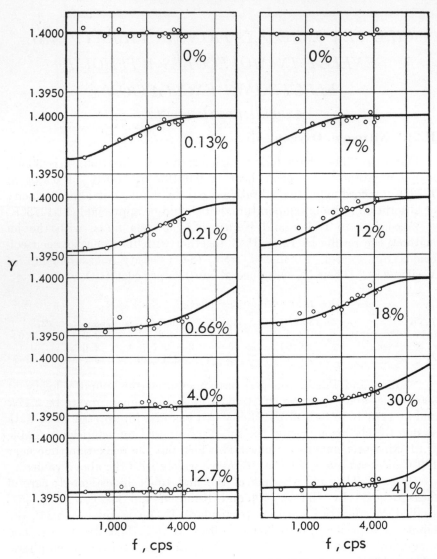

Fig. H,21a. Vibrational dispersion in O_2 mixed with NH_3 (left) and H_2O (right). Curves illustrate dependency of γ on frequency f (atmospheric pressure and 19°C). NH_3 addition in molecular per cent; H_2O addition in per cent relative humidity. Data from H. and L. Knötzel [20, Fig. 5].

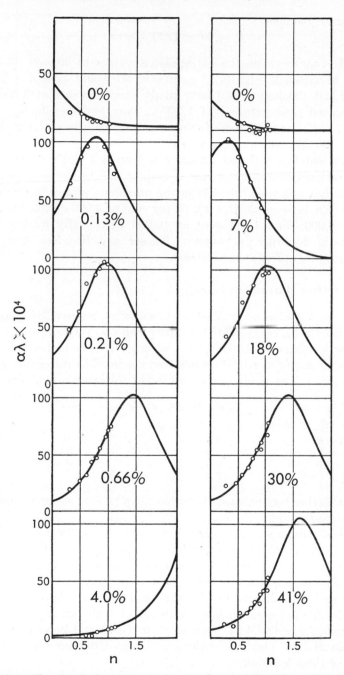

Fig. H,21b. Vibrational absorption in O_2 mixed with NH_3 (left) and H_2O (right). Curves illustrate molecular absorption per wavelength as a function of n (ordinal number of the harmonic of the tube). NH_3 addition in molecular per cent; H_2O addition in per cent relative humidity. Data from H. and L. Knötzel [20, Fig. 4].

as impurity, one has

$$f' = 60 + 1220(1000X)$$

The difference between the extrapolated values of 40 and 60 for dry oxygen is within the limits of accuracy; 50 would give $Z = 2 \times 10^7$. Shilling and Partington [62] have made measurements at 3,000 cycles and elevated temperatures. At 1273°K, they find an effective specific heat of $2.68R$; from this there follows a relaxation time of 1.4×10^{-5} sec, or a Z of 30,000, which seems low.

Air. Knudsen [61] and Kneser and Knudsen [60] have shown that the vibrational absorption in air is mainly due to the oxygen present. Knudsen has measured the shift of the maximum absorption with water content (e.g. it lies at 20°C, for 0.25 per cent at 3,000 cycles, for 0.33 per cent at 6,000, for 0.4 per cent at 10,000 cycles). By mixing varying amounts of N_2 with dry oxygen, Kneser and Knudsen find for the collision O_2-N_2 a Z of about 100,000.

H,22. Other Diatomic Gases.

Chlorine. Chlorine, washed with water to remove HCl, and then dried with $CaCl_2$, concentrated sulfuric acid, and P_2O_5, has been investigated by Eucken and Becker [64], who measured the dispersion curve in the interferometer at relatively low frequencies. The dispersion is due to the vibration. The results are found in the following table.[6] The absorp-

Table H,22a. Chlorine.

T, °K	241	291	347	415
C_{vib}/R	0.43	0.55	0.66	0.74
$\tau_c \times 10^{10}$ sec	0.88	1.05	1.24	1.46
$\tau \times 10^6$ sec	6.3	4.2	2.6	1.6
$Z \times 10^{-4}$	7.2	4	2	1.1

tion not having been measured, nothing can be said about the relaxation of rotational energy.

Carbon monoxide. For carbon monoxide, $\theta = 3080°$, $C_{vib}/R = 4.5 \times 10^{-3}$ at 300°C. The effect of vibration on velocity at that temperature is therefore negligible. Bender [58] has found, for 1 Mc, an appreciable effect at 400°K, and one can, therefore, estimate τ there to be 1.5×10^{-7} sec. Bender measured dispersion with the fixed path interferometer. Sherrat and Griffiths [65] used an interferometer at high temperature and frequencies of 7.9 and 27.4 kc. Some of their results and Bender's are shown in Table H,22b. There is obviously strong disagreement between the results of these authors.

---

[6] Eucken and Becker use $\theta = 841°$, while Mayer and Mayer give 797°, which was used here to calculate C_V; however, Eucken's results have not otherwise been recalculated.

Table H,22b. Carbon monoxide.

T, °K	400	1273	1673	2073
$\tau_c \times 10^{10}$	1.74	4.7	5.6	6.2
$\tau \times 10^8$	15	1000	1150	1000
Z	860	21,000	21,000	16,000

Van Itterbeek and Mariens [*36*] find at room temperature $\alpha/\alpha_{class} = 3.9$, which, according to Eq. 7-9, means

$$0.069 Z_{rot} + 3 \times 10^{-4} Z_{vib} = 2.9$$

or

$$Z_{rot} + 4.2 \times 10^{-3} Z_{vib} = 42$$

If $Z_{rot} \cong 4$, $Z_{vib} = 9,000$. This lies closer to the values of Sherrat and Griffiths. To get agreement with Bender, one must choose $Z_{rot} \cong 38$.

NO. Bender has also measured NO, with results similar to those for CO. Van Itterbeek and Thys [*36*] find $\alpha/\alpha_{class} = 1.17$.

H,23. Triatomic Linear Molecules. These molecules have been the subject of many careful investigations. In CO_2, Kneser [*67*] measured for the first time the whole absorption and dispersion curve.

These molecules have two "valence bond" vibrations, one symmetrical, one antisymmetrical, and one degenerate bending vibration. The data and the corresponding specific heats are shown in Table H,23a.

Table H,23a. Data for linear triatomic molecules.

	CO_2			COS		
	Asymmetric	Symmetric	Bending	Asymmetric	Symmetric	Bending
θ	3380	1920	959	2988	1370	758
C'/R at 300°K	1.57×10^{-3}	0.069	0.454	4.7×10^{-3}	0.221	0.602
	CS_2			N_2O		
	Asymmetric	Symmetric	Bending	Asymmetric	Symmetric	Bending
θ	2190	1043	570	3200	1850	847
C'/R at 300°K	0.04	0.397	0.747	2.6×10^{-3}	0.082	0.536

Careful absorption measurements, including the effect of impurities, have been made by Leonard [*69*], Fricke [*66*], and Fricke and Knudsen [*68*]. Leonard also made dispersion measurements on CO_2, which agree well with his results on absorption, although the relaxation time found is only $\frac{2}{3}$ of that found by others (trace of H_2O?). The data of Fricke and Knudsen are shown in Table H,23b. The change of f' (i.e. of τ^{-1}) is

Table H,23b. Effect of impurities.

Pure gases	CO_2	COS	CS_2	N_2O
f', kc	20	287	379	153
Z	86,000	9600	8700	11,800

$\Delta f'$, kc for 1 % of	H_2	H_2O	CH_3OH	C_2H_7OH	$C_6H_5CH_3$
in CO_2	155	2250	550	1100	1780
COS	336	4200	930	1830	
CS_2	296	2460	496	871	316
N_2O	342	427	304	575	300

strictly linear in the mole fraction of the impurity (see Fig. H,10). By use of the impact tube M. Gustavson [*70*] gets $\tau = 2.5 \times 10^{-6}$ sec or $Z = 22,000$, with an indication of several relaxation times.

Angona [*70a*] finds by absorption measurement a relaxation time of 6.61×10^{-6} sec for CO_2, 0.727×10^{-6} sec for CS_2, or $Z = 52,000$ for CO_2, 8,000 for CS_2.

The Iowa group [*19a*] gets $\tau = 0.93 \times 10^{-6}$ sec for N_2O or $Z = 8500$.

Eucken and Becker [*64*] determined the temperature dependence of Z for CO_2, Bushmann and Schäfer [*17*] for N_2O. The data are reported in Table H,23c.

Table H,23c. Temperature dependence of Z for CO_2 and N_2O.

T, °C	−32	18	74	142
Z for pure CO_2	100,000	51,000	36,000	23,000
Z for CO_2-HCl		120	35	

T, °C	−25.5	3	19	73
Z for N_2O	12,500	6800	5600	3800

The last named authors have attempted to decide on the mechanism of excitation of the different degrees of freedom by careful dispersion measurements. There is some indication in their results that the velocity is not a function of ω/p alone for CO_2. The authors explain the effect by triple collisions (see Art. 12).

They give two relaxation times each for CO_2 and COS, which they ascribe to the symmetric valence bond and to the bending vibration. Pielemeier, Sexton, and Telfair [71] also find two relaxation times in CO_2; their reciprocals are linear, but are different functions of the H_2O concentration; this would prove either parallel excitation or series excitation by collision. Their expressions are

$$1/\tau = 2.7 \times 10^5 + 3.8 \times 10^8 X, \qquad 1/\tau = 3.2 \times 10^5 + 9 \times 10^7 X$$

The direct measurements of Slobodskaya [30c] gave for the bending vibration $\tau = 1.6 \times 10^{-6}$ sec or $Z = 14{,}000$, for the asymmetric vibration 7×10^{-6} sec or $Z = 63{,}000$. These times do not agree closely with those extrapolated by Pielemeier, Sexton, and Telfair.

H,24. Nonlinear Triatomic and Four-Atomic Molecules.

Water. There are three vibrations, with $\theta = 5117°, 5400°$, and $2294°$. The vibrational specific heat at $300°K$ is $0.0296R$.

In spite of its importance, there are no extensive ultrasonic measurements on water vapor, although preliminary experiments by Kinnier [72] show that the relaxation time is short. Huber and Kantrowitz's jet method [33] gives relaxation times given in Table H,24.

Table H,24. Relaxation time for water vapor.

T, °K	486	586	706
$\tau \times 10^8$ sec	3.7	2.6, 3.1	2.1
Z	400	260, 310	190

SO_2. Vibrational $\theta = 1656°, 1956°$, and $752°$; vibrational specific heats at $300°K$ are $0.223R$, $0.064R$, and $0.609R$. Fricke [66] finds from ultrasonic dispersion $f' = 1.04$ Mc, $Z = 1900$. Griffith [30] finds with the jet method $\tau = 3.7 \times 10^{-7}$ sec, $Z = 1500$.

NH_3, *ammonia*. $\theta = 4790°$ and $4620°$ (degenerate) and $950°$ and $1630°$ (degenerate). At $300°K$, only the last two contribute appreciably to the vibrational specific heat, namely $0.211R$ and $2 \times 0.025R$. Bushmann and Schäfer [17] interpret their results as due to two relaxation times, 1.8 and 14.5×10^{-2} sec, at $40°C$, or $Z = 1700$ and $13{,}600$, with a decrease to 620 and 2500 at $100°C$. Griffith finds with the jet method $\tau = 1.2 \times 10^{-7}$ sec at $20°C$, or $Z = 1300$. There is some doubt now that affects the interpretation of Keller's measurements (Art. 20).

H,25. Larger Molecules.

CH_4. For methane, vibrational $\theta = 2915°, 3022°$ (triply degenerate), and bending vibrations are $1304°$ (triply degenerate) and $1520°$ (doubly degenerate). The specific heats at 300°K are $1.6 \times 10^{-4}R$, $3 \times 1.1 \times 10^{-4}R$, $3 \times 0.0756R$, and $2 \times 0.0364R$. Eucken and Aybar [75], using both absorption and dispersion measurements with good agreement, find $Z = 8400$ at 382°K, 5700 at 473°K, and 3400 at 625°K. Griffith [30] found 4.8×10^{-7} sec at 303°K with the jet method, or $Z = 4400$.

CH_3OH, *methyl alcohol.* Ener, Busala, and Hubbard [74] find, at 303°K, a dispersion curve going from $C_V = 4.25R$ to an extrapolated value of $3R$ with $\tau = 2.27 \times 10^{-8}$ sec, or $Z = 220$. According to Weltner [83], the static value of C_V is $5.27R$, or $\gamma = 1.19$.

Benzene. Benzene has 30 vibrational degrees of freedom, with 20 different frequencies, and with θ ranging from 582° to 4430°. The vibrational specific heat at 303°K is $6.45R$.

Cheng [15] has measured velocity and absorption at 303°K, the total effective C_V going from $8.17R$ (equilibria nearly established) near 2 Mc/atm to $3.02R$ (only $0.02R$ vibrational specific heat left) near 37 Mc/atm. She can represent her data with one relaxation time of 5×10^{-8} sec, that is, with a time between collisions of 0.77×10^{-10} sec, a Z of 700. A representation by two times, 6.8 and 2×10^{-8} sec, is also possible. Lambert and Rawlinson [77] have measured the dispersion at 117°C ($C_{\text{vib}} = 9.12R$) and found $\tau' = 1.33 \times 10^{-7}$ sec which is somewhat longer than Cheng's value. More data are given in Table H,25b. Matta and Richardson [78] have also measured the dispersion, but without evaluating τ.

$HClC_2HCl$, *dichlorethylene.* Busala, Sette, and Hubbard [81] have measured *cis-* and *trans-*dichlorethylene. The two differ only by the orientation of one CHCl group. The *cis-*compound, which has a dipole moment, and the *trans-*compound, which has no dipole, seem to behave nearly alike [19b].

Other gases. Results are contained in Table H,25b, which is taken from Lambert and Rawlinson and supplemented from Griffith [30].

Lambert and his coworkers [81a] have measured, at 100°C, a considerable series of related compounds, CH_3F, CH_3Cl (see Table H,25b), CH_3BR, CH_3I; CH_2F_2, CH_2Cl_2; CHF_3, $CHCl_3$; CF_4, CCl_4 and calculated the relaxation times. Some of these (CH_3Cl, CH_2Cl_2, $CHCl_3$, CCl_4) have also been investigated by Busala, Sette, and Hubbard [81b]. For all but CH_2Cl_2 the corresponding specific heats go from the spectroscopically determined value at low frequency to $3.00 \pm 0.02R$ at high frequency. CH_2Cl_2 is the only substance with two distinct relaxation times. The relaxation times and direct measurements of Hubbard, et al. do not agree with those of Lambert, et al. For example, the specific heat $C_{V\text{eff}} = 8R$ is reached for CCl_4 by Lambert at about 1.6 Mc/atm, by Hubbard at 7 Mc/atm. Of course, the temperatures are different, 30°C and 100°C respectively.

Table H,25b.   Relaxation times in organic vapors.

Gas	Reference	T, °C	τ, sec	Z
C_2H_6 ethane	[77] [30]	20 20	5.24×10^{-9} 3×10^{-9}	52 30
C_3H_8 propane	[77] [30]	20 20	$<10^{-8}$ $<7 \times 10^{-9}$	<90 <60
C_3H_6 cyclopropane	[77]	18 100	3.64×10^{-7} 2.70×10^{-7}	4000 2570
C_4H_{10} butane	[30]	20	1.8×10^{-8}	
C_6H_{14} n-hexane	[77]	100	$<10^{-8}$	<90
C_2H_4 ethylene	[80]	30	2.38×10^{-7}	2240
C_3H_6 propylene	[82] [30]	0–217 20	$<10^{-8}$ $<6 \times 10^{-9}$	<90 <50
C_4H_8 butadiene	[30]	20	$<1.3 \times 10^{-8}$	
CH_3Cl methyl chloride	[30] [81a]	22 100	2.02×10^{-7} 1.8×10^{-7}	
C_2H_2O ethylene oxide	[30] [70a]	30 23	1.23×10^{-6} 0.36×10^{-6}	
C_6H_6 benzene	[15] [77]	30 96 117 165	5×10^{-8} 1.5 1.33 1.18×10^{-7}	700 1070 950 847

Matta and Richardson [78] have measured dispersion in ethylene ethyl ether, acetaldehyde, and CS_2. Older measurements in vapor are due to Railston [79] and Jatkar [76].

MECHANISM OF EXCITATION

H,26.   Introductory Remarks.   The discussion of the mechanism of excitation is more clear-cut for gases than for liquids, since in the former case the molecules are in interaction only during a small fraction of their path (collision).

The first attempt at calculating the excitation process by quantum theory was made by Kallmann and London [84] and was followed by other papers by O. K. Rice [*85*] and Zener [*86*]. The latter treated the question both classically and quantum theoretically; it became understandable why, in general, energy exchange between translation and rotation is rather efficient, exchange between translation and vibration rather inefficient. However, these papers did not permit a successful calculation of Z for given molecules. This is also true for the paper of Landau and Teller [*4*] which will be discussed next; however this paper led to an expression for the temperature dependence of Z.

Before proceeding it should be pointed out that, since Z is the number of collisions which on the average are needed for deactivation, $1/Z$ is the probability that one collision will result in such deactivation, and for the sake of simplicity, this expression will be used. (For the exact meaning, see Art. 3.)

Both in Landau and Teller's paper and in the quantum theoretical calculation given in Art. 28–33, the problem is simplified by the following assumptions. Rotation is neglected. Landau and Teller, since they do not aim at numerical calculation of Z, do not specify the orientation. In the quantum theoretical calculation of Z, head-on collision is assumed, i.e. translation along the molecular axis. Both calculations deal with the vibrational energy change in one molecule on colliding with another, due to the mutual translational energy, so that the model is really of a monatomic molecule colliding with a diatomic one and changing its vibrational state. This last restriction will be removed in the quantum theoretical calculation of Art. 32 and 33. Landau and Teller's paper treats the problem classically; it insists on the importance of distinguishing adiabatic and nonadiabatic processes. The expression had been introduced into quantum theory by Ehrenfest. If we deal with a periodic phenomenon, like a molecular vibration, we say the external conditions, e.g. a force field, change adiabatically, if the relative change is infinitely small during one period; otherwise, the change is nonadiabatic.

The point of interest for us is the proof of Landau and Teller; that is, if the molecular collision can be treated adiabatically, it leaves the molecule, according to classical theory, in the vibrational state in which it was before the collision. A collision is strictly adiabatic if the molecule is able to make an infinite number of vibrations during the time of the collision.

It is also a well-known result of the perturbation theory of wave mechanics, that if a system, here a vibrating molecule, is subject to a perturbation which varies adiabatically, the quantum state of the system does not vary. On the other hand, if the perturbation changes rapidly, i.e. varies nonadiabatically, it produces quantum jumps in the system; in our case, changes the vibrational quantum number. For the details of such general calculations, see, for example, the books of Schiff; Eyring, Walter, and Kimball; and Sec. B of this volume.

H,27. The Theory of Landau and Teller (Classical). In this theory [4], consider a molecule consisting of two atoms B and C. Let C at first have infinite mass, so that it can be considered fixed in space. B is tied to C by a force obeying Hooke's law. Let B at first also be at rest. The molecule BC is approached along the molecular axis by a particle A, which is going to make a head-on collision. Consider now two extreme cases:

1. A and B interact as perfectly elastic hard spheres, so that the time during which they are in contact is infinitely short. In that case, B receives a sharp head-on blow by A, and linear momentum is transmitted to it, so that it is set into motion toward C, compressing the springlike force between B and C. The hitting particle, A, is thrown back. But because A and B act as hard spheres—or "their force of interaction has range zero"—A is out of contact with B before B has had time to move appreciably; B has acquired a velocity, but this has taken so little time that this velocity has not resulted in an appreciable displacement, and therefore no compression of the spring has yet taken place. Accordingly, during the collision B behaves as if it were a free particle.

Particle B now moves toward C with the impulse received from the collision, compresses the "spring," is finally stopped, and returns in a simple harmonic motion of its own characteristic frequency. If the velocity direction of particle A were inverted in the collision (which depends on whether the mass of B is larger than that of A, as will be shown below), particle A is gone when B returns to the place of the collision, and B, i.e. the vibrational motion, keeps all the energy it received in the first collision. This is the extreme nonadiabatic case. If the mass of B is not larger than that of A, one or more further collisions will follow immediately, with further energy changes.

2. The other extreme is one in which the force of interaction is very "soft," i.e. has a very long range. Then, when A and B are still far apart, A starts acting on B with a weak force. This does not give an appreciable momentum to B, but just shoves it toward or away from C (depending on whether the force between A and B is at first repulsive or attractive) until the Hooke's law inner molecular force just compensates the force between A and B. Since the external force between A and B changes only slowly with time, B changes its position only slowly and has only negligible kinetic energy. The position of B is determined quasi-statically; at every moment it is such that there is equilibrium between the inner molecular restoring force and the force exerted by the hitting particle. Of course, there finally comes a moment when particle A is completely stopped, when its kinetic energy is changed into potential energy, which is stored partly in the interaction between A and B, and partly in the compressed bond BC. Now the motion is reversed; in this part too, B is always in quasi-equilibrium and therefore never acquires appreciable

kinetic energy, while the stored up potential energy is changed back into kinetic energy of A. Finally, when A has again moved out of reach, B is at rest with no forces acting on it; no energy has been transferred to the vibration. The fact that B can "give" if acted upon by A appears as an apparent modification of the force between A and the molecule BC.

In the preceding we have talked about giving energy to the vibration, while, according to Art. 3, the relaxation time is mainly determined by the rate of deactivation. These concepts, however, differ mainly (apart from the weight factor) by the exponential factor, which in turn has its origin in the relative scarcity of colliding molecules which have enough energy to excite a vibration.

The assumption which was made first, that atom C is fixed in space, is not essential.

One has only to use, in the collision equations, the effective mass of the whole system

$$\tilde{m} = \frac{m_A(m_B + m_C)}{m_A + m_B + m_C} \tag{27-1}$$

while for the internal vibration one uses

$$m_{BC} = \frac{m_B m_C}{m_B + m_C}$$

Landau and Teller assume in accordance with the previous argument that the probability of energy exchange depends roughly on the ratio of the duration of a collision to the period of vibration of the molecule. They set the duration of collision equal to the ratio of a length l', characteristic of the interaction forces (they use a instead of l') to the relative velocity of motion w, so that the above ratio is roughly

$$\frac{\nu l'}{w}$$

Specifically, they use for the probability the function

$$\frac{1}{Z} = \frac{1}{Z'_0} e^{-\frac{2\pi \nu l'}{w}} \tag{27-2}$$

where Z'_0 is a constant. Eq. 27-2 expresses the fact that the faster the molecule, the more nonadiabatic is the collision, and the larger is the chance of energy exchange. The molecules are distributed according to the Maxwell distribution law, which states that the fraction of molecules hitting per second with speeds between w and $w + dw$ is given by

$$\frac{dN}{N_0} = 2\left(\frac{m}{2kT}\right)^2 w^3 dw e^{-\frac{m}{2}\frac{w^2}{kT}} \tag{27-3}$$

This is slightly different from the Maxwell distribution law in its usual form, because when one considers the molecules hitting an area per second, instead of the molecules contained in a certain volume, the faster molecules are relatively favored. This condition results in the introduction of another factor w, with corresponding change in the constant factor.

One has to multiply Eq. 27-2 by 27-3 and integrate w from zero to infinity to get the average probability. This, however, is too complicated. Instead, one considers that the product has a sharp maximum, since Eq. 27-2 increases with increasing w, while Eq. 27-3 decreases with increasing w for the large velocities involved. One then looks for the maximum of the exponent and develops it into a power series around the maximum. The variation of w^3 is neglected in comparison with that of the exponential functions; it is replaced by its value at the maximum, since only values of w not very different from that of the maximum contribute appreciably to the integral. The combined exponent is

$$-\left(\frac{2\pi \nu l'}{w} + \frac{\widetilde{m}}{2}\frac{w^2}{kT}\right)$$

Its maximum lies at

$$-\frac{2\pi \nu l'}{w^2} + \frac{\widetilde{m}w}{kT} = 0$$

or

$$w_m^3 = \frac{2\pi \nu l'}{\widetilde{m}}kT \tag{27-4}$$

The value of the exponent near the maximum is then

$$-\frac{3}{2}\frac{2\pi \nu l'}{w_m} - \frac{3\widetilde{m}}{2kT}(w - w_m)^2 = -\frac{3}{2}\left(\frac{\epsilon'}{kT}\right)^{\frac{1}{3}} - \frac{3\widetilde{m}}{2kT}(w - w_m)^2 \tag{27-5a}$$

with

$$\epsilon' = \widetilde{m}(2\pi \nu l')^2 \tag{27-5b}$$

ϵ' is twice the energy of the molecular vibration with maximum amplitude l'. One then finds

$$\frac{1}{Z} = \frac{1}{Z_0'}2\left(\frac{\widetilde{m}}{2kT}\right)^2\frac{2\pi \nu l'}{\widetilde{m}}kTe^{-\frac{3}{2}\left(\frac{\epsilon'}{kT}\right)^{\frac{1}{3}}}\int_{-\infty}^{+\infty}e^{-\frac{3\widetilde{m}}{2kT}(w-w_m)^2}dw \tag{27-6}$$

Using as integration variable $w - w_m$ and as limits in the integral $-\infty$ to $+\infty$, instead of $-w_m$ to $+\infty$, the integral is $(2\pi kT/3\widetilde{m})^{\frac{1}{2}}$ and one has[7]

$$Z = Z_0''e^{\frac{3}{2}\left(\frac{\epsilon'}{kT}\right)^{\frac{1}{3}}} \tag{27-7a}$$

[7] That ϵ'/kT is a measure of the approach to adiabatic condition may be seen from the fact that the root mean square thermal velocity is $\sqrt{3kT/\widetilde{m}}$, and therefore the average collision time $\cong 2l'\sqrt{\widetilde{m}/3kT}$

$$\frac{\epsilon'}{kT} = 3\pi^2\left(\nu 2l'\sqrt{\frac{\widetilde{m}}{3kT}}\right)^2$$

with

$$Z_0'' = 2Z_0' \sqrt{\frac{3kT}{2\pi\tilde{m}}} \frac{1}{2\pi\nu l'} = 2Z_0' \sqrt{\frac{3}{2\pi} \frac{kT}{\epsilon'}} \tag{27-7b}$$

$\sqrt{3kT/2\tilde{m}}$ is the root mean square thermal velocity of the molecules, $\sqrt{\gamma kT/2\tilde{m}} = \sqrt{\gamma RT/\mathfrak{M}}$ the sound velocity, so that $\sqrt{3kT/2\pi\tilde{m}}$ is equal to $\sqrt{3/2\pi\gamma_0}\, a_0$, or for a gas like air about 2.9×10^4. $2\pi\nu l'$ is the maximum velocity the oscillating atom in the molecule would have if the amplitude were l'. With $\nu \cong 3 \times 10^{13}$, $l' = 10^{-8}$ cm, $2\pi\nu l' \cong 2 \times 10^6$ cm/sec. Therefore Z_0 is in this case $\cong Z_0'/40$.

The first measurements of the dependence of Z on temperature were made by Eucken and Becker (Table H,23c) on CO_2. They represented their results by $Z = Z_0 e^{Q/RT}$. However, Eq. 27-7a fits their results as well, as Kantrowitz [31] has shown.

H,28. Fundamental Quantum Considerations. In the preceding article it is shown that classically the deactivation is only efficient if the duration of the collision is short compared to the period of vibration, i.e. if the molecules have high speed. In Art. 26 it is also mentioned that, from the standpoint of general perturbation theory, a quantum jump is likely only if the perturbing interaction field varies rapidly with time. But the same point can also be viewed from another aspect. Those processes are most likely in which the linear momentum of a particle (like particle A) changes little.

If, for the moment, the center of gravity of the molecule BC is fixed, then from the standpoint of conservation of energy, one has for deactivation by one vibrational quantum (m for m_A)

$$\frac{1}{2m}\left[(mw_A')^2 - (mw_A)^2\right] = h\nu$$

or

$$mw_A' - mw_A = \sqrt{(mw_A)^2 + 2mh\nu} - mw_A \tag{28-1a}$$

This decreases steadily, from $\sqrt{2mh\nu}$ for $mw_A = 0$ to $mh\nu/mw_A$ for large initial momenta mw_A.

The general method to treat this collision problem has been developed by Zener [86] and improved in papers of O. K. Rice [85], and Jackson and Mott [87].

One considers a stream of particles A flying parallel to one another, with speed w_A and a linear momentum $p_A = m_A w_A$. (The letter p will be reserved for linear momentum in Art. 28 and 29, since the hydrostatic pressure for which this letter is used elsewhere does not appear in these articles.) This stream is represented by a plane wave, of de Broglie wavelength

$$\lambda = \frac{h}{p} \tag{28-2}$$

The square of the amplitude of that wave represents the number of particles per unit volume, and this number multiplied by the speed $w_A = p/m_A$ represents the number of particles passing per second through unit area. One should really use $\tilde{m}$ (Eq. 27-1a) the effective mass of the whole system, instead of m_A, since w_A represents the relative motion of A with respect to BC.

The molecule BC is then located at the origin as "scatterer." To satisfy the conditions at the origin, one has to add to the plane incoming wave "scattered waves," some with the same wavelength (and therefore the same linear momentum and the same energy) as the incoming wave, some with altered wavelength. The former represent "elastic scattering," the latter "inelastic scattering," which is accompanied by a change of excitation of molecule BC. Again the amplitude squared of each scattered wave represents the local density of the corresponding outgoing scattered particle.

However, the program just described is not carried through because the three-dimensional case is still too complicated. It is changed to a one-dimensional case by imagining a plane arrangement of molecules BC, parallel to each other so that the picture is that of two solid planes which can vibrate against each other with frequency ν, the planes so densely packed that no incident particle can get through. Nonetheless, the interaction energy is assumed to be only between one particle A and one particle B.

Since in Art. 30 we use as interaction energy between A and B the expression

$$H' = -4\epsilon \left[\left(\frac{r_0}{r} \right)^6 - \left(\frac{r_0}{r} \right)^{12} \right] \qquad (28\text{-}3a)$$

it would be more consistent to have $\delta/\pi r_0^2$ molecules BC per unit surface, and to use as potential energy of A in respect to that surface

$$\overline{H}' = -4\epsilon \frac{\delta}{\pi r_0^2} \int_0^\infty \left[\frac{r_0^6}{(R^2 + X^2)^3} - \frac{r_0^{12}}{(R^2 + X^2)^6} \right] 2\pi R\, dR \quad (28\text{-}3b)$$

where X is the distance normal to the plane and R a radius in the plane. This gives

$$\overline{H}' = -2\epsilon\delta \left[\left(\frac{r_0}{X} \right)^4 - \frac{2}{5} \left(\frac{r_0}{X} \right)^{10} \right] \qquad (28\text{-}3c)$$

The incident particles are then represented by a plane wave of amplitude 1 (i.e. $p_0/\tilde{m}$ incident particles per second on unit area) falling normally on the wall, and a set of "reflected" (instead of scattered) waves. These will be plane at some distance from the surface. If the amplitude of a wave with wavelength $\lambda_j = h/p_j$ is equal to a_j, then there is the number of particles equal to $|a_j|^2 p_j/\tilde{m}$ passing per second through unit surface; i.e. the fraction $|a_j|^2(p_j/p_i)$ of the incident particles. Since all particles are reflected—elastically or inelastically—this is taken as the one-dimensional analogue of one collision, so that (Art. 3)

$$k_{ij} = |a_j|^2 \frac{p_j}{p_i} \frac{1}{\tau_0} \tag{28-4}$$

which then has to be averaged over a Maxwell distribution for the p of the incoming particles.

The next problem is therefore the calculation of a_j which is a perturbation problem.[8]

In the usual manner one sets, in the lowest approximation, the wave function of the total initial state, Ψ_0, as a product of the wave function of the incoming wave (incident particles A), $\psi_0^{(A)}$, and the molecule BC in vibrational state i, $\psi_i^{(BC)}$

$$\Psi_0 = \psi_0^{(A)} \psi_i^{(BC)} \tag{28-5a}$$

The wave function of the state after reflection, Ψ_j, is written again as the product of the wave function of the reflected wave with a possibly modified p_j, $\psi_j^{(A)}$ and the wave function $\psi_j^{(BC)}$ of molecule BC in a possibly different quantum state j, the whole multiplied with an amplitude factor a_j, both $\psi^{(A)}$ and $\psi^{(BC)}$ being assumed chosen as normalized.

$$\Psi_j = a_j \psi_j^{(A)} \psi_j^{(BC)} \tag{28-5b}$$

From the principle of conservation of energy one has, in generalization of Eq. 28-1a

$$p_j - p_0 = \sqrt{p_0^2 + 2\widetilde{m}(j - i)h\nu} - p_0 \tag{28-1b}$$

In Eq. 28-5a and 28-5b, one uses as the wave functions $\psi^{(BC)}$ the undisturbed wave functions of the simple harmonic oscillator. This contains as variable $x_B - x_C$, which is,

$$x_B - x_C = \frac{m_B + m_C}{m_C}(x_B - x_{BC}) \tag{28-6a}$$

where x_{BC} is the coordinate of the center of gravity of molecule BC. Call

$$x_A - x_{BC} = X \tag{28-6b}$$

$$x_B - x_C = x \tag{28-6c}$$

If one calls H' the interaction energy between A and B, then the usual perturbation calculation gives

$$a_j = \frac{4\pi\widetilde{m}}{hp_j} H'_{0j} \tag{28-7a}$$

---

[8] In this form, the problem is quite similar to that of calculating the accommodation coefficient of a molecule impinging on the boundary of a solid [*88*]. The main difference is that there the solid has a continuous spectrum with an upper cut-off, while here the spectrum of the wall is monochromatic.

where H'_{0j} is defined as

$$H'_{0j} = \int \Psi_0 H' \Psi_j dX dx \qquad (28\text{-}7b)$$

the integration going over the whole relative motion X and the whole vibration x.

The important point is now that H' depends on the distance between A and B, which can be written as

$$x_A - x_B = x_A - x_{BC} - (x_B - x_{BC}) = x_A - x_{BC}$$

$$- \frac{m_C}{m_B + m_C}(x_B - x_C) = X - \frac{m_C}{m_B + m_C}x \qquad (28\text{-}8)$$

according to Eq. 28-6.

If H' would not contain x, the vibrational amplitude, the collision could not produce transitions to other vibrational states, because then

$$H'_{0j} = \int \psi_0^{(A)} H' \psi_j^{(A)} dX \int \psi_i^{(BC)} \psi_j^{(BC)} dx = 0, \quad \text{if } i \neq j$$

due to the orthogonality of different wave functions of the harmonic oscillator BC.

If, as is usually the case, the collision efficiency is small, the transition is nearly adiabatic and the vibration amplitude is a small fraction of the length l which characterizes the force.

It is then possible to use a power series

$$H'\left(X - \frac{m_C}{m_B + m_C}x\right) = H'(X) - \frac{dH'(X)}{dX}\frac{m_C}{m_B + m_C}x \qquad (28\text{-}9)$$

and then to calculate H'_{0j} as the product

$$H'_{0j} = -\frac{m_C}{m_B + m_C} H'^{(tr)}_{ij} H'^{(osc)}_{ij} \qquad (28\text{-}10a)$$

Here $H'^{(tr)}_{ij}$ depends only on the relative motion of A and BC

$$H'^{(tr)}_{ij} = l \int \psi_0^{(A)} \frac{dH'}{dx} \psi_j^{(A)} dX \qquad (28\text{-}10b)$$

l is a conveniently chosen length, and has been introduced to give $l(\partial H'/\partial x)$ the dimensions of an energy; $H'^{(osc)}_{ij}$ depends only on the oscillation

$$H'^{(osc)}_{ij} = \frac{1}{l} \int \psi_i^{(BC)} x \psi_j^{(BC)} dx \qquad (28\text{-}10c)$$

However, for a harmonic oscillator, this is different from zero only if $j = i \pm 1$; i.e. only quantum jumps by one are permissible, just as in radiation. This had been assumed already by Landau and Teller [4]. One has then (see the book by Schiff or Sec. B)

$$H'^{(\text{osc})}_{ij} = +\frac{1}{2\pi l}\sqrt{\frac{h}{2m_{\text{BC}}\nu}}\left(i + \frac{1}{2} \pm \frac{1}{2}\right) \qquad (28\text{-}10\text{d})$$

The upper sign, $i + \frac{1}{2} + \frac{1}{2} = i + 1$, has to be chosen if $j = i + 1$; the lower sign, $i + \frac{1}{2} - \frac{1}{2} = i$, if $j = i - 1$. In other words, $i + \frac{1}{2} \pm \frac{1}{2}$ is always the bigger of the two numbers, i or j.

We have, therefore,

$$|a|^2_j \frac{p_j}{p_i} = \frac{1}{4p_i p_j}\left(\frac{m_{\text{C}}}{m_{\text{B}} + m_{\text{C}}}\right)^2 \frac{h}{2\pi^2 m_{\text{BC}}\nu l^2}\left(i + \frac{1}{2} \pm \frac{1}{2}\right)\left(\frac{4\pi\tilde{m}}{h}H'^{(\text{tr})}_{ij}\right)^2 \quad (28\text{-}11)$$

The factor

$$\frac{h(i + \frac{1}{2} \pm \frac{1}{2})}{2\pi^2 m_{\text{BC}}\nu l^2} = \frac{h\nu(i + \frac{1}{2} \pm \frac{1}{2})}{2\pi^2 m_{\text{BC}}\nu^2 l^2}$$

is the ratio of the energy of the oscillator of quantum number $i + \frac{1}{2} \pm \frac{1}{2}$ to the energy which the oscillator would have if it had the classical amplitude l; e.g. if l is chosen 10^{-8} cm, $\nu = 3 \times 10^{13}$ sec^{-1}, $\tilde{m} = 27 \times 10^{-24}$ g, the above quantity is about $0.004(i + \frac{1}{2} \pm \frac{1}{2})$. The validity of the method requires that Eq. 28-10d $\ll 1$, which, according to these data, is fulfilled. It is clear from Eq. 28-11 that $H'^{(\text{tr})}/l$ is the only quantity which may vary widely for different molecules and which may depend strongly on the temperature.

If one considers Eq. 28-10b, one may first remark that the wave functions $\psi^{(\text{A})}$ are, at some distance from B, plane waves; but the product of two functions representing plane waves of different wavelength gives zero when integrated over an appreciable distance. Therefore the only contribution to $H'^{(\text{tr})}$ comes from regions where dH'/dX is not constant and/or where, due to the presence of B, the incident and reflected waves do not have constant wavelength.

To make the calculation successful, however, it is necessary to start out with the proper wave functions $\psi^{(\text{A})}$. If one started out with plane waves of constant wavelength, as they exist at large distances from BC, the mere presence of the scatterer would necessitate a perturbation calculation, even if no change of excitation occurred in BC by collision. This means that even the elastic collisions—in which we are not interested—would first have to be calculated, including the first term $H'(X)$ in Eq. 28-9, to find H'_{ii}.

The progress made by Jackson and Mott lies in the fact that they selected as unperturbed wave functions $\psi^{(\text{A})}$ such functions as were already solutions of the elastic scattering problem. Thus, only the inelastic scattering constitutes the perturbation, and only the second term on the right side of Eq. 28-9 the perturbation energy (method of distorted waves).

Accordingly, the $\psi^{(A)}$ are solutions of the Schrödinger equation (see Sec. B)

$$\frac{d^2}{dX^2}\,\psi^{(A)} + \frac{8\pi^2\tilde{m}}{h^2}\,[E - H'(X)]\psi^{(A)} = 0 \qquad (28\text{-}12)$$

H,29. Inelastic Scattering for an Exponential Interaction Potential. Jackson and Mott [*87*] solved Eq. 28-12 for an interaction potential

$$H' = H_0' e^{-X/l} \qquad (29\text{-}1)$$

This was selected for mathematical reasons. They solve the Schrödinger equation (28-12) for this potential and find for $H'^{(\text{tr})}$:[9]

$$\frac{4\pi\tilde{m}}{hp_j}\,H_{ij}'^{(\text{tr})} = \frac{h}{p_j l}\,\frac{1}{8\pi^3}\,(g_j g_i \sinh g_i \sinh g_j)^{\frac{1}{2}}(g_j^2 - g_i^2)(\cosh g_j - \cosh g_i)^{-1}$$
$$(29\text{-}2)$$

Here, g is an abbreviation:

$$g = \frac{4\pi^2 p l}{h} \qquad (29\text{-}3)$$

sinh, cosh are the hyperbolic functions, pl/h is the ratio of the length l to the de Broglie wavelength h/p as it exists at a great distance from BC. (Jackson and Mott write πg for our g, $1/a$ for our l; they do not introduce the factor $1/l$ in $H'^{(\text{osc})}$ and l in $H'^{(\text{tr})}$, the separation into factors being arbitrary.)

One has the energy equation

$$g_j^2 - g_i^2 = \pm\,\frac{32\pi^4 l^2 \tilde{m}}{h^2}\,h\nu \qquad (29\text{-}4)$$

One can then rewrite

$$\frac{4\pi\tilde{m}}{h\,\sqrt{p_i p_j}}\,H_{ij}'^{(\text{tr})} = 16\pi^3\,\frac{\tilde{m}\nu l^2}{h}\,(\sinh g_i \sinh g_j)^{\frac{1}{2}}[\cosh g_j - \cosh g_i]^{-1} \quad (29\text{-}5)$$

or, inserting Eq. 29-4 and 29-5 in Eq. 28-11

$$|a_j|^2 \frac{p_j}{p_i} = \left(\frac{16\pi^3 \tilde{m}\nu^2 l^2}{h\nu}\right)^2 \left(\frac{m_{\text{C}}}{m_{\text{C}} + m_{\text{B}}}\,H_{ij}'^{(\text{osc})}\right)^2 \frac{(e^{g_i} - e^{-g_i})(e^{g_j} - e^{-g_j})}{(e^{g_j} + e^{-g_j} - e^{g_i} - e^{-g_i})^2} \quad (29\text{-}6a)$$

If we now assume that only the very fast collisions are important, we assume $1 \ll g_i, g_j, g_j - g_i$ and may neglect all exponentials with negative

[9] It is remarkable that $H'^{(\text{tr})}$ no longer contains H_0', the strength of the interaction potential. This comes about so that the region of X in which there is constructive interference between the two distorted de Broglie waves of different wavelength is inversely proportional to H_0' which therefore cancels out. Physically, this is due to the nature of the exponential function, since a change in H_0' corresponds only to a shift in origin of X or "collision radius"; in other words, for a given l there exists only one potential energy curve. By defining $X_0 = l \ln H_0'$, one has $H_0' e^{-X/l} = e^{-(X-X_0)/l}$.

exponents. The fraction written above may then be reduced to

$$e^{-|g_j - g_i|}$$

or

$$|a_j|^2 \frac{p_j}{p_i} = \left(\frac{16\pi^3 \tilde{m}\nu^2 l^2}{h\nu}\right)^2 \left(\frac{m_C}{m_C + m_B} H_{ij}'^{(osc)}\right)^2 e^{-|g_j - g_i|} \qquad (29\text{-}6b)$$

The exponent may now be rewritten with the help of Eq. 29-4

$$-|g_j - g_i| = -\frac{|g_j^2 - g_i^2|}{g_j + g_i} = -\frac{8\pi^2 l\nu}{w_i + w_j} = -2 \times 2\pi \frac{2\pi l\nu}{w_i + w_j} \qquad (29\text{-}7a)$$

On comparing this with Landau and Teller's expression (27-2) one sees that their $l' = 2\pi l$, and their w is replaced by $(w_i + w_j)/2$. We may write

$$\frac{w_i + w_j}{2} = \frac{w_i}{2} + \frac{1}{2}\sqrt{w_i^2 \pm \frac{2h\nu}{\tilde{m}}} = \frac{w_i}{2} + \frac{w_i}{2}\left(1 \pm \frac{h\nu}{\tilde{m}w_i^2}\right)$$

$$= w_i\left(1 \pm \frac{h\nu}{2\tilde{m}w_i^2}\right) \qquad (29\text{-}8)$$

In this development it is assumed again that the significant kinetic energies $(\tilde{m}/2)w_i^2$ are large compared to $h\nu$, the change in energy. In Eq. 29-8, the positive upper sign corresponds to $j = i + 1$, activation, the negative lower sign to $j = i - 1$, deactivation. Accordingly, the exponent (29-7a) may be written

$$-4\pi^2 \frac{l\nu}{w_i}\left(1 \mp \frac{h\nu}{2mw_i^2}\right) \qquad (29\text{-}7b)$$

Eq. 29-6b, with Eq. 29-7b as exponent, is then treated as was expression (27-2). It is multiplied with the Maxwell distribution in the proper form (27-3), w being w_i, the velocity before the inelastic collision. Proceeding exactly as in Art. 27 and introducing the energy

$$\epsilon' = 16\pi^4 \tilde{m}\nu^2 l^2 \qquad (29\text{-}9a)$$

one finds, just as in (27-7a), (27-7b),

$$\left(e^{-|g_j - g_i|}\right)_{av} = \frac{1}{2}\sqrt{\frac{2\pi\epsilon'}{3kT}}\, e^{-\frac{3}{2}\left(\frac{\epsilon'}{kT}\right)^{\frac{1}{3}} \mp \frac{h\nu}{2kT}} \qquad (29\text{-}9b)$$

where the upper signs apply to activation, the lower signs to deactivation. Since (see Eq. 28-10d) $H_{i,i+1}'^{(osc)} = H_{i+1,i}'^{(osc)}$, one gets properly, from Eq. 29-9b and 28-11, that for the ratio of activation and deactivation

$$k_{i,i+1} : k_{i+1,i} = e^{-\frac{h\nu}{kT}}$$

as it must be according to Eq. 3-4.

The factor occurring in Eq. 29-6a may be rewritten using Eq. 29-9a

$$\left[\frac{16\pi^3 \tilde{m} \nu^2 l^2}{h\nu}\right]^2 = \left(\frac{\epsilon'}{\pi h\nu}\right)^2$$

so that

$$\left[\frac{1}{p_i p_j}\left(\frac{4\pi \tilde{m}}{h} H'^{(tr)}_{i+1,i}\right)^2\right]_{av} = \frac{1}{2\pi^2}\left(\frac{\epsilon'}{h\nu}\right)^2\left(\frac{2\pi\epsilon'}{3kT}\right)^{\frac{1}{2}} e^{-\frac{3}{2}\left(\frac{\epsilon'}{kT}\right)^{\frac{1}{3}}+\frac{h\nu}{2kT}} \quad (29\text{-}10a)$$

Furthermore, Landau and Teller have shown (3-23) that, for the relaxation of the total vibrational energy, the transition $1 \rightarrow 0$ ought to be chosen. Then from Eq. 28-10d and 29-9a

$$(H'^{(osc)}_{1,0})^2 = 2\pi^2 \frac{h\nu}{\epsilon'} \frac{\tilde{m}}{\tilde{m}_{BC}} = 2\pi^2 \frac{m_A(m_B + m_C)^2}{m_B m_C(m_A + m_B + m_C)} \frac{h\nu}{\epsilon'} \quad (29\text{-}10b)$$

We find then, summing up

$$Z = Z_0 \cdot \left(\frac{h\nu}{\epsilon'}\right)\left(\frac{3kT}{2\pi\epsilon'}\right)^{\frac{1}{2}} \frac{m_B(m_A + m_B + m_C)}{m_A m_C} e^{\frac{3}{2}\left(\frac{\epsilon'}{kT}\right)^{\frac{1}{3}}-\frac{h\nu}{2kT}} \quad (29\text{-}11)$$

Here Z_0 is a geometrical factor, taking care of the fact that not all collisions are head-on. It is probably between 1 and 10.

H,30. Introduction of a Better Interaction Potential. One may ask whether the interaction potential (29-1) is applicable to the molecular problem, since it represents a purely repulsive potential while the actual interaction can be represented as the sum of an attractive potential which predominates at large distances and a repulsive potential which predominates and rises steeply at small distances. However, it follows from Eq. 28-10b, that the regions where the force of interaction, $-dH'/dx$, is strongest are the ones which contribute most to the transitions. Since the potential curve is steepest at the closest approach of the particles concerned, in which region the repulsive force predominates, the application of Eq. 29-1 may be justified.

Lennard-Jones [89] has introduced as interaction potential an expression of the form

$$H'' = -4\epsilon\left[\left(\frac{r_0}{r}\right)^6 - \left(\frac{r_0}{r}\right)^{12}\right] \quad (30\text{-}1)$$

The sixth power in the attractive first term is theoretically deducible (Sec. B); the twelfth power for the repulsive energy is chosen for mathematical convenience, but fits the facts pretty well. Hirschfelder and his coworkers (Sec. B) have recently determined the constants r_0 and ϵ for many gases and pairs of gases by fitting viscosities, temperature dependence, and diffusion constants.

Schwartz [90] has made the transition from the potential energy (30-1) to the exponential form (29-1), fitting the exponential curve to the former at the point where collisions are most effective and at the minimum of H'', so that $H'' + \epsilon$ is an exponential expression.

One has from Eq. 30-1

$$\left(\frac{r_0}{r}\right)^6 = \frac{1}{2}\left(1 \pm \sqrt{1 + \frac{H''}{\epsilon}}\right) \qquad (30\text{-}2)$$

Furthermore

$$-r\frac{dH''}{dr} = 12 \times 4\epsilon\left[\left(\frac{r_0}{r}\right)^{12} - \frac{1}{2}\left(\frac{r_0}{r}\right)^6\right]$$

$$= 12(H'' + \epsilon)\left(1 \pm \sqrt{\frac{\epsilon}{H'' + \epsilon}}\right) \qquad (30\text{-}3)$$

Here the plus sign refers to distances smaller than the equilibrium distance $2^{\frac{1}{6}}r_0$, the minus sign to larger distances.

As mentioned earlier, molecules with high kinetic energy are effective in collision. Except at very low temperatures or for gases with an exceptionally high ϵ, the kinetic energy of the most effective molecules is large compared to ϵ.

The differential equation of a purely exponential curve would be

$$-l\frac{dH'}{dr} = H' \qquad (30\text{-}4a)$$

Therefore, to find the best l for Eq. 30-1, one plots from Eq. 30-3, for the repulsive part of the curve

$$-\frac{1}{H'' + \epsilon'}\frac{dH''}{dr} = \frac{12}{r}\left(1 + \sqrt{\frac{\epsilon}{H'' + \epsilon}}\right) \qquad (30\text{-}4b)$$

This shows a broad maximum in the right-hand region giving

$$l \cong \frac{r_0}{17.5} \qquad (30\text{-}5a)$$

For more accurate results, one has to make successive numerical calculations using Eq. 30-4b with $H'' = \tilde{m}w^2/2$, and (see Eq. 27-4)

$$w^3 = \frac{4\pi^2 \nu l}{\tilde{m}}kT \qquad (30\text{-}5b)$$

A closer scrutiny of the application of Eq. 27-3 also shows that Eq. 29-11 should be multiplied by $e^{-\epsilon/kT}$, to take care of the velocity gains of the molecules while moving through the attractive regions of the potential (30-1). Accordingly, one has finally, replacing Eq. 29-11,

$$Z = Z_0\left(\frac{h\nu}{\epsilon'}\right)\left(\frac{3kT}{2\pi\epsilon'}\right)^{\frac{1}{2}} 2\,\frac{m_B m_C(m_A + m_B + m_C)}{m_A(m_B^2 + m_C^2)}e^{\frac{3}{2}\left(\frac{\epsilon'}{kT}\right)^{\frac{1}{3}} - \frac{\theta}{2T} - \frac{\epsilon}{kT}} \qquad (30\text{-}6)$$

Here, θ is the characteristic temperature of the vibration,

$$\theta = \frac{h\nu}{k}$$

In the mass factor of Eq. 28-11 and 29-11, m_B/m_C has been replaced by

$$\frac{1}{2}\left(\frac{m_B}{m_C} + \frac{m_C}{m_B}\right) = \frac{1}{2}\frac{m_B^2 + m_C^2}{m_B m_C}$$

since there is equal chance that particle A will hit the B or the C end of molecule BC.

H,31. Numerical Calculations. It is convenient to use $\epsilon'/k = \theta'$ which has as units degrees K, instead of ϵ'. The vibration frequency ν, which enters into ϵ', may be conveniently expressed either in wave numbers in cm^{-1} (which shall be called $\bar{\nu}$ here) or in characteristic temperatures θ

$$\theta = \frac{h}{k}\nu = \frac{hc}{k}\bar{\nu} = 1.440\bar{\nu} \tag{31-1}$$

Then

$$\theta' = \frac{\epsilon'}{k} = 1.087\mathfrak{M}\bar{\nu}^2 l^2 \quad °K \tag{31-2}$$

Here l is measured in angstrom units, $\bar{\nu}$ the wave number in cm^{-1}, and $\mathfrak{M}$ the effective molecular weight

$$\mathfrak{M} = \frac{\mathfrak{M}_A \mathfrak{M}_{BC}}{\mathfrak{M}_A + \mathfrak{M}_{BC}}$$

One may also write, using Eq. 31-1,

$$\theta' = 0.8153\mathfrak{M}\theta^2 l^2 \tag{31-3}$$

where θ is the characteristic temperature of the vibrations. Finally, if one sets (see Eq. 30-5a)

$$l = \frac{1}{17.5}r_0 = \frac{4}{70}r_0 \tag{31-4}$$

and measures r_0 in angstrom units. One may rewrite Eq. 30-6 in this form:

$$Z = Z_0 \frac{2\mathfrak{M}_B \mathfrak{M}_C (\mathfrak{M}_A + \mathfrak{M}_B + \mathfrak{M}_C)}{\mathfrak{M}_A (\mathfrak{M}_B^2 + \mathfrak{M}_C^2)} Z_{vib} Z_{tr} \tag{31-5a}$$

with

$$Z_{vib} = \frac{1}{2\pi^2}\frac{\theta'}{\theta} \tag{31-5b}$$

$$Z_{tr} = 2\pi^2\left(\frac{\theta}{\theta'}\right)^2 \sqrt{\frac{3T}{2\pi\theta'}} \, e^{\frac{3}{2}\left(\frac{\theta'}{T}\right)^{\frac{1}{3}} - \frac{\theta}{2T} - \frac{\epsilon}{kT}} \tag{31-5c}$$

The effect of an uncertainty in l on Eq. 31-5a is given by

$$\frac{\Delta Z}{Z} = \frac{\Delta l}{l}\left[\left(\frac{\theta'}{T}\right)^{\frac{1}{3}} - 3\right] \tag{31-6}$$

From the examples given below, one sees that an error of 1 per cent in l means an error of less than 10 per cent in Z for θ' below 5×10^5, and an error of 27 per cent in Z for θ' equal to 6×10^6.

To give numerical examples, Tables H,31a to H,31c show results for $r_0 = 5 \times 10^{-8}$ cm, $l = 0.2857 \times 10^{-8}$ cm.

Table H,31a. θ' in degrees K (Eq. 31-3).

$\mathfrak{M}$ \ θ	150	300	600	1000	1500	2000
1	1500	6000	2.40×10^4	6.66×10^4	1.50×10^5	2.66×10^5
20	3.00×10^4	1.20×10^5	4.79×10^5	1.33×10^6	3.00×10^6	5.32×10^6
40	6.00×10^4	2.40×10^5	9.59×10^5	2.66×10^6	6.00×10^6	
80	4.20×10^5	4.79×10^5	1.92×10^6	5.32×10^6		

Table H,31b. Z_{vib} (Eq. 31-5b).

$\mathfrak{M}$ \ θ	150	300	600	1000	1500	2000
1	0.5	1	2	3.4	5	6.7
40	10	20	40	67	100	133
20	20	40	80	133	200	
80	40	80	166	266		

Table H,31c. Z_{tr} multiplied by $e^{\epsilon/kT}$ (Eq. 31-5c).

$\mathfrak{M}$ \ θ	150	300	600	1000	1500	2000
1	2.48	1.08	0.904	0.202	0.170	0.448
20	0.112	0.66	33.4	716	6.9×10^4	3.06×10^7
40	0.134	2.24	548	7.88×10^4	5.8×10^7	
80	0.150	13.38	2250	4.62×10^7		

Since the perturbation method used is valid only if the probability of an inelastic collision is small, i.e. if Z is large, it is obvious that those calculations in the above tables which give a total Z less than 10 cannot be trusted quantitatively.

If one uses the one-dimensional Maxwell distribution

Table H,31d. Comparison of calculated and experimental Z.

Gas partners	l, A	$\frac{\epsilon}{k}$, °K	$\widetilde{\mathfrak{M}}$	$\theta°$	θ'	T,°K	Z_{calc}	Z_{exptl}
N_2-N_2	0.211	91.5	14	3380	4.786×10^6	600	1.5×10^9	$\cong 2 \times 10^7$
N_2-H_2	0.183	55.2	1.87	3380	618,000	600	5,000	
O_2-O_2	0.189	113.2	16	2260	2.424×10^6	288	1.0×10^8	2.5×10^7
O_2-H_2	0.173	61.4	1.88	2260	236,000	288	1100	20,000
Cl_2-Cl_2	0.189	357	35	810	638,000	288	13,000	34,000
Cl_2-He	0.180	46.4	3.78	810	34,100	288	75	900
Cl_2-N_2	0.195	181	20	810	410,000	288	9500	43,000
Br_2-Br_2	0.171	400	80	470	404,000	288	1600	

$$\frac{dN}{N_0} = \frac{\widetilde{m}}{kT} e^{-\frac{\widetilde{m}w^2}{2kT}} w\,dw \tag{31-7}$$

instead of Eq. 27-3, which is more consistent with the one-dimensional model, one finds, instead of the factor

$$\sqrt{\frac{3kT}{2\pi\epsilon'}} = \sqrt{\frac{3T}{2\pi\theta'}}$$

in Eq. 27-7b, 29-11, 30-6, 31-5c, 32-6, the factor

$$\frac{1}{2}\sqrt{\frac{3}{2\pi}}\left(\frac{T}{\theta'}\right)^{\frac{1}{3}}$$

The equivalent applies to the reciprocals, appearing in Eq. 29-9b, 29-10a, and 32-5. It turns out [91] that, for the three-dimensional case, one finds the same result, apart from a factor of the order of unity. In this calculation, the quasipotential of the centrifugal force acts mainly in slowing down the molecules before collision. One has then instead of Eq. 31-5c

$$Z_{tr} = \pi^2 \sqrt{\frac{3}{2\pi}}\left(\frac{\theta}{\theta'}\right)^2 \left(\frac{T}{\theta'}\right)^{\frac{1}{3}} e^{\frac{3}{2}\left(\frac{\theta'}{T}\right)^{\frac{1}{3}} - \frac{\theta}{2T} - \frac{\epsilon}{kT}} \tag{31-8}$$

The direct comparison of Eq. 31-8 with experimental data is shown in Table H,31d, with $Z_0 = 3$.

The problem for the one-dimensional case was first solved by Slawsky, Schwartz, and Herzfeld [90], that for the three-dimensional case by Schwartz and Herzfeld [91]. Takayanagi deduced the same results independently at the same time [91a].

H,32. More Than One Vibration Is Involved. A polyatomic molecule has more than one vibration; these can be expressed by the so-called characteristic vibrations, one of which may be

$$y_s = y_s^0 \cos 2\pi\nu_s t$$

with effective mass m_s associated with it. This y_s is called a normal coordinate. One can then always write

$$x = \sum_s b_s y_s \qquad (32\text{-}1)$$

where the b_s are dimensionless numerical coefficients (of the character of direction cosines).

The series (28-9) for the potential may now be carried further

$$H\left(X - \frac{m_C}{m_B + m_C}x\right) = H'(X) - \frac{dH'(X)}{dX}\frac{m_C}{m_B + m_C}\sum b_s y_s$$

$$+ \frac{1}{2}\left(\frac{m_C}{m_B + m_C}\right)^2 \frac{d^2H'(X)}{dX^2}\left(\sum_j \sum_s b_j b_s y_s y_j\right) \cdots \qquad (32\text{-}2)$$

To the terms linear in y_s there correspond transitions of one quantum in the normal coordinates s.

For such a transition, Eq. 30-6 is valid if divided by $(b_s)^2$ and if m_s, ν_s is used for m_B, ν. However, the quadratic terms correspond to two simultaneous one-quantum transitions; one in characteristic vibration j, the other in the characteristic vibration s. There may be two cases for deactivation:

1. Both j and s lose one quantum, the kinetic energy is increased by $h(\nu_j + \nu_s)$.
2. Assuming $\nu_s > \nu_j$, s loses one quantum, j gains one, and the kinetic energy is increased by $h(\nu_s - \nu_j)$.

In both cases we get for the transition probabilities two vibrational factors (28-11)

$$\left(\frac{m_C}{m_B + m_C}b_s H_{1,0}'^{s(\text{osc})}\right)^2 \left(\frac{m_C}{m_B + m_C}b_j H_{1,0}'^{j(\text{osc})}\right)^2$$

$$= 2\pi^2 \frac{\mathfrak{M}_A \mathfrak{M}_C}{\mathfrak{M}_B(\mathfrak{M}_A + \mathfrak{M}_B + \mathfrak{M}_C)}b_s^2\frac{\theta_s}{\theta_s'} \cdot 2\pi^2 \frac{\mathfrak{M}_A \mathfrak{M}_C}{\mathfrak{M}_B(\mathfrak{M}_A + \mathfrak{M}_B + \mathfrak{M}_C)}b_j^2\frac{\theta_j}{\theta_j'}$$

$$= \left(2\pi^2 \frac{\mathfrak{M}_A \mathfrak{M}_C}{\mathfrak{M}_B(\mathfrak{M}_A + \mathfrak{M}_B + \mathfrak{M}_C)}b_s b_j\right)^2 \frac{\theta_s}{\theta_s'}\frac{\theta_j}{\theta_j'} \qquad (32\text{-}3)$$

Here θ_s', θ_s refer to vibration s; θ_j', θ_j to vibration j according to Eq. 31-1 and 31-3.

In the following formula θ'_{sj} is used. $(\theta'_{sj})^{\frac{1}{2}}$ is proportional to

$$\frac{\nu_s \pm \nu_j}{(\nu_s \pm \nu_j)^{\frac{1}{2}}} = (\nu_s \pm \nu_j)^{\frac{1}{2}}$$

Therefore

$$\theta'_{sj} = (\sqrt{\theta'_s} \pm \sqrt{\theta'_j})^2 = \theta'_s + \theta'_j \pm 2\sqrt{\theta'_s \theta'_j} \qquad (32\text{-}4)$$

The translational factor (31-5c) is

$$\left[\frac{1}{p_0 p_1}\left(\frac{4\pi\tilde{m}}{h} H'^{(\mathrm{tr})}_{1,0}\right)^2\right]_{\mathrm{av}} = \frac{1}{2\pi^2}\left(\frac{\theta'_{sj}}{\theta_s \pm \theta_j}\right)^2\left(\frac{2\pi}{3}\frac{\theta'_{sj}}{T'}\right)^{\frac{1}{2}} e^{-\frac{3}{2}\left(\frac{\theta'_{sj}}{T}\right)^{\frac{1}{3}} + \frac{\theta_s \pm \theta_j}{2T}} \qquad (32\text{-}5)$$

One ends up therefore with the following expression:

$$Z_{sj} = 2Z_0\left[\pi\,\frac{\mathfrak{M}_A(\mathfrak{M}_B^2 + \mathfrak{M}_C^2)}{\mathfrak{M}_B\mathfrak{M}_C(\mathfrak{M}_A + \mathfrak{M}_B + \mathfrak{M}_C)}\,b_s b_j\right]^{-2}\frac{\theta'_s\,\theta'_j}{\theta_s\,\theta_j}\left(\frac{\theta_s \pm \theta_j}{\theta'_{sj}}\right)^2 \cdot$$

$$\left(\frac{3T}{2\pi\theta'_{sj}}\right)^{\frac{1}{2}} e^{\frac{3}{2}\left(\frac{\theta'_{sj}}{T}\right)^{\frac{1}{3}} - \frac{\theta_s \pm \theta_j}{2T} - \frac{\epsilon}{kT}} \qquad (32\text{-}6)$$

These equations may be generalized to include more than two quantum jumps.

It is obvious from Tables H,31 that it is profitable to have a two-quantum process if Z_{tr} is very large. One increases Z by having a second vibrational factor, but since Z_{tr} is so strongly dependent on $h\nu$ for large $h\nu$, this increase by the additional vibrational factor is strongly over-compensated by the decrease in Z_{tr}, because only the difference of the two values of $h\nu$ has to be changed into translational energy (see Eq. 32-4).

This is the second reason why impurities may be very efficient in transferring vibrational energy into translational energy.

H,33. Energy Exchange at Exact Resonance. It may happen that two colliding particles, both with vibrational degrees of freedom, have a vibration of the same frequency ν. This, of course, would be the case if two molecules of the same kind collide. It is then possible that one vibration loses one quantum and that the other vibration gains one quantum, with no change occurring in the translational energy. Such a process is of no importance in sound propagation, but is of importance in the energy supply of chemical reactions.

In this case one has for the interaction energy

$$H'\left[X - \frac{m_C}{m_C + m_B}(x_B - x_A)\right] = H'(X) - \frac{m_C}{m_C + m_B}\frac{dH'}{dX}(x_B - x_A)$$

$$+ \frac{1}{2}\left(\frac{m_C}{m_C + m_B}\right)^2\frac{d^2H'}{dx^2}(x_B - x_A)^2 \cdots \qquad (33\text{-}1)$$

The term of this development which is important to us is

$$\left(\frac{m_C}{m_C + m_B}\right)^2 \frac{d^2 H'}{dX^2}\, x_B x_A \tag{33-2}$$

For the vibrational energy, one has the factor (see Eq. 28-11)

$$4\pi^4 \left(\frac{m_C}{m_C + m_B}\right)^4 \left(\frac{h\nu}{\epsilon'}\right)^2 \tag{33-3}$$

with ϵ' given by Eq. 29-9a.

The translational contribution, however, must be recalculated for $g_i = g_j$ directly from Eq. 29-2, since we had assumed in our previous calculations $|g_j - g_i| \gg 1$.

One finds

$$\lim_{g_i = g_j} \frac{g_j^2 - g_i^2}{\cosh g_j - \cosh g_i} = 4ge^{-g}$$

and

$$\frac{4\pi\tilde{m}}{hp} H_0'^{(tr)} = 4\frac{\pi pl}{h} \tag{33-4}$$

The average value of the square of Eq. 33-4 is given by the fact that, in collisions,

$$\overline{p^2} = 2\tilde{m} \cdot 2kT$$

Therefore

$$\left[\left(\frac{4\pi\tilde{m}}{p} H_0'^{(tr)}\right)^2\right] = 64\pi^2 \frac{\tilde{m}l^2 kT}{h^2} = \frac{4}{\pi^2} \frac{\epsilon' kT}{(h\nu)^2} \tag{33-5}$$

Combining Eq. 33-3 and 33-5, one gets (using again the argument that either B or C might be hit)

$$Z = Z_0 \frac{1}{4\pi^2} \left[\frac{(m_C + m_B)^2}{m_C^2 + m_B^2}\right]^2 \frac{\epsilon'}{kT} e^{-\epsilon/kT}$$

$$= Z_0 \frac{1}{4\pi^2} \left[\frac{\mathfrak{M}_{BC}^2}{\mathfrak{M}_B^2 + \mathfrak{M}_C^2}\right]^2 \frac{\theta'}{T} e^{-\epsilon/kT} \tag{33-6}$$

An example is CO_2 (see Table H,23a). (Tridimensional calculation.)

Table H,33. Calculated Z for CO_2 at 288°K.

θ_1	$0 \to 0$	$1 \to 0$	$1 \to 0$	$1 \to 0$
θ_2	$1 \to 0$	$0 \to 0$	$0 \to 1$	$0 \to 2$
Z	22,000	6×10^{10}	6×10^8	700
				exptl. 50,000

H,34. Summary of Comparison of Theory and Experiment. From the preceding articles it appears that in general the theory can account for both the numerical values of Z in pure gases, and for the effect of impurities. In most gases the calculated Z is somewhat (by a factor of up to 10) lower than the experimental value, but this can be explained by the simplification which is necessary for the calculation. The quantity which is decisive for the order of magnitude involved is the amount of energy transferred [95] to translation divided by the average time the molecules interact.

The high efficiency of impurities is possible if they have either a small mass or a vibrational frequency small, but not negligible, compared to the substrate, so that a double quantum jump is possible.

There are two cases which do not conform to such a system: the high efficiency of CO as the impurity in Cl_2 [93] and the exceptional effectiveness of H_2O.

The explanation for the former might fall under the general suggestion of Franck and Eucken [92] that collisions are very effective between partners if such partners have a chemical affinity for each other. This might mean the appearance of additional short range forces [93a].

In the case of water, the first characteristic that comes to mind is its dipole moment (the molecular weight of 18 is low, but not exceptionally so). However, according to the theory, dipole forces, being long range forces, should have no direct effect on the transfer probability.

Actually, Busala, Sette, and Hubbard [81] have compared *cis*- and *trans*-dichlroethylene, the former with a dipole moment, the latter without. The result was that the *cis*- form has nearly the same absorption (see Art. 25).

One might think that the effectiveness of water vapor might be due to a transfer of vibrational to rotational energy, since water with its small moment of inertia has relatively large rotational quanta. This can be tested, according to a remark in a discussion with J. C. Slater, by comparing the effectiveness of H_2O and D_2O. These have the same dipole moment, but their moments of inertia are in the ratio of about 1:2. Van Itterbeek and Mariens [94] found by absorption measurements that H_2O in CO_2 is only about 1.5 times as effective as D_2O, and this was confirmed by Sette and Hubbard [96]. This result can be explained by the slightly higher total mass of D_2O (lower thermal velocity) and precludes any strong influence of the moment of inertia; i.e. transfer from vibrational to rotational energy does not contribute appreciably to vibrational deactivation. The phenomenon has been explained by Widom and Bauer [96a] as being due to the large attractive forces between CO_2 and water, which speed up the molecules just before they collide with the repulsion which is responsible for the transition. Although the theory presented in Art. 28–31 is not really applicable when the attractive forces are strong, the factor $e^{\epsilon/kT}$ represents such an effect. If $N_A\epsilon$ is chosen 4 kcal/mole, the exponential represents at room temperature a factor 790. For more detailed discussion of the effect of attractive forces see [96b].

VIBRATIONAL RELAXATION IN CHEMICAL REACTIONS

H,35. Energy Transfer and the Kinetics of Chemical Gas Reactions. Unimolecular decompositions in which the molecule needs a minimum energy before it can react are the only ones which go slow enough to be measured. This energy, which is many (15 to 20) times RT, must therefore be furnished first to the molecule which is to react. Supply through radiant energy is much too slow, so collisions with other molecules are the only source of the energy necessary for decomposition. The energy supply process is a second-order reaction because the number of collisions occurring per second in a unit volume is proportional to the square of the number of molecules. The actual decomposition of molecules, once they have sufficient energy, is a first-order reaction, i.e. it is proportional to the first power of the number of sufficiently excited molecules. Therefore the processes of energy supply and of actual decomposition present two reactions in series. In such a case, the rate of the over-all reaction—the measured rate—is determined by the slower of the two processes, which forms a bottleneck.[10] If the actual decomposition is the slower process, most of the molecules acquiring by collisions sufficient energy for decomposition lose it again by ensuing collisions before they decompose. In this case the number of molecules with sufficient energy is practically equal to the equilibrium number—a temperature dependent, pressure independent, fraction of the total number of molecules—and a given fraction of these decompose per second. The over-all reaction is therefore unimolecular (first order). If, on the other hand, the supply of energy is the much slower process, then practically all molecules decompose in a very short time after they have acquired sufficient energy, and the collisions are so far apart that practically all molecules of sufficient energy have decomposed when the next collision after the activating collision is due. Therefore practically no molecules lose their activation energy by a deactivating collision. In this case, the over-all rate is equal to the rate of activating collisions, i.e. it is bimolecular, or for a given temperature proportional to the square of the pressure.

Since the activation-deactivation process is proportional to the square of the pressure (the actual decomposition to the first power), it follows that at sufficiently low pressures the activation process must be the slower one and therefore the over-all process must be bimolecular; at high pressures the activation process must be the faster one and therefore the over-all rate must be monomolecular.

If one then follows the rate and finds it monomolecular at higher pressures, the monomolecular rate constant k_2 means that during dt the

---

[10] In the case of two reactions in parallel, the over-all rate is determined by the *faster* of the two. For the details of the theory presented above see a book by Laidler (Bibliography); for the experimental data see a book by Schumacher (Bibliography).

fraction $k_2 dt$ of molecules decomposes. If at lower pressures the rate constant decreases, it means that the rate of activation is now comparable to the decomposition rate. In particular, when the apparent mono-molecular rate constant has fallen to $k_2/2$, it means that during dt the fraction of molecules which acquire sufficient energy by collision is $k_2 dt$. Half of these decompose, and half are deactivated by collision.

Thus knowing experimentally the rate at which molecules acquire sufficient energy, one can calculate Z, the efficiency of energy transfer.

There is still another point to be considered [94]. From the standpoint of classical physics, the question may be formulated as follows: One is interested in the probability of any particular vibration or bond having an energy larger than a prescribed energy E_0 (per mole), E_0 being larger than RT. The different degrees of freedom of vibration would have an average energy RT. The whole energy of the molecule migrates from time to time, either into a particular bond by interference, or into a particular vibration by the nonlinear coupling terms. The larger the numbers of degrees of freedom, the smaller the energy the last collision has to add to bring the total energy above E_0. A more precise statement comes from the theory of probability, according to which the probability of getting a certain high energy is greater, the greater the number of ways of making it up. Mathematically, the statement is as follows: Consider a molecule with s degrees of vibrational freedom. The fraction of molecules in which the total vibrational energy is larger than E_0 is

$$\frac{1}{(s-1)!}\left(\frac{E_0}{RT}\right)^{s-1} e^{-\frac{E_0}{RT}} \tag{35-1}$$

If one assumes that it takes Z collisions to take away sufficient energy to make the molecule chemically inactive, then among N molecules the number of deactivation processes per second is, in equilibrium,

$$\frac{1}{Z\tau_c}\frac{N}{(s-1)!}\left(\frac{E_0}{RT}\right)^{s-1} e^{-\frac{E_0}{RT}} \tag{35-2}$$

This is also the rate of production of activated molecules. If the rate of the decomposition is put equal to $Ae^{-E_0/RT}$ where A is the so-called frequency factor of the unimolecular reaction, then we have, at the pressure at which the high pressure rate constant has fallen to half its former value

$$\frac{1}{2Z}\left(\frac{1}{\tau_c}\right)_{\frac{1}{2}}\frac{1}{(s-1)!}\left(\frac{E_0}{RT}\right)^{s-1} e^{-\frac{E_0}{RT}} = Ae^{-\frac{E_0}{RT}} \tag{35-3}$$

There are more elaborate theories by Kassel [98] and by O. K. Rice [103] which assume a dependence of A on the energy of the reacting molecule; however, they do not change the order of magnitude of Eq. 35-3.

Experimentally it has been found that the rate constants of some monomolecular reactions decrease at low pressure, which fact is in agreement with the theory. In such cases, the admixture of a foreign gas very often restores the monomolecular rate constant to the value it had at higher pressures, or at least diminishes the drop. H_2 and He seem to be particularly effective. All this can be understood from the theory. Unfortunately, the interpretation is less certain than might be wished, because in the case of many apparently monomolecular reactions it is doubtful whether they really occur in a single step or whether they are chain reactions (or even occur at the wall).

The following table shows relative values for $1/Z$:

Table H,35a. Efficiency of collision partners compared to the pure gas.

Decomposition of	Temp., °C	Impurity						
		He	A	D_2	N_2	O_2	H_2O	CO_2
F_2O [100]	250	0.40	0.52		1.01	1.13		
F_2O_2 [105]	−37	0.07	0.40		0.21	1.2		0.45
N_2O [107]	653	0.66	0.20		0.24	0.23	1.5	1.32
Azomethane CH_2-N_2-CH_2 [103]	310	0.07		0.37	0.21		0.46	0.25

For F_2O the reaction is bimolecular in the whole pressure range, which means that the process of supplying energy is rate determining. Since the molecule is triangular, it has three vibrational degrees of freedom. All three of them, with $Z \cong 1$, are needed so as to make the rate of production of activated molecules equal to the measured reaction rate.

F_2O_2 has six vibrational degrees of freedom. To represent the change of reaction rate constant (at −37°C it falls to half its high-pressure value at around 50 mm Hg), one needs all six degrees of freedom, again with $Z \cong 1$.

For N_2O, which is linear, Volmer calculates Z for several assumptions concerning the number s of cooperating degrees of freedom:

for $s = 4$, $Z = 1700$;   for $s = 3$, $Z = 190$;   for $s = 2$, $Z = 12$

Only the order of magnitude of these numbers is to be considered. Patat and Bartholomé [101] argue in favor of the last of these values, with the following arguments:

From sound absorption measurements, Eucken and Jaaks [97] had found the following Z numbers for H_2O as impurity in N_2O (see Art. 23):

at 20°C, $Z = 60$; at 195°C, $Z = 10$. Therefore, they conclude that at 635°C, Z must be surely smaller, say $Z \cong 5$. But according to Table H,35a, Z for $N_2O = 1.5\ Z\ (H_2O)$, and therefore $2 < Z(N_2O) < 8$, at 635°C.

Measurements have also been made on NO_2Cl [104]. Since the decomposition of azomethane and of many organic compounds involves radical chains, we will not try to draw conclusions as to collision efficiencies here. A considerable amount of work has been done in this field, particularly by Hinshelwood and his collaborators. It should be noted in this connection that in some of those organic reactions where the rate constant decreases at low initial pressure, the rate constant does not change while the reaction progresses, although the amount of initial substance is diminishing. This is usually explained by saying that the products of the reaction have efficiency equal to that of the original substance; such a statement, however, is very astonishing in view of the different behavior of different substances as shown in ultrasonic absorption as well as in the above inorganic reactions. There seems to be nothing in the structure of the decomposition products, as compared with the initial substance, to give them equal efficiency in energy transfer; this increases the suspicion that the effect of pressure here lies in the complication of the chemical mechanism. No measurements of the effect of helium admixtures on the rate of unimolecular organic reactions has been made in the low pressure region, where the rate constant of the pure substance falls off. Patat and Bartholomé [101] point out that in pure gases transfer of excitation energy from a particular vibration in one molecule to the corresponding vibration in a colliding molecule—with no change in translation energy—does not show up in ultrasonics at all. On the other hand, in chemical reactions, where it is a matter of total energy in a molecule, these "resonance transfers" do matter. If the transfer of energy between translation and vibration is inefficient, but the resonance transfer between vibrations is very efficient, then the large Z found in ultrasonics and low Z found in reaction rates are compatible. From the quantum mechanics calculations of Art. 33, one sees that the difficulty is that the theoretical resonance transfers do not seem efficient enough. (The N_2O case seems to make no difficulty.) A third possibility is a wrong interpretation of the chemical results. This might either be quite radical, insofar as the reaction might really be a wall reaction, or the effect of pressure and of foreign gases may produce a relative change among complicated elementary reactions making up the over-all measured rate. While this is very probably the case for some of the organic reactions, the effect of He in increasing the rate constant can probably not be explained except as an increase in heat transfer. A less radical error might be an underestimate of the number of degrees of freedom participating, which would also mean underestimating Z.

A related effect appears in the measurement of the recombination of atoms, which is possible in triple collisions (or on the wall) where the heat of formation may be removed by the third partner (or the wall). The most reliable measurements for the recombination of Br and I atoms n the presence of other gases have been made, after earlier attempts by others, by Rabinowitsch and Wood [102]. They produced the atoms by photodissociation and measured optically the Br_2 or I_2 concentration in the stationary state.

Table H,35b gives the fraction of the collision between atoms which combine in the presence of 1 atm of the foreign gas, i.e. essentially $(b/12,300)Z$. This shows that Z is of the order of magnitude of 1. The same seems to be true for the recombination of two H atoms with H_2 as third partner, while H is only about one-tenth as efficient [106].

Table H,35b. Fraction of atomic collisions leading to recombination in presence of 1 atm of foreign gas.

Foreign gas		He	A	H_2	N_2	O_2	CO_2	C_6H_6
Fraction of atomic collisions $\times 10^3$	Br	0.82	1.4	2.2	2.7	3.4	5.7	
	I	1.7	3.6	3.9	6.3	10	17	97

To sum up the results reported here, one finds high efficiency of some triple collisions in recombination reactions. For double collisions also the calculated efficiencies are much higher than usually found in ultrasonic experiments.

CHAPTER 6. *ELECTRONICALLY EXCITED* *MOLECULES*

H,36. Transfer of Vibrational and Rotational Energy in Electronically Excited Molecules. If one brings a diatomic molecule into its first excited state, with a vibrational quantum number v' and an angular momentum quantum number j', it will, if not otherwise disturbed, return to the ground electronic state after an average lifetime τ_R (R signifying radiation). This return may be to a limited set of vibrational quantum numbers v, which are allowed by the Franck-Condon principle; but it may change its rotational quantum number only by 1, i.e. $j' \to j' + 1$ or $j' \to j' - 1$. Accordingly, the fluorescence spectrum consists of a few pairs of lines. Such a pair is due to a particular transition $v' \to v''$, and the two possible rotational transitions just mentioned.

As Wood [116] discovered, this can actually be shown in iodine vapor, where the mercury line of 5461A coincides with one of the absorption lines of I_2. If I_2 is illuminated by this line, a molecule in the ground state with $v'' = 0$ is brought into the electronically excited state with $v' = 26$ and $j' = 30$.

If now a foreign gas is admitted, the fluorescence spectrum becomes much richer; the whole band of rotation lines—instead of only a pair—and many other bands (besides the one corresponding to $v' = 26 \rightarrow v''$) appear. This means that in many excited molecules a collision has taken place before the molecule could emit. This collision has not affected the electronic excitation but has produced a change in the vibrational state v' and rotational state j'. In particular, there is an intensity shift to the red, since many excited iodine molecules lose in collision part of their high vibrational energy. The effect of foreign gases was first observed by Franck and Wood [118,110]. Wood and Loomis [119] showed that in each transferring collision with a He atom, j' changes by two; v' usually changes by only 1 or 2 in a transferring collision. To get a quantitative estimate, one sees that the intensity of the newly produced transition is roughly proportional to

$$\frac{1}{\tau}\left(\frac{1}{\tau_R} + \frac{1}{\tau}\right)^{-1} = \left(1 + \frac{\tau}{\tau_R}\right)^{-1}$$

where τ is the average time between "transferring" collisions. One sees that one can only determine τ/τ_R directly, and to find τ, τ_R must be known. This had been assumed to be 10^{-8} sec in analogy with "allowed" atomic transitions. One can then calculate effective cross sections for transfer collisions, which are given below.

Table H,36. Apparent effective cross sections for transferring collisions.

Gas	I_2-He	I_2-Ne	I_2-A	I_2-Kr	I_2-Xe
Cross section, A^2	113	159	240	309	480

These cross sections are considerably larger than the gas kinetic ones so that not only every collision would be effective, but there would be considerable effect before collision.

However, it is now known that while the I_2 ground state is a singlet state, the first excited state is a triplet state; the triplet-singlet transition is weak, i.e. τ_R should be much longer than 10^{-8} sec. How much longer is not known; an upper limit is given by the old experiment of Stern and Volmer [115] showing that the fluorescence does not extend measurably beyond the sharply limited illuminated spot, which means that the I_2 molecules have not traveled during τ_R say, 0.5 mm. This means $\tau_R < 3 \times 10^{-6}$ sec. If we assume $\tau_R = 10^{-6}$ sec, the cross sections in Table H,36 are too high by a factor of 100, which would mean a reasonable Z of the order of 5 to 10. A $Z_v = 10$ for $v = 26$ would then, since the transition probability for vibration is proportional to v, mean a $Z_v = 250$ for the transition $1 \rightarrow 0$, which is entirely reasonable.

Durand [109] had investigated the effect of foreign gases on S_2. He finds, for S_2 molecules with $v' = 8$, the transfer efficiency nearly equal for vibrational and rotational energy; it is greater for He than for the heavier gases.

In some molecules and radicals, like Hg_2, HgH, and OH, there are some effects not yet quite understood [111,112]. In OH bands where the OH radical is produced by photochemical processes, the high rotational levels show too high an intensity (too large a population) which would indicate that they take longer to achieve equilibrium.

Shuler [114] has shown that 3 in. above the tip of the inner cone of an oxygen-natural gas flame there is equilibrium between all degrees of freedom of OH, while in the outer cone of an oxygen-acetylene flame only rotation has established equilibrium with translation, while the vibrational temperature is higher.

Schüler [113] has made observations in which he produced metal hydride radicals in a hollow cathode discharge; at the place of origin, the temperature is very high, decreasing outward. He finds also that the temperature of the higher rotation states decreases less rapidly, i.e. is exchanged less easily, than for the lower ones.

If HgH is produced in a highly excited vibrational state, $v' = 5$, the addition of nitrogen removes the vibrational excitation of HgH, but produces high rotational energy of the HgH [112]. That indicates that the transfer (vibrational energy $\rightarrow$ rotational energy) of HgH is easier than the transfer (vibrational energy $\rightarrow$ translational energy) of N_2.

H,37. Deactivation of Electronic Excitation. Quenching of Fluorescence. In the transfer of electronic energy, the general result which says that large changes of translational energy are very improbable, is reemphasized by the Franck-Condon principle; because of the wide difference in electron and atomic masses, there should not be a large change in momentum of the latter during the short time—in Bohr language— during which the electronic transition takes place.

Accordingly, if electronic excitation energy is to be removed in a collision, it will be taken up in the largest possible degree by some other electronic excitation energy—either in the original or in the colliding particle. Only the difference appears as translational kinetic energy. As much as possible will be taken up as vibrational energy, or as chemical energy, and only if none of these processes is possible, will the whole electronic excitation appear as translational energy. It was first thought that the high efficiency of many gases [120] in suppressing the resonance radiation of Hg was due to quenching (return to the ground state). However it turned out to be due to a transfer from the $^3P_1$ to the metastable

$^3P_0$ state which lies 0.218 ev lower. Even this effect is more efficient with NO [125]—where vibrations may be excited—than with monatomic gases. With the former, one can estimate $Z \cong 5$. If one excites in sodium the D line which has the higher frequency, the other one appears also if sufficient foreign gas is present [128,129]. For argon $Z \cong 1$ (half pressure about 3 mm Hg). The energy difference between the two levels $^2P_{\frac{3}{2}}$ and $^2P_{\frac{1}{2}}$ is about 2×10^{-3} ev.

Atoms of the same kind are much more effective, probably because, for example in sodium, the process is

A $(^2P_{\frac{3}{2}})$ + B (ground state)

$$\to \text{A (ground state)} + \text{B } (^2P_{\frac{1}{2}}) + \text{kinetic energy}$$

and even two transitions involving the ground state are more probable than a single one which involves reversing a spin. Direct transition to the ground state (quenching) is much less probable, but seems to give smaller Z than expected; e.g. for the resonance line of mercury, argon at 2 mm seems to quench the fluorescence by about 5 per cent, or $Z \cong 120$.

According to Oldenberg [124] the effectiveness of argon in quenching mercury is about 4 times higher at 750°C than at room temperature. As an explanation for the relatively high effectiveness of rare gas atoms, a distortion of the energy levels of the radiating atom by the hitting atom has been proposed [121,122]. Hence the potential energy curve of the pair-excited atom-hitting atom is, at the place of closest approach, very close to the interaction curve of the pair-unexcited atom-hitting atom, resulting in an easy transition between these two potential curves.

For N_2, the effect on Hg is about 3 times that of argon; the effect of N_2 on excited Na however, seems to be only one-third that on Hg [123], which is astonishing.

If the energy of excitation can be used to produce chemical changes (dissociation, as in H_2 [120,122]), Z is much smaller ($\cong 2$).

Quenching also exists in electronically excited molecules with more than one atom, e.g. I_2 [126].

H,38.   Cited References and Bibliography.

Cited References

1. Bourgin, D. G.   *Phil. Mag.* 7, 821 (1929); *Phys. Rev. 34*, 521 (1929); 42, 721 (1932); 49, 411 (1936); 50, 355 (1936); *J. Acoust. Soc. Amer. 4*, 108 (1932).
2. Kneser, H. O.   *Ann. Physik 11*, 761 (1931).
3. Kneser, H. O.   *Ann. Physik 16*, 360 (1933).
4. Landau, L., and Teller, E.   *Physik. Z. Sowjetunion 11*, 18 (1937).
5. Rutgers, A. J.   *Ann. Physik 16*, 350 (1933).
6. Eucken, A.   *Physik. Z. 14*, 324 (1913).
7. Kirchhoff, G.   *Pogg. Ann. Phys. 134*, 177 (1868).
8. Kohler, M.   *Z. Physik 125*, 715 (1949).
9. Stokes, G. G.   *Trans. Cambridge Phil. Soc. 8*, 287 (1845); *Coll. papers I*, 75.

10. Abello, T. B.   *Proc. Natl. Acad. Sci. 13*, 699 (1927).
11. Herzfeld, K. F., and Rice, F. O.   *Phys. Rev. 31*, 691 (1928).
12. Jeans, J. J.   *The Dynamical Theory of Gases.* Cambridge Univ. Press, 1904.
13. Pierce, G. W.   *Proc. Am. Acad. Arts Sci. 60*, 271 (1925).
14. Watson, H. W.   *A Treatise on the Kinetic Theory of Gases,* 2nd ed. Oxford Univ. Press, 1898.
15. Cheng, L.   *J. Chem. Phys. 19*, 693 (1951).
16. Richards, W. T.   *J. Chem. Phys. 1*, 863 (1933).
17. Schäfer, K.   *Z. physik. Chem. B46*, 212 (1940).
    Buschmann, K. F., and Schäfer, K.   *Z. physik. Chem. B50*, 73 (1941).
18. Schwartz, R. N., and Slawsky, Z. I.   *Nav. Ord. Lab. Tech. Rept.* Unpublished.
19. Eucken, A., and Becker, R.   *Z. physik. Chem. B20*, 467 (1933).
19a. Walker, R. A., Rossing, T. D., and Legvold, S.   *NACA Tech. Note 3210*, 1954.
19b. Boudart, M.   *J. Chem. Phys. 21*, 955 (1953).
20. Knötzel, H., and Knötzel, L.   *Ann. Physik 2*, 393 (1948).
21. Grüneisen, E., and Merkel, E.   *Ann. Physik 66*, 344 (1921).
22. Kneser, H. O., and Knudsen, V. O.   *Ann. Physik 21*, 684 (1934).
23. Knudsen, V. O.   *J. Acoust. Soc. Amer. 5*, 112 (1933).
    Meyer, E., and Tamm, K.   *Akust. Z. 4*, 145 (1939).
24. Alleman, R. S.   *J. Acoust. Soc. Amer. 10*, 88 (1938); *13*, 23 (1941); *Phys. Rev. 55*, 87 (1939).
25. Hubbard, J. C.   *Phys. Rev. 38*, 1011 (1931); *41*, 523 (1932); *46*, 525 (1934); *59*, 934 (1941).
26. Swomley, E. S. (Stewart, E. S.)   *Ph.D. Dissertation.* The Johns Hopkins Univ., 1946.
27. Zmuda, A.   *J. Acoust. Soc. Amer. 23*, 472 (1951).
28. Grobe, H.   *Physik. Z. 39*, 333 (1938).
28a. Parker, J. S., Adams, C. E., and Stavseth, R. H.   *J. Acoust. Soc. Amer. 25*, 263 (1953).
28b. Greenspan, M., and Thompson, C. M., Jr.   *J. Acoust. Soc. Amer. 25*, 92 (1953).
28c.   Theory
    Eckart, C.   *Phys. Rev. 73*, 68 (1948).
    Fox, F. E., and Herzfeld, K. F.   *Phys. Rev. 78*, 156 (1950).
       Experiments
    Liebermann, L. N.   *Phys. Rev. 75*, 1415 (1949).   } (liquids)
    Karim, S. M.   *J. Acoust. Soc. Amer. 25*, 997 (1953). }
    Medwin, H.   *J. Acoust. Soc. Amer. 26*, 332 (1954).   (gases)
29. Petersen, O.   *Physik. Z. 41*, 29 (1940).
30. Griffith, W.   *J. Appl. Phys. 21*, 1319 (1950).
30a. Griffith, W.   *Phys. Rev. 87*, 234 (1952).
30b. Greene, E. F., Cowan, G. R., and Hornig, D. F.   *J. Chem. Phys. 19*, 427 (1951).
30c. Gorelik, G.   *Compt. rend. Acad. Sci. U.R.S.S. 54*, 779 (1946).
    Slobodskaya, P. V.   *Izvest. Akad. Nauk S.S.S.R., Ser. Fiz. 12*, 656 (1948).
    Cottrell, T. L.   *Trans. Faraday Soc. 46*, 1025 (1950).
31. Kantrowitz, A.   *J. Chem. Phys. 14*, 150 (1946).
32. Smiley, E. F., Winkler, E. H., and Slawsky, Z. I.   *J. Chem. Phys. 20*, 923 (1952).
33. Huber, P. W., and Kantrowitz, A.   *J. Chem. Phys. 15*, 275 (1947).
34. Greenspan, M.   *J. Acoust. Soc. Amer. 22*, 568 (1950).
35. Keller, H. H.   *Physik. Z. 41*, 386 (1940).
36. van Itterbeek, A., and Mariens, P.   *Physica 4*, 609 (1937).
    van Itterbeek, A., and Thys, L.   *Physica 5*, 889 (1938).
37. van Itterbeek, A., and Verhaegen, L.   *Nature 167*, 478 (1951).
38. Boyer, R.   *J. Acoust. Soc. Amer. 23*, 176 (1951).
39. Brillouin, M.   *Ann. chim. et phys. 20*, 440 (1900).
40. Burnett, D.   *Proc. London Math. Soc. 40*, 382 (1935).
41. de Boer, J., and Michels, A.   *Physica 5*, 945 (1938); *6*, 409 (1939).
42. Wang Chang, C. S., and Uhlenbeck, G. E.   *Appl. Phys. Lab. Johns Hopkins Univ. Rept. CM-433, UMH-3-F*, Feb. 1948.
    Wang Chang, C. S.   *Appl. Phys. Lab. Johns Hopkins Univ. Rept. CM-467, UMH-3-F*, May 1948.

43. Herzfeld, K. F.   *Ann. Physik 23*, 465 (1935).
44. Jones, J. E.   *Trans. Roy. Soc. London 223*, 1 (1923).
45. Lucas, R.   *Compt. rend. 206*, 658 (1938).
46. Primakoff, H.   *J. Acoust. Soc. Amer. 14*, 14 (1942).
47. Rocard, Y.   *Ann. physique 8*, 1 (1927).
48. Tsien, H. S., and Schamberg, R.   *J. Acoust. Soc. Amer. 18*, 334 (1946).
48a. Truesdell, C.   *J. Rat. Mech. and Anal. 2*, 643 (1953).
49. Kohler, M.   *Z. Physik 127*, 40 (1949).
50. Meixner, J.   *Ann. Physik 43*, 470 (1943).
51. Rocard, Y.   *Propagation et absorption du son.* Hermann, Paris, 1935.
52. Rhodes, J. E.   *Phys. Rev. 70*, 91, 932 (1946).
53. Stewart, E. S., Stewart, J. L., and Hubbard, J. C.   **Phys. Rev. 68, 231 (1945).**
    Stewart, E. S.   *Phys. Rev. 69*, 632 (1946).
    Stewart, J. L., and Stewart, E. S.   *J. Acoust. Soc. Amer. 20*, 585 (1948).
54. Zartmann, I. F.   *J. Acoust. Soc. Amer. 21*, 171 (1949).
55. Braithwaite, J. W., and Werner, F. D.   *Univ. Minn. Research Rept. 58, Contract N6-onr-264 VII*, Apr. 1950.
56. Ener, C., Gabrysh, A. F., and Hubbard, J. C.   *J. Acoust. Soc. Amer. 24*, 474 (1952).
57. Thaler, W.   *J. Acoust. Soc. Amer. 24*, 15 (1952).
58. Bender, D.   *Ann. Physik 38*, 199 (1940).
59. Henry, P. S.   *Nature 129*, 200 (1932).
60. Kneser, H. O.   *J. Acoust. Soc. Amer. 5*, 122 (1933).
    Kneser, H. O., and Knudsen, V. O.   *Ann. Physik 21*, 682 (1934).
61. Knudsen, V. O.   *J. Acoust. Soc. Amer. 5*, 112 (1933).
    Knudsen, V. O., and Obert, L.   *J. Acoust. Soc. Amer. 7*, 210 (1930); *Phys. Rev. 47*, 256 (1930).
62. Shilling, W. G., and Partington, J. R.   *Phil. Mag. 3*, 273 (1927); *6*, 920 (1928).
63. Vasilesco, V.   *Ann. physique 20*, 137 (1945).
64. Eucken, A., and Becker, R.   *Z. physik. Chem. B27*, 235 (1935).
65. Sherrat, G. G., and Griffiths, E.   *Proc. Roy. Soc. London A147*, 292 (1934).
66. Fricke, E. F.   *J. Acoust. Soc. Amer. 12*, 245 (1950).
67. Kneser, H. O.   *Ann. Physik 11*, 777 (1931); *12*, 1015 (1932).
68. Knudsen, V. O., and Fricke, E.   *J. Acoust. Soc. Amer. 9*, 273 (1938); *10*, 89 (1938); *12*, 255 (1938).
69. Leonard, R. W.   *J. Acoust. Soc. Amer. 12*, 466 (1940).
70. Gustavson, M.   *Ph.D. Thesis.* Cornell Univ., 1952.
70a. Angona, F. A.   *J. Acoust. Soc. Amer. 25*, 1116 (1953).
71. Pielemeier, W. H., Sexton, H. L., and Telfair, D.   *J. Chem. Phys. 8*, 106 (1940).
72. Kinnier, J.   *M.S. Dissertation.* Catholic Univ., 1949.
73. Alexander, E. A., and Lambert, J. D.   *Proc. Roy. Soc. London A179*, 499 (1942).
74. Ener, C., Busala, A., and Hubbard, J. C.   *J. Chem. Phys. 23*, 155 (1955).
75. Eucken, A., and Aybar, L.   *Z. physik. Chem. B46*, 195 (1940).
76. Jatkar, S. K. K.   *Indian J. Phys. 22A*, 19, 39, 59 (1939).
77. Lambert, J. D., and Rawlinson, J. S.   *Proc. Roy. Soc. London A204*, 424 (1950).
78. Matta, K., and Richardson, E. G.   *J. Acoust. Soc. Amer. 23*, 58 (1951).
79. Railston, W.   *J. Acoust. Soc. Amer. 11*, 107 (1939).
80. Richards, W. T., and Reid, J. A.   *J. Chem. Phys. 2*, 206 (1934).
81. Busala, A., Sette, D., and Hubbard, J. C.   *J. Chem. Phys. 20*, 1899 (1952).
81a. Fogg, P. G. T., Hanks, P. A., and Lambert, J. D.   *Proc. Roy. Soc. London A219*, 490 (1953).
81b. Busala, A., Sette, D., and Hubbard, J. C.   *J. Chem. Phys 23*, May 1955.
82. Telfair, D.   *J. Chem. Phys. 10*, 167 (1942).
83. Weltner, A.   *Dissertation.* Univ. Calif., 1950.
84. Kallmann, H., and London, F.   *Z. physik. Chem. B2*, 207 (1929).
85. Rice, O. K.   *Proc. Natl. Acad. India 17*, 34 (1931); *Phys. Rev. 38*, 1943 (1931).
86. Zener, C.   *Phys. Rev. 38*, 277 (1931); *Proc. Cambridge Phil. Soc. 29*, 136 (1933).
87. Jackson, J. M., and Mott, N. F.   *Proc. Roy. Soc. London A137*, 703 (1932).
88. Jackson, J. M., and Howarth, A.   *Proc. Roy. Soc. London A142*, 447 (1933).
    Devonshire, A. F.   *Proc. Roy. Soc. London A158*, 269 (1937).

89. Lennard-Jones, J. E.   *Proc. Roy. Soc. London A106*, 441 (1924).
90. Slawsky, Z., Schwartz, R. N., and Herzfeld, K. F.   *J. Chem. Phys. 20*, 1591 (1952).
91. Schwartz, R. N., and Herzfeld, K. F.   *J. Chem. Phys. 22*, 767 (1954).
91a. Takayanagi, T.   *Progress Theoret. Phys. Japan 8*, 111 (1952).
     Takayanagi, T., and Kishimoto, T.   *Progress Theoret. Phys. Japan 9*, 578 (1953).
92. Franck, J., and Eucken, A.   *Z. physik. Chem. B20*, 460 (1933).
93. Eucken, A., and Kuchler, L.   *Physik. Z. 39*, 831 (1938).
93a. Slawsky, Z. I., de Wette, F., and de Groot, S. R.   Intern. Conf. on ultrasonics, Brussels. *Kon. Vlaamse Acad. voor Wet.*, 82 (1951).
94. van Itterbeek, A., and Mariens, P.   *Physica 7*, 125 (1940).
95. Oldenberg, O., and Frost, A. A.   *Chem. Revs. 20*, 99 (1937).
96. Sette, D., and Hubbard, J. C.   *J. Acoust. Soc. Amer. 25*, 994 (1953).
96a. Widom, B., and Bauer, S. H.   *J. Phys. Chem. 21*, 1670 (1953).
96b. de Wette, Z., and Slawsky, Z.   To be submitted to *Physica*.
97. Eucken, A., and Jaaks, H.   *Z. physik. Chem. B30*, 85 (1935).
98. Kassel, L.   *Chem. Revs. 10*, 14 (1932).
99. Lindemann, F. A.   *Trans. Faraday Soc. 17*, 598 (1922).
100. Koblitz, W. H., and Schumacher, H. J.   *Z. physik. Chem. B25*, 283 (1934).
101. Patat, E., and Bartholomé, E.   *Z. physik. Chem. B32*, 396 (1936).
102. Rabinowitsch, E., and Wood, W. C.   *J. Chem. Phys. 4*, 497 (1936).
103. Rice, O. K., and Ramsperger, H. C.   *J. Am. Chem. Soc. 49*, 1617 (1927).
104. Schumacher, H. J., and Sprenger, P.   *Z. physik. Chem. B12*, 115 (1931).
105. Schumacher, H. J., and Frisch, P.   *Z. physik. Chem. B37*, 18 (1937).
106. Steiner, W.   *Trans. Faraday Soc. 31*, 623 (1935).
107. Volmer, M., and Fröhlich, H.   *Z. physik. Chem. B19*, 85 (1932).
108. Volmer, M., and Bogdan, M.   *Z. physik. Chem. B21*, 257 (1933).
109. Durand, E.   *J. Chem. Phys. 8*, 46 (1940).
110. Franck, J.   *Verhandl. deut. physik Ges. 14*, 419 (1912).
111. Oldenberg, O.   *Phys. Rev. 37*, 194 (1931).
112. Rieke, F. F.   *Phys. Rev. 42*, 587 (1932); *46*, 236 (1934); *47*, 488 (1935).
113. Schüler, H.   Unpublished talk given at meeting of the Phys. Soc. of Würtemberg-Baden at Stuttgart. June 1948.
114. Shuler, K. E.   *J. Chem. Phys. 18*, 1221, 1466 (1950).
115. Stern, O., and Volmer, M.   *Physik. Z. 20*, 183 (1919).
116. Wood, R. W.   *Phil. Mag. 12*, 329 (1906); *21*, 261 (1911); *22*, 469 (1911).
117. Wood, R. W., and Kimura, M.   *Phil. Mag. 35*, 236 (1918).
118. Wood, R. W., and Franck, J.   *Phil. Mag. 21*, 265 (1911).
119. Wood, R. W., and Loomis, F. W.   *Phil. Mag. 6*, 231 (1928).
120. Cario, G., and Franck, J.   *Z. Physik 11*, 161 (1922); *37*, 619 (1926).
121. Jablonski, A.   *Z. Physik 70*, 723 (1931).
122. Laidler, K. J.   *J. Chem. Phys. 10*, 34, 43 (1942).
123. Norrish, R. G., and Smith, W. Mac F.   *Proc. Roy. Soc. London A176*, 295 (1940).
124. Oldenberg, O.   *Z. Physik 49*, 609 (1928); *50*, 580 (1928).
125. Bates, J. R.   *J. Am. Chem. Soc. 54*, 569 (1932).
126. Wood, R. W.   *Phil. Mag. 21*, 309 (1911); *22*, 469 (1911).
127. Wood, R. W.   *Phil. Mag. 50*, 774 (1925); *Proc. Roy. Soc. London A106*, 679 (1929).
128. Wood, R. W., and Dunoyer, L.   *Phil. Mag. 27*, 1018 (1914).
129. Wood, R. W., and Mohler, F. L.   *Phys. Rev. 11*, 70 (1918).

Bibliography

Reviews and books dealing with ultrasonic dispersion and absorption

Bergmann, L.   *Der Ultraschall*, English transl. of the 1st German ed. by H. S. Hatfield. Wiley, 1938 and 1944. 6th German ed., S. Hirzel, Stuttgart, 1954.

Beyer, R. T.   A review of sound absorption in fluids. *Brown Univ. N7-onr-35808*, March 1951.

Herzfeld, K. F.   A forthcoming book on propagation of ultrasonic waves from which most of this section is taken, partly verbatim, partly in content only (Academic Press).

Hiedemann, E.   *Ultraschallforschung.* De Gruyter, Berlin, 1939.
Kneser, H.   Molekulare Schallabsorption und-dispersion. *Ergebnisse der Exakten Naturwissenschaften,* Vol. XXII. Springer, Berlin, 1949.
Markham, J. G., Beyer, R. T., and Lindsay, R. B.   *Revs. Mod. Phys. 23,* 353 (1951).
Richards, W. T.   *Revs. Mod. Phys. 11,* 36 (1939).
Vigoureux, P.   *Ultrasonics.* Chapman and Hall, London, 1950.

Books on other subjects.

Art. 21–25

Sponer, H.   *Molekülspectren.* Springer, Berlin, 1935.
Mayer, J. E., and Mayer, M. G.   *Statistical Mechanics.* Wiley, 1939.

Art. 28–29

Eyring, H., Walter, J., and Kimball, S. E.   *Quantum Chemistry.* Wiley, 1944.
Massey, H. S. W., and Burlap, E. H. S.   *Electronic and Ionic Impact Phenomena.* Oxford Univ. Press, 1952.
Mott, N. F., and Massey, H. S. W.   *The Theory of Atomic Collisions,* 2nd ed. Oxford Univ. Press, 1949.
Schiff, L.   *Quantum Mechanics.* McGraw-Hill, 1943.

Art. 29–32

Hirschfelder, J. O., Curtiss, C. F., and Bird, R. B.   *Molecular Theory of Gases and Liquids.* Wiley, 1954.

Art. 35

Laidler, K.   *Chemical Kinetics.* McGraw-Hill, 1950.
Schumacher, H. J.   *Chemische Gas Reaktionen.* T. Steinkopff, Dresden, 1938.

Art. 36–37

Pringsheim, P.   *Fluorescence and Phosphorescence.* Interscience, 1949.

SECTION I

GASES AT LOW DENSITIES

IMMANUEL ESTERMANN

CHAPTER 1. LIMITS OF CONTINUUM THEORY

I,1. Role of Dimensionless Numbers for the Classification of Physical Processes. There are many physical phenomena in which the character of the process depends on the ratio of two quantities of the same physical dimension. One of these quantities may represent an external length, e.g. the length of a characteristic part of the apparatus in which the process takes place; the other may represent a natural length associated with the process itself. As an example we may consider the passage of a plane wave (light, sound, de Broglie wave, etc.) of wavelength λ through a slit of width d. If the dimensionless ratio λ/d is very small, the process can be described by the laws of geometrical optics; the deviation from the rectilinear propagation is negligible, and the wave nature of the process is not essential for its description. In the opposite case, if λ/d is not small, the laws of geometrical optics no longer describe the process satisfactorily, and its essential features, namely the diffraction patterns which are observed, have to be derived from the wave theory.

Since the units used in physics are completely arbitrary, it is obvious that dimensionless quantities, which are independent of any particular system of units, are of great importance in the description of physical phenomena. Dimensionless numbers of this kind are, for example, β the ratio of the velocity v of a particle to the velocity of light c ($\beta = v/c$) whose magnitude determines the limits of applicability of classical mechanics; the Reynolds number, $Re = uL/v$, which limits the region of laminar flow; the Mach number, $M = u/a$, which divides the regions of subsonic and supersonic flow; and many others.

I,2. Molecular and Continuum Theory of Fluids. The molecular theory of matter considers a solid, liquid, or gas as composed of a large number of discrete particles. In the first two states of aggregation these particles are close together, i.e. separated by distances of the order of magnitude of their diameters; in the gaseous state they are separated by distances which are large compared to their diameters. The continuum theory, as applied in the classical theories of elasticity and hydro-dynamics, treats the physical parameters of systems as continuous variables of the coordinates. Each system is divided into small volume elements dv, and it is assumed that its parameters, like pressure, temperature, or density, have constant values throughout each element, changing from one element to the next according to a specific law. No assumption is made regarding the size of these volume elements except that they are small. In order to obtain a truly continuous function for the parameters, the volume of these elements must be permitted to approach zero without limitations. On the other hand, the discrete character of the molecular theory limits the size of these elements to a volume containing a number of particles which is large enough to allow an interpretation of the *macroscopic* concepts of temperature, pressure, density, or composition in terms of the proper averages over the *microscopic* properties of the individual particles, like velocity, mass, or number per unit volume. Therefore, it is apparent that the application of the continuum theory is limited to cases where the external parameters vary so slowly that they can be assumed to remain constant over volume elements containing very many particles. Only under this condition can the results of the continuum theory be expected to agree with those of the molecular theory and of the experiment. It seems desirable to express this condition by means of a dimensionless number.

For gases at room temperature and atmospheric pressure, the average distance between molecules is about 3×10^{-7} cm, while the molecular diameters are about one order of magnitude smaller. A more detailed analysis of the transport phenomena in gases shows, however, that another length occurring in gases, which depends on these two quantities, has a more fundamental importance. This is the mean free path l of a gas molecule, which describes the average length of a path of a gas molecule between collisions with others. It is related to the effective diameter of the particles and to the average distance between them, or better to the number of particles per cm^3 and to their effective collision cross section.

I,3. The Mean Free Path and the Knudsen Number. The early development of the kinetic theory of gases led to values for the average velocity of gas molecules of the order of $v_m = 5 \times 10^4$ cm/sec, while experimental measurements of the rate of diffusion in gases made it evident that the actual progress of a molecule in a gas under normal conditions is many orders of magnitude slower. This apparent contradiction, which was for some time considered as a valid objection against the kinetic theory, was resolved by Clausius [1] through a consideration of the collisions between molecules. Because of the finite size and finite number of molecules in a gas, an individual molecule will be able to proceed along a straight line and with its "molecular" velocity only for a very short distance, after which it will collide with another molecule and change its direction. The resulting path is, therefore, a zigzag line, and the progress in any given direction is much less rapid than the molecular velocities indicate. The average distance between collisions is known as the mean free path l and its value was first calculated by Clausius (see Sec. B) as

$$l_{\text{Clausius}} = \frac{1}{N\pi\sigma^2} \tag{3-1}$$

where N is the number of molecules per cm³ and σ their collision diameter.

Better calculations carried out by Maxwell [2] under consideration of the velocity distribution of the molecules led to the slightly different value

$$l = \frac{\sqrt{2}}{N\pi\sigma^2} \tag{3-2}$$

Introducing the density of the gas, $\rho = Nm$ where m represents the mass of a molecule, Eq. 3-2 becomes

$$l = \frac{m\sqrt{2}}{\pi\sigma^2\rho} \tag{3-3}$$

which shows that the mean free path is inversely proportional to the density and, at constant temperature, to the pressure of the gas. This result is of particular importance for further discussions in this section. Since σ is not directly measurable, l cannot be calculated from Eq. 3-3. There exist, however, relations between the mean free path and the transport phenomena, namely heat conduction, viscosity, and diffusion in gases, which permit numerical calculations of l from measurable quantities for which we refer to Art. 13 and to Sec. D. A method for the direct experimental determination of the mean free path is discussed in Art. 22.

If we consider a gas enclosed in a vessel of a given size, the transport phenomena will clearly depend on the ratio between the mean free path and the dimensions of the vessel. If, as under normal conditions, the mean free path is small compared to the dimensions of the vessel, the transport of matter, momentum, or energy through the gas will be governed essentially by the collisions of the gas molecules with each other; if, however, the mean free path is large compared with the dimensions of the vessel, collisions between gas molecules will occur only rarely, and the important effects will be those which are determined by the collisions between a gas molecule and the walls of the vessel. For the purpose of the discussions in this section, a system fulfilling the latter condition shall be considered a *gas at low density*, and we shall use the dimensionless number

$$K = \frac{l}{L} \tag{3-4}$$

as a measure of the degree of low density, where L is a characteristic linear dimension of the system. For $K \gg 1$ (in practice $K > 10$) the laws derived for gases at low density are applicable within the customary experimental accuracy, for $K \ll 1$ (in practice $K < 0.1$) the laws of continuum theory will hold. The intermediate region, $0.1 < K < 10$, is known as transition or slip-flow region for which very little is known in general terms. The number K is designated as Knudsen number, in honor of Martin Knudsen who pioneered in the theoretical and experimental research on gases at low densities.

I,4. Relations between Mach Number, Reynolds Number, and Knudsen Number. From the definition of the Reynolds number, we have

$$Re = \frac{uL}{\nu} = \frac{uL\rho}{\mu} \tag{4-1}$$

where ν is the dynamic viscosity, μ the viscosity coefficient, ρ the gas density, and L the characteristic length.[1] The Mach number is defined as

$$M = \frac{u}{a} \tag{4-2}$$

when u represents the free stream velocity of the gas, and a the local velocity of sound. Their ratio is, therefore

$$\frac{M}{Re} = \frac{\mu}{aL\rho} \tag{4-3}$$

But, according to Chapman [3] and Enskog [4] (see also Art. 13),

$$\mu = 0.499\rho\bar{v}_m\bar{l} \tag{4-4}[2]$$

hence

$$\frac{M}{Re} = 0.499 \frac{\bar{v}_m}{a} \cdot \frac{\bar{l}}{L} \tag{4-5}$$

and, since

$$a = \sqrt{\frac{\gamma RT}{\mathfrak{M}}} \quad \text{and} \quad \bar{v}_m = \sqrt{\frac{8}{\pi}\frac{RT}{\mathfrak{M}}} \tag{4-6}$$

(where γ is the ratio of the specific heats at constant pressure and constant volume, $\gamma = C_p/C_V$, R the universal gas constant, $\mathfrak{M}$ the molecular weight, and T the absolute temperature) we obtain

$$\frac{M}{Re} = 0.499\sqrt{\frac{8}{\pi\gamma}}\frac{l}{L} = 0.499\sqrt{\frac{8}{\pi\gamma}}K \tag{4-7}$$

[1] At small values of Re, the length L may usually be associated with a dimension of the body or of the flow channel; at large values of Re, the boundary layer thickness is a more significant quantity. See IV,B.

[2] In Art. 13, we derive the expression $\mu = \frac{1}{3}\rho\bar{v}_m\bar{l}$ under certain simplified assumptions. The factor 0.499 in Eq. 4-4 requires a very elaborate calculation.

Since γ is a constant for each gas, this result means that the Knudsen number is equal to the ratio of the Mach and Reynolds numbers, multiplied by a constant factor of the order of magnitude 1.

The main usefulness of the Reynolds and Knudsen numbers does not lie in their absolute value, which is somewhat uncertain, as the characteristic length L is frequently hard to define. They are, however, extremely important as scaling factors. This means that when a phenomenon is studied in a model of certain dimensions and geometrical shape the flow properties remain unchanged if the parameters of the system are changed in such a way that these numbers remain the same. For example, if we consider the flow of a gas through an orifice of the diameter d at a certain pressure p, the flow conditions (hydrodynamic, free molecular, or intermediate flow) will remain unchanged as long as the Knudsen number remains unchanged, that means, for instance, if an increase in p is associated with a proportionate decrease in d. Therefore, low density behavior may exist in a gas at very low pressure with regard to an orifice of large diameter, and also in a gas of, say, atmospheric pressure with regard to extremely fine pores or holes.

I,5. Numerical Values of the Mean Free Path. Table I,5 contains numerical values for $\bar{l}$ and $\bar{v}_m$ for 0°C and atmospheric pressure, calculated from experimental data according to Eq. 4-4 and 4-6.

Table I,5. Numerical values for the average thermal velocity and the mean free path for various gases at 0°C and 1 atm.

Gas	Symbol	$\bar{v}_m \times 10^{-4}$, cm/sec	$\bar{l} \times 10^6$, cm
Hydrogen	H₂	16.92	11.2
Helium	He	12.04	18.0
Neon	Ne	5.35	12.6
Argon	A	3.81	6.4
Nitrogen	N₂	4.54	6.0
Oxygen	O₂	4.25	6.5
Air		4.47	6.1
Carbon dioxide	CO₂	3.63	4.0
Water vapor	H₂O	5.67	4.0
Ammonia	NH₃	5.83	4.4
Methane	CH	6.01	4.9
Mercury vapor	Hg	1.70	2.2

The values of the mean free path used in Table I,5 are calculated under the assumption that the molecules behave like elastic spheres of fixed radius. As a result the mean free path becomes independent of temperature. Experiments show, however, that $\bar{l}$ increases with temperature. This is due to the fact that gas molecules can be represented as rigid spheres of a definite diameter only in a first approximation. A more accurate model has to consider the existence of attractive forces between molecules proportional to r^{-N} where r is the distance between the centers of the molecules and the exponent N approximately equal to 5 or 6. The rigidity may be replaced by repulsive forces falling off with a higher inverse power of the distance, N about equal to 9. A theoretical development on the basis of such a model does not lead to a definite diameter for a molecule, but to a sphere of influence, whose diameter increases with a decrease in the amount of energy transmitted by an individual interaction between the molecules. The value of the mean free path, therefore, depends on refinement of methods for its measurement. It should also be stated that from the standpoint of quantum mechanics the interaction between molecules has to be considered as an interference process between the de Broglie waves associated with the colliding molecules. The last two problems are discussed in Art. 22 and 23.

CHAPTER 2. FLOW OF GASES AT LOW DENSITIES

I,6. Flow through an Ideal Orifice: Effusion. We consider a vessel A (Fig. I,6a) containing a gas of pressure p_A surrounded by a vacuum envelope B, in which a very low pressure $p_B \cong 0$ is maintained by a suitable vacuum pump. One of the walls of vessel A is equipped

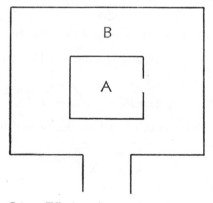

Fig. I,6a.   Effusion of a gas through an orifice.

with an orifice of area σ and diameter d, the wall thickness being assumed to be very small compared to d. If the gas pressure p_A or the diameter d are so small that the Knudsen number $K = \bar{l}/d$ is large, a molecule from the inside of vessel A moving toward the orifice will normally pass through without collisions. The rate of flow through an orifice of area σ can, therefore, be calculated simply by computing the number of molecules impinging upon an area σ of the wall per unit time.

For a calculation of this number, we consider an area element $d\sigma$ of the wall of a gas vessel containing N molecules per cm³. The number of molecules striking this element and having a direction making an angle between θ and $\theta + d\theta$ with the normal to $d\sigma$ is (Fig. I,6b)

$$dZ' = \tfrac{1}{2}N\bar{v}_m \sin\theta \cos\theta d\theta d\sigma \tag{6-1}$$

(see Sec. B). By integration, we obtain

$$dZ = \int_0^{\pi/2} \tfrac{1}{2}N\bar{v}_m \sin\theta d\sin\theta d\sigma = \tfrac{1}{4}N\bar{v}_m d\sigma \tag{6-2}$$

Expressing $N\bar{v}_m$ in terms of the pressure p_A, the absolute temperature T, the molecular weight $\mathfrak{M}$, Avogadro's number N_A and the gas constant R,

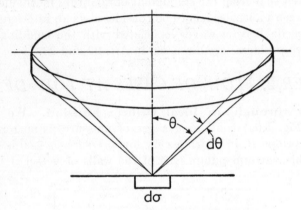

Fig. I,6b.   Illustration of the cosine law.

and integrating over the area σ of the orifice,[3] Eq. 6-1 becomes

$$Z = \frac{p_A N_A \sigma}{\sqrt{2\pi \mathfrak{M} RT}} = \frac{p_A \sigma}{\sqrt{2\pi mkT}} \; \text{sec}^{-1} \tag{6-3}$$

where $k = R/N$ is Boltzmann's constant. Expressed in grams, we obtain

$$G = \frac{p_A \sigma}{\sqrt{2\pi R}} \sqrt{\frac{\mathfrak{M}}{T}} \; \text{g/sec} \tag{6-4}$$

or, in mole numbers

$$Q = \frac{p_A \sigma}{\sqrt{2\pi \mathfrak{M} RT}} = \frac{5.83 \times 10^{-2}}{\sqrt{\mathfrak{M}T}} p_A \sigma \; \text{mole/sec} \tag{6-5}$$

if p_A is expressed in dynes/cm². Finally, we may introduce the volume V as measure for the quantity of the gas, and obtain

$$V = \frac{QRT}{p} = \sigma \sqrt{\frac{RT}{2\pi \mathfrak{M}}} \tag{6-6}$$

[3] The symbol σ is used here for the area of the orifice, while in Art. 3 and 22 σ stands for the molecular collision diameter.

(The last expression shows that the volume of an effusing gas is independent of the pressure.) For air ($\mathfrak{M} = 29$) and room temperature ($T = 300°\text{K}$), $V = 11{,}700$ cm³ per sec per cm² or 11.7 liters per sec per cm².

The expressions given above were first tested experimentally by Knudsen [5] who wrote them in a slightly different form, introducing a quantity

$$\rho_1 = \frac{\mathfrak{M}}{RT}$$

which represents the density of the gas at the temperature T and the pressure of 1 dyne per cm². Using this quantity, Eq. 6-4 and 6-6 take the form

$$G = \frac{\sigma}{\sqrt{2\pi}} p_A \sqrt{\rho_1} \tag{6-7}$$

and

$$V = \frac{\sigma}{2\pi} \frac{1}{\sqrt{\rho_1}} \tag{6-8}$$

It is practical to consider the quantity $W_0 = \sqrt{2\pi}/\sigma$ as the flow resistance of the orifice, and to write Eq. 6-7 and 6-8

$$G = \frac{p_A \sqrt{\rho_1}}{W_0} \tag{6-7a}$$

and

$$V = \frac{1}{W_0 \sqrt{\rho_1}} \tag{6-8a}$$

This form is advantageous for the treatment of a flow through several orifices (or tubes) in series; the total resistance of such a system is simply the sum of the resistances of its elements

$$W_0 = W_1 + W_2 + \cdots \tag{6-9}$$

I,7. Rate of Evaporation. The equilibrium between a condensed phase and its vapor cannot be considered as a static condition. It must be regarded as a dynamic equilibrium between evaporation and condensation processes going on at the same rate so that a pressure p_s equal to the vapor pressure is maintained in the gas phase. The maximum rate of condensation is easily computed. It corresponds to the case that every molecule impinging on the surface from the gas phase is incorporated into the condensate. The number of these molecules per unit time *and unit surface area* is, according to Eq. 6-3,

$$Z = \frac{p_s N_A}{\sqrt{2\pi \mathfrak{M} RT}} \tag{7-1}$$

This number is also the *maximum* rate of vaporization if the condensed phase is exposed to a perfect vacuum, with p_s now representing the vapor pressure.

If only a fraction α of the impinging molecules is incorporated into the condensed phase, the rate of vaporization must be reduced by a factor α in order to maintain equilibrium. The actual rate of vaporization, (or the coefficient α) can be measured if the process is so arranged that the number of molecules striking the surface of the condensate from the gas phase is negligible. This requires an apparatus where the Knudsen number is large and where the evaporating molecules are removed continuously by a vacuum pump or by condensation. Experiments carried out under these conditions [6] have shown that α may approach unity for extremely clean surfaces of liquids. For crystalline surfaces, α has been found to be somewhat smaller; it has probably also different values for different crystallographic lattice planes. Small impurities of surface active materials may reduce α to very small values [7,8].

Eq. 7-1 has been used for the experimental determination of vapor pressures. Because of the generally unknown value of α, this method is not always reliable. A modification of the method avoids this difficulty. The condensate is enclosed in a vessel equipped with a small orifice and this vessel is enclosed in a vacuum envelope. If the evaporating surface is very large compared with the area of the orifice, the pressure behind the orifice will equal the vapor pressure even when α is small, and the rate of effusion through the orifice will depend only on the vapor pressure, the temperature, and the area of the orifice, provided the Knudsen number is large enough.

I,8. Flow Through Long Tubes. We shall now consider the case where two vessels A and B are connected by a tube of cross-sectional area σ and length L. One of the vessels (A) may contain a gas maintained at the pressure p_A; in the other vessel (B) the pressure is kept at a very low value ($p_B \cong 0$) by a vacuum pump (Fig. I,8a).

A molecule entering the tube from A will strike the inner wall of the tube, except in the rare case where the direction of its velocity is almost parallel to the tube axis. The progress of such a molecule depends on the way in which it is reflected from the wall. If the impact between the molecule and the wall is perfectly elastic, i.e. if the reflection is specular, every molecule will proceed along a zigzag path through the tube, maintaining always its component of velocity parallel to the axis of the tube. Since for large Knudsen numbers, or $\bar{l} \gg d$, the number of molecules leaving A per unit time is the same as if the tube were replaced by an orifice, and since all these molecules would pass through the tube, the rate of flow would be equal to that given by Eq. 6-4, 6-5, or 6-6. Experiments show, however, that the rate of flow is much smaller, and that it depends inversely on the length of the tube. For an explanation of this phenomenon, Knudsen has assumed that a molecule impinging on a surface is not reflected like an elastic body, but is scattered from the surface according to a cosine law, i.e. that the probability of its leaving the surface in a direction having an angle θ with the normal is proportional to $\cos \theta$ and independent of the angle of incidence. This law is formally identical with the cosine law governing the scattering of light from a rough surface (Lambert's law) and is justified by the fact that even a highly polished surface is rough compared to molecular dimensions. As a result, the probability for a molecule to continue after an impact in the forward direction is equal to its probability to continue in the backward

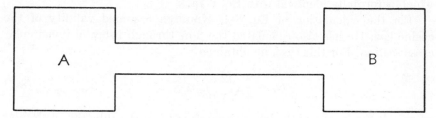

Fig. I,8a.   Molecular flow through a tube.

direction. A fraction of the molecules which enter the tube will, therefore, return to A, and the number of molecules which succeed in passing through the whole length of the tube becomes considerably smaller than the number entering, and decreases with the length of the tube. We may, therefore, express the rate of flow through the tube by multiplying the rates given by the equations of Art. 6 by a factor P [9] which represents the probability that a molecule entering the tube from A actually reaches B. Eq. 6-7, for instance, will become

$$G_t = P \frac{p_A \sigma \sqrt{\rho_1}}{\sqrt{2\pi}} \tag{8-1}$$

For a circular cross section, $\sigma = \pi r^2 = \pi d^2/4$ and

$$G_t = P\pi r^2 \frac{p_A \sqrt{\rho_1}}{\sqrt{2\pi}} = Pd^2 \sqrt{\frac{\pi \rho_1}{32}}\, p_A \tag{8-2}$$

The calculation of P requires a detailed analysis of the progress of the molecules after each collision with the wall. It is obvious that P depends on the length of the tube and on the wall *area*, not only on the cross-sectional area. The first calculation of P was carried out by Knudsen [10] who found for a circular tube of radius r and length L

$$P = \frac{8r}{3L} \tag{8-3}$$

and

$$G_t = \frac{8\pi r^3}{3L} \frac{p_A \sqrt{\rho_1}}{\sqrt{2\pi}} = \frac{d^3}{L} \sqrt{\frac{\pi \rho_1}{18}}\, p_A \qquad (8\text{-}4)$$

or, if we introduce

$$W_t = \frac{L}{d^3} \sqrt{\frac{18}{\pi}} \qquad (8\text{-}5)$$

as the flow resistance of the tube,

$$G_t = \frac{p_A \sqrt{\rho_1}}{W_t} \qquad (8\text{-}6)$$

which is formally identical with Eq. 6-7a.

For the calculation of Eq. 8-4, Knudsen assumed validity of the cosine law. He has also calculated the flow through tubes of noncircular cross section. For this case, he obtained

$$G_t = \frac{8}{3} \sqrt{\frac{2}{\pi}} \frac{\sigma^2}{sL}\, p_A \sqrt{\rho_1} \qquad (8\text{-}7)$$

where s is the length of the inner circumference of the tube. For a circular cross section,

$$s = 2\pi r \quad \text{and} \quad \sigma = \pi r^2$$

and Eq. 8-7 reduces to Eq. 8-4.

The equations given above cannot be correct for a short tube, since they would lead to $G = \infty$ for $L = 0$; i.e. for an orifice in a thin wall.

Moreover, it has been shown by Smoluchowski [11] that Eq. 8-7 is not quite correct, and that it ought to be replaced by

$$G_t = \frac{1}{\sqrt{8\pi}} \frac{K}{L} \sqrt{\rho_1}\, p_A \qquad (8\text{-}8)$$

where

$$K = \int_s \int_{-\pi/2}^{\pi/2} \tfrac{1}{2} \tau \cos \theta\, d\theta\, ds \qquad (8\text{-}9)$$

where τ is a chord forming an angle θ with the normal to the element ds. For a circular cross section, Eq. 8-8 and 8-9 lead again to Knudsen's equation (8-4).

Another interesting case which occurs frequently in experiments is the flow through a tube with rectangular cross section (canal). If we designate the width of the rectangle forming the cross section of the canal with b, the length with a, and the depth or length of the canal with L (Fig. I,8b), and if $L \gg a \gg b$, the probability P is, according to Smoluchowski,

$$P = \frac{b}{L}\left(\frac{1}{2} + 2.3 \ln \frac{2a}{b}\right) \qquad (8\text{-}10)$$

while the incorrect equation of Knudsen (8-7) would lead to $P = 8b/3L$. For a short canal or a slit whose jaws are not infinitely thin, i.e. if

$$a \gg L \gg b$$

Clausing [*12*] derived the equation

$$P = \frac{b}{L}\left(\frac{1}{2} + 2.3 \ln \frac{L}{b}\right) \tag{8-11}$$

If the assumption that all the collisions between the molecules and the wall of the tube obey the cosine law is dropped, the equations given above have to be modified. If only a fraction f leads to cosine reflection

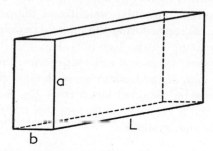

Fig. I,8b. Channel with rectangular cross section.

and a fraction $1 - f$ to specular reflection, P has to be multiplied, according to Smoluchowski, by a factor $R = (2 - f)/f$. This factor is only an approximation and, of course, valid only for sufficiently large values of f, since it would become divergent for $f = 0$ (see Art. 17).

Other possibilities regarding the interaction between gas molecules and solid surfaces are discussed in Art. 23.

I,9. Flow Through Short Tubes.   It has been stated in the preceding article that Eq. 8-3 and the equations derived from it become divergent for $L \rightarrow 0$, instead of leading to Eq. 6-4 to 6-9. An equation which gives the desired result has been obtained by Dushman [*13*] for circular tubes by combining Eq. 6-8 and 8-5. The flow resistance of a short tube is regarded as the sum of the resistances W_0 and W_T or

$$W_{s.t.} = \frac{1}{d^2}\sqrt{\frac{32}{\pi}} + \frac{L}{d^3}\sqrt{\frac{18}{\pi}} = \left[\frac{4}{d^2} + \frac{3L}{d^3}\right]\sqrt{\frac{2}{\pi}} \tag{9-1}$$

The rate of flow is given by $G_{s.t.} = p_A \sqrt{\rho_1}/W_{s.t.}$ as in Eq. 6-7 and 8-6. For $L \gg d$, $4/d^2$ can be neglected, while for $L \rightarrow 0$, $3L/d^3$ is negligible.

Clausing [*14*] has shown, however, that Eq. 9-1 is only correct in the two limiting cases listed above. For the general case, he obtains a complicated integral equation which he was able to solve for circular tubes for which $L \gg r$ or $r/L \gtrsim 1$. Similar calculations were carried out by him for a short canal of rectangular cross section.[4]

As in the case of an orifice, the flow rates G can be transformed to mole numbers or volume, and equations analogous to Eq. 6-5 and 6-6 will result. In particular, the volume of a gas streaming through a tube in molecular flow is again independent of the pressure. It is therefore possible to express the "conductance" $1/W$ of a tube in cm³/sec for a given gas and a given temperature. Nomograms showing this quantity for air at room temperature are to be found in the literature [13] and are of great convenience for the computation of flow rates in vacuum systems. For other gases and temperatures, the flow rates can be obtained by multiplication with a correction factor $\sqrt{29/\mathfrak{M}}$ or $\sqrt{T/290}$, where $\mathfrak{M}$ and T are the actual molecular weight and temperature of the gas under consideration, 29 representing the molecular weight of the air, and 290 the room temperature on the Kelvin scale.

For a train of several tubes and orifices in series, the total flow resistance is equal to the sum of the resistances of the individual components, and the flow rate can be obtained again from Eq. 8-5 by replacing W with $\sum W$. This method is very convenient for the evaluation of flow rates through complex vacuum systems.

I,10. Molecular Flow Between Two Gas Vessels and Related Effects. If the pressures in the vessels A and B and the dimensions of the connecting tube or orifice are such that the Knudsen number is small, the flow between the vessels will be governed by the laws of hydrodynamics. These laws set as a condition for equilibrium that the *total* pressures in A and B are equal. If the gases in A and B are different and have the initial pressures p_A and p_B, $(p_A > p_B)$, gas will flow from A to B until $p_A = p_B$, regardless of the composition of the resulting gas mixtures or the temperatures in A and B. It is true that ultimately the compositions and temperatures in A and B will also equalize by diffusion and heat conduction, but these processes are so slow compared to the equilibration of the total pressures that they can generally be disregarded. If, however, the Knudsen number is large, the flows from A to B and from B to A will be completely independent. If composition and temperature in A and B are the same, the net flow will be simply represented by

$$G = \frac{p_A - p_B}{W} \sqrt{\rho_1} \qquad (10\text{-}1)$$

and will continue until $p_A = p_B$, just as in the case of hydrodynamic flow.

If the temperatures in A and B are different, this will no longer be

[4] See AEC Report BR 296A (1944) by A. S. D. Barrett and C. H. Bosanquet for the resistance of ducts to molecular flow.

the case. Remembering that $\rho_1 = \mathfrak{M}/RT$, the flow from A to B will be given by

$$G_{AB} = \frac{1}{W} \sqrt{\frac{\mathfrak{M}}{R}} \frac{p_A}{\sqrt{T_A}} \qquad (10\text{-}2)$$

and from B to A by

$$G_{BA} = \frac{1}{W} \sqrt{\frac{\mathfrak{M}}{R}} \frac{p_B}{\sqrt{T_B}} \qquad (10\text{-}3)$$

Equilibrium will be reached if $G_{AB} = G_{BA}$, that means if

$$\frac{p_A}{\sqrt{T_A}} = \frac{p_B}{\sqrt{T_B}} \qquad (10\text{-}4)$$

or

$$\frac{p_A}{p_B} = \sqrt{\frac{T_A}{T_B}} \qquad (10\text{-}4a)$$

and not if $p_A = p_B$. This interesting result means that even if initially $p_A = p_B$, but $T_A \neq T_B$, gas will flow between A and B until Eq. 10-4 is satisfied. Similarly, if the system is originally in equilibrium ($T_A = T_B$, $p_A = p_B$) and the temperature in one of the parts of the system is changed, gas flow will result. This phenomenon was pointed out first by Knudsen [15] and has been called *thermal molecular flow*. It is important to consider this effect in connection with pressure measurements in high vacuum systems where the temperature of the measuring element (Pirani or ionization gauge) is frequently different from the temperature in the part of the system where the knowledge of the pressure is desired.

An interesting effect can be observed at large Knudsen numbers if the two vessels are filled with different gases, say A with hydrogen and B with oxygen. Here again, the flows from A to B and from B to A will be completely independent. Equilibrium will be reached when the *partial* pressures of both gases in A and B have been equalized, not, as in the hydrodynamic case, if the *total* pressures are equal. Flow will therefore result even if the initial pressures and temperatures in A and B are equal. The final total pressure in A and B will then, of course, be equal to the initial pressure, but a transient increase in the pressure in B will occur. To prove this, we express the flow rate in terms of the gas volume, which is proportional to $\sqrt{1/\mathfrak{M}}$ (see Eq. 6-6). Since $1/\mathfrak{M}$ for hydrogen is 16 times as large as for oxygen, the initial hydrogen flow rate from A to B will be 4 times as large as the oxygen flow rate from B to A. Consequently, the total pressure in B will at first increase, but when the partial pressures of hydrogen are practically equalized, oxygen will still stream from B to A and the total pressure in B will now decrease until it reaches its original value.

Finally, we want to call attention to the fact that the mass flow rates as given, for instance, in Eq. 6-5 are inversely proportional to $\sqrt{\mathfrak{M}}$. As a result, effusion, vaporization, and diffusion through porous materials may be used for isotope separation [16,17,18]. The diffusion process can be considered as flow through a large number of very small capillaries, and since the diameter of these tubes is extremely small, the Knudsen number remains large up to moderately high pressures. The separation process has to be so arranged that it goes only in one direction, i.e. that the back reaction is suppressed as much as possible, because the back reaction has the same rate dependence on $\mathfrak{M}$ as the forward reaction. This is the reason why equilibrium or near equilibrium processes like ordinary distillation do not produce isotope separation, except in those special cases where the thermodynamic functions determining the equilibrium are sufficiently different for the isotopes, as for example, the hydrogen isotopes in H and D. A very effective separation process is thermal diffusion. A discussion with numerous references is given in [18a].

I,11. Directional and Velocity Distribution of Molecules Passing Through an Orifice or a Tube. For an "ideal" orifice and large Knudsen numbers, the directional distribution may be expected to follow closely the cosine law stated in Art. 8 and illustrated by Fig. I,6b. The only assumptions required for this result are that the molecules inside the gas vessel have a random distribution of direction and that this distribution is not appreciably disturbed by the replacement of a wall element $d\sigma$ with an equal element of the orifice. Any disturbance produced by this replacement will be limited to a hemisphere of a radius equal to the diameter d of the orifice, or in the case of a rectangular slit, to a semicylinder of a radius equal to the width b of the slit. Since at large Knudsen numbers ($\bar{l} \gg d$ or $\bar{l} \gg b$) most of the effusing molecules had their last collision at a distance of the order $\bar{l}$ from the orifice, their directional distribution will represent that of the undisturbed part of the gas. For increasing pressures, this will no longer be the case, and an increasing fraction of the molecules will have had their last collision in the disturbed region. This leads to a preponderance of a forward component of velocity in the effusing molecules and, if we go to small Knudsen numbers, to the formation of a jet as in hydrodynamic flow.

The flow conditions from a tube are much more complicated. Here, even at large Knudsen numbers, many of the emitted molecules have had their last collision with the wall of the tube, not with the walls of the original container or with another molecule. Their directional distribution depends therefore on the geometrical shape of the tube and on the type of interaction between the molecules and the wall. Assuming the validity of the cosine law for this interaction, Clausing [19,20] calculated the directional distribution for molecules emitted from a short circular tube whose length L is equal to the diameter $2r$. His results are shown in Fig. I,11. The solid curve shows the actual distribution; the dotted line the cosine distribution. It is worth noting that the number of molecules emitted in the direction of the axis of the tube is the same for both distributions, while the total number emitted from the tube is only about one half of that emitted from an orifice of equal diameter.

The effects of deviations from the cosine law are discussed in Art. 17.

Regarding the velocity distribution in magnitude, one might assume that it is represented by the ordinary Maxwellian distribution in a gas at rest. It has been shown by Stern [21] that this distribution has to be

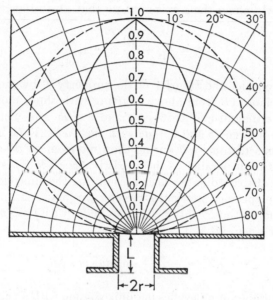

Fig. I,11. Angular distribution of molecules effusing
from a short canal (after Clausing [20]).

modified because the probability of a molecule escaping through an orifice is also proportional to its velocity v. The modified Maxwell distribution will, therefore, contain the factor v^3 instead of v^2, and is given by

$$\frac{dZ'_v}{Z'} = \frac{2v^3}{\alpha^3} e^{-\frac{v^2}{x^2}} d\left(\frac{v}{\alpha}\right) \tag{11-1}$$

where dZ'_v/Z' is the fraction of molecules having a velocity between v and $v + dv$, and $\alpha = \sqrt{2RT/\mathfrak{M}}$ the most probable velocity in the gas at rest. For not very large Knudsen numbers it is to be expected that the distribution given by Eq. 11-1 is distorted by collisions within the sphere of influence of the orifice or slit, i.e. within a "depth" d (or b) behind the orifice. This distortion leads to a depletion of the number of very slow molecules and has been found experimentally and discussed theoretically by Estermann, Simpson, and Stern [22].

CHAPTER 3. TRANSPORT PHENOMENA
AT LOW DENSITIES

I,12. The Transfer Equation. We consider a gas in a cylindrical container of unit cross section, placing the z axis in the direction of the cylinder axis. A plane AB normal to the z axis is placed across the cylinder at $z = z_0$. A molecular property Γ (e.g. kinetic energy or momentum) may vary slowly along the z axis only, so that at any nearby level z its value is given by

$$\Gamma_z = \Gamma_{z_0} + \frac{\partial \Gamma}{\partial z}\,(z - z_0) \qquad (12\text{-}1)$$

We now consider the transfer of the property Γ by molecules going through the plane AB from above, starting with those molecules whose velocities have magnitudes between v and $v + dv$ and whose directions form an angle between θ and $\theta + d\theta$ with the z axis. Each of these molecules traverses a distance vdt during the time element dt, and the component of this path parallel to the z axis is $v \cos \theta dt$. This expression is negative since the coordinate z decreases during the time element dt. The number of the specified molecules passing through AB in the time element dt is equal to those contained in a cylinder with base AB and height $-v \cos \theta dt$, or since $AB = 1$,

$$dZ'_v = -\,\frac{dN_v}{2}\,\sin \theta d\theta v \cos \theta dt \qquad (12\text{-}2)$$

if dN_v is the number of molecules per unit volume with a velocity between v and $v + dv$ and $2\pi \sin \theta d\theta/4\pi$ the fraction of molecules whose direction forms an angle between θ and $\theta + d\theta$ with the z axis. Per unit time, we obtain

$$dZ = \tfrac{1}{2}dN_v v \sin \theta \cos \theta d\theta \qquad (12\text{-}3)$$

If a particle has covered a distance l since its last collision, it has come from a level $z = z_0 - l \cos \theta$. The corresponding value of Γ is, provided l is small,

$$\Gamma_z = \Gamma_{z_0} - l \cos \theta \left(\frac{\partial \Gamma}{\partial z}\right) \qquad (12\text{-}4)$$

The amount of Γ transported by dz molecules per unit time is

$$d\Gamma' = dZ\Gamma_{z_0} - \left(\frac{\partial \Gamma}{\partial z}\right) \cos \theta \sum l = dZ \left[\Gamma_{z_0} - \bar{l}\left(\frac{\partial \Gamma}{\partial z}\right) \cos \theta\right] \qquad (12\text{-}5)$$

where $\bar{l}$ is now the mean free path. The total amount of Γ transported from above through the plane AB by molecules with velocities between

v and $v + dv$ is obtained by integration over θ from $\pi/2$ to π

$$dГ_1 = \frac{v}{4} dN_v Г_{z_\bullet} + \frac{v\bar{l}dN_v}{6} \left(\frac{\partial Г}{\partial z}\right) \tag{12-6}$$

The amount transported through AB from below is correspondingly

$$dГ_2 = \frac{v}{4} dN_v Г_{z_\bullet} - \frac{v\bar{l}dN_v}{6} \left(\frac{\partial Г}{\partial z}\right) \tag{12-7}$$

and the net transfer

$$dГ = dГ_1 - dГ_2 = \frac{v\bar{l}dN_v}{3} \left(\frac{\partial Г}{\partial z}\right) \tag{12-8}$$

The total transfer is obtained by integration over dN_v under consideration of Maxwell's law. If we assume for simplicity that all the molecules have the same velocity $\bar{v}$, then $\int dN_v = N$ and

$$\Delta Г = \frac{1}{3} \bar{v}_m \bar{l} N \left(\frac{\partial Г}{\partial z}\right) \tag{12-9}$$

I,13. Transfer of Momentum. Internal Friction. We consider as property $Г$ the momentum of a streaming gas in the x, y plane, the direction of its velocity u being parallel to the positive x direction, so that $u = u(x)$. From Eq. 12-9 we obtain, setting $Г = mu$ and $Nm = \rho$

$$\Delta Г = \frac{1}{3} \bar{v}_m \bar{l} N m \frac{\partial u}{\partial z} = \frac{1}{3} \bar{v}_m \bar{l} \rho \frac{\partial u}{\partial z} \tag{13-1}$$

The quantity u is now the average velocity component of the gas molecules in the x direction (which would be 0 for a gas at rest), m the mass of a molecule, and ρ the density. Eq. 13-1 gives the transfer of momentum per unit time and per unit area in the x, y plane. For an element of the x, y plane, $dxdy$, the transferred momentum per unit time is equal to the force of friction, or

$$\frac{1}{3} \rho \bar{v}_m \bar{l} dxdy \frac{\partial u}{\partial z} = \mu dxdy \frac{\partial u}{\partial z} \tag{13-2}$$

where μ by definition is the friction coefficient or viscosity coefficient. From the kinetic theory, we thus obtain

$$\mu = \tfrac{1}{3}\rho\bar{v}_m\bar{l} \tag{13-3}$$

A more accurate calculation, taking into account the Maxwellian velocity distribution law and the persistence of velocities after the impact led Chapman [3] to the same relation, but with the numerical factor 0.499 instead of 0.333, which already has been mentioned in Art. 4, Eq. 4-4. It should be pointed out that μ as expressed in these equations is independent of the pressure, since the product $\rho\bar{l}$ is pressure independent,

l being inversely proportional to ρ at constant temperature. For the temperature dependence of μ see Art. 22.

I,14. External Friction and Slip. The process discussed in Art. 12 and 13 may be caused by the relative motion of two plane plates separated by a distance d, parallel to each other and to the x, y plane. The x axis may be in the direction of the relative velocity. Let the velocity of the lower plate be U_1, and of the upper plate U_2. In the stationary state, a velocity gradient $\partial u/\partial z$ will establish itself in the gas between the plates, so that

$$\int_0^d \frac{\partial u}{\partial z}\, dz = U_2 - U_1 \tag{14-1}$$

The continuum theory would suggest a linear dependence of u on z

$$\frac{\partial u}{\partial z} = \frac{U_2 - U_1}{d} = \alpha$$

as shown in Fig. I,14, u being the free stream velocity of the gas at a distance z from the plate with the velocity U_1.

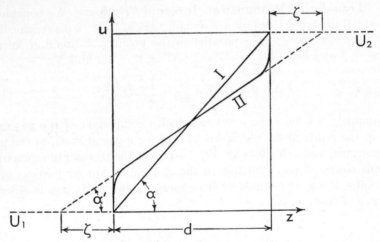

Fig. I,14.   Velocity gradient in laminar flow.

This situation may be expected to hold for $\bar{l} \ll d$, i.e. at large gas pressures or at a large distance between the plates. If the gas pressure is reduced so that the mean free path cannot be neglected in comparison with d, a change in the velocity gradient is to be expected. If we consider a thin layer of gas adjacent to the lower plate, the average velocity component in the x direction of the gas molecules in this layer at a distance δz from the lower plate *will not* be

$$\bar{u} = U_1 + \left(\frac{\partial u}{\partial z}\right)\delta z \tag{14-2}$$

but has to be calculated as follows: One half of the molecules contained in this layer had their last collision with the wall, while the other half had their last collision with a gas molecule at a distance $z \cong \bar{l}$ from the wall. The latter group will, therefore, have an average velocity component in the x direction of U_1 which is approximately equal to the free stream velocity of the gas at $z = \bar{l}$, while the first group, if we assume cosine reflection from the wall, will have an average velocity component equal U_1. The average for the whole layer is, therefore

$$\bar{u}_1 = \tfrac{1}{2}(U_1 + u_1') \tag{14-3}$$

and is independent of z. Similarly, the molecules in the layer near the upper plate will have an average velocity component $\bar{u}_2$ equal to

$$\bar{u}_2 = \tfrac{1}{2}(U_2 + u_2') \tag{14-4}$$

where u_2' is the free stream velocity in the gas at about the distance $\bar{l}$ from the upper plate.

Eq. 14-3 and 14-4 show that there is a discontinuity of velocity in the immediate vicinity of the wall; that means that the infinitesimal gas layer adjacent to the wall does not have the same velocity as the wall. In a formal way, such a velocity jump can be obtained by the following method: We consider a layer of the thickness δ and the frictional forces acting on it. On the side facing the gas, the frictional force acting on a surface element $dx\,dy$ is

$$dF_{\text{int}} = \mu\, dx\, dy\, \frac{\partial u}{\partial z} \tag{14-5}$$

according to the definition of the coefficient of internal friction. In order to obtain a stationary state, this force must be opposed by an equal frictional force between the gas layer and the wall, which we shall assume to be proportional to the velocity difference between the gas layer and the wall. Introducing the proportionality constant ϵ as a "coefficient of external friction" we obtain

$$dF_{\text{ext}} = \epsilon\, dx\, dy\, (\bar{u}_1 - U_1) \tag{14-6}$$

Equating dF_{int} and dF_{ext}, we obtain

$$\mu\, dx\, dy\, \frac{\partial u}{\partial z} = \epsilon\, dx\, dy\, (\bar{u}_1 - U_1) \tag{14-7}$$

and

$$\bar{u}_1 - U_1 = \frac{\mu}{\epsilon}\frac{\partial u}{\partial z} = \zeta\, \frac{\partial u}{\partial z} \tag{14-8}$$

Similarly

$$U_2 - \bar{u}_2 = \frac{\mu}{\epsilon}\frac{\partial u}{\partial z} = \zeta\, \frac{\partial u}{\partial z} \tag{14-9}$$

We may call $\zeta \equiv \mu/\epsilon$ the slip coefficient.

Solving for $\partial u/\partial z$ we have

$$\frac{\partial u}{\partial z} = \frac{\bar{u}_2 - \bar{u}_2}{d} = \frac{U_2 - U_1 - 2\zeta\dfrac{\partial u}{\partial z}}{d} \tag{14-10}$$

or

$$\frac{\partial u}{\partial z} = \frac{U_2 - U_1}{d + 2\zeta} = \alpha' \tag{14-11}$$

The slip therefore produces an apparent increase in the effective distance between the plates, or a decrease in the velocity gradient. Curve II in Fig. I,14 shows schematically the flow distribution under consideration of the slip region.

An interpretation of the slip coefficient on the basis of the kinetic theory can be obtained as follows: The external frictional force per unit area is equal to the tangential component of the momentum transferred to a unit area of the wall per unit time. The molecules striking the wall from the gas have an average momentum in the x direction of mu'_1; after the impact, and assuming the validity of the cosine law, their average momentum is mU_1. The momentum transfer per unit time and area is, therefore

$$\tfrac{1}{4}N\bar{v}_m m(u'_1 - U_1)$$

since the number of impacts per unit time is $\tfrac{1}{4}N\bar{v}_m$. The external frictional force is according to Eq. 14-6 and 14-3

$$F_{\text{ext}} = \epsilon(\bar{u}_1 - U_1) = \epsilon\left(\frac{U_1 + u'_1}{2} - U_1\right) = \epsilon\frac{u'_1 - U_1}{2} \tag{14-12}$$

Hence

$$\epsilon = \tfrac{1}{2}Nm\bar{v}_m$$

But, according to Eq. 13-3

$$\mu = \tfrac{1}{3}Nm\bar{v}_m\bar{l}$$

and

$$\zeta = \frac{\mu}{\epsilon} = \frac{2}{3}\bar{l} \tag{14-13}[5]$$

Consequently, the effect of slip increases rapidly with decreasing pressure or increasing Knudsen number.

The slip effect was first observed by Kundt and Warburg [*23,24*] in connection with their observations of the damping of an oscillating disk in a gas. They found that ζ is inversely proportional to the pressure in the pressure region from 0.6 to 20 mm Hg in agreement with Eq. 14-13. The slip coefficient is also of importance for the flow of gases through tubes and for the fall of small droplets in a gas; for details see the cited references [*10,25,26,27*].

---

[5] If we had used the more accurate factor 0.499, i.e. Eq. 4-4 instead of Eq. 13-3, the numerical factor in Eq. 14-13 would have become approximately 1 instead of $\tfrac{2}{3}$.

At still lower pressures, $\bar{l} \gg d$ we can neglect d in the denominator of Eq. 14-11 because of Eq. 14-13. We then obtain

$$\frac{\partial u}{\partial z} = \frac{U_2 - U_1}{2\varsigma} = \frac{U_2 - U_1}{\frac{4}{3}\bar{l}} \tag{14-14}$$

and for the frictional force under consideration of Eq. 13-3

$$\mu \frac{\partial u}{\partial z} = \frac{\mu}{\frac{4}{3}\bar{l}}(U_2 - U_1) = \frac{1}{4}\rho\bar{v}_m(U_2 - U_1) \tag{14-15}[6]$$

The flow distribution, as shown in Fig. I,14, becomes an almost horizontal line for $\bar{l} \gg d$.

The direct kinetic interpretation is simple. Assuming again validity of the cosine law for the interaction between gas molecules and the wall, we obtain for the average velocity component of the molecules striking the lower plate the value U_2, since all these molecules had their last collision with the upper plate. After a collision with the lower plate, their average velocity will be U_1. The total momentum transfer in the x direction per molecule is, therefore, $m(U_2 - U_1)$. Since the number of molecules impinging on a square centimeter per unit time is $\frac{1}{4}N\bar{v}_m$, and since the momentum transfer per unit time on a surface element $dxdy$ is equal to the frictional force $\mu(\partial u/\partial z)dxdy$, we obtain

$$\mu \frac{\partial u}{\partial z} dxdy = \frac{1}{4} N\bar{v}_m dxdy m(U_2 - U_1)$$

or

$$\mu \frac{\partial u}{\partial z} = \frac{1}{4} \rho\bar{v}_m(U_2 - U_1) = p\sqrt{\frac{\mathfrak{M}}{2\pi RT}}(U_2 - U_1) \tag{14-16}$$

in agreement with Eq. 14-15.

The frictional force in a gas at low density will, according to Eq. 14-15 and 14-16, decrease in proportion to the pressure and will approach zero for $p = 0$. This behavior is in striking contrast to the behavior at higher pressures, where the frictional force, according to Eq. 4-4 and 13-3, is independent of the pressure.

Effects of partial specular reflection are discussed in Chap. 4.

The simple treatment given in this article is only valid for small velocity gradients; a more detailed discussion can be found in IV,E.

I,15. Heat Conduction. The transport equation, Eq. 12-9, leads immediately to an equation for the thermal conductivity if we consider the kinetic energy as the property to be transported. Assuming for simplicity monatomic molecules, we can express the kinetic energy as product of temperature and specific heat. From the well-known equation of

---

[6] Regarding the factor $\frac{1}{4}$ in Eq. 14-15, see footnote 5.

the kinetic theory of gases

$$p = \tfrac{1}{3}Nm\overline{v^2} \tag{15-1}$$

we obtain by multiplication with the molar volume V

$$pV = \tfrac{1}{3}NVm\overline{v^2} = N_\text{A}kT = RT \tag{15-2}$$

and for the average kinetic energy per mole

$$E = \tfrac{1}{2}m\overline{v^2} = \tfrac{3}{2}N_\text{A}kT \tag{15-3}$$

The specific heat is by definition

$$C_V = \left(\frac{\partial E}{\partial T}\right)_V \tag{15-4}$$

or in our case (with $k = 1.37 \times 10^{-16}$ ergs/°K)

$$C_V = \tfrac{3}{2}N_\text{A}k = \tfrac{3}{2}R \text{ erg/mole} \tag{15-5}$$

For diatomic or multiatomic molecules, this value for C_V has to be multiplied by a factor which may be a function of temperature.

In order to have heat flow by conduction[7] between two plates at a distance d separated by a gas, the plates must be at different temperatures T_1 and T_2. As in Art. 14, we expect for small values of $\bar{l}$, i.e. for large pressures, a linear temperature distribution in the gas between the plates. At a distance δz from the lower plate, the temperature will be given by

$$T = T_1 + \left(\frac{\partial T}{\partial z}\right)\delta T \tag{15-6}$$

and the temperature gradient $\partial T/\partial z$ by

$$\frac{\partial T}{\partial z} = \frac{T_2 - T_1}{d} \tag{15-7}$$

The coefficient of heat conduction Λ is formally defined by

$$\frac{dE}{dt} = -\Lambda\,\frac{\partial T}{\partial z} \tag{15-8}$$

where dE/dt is the amount of heat (in ergs) flowing per second through a column of unit cross-sectional area. We want to express Λ in terms of the properties of the gas molecules. The minus sign in Eq. 15-8 means that, if T increases with z, the heat flow is in the opposite direction of the positive z axis.

Writing from Eq. 15-3, 15-4, and 15-5

$$\overline{E} = C_V T = \Gamma \tag{15-9}$$

---

[7] Convection is not discussed here.

we obtain from Eq. 12-9 and 15-8

$$\Delta\Gamma = \frac{1}{3}N\bar{v}_m\bar{l}\frac{\partial\Gamma}{\partial z} = \frac{1}{3}N\bar{v}_m\bar{l}\frac{C_V}{N_A}\frac{\partial T}{\partial z} = \Lambda\frac{\partial T}{\partial z} \qquad (15\text{-}10)$$

or

$$\Lambda = N\frac{\bar{v}_m\bar{l}C_V}{3N_A} \qquad (15\text{-}11)$$

Since $N_A/N = V = \mathfrak{M}/\rho$, we can write

$$\Lambda = \rho\frac{\bar{v}_m\bar{l}C_V}{3\mathfrak{M}} \qquad (15\text{-}12)$$

Comparing this result with Eq. 13-3, we find the important result that

$$\Lambda = \frac{\mu C_V}{\mathfrak{M}} \qquad (15\text{-}13)$$

Since μ was found to be independent of pressure, the heat conductivity is also independent of pressure. The temperature dependence of Λ reflects not only the temperature dependence of μ, but also that of C_V, which is temperature independent only for monatomic cases.

The treatment given above, like that used in Art. 13 for the internal friction, is only the first approximation, assuming a constant velocity $\bar{v}_m$ for all molecules. A more exact theory, developed by Chapman [3] and Enskog [4] leads to a numerical factor in Eq. 15-10, 15-11, and 15-12 different from $\frac{1}{3}$. For details, we have to refer to the cited references.[8]

If the molecules are not monatomic, the contributions of the rotational and vibrational energies to the heat conduction have to be considered. This leads not only to a larger and temperature dependent value of Λ, but also to a different numerical factor. An approximate treatment of this case is due to Eucken; more exact calculations have been carried out by Pidduck [28] and by Chapman and Hainsworth [29].

I,16. Temperature Discontinuity at the Wall.   We consider, as in Art. 15, two horizontal plates of temperatures T_1 and T_2, separated by a gas of thickness d. At small Knudsen numbers, the temperature gradient will be linear and is given by

$$\frac{\partial T}{\partial z} = \frac{T_2 - T_1}{d}$$

If the pressure is reduced, a temperature jump at the wall will develop for the same reasons as stated in Art. 14. Let us call the temperature in the layer adjacent to the lower plate $\bar{l}_1$. The heat transfer between a unit

---

[8] A more detailed discussion of the transport phenomena, particularly in the slip region, is given in Vol. IV and V.

area of wall and the adjacent gas layer will then be given by (Poisson's law)

$$\frac{dE}{dt} = -\Lambda \frac{\partial T}{\partial z} = \lambda (\bar{t}_1 - T_1) \tag{16-1}$$

or

$$\bar{t}_1 - T_1 = \frac{\Lambda}{\lambda} \frac{\partial T}{\partial z} = \gamma \frac{\partial T}{\partial z} \tag{16-2}$$

where $\Lambda/\lambda = \gamma$ may be defined as the temperature jump coefficient. Following exactly the same procedure as in Art. 14, we obtain for the actual temperature gradient in the gas

$$\frac{\partial T}{\partial z} = \frac{T_2 - T_1}{d + 2\gamma} \tag{16-3}$$

This case is represented completely by Fig. I,14 if the ordinates indicate temperature instead of velocity.

Measurements of the temperature jump at the wall were made by several investigators. Very accurate measurements of γ as a function of the pressure were reported by Lasareff [30], who found that γ is inversely proportional to p in agreement with the results obtained in Art. 14 for ζ which also apply in this case.

For very large Knudsen numbers, d in Eq. 16-3 can be neglected against 2γ, and we obtain in analogy to Eq. 14-14 and 14-15

$$\frac{dE}{dt} = -\Lambda \frac{\partial T}{\partial z} = \frac{\Lambda}{l} (T_2 - T_1) = \frac{\rho \bar{v}_m C_V}{3M} (T_2 - T_1) \tag{16-4}$$

This equation shows that the heat conductivity for large Knudsen numbers is proportional to the pressure and independent of d, in contrast to the result obtained in Art. 15, where a pressure independent heat conductivity was found. Eq. 16-4 explains the possibility of producing thermal insulation by vacuum jackets (Dewar vessels) which would not have been possible on the basis of Eq. 15-12.

The factor $\frac{1}{3}$ in Eq. 16-4 is obtained by the use of very crude assumptions. More elaborate treatments lead to the same general result, only with slightly different numerical factors.

We give now the kinetic calculation for heat transfer between two parallel plates at very low gas densities according to Knudsen [31]:

The number of gas molecules per unit volume moving upward, i.e. from the lower plate of temperature T_1 toward the upper plate of temperature T_2 with a velocity between v and $v + dv$ shall be denoted by dN_v. The number reaching a unit area of the upper plate per unit time is then

$$dZ_1 = \tfrac{1}{2} v dN_v \tag{16-5}$$

the factor $\frac{1}{2}$ replacing the factor $\frac{1}{4}$ used in Art. 6, Eq. 6-2, because dN_v

represents only one half of the molecules per unit volume between the plates. Each molecule carries the energy $\frac{1}{2}mv^2$ to the upper plate, assuming again that it is monatomic and that it transfers all of its energy to the plate. The energy thus transferred is

$$dE_1 = \tfrac{1}{4}mv^3 dN_v \tag{16-6}$$

Under consideration of the Maxwellian distribution law

$$dN_v = \frac{4N}{\alpha^3 \sqrt{\pi}} v^2 e^{-\frac{v^2}{\alpha^2}} dv$$

we obtain for the total energy transferred to the upper plate

$$E_1 = \int_0^{\infty} \frac{N_1 m}{\alpha_1^3 \sqrt{\pi}} v^5 e^{-\frac{v^2}{\alpha^2}} dv = \frac{mN_1 \alpha_1^3}{\sqrt{\pi}} \tag{16-7}$$

where N_1 is the total number of molecules per cm³ moving upward between the plates, and $\alpha_1 = \sqrt{2kT_1/m}$ their most probable velocity, assuming that all of them had their last collision with the lower plate of the temperature T_1. Since

$$\bar{v}_m = \sqrt{\frac{8kT}{\pi m}} = \frac{2\alpha}{\sqrt{\pi}}$$

we obtain

$$E_1 = \frac{\pi}{8} mN_1 \bar{v}_{m_1}^3 \tag{16-8}$$

Correspondingly, the lower plate receives from the upper plate per unit time and area

$$E_2 = \frac{\pi}{8} mN_2 \bar{v}_{m_2}^3 \tag{16-9}$$

The net energy loss of the upper plate per unit time and unit area is, therefore,

$$\frac{dE}{dt} = E_2 - E_1 = \frac{\pi}{8} m(N_2 \bar{v}_{m_2}^3 - N_1 \bar{v}_{m_1}^3) \tag{16-10}$$

If the plates are in a large vessel whose walls have a temperature $T = \frac{1}{2}(T_1 + T_2)$, and if T_1 and T_2 are not very different, the number of impacts per unit time on a unit area of each plate and of the walls of the vessel must be the same, or

$$\tfrac{1}{2}N_1 \bar{v}_{m_1} = \tfrac{1}{2}N_2 \bar{v}_{m_2} = \tfrac{1}{4}N\bar{v}_m$$

if N is the number of molecules per unit volume in the vessel and $\bar{v}_m$ their average velocity. We may then write Eq. 16-10

$$\frac{dE}{dt} = \frac{\pi}{16} Nm\bar{v}_m(\bar{v}_{m_2}^2 - \bar{v}_{m_1}^2) \tag{16-10a}$$

But

$$\bar{v}_{m_2}^2 = \frac{8kT_2}{\pi m} \quad \text{and} \quad v_{m_1}^2 = \frac{8kT_1}{\pi m}$$

hence

$$\frac{dE}{dt} = \frac{1}{2} Nk\bar{v}_m(T_2 - T_1) = \frac{2pk}{\sqrt{2\pi mkT}} (T_2 - T_1) \qquad (16\text{-}11)[9]$$

For monatomic gases, $C_v = \frac{3}{2}R = \frac{3}{2}N_A k$, and under consideration of $N = \rho N_A/\mathfrak{M}$, we obtain from Eq. 16-11

$$\frac{dE}{dt} = \frac{\rho \bar{v}_m C_V}{3\mathfrak{M}} (T_2 - T_1) \qquad (16\text{-}12)$$

in agreement with Eq. 16-4. To consider the general case of diatomic or polyatomic molecules where contributions to the energy from rotational and vibrational motion of the atoms within the molecule lead to a larger value of the specific heat, we write for the total energy per mole

$$E = E_{tr} + E_{int}$$

where $E_{tr} = \frac{3}{2}RT$ represents the translational and E_{int} the internal, i.e. the sum of the rotational and the vibrational energies. For a given molecule, we may set

$$\frac{E_{tr} + E_{int}}{E_{tr}} = \beta = \frac{\frac{2}{3}}{\gamma - 1} \qquad (16\text{-}13)$$

where $\gamma = C_p/C_v$ and $E_{int} = (\beta - 1)E_{tr}$.

If β were constant for each molecule, the total heat transferred by a gas consisting of polyatomic molecules would be β times larger than the amount transported by a monatomic gas. Knudsen has pointed out that this is not necessarily the case, because molecules with a relatively small amount of translational energy may carry relatively large amounts of internal energy and vice versa, and that β represents only the ratio of the average total energy over the average translational energy for all molecules. The average internal energy of the molecules with a velocity between v and $v + dv$ is under this assumption $\frac{1}{2}mv^2(\beta - 1)$ and the amount of internal energy transferred to the upper plate

$$dE_1^{(int)} = \frac{1}{2}vdN_v \times \frac{1}{2}mv^2(\beta - 1) \qquad (16\text{-}14)$$

For the total energy transferred through the internal energy of the molecules, we have to integrate this equation considering the internal energy of each molecule as independent of its translational energy and obtain

$$dE_1^{(int)} = \frac{1}{4}m\bar{v}_1^2(\beta - 1) \int_0^\infty vdN_v = \frac{1}{4}m\bar{v}_1^2(\beta - 1)\bar{v}_1 N_1 \qquad (16\text{-}15)$$

[9] In [5], Knudsen introduces the quantity $\rho_0 = \mathfrak{M}/273R = m/273k$ which represents the density of the gas between the plates at the icepoint and at the pressure of 1 dyne/cm². Using this terminology,

$$\frac{dE}{dt} = \frac{2p}{\sqrt{2\pi\rho_0 \times 273T}} (T_2 - T_1)$$

The net heat loss of the upper plate by this process per unit time and area is therefore

$$\frac{dE_1^{(int)}}{dt} = \frac{1}{4} m(\beta - 1)[\bar{v}_2^2 v_{m_2} N_2 - \bar{v}_1^2 \bar{v}_{m_1} N_1]$$

With $\bar{v}_{m_1} N_1 = \bar{v}_{m_2} N_2 = \frac{1}{2} \bar{v}_m N$ and $\bar{v}^2 = \frac{3kT}{m}$,

$$\frac{dE_1^{(int)}}{dt} = \frac{3}{8} Nk\bar{v}_m(\beta - 1)(T_2 - T_1) \qquad (16\text{-}16)$$

For the total heat transfer, we obtain

$$\frac{dE}{dt} = \frac{1}{2} Nkv_m \left[1 + \frac{3}{4}(\beta - 1)\right](T_2 - T_1)$$

$$= \frac{2pk}{\sqrt{2\pi mkT}} \left[1 + \frac{3}{4}(\beta - 1)\right](T_2 - T_1)$$

$$= \frac{1}{2}\frac{p}{\sqrt{2\pi mkT}} (3\beta - 1)(T_2 - T_1) \qquad (16\text{-}17)$$

For large temperature differences, β will usually depend on the temperatures, and this effect has to be considered in the integration of Eq. 16-15.

The equations for heat conduction obtained above are based on the assumption that the molecules leaving a solid surface after an impact have a velocity distribution corresponding to the temperature of the solid, just as the equations derived in Art. 13 and 14 were based on the assumption of complete cosine scattering. Both assumptions are not necessarily valid. The conditions governing the interactions between gas molecules and solid surfaces and their effect on the transport phenomena are discussed in Chap. 4.

The theoretical treatment of heat transfer through a flowing gas involves very considerable difficulties which have not yet been overcome except for very special cases. A survey of the present status of this problem, including convection, for continuum, free molecular, and intermediate flow conditions, is contained in an ONR report by R. M. Drake and E. D. Kane [32] and is also discussed in IV,E.

CHAPTER 4. INTERACTION WITH SURFACES

I,17. Cosine Scattering and Specular Reflection. Transport of a physical quantity, like momentum or energy, through a gas is always transport between two condensed surfaces. It involves, therefore, two phenomena: transfer from the surfaces to the gas, and transfer through the gas itself. The individual steps involved are collisions, either between gas molecules and the wall, or between gas molecules and gas molecules.

At small Knudsen numbers, i.e. if the distances over which the transport takes place are large compared with the mean free path, the second type of collision will greatly outnumber the first type and will completely control the process. In this region, the transport coefficients are independent of the density. This is easily understood; an increase in density increases the number of available carriers, but decreases, in compensation, the mean free path between collisions or the distance over which the transport can proceed without interference. At large Knudsen numbers, the first type of collision is the controlling process since most of the molecules travel the whole distance without collisions with one another. In the intermediate zone, we find the development of layers in which collisions with the wall are of equal importance as collisions between gas molecules; the layer thicknesses increase with decreasing gas density until they finally fill the whole volume of the system.

In the preceding chapter two assumptions were made in regard to the interaction between gas molecules and the wall. The first stated that a group of gas molecules striking a wall with an average velocity component $\bar{u}$ in a certain direction will, after the impact, have a perfectly random distribution of the direction of their velocities. The second one stated that a group of molecules having a velocity distribution (in magnitude) corresponding to a temperature T_1 will, after an impact with a wall of temperature T_2, possess a velocity distribution corresponding to the temperature T_2 of the wall.

The first assumption is essentially equivalent to the cosine law.[10] It is based on the consideration that in a stationary gas, the number of molecules arriving at a surface element of a wall from a direction making an angle between θ and $\theta + d\theta$ with the normal to the wall is proportional to $\cos \theta$ (compare Eq. 6-1). This is simply an expression of the random distribution in direction of the molecular velocities. The law of detailed balance requires that for an equilibrium state the number of molecules leaving the surface into any given direction is equal to the number arriving from that direction. As a result, we may conclude that the molecules leaving a surface will obey the cosine law.

These considerations do not apply, however, to nonequilibrium processes, for instance to the directional distribution acquired by a group of molecules after striking a surface from a given direction. One may of course *postulate* that the cosine law shall hold for this case also, i.e. that after the impact the number of molecules leaving in a certain direction shall be proportional to the cosine of the angle between this direction and the normal and be independent of the angle of incidence. One could also postulate that the molecules shall be reflected specularly, or, with Maxwell, that a fraction f is scattered according to the cosine law, while a fraction $1 - f$ is reflected specularly. (The quantity f is denoted as

[10] For a detailed discussion of the implications of the cosine law see [34].

scattering coefficient; $1 - f$ as reflection coefficient.) Even more complicated distributions are possible, and have been found experimentally in some cases, e.g. in the scattering of molecular beams by crystal surfaces (Art. 23). It is obvious that such assumptions will influence the calculated values for the transport coefficients for large Knudsen numbers, while at high densities their influence will be negligible, since then the interaction between the gas molecules and the wall is of little importance.

We shall now consider the viscosity of a gas under Maxwell's assumption that only a fraction f of the molecules obey the cosine law. The molecules in the "boundary layer" (compare Art. 14) will then assume an average velocity $\bar{u}_1$ which can be found as follows: One half of the molecules, namely those which had their last collision with another gas molecule at a distance of approximately $\bar{l}$ from the wall, will have an average velocity u_1' which is the free stream velocity at $z = \bar{l}$; of the other half, the fraction f will have the velocity of the lower plate U_1, while the fraction $1 - f$, which are reflected in specular fashion, will retain the velocity u_1'. The average velocity is therefore

$$\bar{u}_1 = (1 - \tfrac{1}{2}f)u_1' + \tfrac{1}{2}fU_1$$

and for those adjacent to the upper plate

$$\bar{u}_2 = (1 - \tfrac{1}{2}f)u_2' + \tfrac{1}{2}fU_2$$

The momentum transfer and the external frictional force per unit time and area are therefore

$$\tfrac{1}{4}N\bar{v}_m fm(u_1' - U_1) = \epsilon'(\bar{u}_1 - U_1) = \epsilon'[(1 - \tfrac{1}{2}f)u_1' + \tfrac{1}{2}fU_1 - U_1]$$

$$= \epsilon'\frac{2 - f}{2}(u_1' - U_1)$$

Hence

$$\epsilon' = \frac{1}{2}N\bar{v}_m m\frac{2 - f}{f} \tag{17-1}$$

and

$$\zeta' \equiv \frac{\mu}{\epsilon'} = \frac{2}{3}\bar{l}\frac{2 - f}{f} \tag{17-2}[11]$$

For extremely large Knudsen numbers, Eq. 14-15 will give for the frictional force

$$\mu\frac{\partial u}{\partial z} = \mu\frac{U_2 - U_1}{2\zeta'} = \frac{1}{4}\rho\bar{v}_m\frac{f}{2 - f}(U_2 - U_1) \tag{17-3}$$

For the flow through tubes we obtain the same equations as in Art. 8 and 9, except that the resistance given in Eq. 8-5 has to be multiplied by a factor, $f/(2 - f)$, or the flow rate by the inverse factor $(2 - f)/f$.

---

[11] If the Chapman-Enskog factor $0.499 \cong \tfrac{1}{2}$ instead of the Clausius factor $\tfrac{1}{3}$ is used, $\zeta' = \bar{l}[(2 - f)/f]$. (See also footnote 5.)

This factor is valid only for sufficiently long tubes, since it would give an infinite flow for $f \to 0$. In reality, the resistance should then become equal to that of an orifice of the same cross-sectional area. In other words, the resistance of a tube has to be expressed by the following modification of Eq. 9-1, in which only the second term is multiplied by $f/(2-f)$. This leads to

$$W_t = \frac{1}{d^2}\sqrt{\frac{32}{\pi}} + \frac{f}{2-f}\frac{L}{d^3}\sqrt{\frac{18}{\pi}} \qquad (17\text{-}4)$$

The coefficients ζ' and f can be determined experimentally from measurements of the frictional forces in gases. These may be carried out by a determination of the damping of oscillating disks and spheres [45], the fall of small droplets in air and other gases [26], the flow through tubes at low pressure [24], and the deflection of a cylinder surrounded by a revolving cylinder in a gas at low pressures [33]. A few values are given in Table I,17.

Table I,17. Scattering and slip coefficients.

Gas	Surface	$\zeta \times 10^7$, cm for 1 atm and room temp	f	Method	Observer	Reference
Air	Glass	82	–	Flow	Warburg	[24]
Air	Oil	81	0.9	Droplets	Millikan	[26]
He	Oil	230	0.87	"	"	"
H_2	Oil	88	0.93	"	"	"
Air	Hg	66	1.00	"	"	"
Air	Ag_2O	69	0.89	Deflection	Blankenstein	[33]
He	Ag_2O	190	1.0	"	"	"
H_2	Ag_2O	121	1.0	"	"	"
O_2	Ag_2O	72	0.99	"	"	"

On the basis of his flow experiments, Gaede [59] has suggested that molecules may be reflected back into the direction of their incidence, but this explanation does not seem to be supported by other evidence [34].

Direct experimental tests of the cosine law using the molecular beam method are discussed in Chap. 5.

I,18. Thermal Accommodation Coefficient. Experimental determinations of the heat conduction through gases at low pressures lead to the result that the observed thermal conductivity is always smaller than calculated from kinetic theory as outlined in Art. 15 and 16. This discrepancy was found to be larger in hydrogen than in air, and it increases in general with decreasing density of the gas. The qualitative explanation given by several observers [36, p. 46] was that the energy exchange between a gas molecule and a wall is generally incomplete. As a measure for the degree of energy exchange, Knudsen introduced a quantity which he called the accommodation coefficient, and which he defined by the equation

$$\alpha_K = \frac{T_1' - T_0}{T_1 - T_0} \tag{18-1}$$

where T_0 denotes the temperature of the impinging gas molecules, T_1 that of the wall, and T_1' that of the gas molecules reemitted from the wall.

Table I,18. Thermal accommodation coefficients.

Gas	Surface	Temperature	α	Observer	Reference
H_2	bright Pt		0.32	Knudsen	[36]
H_2	black Pt		0.59	"	"
O_2	bright Pt		0.808	"	"
O_2	black Pt		0.934	"	"
CO_2	bright Pt		0.843	"	"
CO_2	black Pt		0.959	"	"
He	Wo	0°C	0.057	Roberts	[61]
He	Wo	−80°C	0.047	"	"
He	Wo	−192°C	0.025	"	"
He	Pt	450°K	0.21	Oliver	[35]
N_2	Pt	700°K	0.50	"	"
A	Pt	650°K	0.65	"	"
He	Wo	800°K	0.12	"	"
N_2	Wo	850°K	0.35	"	"
A	Wo	850°K	0.45	"	"

Obviously, $\alpha_K = 0$ for $T_1' = T_0$, i.e. for no energy exchange between wall and gas molecules, and $\alpha_K = 1$ for $T_1' = T_1$ or for complete energy exchange.

While the velocity distribution of the impinging molecules may be assumed to be Maxwellian, that of the molecules leaving the wall will be Maxwellian only if $\alpha_K = 0$ or $\alpha_K = 1$, or if the temperatures T_1 and T_2 are not far apart. Otherwise, the velocity distribution will be distorted and, as Blodgett and Langmuir [60] pointed out, the temperature T_1' will not have a clearly defined meaning. They suggested, therefore, another definition for the accommodation coefficient, namely the actual heat transferred, W_{act}, from the wall to the gas as found by experiments, divided by the theoretical heat transferred, W_{th}, as defined in Art. 16, or

$$\alpha_L = \frac{W_{act}}{W_{th}} \tag{18-2}$$

Under consideration of Eq. 16-4, we can write for monatomic gases,

$$\alpha_L = \frac{W_{\text{act}} \cdot 3\mathfrak{M}}{\rho \bar{v}_m C_V (T_1 - T_0)} = \frac{W_{\text{act}} \cdot 2\mathfrak{M}}{\rho \bar{v}_m R (T_1 - T_0)} = \frac{W_{\text{act}} \sqrt{2\pi m k T}}{\rho \cdot 2k (T_1 - T_0)} \quad \text{(18-3)}$$

where W_{act} is expressed per unit wall area and unit time, and $C_V = \frac{3}{2}R$. T is the average temperature of the gas.

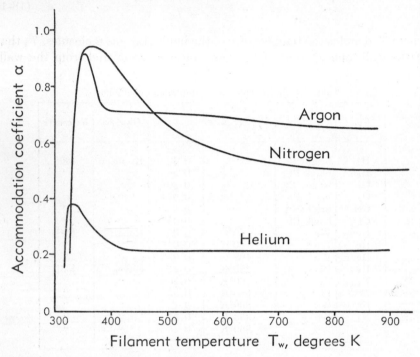

Fig. I,18a. Accommodation coefficient of helium, nitrogen, and argon on a platinum filament as function of the filament temperature; bulb temperature 300°K (after Oliver).

For polyatomic gases, if the notation of Art. 16 is used, the factor $C_V(T_1 - T_0)$ has to be replaced in accordance with Eq. 16-17 by

$$\frac{k}{4} \int_{T_0}^{T_1} (3\beta - 1)dT$$

In the notation used by Langmuir, $C_V = \beta' k$ and the factor assumes the form

$$k \int_{T_0}^{T_1} (\beta' + \tfrac{1}{2})dT$$

In most experimental arrangements for the determinations of accommodation coefficients, a thin wire is surrounded by a gas at low pressure contained in a cylindrical tube whose walls are kept at a constant temperature T_0, and the amount of the electrical energy W_{act} per unit area and time required to maintain the temperature of the wire at a value T_1 is measured. If the radius of the wire is small compared to that of the tube, each molecule leaving the wire will collide many times with the wall before striking the wire again. Consequently, the velocity distribution of the gas molecules before the impact with the wire can be assumed to correspond to the temperature of the wall T_0 even if the accommodation coefficient between the gas and the wall is not unity, and T_0 may replace

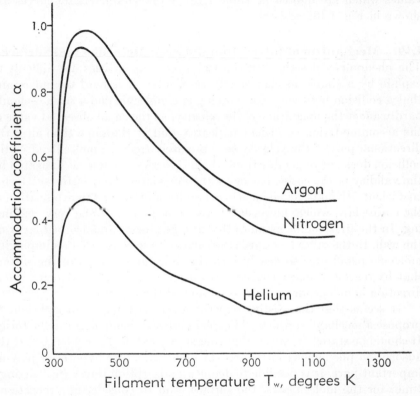

Fig. I,18b.   Accommodation coefficient of helium, nitrogen, and argon on a tungsten filament as function of the filament temperature; bulb temperature 300°K (after Oliver).

the average temperature T in the numerator of Eq. 18-3. Corrections for radiation loss, heat conduction to the ends of the wire, and nonuniformity of temperature have to be applied.

In Knudsen's earlier investigations [36], heat transfer was measured between concentric cylinders and between a wire and the wall of a tube as described above. As stated before, Knudsen's definition of the accommodation coefficient is only applicable for small temperature differences, while for the more recent work, where large temperature differences were used, the definition given by Langmuir is preferable.

In general, the accommodation coefficient varies over a wide range with the nature of the gas, the material and the condition of the surface, and the temperatures of the gas and the wire. Results from a recent thesis by Oliver [*35*] show that the effect of pressure is negligible, but that the variation with temperature is most rapid when the temperature difference between wire and gas is about 50°C. For large temperature differences, the accommodation coefficients given in [*35*] approach constant values which are quoted in Table I,18. A few characteristic curves are shown in Fig. I,18a and 18b.

I,19. Mechanism of Interaction Between Molecules and Surfaces. The phenomena described in the two preceding articles are difficult to explain by a simple mechanism. In particular, it is hard to understand that a collision between a fast-moving gas molecule and a surface should hardly affect the magnitude of its velocity, as the small observed value of the accommodation coefficient indicates, and at the same time alter the directional part of the velocity so completely that the molecule after the collision does not remember from which direction it came, as indicated by the validity of the cosine law or by the very large value of the scattering coefficient f. Knudsen [*36*] mentions two hypotheses for an explanation of the cosine law, which, however, he does not consider to be very convincing. In the first one he assumes that the gas forms an adsorbed layer on the wall. In the other he regards the surface as so rough that an impinging molecule penetrates so deeply into the holes and valleys of the surface that by reason of many collisions it finally leaves with a velocity whose direction is independent of the direction of the incidence.

It seems that the existing experimental material is not sufficient to propose a mechanism which will explain all the phenomena satisfactorily. It should be stated, however, that there is a great deal of evidence that the adsorption phenomena introduced in Knudsen's first hypothesis play an important part. It is possible to define an adsorption time τ (or "sitting" time) for the molecules on the surface, and to consider as "reflection" the case where τ is very small, using for comparison the natural period of the vibrations of the molecules in the surface. One might expect that for large values of τ the accommodation coefficient α and the scattering coefficient f are both unity, while for small values they approach zero. The observations stated in the preceding paragraph would lead to the assumption that the values of τ required for energy exchange are much larger than those required for momentum exchange.

Measurements of the adsorption time τ by nonsteady flow experiments were carried out by Clausing [*37*]. His results can be interpreted in terms of an equation developed by Frenkel [*38*] on the basis of statistical mechanics:

$$\tau = \tau_0 e^{-\frac{\varphi}{kT}} = \tau_0 e^{\frac{U}{kT}} \tag{19-1}$$

in which τ_0 represents the oscillation period of the adsorbed molecules and φ their potential energy. The heat of adsorption in calories per mole is $-U = N_A\varphi$. Clausing's measurements for argon on glass gave $\tau_0 = 1.7 \times 10^{-14}$ seconds and $U = 3800$ cal/mole; for τ he found 7.5×10^{-4} seconds at 78°K and 3.1×10^{-5} seconds at 90°K. For such long times, accommodation coefficients close to unity may be expected, but unfortunately, no experimental data are available for this system. The data given by Oliver show that the accommodation coefficient for argon on platinum may exceed 0.9, but they also indicate that it falls off sharply below a surface temperature of 350°K. Clausing's values for neon on glass gave sitting times of 10^{-7} seconds but were good only in order of magnitude. He also noticed that the treatment of the surface has a great effect on the sitting time.

Other experimental studies have shown that adsorbed phases of the nature of a two-dimensional gas exist as an intermediate phase between gases and solid surfaces; for further details we refer to the cited references. Additional information obtained by the use of the molecular beam method is given in Chap. 5.

CHAPTER 5. MOLECULAR BEAMS

I,20. Method and Technique. In the preceding chapters, the composition of a gas as consisting of individual, discrete particles was always presupposed, and the mechanical properties of these particles were entered as parameters in the theoretical arguments. The observations referred to, however, were taken under conditions where these properties could be deduced from measured quantities only in an indirect way. The molecular beam method, used first by Dunoyer [*39*] but developed into an extremely powerful tool for the investigation of fundamental problems by O. Stern and his collaborators, makes it possible to determine these quantities in a direct and, at least theoretically, very simple manner.

A molecular beam is defined as a stream of molecules which are moving in a highly evacuated space in almost parallel trajectories within the geometrical limits imposed by a set of apertures. Such a beam is produced if a vessel A (Fig. I,20), containing a gas or vapor and equipped with a small orifice or slit O, is brought into a highly evacuated envelope B. The molecules inside A whose velocity vectors are pointing toward O will escape through O and continue in the evacuated space B along a straight path. A second aperture C selects from the molecules effusing from O in all directions those whose velocity vectors lie within the solid angle determined by the limits of O and C and the distance d between them. This group of molecules forms the molecular beam. If O and C are small compared to d, the paths of the molecules in the beam are practically parallel. Consequently, collisions between molecules will occur only when a faster molecule overtakes a slower one moving in the same direction; since this happens only rarely, the beam may be considered for all practical purposes as unidirectional and collision free.

In the absence of forces acting on the molecules, they move along straight trajectories with the velocity obtained at their last collision before leaving the vessel A. Conversely, forces acting on them will produce a deflection which can be measured and from which the nature and magnitude of these forces can be deduced.

It follows from the above that molecular beams require large Knudsen numbers for the emitting orifice as well as for the rest of the apparatus. If the pressure behind the orifice is so large that the mean free path is not large compared to the diameter, collisions will occur in front of the slit and the velocity distribution will be distorted. At still higher pressures, hydrodynamic flow will set in, leading to the formation of a jet

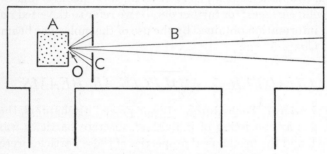

Fig. I,20.   Molecular beam apparatus.

which will not remain confined to the geometrical pattern determined by the apertures of O and C but will spread out with turbulent motion at its boundaries. Moreover, the velocity distribution of the molecules in a jet is not Maxwellian and does not correspond to a temperature, while that in an ideal molecular beam is governed by Maxwell's law, as modified in Art. 11.

A molecular beam apparatus consists of at least these four components: (1) a source, (2) a collimating system, (3) a detector, and (4) a vacuum envelope in which the other components are arranged and where the pressure can be maintained at such a low level that the mean free path is several times as large as the distance between the source and the detector. Additional components may be installed depending on the type of investigation desired, for instance: velocity selectors, scattering chambers, reflecting surfaces, electric or magnetic fields, and others.

A molecular beam source for use with a vapor consists of a small oven equipped with a heater and a defining orifice which contains the beam substance. The orifice usually has the cross section of a long rectangle (slit), since in most applications the beam deflection in only one direction is important. For use with permanent gases, the source consists of a slit connected to a reservoir containing the gas. Heating and cooling arrangements are provided if it is desired to vary the temperature of the beam. Since the earlier molecular beam experiments were carried out with vapors, the source is frequently referred to as oven and its orifice as oven slit even when it is not heated.

Molecular beams consist of neutral particles which cannot be focused like charged particles by electric or magnetic fields. The collimating system of a molecular beam apparatus therefore consists, in the simplest case, of a second slit. This collimating slit and the oven slit define the beam, consisting for geometrical reasons of a central region with constant intensity, the umbra, and a region on either side, the penumbra, where the intensity drops linearly from the value in the umbra to zero. Additional slits may be introduced, either for better geometrical definition of the beam or for other purposes, like ease of alignment or vacuum control. Slits are frequently only a few hundredths of a millimeter wide and several millimeters long, requiring extremely careful alignment and mechanical stability of their supports.

The detector technique depends in a large measure on the physical and chemical properties of the beam substance. For many vapors, a condensation target, i.e. a highly polished and usually cooled metal or glass plate, forms a sensitive detector, though the intensity distribution cannot easily be deduced from the appearance of the trace. For permanent gases, a small chamber equipped with an entrance canal and a sensitive pressure gauge is frequently used. Other detectors utilize specific chemical or electric properties of the beam substance, like the surface ionization detector for alkali metal atoms.

The length of a molecular beam may vary between a few centimeters and several meters. As a result, the vacuum envelopes will offer many different design problems. In any case, the vacuum pumps must be able to maintain a pressure which corresponds to a sufficient mean free path; for long beams pressures of 10^{-7} mm Hg or less are required. Cooled surfaces or traps can be used to assist the pumps in the removal of condensable vapors, one cm² of surface cooled by liquid air has an equivalent pumping speed of 10 liters/sec for vapors. Vacuum envelopes as large as 30 cm in diameter and several meters in length have been used in actual experiments.

For more details regarding the molecular beam technique in general, we refer particularly to [40]. In the following articles, we shall deal with its applications to problems related to the kinetic theory of gases.

I,21. Molecular Velocities. The first molecular beam experiment performed by Dunoyer [39] did nothing more than demonstrate the straight-line propagation of gas molecules when undisturbed by collisions. The apparatus consisted of an evacuated glass tube, about 20 cm long, divided by two circular diaphragms into three compartments. A small amount of redistilled sodium was introduced into the first chamber which was then heated from the outside until the sodium began to vaporize. After several minutes, a deposit of metallic sodium appeared on the closed bottom of the third compartment, having exactly the form and dimensions of the umbra and penumbra to be expected.

The next experiment which marks the beginning of the molecular beam method as a research tool consisted of the measurement of the molecular velocity by Stern [41]. A framework, holding source, collimating slit, and detector, was rotated under an evacuated bell jar. The deflections from the straight path caused by clockwise and counterclockwise rotation of the frame allowed an estimate of the average velocity of the molecules with an accuracy of about 10 per cent, but the rather primitive arrangement did not permit an analysis of the velocity distribution in the beam. This distribution is not, as mentioned in Art. 11, the ordinary Maxwellian velocity distribution of a gas at rest, but is modified by the replacement of the factor v^2 by v^3. The first attempt to measure this distribution, which is represented by Eq. 11-1, is due to Costa, Smyth, and Compton [42]; more decisive results were obtained by the use of a rotating system of two toothed wheels (as in Fizeau's method for the measurement of the velocity of light) by Lammert [43] for mercury, and by Estermann, Frisch, and Stern [44] for helium. Other methods employed the deflection of alkali metal beams by magnetic fields [46] and the gravitational field [22] or the direct measurement of the time of flight from the source to the detector [47,48,49]. In all these cases, the distribution given by Eq. 11-1 was verified within experimental errors of a few per cent, except that very accurate experiments [22], using gravity deflection, showed a deficiency of slow molecules produced by molecular collisions in the vicinity of the oven slit.

I,22. Mean Free Path and Collisions. The attenuation of a molecular beam passing through a residual gas can be expressed by the equation

$$I = I_0 e^{-\frac{L}{l}} \qquad (22\text{-}1)$$

where I_0 is the intensity of the "unweakened" or "vacuum" beam, I the intensity of the attenuated beam, L the length of its passage through the gas, and l the mean free path. Experiments of this kind provide, therefore, a direct method for the determination of the mean free path and allow a comparison with the values obtained from measurements of the viscosity or the heat conduction as discussed in Art. 13 and 15.

Measurements by Knauer and Stern [50] indicated that the mean free path calculated from the weakening of a hydrogen beam in hydrogen gas was only 44 per cent of the value derived from viscosity measurements. This discrepancy is not accidental; it is due to a different physical interpretation of the collision process in both cases. The viscosity method registers only such encounters which are associated with a considerable amount of momentum transfer, while the molecular beam method regards as collision any interaction which removes the molecule from the beam, that is, any interaction which deflects it by a very small angle.

It would appear, therefore, that the mean free path as deduced from the attenuation of a molecular beam should decrease as the solid angle occupied by the beam becomes smaller or as the angle necessary to remove the molecules from the beam decreases, or as the resolving power of the apparatus increases. Actually, this is true only to a certain degree if quantum mechanics is applied to the scattering process.

Even on the basis of classical mechanics, the simple model used in Art. 3 considering the molecules as hard elastic spheres of a definite diameter σ is not able to explain the observed behavior of gases. Measurements of the viscosity at different temperatures show that the mean free path increases with temperature. This means that μ is not proportional to $\bar{v}_m$ or $\sqrt{T}$ as indicated by Eq. 13-3, but that it increases somewhat more rapidly with temperature. This behavior was explained by Sutherland [51] through the assumption of attractive forces between molecules. But even the theoretical results obtained on the basis of the hard sphere model without attractive forces differ in classical and quantum theory.

Since the mean free path varies with pressure, it is more practical to use the concept of the scattering cross section Q as a basis for discussion. For hard spheres, this quantity is classically

$$Q = \pi\sigma^2 \tag{22-2}$$

where σ is the diameter of the molecules, or, in the case of encounters between different sized molecules, the sum of their respective radii. In quantum mechanics, the collision is pictured as the scattering of the de Broglie waves associated with the two particles. If we consider one particle at rest and the other moving with the relative velocity v_{rel}, the de Broglie wave of the moving particle has the wavelength $\lambda = h/mv_{rel}$ where $m = (m_1 + m_2)/m_1m_2$ is the reduced mass of the two particles. This wave is scattered from an opaque sphere of radius σ. The scattering cross section in this case is, according to Massey and Mohr [52],

$$Q = 2\pi \int_0^\pi I(\theta) \sin\theta d\theta \tag{22-3}$$

where $I(\theta)$ is the scattering function, namely the scattered intensity of beam atoms per unit solid angle forming an angle θ with the direction of the incident beam. This function shows a large increase for small angle scattering and leads to a cross section Q about twice as large as the classical value $\pi\sigma^2$. While for "classical" hard elastic spheres the scattering probability is the same for all angles, "quantum" scattering results in a preference for forward scattering. This result is similar to that obtained classically for hard spheres exerting attractive forces on one another, but with this important distinction: any classical theory involving attractive forces leads to an infinite cross section for scattering angles approaching zero, while quantum theory under the same conditions leads to a finite value of Q even for zero angle scattering. As a result, molecular beam experiments lead to meaningful results for the scattering cross section if the resolving power is sufficiently large so that an increase toward smaller angles will not materially alter the number of scattered molecules.

Measurements of the scattering cross sections of alkali metal atoms in various gases were carried out by Mais [53] with a resolving power of 4 minutes of arc, Rosin and Rabi [54] with a resolving power of 1 minute of arc, and Estermann, Foner, and Stern [55] and Foner [56] with a resolving power of 5 seconds of arc. In the last cited work, the variation of the mean free path with the velocity of the beam atoms was also measured directly. Values for the sums of the classical radii obtained in [53–55] are given in Table I,22. It is apparent that the scattering cross sec-

Table I,22. Effective collision radii σ for alkali atoms in various gases.

Encounter	$\sigma = r_1 + r_2 \ (\times 10^8 \ \text{cm})$		
	[53]	[54]	[55]
K-He	6.91	7.25	
K-Ne	8.74	9.10	
K-A	13.0	13.6	
Cs-He		7.18	12.0
Cs-Ne		9.56	
Cs-A		13.5	
Cs-N$_2$			17.2
Cs-Cs			27.3

tions seem to increase with the resolving power of the apparatus, and it is also interesting to note that the sum of the radii for the Cs-He encounter appears to be smaller than the classical radius of the Cs atom itself. This is another indication of the presence of attractive forces in these encounters.

I,23. Scattering from Surfaces. The wave nature of a molecular beam is even more evident in the scattering of molecules from solid crystal surfaces. The de Broglie wavelength $\lambda = h/mv$ for He or H_2 molecules with thermal velocities is of the order of 10^{-8} cm, or of the order of magnitude of the lattice constants of crystals. Molecular beams of He atoms or H_2 molecules were "reflected" from freshly cleaved surfaces of LiCl crystals by Estermann, Frisch, and Stern [*57,44*] and those of H atoms by Johnson [*58*]. The intensity distribution observed in these experiments agrees in all details with the diffraction patterns calculated for plane waves diffracted from a crossed grating, and it shows a "spectral" distribution of wavelengths corresponding to the velocity distribution in a molecular beam. Variation of the temperature of the beam at the source produced a corresponding shift in the diffraction pattern. Using a velocity selector as described in Art. 21, Estermann, Frisch, and Stern [*44*] were able to compare the de Broglie wavelength λ measured by the angle of diffraction ϕ and the lattice constant a of the crystal with λ computed from the mass of the molecule and the velocity v measured by the dimensions and the angular velocity of the selector, and to verify the de Broglie relation with an accuracy of one per cent. These results are of fundamental importance since they not only affirm the validity of the basic concepts of wave mechanics, but also show that the de Broglie relation applies not only to elementary particles, but also to atoms and even to polyatomic molecules.

Since the spectral distribution in the reflected beam represents the velocity of the incident beam and not that of the temperature of the reflecting surface, these experiments are an illustration of a case where the thermal accommodation coefficient α is zero. An estimate of the integrated intensity over the diffraction pattern leads to the result that the scattering coefficient f must also be very small. Both these results may be explained by the assumption that the time of adsorption τ (Art. 19) is short compared to the natural frequency of the ions forming the crystal lattice. If this condition were not fulfilled, cosine scattering would have to be expected.

For beams of heavier molecules, the de Broglie wavelength becomes considerably shorter than the lattice constant. As stated in Art. 1, the wave properties of the beam should then become unimportant and diffraction patterns should no longer be observable. But specular reflection should still exist in accordance with the laws of geometrical optics. Experiments have shown, however, that the fraction of specularly reflected molecules for neon, argon, or nitrogen beams is relatively small. This result indicates that the adsorption time for these gases is considerably longer, but further experiments are needed in order to throw more light on the problem of interaction between gas molecules and solid surfaces.

I,24. Cited References.

1. Clausius, R. *Mechanische Warmetheorie*. Braunschweig, 1867.
2. Maxwell, J. C. *Phil. Mag. 19*, 28 (1860).
3. Chapman, S. *Phil. Trans. 217*, 115 (1918).
4. Enskog, D. *Physik. Z. 12*, 56, 533 (1911); *Dissertation*, Uppsala, 1917.
5. Knudsen, M. *Ann. Physik 28*, 999 (1909).

6. Volmer, M., and Estermann, I.   *Z. Physik 7*, 1 (1921).
7. Knudsen, M.   *Ann. Physik 47*, 697 (1915).
8. Bennewitz, K.   *Ann. Physik 59*, 193 (1919).
9. Clausing, P.   *Ann. Physik 4*, 567 (1930).
10. Knudsen, M.   *Ann. Physik 28*, 75 (1909).
11. Smoluchowski, M. V.   *Ann. Physik 33*, 1559 (1910).
12. Clausing, P.   *Ann. Physik 14*, 134 (1932).
13. Dushman, S.   *Scientific Foundations of Vacuum Technique.* Wiley, 1949.
14. Clausing, P.   *Ann. Physik 12*, 961 (1932).
15. Knudsen, M.   *Ann. Physik 33*, 1435 (1910).
16. Bronsted, M., and Hevesy, G. v.   *Z. physik. Chem. 99*, 189 (1921).
17. Harkins, W., and Madorsky, S. L.   *Phys. Rev. 21*, 385 (1923).
18. Stern, O., and Volmer, M.   *Ann. Physik 59*, 225 (1919).
18a. Cohen, K.   *The Theory of Isotope Separation.* McGraw-Hill, 1951.
19. Clausing, P.   *Physica 9*, 65 (1929).
20. Clausing, P.   *Z. Physik 66*, 471 (1930).
21. Stern, O.   *Z. Physik 3*, 417 (1920).
22. Estermann, I., Simpson, O. C., and Stern, O.   *Phys. Rev. 65*, 346 (1944).
23. Kundt, A., and Warburg, E.   *Ann. Physik 155*, 337 (1875).
24. Warburg, E.   *Ann. Physik 159*, 339 (1876).
25. Knudsen, M., and Weber, S.   *Ann. Physik 36*, 981 (1911).
26. Millikan, R. A.   *Phys. Rev. 21*, 222 (1923); *22*, 1 (1923).
27. Epstein, P. S.   *Phys. Rev. 23*, 710 (1924).
28. Pidduck, F. B.   *Proc. Roy. Soc. London 101*, 101 (1922).
29. Chapman, S., and Hainsworth, W.   *Phil. Mag. 48*, 593 (1924).
30. Lasareff, P.   *Ann. Physik 37*, 233 (1912).
31. Knudsen, M.   *Ann. Physik 34*, 593 (1911).
32. Drake, R. M., and Kane, E. D.   A summary of the present status of heat transfer in a rarefied gas. *Office of Nav. Research Rept. He-150-73, Univ. Calif. Berkeley*, 1950.
33. Blankenstein, E.   *Phys. Rev. 22*, 582 (1923).
34. Clausing, P.   *Ann. Physik 4*, 533 (1930).
35. Oliver, R. N.   *Thesis.* Calif. Inst. Technol., 1950.
36. Knudsen, M.   *Kinetic Theory of Gases.* Methuen, London, 1934.
37. Clausing, P.   *Ann. Physik 7*, 489 (1930).
38. Frenkel, J.   *Z. Physik 26*, 117 (1924).
39. Dunoyer, L.   *Compt. rend. 152*, 594 (1911).
40. Estermann, I.   *Revs. Mod. Phys. 18*, 300 (1946).
41. Stern, O.   *Z. Physik 2*, 49 (1920); *3*, 417 (1920).
42. Costa, J. L., Smyth, H. D., and Compton, K. T.   *Phys. Rev. 30*, 349 (1927).
43. Lammert, B.   *Z. Physik 56*, 244 (1929).
44. Estermann, I., Frisch, R., and Stern, O.   *Z. Physik 73*, 348 (1931).
45. Vogel, H.   *Ann. Physik 43*, 1235 (1914).
46. Ellett, A., and Cohen, V.   *Phys. Rev. 51*, 64 (1937).
47. Knauer, F.   *Z. Physik 125*, 278 (1948).
48. Kofsky, I. L.   *Thesis.* Syracuse University, 1945.
49. Marple, D. T. F.   *Thesis.* Syracuse University, 1950.
50. Knauer, F., and Stern, O.   *Z. Physik 53*, 766 (1929).
51. Sutherland, W.   *Phil. Mag. 36*, 507 (1893).
52. Massey, H. S. W., and Mohr, C. B. O.   *Proc. Royal Soc. London 141*, 454 (1933).
53. Mais, H. W.   *Phys. Rev. 45*, 773 (1934).
54. Rosin, S., and Rabi, I. I.   *Phys. Rev. 48*, 373 (1935).
55. Estermann, I., Foner, S. N., and Stern, O.   *Phys. Rev. 71*, 250 (1947).
56. Foner, S. N.   *Thesis.* Carnegie Inst. Technol., 1945.
57. Estermann, I., Frisch, R., and Stern, O.   *Z. Physik 73*, 348 (1931).
58. Johnson, T. H.   *Phys. Rev. 35*, 1299 (1930).
59. Gaede, W.   *Ann. Physik 41*, 289 (1913).
60. Blodgett, K. B., and Langmuir, I.   *Phys. Rev. 40*, 78 (1932).
61. Roberts, J. K.   *Proc. Roy. Soc. London 129*, 146 (1930); *135*, 192 (1932).

SECTION J

THE THERMODYNAMICS
OF IRREVERSIBLE PROCESSES

C. F. CURTISS

Considerable success has been attained in the application of statistical methods to the study of both equilibrium and nonequilibrium states of matter. Thermodynamics may be considered as a particular phase of statistical mechanics in which one investigates the implications of a few basic results. These results are the three laws of thermodynamics which were originally taken to be first principles which were not deduced from more fundamental ones but which now may be derived by statistical methods from the laws of mechanics. Thermodynamics has proved quite useful in understanding and correlating the properties of equilibrium systems and reversible changes. However, the usual three laws do not contain sufficient information to describe nonequilibrium systems or irreversible processes, except qualitatively.

Because of the success of the ordinary thermodynamics of reversible systems there arises the question of the possible applications of similar methods to the study of irreversible processes. Although this extension has not attained the firm foundation of the equilibrium theory, nevertheless considerable success has been attained in the applications to processes such as transport phenomena, chemical kinetics, etc. If the system is close to equilibrium, it is possible to describe in general terms its rate of approach to equilibrium.

The principles and formulation are known as the thermodynamics of irreversible processes,[1] and have been discussed in considerable detail in books by de Donder [1], Prigogine and Defay [2], Prigogine [3], and de Groot [4]. The extension is based upon two important concepts: (1) the linear law and (2) the Onsager reciprocal relations. Special examples of the applications of these laws have been known for a long time. Such examples are Newton's law of cooling, Lord Kelvin's discussion of the thermoelectric effect, the distribution of current in the elements of an electrical network (so as to minimize the generation of heat), etc. Thus the linear law is a generalization of the empirical relations found to

[1] The material in this section is similar to that in section 11.2 of reference [13].

apply to many special systems only slightly removed from equilibrium. At the present time the linear law is empirical and has no foundation except as a working postulate which seems to be justified by the results. However, the study of the approach of a system to equilibrium is possible through the use of the statistical theory of fluctuations, and it is very likely that the linear law can be justified on this basis. Onsager [5] has shown that if a system is slightly removed from equilibrium the most probable path to equilibrium is well defined. In this manner he was able to prove that the reciprocal relations are closely related to the principle of microscopic reversibility.

J,1. The Linear Law. The time rate of change of the entropy of a system, $\dot{S}$, may be written as the product of two factors or the sum of such terms, i.e.

$$\dot{S} = \frac{1}{T} \sum_i F_i v_i \tag{1-1}$$

Here, the "i" represents the particular dissipative mechanism; the F_i represent the displacements of the system from equilibrium, and the v_i represent the rate of approach to equilibrium. The linear law postulates that the velocities are proportional to the "driving forces," F_i, when the system is near equilibrium:

$$v_i = \sum_j \alpha_{ij} F_j \tag{1-2}$$

The linear law may best be explained by means of several examples. Let us consider a particularly simple system. This system is composed of two parts both enclosed within the same rigid adiabatic enclosure. One part is at a uniform temperature T_1, the other at a uniform temperature T_2. Let us consider a flow of heat from one part to the other. If this flow is slow and if the temperature of each part remains uniform, this change may be considered reversible from the point of view of each part but not from that of the system as a whole. Thus the change of entropy of part one is

$$dS_1 = \frac{\delta Q_1}{T_1} \tag{1-3}$$

and that of part two is

$$dS_2 = \frac{\delta Q_2}{T_2} \tag{1-4}$$

But the entire system is adiabatically isolated, i.e.

$$\delta Q = \delta Q_1 + \delta Q_2 = 0 \tag{1-5}$$

Thus the change in entropy of the system is

$$dS = dS_1 + dS_2 = dQ_1 \left[\frac{1}{T_1} - \frac{1}{T_2} \right] \tag{1-6}$$

Incidentally, according to the second law

$$dS \geqq 0 \tag{1-7}$$

for an adiabatic, isolated system. Hence, as an immediate consequence of Eq. 1-6, we note that if $\delta Q_1 > 0$ (heat flowing into part one) then $T_1 < T_2$; that is, according to the second law, heat flows from the high temperature to the low temperature.

Let us consider a continuous process. Let $\dot{S}$ be the time rate of change of entropy of the system and $\dot{Q}$ the rate of flow of heat. Then from Eq. 1-6

$$\dot{S} = \frac{T_2 - T_1}{T_1 T_2} \dot{Q} \tag{1-8}$$

Now let us consider a limiting case in which the two temperatures are nearly the same. In this case

$$\dot{S} = \frac{\Delta T}{T^2} \dot{Q} \tag{1-9}$$

where $\Delta T = T_2 - T_1$ and T is the geometric mean temperature. Eq. 1-9 gives the rate of increase of entropy as the product of two factors. The first factor $(\Delta T/T^2)$ describes quantitatively the extent of nonequilibrium while the second factor $(\dot{Q})$ represents the flux or flow tending to re-establish equilibrium.

It is clear that whenever ΔT is zero, so is $\dot{Q}$. The "linear law" states that for systems only slightly removed from equilibrium $\dot{Q}$ is proportional to ΔT, i.e.

$$\dot{Q} = \alpha \left(\frac{\Delta T}{T} \right) \tag{1-10}$$

We note that in this case the result is Newton's law of cooling, a well-known empirical result. In many other cases the linear law implies a well-established empirical relation, and may be considered as an extension and generalization of many empirical results.

In any case the rate of creation of entropy can be written in the form

$$\dot{S} = \frac{1}{T} \sum_i F_i v_i \tag{1-11}$$

This is a sum of terms in which the v_i represent, in a generalized sense, rates of flow tending to establish equilibrium and the F_i represent magnitudes of displacement from equilibrium. The linear law asserts that the

F_i act as "driving forces" for the flows and that in the limit that the system is close to equilibrium,

$$v_i = \sum_j \alpha_{ij} F_j \qquad (1\text{-}12)$$

The diagonal elements represent the direct effect of a displacement in producing an associated flow, while the cross terms represent interesting coupling terms. Using Eq. 1-11 and 1-12, it follows that

$$\dot{S} = \frac{1}{T} \sum_{i,j} \alpha_{ij} F_i F_j \qquad (1\text{-}13)$$

The second law states that

$$\dot{S} \geqq 0 \qquad (1\text{-}14)$$

i.e. that the quadratic form of Eq. 1-13 is positive or zero.

As another example of the use of the linear law let us consider a system in which chemical reactions are taking place. It will be shown that the linear law is consistent with the usual expressions for the rates of chemical reactions (when the system is near equilibrium). The entropy of the system is defined as a state function by the relation

$$dS = \frac{1}{T}\left(dE + pdV - \sum_k \mu_k dN_k\right) \qquad (1\text{-}15)$$

where E is the internal energy; p the pressure; V the volume; N_k the number of moles of component k, and μ_k is the chemical potential or partial molar Gibbs free energy.

In discussing the simple system above, we made use of the first term of Eq. 1-15, only, since the system was such that both V and the chemical composition remained constant. In the present case, let us consider a system in which the volume and internal energy remain constant but in which the chemical composition changes. Thus for this example

$$dS = -\frac{1}{T} \sum_k \mu_k dN_k \qquad (1\text{-}16)$$

and the time rate of production of entropy is

$$\dot{S} = -\frac{1}{T} \sum_k \mu_k \Gamma_k \qquad (1\text{-}17)$$

where Γ_k is the net rate of production of molecules of k due to the chemical reactions. This expression may be rearranged by considering explicitly the various reactions which may occur.

Each reaction may be described by the stoichiometric relation

$$\beta_{1j}[1] + \beta_{2j}[2] + \cdots \rightarrow \eta_{1j}[1] + \eta_{2j}[2] + \cdots \qquad (1\text{-}18)$$

the β_{ij} and the η_{ij} being integers and the $[i]$ indicating the ith species. Let the rate constant for the forward reaction be k_j and that for the backward reaction be k_j', so that the rate of the forward reaction is

$$k_j f_1^{\beta_{1j}} f_2^{\beta_{2j}} \cdots \qquad (1\text{-}19)$$

where f_j is the fugacity of component i. A similar expression applies to the backward reaction. Thus the total rate of formation of molecules of i by all of the chemical reactions is

$$\Gamma_i = \sum_j (\eta_{ij} - \beta_{ij})[k_j f_1^{\beta_{1j}} f_2^{\beta_{2j}} \cdots - k_j' f_1^{\eta_{1j}} f_2^{\eta_{2j}} \cdots] \qquad (1\text{-}20)$$

The affinity of the jth reaction is defined as

$$A_j = -\sum_i (\eta_{ij} - \beta_{ij})\mu_i \qquad (1\text{-}21)$$

In terms of these quantities, Eq. 1-17 for the rate of production of entropy becomes

$$\dot{S} = \frac{1}{T} \sum_j A_j v_j \qquad (1\text{-}22)$$

where

$$v_j = k_j f_1^{\beta_{1j}} f_2^{\beta_{2j}} \cdots - k_j' f_1^{\eta_{1j}} f_2^{\eta_{2j}} \cdots \qquad (1\text{-}23)$$

is the net rate of the jth reaction.

It will be noticed that Eq. 1-22 is of the form of Eq. 1-11 described above in connection with the discussion of the linear law. The affinities, A_j, represent the displacement from equilibrium. The usual thermodynamic criterion for chemical equilibrium is obtained by setting the A_j equal to zero. The net rates of the chemical reactions, v_j, represent the rate of approach to equilibrium. Thus for situations in which the chemical composition is close to equilibrium, the linear law states that

$$v_i = \sum_j \alpha_{ij} A_j \qquad (1\text{-}24)$$

It is shown below that this expression is consistent with the usual rate laws of chemical kinetics.

Let us consider as an example a system in which the single reaction

$$\mathrm{H_2 + I_2} \overset{k_f}{\underset{k_r}{\rightleftarrows}} 2\mathrm{HI} \qquad (1\text{-}25)$$

takes place. If this equation represents the actual kinetics of the reaction then

$$v = k_f f_{\mathrm{H_2}} f_{\mathrm{I_2}} - k_r f_{\mathrm{HI}}^2 \qquad (1\text{-}26)$$

where k_f and k_r are the rate constants of the forward and reverse reactions and the f_k are the fugacities of the various components. Rearranging this expression, one obtains for the rate of the reaction,

$$v = k_r f_{\mathrm{HI}}^2 \left[K \left(\frac{f_{\mathrm{H}_2} f_{\mathrm{I}_2}}{f_{\mathrm{HI}}^2} \right) - 1 \right] \tag{1-27}$$

Here $K = k_f/k_r$ is the equilibrium constant. Now using the thermo-dynamic relations

$$\mu_k = \mu_k^{(0)} + RT \ln f_k \tag{1-28}$$

and

$$\sum_k (\eta_k - \beta_k) \mu_k^{(0)} = -RT \ln K \tag{1-29}$$

it can easily be shown that the affinity of the reaction is

$$A_1 = RT \ln K - RT \ln \left(\frac{f_{\mathrm{HI}}^2}{f_{\mathrm{H}_2} f_{\mathrm{I}_2}} \right) \tag{1-30}$$

From this expression it is clear that whenever the composition is an equilibrium composition, the affinity A_1 is zero. Then from Eq. 1-27 and 1-30, it follows that

$$v = k_r f_{\mathrm{HI}}^2 (e^{A_1/RT} - 1) \tag{1-31}$$

Eq. 1-31 is simply a reformulation of the usual rate law, Eq. 1-26, in somewhat different terms and consequently has the same range of validity. However, near equilibrium the affinity A_1 is small compared to RT,

$$A_1 \ll RT \tag{1-32}$$

and the exponential may be expanded to obtain a limiting form,

$$v = \left(\frac{k_r f_{\mathrm{HI}}^2}{RT} \right) A_1 \tag{1-33}$$

This is the form predicted by the linear law. In this case the proportionality constant is $k_r f_{\mathrm{HI}}^2/RT$. It is clear that a similar result would apply to any reaction in which the actual mechanism is a single step. The linear law, however, is quite general and independent of the mechanism of the reaction. The linear law has been verified experimentally for some heterogeneous reactions by Prigogine, Outer, and Herbo [6].

The most interesting applications of the thermodynamics of irreversible processes involve coupled mechanisms. As an example of coupled irreversible processes, Onsager [5] examined a particularly simple hypothetical system. He considered a mixture of three interacting chemical species A, B, and C. If it is assumed that from the point of view of the conservation of mass any one of these three species may be converted into any other one, then the only possible chemical mechanisms are

$$A \rightleftarrows B \tag{1-34}$$

$$A \rightleftarrows C \tag{1-35}$$

$$B \rightleftarrows C \tag{1-36}$$

A rate constant of zero is equivalent to the statement that this reaction is not part of the actual mechanism. For this system the rate of production of entropy is, according to Eq. 1-17,

$$\dot{S} = -\frac{1}{T} (\mu_A \Gamma_A + \mu_B \Gamma_B + \mu_C \Gamma_C) \tag{1-37}$$

But from the concept of the conservation of mass, the total number of moles remains constant and

$$\Gamma_A + \Gamma_B + \Gamma_C = 0 \tag{1-38}$$

Thus from Eq. 1-37

$$\dot{S} = \frac{1}{T} (A_1 \Gamma_B + A_2 \Gamma_C) \tag{1-39}$$

where

$$A_1 = -(\mu_B - \mu_A) \tag{1-40}$$

and

$$A_2 = -(\mu_C - \mu_A) \tag{1-41}$$

are the affinities of the reactions (1-34) and (1-35).

Eq. 1-39 is of the form of the general expression (1-11). Thus according to the linear law we have as a special case of Eq. 1-12,

$$\Gamma_B = \alpha_{11} A_1 + \alpha_{12} A_2 \tag{1-42}$$

and

$$\Gamma_C = \alpha_{21} A_1 + \alpha_{22} A_2 \tag{1-43}$$

But from the usual concepts of chemical kinetics

$$\Gamma_B = k_{AB} f_A - k_{BA} f_B - k_{BC} f_B + k_{CB} f_C \tag{1-44}$$

and

$$\Gamma_C = k_{AC} f_A - k_{CA} f_C + k_{BC} f_B - k_{CB} f_C \tag{1-45}$$

where k_{AB} is the rate constant for the reaction $A \rightarrow B$ and similarly for the other k_{ij}. These expressions may be rearranged in a manner similar to that described above to obtain expressions applying to systems only slightly displaced from equilibrium.

$$\Gamma_B = (k_{BA} f_B + k_{CB} f_C) \frac{A_1}{RT} - k_{CB} f_C \frac{A_2}{RT} \tag{1-46}$$

and

$$\Gamma_C = -k_{CB} f_C \frac{A_1}{RT} + (k_{CA} f_C + k_{CB} f_C) \frac{A_2}{RT} \tag{1-47}$$

These equations are consistent with those obtained by use of the linear law, Eq. 1-42 and 1-43, and they exhibit several interesting facts.

If the actual mechanism of the kinetics involves only the Eq. 1-34 and 1-35, then k_{CB} is zero and the coupling terms are absent. That is, the third mechanism acts as a coupling mechanism; if this reaction does not take place, then each of the other two progress at rates which depend only upon the respective affinities. The second point is that the two coupling coefficients are identical,

$$\alpha_{12} = \alpha_{21} \tag{1-48}$$

This is an example of the law of reciprocity, the second important concept entering into the thermodynamics of irreversible processes. By an examination of more general types of chemical reactions and other types of physical processes, as discussed in Art. 2, Onsager came to the conclusion that, in general,[2]

$$\alpha_{ij} = \alpha_{ji} \tag{1-49}$$

J,2. The Reciprocal Relations. By very general statistical mechanics arguments based on the concept of microscopic reversibility, Onsager [5] proved the basic relation, $\alpha_{ij} = \alpha_{ji}$, of Eq. 1-49. These relations are referred to as the reciprocal relations, and in the thermodynamics of irreversible processes they play a role similar in importance and in concept to the second law. The proof is based on an exceedingly formal treatment of the kinetics of irreversible processes in general.

It is assumed that the rate of a macroscopic irreversible process is the same as the average rate of regression of statistical fluctuations in the state of the system. Let us consider a system in a particular nonequilibrium state. We wish to determine the rate of approach to equilibrium. To accomplish this, let us consider the same system in the corresponding equilibrium state. Due to statistical fluctuations, there is a small but finite probability of finding this system in any microscopic state. Let us wait until a fluctuation occurs which brings the system into a state corresponding to the particular nonequilibrium state which we are studying. Again after a time, t, the system may be found in any one of the microscopic states of the system. However, one class of these states is much more probable than any other, and this corresponds to a new nonequilibrium state of the system. In this manner on the basis of the theory of fluctuations one can trace out the approach of the system to equilibrium.

Because of the large number of degrees of freedom of the macroscopic system, the probability of a fluctuation is small and the system is much more likely to be found in a microscopic state corresponding directly to the equilibrium state than in any other. This is the basis of the usefulness

[2] This statement of the principle covers all usual cases. For a more precise statement see II,F.

of the statistical method. For a similar reason the path of the regression of a fluctuation is well defined with the probability of a deviation from this path being of a still smaller order of magnitude. Physically this corresponds to the fact that the irreversible process is well specified.

On these arguments Onsager developed a formal theory of the rates of irreversible processes. Then assuming the linear law he obtained expressions for the coefficients. The principle of microscopic reversibility then implies the reciprocal relations (1-49).

J,3. Application to Flow Processes [7–13]. Let us consider the application of the thermodynamics of irreversible processes to a general system. Let us assume that the system is a continuous medium in which the temperature, pressure, and other thermodynamic quantities vary continuously in space. In order to apply these methods, it is necessary to obtain an equation of change for the entropy and from this obtain an expression for the local rate of production of entropy.

The equations of change may be derived by very general statistical mechanics arguments [14] and apply to any system in which the gradients are not so large that the local values of the macroscopic variables lose their physical interpretation.[3] Let n_i be the number of moles of species i per cm^3, ρ the density, and e the internal energy per gram. Let $\mathbf{v}_i$ be the average velocity of molecules of species i defined in such a manner that $n_i\mathbf{v}_i$ is the average flux of component i in moles per cm^2 sec. Then the mass average velocity of the fluid is defined by

$$\mathbf{v} = \frac{1}{\rho} \sum_i n_i \mathfrak{M}_i \mathbf{v}_i \qquad (3\text{-}1)$$

where $\mathfrak{M}_i$ is the molecular weight of species i. The velocity $\mathbf{v}$ is the macroscopically observed stream velocity. The diffusion velocity of component i is defined as

$$\mathbf{V}_i = \mathbf{v}_i - \mathbf{v} \qquad (3\text{-}2)$$

Because of this definition

$$\sum_i n_i \mathfrak{M}_i \mathbf{V}_i = 0 \qquad (3\text{-}3)$$

The equations of change are written in terms of $\mathbf{q}$ the total energy flux vector, $\mathbf{p}$ the pressure tensor (representing the momentum flux), Γ_i the rate of formation of molecules of i by chemical reactions in moles per cm^3, and $\mathbf{V}_i$ the diffusion velocity of species i. These quantities describe the irreversibility of the hydrodynamic flow and are discussed in more detail

---

[3] The present treatment does not apply to shock wave phenomena because (1) in a shock wave the gradients are sufficiently large that this condition is violated and (2) in a strong shock wave portions of the system are in conditions far removed from equilibrium and the present thermodynamic methods do not apply.

later. We shall use the operator D/Dt to indicate the time rate of change of a property following the fluid element. In terms of $\partial/\partial t$ the rate of change at a particular point,

$$\frac{D}{Dt} = \frac{\partial}{\partial t} + \mathbf{v} \cdot \nabla \tag{3-4}$$

The equations of change (in the absence of external forces) are
  (1) the equation of continuity of component i

$$\rho \frac{D(n_i/\rho)}{Dt} = \Gamma_i - \nabla \cdot n_i \mathbf{V}_i \tag{3-5}$$

  (2) the over-all equation of continuity

$$\rho \frac{D(1/\rho)}{Dt} = \nabla \cdot \mathbf{v} \tag{3-6}$$

  (3) the equation of motion

$$\rho \frac{D\mathbf{v}}{Dt} = -\nabla \cdot \mathbf{p} \tag{3-7}$$

  (4) the energy balance equation[4]

$$\rho \frac{De}{Dt} = -\nabla \cdot \mathbf{q} - \mathbf{p} : \nabla \mathbf{v} \tag{3-8}$$

According to the fundamental relation (1-15)

$$\frac{D\sigma}{Dt} = \frac{1}{T}\left[\frac{De}{Dt} + p \frac{D(1/\rho)}{Dt} - \sum_i \mu_i \frac{D(n_i/\rho)}{Dt} \right] \tag{3-9}$$

where σ is the entropy per gram of the system. Here p is the static pressure, as distinct from the pressure tensor $\mathbf{p}$. Actually, the static pressure p is defined by this relation.

Making use of the usual equations of change, Eq. 3-5, 3-7, and 3-8, it follows from Eq. 3-9 that the rate of increase of entropy of a small element of volume moving with the fluid is

$$\rho \frac{D\sigma}{Dt} = -\nabla \cdot \boldsymbol{\phi} + \dot{s} \tag{3-10}$$

where

$$\boldsymbol{\phi} = \frac{1}{T}\mathbf{q} - \sum_i \frac{1}{T}\mu_i n_i \mathbf{V}_i \tag{3-11}$$

[4] The tensor operation $A:B$ is defined in the following manner:

$$A:B = \sum_{i,j} A_{ij}B_{ji}$$

$$\dot{s} = -\frac{1}{T^2}\,\mathbf{q}\cdot\nabla T - \sum_i n_i \mathbf{V}_i \cdot \nabla\left(\frac{\mu_i}{T}\right)$$

$$-\frac{1}{T}\,(\mathbf{p} - p\mathbf{1}):\nabla\mathbf{v} - \frac{1}{T}\sum_i \mu_i \Gamma_i \quad (3\text{-}12)$$

and **1** is the unit tensor.

The vector ϕ represents the reversible flow of entropy while the second term, $\dot{s}$, represents the local rate production of entropy due to irreversible processes. This may be indicated by the following arguments. The total energy flux vector $\mathbf{q}$ is made up of two terms,

$$\mathbf{q} = \omega + \sum_i n_i \,\mathrm{H}_i \mathbf{V}_i \qquad (3\text{-}13)$$

where H_i is the partial molar enthalpy. The second term is the flux of energy incidental to the diffusion processes, while ω (which is defined as the difference) is the flow of thermal energy due to the collision processes. Then introducing the partial molar entropy s_i it follows from Eq. 3-11 and 3-13 that

$$\phi = \frac{1}{T}\,\omega + \sum_i n_i s_i \mathbf{V}_i \qquad (3\text{-}14)$$

In this form it is seen that ϕ is the sum of two terms. The first term is the reversible flow of entropy due to the heat flow, while the second term is the flow incidental to the diffusion processes. The peculiar form of ϕ given by Eq. 3-11 is due to the fact that the transport of thermal energy and the transport of energy due to the diffusion enter in different ways into the energy flux vector and the entropy flux vector.

The expression for $\dot{s}$, the rate of production of entropy, is of the form given by Eq. 1-11 and therefore one may apply the linear law. The effect of the chemical reactions enters in exactly the same manner as discussed in Art. 1. Here we have in addition the effects of the transport of mass, momentum, and energy. The various gradients which enter describe the displacement from equilibrium, while the corresponding fluxes represent the rate of approach to equilibrium. Although it is possible to apply the linear law directly to this form, it is more convenient to transform the expression making use of Eq. 3-13 so that ω, representing the flow of purely thermal energy, enters rather than $\mathbf{q}$, the total energy flux vector. Making use of simple thermodynamic relations the result is

$$\dot{s} = -\frac{1}{T^2}\,\omega\cdot\nabla T - \frac{1}{T}\sum_i \mathbf{J}_i\cdot\mathbf{\Lambda}_i - \frac{1}{T}\,(\mathbf{p} - p\mathbf{1}):\nabla\mathbf{v} - \frac{1}{T}\sum_i \mu_i \Gamma_i \quad (3\text{-}15)$$

where

$$\mathbf{J}_i = n_i \mathfrak{M}_i \mathbf{V}_i \qquad (3\text{-}16)$$

is the mass diffusion flux of species i, and

$$\mathbf{\Lambda}_i = \nabla\left(\frac{\mu_i}{\mathfrak{M}_i}\right) + \left(\frac{s_i}{\mathfrak{M}_i}\right)\nabla T \tag{3-17}$$

The vector $\mathbf{\Lambda}_i$ which plays the role of a displacement in the case of diffusion is the sum of two terms. If the temperature is uniform, the second term is zero and the "driving force" becomes simply the gradient of the chemical potential. In the case of a perfect gas

$$\mu_i = F_i^{(0)}(T) + RT \ln p_i \tag{3-18}$$

where $F_i^{(0)}(T)$ is the Gibbs free energy at temperature T and unit pressure, and p_i is the partial pressure of component i. In this case

$$\mathbf{\Lambda}_i = \frac{RT}{\mathfrak{M}_i}\nabla \ln p_i \tag{3-19}$$

In the general case, the driving force $\mathbf{\Lambda}_i$ cannot be written as the gradient of any thermodynamic function.

The term in Eq. 3-15 representing the effect of chemical reactions is given by Eq. 1-17. By considering the various reactions explicitly this term may be rearranged into the form given by Eq. 1-22. Making use of this transformation, the expression for the rate of production of entropy, Eq. 3-15, may now be written in the form of Eq. 1-11. The result is a sum of terms each representing the effect of a particular physical process,

$$\dot{s} = \frac{1}{T}\left[\mathbf{F}_T \cdot \boldsymbol{\omega} + \sum_i \mathbf{F}_{D_i} \cdot \mathbf{J}_i + \mathbf{F}_v : (\mathbf{p} - p\mathbf{1}) + \sum_i F_{c_i}v_i\right] \tag{3-20}$$

Here the F's are generalized affinities, defined by

$$\mathbf{F}_T = -\frac{1}{T}\nabla T \tag{3-21}$$

$$\mathbf{F}_{D_i} = -\mathbf{\Lambda}_i = -\frac{1}{\mathfrak{M}_i}(\nabla\mu_i + s_i\nabla T) \tag{3-22}$$

$$\mathbf{F}_v = -\nabla\mathbf{v} \tag{3-23}$$

and

$$F_{c_i} = A_i \tag{3-24}$$

The affinities are a measure of the displacement from equilibrium. The corresponding flux vectors measure the rate of approach to equilibrium.

According to the linear law, the affinities act as "driving forces" for the corresponding flux vectors. Situations only slightly removed from equilibrium are characterized by small values of the gradients, i.e. small values of the affinities. Under these conditions one may apply the linear law as formulated by Eq. 1-11. This equation states that the components of the generalized fluxes or flows are linear combinations of the components of the generalized affinities.

The fluxes are tensors of various ranks, which according to the linear law are linear combinations of the tensors representing the affinities. On the basis of the transformation properties of the tensors, it may be shown that certain types of coupling do not occur. If the system is isotropic, then coupling can occur only between tensors such that the difference in rank is even. Basically this is due to the fact that the contraction of a tensor is also a tensor (of two lower rank) in that the contraction also satisfies the necessary transformation properties.

Since both $\mathbf{F}_T$ and $\mathbf{F}_{D_i}$ are vectors (tensors of rank one), there is coupling between the diffusion processes and thermal conductivity. This coupling is observed experimentally as the phenomena of thermal diffusion. A complementary phenomenon, the direct effect of the composition gradients on the thermal conductivity, also exists and is known as the Dufour effect, although it is less well recognized.

The generalized affinities, F_{C_i} and $\mathbf{F}_v$, are tensors of rank zero and two, respectively. Hence in the case of isotropic systems there can be no coupling between either of these processes and either the diffusion or thermal conductivity. That is, for example, the rates of the chemical reactions are not affected by gradients in either the composition or the temperature. However, since the difference in rank between F_{C_i} and $\mathbf{F}_v$ is two (an even number), in general coupling may occur between these processes. This particular coupling does not occur in the special case that the trace (the contraction) of the tensor $(\mathbf{p} - p\mathbf{1})$ is zero. Although in general this trace is not zero, it is zero in the case of perfect gas or in any system in which the coefficient of bulk viscosity is zero.

Neglecting the possible coupling terms between the reaction rates and the pressure tensor, the implications of the linear law may be written in the form:

$$\boldsymbol{\omega} = \alpha_{TT} \cdot \mathbf{F}_T + \sum_i \alpha_{TD_i} \cdot \mathbf{F}_{D_i} \tag{3-25}$$

$$\mathbf{J}_i = \alpha_{D_iT} \cdot \mathbf{F}_T + \sum_j \alpha_{D_iD_j} \cdot \mathbf{F}_{D_j} \tag{3-26}$$

$$(\mathbf{p} - p\mathbf{1})_{ij} = \sum_{k,l} \alpha_{ij}^{kl}(\mathbf{F}_v)_{kl} \tag{3-27}$$

$$v_i = \sum_j \alpha_{C_iC_j}F_{C_j} \tag{3-28}$$

The applications of the reciprocity relations to the theory of the rates of chemical reactions were discussed in Art. 1 and these terms are not considered further here.

J,4. Viscosity. Let us consider the applications of the reciprocity relations to the theory of viscosity. Let

$$\Phi = \mathbf{p} - p\mathbf{1} \tag{4-1}$$

Then according to the linear law

$$\phi_{ij} = \sum_{k,l} \alpha_{ij}^{kl}(\mathbf{F}_v)_{kl} = -\sum_{k,l} \alpha_{ij}^{kl}\frac{\partial v_l}{\partial x_k} \tag{4-2}$$

Onsager's reciprocity relations state that

$$\alpha_{ij}^{kl} = \alpha_{kl}^{ij} \tag{4-3}$$

In the statistical mechanical derivations of the equations of change, the pressure tensor is defined in such a manner that it is symmetric. Phenomenologically this is necessary, since otherwise each small element of volume would be subject to a torque. Hence

$$\alpha_{ij}^{kl} = \alpha_{ji}^{kl} \tag{4-4}$$

and from Eq. 4-3 and 4-4,

$$\alpha_{ij}^{kl} = \alpha_{ij}^{lk} \tag{4-5}$$

Thus Eq. 4-2 may be written in the more familiar form

$$\phi_{ij} = -\frac{1}{2}\sum_{k,l} \alpha_{ij}^{kl}\left(\frac{\partial v_l}{\partial x_k} + \frac{\partial v_k}{\partial x_l}\right) \tag{4-6}$$

The set of coefficients α_{ij}^{kl} is a matrix of 81 elements. However, because of the symmetry relations there are only 21 independent coefficients. These are the elastic constants of the medium. The same symmetry requirements may be obtained by assuming that Φ is identically zero for motions corresponding to rigid-body translations and rotations. Hence in this case Onsager's reciprocal relations have a simple physical interpretation.

If the medium has any amount of symmetry, the number of independent elastic constants is considerably less than 21. Let us define

$$(\nabla\mathbf{v})_{ij}^{(s)} = \frac{1}{2}\left(\frac{\partial v_j}{\partial x_i} + \frac{\partial v_i}{\partial x_j}\right) \tag{4-7}$$

Then if the medium is isotropic the relation between Φ and $(\nabla\mathbf{v})^{(s)}$ is independent of a rotation of the coordinate frame. Under these conditions it may be shown that the α_{ij}^{kl} are of such a form that

$$\Phi = \mathbf{p} - p\mathbf{1} = -2\mu(\nabla\mathbf{v})^{(s)} - \lambda(\nabla\cdot\mathbf{v})\mathbf{1} \tag{4-8}$$

where μ and λ are the two independent elements. This form follows immediately from the condition of isotropy since in this case the only tensors upon which Φ may depend are $\mathbf{1}$, $\nabla\mathbf{v}$, and the transpose of $\nabla\mathbf{v}$.

Hence Φ must be a linear combination of these three tensors. However, the antisymmetric combination of ∇v and its transpose are eliminated by the symmetry arguments above. Hence the form given by Eq. 4-8 follows.

Thus in an isotropic medium there are two coefficients of viscosity. The coefficient μ is termed the shear viscosity and is important in flows in which successive plane layers of the fluid move with different velocities. The combination

$$\phi = \tfrac{2}{3}\mu + \lambda \tag{4-9}$$

is the coefficient of bulk viscosity. This coefficient is important in the pure expansion of a fluid.

From Eq. 3-20, 4-8, and 4-9 it follows that the contribution of viscous effects to the rate of production of entropy is

$$\dot{s}_v = \frac{1}{T}\left[2\mu(\nabla v)^{(s)} - \left(\frac{2}{3}\mu - \phi\right)(\nabla \cdot v)\mathbf{1} \right]:\nabla v \tag{4-10}$$

This expression may be rearranged into the form

$$\dot{s}_v = \frac{2\mu}{T}\left[(\nabla v)^{(s)} - \frac{1}{3}(\nabla \cdot v)\mathbf{1} \right]:\left[(\nabla v)^{(s)} - \frac{1}{3}(\Delta \cdot v)\mathbf{1} \right] + \frac{\phi}{T}(\nabla \cdot v)^2 \tag{4-11}$$

The factors multiplying both μ and ϕ are sums of squares and hence both are positive. According to the second law

$$\dot{s}_v \geqq 0 \tag{4-12}$$

for all ∇v. Since either factor may be zero while the other factor is not it follows that

$$\mu \geqq 0 \quad \text{and} \quad \phi \geqq 0 \tag{4-13}$$

The kinetic theory of dilute gases in the Navier-Stokes approximation leads to an expression for the pressure tensor in complete agreement with the form of Eq. 4-8. However, in this limit the coefficient of bulk viscosity ϕ is zero. The integral expressions for the coefficient of shear viscosity μ are such as to lead to positive values.

J,5. Thermal Conductivity and Diffusion.

The effects of thermal conductivity and diffusion are coupled. Considering only these terms, the rate of entropy production is

$$\dot{s} = \frac{1}{T}\left(-\frac{1}{T}\nabla T \cdot \omega - \sum_i \mathbf{A}_i \cdot \mathbf{J}_i \right) \tag{5-1}$$

Because of the definition of the diffusion velocity,

$$\sum_i \mathbf{J}_i = 0 \tag{5-2}$$

and hence one $\mathbf{J}_i$ may be eliminated from Eq. 5-1. Let us eliminate $\mathbf{J}_k$ in particular. Then

$$\dot{s} = \frac{1}{T}\left[-\frac{1}{T}\nabla T \cdot \boldsymbol{\omega} - \sum_{i \neq k}(\boldsymbol{\Lambda}_i - \boldsymbol{\Lambda}_k) \cdot \mathbf{J}_i \right] \tag{5-3}$$

Applying the linear law one obtains[5]

$$\boldsymbol{\omega} = -\frac{\alpha_{00}}{T}\nabla T - \sum_{j \neq k}\alpha_{0j}(\boldsymbol{\Lambda}_j - \boldsymbol{\Lambda}_k) \tag{5-4}$$

and

$$\mathbf{J}_i = -\frac{\alpha_{i0}}{T}\nabla T - \sum_{j \neq k}\alpha_{ij}(\boldsymbol{\Lambda}_j - \boldsymbol{\Lambda}_k) \quad (i \neq k) \tag{5-5}$$

The coefficients with either lower index k are not defined (at present).

In the general case the coefficients are tensors. Onsager's reciprocal relations then imply that

$$\alpha_{ij} = \alpha_{ji}^\dagger \tag{5-6}$$

where the $\dagger$ indicates the transpose. In the case of an isotropic system it is clear that the coefficients are scalar multiples of the unit tensor. We will consider only this case.

Using Eq. 5-2 and 5-5, it follows that

$$\mathbf{J}_k = \frac{\nabla T}{T}\sum_{i \neq k}\alpha_{i0} + \sum_{j \neq k}\sum_{i \neq k}\alpha_{ij}(\boldsymbol{\Lambda}_j - \boldsymbol{\Lambda}_k) \tag{5-7}$$

Thus Eq. 5-5 may be made formally correct for $i = k$ by defining

$$\alpha_{kj} = -\sum_{i \neq k}\alpha_{ij} \quad j = 0, 1, 2, \cdots \; j \neq k \tag{5-8}$$

Let us define the α_{jk} so as to extend the reciprocity relations correspondingly,

$$\alpha_{jk} = \alpha_{kj} = -\sum_{i \neq k}\alpha_{ji} \quad j = 0, 1, 2, \cdots \tag{5-9}$$

Thus Eq. 5-4 and 5-5 can be written

$$\boldsymbol{\omega} = -\frac{\alpha_{00}}{T}\nabla T - \sum_{j}\alpha_{0j}\boldsymbol{\Lambda}_j \tag{5-10}$$

and

$$\mathbf{J}_i = -\frac{\alpha_{i0}}{T}\nabla T - \sum_{j}\alpha_{ij}\boldsymbol{\Lambda}_j \tag{5-11}$$

---

[5] In this and the succeeding equations it is understood that the sum does not include zero. Also for simplicity, we use a slightly different notation than in Eq. 3-25 and 3-26.

This form may have been obtained directly by application of the linear law to the original expression for $\mathbf{J}_i$ (5-11). However, the linear relations among the $\mathbf{J}_i$ imply the linear relations among the α_{ij} given by Eq. 5-8 and 5-9, which may be written in the more symmetric form

$$\sum_i \alpha_{ij} = \sum_i \alpha_{ji} = 0 \tag{5-12}$$

Let us define a set of quantities,

$$\mathbf{d}_i = \frac{n_i \mathfrak{M}_i}{p} \mathbf{\Lambda}_i - \frac{n_i \mathfrak{M}_i}{\rho p} \nabla p \tag{5-13}$$

It can be shown on purely thermodynamic grounds that[6]

$$\sum_i n_i \mathfrak{M}_i \mathbf{\Lambda}_i = \nabla p \tag{5-14}$$

and hence

$$\sum_i \mathbf{d}_i = 0 \tag{5-15}$$

In the case of a perfect gas where $\mathbf{\Lambda}_i$ is given by Eq. 3-19,

$$\mathbf{d}_i = \nabla \left(\frac{n_i}{n}\right) + \left(\frac{n_i}{n} - \frac{n_i \mathfrak{M}_i}{\rho}\right) \nabla p \tag{5-16}$$

Eq. 5-10 and 5-11 may be written in terms of the $\mathbf{d}_i$; then using the condition given by Eq. 5-12 one obtains,

$$\boldsymbol{\omega} = -\frac{\alpha_{00}}{T} \nabla T - p \sum_j {}'\frac{\alpha_{0j}}{n_i \mathfrak{M}_i} \mathbf{d}_j \tag{5-17}$$

and

$$\mathbf{J}_i = -\frac{\alpha_{i0}}{T} \nabla T - p \sum_j {}'\frac{\alpha_{ij}}{n_j \mathfrak{M}_j} \mathbf{d}_j \tag{5-18}$$

It can be shown by means of kinetic theory that for a gas at sufficiently low pressure, the thermal flux vector $\boldsymbol{\omega}$ may be written in the form

$$\boldsymbol{\omega} = -\lambda' \nabla T - p \sum_j {}'\frac{D_j^T}{n_j \mathfrak{M}_j} \mathbf{d}_j \tag{5-19}$$

and that the diffusion flux of i may be written in the form

$$\mathbf{J}_i = n_i \mathfrak{M}_i \mathbf{V}_i = -\frac{D_i^T}{T} \nabla T + \frac{n^2}{\rho} \sum_j {}'\mathfrak{M}_i \mathfrak{M}_j D_{ij} \mathbf{d}_j \tag{5-20}$$

Here λ' is closely related to the coefficient of thermal conductivity, which,

[6] This is essentially the Gibbs-Duhem relation.

however, is usually defined in a somewhat different manner, by an equation discussed later (5-32). The D_i^T are generalized coefficients of thermal diffusion, while the D_{ij} are generalized ordinary diffusion coefficients. Since the $\mathbf{d}_j$ are not linearly independent, the D_{ij} are not uniquely specified by Eq. 5-20. A unique set is usually chosen by requiring that, in addition,

$$D_{ii} = 0 \tag{5-21}$$

In the case of the α_{ij} the uniqueness is imposed in an entirely different manner by the reciprocal relations.

From Eq. 5-19 and 5-20, it is clear that the kinetic theory results are consistent with some of the reciprocal relations in that

$$\alpha_{i0} = \alpha_{0i} = D_i^T \tag{5-22}$$

It may also be shown that the remaining reciprocal relations are satisfied. Making use of the linear relations among the $\mathbf{d}_i$, Eq. 5-15, to eliminate the "diagonal" elements, and using Eq. 5-12 it follows that the D_{ij} are related to the α_{ij} in the following manner:

$$D_{ij} = -\frac{\rho p}{n^2 \mathfrak{M}_i \mathfrak{M}_j} \left(\frac{\alpha_{ij}}{n_j \mathfrak{M}_j} + \frac{1}{n_i \mathfrak{M}_i} \sum_{k \neq i} \alpha_{ik} \right) \tag{5-23}$$

This equation may be solved for the α_{ij} to obtain the relation

$$\alpha_{ij} = \frac{n^2 n_j \mathfrak{M}_j \mathfrak{M}_i}{\rho^2 p} \left(-\rho \mathfrak{M}_j D_{ij} + \sum_{k \neq i} n_k \mathfrak{M}_k^2 D_{ik} \right) \tag{5-24}$$

Thus the D_{ij} must be such that this linear combination is symmetric.

In the case of a two-component mixture, Eq. 5-24 reduces to

$$\alpha_{ij} = -\frac{n^2}{\rho^2 p} n_i n_j \mathfrak{M}_i^2 \mathfrak{M}_j^2 D_{ij} \tag{5-25}$$

and hence the symmetry relations imply that

$$D_{ij} = D_{ji} \tag{5-26}$$

In this simple case, the result is trivial in that it can be obtained directly from Eq. 5-20 making use of Eq. 5-2. In general, however, the reciprocal relations impose important restrictions.

Let s be the number of components. Then because of the $\frac{1}{2}s(s-1)$ reciprocal relations, the $s(s-1)$ values of D_{ij} may be expressed in terms of $\frac{1}{2}s(s-1)$ quantities. In the case of a dilute gas, the kinetic theory expressions for the D_{ij} have been expressed in terms of the $\frac{1}{2}s(s-1)$ values of the binary diffusion constants $\mathfrak{D}_{ij}$ for the various pairs of components.[7]

---

[7] $\mathfrak{D}_{ij}$ is the diffusion constant for a mixture of i and j at the same total pressure as that of the multicomponent mixture under consideration.

(As discussed above, the binary diffusion coefficients are symmetric.) In the case of a ternary mixture, the kinetic theory expressions give

$$D_{12} = \mathfrak{D}_{12}\left[1 + \frac{n_3[(\mathfrak{M}_3/\mathfrak{M}_2)\mathfrak{D}_{13} - \mathfrak{D}_{12}]}{n_1\mathfrak{D}_{23} + n_2\mathfrak{D}_{13} + n_3\mathfrak{D}_{12}}\right] \qquad (5\text{-}27)$$

and similar expressions for the other D_{ij}.

Using Eq. 5-24, one obtains for a ternary mixture,

$$\alpha_{12} = \frac{n^2 n_2 \mathfrak{M}_1 \mathfrak{M}_2}{\rho^2 p}\left[-\mathfrak{M}_2(\rho - n_2\mathfrak{M}_2)D_{12} + n_3\mathfrak{M}_3^2 D_{13}\right] \qquad (5\text{-}28)$$

Then using the kinetic theory result, Eq. 5-27, it follows that for a dilute gas,

$$\alpha_{12} = \frac{n^2 n_1 n_2 \mathfrak{M}_1 \mathfrak{M}_2[n_3\mathfrak{M}_3^2\mathfrak{D}_{13}\mathfrak{D}_{23} - \mathfrak{M}_2(\rho - n_2\mathfrak{M}_2)\mathfrak{D}_{12}\mathfrak{D}_{23} - \mathfrak{M}_1(\rho - n_1\mathfrak{M}_1)\mathfrak{D}_{12}\mathfrak{D}_{13}]}{\rho^2 p(n_1\mathfrak{D}_{23} + n_2\mathfrak{D}_{13} + n_3\mathfrak{D}_{12})} \qquad (5\text{-}29)$$

This expression is symmetric in "1" and "2"; hence in this case the kinetic theory result is consistent with the reciprocity relations. It should be possible to show that the result for a general multicomponent mixture is consistent.

The kinetic theory expressions for the D_{ij} in terms of the binary diffusion coefficients $\mathfrak{D}_{ij}$ are such that Eq. 5-20 may be arranged to give

$$\sum_{j \neq i} \frac{n_i n_j}{n^2 \mathfrak{D}_{ij}}(\mathbf{V}_j - \mathbf{V}_i) = \mathbf{d}_i - \frac{1}{T}\nabla T \sum_j \frac{n_i n_j}{n^2 \mathfrak{D}_{ij}}\left(\frac{D_j^T}{n_j\mathfrak{M}_j} - \frac{D_i^T}{n_i\mathfrak{M}_i}\right) \qquad (5\text{-}30)$$

Using this result it follows that the equation for the thermal flux, Eq. 5-19, may be rewritten in the form

$$\omega = -\lambda\Delta T - p\sum_{j,k} \frac{n_k D_j^T}{n^2 \mathfrak{M}_j \mathfrak{D}_{jk}}(\mathbf{V}_k - \mathbf{V}_j) \qquad (5\text{-}31)$$

where

$$\lambda = \lambda' - \frac{p}{2T}\sum_{j,k}\frac{n_j n_k}{n^2\mathfrak{D}_{jk}}\left(\frac{D_k^T}{n_k\mathfrak{M}_k} - \frac{D_j^T}{n_j\mathfrak{M}_j}\right)^2 \qquad (5\text{-}32)$$

is the constant usually referred to as the coefficient of thermal conductivity.

The rate of production of entropy due to thermal conductivity and diffusion processes is given by Eq. 5-1. Introducing the $\mathbf{d}_i$ defined by Eq. 5-13 and making use of the relation (5-15) it follows that

$$\dot{s} = \frac{1}{T^2}\nabla T \cdot \omega - \frac{p}{T}\sum_i \mathbf{V}_i \cdot \mathbf{d}_i \qquad (5\text{-}33)$$

Then using Eq. 5-30 and 5-31,

$$\dot{s} = \frac{\lambda}{T^2} (\nabla T)^2 + \frac{p}{2T} \sum_{i,j} \frac{n_i n_j}{n^2 \mathcal{D}_{ij}} (\mathbf{V}_j - \mathbf{V}_i)^2 \qquad (5\text{-}34)$$

Since each term in this expression can separately be zero, it follows that the second law which states that

$$\dot{s} \geqq 0 \qquad (5\text{-}35)$$

implies that

$$\lambda \geqq 0 \qquad (5\text{-}36)$$

and

$$\mathcal{D}_{ij} \geqq 0 \qquad (5\text{-}37)$$

J,6. Cited References.

1. de Donder, T.   *L'Affinité*. Gauthier-Villars, Paris, 1927, 1931, 1934, 1936.
2. Prigogine, I., and Defay, R.   *Thermodynamique Chimique, Conformementaux Methods de Gibbs et de Donder*. Desoer, Liège, 1946.
3. Prigogine, I.   *Etude Thermodynamique des Phenomenes Irreversibles*. Desoer, Liège, 1947.
4. de Groot, S. R.   *Thermodynamics of Irreversible Processes*. North Holland, 1951.
5. Onsager, L.   *Phys. Rev. 37*, 405 (1931); *38*, 2265 (1931).
6. Prigogine, I., Outer, P., and Herbo, C.   *J. Phys. & Colloid Chem. 52*, 321 (1940).
7. Eckart, C.   *Phys. Rev. 58*, 267, 269, 919 (1940).
8. de Groot, S. R.   *L'Effet Soret. Diffusion Thermique dans Les Phases Condensées*. N. V. Noord Hollandsche Uitgevers Maatschappij, Amsterdam, 1945.
9. Tolman, R. C., and Fine, P. C.   *Revs. Mod. Phys. 20*, 51 (1948).
10. Leaf, B.   *Phys. Rev. 70*, 748 (1946).
11. Curtiss, C. F., and Hirschfelder, J. O.   *J. Chem. Phys. 18*, 171 (1950).
12. Cox, R. T.   *Revs. Mod. Phys. 22*, 238 (1950).
13. Hirschfelder, J. O., Curtiss, C. F., and Bird, R. B.   *The Molecular Theory of Gases and Liquids*. Wiley, 1954.
14. Irving, J. H., and Kirkwood, J. G.   *J. Chem. Phys. 18*, 817 (1950).

INDEX